Physics 12

Physics *12*

Authors

Alan J. Hirsch
Formerly of Peel District School Board

David Martindale
Formerly of Waterloo Region District School Board

Charles Stewart
Toronto District School Board

Maurice Barry
Memorial University of Newfoundland

Program Consultant

Maurice Di Giuseppe
Toronto Catholic District School Board

THOMSON
★
NELSON

Australia   Canada   Mexico   Singapore   Spain   United Kingdom   United States

Nelson Physics 12

Authors
Alan J. Hirsch, David Martindale,
Charles Stewart, Maurice Barry

Contributing Authors
Robert Heath, Philip Eastman

Contributing Writers
Alison Armstrong,
Maurice Di Giuseppe,
Barry LeDrew

Director of Publishing
David Steele

Publisher
Kevin Martindale

Program Manager
John Yip-Chuck

Developmental Editors
Julie Bedford
Betty Robinson

Editorial Assistant
Lisa Kafun

Senior Managing Editor
Nicola Balfour

Senior Production Editor
Linh Vu

Online Quiz Editor
Karim Dharssi

Copy Editor
Toomas Karmo

Proofreader
Trish Letient

Production Coordinator
Sharon Latta Paterson

Creative Director
Angela Cluer

Art Director
Ken Phipps

Art Management
Suzanne Peden

Illustrators
Andrew Breithaupt
Steven Corrigan
Deborah Crowle
Dave Mazierski
Dave McKay
Irma Ikonen
Peter Papayanakis
Ken Phipps
Marie Price
Katherine Strain

Design and Composition Team
Marnie Benedict
Susan Calverley
Zenaida Diores
Krista Donnelly
Erich Falkenberg
Nelson Gonzalez
Alicja Jamorski
Janet Zanette

Interior Design
Kyle Gell
Allan Moon

Cover Design
Ken Phipps

Cover Image
© Kevin Fleming/CORBIS/Magma

Photo Research and Permissions
Vicki Gould

Printer
Transcontinental Printing Inc.

National Library of Canada Cataloguing in Publication Data

Main entry under title:
Nelson physics 12 / Alan J. Hirsch ... [et al.].

Includes index.
For use in grade 12 Ontario curriculum.
ISBN 0-17-625988-0

1. Physics. I. Hirsch, Alan J II. Title: Physics 12. III. Title: Physics twelve. IV. Title: Nelson physics twelve.

QC23.N44 200   530
C2002-901565-0

Reviewers

CONTENTS

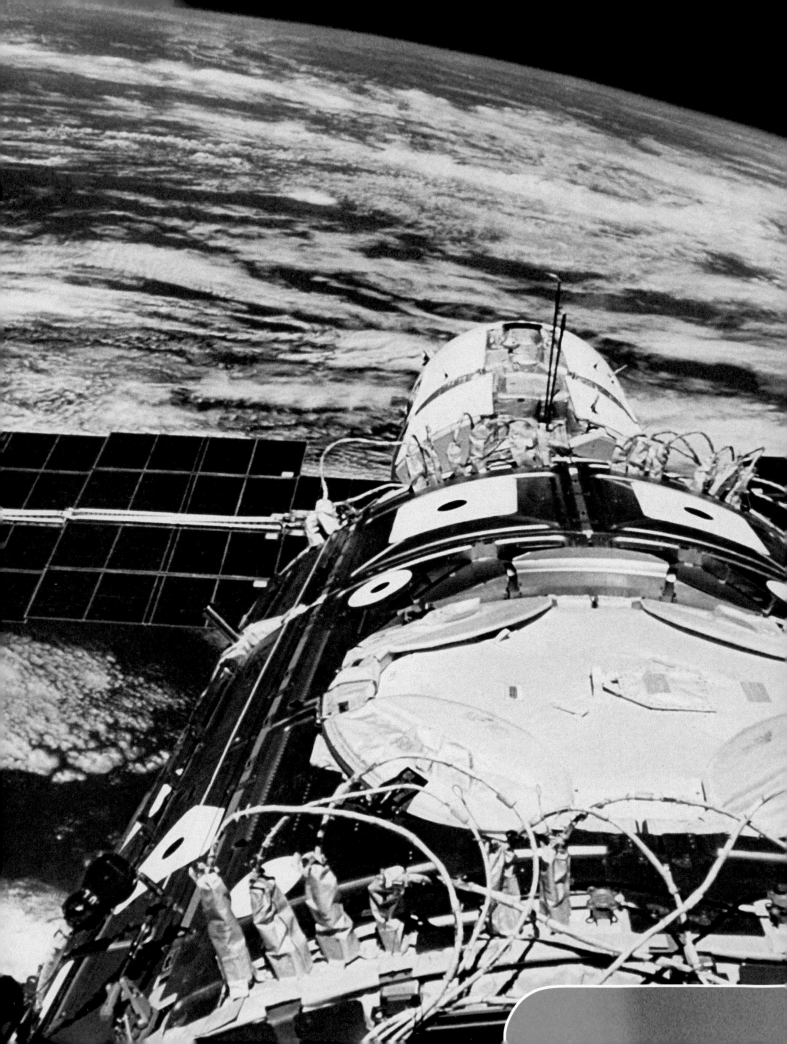

Forces and Motion: Dynamics

Dr. Kimberly Strong
Atmospheric Physicist, University of Toronto

Kimberly Strong became an atmospheric physicist because of her keen interest in why and how climate change affects the health of our planet. She is interested in making new discoveries that will better allow scientists to understand and respond to pressing issues like ozone depletion, atmospheric pollution, and global warming.

Dr. Strong teaches physics at the University of Toronto and studies Earth's atmosphere using specially designed instruments attached to satellites and weather balloons. Her team deploys huge balloons—as high as 25 stories—equipped with instruments used to detect gases in the atmosphere. Satellites, with their global view, play a vital role in helping scientists to monitor environmental changes over time, and Strong's knowledge of dynamics and circular motion is used consistently in her work. Strong and her colleagues also design many of the instruments that are carried on satellites that orbit Earth.

Atmospheric and space physicists working in companies and universities build satellites and instrumentation for environmental monitoring with the support of the Canadian Space Agency. They also work for organizations such as Environment Canada interpreting and measuring changes in the atmosphere. This field of research is highly collaborative and often involves international partnerships.

▶ Overall Expectations

In this unit, you will be able to

- analyze the motions of objects in horizontal, vertical, and inclined planes, and predict and explain the motions by analyzing the forces acting on the objects
- investigate motion in a plane using experiments and/or simulations
- analyze and solve problems involving forces acting on an object in linear, projectile, or circular motion using vectors, graphs, and free-body diagrams
- analyze ways in which the study of forces relates to the development and use of technological devices, such as vehicles and sports equipment

ARE YOU READY?

▶ **Prerequisites**

Concepts

- distinguish between scalar and vector quantities
- describe and analyze one-dimensional motion with constant velocity and motion with constant acceleration, using mathematics
- recognize common types of forces
- understand Newton's three laws of motion and his law of universal gravitation
- distinguish between static friction and kinetic friction

Skills

- analyze graphs
- analyze vectors
- manipulate algebraic equations
- define terms and use them in context
- apply basic trigonometric functions
- draw scale diagrams and free-body diagrams
- analyze dimensions of quantities
- use SI units
- perform controlled investigations
- communicate in writing, both verbally and using mathematics
- manipulate computer software
- conduct research using printed resources and the Internet

Knowledge and Understanding

1. List four scalar and four vector quantities associated with motions and forces, and for each indicate the SI units and a typical example.

2. A 20-g mass and a 50-g mass are dropped from rest from the same height above the floor.
   (a) Will the masses land simultaneously? If not, which will land first? Explain your choice.
   (b) Draw a free-body diagram showing all the forces acting on the 50-g mass as it is falling.
   (c) What is the weight of the 20-g mass?
   (d) Give one example of an action–reaction pair of forces in this situation.

3. On what does the magnitude of the force of gravity between Earth and the Moon depend? Be as detailed as possible in your answer.

4. Compare and contrast each of the following pairs of quantities or concepts, illustrating your answer with examples where appropriate:
   (a) kinematics, dynamics
   (b) average speed, average velocity
   (c) static friction, kinetic friction
   (d) helpful friction, unwanted friction
   (e) frequency, period
   (f) rotation, revolution

Inquiry and Communication

5. A safety inspector at a playground takes measurements to determine the acceleration of a child undergoing circular motion on a rotating ride. The inspector uses two common, nonelectric measuring devices.
   (a) Based on the units of acceleration, what measuring devices could the inspector use to take measurements to determine the acceleration?
   (b) Name the independent and dependent variables.

6. In an investigation to measure the magnitude of the acceleration due to gravity where the known value is 9.8 m/s^2, group A gets 9.4 m/s^2 and group B gets 9.7 m/s^2.
   (a) Determine the possible error in the value obtained by group A.
   (b) Determine the percent possible error in the value obtained by group A.
   (c) Determine the percentage error in the value obtained by group A.
   (d) Determine the percentage difference between the values of the two groups.

7. What is the difference between a prediction and a hypothesis?

Making Connections

8. You have a test tube containing a liquid and a mixture of substances of different densities. Would the substances mix more thoroughly or tend to settle out and separate if the test tube were spun rapidly in a centrifuge? Explain your answer.

9. **Figure 1** shows three possible ways of angling an exit ramp from an expressway for traffic travelling away from the observer and turning to the right.
   (a) Draw a free-body diagram for each case, showing all the forces acting on the truck.
   (b) Which choice of design would be best for vehicles travelling to the right? Why?

Math Skills

10. Consider the equation $\Delta \vec{d} = \vec{v_i}\Delta t + \frac{1}{2}\vec{a}(\Delta t)^2$.

    (a) Rearrange the equation to solve for $\vec{a}$.
    (b) Write the quadratic-formula solution for Δt.

11. **Figure 2** shows vectors $\vec{A}$ and $\vec{B}$ drawn to the scale 1.00 cm = 10.0 m/s.
    (a) Determine the north and east components of vector $\vec{A}$.
    (b) Describe as many ways as possible of determining the vector sum $\vec{A} + \vec{B}$.
    (c) Determine $\vec{B} + \vec{A}$ and $\vec{A} - \vec{B}$, using any method you find convenient.

Technical Skills and Safety

12. **Figure 3** depicts a puck moving on an x-y plane. The dots represent the location of the puck at equal time intervals of 0.10 s.
    (a) What total time elapses between the start and finish of this motion?
    (b) Copy the pattern of dots into your notebook, and determine the x-component of the displacement between each set of dots. What do you conclude about the motion in the x direction?
    (c) Determine the y-component of the displacement between each set of dots. What do you conclude about the motion in the y direction?
    (d) Assuming that the diagram is drawn to the scale 1.0 cm = 5.0 cm, determine the average velocity between the start and finish of the motion.

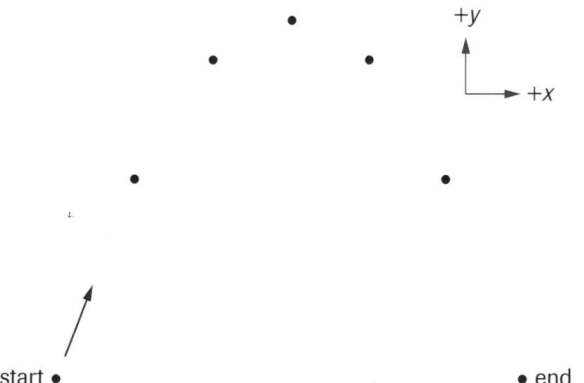

Figure 3
Motion of an air puck on an air table

13. Your lab partner ties a one-holed rubber stopper to a string, then twirls the stopper in a horizontal circle of known radius at a constant speed.
    (a) Describe how you would measure the period and frequency of revolution of the stopper's motion. Include a list of the apparatus you would need.
    (b) What safety precautions would you and your lab partner follow in taking the measurements?
    (c) What sources of error would you expect in this experiment?

(a)

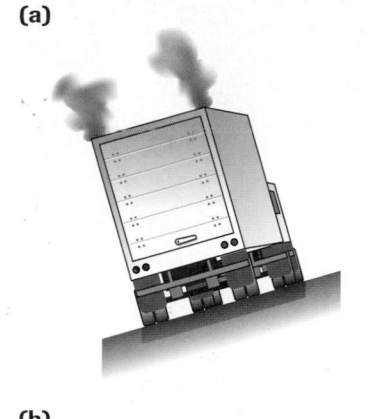

(b)

(c)

Figure 1
The truck is moving away and turning to the right in each case. (for question 9)

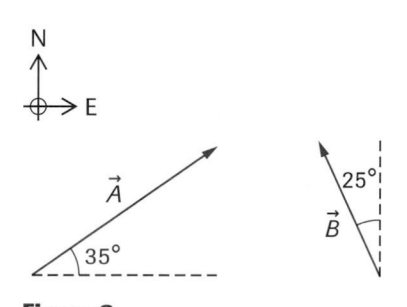

Figure 2
Vectors $\vec{A}$ and $\vec{B}$ (for question 11)

Kinematics

- analyze and predict in quantitative terms and explain the linear motion of objects in horizontal, vertical, and inclined planes

- analyze and predict in quantitative terms and explain the motion of a projectile in terms of the horizontal and vertical components of its motion

- carry out experiments or simulations involving objects moving in two dimensions, and analyze and display the data in an appropriate form

- predict the motion of an object given its initial speed and direction of motion, and test the prediction experimentally

- design or construct technological devices based on the concepts and principles of projectile motion

Engineers who design ski jumps, like the one shown in **Figure 1**, must decide on the angles and lengths of various components of the hill, such as the approach slope, the takeoff angle, and the landing slope. Upon becoming airborne, the jumper follows a curved path of motion known as a trajectory. One of the things you will discover in this chapter is how to analyze that trajectory, using physics concepts and equations.

You are likely familiar with concepts and equations for displacement, velocity, and acceleration in one-dimensional motion. In this chapter, we extend these concepts and equations to motions in two dimensions.

REFLECT on your learning

1. The arrows in **Figure 2** represent the initial velocities of four identical balls released simultaneously from the top of a cliff. Air resistance is negligible. Ball A is dropped. Balls B, C, and D are thrown with initial velocities of equal magnitude but at the different angles shown.
   (a) In your notebook, use a sketch to predict the flight path of each ball.
   (b) Indicate in what order you think the balls land. Explain your reasons.

2. In **Figure 3**, one canoeist is paddling across a still lake, while another is paddling across a flowing river. The two canoeists are equally strong and the two bodies of water equally wide. The arrows are all velocity vectors.
   (a) Redraw the diagrams in your notebook, showing the path of each canoe as it travels from one shore to the other.
   (b) If the canoeists set out from the south shores at the same time, who arrives at the north shore first? Explain.
   (c) Use another diagram to show how the canoeist in the river can arrange to arrive on the north shore directly opposite the starting position on the south shore. Will the trip across the river take the same time as before? Explain.

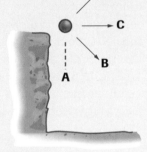

Figure 2
Will four balls launched at the same instant all land at the same time?

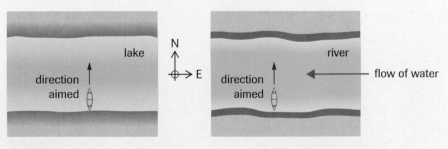

Figure 3
The distance across the lake is equal to the distance across the river.

approach

launch

60 m

start of
flatter slope

θ

$\theta = 37°$ landing

Figure 1
Physics principles can be used to understand the
motion of a ski jumper. Those same principles can
also be applied to design the ski jump's approach
and landing slopes.

▶ **TRY THIS** activity   *Choose the Winner*

Figure 4 shows a device that allows steel ball A to fall straight
downward while projecting steel ball B horizontally outward.
Assume that the balls start moving at the same instant. How do
you think the times they take to hit the floor compare?

(a) In your notebook, sketch the path of each ball. Predict, with
an explanation, whether the balls land at the same time or
at different times.

(b) Observe a demonstration of the device shown (or of some
alternative setup). Compare the demonstration with your
prediction. If your observations are different from your predictions, try to resolve the differences.

 **Observers must remain a safe distance away from
the sides of the device.**

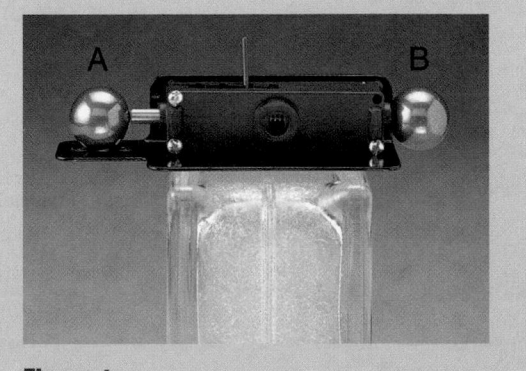

Figure 4
This device can project one ball horizontally
while simultaneously allowing a second ball to
fall straight downward.

Visitors to an amusement park, such as the one in **Figure 1**, experience a variety of motions. Some people may walk at a constant speed in a straight line. Others, descending on a vertical drop ride, plummet at a very high speed before slowing down and stopping. All these people undergo motion in one dimension, or *linear motion*. Linear motion can be in the horizontal plane (walking on a straight track on level ground, for example), in the vertical plane (taking the vertical drop ride), or on an inclined plane (walking up a ramp). Linear motion can also involve changing direction by 180°, for example, in going up and then down, or moving east and then west on level ground.

Figure 1
How many different types of motion can you identify at this amusement park?

kinematics the study of motion

(a)

start

N

E

(b)

start

N

E

Figure 2
(a) A dog running on level ground 24 m eastward and then 11 m westward undergoes motion in one dimension.
(b) A dog running on level ground 24 m eastward and then 11 m southward undergoes motion in two dimensions.

scalar quantity quantity that has magnitude but no direction

instantaneous speed speed at a particular instant

Visitors to an amusement park also experience motion in two and three dimensions. Riders on a merry-go-round experience two-dimensional motion in the horizontal plane. Riders on a Ferris wheel experience two-dimensional motion in the vertical plane. Riders on a roller coaster experience motion in three dimensions: up and down, left and right, around curves, as well as twisting and rotating.

The study of motion is called **kinematics**. To begin kinematics, we will explore simple motions in one and two dimensions, like those in **Figure 2**. Later, we will apply what we have learned to more complex types of motion.

Speed and Other Scalar Quantities

Consider the speed limits posted on roads and highways near where you live. In a school zone, the limit may be posted as 40 km/h, while 100 km/h may be permitted on a highway. The unit km/h (kilometres per hour) reminds you that speed is a distance divided by a time. Speed, distance, and time are examples of **scalar quantities**, which have magnitude (or size) but no direction.

In car racing, the starting lineup is determined by qualifying time trials in which the average speeds of the drivers are compared. Each driver must cover the same distance around the track, and the driver with the shortest time gets the pole (or first) position. During some parts of the qualifying trials, other drivers may have achieved a higher **instantaneous speed**, or speed at a particular instant. But the winner has the greatest

average speed, or total distance travelled divided by total time of travel. The equation for average speed is

$$v_{av} = \frac{d}{\Delta t}$$

where d is the total distance travelled in a total time Δt.

average speed (v_{av}) total distance of travel divided by total time of travel

LEARNING TIP

Scalar Quantities
"Scalar" stems from the Latin *scalae*, which means "steps" or "ladder rungs," and suggests a magnitude or value. Scalars can be positive, zero, or negative.

> **SAMPLE** problem **1**

At the Molson Indy race in Toronto, Ontario, a driver covers a single-lap distance of 2.90 km at an average speed of 1.50×10^2 km/h. Determine

(a) the average speed in metres per second
(b) the time in seconds to complete the lap

Solution

(a) To convert units, we multiply by factors that are equivalent to 1. We know that
1 km = 1000 m and 1 h = 3600 s

$$\therefore 1.50 \times 10^2 \text{ km/h} = 1.50 \times 10^2 \frac{\text{km}}{\text{h}} \times \frac{1000 \text{ m}}{1 \text{ km}} \times \frac{1 \text{ h}}{3600 \text{ s}} = 41.7 \text{ m/s}$$

The average speed is 41.7 m/s.

(b) v_{av} = 41.7 m/s
d = 2.90 km = 2.90×10^3 m
Δt = ?

Rearranging the equation $v_{av} = \frac{d}{\Delta t}$ to isolate Δt, we have

$$\Delta t = \frac{d}{v_{av}}$$
$$= \frac{2.90 \times 10^3 \text{ m}}{41.7 \text{ m/s}}$$
$$\Delta t = 69.6 \text{ s}$$

The time to complete the lap is 69.6 s. (Refer to the Learning Tip, Significant Digits and Rounding.)

LEARNING TIP

The Average Speed Equation
In the equation $v_{av} = \frac{d}{\Delta t}$, the symbol v comes from the word velocity (a vector quantity) and the subscript "av" indicates average. The Greek letter Δ (delta) denotes the change in a quantity, in this case time. The symbol t usually represents a time at which an event occurs, and Δt represents the time between events, or the elapsed time.

LEARNING TIP

Significant Digits and Rounding
In all sample problems in this text—take a close look at Sample Problem 1—the answers have been rounded off to the appropriate number of significant digits. Take special care in answering a question with two or more parts. For example, when working on a two-part problem, keep the intermediate (excess-precision) answer for part (a) in your calculator so that you can use it to solve part (b) without rounding error. Appendix A reviews the rules for significant digits and rounding-off.

> ### Practice

Understanding Concepts

1. For each of the following motions, state whether the number of dimensions is one, two, or three:
   (a) A tennis ball falls vertically downward after you release it from rest in your hand.
   (b) A tennis ball falls vertically downward after you release it from rest in your hand, hits the court, and bounces directly upward.
   (c) A basketball flies in a direct arc into the hoop.
   (d) A baseball pitcher tosses a curveball toward the batter.
   (e) A passenger on a Ferris wheel travels in a circle around the centre of the wheel.
   (f) A roller coaster moves around the track.

vector quantity quantity that has both magnitude and direction

position ($\vec{d}$) the distance and direction of an object from a reference point

displacement ($\Delta\vec{d}$) change in position of an object in a given direction

2. Which of the following measurements are scalar quantities?
   (a) the force exerted by an elevator cable
   (b) the reading on a car's odometer
   (c) the gravitational force of Earth on you
   (d) the number of physics students in your class
   (e) your age

3. Does a car's speedometer indicate average speed or instantaneous speed? Is the indicated quantity a scalar or a vector? Explain.

4. In the Indianapolis 500 auto race, drivers must complete 200 laps of a 4.02-km (2.50-mile) track. Calculate and compare the average speeds in kilometres per hour, given the following times for 200 laps:
   (a) 6.69 h (in 1911, the first year of the race)
   (b) 3.32 h (in 1965)
   (c) 2.69 h (in 1990, still a record more than a decade later)

5. A swimmer crosses a circular pool of diameter 16 m in 21 s.
   (a) Determine the swimmer's average speed.
   (b) How long would the swimmer take to swim, at the same average speed, around the edge of the pool?

6. Determine the total distance travelled in each case:
   (a) Sound propagating at 342 m/s crosses a room in 3.54×10^{-2} s.
   (b) Thirty-two scuba divers take turns riding an underwater tricycle at an average speed of 1.74 km/h for 60.0 h. (Express your answer both in kilometres and in metres.)

Velocity and Other Vector Quantities

Many of the quantities we measure involve a direction. A **vector quantity** is a quantity with a magnitude and direction. Position, displacement, and velocity are common vector quantities in kinematics. In this text, we indicate a vector quantity algebraically by a symbol containing an arrow with the direction stated in square brackets. Examples of directions and their specifications are east [E], upward [up], downward [down], and forward [fwd].

Position, $\vec{d}$, is the directed distance of an object from a reference point. **Displacement**, $\Delta\vec{d}$, is the change of position—that is, the final position minus the initial position. In **Figure 3**, a cyclist initially located 338 m west of an intersection moves to a new position 223 m west of the same intersection.

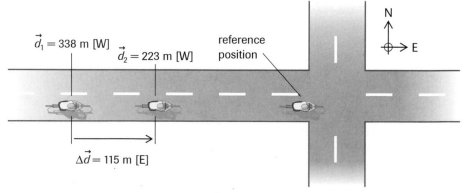

Figure 3
In moving from position $\vec{d}_1$ to $\vec{d}_2$, the cyclist undergoes a displacement $\Delta\vec{d} = \vec{d}_2 - \vec{d}_1$.

We can determine the cyclist's displacement as follows:

$$\Delta \vec{d} = \vec{d}_2 - \vec{d}_1$$
$$= 223 \text{ m [W]} - 338 \text{ m [W]}$$
$$= -115 \text{ m [W]}$$
$$\Delta \vec{d} = 115 \text{ m [E]}$$

The quantities "-115 m [W]" and "115 m [E]" denote the same vector.

A fundamental vector quantity involving position and time is **velocity**, or rate of change of position. The velocity at any particular instant is called the **instantaneous velocity**, $\vec{v}$. If the velocity is constant (so that the moving body travels at an unchanging speed in an unchanging direction), the position is said to change uniformly with time, resulting in *uniform motion*.

The **average velocity**, $\vec{v}_{av}$, of a motion is the change of position divided by the time interval for that change. From this definition, we can write the equation

$$\vec{v}_{av} = \frac{\Delta \vec{d}}{\Delta t}$$

where $\Delta \vec{d}$ is the displacement (or change of position) and Δt is the time interval. For motion with constant velocity, the average velocity is equal to the instantaneous velocity at any time.

> ▶ **SAMPLE** problem **2**

The cyclist in **Figure 3** takes 25.1 s to cover the displacement of 115 m [E] from $\vec{d}_1$ to $\vec{d}_2$.

(a) Calculate the cyclist's average velocity.

(b) If the cyclist maintains the same average velocity for 1.00 h, what is the total displacement?

(c) If the cyclist turns around at $\vec{d}_2$ and travels to position $\vec{d}_3 = 565$ m [W] in 72.5 s, what is the average velocity for the entire motion?

Solution

(a) $\Delta \vec{d} = 115$ m [E]

$\Delta t = 25.1$ s

$\vec{v}_{av} = ?$

$$\vec{v}_{av} = \frac{\Delta \vec{d}}{\Delta t}$$
$$= \frac{115 \text{ m [E]}}{25.1 \text{ s}}$$
$$\vec{v}_{av} = 4.58 \text{ m/s [E]}$$

The cyclist's average velocity is 4.58 m/s [E].

(b) $\Delta t = 1.00$ h $= 3600$ s

$\vec{v}_{av} = 4.58$ m/s [E]

$\Delta \vec{d} = ?$

$$\Delta \vec{d} = \vec{v}_{av} \Delta t$$
$$= (4.58 \text{ m/s [E]})(3600 \text{ s})$$
$$\Delta \vec{d} = 1.65 \times 10^4 \text{ m [E] or 16.5 km [E]}$$

The total displacement is 16.5 km [E].

Comparing Displacements
The displacement from Quebec City to Montreal is 250 km [41° S of W]. The displacement from Baltimore, Maryland, to Charlottesville, Virginia, is 250 km [41° S of W]. Since both displacements have the same magnitude (250 km) and direction [41° S of W], they are the same vectors. Vectors with the same magnitude and direction are identical, even though their starting positions can be different.

velocity ($\vec{v}$) the rate of change of position

instantaneous velocity velocity at a particular instant

average velocity ($\vec{v}_{av}$) change of position divided by the time interval for that change

LEARNING *TIP*

Properties of Vectors
A vector divided by a scalar, as in the equation $\vec{v}_{av} = \dfrac{\Delta \vec{d}}{\Delta t}$, is a vector. Multiplying a vector by a scalar also yields a vector. Appendix A discusses vector arithmetic.

LEARNING *TIP*

Unit and Dimensional Analysis
Unit analysis (using such units as metres, kilograms, and seconds) or dimensional analysis (using such dimensions as length, mass, and time) can be useful to ensure that both the left-hand side and the right-hand side of any equation have the same units or dimensions. Try this with the equation used to solve Sample Problem 2(b). If the units or dimensions are not the same, there must be an error in the equation. For details, see Appendix A.

Other Direction Conventions

In navigation, directions are taken clockwise from due north. For example, a direction of 180° is due south, and a direction of 118° is equivalent to the direction [28° S of E]. In mathematics, angles are measured counterclockwise from the positive x-axis.

(c) $\Delta \vec{d} = \vec{d}_3 - \vec{d}_1$

$\qquad = 565$ m [W] $- 338$ m [W]

$\Delta \vec{d} = 227$ m [W]

$\Delta t = 25.1$ s $+ 72.5$ s $= 97.6$ s

$\vec{v}_{av} = ?$

$$\vec{v}_{av} = \frac{\Delta \vec{d}}{\Delta t}$$

$$= \frac{227 \text{ m [W]}}{97.6 \text{ s}}$$

$\vec{v}_{av} = 2.33$ m/s [W]

The average velocity is 2.33 m/s [W].

(Can you see why this average velocity is so much less than the average velocity in (a)?)

▶ Practice

Understanding Concepts

7. Give specific examples of three different types of vector quantities that you have experienced today.

8. (a) Is it possible for the total distance travelled to equal the magnitude of the displacement? If "no," why not? If "yes," give an example.
   (b) Is it possible for the total distance travelled to exceed the magnitude of the displacement? If "no," why not? If "yes," give an example.
   (c) Is it possible for the magnitude of the displacement to exceed the total distance travelled? If "no," why not? If "yes," give an example.

9. Can the average speed ever equal the magnitude of the average velocity? If "no," why not? If "yes," give an example.

10. A city bus leaves the terminal and travels, with a few stops, along a straight route that takes it 12 km [E] of its starting position in 24 min. In another 24 min, the bus turns around and retraces its path to the terminal.
    (a) What is the average speed of the bus for the entire route?
    (b) Calculate the average velocity of the bus from the terminal to the farthest position from the terminal.
    (c) Find the average velocity of the bus for the entire route.
    (d) Why are your answers for (b) and (c) different?

11. A truck driver, reacting quickly to an emergency, applies the brakes. During the driver's 0.32 s reaction time, the truck maintains a constant velocity of 27 m/s [fwd]. What is the displacement of the truck during the time the driver takes to react?

12. The Arctic tern holds the world record for bird migration distance. The tern migrates once a year from islands north of the Arctic Circle to the shores of Antarctica, a displacement of approximately 1.6×10^4 km [S]. (The route, astonishingly, lies mainly over water.) If a tern's average velocity during this trip is 21 km/h [S], how long does the journey take? (Answer both in hours and days.)

Applying Inquiry Skills

13. Small airports use windsocks, like the one in **Figure 4**.
    (a) Does a windsock indicate a scalar quantity or a vector quantity? What is that quantity?
    (b) Describe how you would set up an experiment to help you calibrate the windsock.

Answers

10. (a) 3.0×10^1 km/h

    (b) 3.0×10^1 km/h [E]

    (c) 0.0 km/h

11. 8.6 m [fwd]

12. 7.6×10^2 h; 32 d

Figure 4
A typical windsock

Position and Velocity Graphs

Graphing provides a useful way of studying motion. We begin by studying position-time and velocity-time graphs for bodies with constant velocity motion.

Consider a marathon runner moving along a straight road with a constant velocity of 5.5 m/s [S] for 3.0 min. At the start of the motion (i.e., at $t = 0$), the initial position is $\vec{d} = 0$. The corresponding position-time data are shown in **Table 1**. The corresponding position-time graph is shown in **Figure 5**. Notice that for constant velocity motion, the position-time graph is a straight line.

Since the line on the position-time graph has a constant slope, we can calculate the slope since it is the ratio of the change in the quantity on the vertical axis to the corresponding change in the quantity on the horizontal axis. Thus, the slope of the line on the position-time graph from $t = 0.0$ s to $t = 180$ s is

$$m = \frac{\Delta \vec{d}}{\Delta t}$$

$$= \frac{990 \text{ m [S]} - 0 \text{ m}}{180 \text{ s} - 0 \text{ s}}$$

$$m = 5.5 \text{ m/s [S]}$$

This value would be the same no matter which part of the line we used to calculate the slope. It is apparent that for constant velocity motion, the average velocity is equal to the instantaneous velocity at any particular time and that both are equal to the slope of the line on the position-time graph.

Figure 6 is the corresponding velocity-time graph of the runner's motion. A practice question will ask you to show that the area under the plot (the shaded area) represents the displacement, in other words, represents $\Delta \vec{d}$ over the time interval that the area covers.

Table 1 Position-Time Data

Time	Position
t (s)	$\vec{d}$ (m [S])
0	0
60	330
120	660
180	990

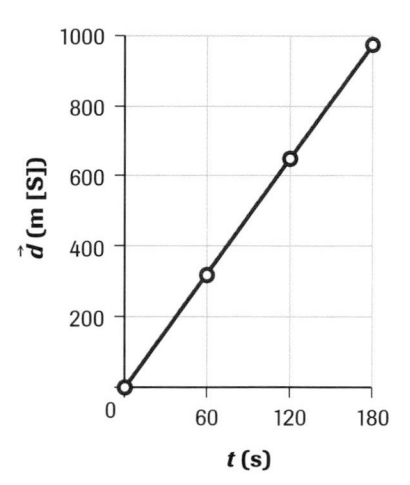

Figure 5
Position-time graph of the runner's motion

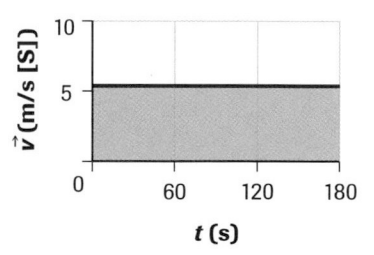

Figure 6
Velocity-time graph of the runner's motion

► **SAMPLE** problem **3**

Describe the motion represented by the position-time graph shown in **Figure 7**, and sketch the corresponding velocity-time graph.

Solution

The slope of the line is constant and it is negative. This means that the velocity is constant in the easterly direction. The initial position is away from the origin and the object is moving toward the origin. The velocity-time graph can be either negative west or positive east as shown in **Figure 8**.

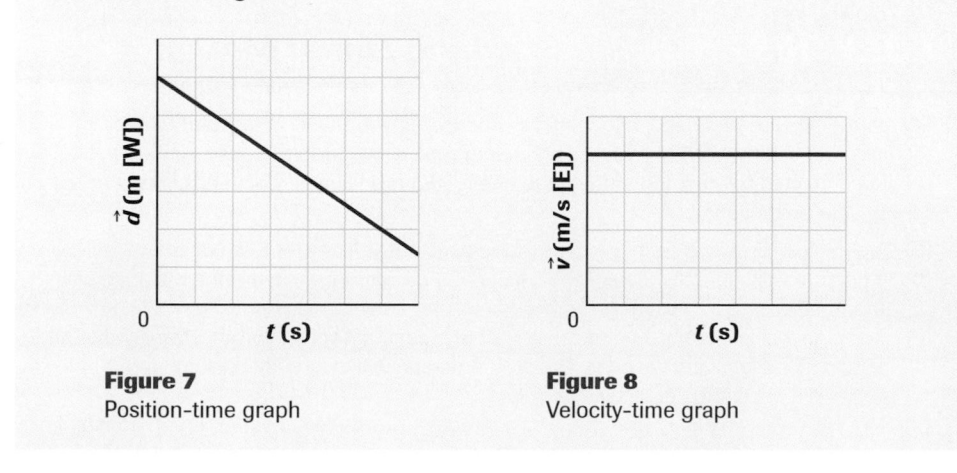

Figure 7
Position-time graph

Figure 8
Velocity-time graph

Table 2 Position-Time Data

Time t (s)	Position $\vec{d}$ (m [fwd])
0	0
2.0	4.0
4.0	16
6.0	36
8.0	64

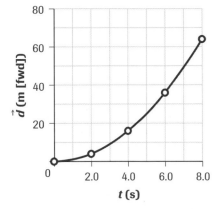

Figure 9
Position-time graph for changing instantaneous velocity. The average velocity between any two times can be found by applying the equation $\vec{v}_{av} = \dfrac{\Delta \vec{d}}{\Delta t}$, but a different approach must be used to find the instantaneous velocity.

tangent a straight line that touches a curve at a single point and has the same slope as the curve at that point

Now let's turn to graphs of motion with changing instantaneous velocity. This type of motion, often called *nonuniform motion*, involves a change of direction, a change of speed, or both.

Consider, for example, a car starting from rest and speeding up, as in **Table 2** and **Figure 9**.

Since the slope of the line on the position-time graph is gradually increasing, the velocity is also gradually increasing. To find the slope of a curved line at a particular instant, we draw a straight line touching—but not cutting—the curve at that point. This straight line is called a **tangent** to the curve. The slope of the tangent to a curve on a position-time graph is the instantaneous velocity.

Figure 10 shows the tangent drawn at 2.0 s for the motion of the car. The broken lines in the diagram show the average velocities between $t = 2.0$ s and later times. For example, from $t = 2.0$ s to $t = 8.0$ s, $\Delta t = 6.0$ s and the average velocity is the slope of line A. From $t = 2.0$ s to $t = 6.0$ s, $\Delta t = 4.0$ s and the average velocity is the slope of line B, and so on. Notice that as Δt becomes smaller, the slopes of the lines get closer to the slope of the tangent at $t = 2.0$ s (i.e., they get closer to the instantaneous velocity, $\vec{v}$). Thus, we can define the instantaneous velocity as

$$\vec{v} = \lim_{\Delta t \to 0} \frac{\Delta \vec{d}}{\Delta t}$$

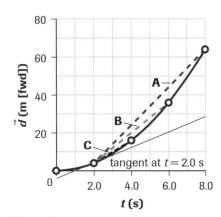

Figure 10
The slopes of lines A, B, and C represent the average velocities at times beyond 2.0 s. As these times become smaller, the slopes get closer to the slope of the tangent at $t = 2.0$ s.

▶ **TRY THIS** activity *Graphing Linear Motion*

Sketch the position-time and velocity-time graphs that you think correspond to each of the following situations. After discussing your graphs with your group, use a motion sensor connected to graphing software to check your predictions. Comment on the accuracy of your predictions.

(a) A person walks away from the sensor at a constant velocity for 5 or 6 steps.
(b) A person walks directly toward the sensor at a constant velocity from a distance of about 4.0 m.
(c) A person walks directly toward the sensor at a constant velocity from 3.0 m away. The person stops for a few seconds. Finally, the person walks directly back toward the origin at a constant, but slower velocity.
(d) A person walks halfway from the origin directly toward the sensor at a high constant velocity, stops briefly, walks the rest of the way at a low constant velocity, and then returns at a high constant velocity to the origin.

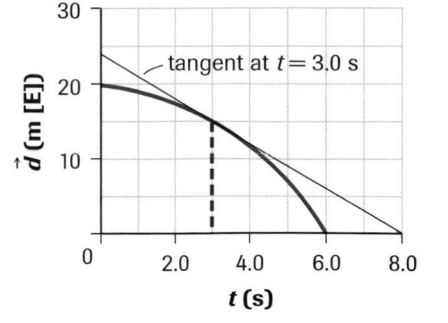

Figure 11
Position-time graph for Sample Problem 4

▶ **SAMPLE** problem **4**

Figure 11 is the position-time graph for a golf ball rolling along a straight trough which slopes downward from east to west. We arbitrarily choose one-dimensional coordinates on which the origin is at the western end of the trough.

(a) Describe the motion.

(b) Calculate the instantaneous velocity at $t = 3.0$ s.

(c) Determine the average velocity between 3.0 s and 6.0 s.

Solution

(a) The slope is zero at $t = 0.0$ s, then it becomes negative. Thus, the velocity starts off at zero and gradually increases in magnitude in the westerly direction. (Negative east is equivalent to positive west.) The object starts at a position east of the reference point or origin and then moves westward arriving at the origin 6.0 s later.

(b) The instantaneous velocity at $t = 3.0$ s is the slope of the tangent at that instant. Thus,

$$\vec{v} = \text{slope} = m = \frac{\Delta \vec{d}}{\Delta t}$$

$$= \frac{0.0 \text{ m} - 24 \text{ m [E]}}{8.0 \text{ s} - 0.0 \text{ s}}$$

$$= -3.0 \text{ m/s [E]}$$

$$\vec{v} = 3.0 \text{ m/s [W]}$$

The instantaneous velocity at 3.0 s is approximately 3.0 m/s [W].
(This answer is approximate because of the uncertainty of drawing the tangent.)

(c) We apply the equation for average velocity:

$$\vec{v}_{av} = \frac{\Delta \vec{d}}{\Delta t}$$

$$= \frac{0.0 \text{ m} - 15 \text{ m [E]}}{6.0 \text{ s} - 3.0 \text{ s}}$$

$$= -5.0 \text{ m/s [E]}$$

$$\vec{v}_{av} = 5.0 \text{ m/s [W]}$$

The average velocity between 3.0 s and 6.0 s is 5.0 m/s [W].

▶ **Practice**

Understanding Concepts

14. Describe the motion depicted in each of the graphs in **Figure 12**.

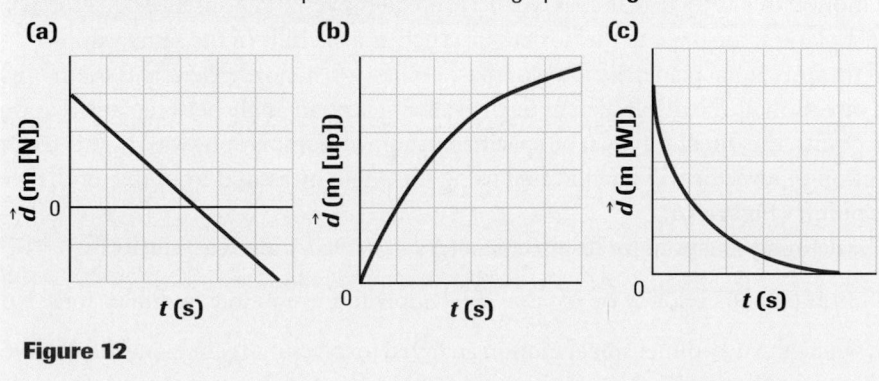

Figure 12

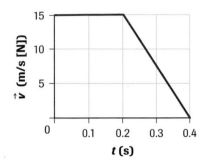

Figure 14
Velocity-time graph for question 16

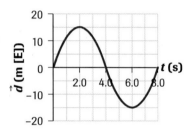

Figure 15
Position-time graph for question 17

15. Use the information on the graphs in **Figure 13** to generate the corresponding velocity-time graphs.

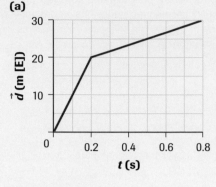

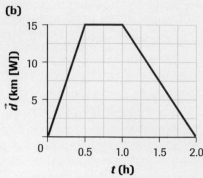

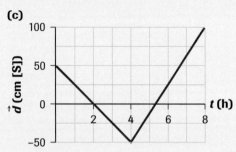

Figure 13
Position-time graphs

16. Determine the area between the line and the horizontal axis on the velocity-time graph in **Figure 14**. What does that area represent? (*Hint:* Include units in your area calculation.)

17. Redraw the position-time graph in **Figure 15** in your notebook and determine the (approximate) instantaneous velocities at $t = 1.0$ s, 2.0 s, 3.0 s, 4.0 s, and 5.0 s.

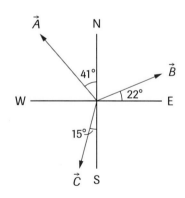

directions of vectors:
$\vec{A}$ [41° W of N]
$\vec{B}$ [22° N of E]
$\vec{C}$ [15° W of S]

Figure 16
Notation for specifying the directions of vectors

Displacement and Velocity in Two Dimensions

As you are driving north on a highway in level country, you come to a bridge closed for repairs. Your destination is across the bridge on the north side of the river. Using a map, you discover a road that goes eastward, then northward across the river, then westward to your destination. The concepts of displacement, velocity, and time interval help you analyze the alternative route as a vector problem in the horizontal plane. You can also analyze motion in a vertical plane (as when a football moves in the absence of a crosswind) or in a plane at an angle to the horizontal (such as a ski hill) in the same way.

In the horizontal plane, the four compass points—east, north, west, and south—indicate direction. If the displacement or the velocity is at an angle between any two compass points, the direction must be specified in some unambiguous way. In this text, the direction of a vector will be indicated using the angle measured from one of the compass points (**Figure 16**).

The defining equations for displacement ($\Delta \vec{d} = \vec{d}_2 - \vec{d}_1$), average velocity $\left(\vec{v}_{av} = \dfrac{\Delta \vec{d}}{\Delta t} \right)$, and instantaneous velocity $\left(\vec{v} = \lim_{\Delta t \to 0} \dfrac{\Delta \vec{d}}{\Delta t} \right)$ apply to motion in two dimensions. However, where the two-dimensional motion analyzed involves more than one displacement, as shown in **Figure 17**, $\Delta \vec{d}$ is the result of successive displacements ($\Delta \vec{d} = \Delta \vec{d}_1 + \Delta \vec{d}_2 + \ldots$), and is called *total displacement*.

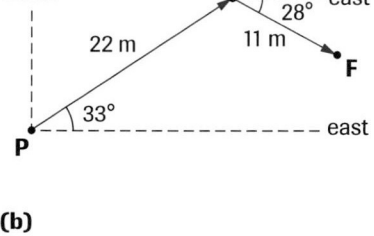

Figure 17
The total displacement is the vector sum of the individual displacements, $\Delta\vec{d} = \Delta\vec{d_1} + \Delta\vec{d_2} + \Delta\vec{d_3}$. Notice that the vectors are added head-to-tail, and the total vector faces from the initial position to the final position.

▶ **SAMPLE** problem **5**

In 4.4 s, a chickadee flies in a horizontal plane from a fence post (P) to a bush (B) and then to a bird feeder (F), as shown in **Figure 18(a)**. Find the following:

(a) total distance travelled

(b) average speed

(c) total displacement

(d) average velocity

Solution

(a) The total distance travelled is a scalar quantity.

$d = 22\text{ m} + 11\text{ m} = 33\text{ m}$

(b) $d = 33\text{ m}$

$\Delta t = 4.4\text{ s}$

$v_{av} = ?$

$$v_{av} = \frac{d}{\Delta t}$$

$$= \frac{33\text{ m}}{4.4\text{ s}}$$

$$v_{av} = 7.5\text{ m/s}$$

The average speed is 7.5 m/s.

(c) We will use the method of sine and cosine laws to solve this problem. (Alternatively, we could use the component technique or a vector scale diagram.) We apply the cosine law to find the magnitude of the displacement, $|\Delta\vec{d}|$. From **Figure 18(b)**, the angle B equals 119°.

$|\Delta\vec{d_1}| = 22\text{ m} \qquad \angle B = 119°$
$|\Delta\vec{d_2}| = 11\text{ m} \qquad |\Delta\vec{d}| = ?$

Applying the cosine law:

$$|\Delta\vec{d}|^2 = |\Delta\vec{d_1}|^2 + |\Delta\vec{d_2}|^2 - 2|\Delta\vec{d_1}||\Delta\vec{d_2}|\cos B$$
$$|\Delta\vec{d}|^2 = (22\text{ m})^2 + (11\text{ m})^2 - 2(22\text{ m})(11\text{ m})(\cos 119°)$$
$$|\Delta\vec{d}| = 29\text{ m}$$

To determine the direction of the displacement, we use the sine law:

$$\frac{\sin P}{|\Delta\vec{d_2}|} = \frac{\sin B}{|\Delta\vec{d}|}$$

$$\sin P = \frac{|\Delta\vec{d_2}|\sin B}{|\Delta\vec{d}|}$$

$$\sin P = \frac{(11\text{ m})(\sin 119°)}{(29\text{ m})}$$

$$\angle P = 19°$$

From the diagram, we see that the direction of the total displacement is $33° - 19° = 14°$ N of E. Therefore, the total displacement is 29 m [14° N of E].

(a)

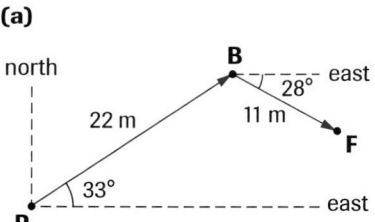

(b)

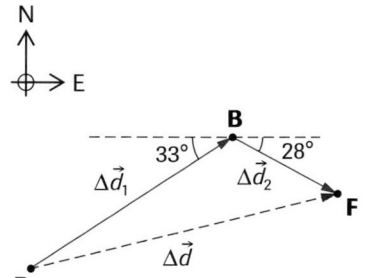

$\angle B = 180° - 33° - 28°$
$\angle B = 119°$

Figure 18
For Sample Problem 5
(a) The chickadee takes 4.4 s to complete the motion shown.
(b) Angle B is found to be 119°.

Answers

18. 5.6 m [24° E of S]

20. (a) 1.3×10^3 m [42° N of E]

    (b) 5.6 m/s; 5.2 m/s [42° N of E]

LEARNING *TIP*

Adding Vectors
In applying the vector addition equation ($\Delta \vec{d} = \Delta \vec{d_1} + \Delta \vec{d_2}$ + ...) to two-dimensional motion, you can choose to add the displacement vectors by whichever of the methods summarized in Appendix A proves most convenient. The vector scale "head-to-tail" diagram method is excellent for visualizing and understanding the situation. However, this method is not as accurate as other methods. The component technique is accurate and can be used for any number of vectors, but it can be time-consuming. The method using the sine and cosine laws is accurate and fairly quick to use, but it is limited to the addition (or subtraction) of only two vectors.

(d) $\Delta \vec{d} = $ 29 m [14° N of E]

$\Delta t = $ 4.4 s

$\vec{v}_{av} = ?$

$$\vec{v}_{av} = \frac{\Delta \vec{d}}{\Delta t}$$

$$= \frac{29 \text{ m } [14° \text{ N of E}]}{4.4 \text{ s}}$$

$$\vec{v}_{av} = 6.6 \text{ m/s } [14° \text{ N of E}]$$

The average velocity is 6.6 m/s [14° N of E].

> ▶ **Practice**

Understanding Concepts

18. Determine the vector sum of the displacements $\Delta \vec{d_1} = $ 2.4 m [32° S of W]; $\Delta \vec{d_2} = $ 1.6 m [S]; and $\Delta \vec{d_3} = $ 4.9 m [27° S of E].

19. Solve Sample Problem 5 using
    (a) a vector scale diagram
    (b) components (referring, if necessary, to Appendix A)

20. A skater on Ottawa's Rideau Canal travels in a straight line 8.5×10^2 m [25° N of E] and then 5.6×10^2 m in a straight line [21° E of N]. The entire motion takes 4.2 min.
    (a) What is the skater's displacement?
    (b) What are the skater's average speed and average velocity?

SUMMARY *Speed and Velocity in One and Two Dimensions*

- A scalar quantity has magnitude but no direction.
- Average speed is the total distance travelled divided by the total time of travel.
- A vector quantity has both magnitude and direction.
- Position is the distance with a direction from some reference point.
- Displacement is the change of position.
- Velocity is the rate of change of position.
- Average velocity is change of position divided by the time interval for that change.
- Instantaneous velocity is the velocity at a particular instant.
- Instantaneous speed is the magnitude of the instantaneous velocity.
- The slope of the line on a position-time graph indicates the velocity.
- The area under the line on a velocity-time graph indicates the change of position.
- In two-dimensional motion, the average velocity is the total displacement divided by the time interval for that displacement.

▶ **Section 1.1** *Questions*

Understanding Concepts

1. State whether each of the following is a scalar or a vector:
   (a) the magnitude of a vector quantity
   (b) a component of a vector quantity in some particular coordinate system
   (c) the mass you gained in the past 15 years
   (d) the product of a scalar and a vector
   (e) the area under the line and above the time axis on a velocity-time graph

2. Give a specific example for each of the following descriptions of a possible motion:
   (a) The velocity is constant.
   (b) The speed is constant, but the velocity is constantly changing.
   (c) The motion is in one dimension, and the total distance travelled exceeds the magnitude of the displacement.
   (d) The motion is in one dimension, the average speed is greater than zero, and the average velocity is zero.
   (e) The motion is in two dimensions, the average speed is greater than zero, and the average velocity is zero.

3. If two measurements have different dimensions, can they be added? multiplied? In each case, give an explanation if "no," an example if "yes."

4. Light travels in a vacuum at 3.00×10^8 m/s. Determine the time in seconds for each of the following:
   (a) Light travels from the Sun to Earth. The average radius of Earth's orbit around the Sun is 1.49×10^{11} m.
   (b) Laser light is sent from Earth, reflects off a mirror on the Moon, and returns to Earth. The average Earth-Moon distance is 3.84×10^5 km.

5. **Figure 19** shows the idealized motion of a car.
   (a) Determine the average speed between 4.0 s and 8.0 s; and between 0.0 s and 8.0 s.
   (b) Calculate the average velocity between 8.0 s and 9.0 s; between 12 s and 16 s; and between 0.0 s and 16 s.
   (c) Find the instantaneous speed at 6.0 s and 9.0 s.
   (d) Calculate the instantaneous velocity at 14 s.

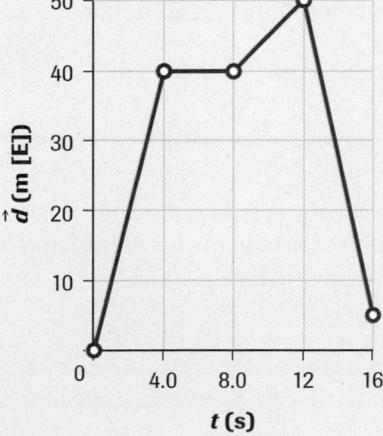

Figure 19
Position-time graph

6. What quantity can be calculated from a position-time graph to indicate the velocity of an object? How can that quantity be found if the line on the graph is curved?

7. Use the information in **Figure 20** to generate the corresponding position-time graph, assuming the position at time $t = 0$ is 8.0 m [E].

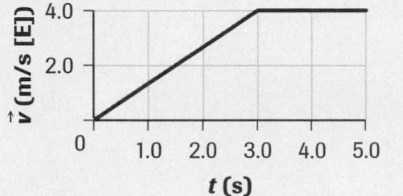

Figure 20
Velocity-time graph

8. In a total time of 2.0 min, a duck on a pond paddles 22 m [36° N of E] and then paddles another 65 m [25° E of S]. Determine the duck's
   (a) total distance travelled
   (b) average speed
   (c) total displacement
   (d) average velocity

Applying Inquiry Skills

9. (a) Review your work in Practice question 17, and use a plane mirror to determine how accurately you drew the tangents used to find the instantaneous velocities.
   (b) Describe how to draw tangents to curved lines as accurately as possible.

Making Connections

10. Research has shown that the average alcohol-free driver requires about 0.8 s to apply the brakes after seeing an emergency. **Figure 21** shows the approximate reaction times for drivers who have been drinking beer. Copy **Table 3** into your notebook, and use the data from the graph to determine the reaction distance (i.e., the distance travelled after seeing the emergency and before applying the brakes).

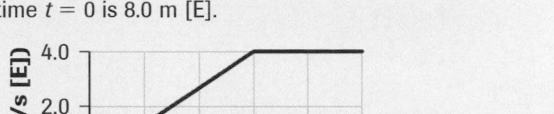

Figure 21
Effect of beer on reaction times for drivers

Table 3 Data for Question 10

Speed	Reaction Distance		
	no alcohol	*4 bottles*	*5 bottles*
17 m/s (60 km/h)	?	?	?
25 m/s (90 km/h)	?	?	?
33 m/s (120 km/h)	?	?	?

1.2 Acceleration in One and Two Dimensions

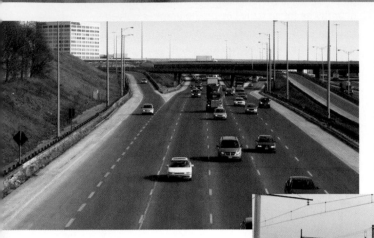

Have you noticed that when you are in a car, you have to accelerate on the ramp of an expressway to merge safely (**Figure 1**)? Drivers experience acceleration whenever their vehicles speed up, slow down, or change directions.

There have been concerns that vehicles using alternative energy resources may not be able to accelerate as quickly as vehicles powered by conventional fossil-fuel engines. However, new designs are helping to dispel that worry. For example, the electric limousine shown in **Figure 2** can quickly attain highway speeds.

Figure 1
As they merge onto the main expressway lanes, cars and motorcycles accelerate more easily than trucks.

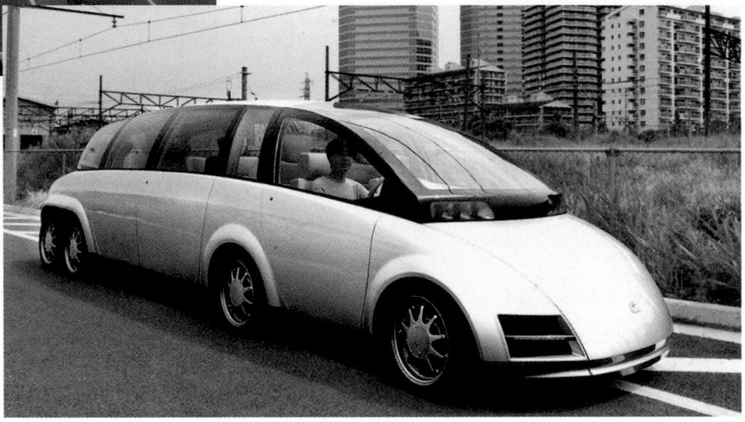

Figure 2
This experimental electric limousine, with a mass of 3.0×10^3 kg, can travel 300 km on an hour's charge of its lithium battery.

DID YOU KNOW?

The Jerk
Sometimes the instantaneous acceleration varies, such as when rockets are launched into space. The rate of change of acceleration is known as the "jerk," which can be found using the relation jerk $= \frac{\Delta \vec{a}}{\Delta t}$ or by finding the slope of the line on an acceleration-time graph. What is the SI unit of jerk?

Acceleration and Average Acceleration in One Dimension

Acceleration is the rate of change of velocity. Since velocity is a vector quantity, acceleration is also a vector quantity. **Average acceleration**, $\vec{a}_{av}$, is the change in velocity divided by the time interval for that change:

$$\vec{a}_{av} = \frac{\Delta \vec{v}}{\Delta t} = \frac{\vec{v}_f - \vec{v}_i}{\Delta t}$$

where $\vec{v}_f$ is the final velocity, $\vec{v}_i$ is the initial velocity, and Δt is the time interval.

The acceleration at any particular instant, or **instantaneous acceleration**—but often just referred to as acceleration—is found by applying the equation:

$$\vec{a} = \lim_{\Delta t \to 0} \frac{\Delta \vec{v}}{\Delta t}$$

In other words, as Δt approaches zero, the average acceleration $\left(\frac{\Delta \vec{v}}{\Delta t}\right)$ approaches the instantaneous acceleration.

As you can see from the following sample problems, any unit of velocity divided by a unit of time is a possible unit of average acceleration and instantaneous acceleration.

acceleration ($\vec{a}$) rate of change of velocity

average acceleration ($\vec{a}_{av}$) change in velocity divided by the time interval for that change

instantaneous acceleration acceleration at a particular instant

▶ *SAMPLE* problem **1**

A racing car accelerates from rest to 96 km/h [W] in 4.1 s. Determine the average acceleration of the car.

Solution

$\vec{v}_i = 0.0$ km/h

$\vec{v}_f = 96$ km/h [W]

$\Delta t = 4.1$ s

$\vec{a}_{av} = ?$

$$\vec{a}_{av} = \frac{\vec{v}_f - \vec{v}_i}{\Delta t}$$

$$= \frac{96 \text{ km/h [W]} - 0.0 \text{ km/h}}{4.1 \text{ s}}$$

$$\vec{a}_{av} = 23 \text{ (km/h)/s [W]}$$

The average acceleration of the car is 23 (km/h)/s [W].

> **LEARNING TIP**
>
> **Comparing Symbols**
> We have already been using the symbols $\vec{v}_{av}$ and $\vec{v}$ for average velocity and instantaneous velocity. In a parallel way, we use $\vec{a}_{av}$ and $\vec{a}$ for average acceleration and instantaneous acceleration. When the acceleration is constant, the average and instantaneous accelerations are equal, and the symbol $\vec{a}$ can be used for both.

▶ *SAMPLE* problem **2**

A motorcyclist travelling at 23 m/s [N] applies the brakes, producing an average acceleration of 7.2 m/s² [S].

(a) What is the motorcyclist's velocity after 2.5 s?

(b) Show that the equation you used in (a) is dimensionally correct.

Solution

(a) $\vec{v}_i = 23$ m/s [N]

$\vec{a}_{av} = 7.2$ m/s² [S] $= -7.2$ m/s² [N]

$\Delta t = 2.5$ s

$\vec{v}_f = ?$

From the equation $\vec{a}_{av} = \dfrac{\vec{v}_f - \vec{v}_i}{\Delta t}$,

$$\vec{v}_f = \vec{v}_i + \vec{a}_{av}\Delta t$$

$$= 23 \text{ m/s [N]} + (-7.2 \text{ m/s}^2 \text{ [N]})(2.5 \text{ s})$$

$$= 23 \text{ m/s [N]} - 18 \text{ m/s [N]}$$

$$\vec{v}_f = 5 \text{ m/s [N]}$$

The motorcyclist's final velocity is 5 m/s [N].

(b) We can use a question mark above an equal sign $\left(\overset{?}{=}\right)$ to indicate that we are checking to see if the dimensions on the two sides of the equation are the same.

$$\vec{v}_f \overset{?}{=} \vec{v}_i + \vec{a}_{av}\Delta t$$

$$\frac{L}{T} \overset{?}{=} \frac{L}{T} + \left(\frac{L}{T^2}\right)T$$

$$\frac{L}{T} \overset{?}{=} \frac{L}{T} + \frac{L}{T}$$

The dimension on the left side of the equation is equal to the dimension on the right side of the equation.

> **LEARNING TIP**
>
> **Positive and Negative Directions**
> In Sample Problem 2, the average acceleration of 7.2 m/s² [S] is equivalent to -7.2 m/s² [N]. In this case, the positive direction of the motion is north: $\vec{v}_i = +23$ m/s [N]. Thus, a positive southward acceleration is equivalent to a negative northward acceleration, and both represent slowing down. Slowing down is sometimes called *deceleration*, but in this text we will use the term "negative acceleration." This helps to avoid possible sign errors when using equations.

▶ **Practice**

Understanding Concepts

1. Which of the following can be used as units of acceleration?
   (a) (km/s)/h (b) mm·s⁻² (c) Mm/min² (d) km/h² (e) km/min/min

2. (a) Is it possible to have an eastward velocity with a westward acceleration? If "no," explain why not. If "yes," give an example.
   (b) Is it possible to have acceleration when the velocity is zero? If "no," explain why not. If "yes," give an example.

3. A flock of robins is migrating southward. Describe the flock's motion at instants when its acceleration is (a) positive, (b) negative, and (c) zero. Take the southward direction as positive.

4. A track runner, starting from rest, reaches a velocity of 9.3 m/s [fwd] in 3.9 s. Determine the runner's average acceleration.

5. The Renault Espace is a production car that can go from rest to 26.7 m/s with an incredibly large average acceleration of magnitude 9.52 m/s².
   (a) How long does the Espace take to achieve its speed of 26.7 m/s?
   (b) What is this speed in kilometres per hour?
   (c) Show that the equation you applied in (a) is dimensionally correct.

6. The fastest of all fishes is the sailfish. If a sailfish accelerates at a rate of 14 (km/h)/s [fwd] for 4.7 s from its initial velocity of 42 km/h [fwd], what is its final velocity?

7. An arrow strikes a target in an archery tournament. The arrow undergoes an average acceleration of 1.37×10^3 m/s² [W] in 3.12×10^{-2} s, then stops. Determine the velocity of the arrow when it hits the target.

Graphing Motion with Constant Acceleration

A speedboat accelerates uniformly from rest for 8.0 s, with a displacement of 128 m [E] over that time interval. **Table 1** contains the position-time data from the starting position. **Figure 3** is the corresponding position-time graph.

Table 1 Position-Time Data

t (s)	$\vec{d}$ (m [E])
0	0
2.0	8.0
4.0	32
6.0	72
8.0	128

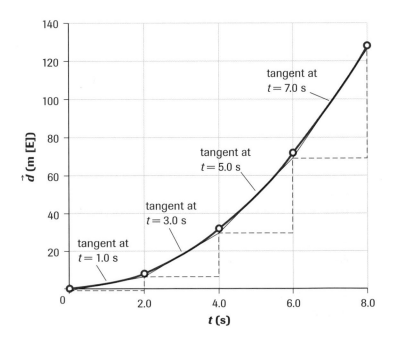

Figure 3
On this position-time graph of the boat's motion, the tangents at four different instants yield the instantaneous velocities at those instants. (The slope calculations are not shown here.)

Recall from Section 1.1 that the slope of the line at a particular instant on a position-time graph yields the instantaneous velocity. Since the slope continuously changes, several values are needed to determine how the velocity changes with time. One way to find the slope is to apply the "tangent technique" in which tangents to the curve are drawn at several instants and their slopes are calculated. **Table 2** shows the instantaneous velocities as determined from the slopes; **Figure 4** shows the corresponding velocity-time graph.

Table 2 Velocity-Time Data

t (s)	$\vec{v}$ (m/s [E])
0	0
1.0	4.0
3.0	12
5.0	20
7.0	28

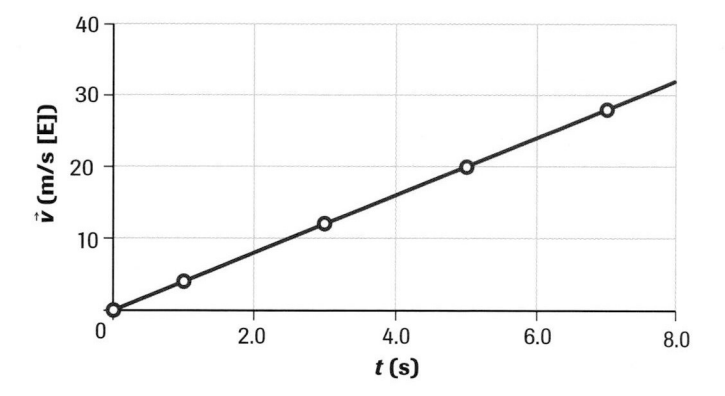

Figure 4
The velocity-time graph of motion with constant acceleration is a straight line. How would you find the instantaneous acceleration, average acceleration, and displacement of the boat from this graph?

The acceleration can be determined from the slope of the line on the velocity-time graph, which is $\dfrac{\Delta \vec{v}}{\Delta t}$. In this example, the slope, and thus the acceleration, is 4.0 m/s² [E]. **Figure 5** is the corresponding acceleration-time graph.

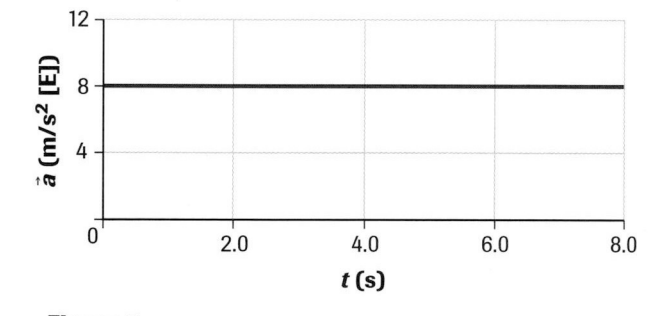

Figure 5
The acceleration-time graph of motion with constant acceleration is a straight horizontal line. How would you find the change in velocity over a given time interval from this graph?

What additional information can we determine from the velocity-time and acceleration-time graphs? As you discovered earlier, the area under the line on a velocity-time graph indicates the change in position (or the displacement) over the time interval for which the area is found. Similarly, the area under the line on an acceleration-time graph indicates the change in velocity over the time interval for which the area is calculated.

Figure 6 is the acceleration-time graph of a car accelerating through its first three gears. Assume that the initial velocity is zero.

(a) Use the information in the graph to determine the final velocity in each gear. Draw the corresponding velocity-time graph.

(b) From the velocity-time graph, determine the car's displacement from its initial position after 5.0 s.

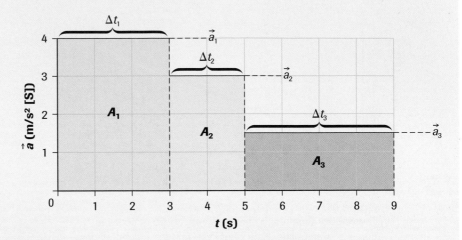

Figure 6
Acceleration-time graph

Solution

(a) The area beneath each segment of the acceleration-time plot is the change in velocity during that time interval.

$$A_1 = \vec{a}_1 \Delta t_1 \qquad\qquad A_2 = \vec{a}_2 \Delta t_2$$
$$= (4.0 \text{ m/s}^2 \text{[S]})(3.0 \text{ s}) \qquad = (3.0 \text{ m/s}^2 \text{[S]})(2.0 \text{ s})$$
$$A_1 = 12 \text{ m/s [S]} \qquad\qquad A_2 = 6.0 \text{ m/s [S]}$$

$$A_3 = \vec{a}_3 \Delta t_3 \qquad\qquad A_{total} = A_1 + A_2 + A_3$$
$$= (1.5 \text{ m/s}^2 \text{[S]})(4.0 \text{ s}) \qquad = 12 \text{ m/s} + 6.0 \text{ m/s} + 6.0 \text{ m/s}$$
$$A_3 = 6.0 \text{ m/s [S]} \qquad\qquad A_{total} = 24 \text{ m/s}$$

The initial velocity is $\vec{v}_1 = 0.0$ m/s. The final velocity in first gear is $\vec{v}_2 = 12$ m/s [S], in second gear is $\vec{v}_3 = 18$ m/s [S], and in third gear is $\vec{v}_4 = 24$ m/s [S].

Figure 7 is the corresponding velocity-time graph.

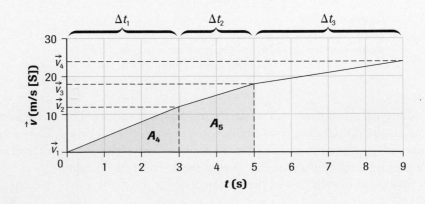

Figure 7
Velocity-time graph

(b) The area beneath each line on the velocity-time graph yields the change in position during that time interval.

$$A_4 = \frac{1}{2}\left(\vec{v}_2 - \vec{v}_1\right)(\Delta t_1)$$

$$= \frac{1}{2}\,(12 \text{ m/s [S]})\,(3.0 \text{ s})$$

$$A_4 = 18 \text{ m [S]}$$

$$A_5 = \left(\vec{v}_2\right)(\Delta t_2) + \frac{1}{2}\left(\vec{v}_3 - \vec{v}_2\right)(\Delta t_2)$$

$$= (12 \text{ m/s [S]})\,(2.0 \text{ s}) + \frac{1}{2}\,(18 \text{ m/s [S]} - 12 \text{ m/s [S]})\,(2.0 \text{ s})$$

$$A_5 = 30 \text{ m [S]}$$

(Area A_5 could also be found by using the equation for the area of a trapezoid.) The car's displacement after 5.0 s is 18 m [S] + 30 m [S] = 48 m [S].

▶ **TRY THIS** activity
Graphing Motion with Acceleration

The cart in **Figure 8** is given a brief push so that it rolls up an inclined plane, stops, then rolls back toward the bottom of the plane. A motion sensor is located at the bottom of the plane to plot position-time, velocity-time, and acceleration-time graphs. For the motion that occurs *after* the pushing force is no longer in contact with the cart, sketch the shapes of the $\vec{d}$-t, $\vec{v}$-t, and $\vec{a}$-t graphs for these situations:

(a) upward is positive
(b) downward is positive

Observe the motion and the corresponding graphs, and compare your predictions to the actual results.

 Catch the cart on its downward motion before it reaches the motion sensor.

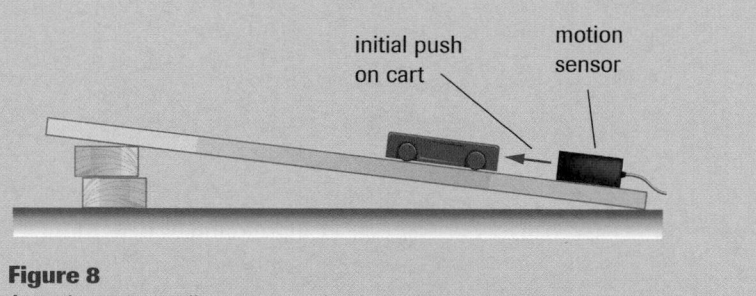

Figure 8
A motion sensor allows you to check predicted graphs.

▶ **Practice**

Understanding Concepts

8. Describe how to determine
   (a) average acceleration from a velocity-time graph
   (b) change in velocity from an acceleration-time graph
9. Describe the motion depicted in each graph in **Figure 9**.

(a)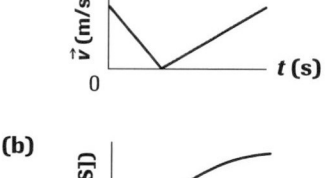

(b)

(c)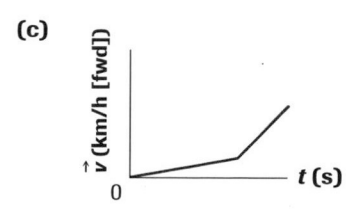

(d)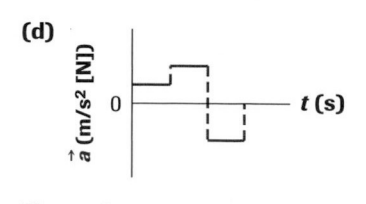

Figure 9
For question 9

10. **Table 3** summarizes observations of a crawling baby experiencing constant accelera-
    tion over several successive 2.0-s intervals.
    (a) Draw a velocity-time graph for this motion.
    (b) Use the information on your velocity-time graph to draw the corresponding
        acceleration-time graph.

Table 3 Data for Question 10

t (s)	0.0	2.0	4.0	6.0	8.0	10	12
$\vec{v}$ (cm/s [E])	10	15	20	15	10	5.0	0.0

11. **Figure 10** is the acceleration-time graph of a football lineman being pushed, from an
    initial velocity of zero, by other players. Draw the corresponding velocity-time graph.

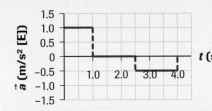

Figure 10
Acceleration-time graph

12. Determine the car's displacement after 9.0 s from the velocity-time graph in
    Figure 7.

Making Connections

13. The acceleration-time graphs in **Figures 6, 9(b)**, and **10** represent idealized situa-
    tions of constant acceleration.
    (a) What does "idealized" mean here?
    (b) Suggest one advantage of presenting idealized, rather than real-life, examples in
        a text of fundamental physics theory.
    (c) Redraw the graph in **Figure 6** to suggest more accurately the real-life motion of
        an accelerating car.

14. Explore the capabilities of graphing tools in acceleration problems. You may have
    access to a graphing calculator and graphing software in such scientific packages as
    IDL®, Maple®, or Mathematica®. Your school may have a planimeter, a mechanical
    instrument for finding the area of paper under a plotted curve. You could begin by
    checking the answers to Sample Problem 3.

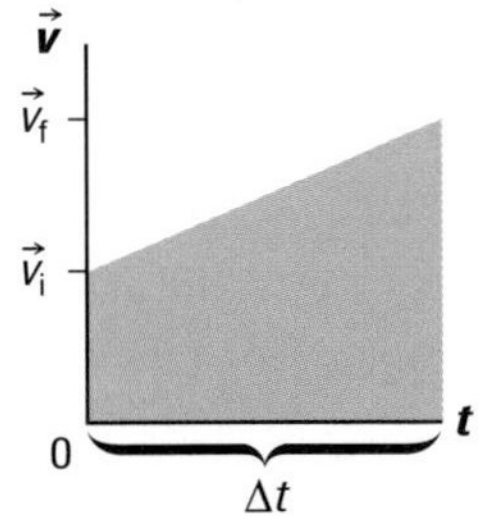

Solving Constant Acceleration Problems

The defining equation for average acceleration, $\vec{a}_{av} = \dfrac{\vec{v}_f - \vec{v}_i}{\Delta t}$, does not include

displacement. You have seen that displacement can be found by determining the area under
the line on a velocity-time graph. We can combine this observation with the defining equation for average acceleration to derive other equations useful in analyzing motion with
constant acceleration. Remember that when the acceleration is constant, $\vec{a} = \vec{a}_{av}$, so we
use the symbol $\vec{a}$ to represent the acceleration.

   Figure 11 shows a velocity-time graph of constant acceleration with initial velocity $\vec{v}_i$.
The area beneath the line is the area of a trapezoid, $\Delta \vec{d} = \dfrac{1}{2}(\vec{v}_f + \vec{v}_i)\Delta t$. This equation,

without the variable $\vec{a}$, can be combined with the defining equation for average acceleration to derive three other equations, each of which involves four of the five possible
variables that are associated with constant acceleration.

   For example, to derive the equation in which Δt is eliminated, we omit the vector
notation; this allows us to avoid the mathematical problem that would occur if we mul-

Figure 11
The shape of the figure under the
line on this graph is a trapezoid, so
the area under the line is the
product of the average length of the

two parallel sides, $\dfrac{\vec{v}_i + \vec{v}_f}{2}$, and the

perpendicular distance between
them, Δt.

tiplied two vectors. We can now rearrange the defining equation to get Δt, which we can substitute to solve for Δd:

$$a = \frac{v_f - v_i}{\Delta t}$$

$$\Delta t = \frac{v_f - v_i}{a}$$

$$\Delta d = \frac{1}{2}(v_f + v_i)\Delta t$$

$$= \frac{1}{2}(v_f + v_i)\left(\frac{v_f - v_i}{a}\right)$$

$$\Delta d = \frac{v_f^2 - v_i^2}{2a}$$

$$2a\Delta d = v_f^2 - v_i^2$$

Therefore $v_f^2 = v_i^2 + 2a\Delta d$.

In a similar way, substitution can be used to derive the final two equations in which $\vec{v}_f$ and $\vec{v}_i$ are eliminated. The resulting five equations for constant acceleration are presented in **Table 4**. Applying dimensional analysis or unit analysis to the equations will allow you to check that the derivations and/or substitutions are valid.

Table 4 Constant Acceleration Equations for Uniformly Accelerated Motion

Variables Involved	General Equation	Variable Eliminated
$\vec{a}, \vec{v}_f, \vec{v}_i, \Delta t$	$\vec{a} = \dfrac{\vec{v}_f - \vec{v}_i}{\Delta t}$	$\Delta \vec{d}$
$\Delta \vec{d}, \vec{v}_i, \vec{a}, \Delta t$	$\Delta \vec{d} = \vec{v}_i \Delta t + \dfrac{1}{2}\vec{a}(\Delta t)^2$	$\vec{v}_f$
$\Delta \vec{d}, \vec{v}_i, \vec{v}_f, \Delta t$	$\Delta \vec{d} = \vec{v}_{av}\Delta t$ or $\Delta \vec{d} = \dfrac{1}{2}(\vec{v}_i + \vec{v}_f)\Delta t$	$\vec{a}$
$\vec{v}_f, \vec{v}_i, \vec{a}, \Delta \vec{d}$	$v_f^2 = v_i^2 + 2a\Delta d$	Δt
$\Delta \vec{d}, \vec{v}_f, \Delta t, \vec{a}$	$\Delta \vec{d} = \vec{v}_f\Delta t - \dfrac{1}{2}\vec{a}(\Delta t)^2$	$\vec{v}_i$

▶ **SAMPLE** problem **4**

A motorcyclist, travelling initially at 12 m/s [W], changes gears and speeds up for 3.5 s with a constant acceleration of 5.1 m/s² [W]. What is the motorcyclist's displacement over this time interval?

Solution

$\vec{v}_i = $ 12 m/s [W] $\Delta t = $ 3.5 s
$\vec{a} = $ 5.1 m/s² [W] $\Delta \vec{d} = $?

$$\Delta \vec{d} = \vec{v}_i\Delta t + \frac{1}{2}\vec{a}(\Delta t)^2$$

$$= (12 \text{ m/s [W]})(3.5 \text{ s}) + \frac{1}{2}(5.1 \text{ m/s}^2 \text{ [W]})(3.5 \text{ s})^2$$

$$\Delta \vec{d} = 73 \text{ m [W]}$$

The motorcyclist's displacement is 73 m [W].

A rocket launched vertically from rest reaches a velocity of 6.3×10^2 m/s [up] at an altitude of 4.7 km above the launch pad. Determine the rocket's acceleration, which is assumed constant, during this motion.

Solution

$\vec{v}_i = 0$ m/s

$\vec{v}_f = 6.3 \times 10^2$ m/s [up]

$\Delta \vec{d} = 4.7$ km [up] $= 4.7 \times 10^3$ m [up]

$\vec{a} = ?$

We choose [up] as the positive direction. Since Δt is not given, we will use the equation

$$v_f^2 = v_i^2 + 2a\Delta d$$

$$v_f^2 = 2a\Delta d$$

$$a = \frac{v_f^2}{2\Delta d}$$

$$= \frac{(6.3 \times 10^2 \text{ m/s})^2}{2(4.7 \times 10^3 \text{ m})}$$

$$a = 42 \text{ m/s}^2$$

Since a is positive, the acceleration is 42 m/s^2 [up].

A curling rock sliding on ice undergoes a constant acceleration of 5.1 cm/s^2 [E] as it travels 28 m [W] from its initial position before coming to rest. Determine (a) the initial velocity and (b) the time of travel.

Solution

Figure 12 shows that the acceleration is opposite in direction to the motion of the rock and that the positive direction is chosen to be west.

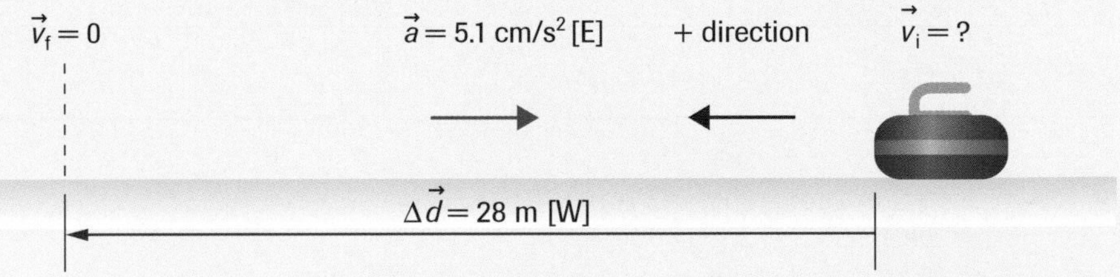

$\vec{v}_f = 0$ $\qquad$ $\vec{a} = 5.1$ cm/s^2 [E] $\qquad$ + direction $\qquad$ $\vec{v}_i = ?$

$\Delta \vec{d} = 28$ m [W]

Figure 12
The situation for Sample Problem 6

(a) $\Delta \vec{d} = 28$ m [W] $\qquad$ $\vec{a} = 5.1$ cm/s^2 [E] $= 0.051$ m/s^2 [E] $= -0.051$ m/s^2 [W]

$\vec{v}_f = 0$ m/s $\qquad$ $\Delta t = ?$

$\vec{v}_i = ?$

$$v_f^2 = v_i^2 + 2a\Delta d$$

$$0 = v_i^2 + 2a\Delta d$$

$$v_i^2 = -2a\Delta d$$

$$v_i = \pm\sqrt{-2a\Delta d}$$

$$= \pm\sqrt{-2(-0.051 \text{ m/s}^2)(28 \text{ m})}$$

$$v_i = \pm 1.7 \text{ m/s}$$

The initial velocity is $v_i = 1.7$ m/s [W].

(b) Any of the constant acceleration equations can be used to solve for Δt.

$$\vec{a} = \frac{\vec{v}_f - \vec{v}_i}{\Delta t}$$

$$\Delta t = \frac{\vec{v}_f - \vec{v}_i}{\vec{a}}$$

$$= \frac{0 - 1.7 \text{ m/s [W]}}{-0.051 \text{ m/s}^2 \text{ [W]}}$$

$$\Delta t = 33 \text{ s}$$

The time interval over which the curling rock slows down and stops is 33 s.

▶ *Practice*

Understanding Concepts

15. You know the initial velocity, the displacement, and the time interval for a certain constant acceleration motion. Which of the five standard equations would you use to find (a) acceleration and (b) final velocity?

16. Show that the constant acceleration equation from which Δt has been eliminated is dimensionally correct.

17. Rearrange the constant acceleration equation from which average acceleration has been eliminated to isolate (a) Δt and (b) $\vec{v}_f$.

18. Starting with the defining equation for constant acceleration and the equation for displacement in terms of average velocity, derive the constant acceleration equation
    (a) from which final velocity has been eliminated
    (b) from which initial velocity has been eliminated

19. A badminton shuttle, or "birdie," is struck, giving it a horizontal velocity of 73 m/s [W]. Air resistance causes a constant acceleration of 18 m/s^2 [E]. Determine its velocity after 1.6 s.

20. A baseball travelling horizontally at 41 m/s [S] is hit by a baseball bat, causing its velocity to become 47 m/s [N]. The ball is in contact with the bat for 1.9 ms, and undergoes constant acceleration during this interval. What is that acceleration?

21. Upon leaving the starting block, a sprinter undergoes a constant acceleration of 2.3 m/s^2 [fwd] for 3.6 s. Determine the sprinter's (a) displacement and (b) final velocity.

22. An electron travelling at 7.72×10^7 m/s [E] enters a force field that reduces its velocity to 2.46×10^7 m/s [E]. The acceleration is constant. The displacement during the acceleration is 0.478 m [E]. Determine
    (a) the electron's acceleration
    (b) the time interval over which the acceleration occurs

Applying Inquiry Skills

23. Describe how you would perform an experiment to determine the acceleration of a book sliding to a stop on a lab bench or the floor. Which variables will you measure and how will you calculate the acceleration? If possible, perform the experiment.

Making Connections

24. Reaction time can be crucial in avoiding a car accident. You are driving at 75.0 km/h [N] when you notice a stalled vehicle 48.0 m directly ahead of you. You apply the brakes, coming to a stop just in time to avoid a collision. Your brakes provided a constant acceleration of 4.80 m/s^2 [S]. What was your reaction time?

Answers

19. 44 m/s [W]

20. 4.6×10^4 m/s^2 [N]

21. (a) 15 m [fwd]
    (b) 8.3 m/s [fwd]

22. (a) 5.60×10^{15} m/s^2 [W]
    (b) 9.39×10^{-9} s

24. 0.13 s

Acceleration in Two Dimensions

Acceleration in two dimensions occurs when the velocity of an object moving in a plane undergoes a change in magnitude, or a change in direction, or a simultaneous change in both magnitude and direction. In **Figure 13**, a parks worker is pushing a lawn mower on a level lawn at a constant speed of 1.8 m/s around a kidney-shaped flowerbed. Is the mower accelerating? Yes: the mower's velocity keeps changing in direction, even though it does not change in magnitude.

The equation for average acceleration introduced for one-dimensional motion also applies to two-dimensional motion. Thus,

$$\vec{a}_{av} = \frac{\Delta \vec{v}}{\Delta t} = \frac{\vec{v}_f - \vec{v}_i}{\Delta t}$$

It is important to remember that $\vec{v}_f - \vec{v}_i$ is a vector subtraction. The equation can also be applied to the components of vectors. Thus,

$$a_{av,x} = \frac{\Delta v_x}{\Delta t} = \frac{v_{fx} - v_{ix}}{\Delta t} \quad \text{and} \quad a_{av,y} = \frac{\Delta v_y}{\Delta t} = \frac{v_{fy} - v_{iy}}{\Delta t}$$

where, for example, v_{fy} represents the *y*-component of the final velocity.

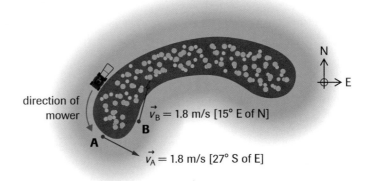

Figure 13

As the lawn mower follows the edge of the flowerbed at constant speed, it is accelerating: its direction of motion keeps changing.

direction of mower

$\vec{v}_B = 1.8$ m/s [15° E of N]

$\vec{v}_A = 1.8$ m/s [27° S of E]

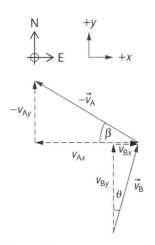

Figure 14

Determining the direction of the change in the velocity vector

---

> ## SAMPLE problem 7

The lawn mower in **Figure 13** takes 4.5 s to travel from A to B. What is its average acceleration?

Solution

$\vec{v}_A = 1.8$ m/s [27° S of E] $\Delta t = 4.5$ s

$\vec{v}_B = 1.8$ m/s [15° E of N] $\vec{a}_{av} = ?$

We begin by finding $\Delta \vec{v}$, which is needed in the equation for average acceleration. In this case, we choose to work with vector components, although other methods could be used (such as the sine and cosine laws). The vector subtraction, $\Delta \vec{v} = \vec{v}_B + (-\vec{v}_A)$, is shown in **Figure 14**. Taking components:

$$\Delta v_x = v_{Bx} + (-v_{Ax})$$
$$= v_B \sin \theta + (-v_A \cos \beta)$$
$$= 1.8 \text{ m/s } (\sin 15°) - 1.8 \text{ m/s } (\cos 27°)$$
$$\Delta v_x = -1.1 \text{ m/s}$$

and

$$\Delta v_y = v_{By} + (-v_{Ay})$$
$$= v_B \cos \theta + (-v_A \sin \beta)$$
$$= 1.8 \text{ m/s } (\cos 15°) + 1.8 \text{ m/s } (\sin 27°)$$
$$\Delta v_y = +2.6 \text{ m/s}$$

Using the law of Pythagoras,

$$|\Delta \vec{v}|^2 = |\Delta v_x|^2 + |\Delta v_y|^2$$
$$|\Delta \vec{v}|^2 = (1.1 \text{ m/s})^2 + (2.6 \text{ m/s})^2$$
$$|\Delta \vec{v}| = 2.8 \text{ m/s}$$

We now find the direction of the vector as shown in **Figure 15**:

$$\phi = \tan^{-1} \frac{1.1 \text{ m/s}}{2.6 \text{ m/s}}$$
$$\phi = 24°$$

The direction is [24° W of N].

To calculate the average acceleration:

$$\vec{a}_{av} = \frac{\Delta \vec{v}}{\Delta t}$$
$$= \frac{2.8 \text{ m/s } [24° \text{ W of N}]}{4.5 \text{ s}}$$
$$\vec{a}_{av} = 0.62 \text{ m/s}^2 \text{ [24° W of N]}$$

The average acceleration is 0.62 m/s² [24° W of N].

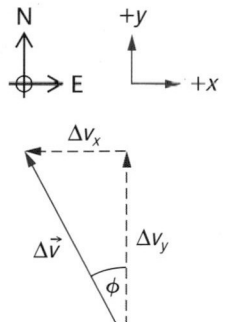

Figure 15
The velocities and their components for Sample Problem 7

▶ *Practice*

Understanding Concepts

25. A car with a velocity of 25 m/s [E] changes its velocity to 25 m/s [S] in 15 s. Calculate the car's average acceleration.

26. A watercraft with an initial velocity of 6.4 m/s [E] undergoes an average acceleration of 2.0 m/s² [S] for 2.5 s. What is the final velocity of the watercraft?

27. A hockey puck rebounds from a board as shown in **Figure 16**. The puck is in contact with the board for 2.5 ms. Determine the average acceleration of the puck over the interval.

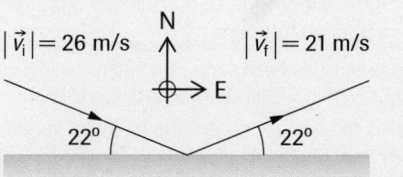

Figure 16
Motion of the puck

28. A passenger in a hot-air balloon throws a ball with an initial unknown velocity. The ball accelerates at 9.8 m/s² [down] for 2.0 s, at which time its instantaneous velocity is 24 m/s [45° below the horizontal]. Determine the ball's initial velocity.

29. At 3:00 P.M. a truck travelling on a winding highway has a velocity of 82.0 km/h [38.2° E of N]; at 3:15 P.M., it has a velocity of 82.0 km/h [12.7° S of E]. Assuming that $+x$ is east and $+y$ is north, determine the x- and y-components of the average acceleration during this time interval.

Answers

25. 2.4 m/s² [45° S of W]

26. 8.1 m/s [38° S of E]

27. 7.3×10^3 m/s² [7.5° N of W]

28. 17 m/s [10° above the horizontal]

29. $a_{av,x} = 9.0 \times 10^{-3}$ m/s²; $a_{av,y} = -2.5 \times 10^{-2}$ m/s²

Acceleration in One and Two Dimensions

- Average acceleration is the average rate of change of velocity.
- Instantaneous acceleration is the acceleration at a particular instant.
- The tangent technique can be used to determine the instantaneous velocity on a position-time graph of accelerated motion.
- The slope of the line on a velocity-time graph indicates the acceleration.
- The area under the line on an acceleration-time graph indicates the change in velocity.
- There are five variables involved in the mathematical analysis of motion with constant acceleration and there are five equations, each of which has four of the five variables.
- In two-dimensional motion, the average acceleration is found by using the vector subtraction $\Delta \vec{v} = \vec{v}_f - \vec{v}_i$ divided by the time interval Δt.

▶ Section 1.2 Questions

Understanding Concepts

1. State the condition under which instantaneous acceleration and average acceleration are equal.

2. Is it possible to have a northward velocity with westward acceleration? If "no," explain why not. If "yes," give an example.

3. A supersonic aircraft flying from London, England, to New York City changes its velocity from 1.65×10^3 km/h [W] to 1.12×10^3 km/h [W] as it prepares for landing. This change takes 345 s. Determine the average acceleration of the aircraft (a) in kilometres per hour per second and (b) in metres per second squared.

4. (a) Sketch a velocity-time graph, over an interval of 4.0 s, for a car moving in one dimension with increasing speed and decreasing acceleration.

   (b) Show how to determine the instantaneous acceleration at $t = 2.0$ s on this graph.

5. **Table 5** gives position-time data for a person undergoing constant acceleration from rest.
   (a) Draw the corresponding velocity-time and acceleration-time graphs.
   (b) Use at least one constant acceleration equation to check the final calculation of acceleration in (a).

Table 5 Position-Time Data

t (s)	0	0.2	0.4	0.6	0.8
$\vec{d}$ (m [W])	0	0.26	1.04	2.34	4.16

6. Describe the motion in each graph in **Figure 17**.

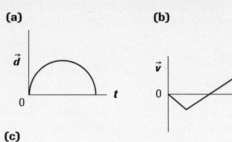
(a)
(b)

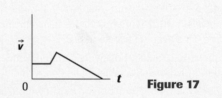
(c)

Figure 17

7. A car, travelling initially at 26 m/s [E], slows down with a constant average acceleration of magnitude 5.5 m/s². Determine its velocity after 2.6 s.

8. The maximum braking acceleration of a certain car is constant and of magnitude 9.7 m/s². If the car comes to rest 2.9 s after the driver applies the brakes, determine its initial speed.

9. Use the information from the velocity-time graph in **Figure 18** to generate the corresponding position-time and acceleration-time graphs.

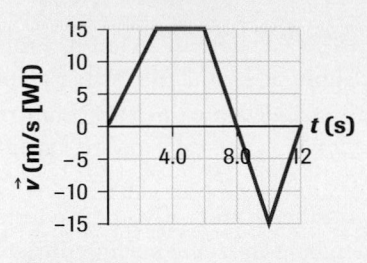

Figure 18

10. A ski jumper, starting from rest, skis down a straight slope for 3.4 s with a constant acceleration of 4.4 m/s² [fwd]. At the end of 3.4 s, determine the jumper's (a) final velocity and (b) displacement.

11. An electron is accelerated uniformly from rest to a velocity of 2.0×10^7 m/s [E] over the displacement 0.10 m [E].
    (a) What is the (constant) acceleration of the electron?
    (b) How long does the electron take to reach its final velocity?

12. During a 29.4-s interval, the velocity of a rocket changes from 204 m/s [fwd] to 508 m/s [fwd]. Assuming constant acceleration, determine the displacement of the rocket during this time interval.

13. A bullet leaves the muzzle of a rifle with a velocity of 4.2×10^2 m/s [fwd]. The rifle barrel is 0.56 m long. The acceleration imparted by the gunpowder gases is uniform as long as the bullet is in the barrel.
    (a) What is the average velocity of the bullet in the barrel?
    (b) Over what time interval does the uniform acceleration occur?

14. A car (C) and a van (V) are stopped beside each other at a red light. When the light turns green, the vehicles accelerate with the motion depicted in **Figure 19**.

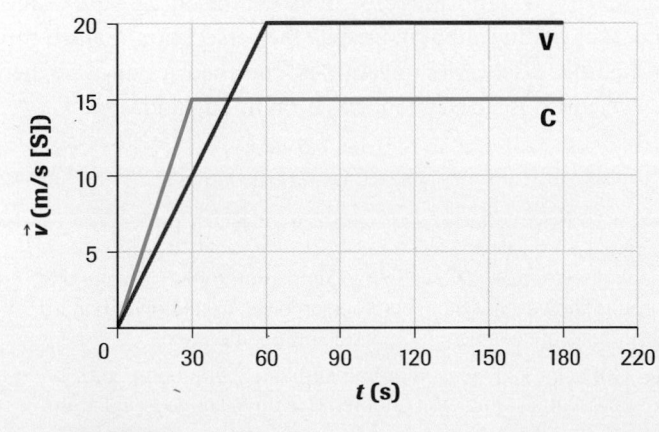

Figure 19
Velocity-time graph of the motions of two vehicles

(a) At what instant after the light turns green do C and V have the same velocity?
(b) At what instant after the light turns green does V overtake C? (*Hint:* Their displacements must be equal at that instant.)
(c) Determine the displacement from the intersection when V overtakes C.

15. A bird takes 8.5 s to fly from position A to position B along the path shown in **Figure 20**. Determine the average acceleration.

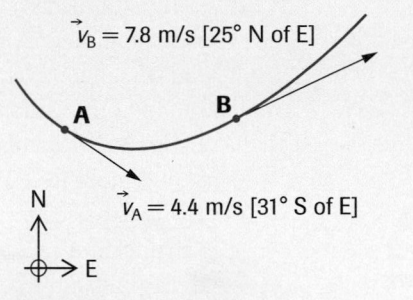

Figure 20

16. A helicopter travelling horizontally at 155 km/h [E] executes a gradual turn, and after 56.5 s flies at 118 km/h [S]. What is the helicopter's average acceleration in kilometres per hour per second?

Applying Inquiry Skills

17. Predict the average acceleration in each of the following situations. State what measurements and calculations you would use to test your predictions.
    (a) A bullet travelling with a speed of 175 m/s is brought to rest by a wooden plank.
    (b) A test car travelling at 88 km/h is brought to rest by a crash barrier consisting of sand-filled barrels.

Making Connections

18. The fastest time for the women's 100-m dash in a certain track-and-field competition is 11.0 s, whereas the fastest time for the four-woman 100-m relay is 42.7 s. Why would it be wrong to conclude that each of the four women in the relay can run a 100-m dash in less than 11.0 s? (*Hint:* Consider acceleration.)

acceleration due to gravity $(\vec{g})$ acceleration of an object falling vertically toward Earth's surface

free fall the motion of an object toward Earth with no other force acting on it than gravity

Figure 1
Aristotle (384 B.C.–322 B.C.)

Figure 2
Galileo Galilei (1564–1642)

A diver using a 3-m high board enters the water at a speed of about 28 km/h. From the 10-m high board, on the other hand, the speed is about 50 km/h. The farther an object falls toward Earth's surface, the faster its landing speed becomes, as long as air resistance remains negligible. The acceleration of an object falling vertically toward Earth's surface is called the **acceleration due to gravity**.

Not all objects accelerate at the same rate toward the ground. If you drop a rubber stopper and a flat piece of paper from the same height at the same instant, the stopper lands first. However, if you crumple the paper into a tight ball, the paper and the stopper land at about the same time. If the air resistance is negligible, the acceleration due to gravity at a particular location is constant, and all dropped objects accelerate downward at the same rate. An object falling toward Earth with no other force acting on it than gravity experiences **free fall**.

In ancient times, people thought that heavier objects fell faster than lighter ones. The Greek philosopher Aristotle (**Figure 1**), who was a successful teacher and scientist and the accepted scientific authority of his day, based his belief on the observation that a rock falls more quickly than a leaf or a feather. He even "proved" that heavy objects fell faster than light ones and that a force is necessary for all motion. Physics based on Aristotle's ideas was known as "Aristotelian physics." (After Newton, physics became known as "Newtonian physics.") Aristotle's ideas, including his theory of falling objects, were accepted for nearly 2000 years.

The renowned Italian scientist Galileo Galilei (**Figure 2**) discovered that both heavy and light objects fall toward Earth with the same acceleration if the effect of air resistance is eliminated. Galileo performed numerous experiments and made many scientific discoveries, some of which led to important inventions, such as the pendulum clock and the astronomical telescope. Using the telescope, he was able to view sunspots on the Sun's surface, close-up views of craters on the Moon, the phases of Venus, and some of the larger moons orbiting Jupiter. His observations supported the view that Earth was not at the centre of the solar system (geocentric theory); rather, Earth and the other planets orbited the Sun (heliocentric theory). Church authorities did not accept this theory and Galileo was placed under house arrest for writing about it. Despite the persecution, Galileo continued to write about his scientific discoveries, inventions, and theories until he died, the same year another great scientist, Isaac Newton, was born in England.

> **Practice**

Understanding Concepts

1. Air resistance is not negligible for a skydiver who has jumped out of an airplane and is falling toward the ground; however, if that same person dives from a diving board into a swimming pool, air resistance is negligible. Explain the difference.

2. Explain the disadvantage of using only reasoning rather than experimentation to determine the dependency of one variable on another. Use an example to illustrate your answer.

Applying Inquiry Skills

3. What experimental setup would demonstrate that in the absence of air resistance, a feather and a coin, released simultaneously, fall toward Earth at the same rate.

Measuring the Acceleration Due to Gravity

Various methods are used to measure the acceleration due to gravity experimentally.
For example, a stroboscope flashing at known time intervals records the position of an
object undergoing free fall (**Figure 3**). To determine the displacement of the object after
each time interval, we measure the photograph with a ruler. We can arrange the kinematics
equation to solve for $\vec{a}$:

$$\Delta \vec{d} = \vec{v}_i \Delta t + \frac{1}{2}\vec{a}(\Delta t)^2$$

If $\vec{v}_i = 0$, then

$$\vec{a} = \frac{2\,\Delta \vec{d}}{(\Delta t)^2}$$

Whichever method is used to determine the average acceleration of a freely falling
object, the result is found to be constant at any specific location. Near Earth's surface, to
two significant digits, the acceleration is 9.8 m/s² [down]. This value is common and
has the symbol $\vec{g}$, the acceleration due to gravity.

Government standards laboratories such as the Bureau International des Poids et
Mesures (BIPM) in Paris determine the local $\vec{g}$ with high precision. At BIPM, a special
elastic band propels an object upward in a vacuum chamber. Mirrors at the top and
bottom of the object reflect laser beams, permitting such an exact measurement of the
time of flight that the local magnitude of $\vec{g}$ is calculated to seven significant digits.

The magnitude of the acceleration due to gravity varies slightly depending on location. In general, the greater the distance from Earth's centre, the lower the acceleration
due to gravity. The value is slightly lower at the equator than at the North and South
Poles (at the same elevation) because Earth bulges outward slightly at the equator. Also,
the value is slightly lower at higher altitudes than at lower ones. **Table 1** lists the value of
$\vec{g}$ at several locations. Notice that the average value is 9.8 m/s² [down] to two significant digits. More details about $\vec{g}$ are presented in Chapters 2 and 3.

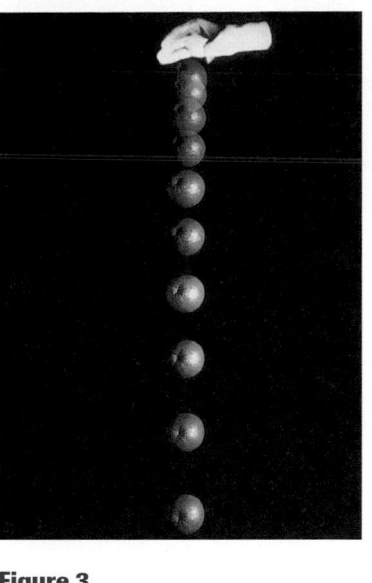

Figure 3
The accelerating object is seen in
the photograph each instant that
the strobe light flashes on. The time
interval Δt between strobe flashes
is constant.

DID YOU KNOW ?

Precise Measurements
Knowing the acceleration due to
gravity to seven or more significant
digits is of great interest to certain
professionals. Geophysicists and
geologists can use the information
to determine the structure of
Earth's interior and near-surface
features, and to help locate areas
with high concentrations of mineral and fossil fuel deposits.
Military experts are concerned
with variations in the acceleration
due to gravity in the deployment of
such devices as cruise missiles.
Space scientists use the data to
help calculate the paths of artificial satellites.

Table 1 $\vec{g}$ at Various Locations on Earth

Location	Latitude	Altitude (m)	$\vec{g}$ (m/s² [down])
North Pole	90° [N]	0	9.832
Equator	0	0	9.780
Java	6° [S]	7	9.782
Mount Everest	28° [N]	8848	9.765
Denver	40° [N]	1638	9.796
Toronto	44° [N]	162	9.805
London, UK	51° [N]	30	9.823
Washington, D.C.	39° [N]	8	9.801
Brussels	51° [N]	102	9.811

Geologists create models of potential earthquake scenarios to analyze the structure of Earth's surface. One such model is the map of ground accelerations in **Figure 4**. This particular map shows the Pacific Northwest region near the border between Canada and the United States. The map shows sideways ground accelerations that may occur from several earthquakes, each with an estimated recurrence time. The colours indicate potential sideways accelerations as a percentage of g. For example, the area in red represents a range of 40% to 60% of g, meaning that the ground would accelerate at approximately 5 m/s^2. The accelerations have a 10% chance of being exceeded in 50 years.

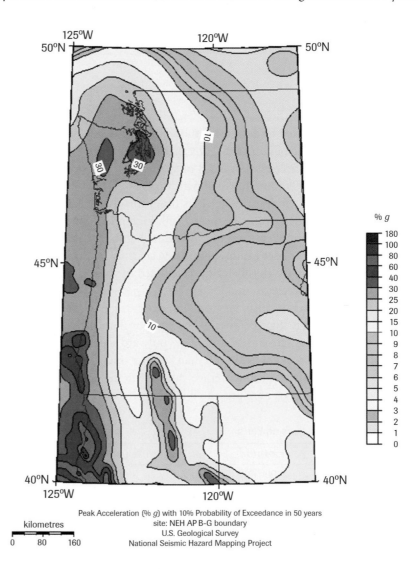

Peak Acceleration (% g) with 10% Probability of Exceedance in 50 years
site: NEH AP B–G boundary
U.S. Geological Survey
National Seismic Hazard Mapping Project

Figure 4
This map of potential ground accelerations from earthquakes covers a large area of the Pacific Northwest. Since latitudes and longitudes are marked, you can find the corresponding locations in an atlas.

(a) Look up the region in a conventional atlas, and write a short scenario for possible earthquakes in the Pacific Northwest, describing which regions are affected severely, moderately, slightly, or not at all.

(b) Explain how you used the acceleration map to construct your scenario.

> ▶ *Practice*

Understanding Concepts

5. A diver steps off a 10.0-m high diving board with an initial vertical velocity of zero and experiences an average acceleration of 9.80 m/s^2 [down]. Air resistance is negligible. Determine the diver's velocity in metres per second and in kilometres per hour, after falling (a) 5.00 m and (b) 10.0 m.

Applying Inquiry Skills

6. You drop an eraser from your hand to your desk, a distance that equals your hand span.
   (a) Estimate the time interval this motion takes in milliseconds.
   (b) Measure your hand span and calculate the time interval, using the appropriate constant acceleration equation(s).
   (c) Compare your answers in (a) and (b). Describe ways in which you can improve your estimation skills.

7. **Table 2** gives position-time data for a very light ball dropped vertically from rest.
   (a) Use the final data pair and the appropriate equation for constant acceleration to determine the acceleration.
   (b) Describe how you would find the acceleration with graphing techniques.
   (c) If the value of the acceleration due to gravity in the place where the ball was dropped is 9.81 m/s^2 [down], what is the percentage error of the experimental value?
   (d) Describe reasons why there is a fairly high percentage error in this example.

Making Connections

8. Olympic events have been held at locations with very different altitudes. Should Olympic records for events, such as the shot put, be adjusted for this?

Answers

5. (a) 9.90 m/s [down];
      35.6 km/h [down]
   (b) 14.0 m/s [down];
      50.4 km/h [down]

7. (a) 8.61 m/s^2 [down]
   (c) 12.2%

Table 2 Position-Time Data

t (s)	$\vec{d}$ (m [down])
0	0
0.200	0.172
0.400	0.688
0.600	1.55

Calculations Involving Free Fall

During free fall, the vertical acceleration is constant, so the kinematics equations developed for constant acceleration in Section 1.2 can be applied. However, the equations can be simplified. Since we are considering vertical motion only, the displacement, velocity, and acceleration variables will be treated as components; thus, we will replace the vector quantities $\Delta\vec{d}$, $\vec{v}_i$, $\vec{v}_f$, and $\vec{a}$ with their corresponding components: Δy, v_{iy}, v_{fy}, and a_y. When using equations involving components, it is essential to choose which direction—up or down—is positive and then assign positive or negative signs to the components appropriately.

Table 3 gives the constant acceleration equations for free-fall motion. Compare this table with **Table 4** in Section 1.2.

> **LEARNING _TIP_**
>
> **Choosing the Positive Direction**
> It is important to use consistent directions with any single motion question. For an object experiencing only downward motion, it is convenient to choose downward as positive. However, if an object is thrown upward or if it bounces upward after falling downward, either upward or downward can be called positive. The important thing is to define your choice for the positive y direction and to use that choice throughout the entire solution.

Table 3 Constant Acceleration Equations for Free-Fall Motion

Variables Involved	General Equation	Variable Eliminated
a_y, v_{fy}, v_{iy}, Δt	$a_y = \dfrac{v_{fy} - v_{iy}}{\Delta t}$	Δy
Δy, v_{iy}, a_y, Δt	$\Delta y = v_{iy}\Delta t + \dfrac{1}{2}a_y(\Delta t)^2$	v_{fy}
Δy, v_{iy}, v_{fy}, Δt	$\Delta y = \dfrac{v_{iy} + v_{fy}}{2}\Delta t$	a_y
Δy, v_{iy}, v_{fy}, a_y	$v_{fy}^2 = v_{iy}^2 + 2a_y\Delta y$	Δt
Δy, v_{fy}, a_y, Δt	$\Delta y = v_{fy}\Delta t - \dfrac{1}{2}a_y(\Delta t)^2$	v_{iy}

A ball is thrown with an initial velocity of 8.3 m/s [up]. Air resistance is negligible.

(a) What maximum height above its starting position will the ball reach?

(b) After what time interval will the ball return to its initial position?

Solution

We will use upward as the $+y$ direction for the entire solution.

(a) We know that $v_{fy} = 0$ m/s because at the maximum height required, the ball stops for an instant before falling downward.

$$a_y = -g = -9.8 \text{ m/s}^2 \qquad v_{fy} = 0 \text{ m/s}$$
$$v_{iy} = +8.3 \text{ m/s} \qquad \Delta y = ?$$

$$v_{fy}^2 = v_{iy}^2 + 2a_y\Delta y$$
$$0 = v_{iy}^2 + 2a_y\Delta y$$
$$\Delta y = \frac{-v_{iy}^2}{2a_y}$$
$$= \frac{-(8.3 \text{ m/s})^2}{2(-9.8 \text{ m/s}^2)}$$
$$\Delta y = +3.5 \text{ m}$$

The maximum height reached by the ball is 3.5 m above its initial position.

(b) One way to solve this problem is to determine the time interval during which the ball rises, then double that value to get the total time. We assume that the time for the ball to fall equals the time for it to rise (a valid assumption if air resistance is neglected).

$$a_y = -g = -9.8 \text{ m/s}^2 \qquad v_{fy} = 0 \text{ m/s}$$
$$v_{iy} = +8.3 \text{ m/s} \qquad \Delta t = ?$$

$$\Delta t = \frac{v_{fy} - v_{iy}}{a_y}$$
$$= \frac{0 - 8.3 \text{ m/s}}{-9.8 \text{ m/s}^2}$$
$$\Delta t = 0.85 \text{ s}$$

total time $= 2 \times 0.85$ s $= 1.7$ s

Therefore 1.7 s will elapse before the ball returns to its initial position.

An arrow is shot vertically upward beside a building 56 m high. The initial velocity of the arrow is 37 m/s [up]. Air resistance is negligible. At what times does the arrow pass the top of the building on its way up and down?

Solution

We take the ground as the origin and [up] as the $+y$ direction.

$$\Delta y = +56 \text{ m} \qquad v_{iy} = +37 \text{ m/s}$$
$$a_y = -g = -9.8 \text{ m/s}^2 \qquad \Delta t = ?$$

LEARNING TIP

Alternative Solutions
There is often more than one way of solving problems involving constant acceleration. A problem usually begins by giving three known quantities. After using one of the five possible equations to solve for one unknown quantity, you now know four quantities. To find the fifth and final quantity, you can choose any of the constant acceleration equations containing the fifth quantity.

LEARNING TIP

Care with Vectors
Some students think that $g = -9.8 \text{ m/s}^2$, which is incorrect. The symbol g represents the magnitude of the vector $\vec{g}$, and the magnitude of a nonzero vector is always positive.

The equation involving these variables is

$$\Delta y = v_{iy}\Delta t + \frac{1}{2}a_y(\Delta t)^2$$

Since both terms on the right-hand side of the equation are not zero, we must apply the quadratic formula to solve for Δt. Thus, we substitute the given quantities into the equation:

$$+56 \text{ m} = 37 \text{ m/s } \Delta t - 4.9 \text{ m/s}^2 (\Delta t)^2$$
$$4.9 \text{ m/s}^2 (\Delta t)^2 - 37 \text{ m/s } \Delta t + 56 \text{ m} = 0$$

Using the quadratic formula:

$$\Delta t = \frac{-b \pm \sqrt{b^2 - 4ac}}{2a} \qquad \text{where } a = 4.9 \text{ m/s}^2, b = -37 \text{ m/s, and } c = 56 \text{ m}$$

$$= \frac{-(-37 \text{ m/s}) \pm \sqrt{(-37 \text{ m/s})^2 - 4(4.9 \text{ m/s}^2)(56 \text{ m})}}{2(4.9 \text{ m/s}^2)}$$

$$\Delta t = 5.5 \text{ s and } 2.1 \text{ s}$$

There are two positive roots of the equation, which means that the arrow passes the top of the building on the way up (at $t = 2.1$ s) and again on the way down (at $t = 5.5$ s).

▶ **Practice**

Understanding Concepts

9. You throw a ball vertically upward and catch it at the height from which you released it. Air resistance is negligible.
   (a) Compare the time the ball takes to rise with the time the ball takes to fall.
   (b) Compare the initial and final velocities.
   (c) What is the instantaneous velocity at the top of the flight?
   (d) What is the ball's acceleration as it is rising? at the top of the flight? as it is falling?
   (e) Sketch the position-time graph, the velocity-time graph, and the acceleration-time graph for the ball's motion during its flight. Use [up] as the positive direction.

10. Write all the equations that could be used to solve for the time interval in Sample Problem 1(b). Choose a different equation and solve for Δt.

11. Determine the speed at impact in the following situations. Air resistance is negligible.
    (a) A seagull drops a shellfish onto a rocky shore from a height of 12.5 m to crack the shell.
    (b) A steel ball is dropped from the Leaning Tower of Pisa, landing 3.37 s later.

12. A steel ball is thrown from the ledge of a tower so that it has an initial velocity of magnitude 15.0 m/s. The ledge is 15.0 m above the ground. Air resistance is negligible.
    (a) What are the total flight time and the speed of impact at the ground if the initial velocity is upward?
    (b) What are these two quantities if the initial velocity is downward?
    (c) Based on your answers to (a) and (b), write a concluding statement.

13. Show that a free-falling ball dropped vertically from rest travels three times as far from $t = 1.0$ s to $t = 2.0$ s as from $t = 0.0$ s to $t = 1.0$ s.

14. A baseball pitcher throws a ball vertically upward and catches it at the same level 4.2 s later.
    (a) With what velocity did the pitcher throw the ball?
    (b) How high does the ball rise?

Answers

11. (a) 15.6 m/s
    (b) 33.0 m/s

12. (a) 3.86 s; 22.8 m/s
    (b) 0.794 s; 22.8 m/s

14. (a) 21 m/s [up]
    (b) 22 m

Answers

15. (a) 63 m

    (b) 35 m/s [down]

16. (a) 1.6 m/s² [down]

    (b) 6.1:1

17. (a) 9.20 m/s² [down];
        9.70 m/s² [down]

    (b) 5.3%

Table 4 Data for Question 17

t (s)	$\vec{d}$ (cm [↓])	$\vec{d}$ (cm [↓])
0	0	0
0.10	4.60	4.85
0.20	18.4	19.4
0.30	41.4	43.6
0.40	73.6	77.6

15. A hot-air balloon is moving with a velocity of 2.1 m/s [up] when the balloonist drops a ballast (a large mass used for height control) over the edge. The ballast hits the ground 3.8 s later.
    (a) How high was the balloon when the ballast was released?
    (b) What was the velocity of the ballast at impact?

16. An astronaut drops a camera from rest while exiting a spacecraft on the Moon. The camera drops 2.3 m [down] in 1.7 s.
    (a) Calculate the acceleration due to gravity on the Moon.
    (b) Determine the ratio of $|\vec{g}_{Earth}|$ to $|\vec{g}_{Moon}|$.

Applying Inquiry Skills

17. A 60.0-Hz ticker-tape timer and a photogate timer are used by two different groups in the lab to determine the acceleration due to gravity of a falling metal mass. The results of the experiments are shown in **Table 4**.
    (a) Use the data to determine the acceleration of the metal mass in each trial.
    (b) Calculate the percent difference between the two accelerations.
    (c) Which results are likely attributable to the ticker-tape timer? Explain why you think so.

Making Connections

18. How would your daily life be affected if the acceleration due to gravity were to increase to twice its present value? Name a few drawbacks and a few advantages.

Terminal Speed

The skydiver who exits a flying aircraft (**Figure 5**) experiences free fall for a short time. However, as the diver's speed increases, so does the air resistance. (You know from the experience of putting your hand out the window of a moving vehicle that air resistance

Figure 5
A skydiver's downward acceleration decreases as the downward velocity increases because of increasing air resistance.

Figure 6
The general shape of a speed-time graph for a falling object that reaches terminal speed

terminal speed maximum speed of a falling object at which point the speed remains constant and there is no further acceleration

becomes high at high speeds.) Eventually this resistance becomes so great that it prevents any further acceleration. At this stage, the acceleration is zero and the diver has reached a constant **terminal speed**, as depicted in the graph in **Figure 6**.

The terminal speeds for various objects falling in air are listed in **Table 5**. An object with a fairly large mass, such as a human, has a high terminal speed. The terminal speed is reduced greatly if the surface area increases, as when a skydiver opens a parachute.

Terminal speeds are also important in fluids other than air. Investigation 1.3.1, in the Lab Activities section at the end of this chapter, looks at the dependence of terminal speed on the mass of an object.

Table 5 Approximate Terminal Speeds of Objects Falling in Air

Object	Terminal speed	
	(m/s)	**(km/h)**
human	53	190
human with open parachute	5 to 10	18 to 36
dandelion seed	0.5	1.8
typical dust particle	0.02	0.07

▶ *Practice*

Understanding Concepts

19. What factors affect an object's terminal speed? How does each factor affect the terminal speed?

20. Does the concept of terminal speed apply on the Moon? Why or why not?

21. Sketch a graph of the vertical speed as a function of time for a skydiver who jumps from an aircraft, reaches terminal speed, opens the parachute, and reaches a new terminal speed.

Applying Inquiry Skills

22. Relief organizations use airplanes to drop packages of supplies in areas inaccessible by surface transport. A package that hits the ground at a high speed may be damaged.
    (a) Describe several factors to consider in the design of a package to maximize the chances of a safe landing.
    (b) Describe how you would test your package design.

Making Connections

23. There are many well-documented cases of people falling from tremendous heights without parachutes and surviving. The record is held by a Russian who fell from an astounding 7500 m. The chances of survival depend on the "deceleration distance" at the time of landing. Why is a fall from a height of 7500 m no more dangerous than one from half that height? How can the deceleration distance upon landing be maximized?

SUMMARY *Acceleration Due to Gravity*

- Free fall is the motion of an object falling toward the surface of Earth with no other force acting on it than gravity.

- The average acceleration due to gravity at Earth's surface is $\vec{g} = 9.8$ m/s^2 [down].

- The acceleration due to gravity depends on latitude, altitude, and local effects, such as the distribution of mineral deposits.

- The constant acceleration equations can be applied to analyze motion in the vertical plane.

- Terminal speed is the maximum speed reached by an object falling in air or other fluids. When a falling object reaches terminal speed, its downward acceleration becomes zero and its velocity becomes constant.

Comparing Terminal Speeds (p. 58)
Flat-bottom coffee filters fall in a fairly straight line when dropped vertically. These filters can be used to study the relation between the mass of an object and its terminal speed. Predict how you think the terminal speed of a stack of flat coffee filters depends on its mass—in other words, on the number of filters in the stack.

DID YOU KNOW ❓

Climate Changes

Dust and smoke particles in the atmosphere can cause climate changes. This 1980 eruption of Mount St. Helens expelled particles of ash high into the atmosphere. Because of their low terminal speed, such particles can remain suspended for months, or even years. These particles can be carried by the prevailing winds all around the world, reducing the amount of solar radiation reaching the ground. The decline in incoming radiation triggers climate changes, including a decline in average temperatures. A similar effect could be caused by smoke and ashes from huge fires, such as major forest fires or fires that would follow nuclear attacks.

Understanding Concepts

1. Describe several different conditions under which air resistance is negligible for a falling object.

2. Compare and contrast Aristotle's and Galileo's notions of falling objects.

3. Determine the landing speed in both metres per second and kilometres per hour for the following situations. Neglect air resistance and assume the object starts from rest.
   (a) Divers entertain tourists in Acapulco, Mexico, by diving from a cliff 36 m above the water.
   (b) A stone falls from a bridge, landing in the water 3.2 s later.

4. Two high jumpers, one in Java, the other in London, UK, each have an initial velocity of 5.112 m/s [up]. Use the data in **Table 1** to calculate, to four significant digits, the heights each jumper attains.

5. During the first minute of blastoff, a space shuttle has an average acceleration of $5g$ (i.e., five times the magnitude of the acceleration due to gravity on the surface of Earth). Calculate the shuttle's speed in metres per second and kilometres per hour after 1.0 min. (These values are approximate.)

6. A person throws a golf ball vertically upward. The ball returns to the same level after 2.6 s.
   (a) How long did the ball rise?
   (b) Determine the initial velocity of the ball.
   (c) How long would the ball remain in flight on Mars, where $\vec{g}$ is 3.7 m/s² [down], if it were given the same initial velocity?

7. In a laboratory experiment, a computer determines that the time for a falling steel ball to travel the final 0.80 m before hitting the floor is 0.087 s. With what velocity does the ball hit the floor?

8. A stone is thrown vertically with a velocity of 14 m/s [down] from a bridge.
   (a) How long will the stone take to reach the water 21 m below?
   (b) Explain the meaning of both roots of the quadratic equation used to solve this problem.

9. A tennis ball and a steel ball are dropped from a high ledge. The tennis ball encounters significant air resistance and eventually reaches terminal speed. The steel ball essentially undergoes free fall.
   (a) Draw a velocity-time graph comparing the motions of the two balls. Take the downward direction to be positive.
   (b) Repeat (a) with the upward direction positive.

10. A flowerpot is dropped from the balcony of an apartment, 28.5 m above the ground. At a time of 1.00 s after the pot is dropped, a ball is thrown vertically downward from the balcony one storey below, 26.0 m above the ground. The initial velocity of the ball is 12.0 m/s [down]. Does the ball pass the flowerpot before striking the ground? If so, how far above the ground are the two objects when the ball passes the flowerpot?

11. Based on your estimates, rank the following objects in order of highest to lowest terminal speed in air: a ping-pong ball, a basketball, a skydiver in a headfirst plunge, a skydiver in a spread-eagle plunge, and a grain of pollen.

Applying Inquiry Skills

12. State the number of significant digits, indicate the possible error, and calculate the percent possible error for each of the following measurements:
    (a) 9.809 060 m/s²
    (b) 9.8 m/s²
    (c) 9.80 m/s²
    (d) 9.801 m/s²
    (e) 9.8×10^{-6} m/s²

13. (a) How could you use a metre stick, together with one or more of the constant acceleration equations, to determine your lab partner's reaction time? Illustrate your method with an example, including a calculation with plausible numerical values.
    (b) How would talking on a cell phone affect the results of the reaction time?

Making Connections

14. In a group, share responsibility for researching the life and contributions of Aristotle or Galileo. Share your results with other groups in your class.

15. There are two different processes of logical thinking. One is called *deductive reasoning*, the other *inductive reasoning*. Use a resource, such as a dictionary or an encyclopedia, to find out more about these types of reasoning.
    (a) Which process did Aristotle and other ancient scientists use?
    (b) Which process did Galileo use?
    (c) Describe other facts you discover about these forms of reasoning.

16. Dr. Luis Alvarez has suggested that the extinction of the dinosaurs and numerous other species 65 million years ago was caused by severe temperature drops following the insertion of dust into the atmosphere. The enormous quantities of dust resulted from an asteroid impact in the Yucatán area of what is now Mexico. Research this topic and write a brief report on what you discover.

 www.science.nelson.com

What do the following situations have in common?

- A monkey jumps from the branch of one tree to the branch of an adjacent tree.
- A snowboarder glides at top speed off the end of a ramp (**Figure 1**).
- A relief package drops from a low-flying airplane.

In each situation, the body or object moves through the air without a propulsion system along a two-dimensional curved trajectory (**Figure 2(a)**). Such an object is called a **projectile**; the motion of a projectile is called *projectile motion*.

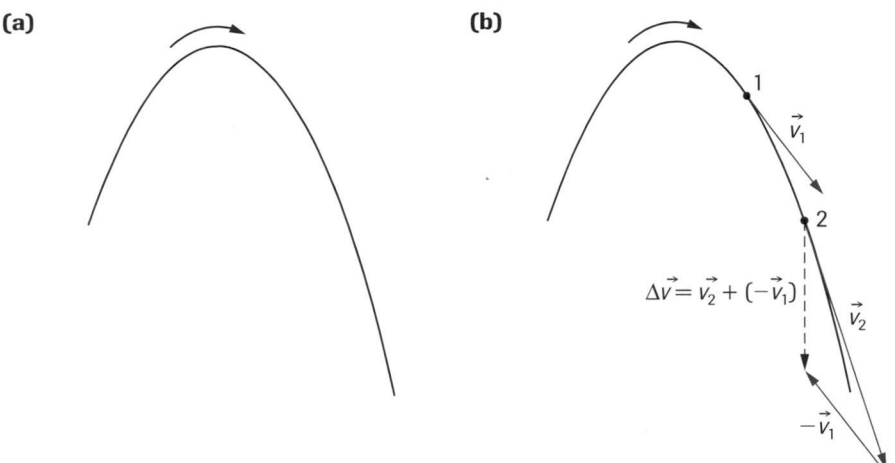

(a)   **(b)**

$$\Delta \vec{v} = \vec{v}_2 + (-\vec{v}_1)$$

Figure 2
(a) A typical trajectory followed by a projectile.
(b) The change in velocity between position 1 and position 2 is $\Delta \vec{v} = \vec{v}_2 - \vec{v}_1$, which is shown as $\Delta \vec{v} = \vec{v}_2 + (-\vec{v}_1)$.
If $\Delta \vec{v}$ is divided by the time Δt required for the motion from position 1 to position 2, the result is the average acceleration for that time interval.

It is evident that a projectile is accelerating because the direction of its instantaneous velocity is continually changing. However, in what direction is that acceleration occurring? Since $\vec{a}_{av} = \dfrac{\Delta \vec{v}}{\Delta t}$, $\vec{a}_{av}$ is in the direction of $\Delta \vec{v}$. **Figure 2(b)** shows that the vector subtraction $\Delta \vec{v} = \vec{v}_2 - \vec{v}_1$ yields a vector directed downward, which indicates that the direction of acceleration is also downward.

In the Try This Activity at the beginning of Chapter 1, you considered two projectiles, balls A and B, which began moving simultaneously. Ball A fell from rest, while ball B was launched horizontally with an initial velocity. Although, as we show in **Figure 3**, B had a longer path than A, the two balls landed simultaneously. The initial horizontal motion of a projectile like ball B does not affect its vertical acceleration.

Other experiments show the same thing. **Figure 4** is a stroboscopic photograph of two balls released simultaneously. The ball on the right was projected horizontally. The interval between strobe flashes was constant. A grid has been superimposed on the photo to facilitate measurement and analysis. In successive equal time intervals, the vertical components of the displacement increase by the same amount for each ball. Note that the projected ball travels a constant horizontal displacement in each time interval. The independent horizontal and vertical motions combine to produce the trajectory.

Figure 1
How would you describe the motion of the snowboarder after leaving the ramp?

projectile an object that moves through the air, along a trajectory, without a propulsion system

DID YOU *KNOW*❓

Dangerous Projectiles
You may have seen soldiers in the television news firing their rifles into the air to celebrate some victory. The bullets travel as high-speed projectiles and, despite air resistance, return to Earth at high enough speeds to be dangerous. Reports indicate that from time to time people are injured by the returning bullets.

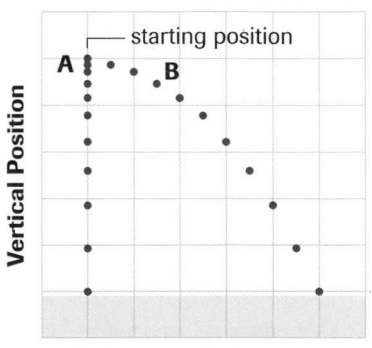

Figure 3
Ball B is projected horizontally at the same instant that ball A is dropped. Although the path of ball B is longer than the path of ball A, the balls land at the same instant.

projectile motion motion with a constant horizontal velocity and a constant vertical acceleration due to gravity

horizontal range (Δx) the horizontal displacement of a projectile

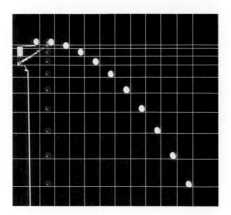

Figure 4
These two balls reached the lowest position at the same instant even though one was projected horizontally. Both balls had an initial vertical velocity of zero, and both experienced free fall.

⚛ INVESTIGATION 1.4.1

Investigating Projectile Motion (p. 58)
There is more than one way to prove that the horizontal and vertical components of a projectile's motion are independent of each other. Describe two or three ways that you could use to analyze the motion of the two balls in **Figure 4** to show that the horizontal motion is independent of the vertical motion. (*Hint:* One way can involve the vector subtraction of instantaneous velocities.) Then perform Investigation 1.4.1 to check your answers.

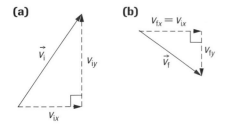

Figure 5
(a) At time $t = 0$, the initial velocity of the projectile, $\vec{v}_i$, has a horizontal component, v_{ix}, and a vertical component, v_{iy}.
(b) After Δt has elapsed, the projectile's velocity, $\vec{v}_f$, has the same horizontal component (neglecting air resistance) and a different vertical component, v_{fy}.

If you look carefully at the grid superimposed on the photograph in **Figure 4**, you can make the following important conclusions about projectile motion:

- The horizontal component of a projectile's velocity is constant. (The horizontal component of acceleration, in other words, is zero.)
- The projectile experiences constant downward acceleration due to gravity.
- The horizontal and vertical motions of a projectile are independent of each other, except they have a common time.

These conclusions are based on the assumption that air resistance can be neglected, an assumption we made when we analyzed the acceleration due to gravity in Section 1.3.

If you were performing an experiment to determine whether the concepts about projectile motion apply to an object on an inclined plane (for example, a puck moving on an air table set up at an angle to the horizontal), what observations would you expect to make? How would you analyze the motion of a projectile on an inclined plane to verify that the horizontal velocity is constant and the vertical acceleration is constant? You will explore these questions in Investigation 1.4.1 in the Lab Activities section at the end of this chapter. ⚛ ▌

Analyzing the Motion of Objects Projected Horizontally

Projectile motion is motion with a constant horizontal velocity combined with a constant vertical acceleration caused by gravity. Since the horizontal and vertical motions are independent of each other, we can apply independent sets of equations to analyze projectile motion. The constant velocity equations from Section 1.1 apply to the horizontal motion, while the constant acceleration equations from Sections 1.2 and 1.3 (with $|\vec{g}| = 9.8$ m/s^2) apply to the vertical motion.

Figure 5 shows the initial and final velocity vectors for a projectile, with their horizontal and vertical components. **Table 1** summarizes the kinematics equations for both components. None of the variables has an arrow over it since these variables represent components of vectors, not vectors themselves. For example, v_{ix} represents the x-component (which is not a vector) of the initial velocity and v_y represents the y-component (also not a vector) of the velocity after some time interval Δt. The horizontal displacement, Δx, is called the **horizontal range** of the projectile.

Table 1 Kinematics Equations for Projectile Motion

Horizontal (*x*) Motion	The constant velocity (zero acceleration) equation is written for the *x*-component only.	$v_{ix} = \dfrac{\Delta x}{\Delta t}$
Vertical (*y*) Motion	The five constant acceleration equations involving the acceleration due to gravity are written for the *y*-component only. The constant acceleration has a magnitude of $\lvert \vec{g} \rvert = g = 9.8 \text{ m/s}^2$.	$a_y = \dfrac{v_{fy} - v_{iy}}{\Delta t}$ or $v_{fy} = v_{iy} + a_y \Delta t$ $\Delta y = v_{iy}\Delta t + \dfrac{1}{2} a_y (\Delta t)^2$ $\Delta y = v_{av,y}\Delta t$ or $\Delta y = \dfrac{1}{2}(v_{fy} + v_{iy})\Delta t$ $v_{fy}^2 = v_{iy}^2 + 2a_y \Delta y$ $\Delta y = v_{fy}\Delta t - \dfrac{1}{2} a_y (\Delta t)^2$

▶ *SAMPLE* problem 1

A ball is thrown off a balcony and has an initial velocity of 18 m/s horizontally.

(a) Determine the position of the ball at $t = 1.0$ s, 2.0 s, 3.0 s, and 4.0 s.

(b) Show these positions on a scale diagram.

(c) What is the mathematical name of the resulting curve?

Solution

(a) Let the $+x$ direction be to the right and the $+y$ direction be downward (which is convenient since there is no upward motion) (see **Figure 6(a)**).

Horizontally (constant v_{ix}):

$v_{ix} = 18$ m/s

$\Delta t = 1.0$ s

$\Delta x = ?$

$$\Delta x = v_{ix}\Delta t$$
$$= (18 \text{ m/s})(1.0 \text{ s})$$
$$\Delta x = 18 \text{ m}$$

Table 2 gives the Δx values for $\Delta t = 1.0$ s, 2.0 s, 3.0 s, and 4.0 s.

Vertically (constant a_y):

$v_{iy} = 0$ $\Delta t = 1.0$ s

$a_y = +g = 9.8 \text{ m/s}^2$ $\Delta y = ?$

$$\Delta y = v_{iy}\Delta t + \frac{1}{2}a_y(\Delta t)^2$$
$$= \frac{1}{2}a_y(\Delta t)^2$$
$$= \frac{(9.8 \text{ m/s}^2)(1.0 \text{ s})^2}{2}$$
$$\Delta y = +4.9 \text{ m}$$

Table 2 gives the Δy values for $\Delta t = 1.0$ s, 2.0 s, 3.0 s, and 4.0 s.

(b) **Figure 6(b)** shows a scale diagram of the ball's position at the required times. The positions are joined with a smooth curve.

(c) The curved path shown in **Figure 6(b)** is a parabola.

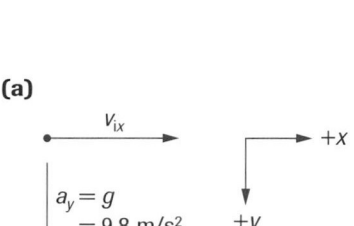
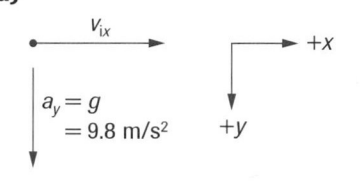

(a)

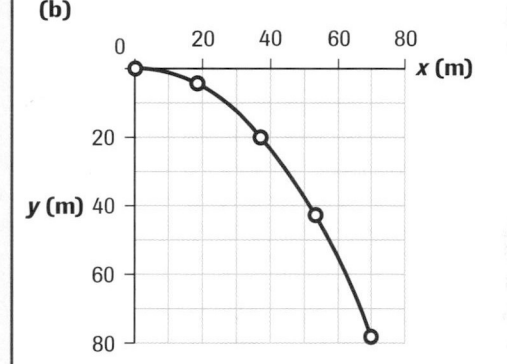

(b)

Figure 6
For Sample Problem 1
(a) Initial conditions
(b) Scale diagram of the motion

Table 2 Calculated Positions at Select Times

t (s)	Δx (m)	Δy (m)
0.0	0.0	0.0
1.0	18	4.9
2.0	36	20
3.0	54	44
4.0	72	78

(a)

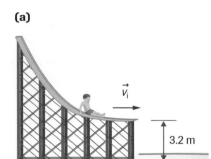

3.2 m

(b)

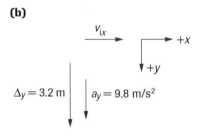

v_{ix}

$+x$

$+y$

$\Delta y = 3.2$ m $a_y = 9.8$ m/s²

Figure 7
For Sample Problem 2
(a) The situation
(b) The initial conditions

A child travels down a water slide, leaving it with a velocity of 4.2 m/s horizontally, as in **Figure 7(a)**. The child then experiences projectile motion, landing in a swimming pool 3.2 m below the slide.

(a) For how long is the child airborne?

(b) Determine the child's horizontal displacement while in the air.

(c) Determine the child's velocity upon entering the water.

Solution

As shown in **Figure 7(b)**, $+x$ is to the right and $+y$ is downward. The initial position is the position where the child leaves the slide.

(a) *Horizontally (constant v_{ix}):*

$v_{ix} = 4.2$ m/s

$\Delta x = ?$

$\Delta t = ?$

Vertically (constant a_y):

$v_{iy} = 0$ $\qquad\qquad\qquad \Delta y = 3.2$ m

$a_y = +g = 9.8$ m/s² $\qquad v_{fy} = ?$

$\Delta t = ?$

The horizontal motion has two unknowns and only one equation $\Delta x = v_{ix}\Delta t$. We can analyze the vertical motion to determine Δt:

$$\Delta y = v_{iy}\Delta t + \frac{1}{2}a_y(\Delta t)^2$$

$$\Delta y = \frac{1}{2}a_y(\Delta t)^2$$

$$(\Delta t)^2 = \frac{2\Delta y}{a_y}$$

$$\Delta t = \pm\sqrt{\frac{2\Delta y}{a_y}}$$

$$= \pm\sqrt{\frac{2(3.2\text{ m})}{9.8\text{ m/s}^2}}$$

$$\Delta t = \pm 0.81 \text{ s}$$

Since we are analyzing a trajectory that starts at $t = 0$, only the positive root applies. The child is in the air for 0.81 s.

(b) We can substitute $\Delta t = 0.81$ s into the equation for horizontal motion.

$$\Delta x = v_{ix}\Delta t$$

$$= (4.2 \text{ m/s})(0.81 \text{ s})$$

$$\Delta x = 3.4 \text{ m}$$

The child reaches the water 3.4 m horizontally from the end of the slide. In other words, the child's horizontal displacement is 3.4 m.

(c) To find the child's final velocity, a vector quantity, we must first determine its horizontal and vertical components. The x-component is constant at 4.2 m/s. We find the y-component as follows:

$$v_{fy} = v_{iy} + a_y\Delta t$$

$$= 0 \text{ m/s} + (9.8 \text{ m/s}^2)(0.81 \text{ s})$$

$$v_{fy} = 7.9 \text{ m/s}$$

We now apply the law of Pythagoras and trigonometry to determine the final velocity as shown in **Figure 8**.

$$v_f = \sqrt{v_{fx}^2 + v_{fy}^2}$$

$$= \sqrt{(4.2 \text{ m/s})^2 + (7.9 \text{ m/s})^2}$$

$$v_f = 8.9 \text{ m/s}$$

$$\theta = \tan^{-1} \frac{v_{fy}}{v_{fx}}$$

$$= \tan^{-1} \frac{7.9 \text{ m/s}}{4.2 \text{ m/s}}$$

$$\theta = 62°$$

The final velocity is 8.9 m/s at an angle of 62° below the horizontal.

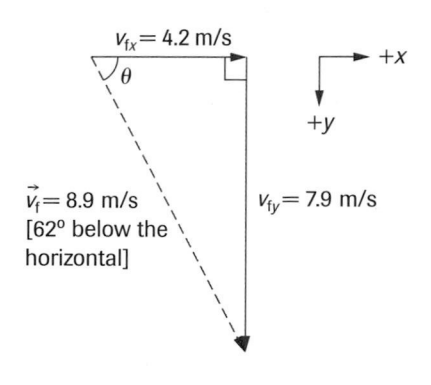

Figure 8
The solution for part (c) of Sample Problem 2

▶ **SAMPLE** problem **3**

A helicopter, travelling horizontally, is 82 m above the ground. The pilot prepares to release a relief package intended to land on the ground 96 m horizontally ahead. Air resistance is negligible. The pilot does not throw the package, but lets it drop. What is the initial velocity of the package relative to the ground?

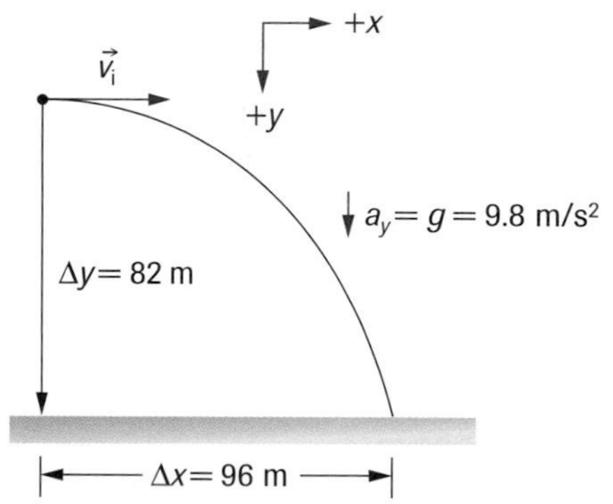

Solution

Figure 9 shows the situation, with the initial position chosen as the point of release, $+x$ chosen to the right, and $+y$ chosen downward. Since the pilot does not throw the package, the initial horizontal velocity of the package is the same as the horizontal velocity of the helicopter.

Horizontally (constant v_{ix}):

$$\Delta x = 96 \text{ m}$$
$$\Delta t = ?$$
$$v_{ix} = ?$$

Figure 9
The situation for Sample Problem 3

Vertically (constant a_y):

$$v_{iy} = 0 \text{ m/s} \qquad\qquad \Delta y = 82 \text{ m}$$
$$a_y = +g = 9.8 \text{ m/s}^2 \qquad \Delta t = ?$$

As in Sample Problem 2, we can determine Δt from the equations for vertical motion. The appropriate equation is

$$\Delta y = v_{iy}\Delta t + \frac{1}{2}a_y(\Delta t)^2$$

$$\Delta y = \frac{1}{2}a_y(\Delta t)^2$$

$$(\Delta t)^2 = \frac{2\Delta y}{a_y}$$

$$\Delta t = \pm \sqrt{\frac{2\Delta y}{a_y}}$$

$$= \pm \sqrt{\frac{2(82 \text{ m})}{9.8 \text{ m/s}^2}}$$

$$\Delta t = 4.1 \text{ s}$$

Since we only consider events after the release of the package at $t = 0$, only the positive root applies.

$$v_{ix} = \frac{\Delta x}{\Delta t}$$

$$= \frac{96 \text{ m}}{4.1 \text{ s}}$$

$$v_{ix} = 23 \text{ m/s}$$

The initial velocity of the package is 23 m/s [horizontally].

▶ Practice

Understanding Concepts

1. Explain why an airplane moving through the air is not an example of projectile motion.

2. A stone is thrown horizontally under negligible air resistance. What are its vertical acceleration and its horizontal acceleration?

3. A marble rolls off a table with a velocity of 1.93 m/s [horizontally]. The tabletop is 76.5 cm above the floor. If air resistance is negligible, determine
   (a) how long the marble is airborne
   (b) the horizontal range
   (c) the velocity at impact

4. A stone is thrown horizontally with an initial speed of 8.0 m/s from a cliff. Air resistance is negligible.
   (a) Determine the horizontal and vertical components of displacement and instantaneous velocity at $t = 0.0$ s, 1.0 s, 2.0 s, and 3.0 s.
   (b) Draw a scale diagram showing the path of the stone.
   (c) Draw the instantaneous velocity vector at each point on your diagram.
   (d) Determine the average acceleration between 1.0 s and 2.0 s, and between 2.0 s and 3.0 s. What do you conclude?

5. A baseball pitcher throws a ball horizontally under negligible air resistance. The ball falls 83 cm in travelling 18.4 m to the home plate. Determine the ball's initial horizontal speed.

Applying Inquiry Skills

6. Figure 10 shows a trajectory apparatus. A vertical target plate allows the horizontal position to be adjusted from one side of the graph paper to the other.
   (a) Describe how this apparatus is used to analyze projectile motion.
   (b) What would you expect to see plotted on graph paper? Draw a diagram. If you have access to a trajectory apparatus, use it to check your prediction.

Making Connections

7. When characters in cartoons run off the edge of a cliff, they hang suspended in the air for a short time before plummeting. If cartoons obeyed the laws of physics, what would they show instead?

Answers

3. (a) 0.395 s
   (b) 76.3 cm
   (c) 4.33 m/s [63.5° below the horizontal]

4. (a) At 3.0 s, $\Delta x = 24$ m, $\Delta y = 44$ m, and $\vec{v} = 3.0 \times 10^1$ m/s [75° below the horizontal].
   (d) 9.8 m/s² [down]

5. 45 m/s

Figure 10
When the steel ball is launched from the ramp and collides with the target plate, the point of contact is recorded on the target paper.

Analyzing More Complex Projectile Motion

In the projectile problems we have solved so far, the initial velocity was horizontal. The same kinematics equations can be used to analyze problems where the initial velocity is at some angle to the horizontal. Since $v_{iy} \neq 0$, you must take care with your choice of positive and negative directions for the vertical motion. For example, a fly ball in baseball

(**Figure 11**) has an initial velocity with an upward vertical component. If the $+y$ direction is chosen to be upward, then v_{iy} is positive, and the vertical acceleration a_y is negative because the gravitational acceleration is downward. Conversely, if the $+y$ direction is chosen to be downward, then v_{iy} is negative and a_y is positive.

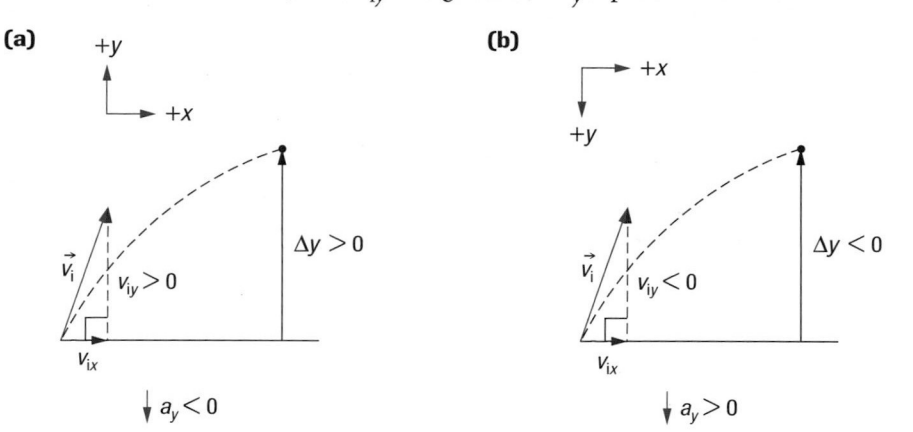

(a) $+y$ $+x$

$\Delta y > 0$

$\vec{v_i}$ $v_{iy} > 0$

v_{ix}

$a_y < 0$

(b) $+x$ $+y$

$\Delta y < 0$

$\vec{v_i}$ $v_{iy} < 0$

v_{ix}

$a_y > 0$

Figure 11
(a) The $+y$ direction is upward.
(b) The $+y$ direction is downward.

► **SAMPLE** problem **4**

A golfer strikes a golf ball on level ground. The ball leaves the ground with an initial velocity of 42 m/s [32° above the horizontal]. The initial conditions are shown in **Figure 12**. If air resistance is negligible, determine the ball's

(a) horizontal range (assuming that it lands at the same level from which it started)

(b) maximum height

(c) horizontal displacement when it is 15 m above the ground

Solution

(a) We begin by finding the horizontal and vertical components of the initial velocity.

$$v_{ix} = |\vec{v_i}|\cos\theta \qquad v_{iy} = |\vec{v_i}|\sin\theta$$

$$= (42\ \text{m/s})(\cos 32°) \qquad = (42\ \text{m/s})(\sin 32°)$$

$$v_{ix} = 36\ \text{m/s} \qquad v_{iy} = 22\ \text{m/s}$$

Horizontally (constant v_{ix}):

$$v_{ix} = 36\ \text{m/s}$$
$$\Delta x = ?$$
$$\Delta t = ?$$

Vertically (constant a_y):

$$a_y = -g = -9.8\ \text{m/s}^2 \qquad \Delta y = 0$$
$$v_{iy} = 22\ \text{m/s} \qquad \Delta t = ?$$
$$v_{fy} = -22\ \text{m/s}$$

Since the horizontal motion has two unknowns and only one equation, we can use the vertical motion to solve for Δt:

$$\Delta y = v_{iy}\Delta t + \frac{1}{2}a_y(\Delta t)^2$$

$$0 = 22\ \text{m/s}\ \Delta t - 4.9\ \text{m/s}^2\ (\Delta t)^2$$

$$0 = \Delta t\ (22\ \text{m/s} - 4.9\ \text{m/s}^2\ \Delta t)$$

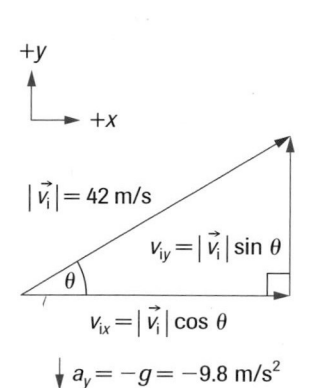

$+y$ $+x$

$|\vec{v_i}| = 42\ \text{m/s}$

$v_{iy} = |\vec{v_i}|\sin\theta$

θ

$v_{ix} = |\vec{v_i}|\cos\theta$

$a_y = -g = -9.8\ \text{m/s}^2$

Figure 12
Initial conditions for Sample Problem 4. The golf tee is chosen as the initial position, and the $+y$ direction is chosen as upward.

Therefore, the ball was hit at $\Delta t = 0$ and the ball lands at 22 m/s – 4.9 m/s^2 $\Delta t = 0$. Solving for Δt, we find that $\Delta t = 4.5$ s, which we can use to find the horizontal range.

$$\Delta x = v_{ix}\Delta t$$
$$= (36 \text{ m/s})(4.5 \text{ s})$$
$$\Delta x = 1.6 \times 10^2 \text{ m}$$

The horizontal range is 1.6×10^2 m.

(b) To determine the maximum height, we start by noting that at the highest position, $v_{fy} = 0$ m/s. (This also happens when an object thrown directly upward reaches the top of its flight.)

$$v_{fy}^2 = v_{iy}^2 + 2a_y\Delta y$$
$$0 = v_{iy}^2 + 2a_y\Delta y$$
$$\Delta y = \frac{v_{iy}^2}{-2a_y}$$
$$= \frac{(22 \text{ m/s})^2}{-2(-9.8 \text{ m/s}^2)}$$
$$\Delta y = 25 \text{ m}$$

The maximum height is 25 m.

(c) To find the horizontal displacement when $\Delta y = 15$ m, we must find the time interval Δt between the start of the motion and when $\Delta y = 15$ m. We can apply the quadratic formula:

$$\Delta y = v_{iy}\Delta t + \frac{1}{2}a_y(\Delta t)^2$$
$$15 \text{ m} = 22 \text{ m/s } \Delta t - 4.9 \text{ m/s}^2\,(\Delta t)^2$$
$$4.9 \text{ m/s}^2\,(\Delta t)^2 - 22 \text{ m/s } \Delta t + 15 \text{ m} = 0$$

Using the quadratic formula,

$$\Delta t = \frac{-b \pm \sqrt{b^2 - 4ac}}{2a} \qquad \text{where } a = 4.9 \text{ m/s}^2, b = -22 \text{ m/s, and } c = 15 \text{ m}$$

$$= \frac{-(-22 \text{ m/s}) \pm \sqrt{(-22 \text{ m/s})^2 - 4(4.9 \text{ m/s}^2)(15 \text{ m})}}{2(4.9 \text{ m/s}^2)}$$

$$\Delta t = 3.7 \text{ s or } 0.84 \text{ s}$$

Thus, the ball is 15 m above the ground twice: when rising and when descending. We can determine the corresponding horizontal positions:

$$\Delta x_{up} = v_{ix}\Delta t \qquad\qquad \Delta x_{down} = v_{ix}\Delta t$$
$$= (36 \text{ m/s})(0.84 \text{ s}) \qquad\qquad = (36 \text{ m/s})(3.7 \text{ s})$$
$$\Delta x_{up} = 3.0 \times 10^1 \text{ m} \qquad\qquad \Delta x_{down} = 1.3 \times 10^2 \text{ m}$$

The horizontal position of the ball is either 3.0×10^1 m or 1.3×10^2 m when it is 15 m above ground.

As you learned in the solution to Sample Problem 4, the range of a projectile can be found by applying the kinematics equations step by step. We can also derive a general equation for the horizontal range Δx of a projectile, given the initial velocity and the angle of launch. What, for example, happens when a projectile lands at the same level from which it began ($\Delta y = 0$), as shown in **Figure 13**? For the horizontal range, the motion is found using the equation $\Delta x = v_{ix}\Delta t$, where the only known variable is v_{ix}. To find the other variable, Δt, we use the vertical motion:

$$\Delta y = v_{iy}\Delta t + \frac{1}{2}a_y(\Delta t)^2$$

where $\Delta y = 0$ because we are considering the situation where the final level is the same as the initial level.

$$v_{iy} = v_i \sin \theta$$
$$a_y = -g$$
$$0 = v_i \sin \theta \Delta t - \frac{1}{2}g(\Delta t)^2$$
$$0 = \Delta t\left(v_i \sin \theta - \frac{1}{2}g(\Delta t)\right)$$

Therefore, either $\Delta t = 0$ (on takeoff) or $v_i \sin \theta - \frac{1}{2}g\Delta t = 0$ (on landing).

Solving the latter equation for Δt gives

$$\Delta t = \frac{2v_i \sin \theta}{g}$$

Now we return to the horizontal motion:

$$\Delta x = v_{ix}\Delta t$$
$$= (v_i \cos \theta)\Delta t$$
$$= v_i \cos \theta \left(\frac{2v_i \sin \theta}{g}\right)$$
$$\Delta x = \frac{v_i^2}{g} 2\sin \theta \cos \theta$$

Since $2\sin \theta \cos \theta = \sin 2\theta$ (as shown in the trigonometric identities in Appendix A), the horizontal range is

$$\Delta x = \frac{v_i^2}{g} \sin 2\theta$$

where v_i is the magnitude of the initial velocity of a projectile launched at an angle θ to the horizontal. Note that this equation applies only if $\Delta y = 0$.

All of the previous discussion and examples of projectile motion have assumed that air resistance is negligible. This is close to the true situation in cases involving relatively dense objects moving at low speeds, such as a shot used in shot put competition. However, for many situations, air resistance cannot be ignored. When air resistance is considered, the analysis of projectile motion becomes more complex and is beyond the intention of this text. The concept of "hang time" in certain sports, especially football, is important and is explored in Lab Exercise 1.4.1 in the Lab Activities Section at the end of this chapter. ✒▮

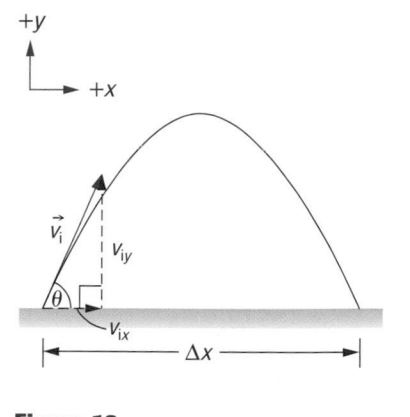

Figure 13
Initial conditions for deriving the horizontal range of a projectile in terms of launch angle and initial velocity

▶ **TRY THIS** *activity*

Comparing Horizontal Range

As a class or in a large group, set up a table using these titles: Launch Angle, Time of Flight, Maximum Height, and Horizontal Range. Complete the table for a projectile that has an initial velocity of magnitude 25.00 m/s and lands at the same level from which it was launched. Perform the calculations using four significant digits, using every third degree from 3° to 87° (i.e., 3°, 6°, 9°, … 81°, 84°, 87°). Write conclusions about maximizing height and horizontal range.

✏ **LAB EXERCISE 1.4.1**

Hang Time in Football (p. 58)
"Hang time" in sports is the time interval between the launch of a ball and the landing or catching of the ball. In football, when a punt is needed, the punter tries to maximize the hang time of the ball to give his teammates time to race downfield to tackle the punt receiver. Of course, at the same time the punter tries to maximize the horizontal range to give his team better field position.

Write your hypothesis and predictions to the following questions, and then explore these concepts further by conducting the lab exercise.
(a) What factors affect the hang time of a punted football? How do they affect hang time?
(b) What launch angle of a punt maximizes the hang time of a football?

Understanding Concepts

8. A field hockey ball is struck and undergoes projectile motion. Air resistance is negligible.
   (a) What is the vertical component of velocity at the top of the flight?
   (b) What is the acceleration at the top of the flight?
   (c) How does the rise time compare to the fall time if the ball lands at the same level from which it was struck?

9. A cannon is set at an angle of 45° above the horizontal. A cannonball leaves the muzzle with a speed of 2.2×10^2 m/s. Air resistance is negligible. Determine the cannonball's
   (a) maximum height
   (b) time of flight
   (c) horizontal range (to the same vertical level)
   (d) velocity at impact

10. A medieval prince trapped in a castle wraps a message around a rock and throws it from the top of the castle wall with an initial velocity of 12 m/s [42° above the horizontal]. The rock lands just on the far side of the castle's moat, at a level 9.5 m below the initial level (**Figure 14**). Determine the rock's
    (a) time of flight
    (b) width of the moat
    (c) velocity at impact

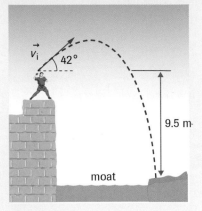

Figure 14
The situation for question 10

Answers

9. (a) 1.2×10^3 m
   (b) 32 s
   (c) 4.9×10^3 m
   (d) 2.2×10^2 m/s [45° below the horizontal]

10. (a) 2.4 s
    (b) 22 m
    (c) 18 m/s [60° below the horizontal]

SUMMARY *Projectile Motion*

- A projectile is an object moving through the air in a curved trajectory with no propulsion system.

- Projectile motion is motion with a constant horizontal velocity combined with a constant vertical acceleration.

- The horizontal and vertical motions of a projectile are independent of each other except they have a common time.

- Projectile motion problems can be solved by applying the constant velocity equation for the horizontal component of the motion and the constant acceleration equations for the vertical component of the motion.

▶ **Section 1.4 Questions**

Understanding Concepts

1. What is the vertical acceleration of a projectile on its way up, at the top of its trajectory, and on its way down?

2. (a) For a projectile with the launch point lower than the landing point, in what part of the flight is the magnitude of the velocity at a maximum? a minimum?
   (b) In what part of the flight is the magnitude of the velocity at a maximum, and in what part is it at a minimum, for a projectile with the launch point higher than the landing point?

3. A projectile launched horizontally moves 16 m in the horizontal plane while falling 1.5 m in the vertical plane. Determine the projectile's initial velocity.

4. A tennis player serves a ball horizontally, giving it a speed of 24 m/s from a height of 2.5 m. The player is 12 m from the net. The top of the net is 0.90 m above the court surface. The ball clears the net and lands on the other side. Air resistance is negligible.

(a) For how long is the ball airborne?
(b) What is the horizontal displacement?
(c) What is the velocity at impact?
(d) By what distance does the ball clear the net?

5. A child throws a ball onto the roof of a house, then catches it with a baseball glove 1.0 m above the ground, as in **Figure 15**. The ball leaves the roof with a speed of 3.2 m/s.
   (a) For how long is the ball airborne after leaving the roof?
   (b) What is the horizontal distance from the glove to the edge of the roof?
   (c) What is the velocity of the ball just before it lands in the glove?

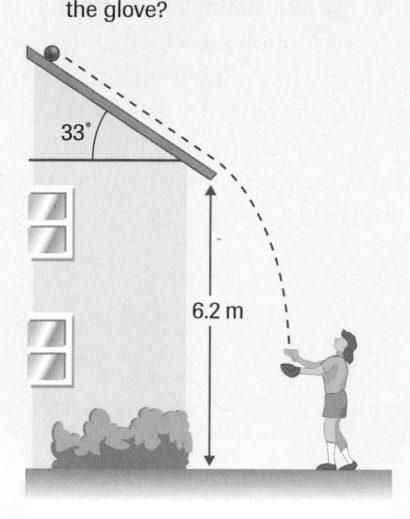

33°

6.2 m

Figure 15

6. For a projectile that lands at the same level from which it starts, state another launch angle above the horizontal that would result in the same range as a projectile launched at an angle of 36°, 16°, and 45.6°. Air resistance is negligible.

7. During World War I, the German army bombarded Paris with a huge gun referred to, by the Allied Forces, as "Big Bertha." Assume that Big Bertha fired shells with an initial velocity of 1.1×10^3 m/s [45° above the horizontal].
   (a) How long was each shell airborne, if the launch point was at the same level as the landing point?
   (b) Determine the maximum horizontal range of each shell.
   (c) Determine the maximum height of each shell.

8. An astronaut on the Moon, where $|\vec{g}| = 1.6$ m/s², strikes a golf ball giving the ball a velocity of 32 m/s [35° above the Moon's horizontal]. The ball lands in a crater floor that is 15 m below the level where it was struck. Determine
   (a) the maximum height of the ball
   (b) the time of flight of the ball
   (c) the horizontal range of the ball

Applying Inquiry Skills

9. A garden hose is held with its nozzle horizontally above the ground (**Figure 16**). The flowing water follows projectile motion. Given a metre stick and a calculator, describe how you would determine the speed of the water coming out of the nozzle.

Figure 16
Projectile motion in the garden

10. Describe how you would build and test a device made of simple, inexpensive materials to demonstrate that two coins launched simultaneously from the same level, one launched horizontally and the other dropped vertically, land at the same instant.

Making Connections

11. In real-life situations, projectile motion is often more complex than what has been presented in this section. For example, to determine the horizontal range of a shot in shot put competitions, the following equation is used:

$$\Delta x = \Delta x_1 + \Delta x_2 + \Delta x_3$$

$$\Delta x = 0.30 \text{ m} + \frac{2v_i^2 \sin\theta \cos\theta}{g} + \frac{v_i \sin\theta \sqrt{v_i^2 \sin^2\theta + |2g\Delta y|}}{g}$$

where 0.30 m is the average distance the athlete's hand goes beyond the starting line, v_i is the magnitude of the initial velocity, θ is the angle of launch above the horizontal, Δy is the height above the ground where the shot leaves the hand, and g is the magnitude of the acceleration due to gravity (**Figure 17**).
   (a) Determine the range of a shot released 2.2 m above the ground with an initial velocity of 13 m/s [42° above the horizontal].
   (b) Compare your answer in (a) to the world record for the shot put (currently about 23.1 m).
   (c) Why do you think the equation given here differs from the equation for horizontal range derived in this section?

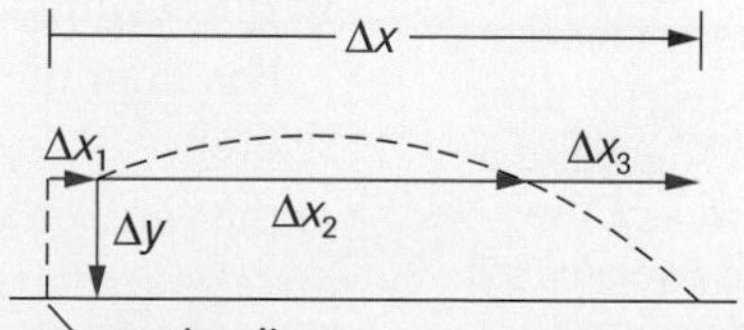

Δx

Δx_1 Δx_3

Δy Δx_2

starting line

Figure 17

frame of reference coordinate system relative to which motion is observed

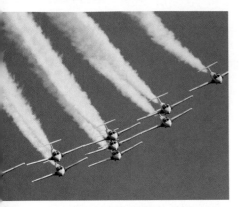

Figure 1
The Canadian Forces Snowbirds fly at velocities of between 400 and 600 km/h (relative to the ground), but when they are flying in formation, as shown here, the velocity of one plane relative to another is zero.

relative velocity velocity of an object relative to a specific frame of reference

Air shows provide elements of both excitement and danger. When high-speed airplanes fly in constant formation (**Figure 1**), observers on the ground see them moving at high velocity. Seen from the cockpit, however, all the planes appear to have zero velocity. Observers on the ground are in one frame of reference, while the pilots are in the plane's frame of reference. A **frame of reference** is a coordinate system relative to which motion is described or observed.

The most common frame of reference that we use as a stationary, or fixed, frame of reference is Earth or the ground. In the examples of motion presented in the previous sections, all objects were assumed to be moving relative to the frame of reference of Earth. Sometimes, however, other frames are chosen for convenience. For example, to analyze the motion of the planets of the solar system, the Sun's frame of reference is used. If we observe a spot near the rim of a rolling wheel, the wheel or the centre of the wheel is the most convenient frame of reference, as in **Figure 2**.

(a)   **(b)**

Figure 2
(a) The motion of a spot near the rim of a rolling wheel is simple if viewed from the frame of reference of the wheel's centre.
(b) The motion of the spot is much more complex when viewed from Earth's frame of reference.

The velocity of an object relative to a specific frame of reference is called **relative velocity**. We have not used this term previously because we were considering motion relative to one frame of reference at a time. Now we will explore situations involving at least two frames of reference. Such situations occur for passengers walking about in a moving train, for watercraft travelling on a flowing river, and for the Snowbirds or other aircraft flying when there is wind blowing relative to the ground.

To analyze relative velocity in more than one frame of reference, we use the symbol for relative velocity, $\vec{v}$, with two subscripts in capital letters. The first subscript represents the object whose velocity is stated relative to the object represented by the second subscript. In other words, the second subscript is the frame of reference.

For example, if P is a plane travelling at 490 km/h [W] relative to Earth's frame of reference, E, then $\vec{v}_{PE} = 490$ km/h [W]. If we consider another frame of reference, such as the wind or air, A, affecting the plane's motion, then $\vec{v}_{PA}$ is the velocity of the plane relative to the air and $\vec{v}_{AE}$ is the velocity of the air relative to Earth. The vectors $\vec{v}_{PA}$ and $\vec{v}_{AE}$ are related to $\vec{v}_{PE}$ using the following relative velocity equation:

$$\vec{v}_{PE} = \vec{v}_{PA} + \vec{v}_{AE}$$

This equation applies whether the motion is in one, two, or three dimensions. For example, consider the one-dimensional situation in which the wind and the plane are both moving eastward. If the plane's velocity relative to the air is 430 km/h [E], and the air's velocity relative to the ground is 90 km/h [E], then the velocity of the plane relative to the ground is:

$$\vec{v}_{PE} = \vec{v}_{PA} + \vec{v}_{AE}$$
$$= 430 \text{ km/h [E]} + 90 \text{ km/h [E]}$$
$$\vec{v}_{PE} = 520 \text{ km/h [E]}$$

Thus, with a tail wind, the ground speed increases—a logical result. You can easily figure out that the plane's ground speed in this example would be only 340 km/h [E] if the wind were a head wind (i.e., if $\vec{v}_{AG} = 90$ km/h [W]).

Before looking at relative velocities in two dimensions, make sure that you understand the pattern of the subscripts used in any relative velocity equation. As shown in **Figure 3**, the left side of the equation has a single relative velocity, while the right side has the vector addition of two or more relative velocities. Note that the "outside" and the "inside" subscripts on the right side are in the same order as the subscripts on the left side.

$$\vec{v}_{PE} = \vec{v}_{PA} + \vec{v}_{AE}$$

$$\vec{v}_{CE} = \vec{v}_{CW} + \vec{v}_{WE}$$

$$\vec{v}_{LO} = \vec{v}_{LM} + \vec{v}_{MN} + \vec{v}_{NO}$$

$$\vec{v}_{DG} = \vec{v}_{DE} + \vec{v}_{EF} + \vec{v}_{FG}$$

Figure 3
The pattern in relative velocity equations

> ## SAMPLE problem 1

An Olympic canoeist, capable of travelling at a speed of 4.5 m/s in still water, is crossing a river that is flowing with a velocity of 3.2 m/s [E]. The river is 2.2×10^2 m wide.

(a) If the canoe is aimed northward, as in **Figure 4**, what is its velocity relative to the shore?

(b) How long does the crossing take?

(c) Where is the landing position of the canoe relative to its starting position?

(d) If the canoe landed directly across from the starting position, at what angle would the canoe have been aimed?

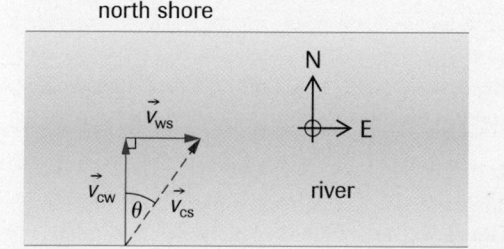

north shore

river

Figure 4
The situation

Solution

Using the subscripts C for the canoe, S for the shore, and W for the water, the known relative velocities are:

$$\vec{v}_{CW} = 4.5 \text{ m/s [N]}$$
$$\vec{v}_{WS} = 3.2 \text{ m/s [E]}$$

DID YOU **KNOW**

Wind Directions
By convention, a west wind is a wind that blows from the west, so its velocity vector points east (e.g., a west wind might be blowing at 45 km/h [E]). A southwest wind has the direction [45° N of E] or [45° E of N].

DID YOU **KNOW**

Navigation Terminology
Air navigators have terms for some of the key concepts of relative velocity. *Air speed* is the speed of a plane relative to the air. *Wind speed* is the speed of the wind relative to the ground. *Ground speed* is the speed of the plane relative to the ground. The *heading* is the direction in which the plane is aimed. The *course*, or *track*, is the path relative to Earth or the ground. Marine navigators use "heading," "course," and "track" in analogous ways.

(a) Since the unknown is $\vec{v}_{CS}$, we use the relative velocity equation

$$\vec{v}_{CS} = \vec{v}_{CW} + \vec{v}_{WS}$$

$$\vec{v}_{CS} = 4.5 \text{ m/s [N]} + 3.2 \text{ m/s [E]}$$

Applying the law of Pythagoras, we find:

$$\left|\vec{v}_{CS}\right| = \sqrt{(4.5 \text{ m/s})^2 + (3.2 \text{ m/s})^2}$$

$$\left|\vec{v}_{CS}\right| = 5.5 \text{ m/s}$$

Trigonometry gives the angle θ in **Figure 4**:

$$\theta = \tan^{-1} \frac{3.2 \text{ m/s}}{4.5 \text{ m/s}}$$

$$\theta = 35°$$

The velocity of the canoe relative to the shore is 5.5 m/s [35° E of N].

(b) To determine the time taken to cross the river, we consider only the motion perpendicular to the river.

$$\Delta\vec{d} = 2.2 \times 10^2 \text{ m [N]}$$
$$\vec{v}_{CW} = 4.5 \text{ m/s [N]}$$
$$\Delta t = ?$$

From $\vec{v}_{CW} = \dfrac{\Delta\vec{d}}{\Delta t}$, we have:

$$\Delta t = \frac{\Delta\vec{d}}{\vec{v}_{CW}}$$

$$= \frac{2.2 \times 10^2 \text{ m [N]}}{4.5 \text{ m/s [N]}}$$

$$\Delta t = 49 \text{ s}$$

The crossing time is 49 s.

(c) The current carries the canoe eastward (downstream) during the time it takes to cross the river. The downstream displacement is

$$\Delta\vec{d} = \vec{v}_{WS}\Delta t$$

$$= (3.2 \text{ m/s [E]})(49 \text{ s})$$

$$\Delta\vec{d} = 1.6 \times 10^2 \text{ m [E]}$$

The landing position is 2.2×10^2 m [N] and 1.6×10^2 m [E] of the starting position. Using the law of Pythagoras and trigonometry, the resultant displacement is 2.7×10^2 m [36° E of N].

(d) The velocity of the canoe relative to the water, $\vec{v}_{CW}$, which has a magnitude of 4.5 m/s, is the hypotenuse of the triangle in **Figure 5**. The resultant velocity $\vec{v}_{CS}$ must point directly north for the canoe to land directly north of the starting position.

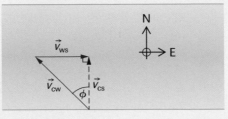

Figure 5
The solution for part (d)

The angle in the triangle is

$$\phi = \sin^{-1} \frac{|\vec{v}_{WS}|}{|\vec{v}_{CW}|}$$

$$= \sin^{-1} \frac{3.2 \text{ m/s}}{4.5 \text{ m/s}}$$

$$\phi = 45°$$

The required heading for the canoe is [45° W of N].

▶ SAMPLE problem 2

The air speed of a small plane is 215 km/h. The wind is blowing at 57 km/h from the west. Determine the velocity of the plane relative to the ground if the pilot keeps the plane aimed in the direction [34° E of N].

Solution

We use the subscripts P for the plane, E for Earth or the ground, and A for the air.

$\vec{v}_{PA} = 215$ km/h [34° E of N]

$\vec{v}_{AE} = 57$ km/h [E]

$\vec{v}_{PE} = ?$

$$\vec{v}_{PE} = \vec{v}_{PA} + \vec{v}_{AE}$$

This vector addition is shown in **Figure 6.** We will solve this problem by applying the cosine and sine laws; however, we could also apply a vector scale diagram or components as described in Appendix A.

Using the cosine law:

$$|\vec{v}_{PE}|^2 = |\vec{v}_{PA}|^2 + |\vec{v}_{AE}|^2 - 2|\vec{v}_{PA}||\vec{v}_{AE}| \cos \phi$$
$$= (215 \text{ km/h})^2 + (57 \text{ km/h})^2 - 2(215 \text{ km/h})(57 \text{ km/h}) \cos 124°$$
$$|\vec{v}_{PE}| = 251 \text{ km/h}$$

Using the sine law:

$$\frac{\sin \theta}{|\vec{v}_{AE}|} = \frac{\sin \phi}{|\vec{v}_{PE}|}$$

$$\sin \theta = \frac{57 \text{ km/h } (\sin 124°)}{251 \text{ km/h}}$$

$$\theta = 11°$$

The direction of $\vec{v}_{PE}$ is 34° + 11° = 45° E of N. Thus $\vec{v}_{PE}$ = 251 km/h [45° E of N].

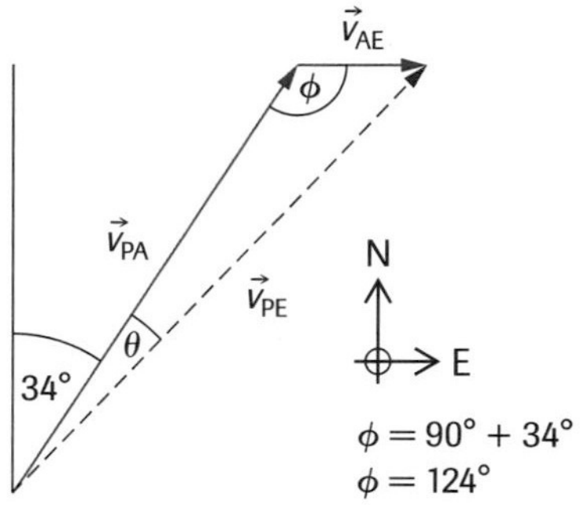

Figure 6
Solving Sample Problem 2 using trigonometry

$\phi = 90° + 34°$
$\phi = 124°$

Sometimes it is helpful to know that the velocity of object X relative to object Y has the same magnitude as the velocity of Y relative to X, but is opposite in direction: $\vec{v}_{XY} = -\vec{v}_{YX}$. Consider, for example, a jogger J running past a person P sitting on a park bench. If $\vec{v}_{JP} = 2.5$ m/s [E], then P is viewing J moving eastward at 2.5 m/s. To J, P appears to be moving at a velocity of 2.5 m/s [W]. Thus $\vec{v}_{PJ} = -2.5$ m/s [E] = 2.5 m/s [W]. In the next Sample Problem, we will use this relationship for performing a vector subtraction.

LEARNING TIP

Subtracting Vectors
When a relative velocity equation, such as $\vec{v}_{PE} = \vec{v}_{PA} + \vec{v}_{AE}$, is rearranged to isolate either $\vec{v}_{PA}$ or $\vec{v}_{AE}$, a vector subtraction must be performed. For example, $\vec{v}_{PA} = \vec{v}_{PE} - \vec{v}_{AE}$ is equivalent to $\vec{v}_{PA} = \vec{v}_{PE} + (-\vec{v}_{AE})$. Appendix A discusses vector arithmetic.

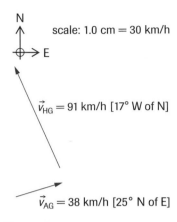

scale: 1.0 cm = 30 km/h

$\vec{v}_{HG}$ = 91 km/h [17° W of N]

$\vec{v}_{AG}$ = 38 km/h [25° N of E]

Figure 7
Situation for Sample Problem 3

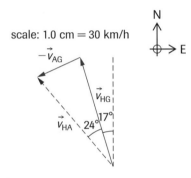

scale: 1.0 cm = 30 km/h

Figure 8
Solution to Sample Problem 3

Answers

2. (a) 3.9 m/s [fwd]

   (b) 1.7 m/s [fwd]

   (c) 3.0 m/s [21° right of fwd]

3. 5.3 m/s [12° E of N]

4. 7.2 × 10² km [30° S of W] from Winnipeg

SAMPLE problem 3

A helicopter, flying where the average wind velocity is 38 km/h [25° N of E], needs to achieve a velocity of 91 km/h [17° W of N] relative to the ground to arrive at the destination on time, as shown in **Figure 7**. What is the necessary velocity relative to the air?

Solution

Using the subscripts H for the helicopter, G for the ground, and A for the air, we have the following relative velocities:

$$\vec{v}_{HG} = 91 \text{ km/h } [17° \text{ W of N}]$$
$$\vec{v}_{AG} = 38 \text{ km/h } [25° \text{ N of E}]$$
$$\vec{v}_{HA} = ?$$

$$\vec{v}_{HG} = \vec{v}_{HA} + \vec{v}_{AG}$$

We rearrange the equation to solve for the unknown:

$$\vec{v}_{HA} = \vec{v}_{HG} - \vec{v}_{AG}$$
$$\vec{v}_{HA} = \vec{v}_{HG} + (-\vec{v}_{AG}) \quad \text{where } -\vec{v}_{AG} \text{ is 38 km/h } [25° \text{ S of W}]$$

Figure 8 shows this vector subtraction. By direct measurement on the scale diagram, we can see that the velocity of the helicopter relative to the air must be 94 km/h [41° W of N]. The same result can be obtained using components or the laws of sines and cosines.

Practice

Understanding Concepts

1. Something is incorrect in each of the following equations. Rewrite each equation to show the correction.
   (a) $\vec{v}_{LE} = \vec{v}_{LD} + \vec{v}_{LE}$
   (b) $\vec{v}_{AC} = \vec{v}_{AB} - \vec{v}_{BC}$
   (c) $\vec{v}_{MN} = \vec{v}_{NT} + \vec{v}_{TM}$ (Write down two correct equations.)
   (d) $\vec{v}_{LP} = \vec{v}_{ML} + \vec{v}_{MN} + \vec{v}_{NO} + \vec{v}_{OP}$

2. A cruise ship is moving with a velocity of 2.8 m/s [fwd] relative to the water. A group of tourists walks on the deck with a velocity of 1.1 m/s relative to the deck. Determine their velocity relative to the water if they are walking toward (a) the bow, (b) the stern, and (c) the starboard. (The bow is the front of a ship, the stern is the rear, and the starboard is on the right side of the ship as you face the bow.)

3. The cruise ship in question 2 is travelling with a velocity of 2.8 m/s [N] off the coast of British Columbia, in a place where the ocean current has a velocity relative to the coast of 2.4 m/s [N]. Determine the velocity of the group of tourists in 2(c) relative to the coast.

4. A plane, travelling with a velocity relative to the air of 320 km/h [28° S of W], passes over Winnipeg. The wind velocity is 72 km/h [S]. Determine the displacement of the plane from Winnipeg 2.0 h later.

Making Connections

5. Airline pilots are often able to use the jet stream to minimize flight times. Find out more about the importance of the jet stream in aviation.

 www.science.nelson.com

Frames of Reference and Relative Velocity

- A frame of reference is a coordinate system relative to which motion can be observed.

- Relative velocity is the velocity of an object relative to a specific frame of reference. (A typical relative velocity equation is $\vec{v}_{PE} = \vec{v}_{PA} + \vec{v}_{AE}$, where P is the observed object and E is the observer or frame of reference.)

▶ Section 1.5 Questions

Understanding Concepts

1. Two kayakers can move at the same speed in calm water. One begins kayaking straight across a river, while the other kayaks at an angle upstream in the same river to land straight across from the starting position. Assume the speed of the kayakers is greater than the speed of the river current. Which kayaker reaches the far side first? Explain why.

2. A helicopter travels with an air speed of 55 m/s. The helicopter heads in the direction [35° N of W]. What is its velocity relative to the ground if the wind velocity is (a) 21 m/s [E] and (b) 21 m/s [22° W of N]?

3. A swimmer who achieves a speed of 0.75 m/s in still water swims directly across a river 72 m wide. The swimmer lands on the far shore at a position 54 m downstream from the starting point.
   (a) Determine the speed of the river current.
   (b) Determine the swimmer's velocity relative to the shore.
   (c) Determine the direction the swimmer would have to aim to land directly across from the starting position.

4. A pilot is required to fly directly from London, UK, to Rome, Italy in 3.5 h. The displacement is 1.4×10^3 km [43° E of S]. A wind is blowing with a velocity of 75 km/h [E]. Determine the required velocity of the plane relative to the air.

Applying Inquiry Skills

5. A physics student on a train estimates the speed of falling raindrops on the train car's window. **Figure 9** shows the student's method of estimating the angle with which the drops are moving along the window glass.

(a) Assuming that the raindrops are falling straight downward relative to Earth's frame of reference, and that the speed of the train is 64 km/h, determine the vertical speed of the drops.

(b) Describe sources of error in carrying out this type of estimation.

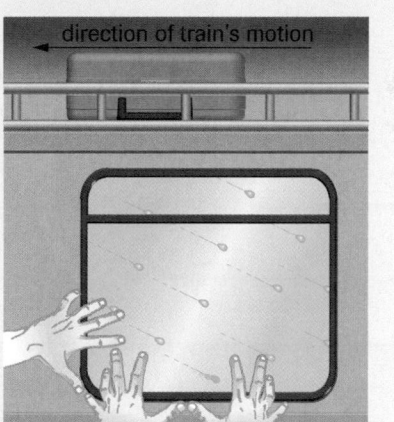

left hand   right hand

Figure 9
Estimating the speed of falling raindrops

Making Connections

6. You have made a video recording of a weather report, showing a reporter standing in the wind and rain of a hurricane. How could you analyze the video to estimate the wind speed? Assume that the wind is blowing horizontally, and that the vertical component of the velocity of the raindrops is the same as the vertical component for the raindrops in the previous question.

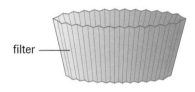 INVESTIGATION 1.3.1

Comparing Terminal Speeds

One way to determine how the terminal speed depends on the mass of an object is to observe the motion of flat-bottomed coffee filters falling vertically toward a motion sensor (**Figure 1**).

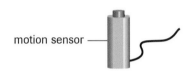

filter —

motion sensor —

Figure 1
Recording the motion of falling coffee filters with a motion sensor

Question

(a) Formulate an appropriate question for this investigation.

Hypothesis/Prediction

(b) Write your hypothesis to answer the question.

(c) On a single speed-time graph, draw three sets of lines to represent your predictions of what you will observe when first one, then two, and finally three filters (inside each other) fall toward a motion sensor that records the speeds. Label each set of lines on the graph.

Inquiry Skills

● Questioning	● Planning	● Analyzing
● Hypothesizing	● Conducting	● Evaluating
● Predicting	● Recording	● Communicating

Experimental Design

(d) Write out the steps of the investigation that your group will follow to answer the question, and to test your hypothesis and predictions. Include any safety precautions.

(e) Have your teacher approve your design before you proceed.

Materials

(f) Make a list of materials and apparatus that you will need to perform this investigation.

Analysis

(g) Carry out your approved design, plotting a single speed-time graph of the results from the motion sensor.

Evaluation

(h) Evaluate your hypothesis and predictions.

(i) List sources of random and systematic errors in this investigation. Suggest ways of minimizing those errors.

Synthesis

(j) Describe how you would design an investigation to determine the factors that affect the terminal speeds of spheres falling through water. Consider not only mass, but at least one other interesting variable.

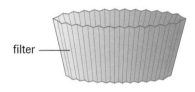 INVESTIGATION 1.4.1

Investigating Projectile Motion

A convenient way of analyzing projectile motion uses an air table in which friction between the moving puck and the surface is minimized (**Figure 1**). If the table is elevated along one side, then a puck that is launched with a horizontal component of velocity will undergo projectile motion. You can analyze that motion using a combination of diagrams and equations.

Inquiry Skills

○ Questioning	○ Planning	● Analyzing
● Hypothesizing	● Conducting	● Evaluating
○ Predicting	● Recording	● Communicating

 There is a danger of electrocution. Leave the spark generator off until you are ready to gather data. Do not touch the air table when the spark generator is activated.

To prevent an electric shock, the two pucks must be in contact with the carbon paper whenever the sparker electricity is activated.

Keep the angle of the air table above the horizontal very small.

⚛ INVESTIGATION 1.4.1 *continued*

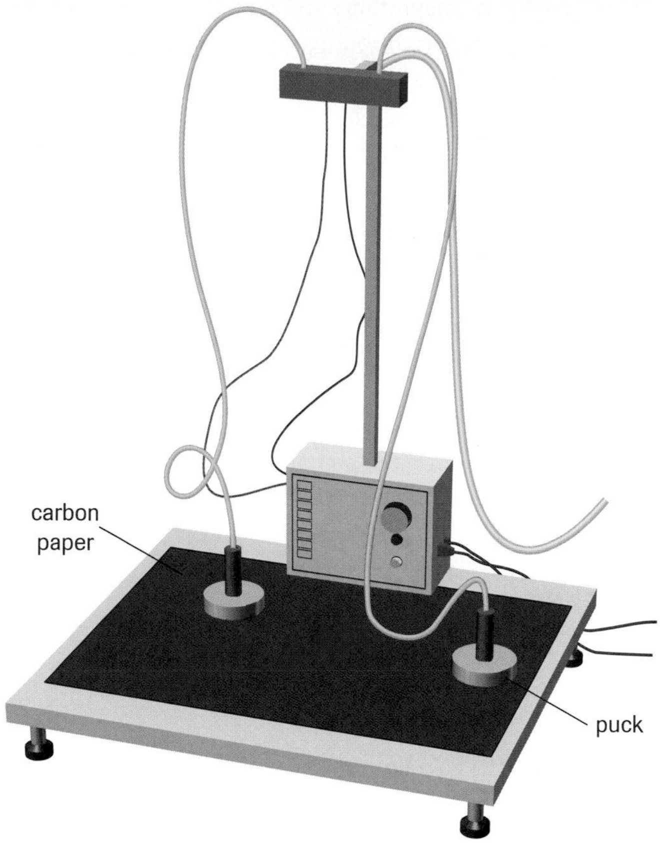

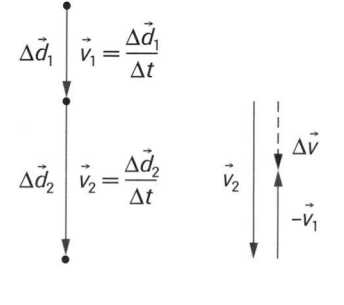

carbon
paper

puck

Figure 1
When using an air table with a sparker puck, keep another puck near the edge of the table in contact with the carbon paper to prevent a break in the current to the sparker.

Questions

(i) What is the direction of the acceleration of a projectile on an inclined plane?

(ii) How can you show that the vertical component of projectile motion on an inclined plane is independent of the horizontal component?

Hypothesis

(a) Hypothesize answers to both questions. Explain each answer.

Materials

For the class:
air table and related apparatus
bricks or books to support the raised end of the table

For each group of 4 or 5 students:
metre stick

For each student:
3 sheets of construction paper
centimetre ruler
protractor

Procedure

1. Working in a group, determine the angle of incline of the air table as accurately as possible. (Apply trigonometry.)

2. With the sparker turned off and the air supply turned on, have one person in the group ready to stop the puck before it hits the edge of the table. Practise setting one of the pucks in motion to satisfy each of the following conditions:

   Motion A: $v_{ix} = 0$; $v_{iy} = 0$
   Motion B: $v_{ix} > 0$; $v_{iy} = 0$
   Motion C: $v_{ix} > 0$; $v_{iy} > 0$

3. When you are satisfied with the motions and with the safe use of the apparatus, turn on the sparker and create Motions A, B, and C on separate pieces of the construction paper for each member of the group. (Do not touch the air table when the spark generator is activated.) Label each motion, indicating the frequency and period of the sparker.

   Note: For the remaining steps, neatness and accuracy are very important.

4. For the linear motion (see **Figure 2**, Motion A), draw between 6 and 10 velocity vectors, $\vec{v}_1, \vec{v}_2, \ldots \vec{v}_n$, by drawing displacement vectors and dividing each one by the time interval for the displacements. Use vector subtraction to determine the corresponding $\Delta\vec{v}$ vectors, as illustrated in the diagram. Next, calculate the average acceleration for each $\Delta\vec{v}$ vector, using the equation

$$\vec{a}_{av,n} = \frac{\vec{v}_{n+1} - \vec{v}_n}{\Delta t}$$

   where Δt is the time interval from the mid-time of $\vec{v}_n$ to the mid-time of $\vec{v}_{n+1}$. Finally, calculate the average acceleration of all $\vec{a}_{av,n}$ values.

$$\Delta\vec{d}_1 \quad \vec{v}_1 = \frac{\Delta\vec{d}_1}{\Delta t}$$

$$\Delta\vec{d}_2 \quad \vec{v}_2 = \frac{\Delta\vec{d}_2}{\Delta t} \qquad \vec{v}_2 \qquad \Delta\vec{v} \quad -\vec{v}_1$$

Figure 2
Determining the change in velocity for frictionless motion on an inclined plane

5. Repeat step 4 for the motion with an initial horizontal velocity (see **Figure 3**, Motion B). Ignore sparker dots created when the pushing force was in contact with the puck or created after the puck came near the edge of the table.

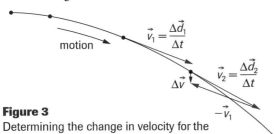

Figure 3
Determining the change in velocity for the projectile motion with an initial horizontal velocity

6. Repeat step 5 for the motion in which the puck was launched upward from the initial position (see **Figure 4**, Motion C).

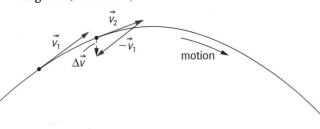

Figure 4
Determining the change in velocity for the projectile motion with an initial velocity at an angle to the horizontal

Analysis

(b) Compare the magnitudes and directions of the accelerations for the three motions tested in this investigation.

(c) Use the angle of the table, θ, to determine the magnitude of the acceleration down the inclined plane. (*Hint:* Use the equation $a = g \sin \theta$, where $g = 9.8$ m/s^2.)

(d) Find the percent difference between your answer in (c) and each of the other average accelerations.

(e) Answer questions (i) and (ii).

Evaluation

(f) Comment on the accuracy of your hypothesis.

(g) Describe random and systematic sources of error in this investigation. How could you minimize these sources of error?

Synthesis

(h) In analyzing the vectors of the motions in this investigation, is it better to use smaller or larger values of Δt? Give your reasons.

(i) Explain why you were asked to calculate the percent difference rather than the percent error in (d).

(j) Prove that the equation $a = g \sin \theta$ is valid for the magnitude of the acceleration down a frictionless plane inclined at an angle θ to the horizontal.

✏ LAB EXERCISE 1.4.1

Hang Time in Football

Inquiry Skills

○ Questioning	○ Planning	● Analyzing
○ Hypothesizing	○ Conducting	● Evaluating
● Predicting	○ Recording	● Communicating

To give the punting team (**Figure 1**) time to get downfield to tackle the receiver, the hang time of the football must be as great as possible. But at the same time, the horizontal range of the ball must be large so that the team can gain field advantage. Factors such as the launch angle, the initial speed, and wind speed and direction affect the ball's motion, which makes experimentation complex. This lab exercise uses a small sampling of data from video recordings of football games. As you analyze the data, consider how you would extract a kinematics data set from a video of your favourite sport.

Figure 1
Think of all the factors that affect the hang time and horizontal range of a football during a football game.

LAB EXERCISE 1.4.1 *continued*

Question

How does maximizing the hang time and horizontal range of a football punt compare with maximizing the time of flight and horizontal range for an "ideal" projectile that has the same landing level as its starting level?

Hypothesis/Prediction

An ideal projectile (one with negligible air resistance acting on it) has a maximum horizontal range when it is launched at an angle of 45°. Its time of flight increases at angles greater than 45° above the horizontal and decreases at angles less than 45°.

(a) Predict what range of launch angles for a football will result in a combination of good hang time and good horizontal range.

Materials

For the data already analyzed:
video recordings of some football games
a VCR machine with stop-action control at known time
intervals (such as 1.0 s)
transparent grid to determine angles and distances on the
video screen
protractor
ruler

For student analysis:
graph paper

Evidence

Several punts were analyzed to determine the angle of launch θ, horizontal range x, hang time Δt, and an estimate of the initial velocity of the ball. For this exercise, only those punts with an initial velocity of magnitude 3.0×10^1 m/s, and with launch angles from 35° to 65° at 5° intervals were chosen. **Table 1** gives the resulting data.

Table 1 Data for Lab Exercise 1.4.1

x (m)	58	60	60	58	54	49	44
Δt (s)	3.1	3.5	3.8	4.2	4.4	4.6	4.7
θ (°)	35	40	45	50	55	60	65

Analysis

(b) Plot a graph of the horizontal range x as a function of hang time Δt. Choose the vertical axis to go from 40 m to 60 m, and the horizontal axis to go from 3.0 s to 5.0 s. Label the launch angle that corresponds to each data point on the graph.

(c) Looking at the graph and the data in the table, state what you think would be a range of launch angles that would achieve a good hang time and a good horizontal range. Explain your choice.

(d) Answer the question.

Evaluation

(e) Do the evidence and the analysis support or refute your hypothesis? Explain your answer.

(f) What assumptions would have to be made to gather the data presented in the data table?

(g) List sources of random and systematic error that are likely in this type of measurement and analysis.

(h) If you were trying to analyze the motion of a projectile in a sports activity, what would you do to obtain the most accurate data possible?

Synthesis

(i) If you had your choice of analyzing football punts in an open stadium or a closed one, which would you choose to obtain the most accurate results? Why?

(j) How could what you learned in this lab exercise be applied to enhance the performance of athletes?

Key Expectations

- analyze and predict, in quantitative terms, and explain the linear motion of objects in the horizontal plane, the vertical plane, and any inclined plane (for example, a skier accelerating down a hillside) (1.1, 1.2, 1.3, 1.5)

- analyze and predict, in quantitative terms, and explain the motion of a projectile in terms of the horizontal and vertical components of its motion (1.4)

- carry out experiments and/or simulations involving objects moving in two dimensions, and analyze and display the data in an appropriate form (1.1, 1.2, 1.3, 1.4)

- predict the motion of an object given its initial speed and direction of motion (e.g., terminal speed and projectile motion) and test the predictions experimentally (1.3, 1.4)

- describe or construct technological devices that are based on the concepts and principles related to projectile motion (1.4)

Key Terms

kinematics	average acceleration
scalar quantity	instantaneous acceleration
instantaneous speed	
average speed	acceleration due to gravity
vector quantity	free fall
position	terminal speed
displacement	projectile
velocity	projectile motion
instantaneous velocity	horizontal range
average velocity	frame of reference
tangent	relative velocity
acceleration	

Key Equations

- $v_{av} = \dfrac{d}{\Delta t}$ (1.1)

- $\Delta \vec{d} = \vec{d_2} - \vec{d_1}$ (1.1)

- $\vec{v}_{av} = \dfrac{\Delta \vec{d}}{\Delta t}$ (1.1)

- $\vec{v} = \lim\limits_{\Delta t \to 0} \dfrac{\Delta \vec{d}}{\Delta t}$ (1.1)

- $\Delta \vec{d} = \Delta \vec{d_1} + \Delta \vec{d_2} + \dots$ (1.1)

- $\vec{a}_{av} = \dfrac{\Delta \vec{v}}{\Delta t} = \dfrac{\vec{v_f} - \vec{v_i}}{\Delta t}$ (1.2)

- $\vec{a} = \lim\limits_{\Delta t \to 0} \dfrac{\Delta \vec{v}}{\Delta t}$ (1.2)

- $\Delta \vec{d} = \vec{v_i}\Delta t + \dfrac{1}{2}\vec{a}(\Delta t)^2$ (1.2)

- $\Delta \vec{d} = \vec{v}_{av}\Delta t = \dfrac{(\vec{v_i} + \vec{v_f})}{2}\Delta t$ (1.2)

- $v_f^2 = v_i^2 + 2a\Delta d$ (1.2)

- $\Delta \vec{d} = \vec{v_f}\Delta t - \dfrac{1}{2}\vec{a}(\Delta t)^2$ (1.2)

- $a_{av,x} = \dfrac{\Delta v_x}{\Delta t} = \dfrac{v_{fx} - v_{ix}}{\Delta t}$ (1.2)

- $a_{av,y} = \dfrac{\Delta v_y}{\Delta t} = \dfrac{v_{fy} - v_{iy}}{\Delta t}$ (1.2)

- $a_y = \dfrac{v_{fy} - v_{iy}}{\Delta t}$ (1.3)

- $\Delta y = v_{iy}\Delta t + \dfrac{1}{2}a_y(\Delta t)^2$ (1.3)

- $\Delta y = \dfrac{(v_{iy} + v_{fy})}{2}\Delta t$ (1.3)

- $v_{fy}^2 = v_{iy}^2 + 2a_y\Delta y$ (1.3)

- $\Delta y = v_{fy}\Delta t - \dfrac{1}{2}a_y(\Delta t)^2$ (1.3)

- $v_{ix} = \dfrac{\Delta x}{\Delta t}$ (1.4)

- $\vec{v}_{PE} = \vec{v}_{PA} + \vec{v}_{AE}$ (1.5)

▸ **MAKE** a summary

Draw a large diagram showing the path of a ball undergoing projectile motion. Label several positions along the path (A, B, C, D, and E), and show as many details of the motion as you can. For example, indicate the magnitude and direction (where possible) of the horizontal and vertical components of the position, displacement, instantaneous velocity, and instantaneous acceleration at each position. Show what happens to those quantities if you assume that air resistance near the end of the path is no longer negligible. Finally, show details related to frames of reference (for instance, one frame of reference could be the playing field and another could be an athlete running parallel to the ball's motion just before catching the ball). In the diagrams and labels, include as many of the key expectations, key terms, and key equations from this chapter as you can.

Write numbers 1 to 11 in your notebook. Indicate beside each number whether the corresponding statement is true (T) or false (F). If it is false, write a corrected version.

1. You toss a ball vertically and step aside. The ball rises and then falls down along the same path and hits the ground. Since the ball reverses direction, it undergoes two-dimensional motion.

2. The magnitude of the velocity of that same ball just before landing is greater than its magnitude of initial velocity upon leaving your hand.

3. The acceleration of that ball at the top of the flight is zero.

4. The time for that ball to rise equals the time for it to fall.

5. A jogger running four laps around a circular track at 4.5 m/s undergoes motion with constant velocity.

6. The slope of the tangent to a curved line on a position-time graph gives the instantaneous velocity.

7. Megametres per hour per day is a possible unit of acceleration.

8. The magnitude of the acceleration due to gravity at Miami is greater than that at St. John's, Newfoundland.

9. The quadratic formula must be used to solve problems involving the quadratic equation $v_f^2 = v_i^2 + 2a\Delta d$.

10. A model rocket launched in a vacuum chamber at an angle of 45° above the horizontal, undergoes projectile motion.

11. If $\vec{v}_{AB} = 8.5$ m/s [E], then $\vec{v}_{BA} = -8.5$ m/s [W].

Write numbers 12 to 19 in your notebook. Beside each number, write the letter corresponding to the best choice.

12. You toss a ball vertically upward from your hand: the initial position is your hand, and $+y$ is upward. Of the position-time graphs shown in **Figure 1**, which best represents the relationship?

13. You drop a rubber stopper from your hand: the initial position is your hand, and $+y$ is upward. Which graph in **Figure 1** best represents the relationship?

14. You toss a ball directly upward: the initial position is your hand, and $+y$ is downward. Which graph in **Figure 1** best represents the relationship?

15. You release a cart from rest at the top of a ramp: the initial position is at the top of the ramp, and $+y$ is up the ramp. Which graph in **Figure 1** best represents the relationship?

16. A car with an initial velocity of 25 m/s [E] experiences an average acceleration of 2.5 m/s² [W] for 2.0×10^1 s. At the end of this interval, the velocity is
    (a) 5.0×10^1 m/s [W]   (d) 75 m/s [W]
    (b) 0.0 m/s   (e) 75 m/s [E]
    (c) 25 m/s [W]

17. An acceleration has an eastward component of 2.5 m/s² and a northward component of 6.2 m/s². The direction of the acceleration is
    (a) [40° E of N]   (d) [68° E of N]
    (b) [50° E of N]   (e) [68° N of E]
    (c) [24° E of N]

18. You are a fullback running with an initial velocity of 7.2 m/s [N]. You swerve to avoid a tackle, and after 2.0 s are moving at 7.2 m/s [W]. Your average acceleration over the time interval is
    (a) 0 m/s²
    (b) 5.1 m/s² [45° N of W]
    (c) 1.0×10^1 m/s² [45° N of W]
    (d) 3.6 m/s² [S]
    (e) 5.1 m/s² [45° W of S]

19. A tennis ball is thrown into the air with an initial velocity that has a horizontal component of 5.5 m/s and a vertical component of 3.7 m/s [up]. If air resistance is negligible, the speed of the ball at the top of the trajectory is
    (a) zero   (c) 5.5 m/s   (e) 9.2 m/s
    (b) 3.7 m/s   (d) 6.6 m/s

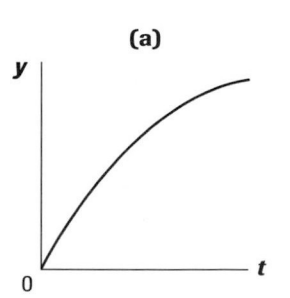
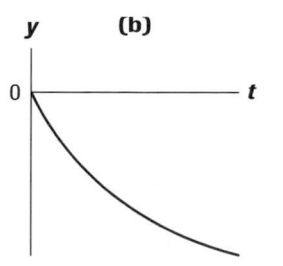
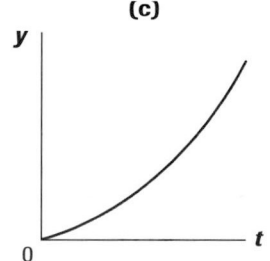
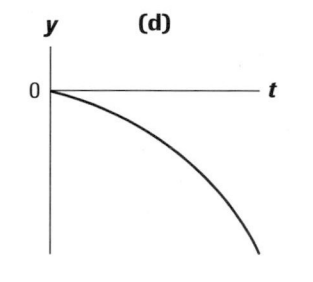

Figure 1
Graphs of vertical position as a function of time for questions 12–15

Understanding Concepts

1. (a) In Canada, the speed limit on many highways is 100 km/h. Convert this measurement to metres per second to three significant digits.
   (b) The fastest recorded speed of any animal is the dive of the peregrine falcon, which can reach 97 m/s. How fast is the dive in kilometres per hour?
   (c) Suggest a convenient way of converting kilometres per hour to metres per second, and metres per second to kilometres per hour.

2. For each dimensional operation listed, state the type of quantity that results (speed, length, etc.).
   (a) $L \times T^{-1}$ (b) $\left(\dfrac{L}{T^3}\right) \times T$ (c) $\left(\dfrac{L}{T^2}\right) \times T \times T$

3. A student reads a test question that asks for a distance, gives a time interval of 3.2 s and a constant acceleration of magnitude 5.4 m/s². Uncertain which equation applies, the student tries dimensional analysis and selects the equation $\vec{d} = \vec{a}(\Delta t)^2$.
   (a) Is the equation dimensionally correct?
   (b) Describe the limitation of relying on dimensional analysis to remember equations.

4. For motion with constant velocity, compare:
   (a) instantaneous speed with average speed
   (b) instantaneous velocity with average velocity
   (c) instantaneous speed with average velocity

5. How can a velocity-time graph be used to determine (a) displacement and (b) acceleration?

6. Can a component of a vector have a magnitude greater than the vector's magnitude? Explain.

7. (a) Can the sum of two vectors of the same magnitude be a zero vector?
   (b) Can the sum of two vectors of unequal magnitudes be a zero vector?
   (c) Can the sum of three vectors, all of unequal magnitudes, be a zero factor?
   In each case, give an example if "yes," an explanation if "no."

8. A golfer drives a golf ball 214 m [E] off the tee, then hits it 96 m [28° N of E], and finally putts the ball 12 m [25° S of E]. Determine the displacement from the tee needed to get a hole-in-one using (a) a vector scale diagram and (b) components. Compare your answers.

9. Determine the vector that must be added to the sum of $\vec{A} + \vec{B}$ in **Figure 1** to give a resultant displacement of (a) 0 and (b) 4.0 km [W].

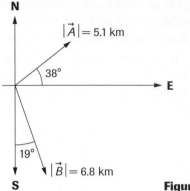

Figure 1

10. Assume that a displacement vector can be drawn from a person's nose to his or her toes. For a town of 2000 people, estimate the resultant displacement vector of the sum of all the nose-to-toes vectors at (a) 5 P.M. and (b) 5 A.M. Explain your reasoning.

11. In the Canadian Grand Prix auto race, the drivers travel a total distance of 304.29 km in 69 laps around the track. If the fastest lap time is 84.118 s, what is the average speed for this lap?

12. According to a drivers' handbook, your safest separation distance from the car ahead at a given speed is the distance you would travel in 2.0 s at that speed. What is the recommended separation distance (a) in metres and (b) in car lengths, if your speed is 115 km/h?

13. An eagle flies at 24 m/s for 1.2×10^3 m, then glides at 18 m/s for 1.2×10^3 m. Determine
    (a) the time interval for this motion
    (b) the eagle's average speed during this motion

14. Describe the motion represented by each graph shown in **Figure 2**.

(a)

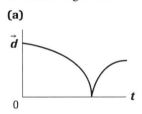

(b)

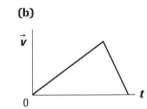

Figure 2

15. A firefighter slides 4.5 m down a pole and runs 6.8 m to a fire truck in 5.0 s. Determine the firefighter's (a) average speed and (b) average velocity.

16. Over a total time of 6.4 s, a field hockey player runs 16 m [35° S of W], then 22 m [15° S of E]. Determine the player's (a) resultant displacement and (b) average velocity.

17. The cheetah, perhaps the fastest land animal, can maintain speeds as high as 100 km/h over short time intervals. The path of a cheetah chasing its prey at top speed is illustrated in **Figure 3**. State the cheetah's instantaneous velocity, including the approximate direction, at positions D, E, and F.

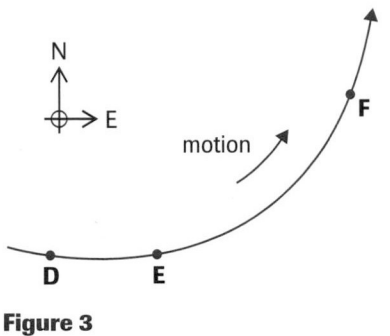

Figure 3

18. A car travelling initially at 42 km/h on the entrance ramp of an expressway accelerates uniformly to 105 km/h in 26 s.
    (a) How far, in kilometres, does the car travel over this time interval?
    (b) Determine the magnitude of the average acceleration in kilometres per hour per second.

19. In a thrill ride at an amusement park, the cars start from rest and accelerate rapidly, covering the first 15 m [fwd] in 1.2 s.
    (a) Calculate the average acceleration of the cars.
    (b) Determine the velocity of the cars at 1.2 s.
    (c) Express the magnitude of the acceleration in terms of $|\vec{g}|$.

20. Determine the constant acceleration needed for a bullet to reach a muzzle velocity of 4.0×10^2 m/s [fwd], provided friction is zero and the muzzle is 0.80 m long.

21. A rocket begins its third stage of launch at a velocity of 2.28×10^2 m/s [fwd]. It undergoes a constant acceleration of 6.25×10^1 m/s^2, while travelling 1.86 km, all in the same direction. What is the rocket's velocity at the end of this motion?

22. In its final trip upstream to its spawning territory, a salmon jumps to the top of a waterfall 1.9 m high. What is the minimum vertical velocity needed by the salmon to reach the top of the waterfall?

23. A bus travels 2.0×10^2 m with a constant acceleration of magnitude 1.6 m/s^2.
    (a) How long does the motion take if the magnitude of the initial velocity is 0.0 m/s?

    (b) How long does the motion take if the magnitude of the initial velocity is 8.0 m/s in the direction of the acceleration?

24. An airplane, travelling initially at 240 m/s [28° S of E], takes 35 s to change its velocity to 220 m/s [28° E of S]. What is the average acceleration over this time interval?

25. A race car driver wants to attain a velocity of 54 m/s [N] at the end of a curved stretch of track, experiencing an average acceleration of 0.15 m/s^2 [S] for 95 s. What is the final velocity?

26. A camera is set up to take photographs of a ball undergoing vertical motion. The camera is 5.2 m above the ball launcher, a device that can launch the ball with an initial velocity 17 m/s [up]. Assuming that the ball goes straight up and then straight down past the camera, at what times after the launch will the ball pass the camera?

27. **Figure 4** shows a velocity-time graph for a squirrel walking along the top of a fence.
    (a) Draw the corresponding acceleration-time graph of the motion.
    (b) Draw the corresponding position-time graph from 0.0 s to 1.0 s. (Be careful: for the first 0.50 s, this graph is not a straight line.)

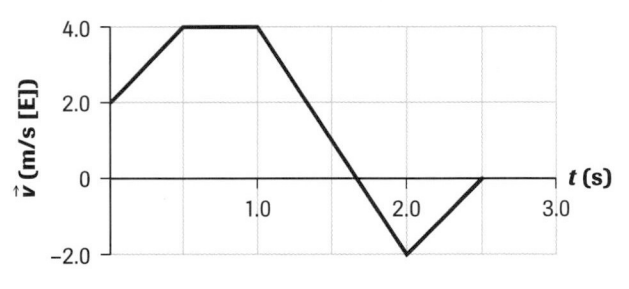

Figure 4

28. Venus, with an orbit of radius 1.08×10^{11} m, takes 1.94×10^7 s to complete one orbit around the Sun.
    (a) What is the average speed in metres per second, and kilometres per hour?
    (b) Determine the magnitude of the average velocity after it has completed half a revolution around the Sun.
    (c) Determine the magnitude of the average acceleration after it has completed a quarter revolution around the Sun.

29. (a) What are the horizontal and vertical components of the acceleration of a projectile?
    (b) How would your answer change if both components of the motion experience air resistance?

30. A child throws a snowball with a horizontal velocity of 18 m/s directly toward a tree, from a distance of 9.0 m and a height above the ground of 1.5 m.
    (a) After what time interval does the snowball hit the tree?
    (b) At what height above the ground will the snowball hit the tree?
    (c) Determine the snowball's velocity as it strikes the tree.

31. Determine the initial velocity of a projectile that is launched horizontally, and falls 1.5 m while moving 16 m horizontally.

32. You are standing in a train moving at constant velocity relative to Earth's frame of reference. You drop a ball to the floor. What is the path of the ball (a) in your frame of reference and (b) from the frame of reference of a person standing stationary beside the train?

33. A plane is travelling with an air speed of 285 km/s [45° S of E]. A wind is blowing at 75 km/h [22° E of N] relative to the ground. Determine the velocity of the plane relative to the ground.

34. A swimmer who can swim at a speed of 0.80 m/s in still water heads directly across a river 86 m wide. The swimmer lands at a position on the far bank 54 m downstream from the starting point. Determine
    (a) the speed of the current
    (b) the velocity of the swimmer relative to the shore
    (c) the direction of departure that would have taken the swimmer directly across the river

35. The displacement from London, UK, to Rome is 1.4×10^3 km [43° E of S]. A wind is blowing with a velocity of 75 km/h [E]. The pilot wants to fly directly from London to Rome in 3.5 h. What velocity relative to the air must the pilot maintain?

36. A football is placed on a line 25 m from the goal post. The placement kicker kicks the ball directly toward the post, giving the ball an initial velocity of 21.0 m/s [47° above the horizontal]. The horizontal bar of the goal post is 3.0 m above the field. How far above or below the bar will the ball travel?

Applying Inquiry Skills

37. A baseball player wants to measure the initial speed of a ball when the ball has its maximum horizontal range.
    (a) Describe how this could be done using only a metre stick or a measuring tape.
    (b) Describe sources of random and systematic error in this activity.

38. You obtain the following data from an experiment involving motion on an essentially frictionless air table inclined at an angle to the horizontal:

length of air table side	62.0 cm
vertical distance from lab bench to the elevated end of the air table	9.9 cm
vertical distance from lab bench to the lower end of the air table	4.3 cm

   (a) Determine the angle of incline of the air table.
   (b) Determine the magnitude of the acceleration of an air puck parallel to the incline of the table. (*Hint:* Use $\vec{g}$ and the value you found for the angle of incline.)
   (c) What are the possible sources of random and systematic error in this experiment?

39. **Figure 5** shows a demonstration of projectile motion that usually warrants applause from the audience. At the instant a dart is launched at a high velocity, a target (often a cardboard monkey) drops from a uspended position downrange from the launching device. Show that if the dart is aimed directly at the target, it will always strike the falling target. (Use a specific set of numbers.)

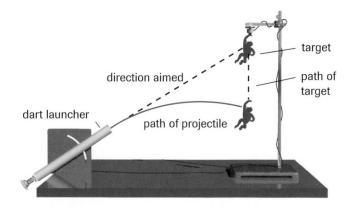

Figure 5
In this "monkey-hunter" demonstration, launching the dart causes the target to drop.

Making Connections

40. An impatient motorist drives along a city bypass at an average speed of 125 km/h. The speed limit is 100 km/h.
    (a) If the bypass is 17 km long, how many minutes does the driver save by breaking the speed limit?
    (b) The driver consumes about 20% more fuel at the higher speed than at the legal limit. Can you suggest a reason?

41. An electromagnetic signal, travelling at the speed of light (3.0×10^8 m/s), travels from a ground station on Earth to a satellite 4.8×10^7 m away. The satellite receives the signal and, after a delay of 0.55 s, sends a return signal to Earth.
    (a) What is the time interval between the transmission from the ground station and the reception of the return signal at the station?
    (b) Relate your answer in (a) to the time delays you observe when live interviews are conducted via satellite communication on television.

42. Kinematics in two dimensions can be extended to kinematics in three dimensions. What motion factors would you expect to analyze in developing a computer model of the three-dimensional motion of asteroids to predict how close they will come to Earth?

43. A patient with a detached retina is warned by an eye specialist that any braking acceleration of magnitude greater than $2\,|\vec{g}|$ risks pulling the retina entirely away from the sclera. Help the patient decide whether to play a vigorous racket sport such as tennis. Use estimated values of running speeds and stopping times.

44. Your employer, a medical research facility specializing in nanotechnology, asks you to develop a microscopic motion sensor for injection into the human bloodstream. Velocity readings from the sensor are to be used to detect the start of blockages in arteries, capillaries, and veins.
    (a) What physics principles and equations would you need to consider in brainstorming the design?
    (b) Describe one possible design of the device. How, in your design, are data obtained from the device?

45. **Figure 6** shows four different patterns of fireworks explosions. What conditions of the velocity of the fireworks device at the instant of the explosion could account for each shape?

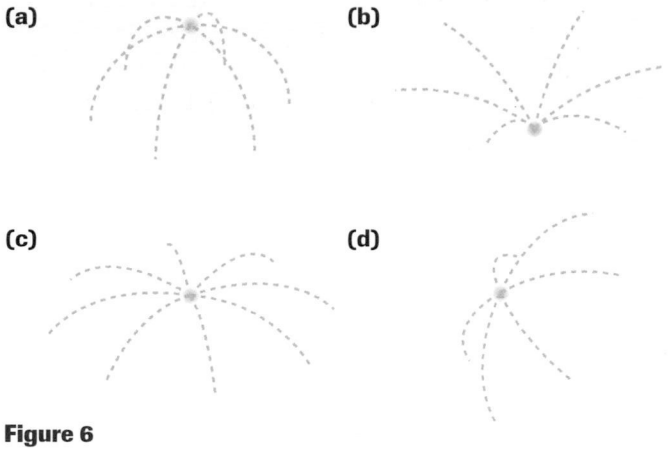

(a) (b) (c) (d)

Figure 6

Extension

46. A helicopter flies directly toward a vertical cliff. When the helicopter is 0.70 km from the cliff face, it transmits a sonar signal. It receives the reflected signal 3.4 s later. If the signal propagates at 3.5×10^2 m/s, what is the speed of the helicopter?

47. A truck with one headlight is travelling at a constant speed of 18 m/s when it passes a stopped police car. The cruiser sets off in pursuit at a constant acceleration of magnitude 2.2 m/s².
    (a) How far does the cruiser travel before catching the truck?
    (b) How long does the pursuit last? (*Hint:* Consider drawing a graph.)

48. A car with an initial velocity of 8.0×10^1 km/h [E] accelerates at the constant rate of 5.0 (km/h)/s, reaching a final velocity of 1.0×10^2 km/h [45° S of E]. Determine (a) the direction of the acceleration and (b) the time interval.

49. Derive an equation for the horizontal range of a projectile with a landing point at a different altitude from its launch point. Write the equation in terms of the initial velocity, the acceleration due to gravity, the launch angle, and the vertical component of the displacement.

50. A sunbather, drifting downstream on a raft, dives off the raft just as it passes under a bridge and swims against the current for 15 min. She then turns and swims downstream, making the same total effort and overtaking the raft when it is 1.0 km downstream from the bridge. What is the speed of the current in the river?

 Sir Isaac Newton Contest Question

Dynamics

To climb a vertical formation like the one shown in **Figure 1**, a rock climber must exert forces against the rock walls. The walls push back with reaction forces, and it is the upward components of those forces that help the climber move upward. In this chapter, you will learn how to analyze the forces and components of forces for stationary and moving objects.

Forces cause changes in velocity. Thus, what you learned in Chapter 1 will be explored further to help you understand why objects speed up, slow down, or change directions. In other words, you will explore the nature of the forces that cause acceleration.

Chapter 2 concludes with a look at motion from different frames of reference. You will find that Newton's laws of motion apply in some frames of reference, but not in others.

REFLECT on your learning

1. A dog-sled team is pulling a loaded toboggan up a snow-covered hill as illustrated in **Figure 2**. Each of the four vectors $\vec{A}$, $\vec{B}$, $\vec{C}$, and $\vec{D}$ represents the magnitude and direction of a force acting on the toboggan.
   (a) Name each labelled force.
   (b) Draw a sketch of the toboggan and its load showing the four forces. Label the positive x direction parallel to force $\vec{A}$ and the positive y direction parallel to force $\vec{B}$. Draw in the components of any vector that is not parallel to either the x or the y direction.

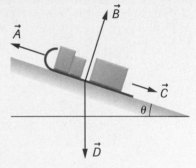

Figure 2

2. A child pushes horizontally against a box, but the box does not move.
   (a) Draw a sketch of the box showing all the forces acting on it. Name each force.
   (b) Determine the vector sum of all the forces acting on the box. Is this sum zero or nonzero? Give a reason.

3. An athlete is in the middle of a long jump. Draw a vector diagram to show all of the forces acting on the jumper
   (a) assuming that there is no air resistance
   (b) assuming that the jumper is experiencing air resistance due to a head wind

4. You apply a horizontal force to the side of your physics textbook that is just large enough to cause the book to move at a slow, constant velocity. How would you have to change the force to cause two identical books, one on top of the other, to move at constant velocity? Explain the physics of your answer.

5. A small rubber stopper is suspended by a string from the inside roof of the school bus in **Figure 3(a)**. At three different points in the journey, this improvised pendulum-style accelerometer is in the three orientations I, J, K shown in **Figure 3(b).**
   (a) In which orientation is the accelerometer when the bus is
      (i) accelerating forward from rest
      (ii) moving forward at a constant velocity
      (iii) braking to a stop while moving to the right
   (b) Draw three vector diagrams for these three cases, showing in each diagram all the forces acting on the stopper.

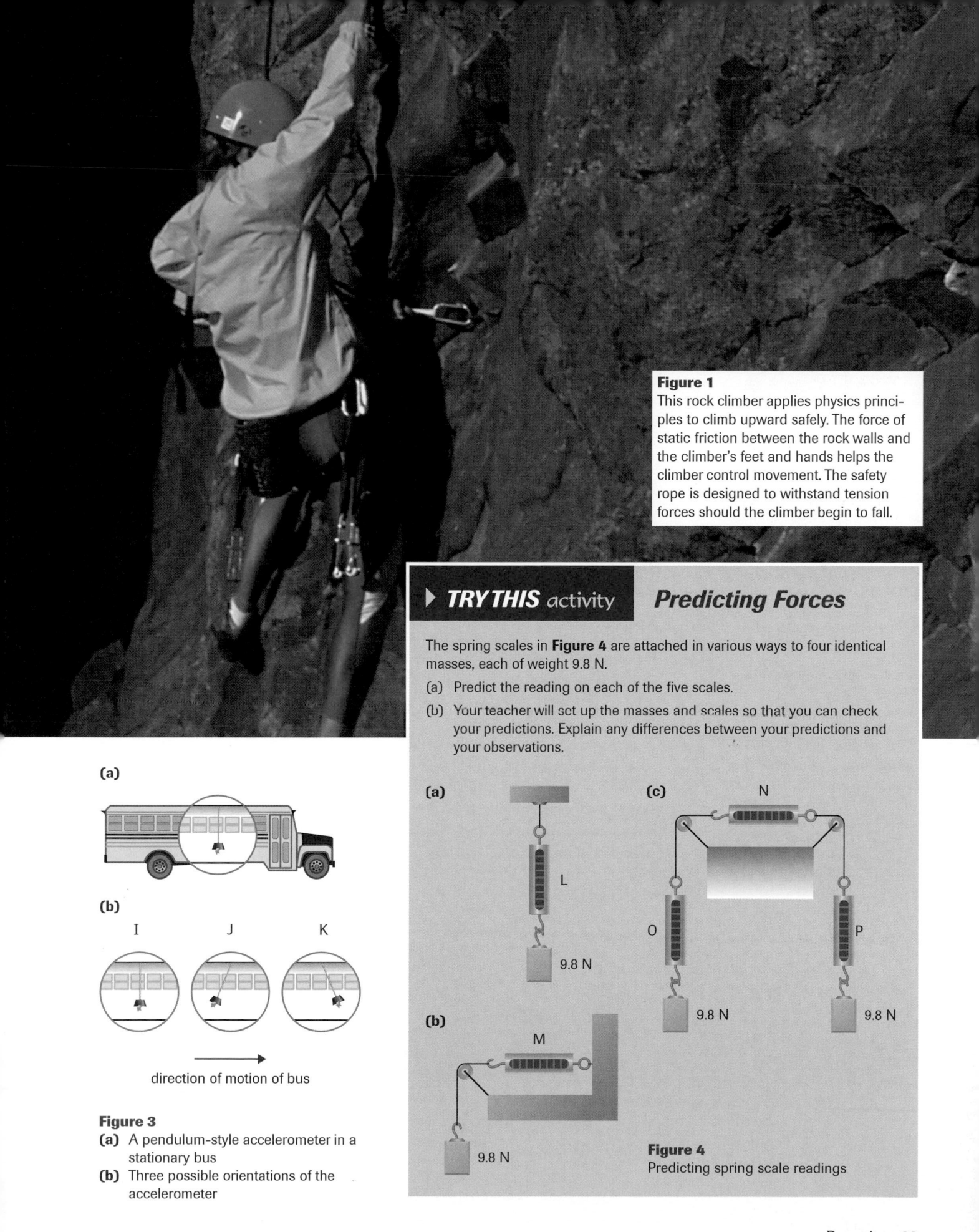

Figure 1

This rock climber applies physics principles to climb upward safely. The force of
static friction between the rock walls and
the climber's feet and hands helps the
climber control movement. The safety
rope is designed to withstand tension
forces should the climber begin to fall.

▶ *TRY THIS* activity   *Predicting Forces*

The spring scales in **Figure 4** are attached in various ways to four identical
masses, each of weight 9.8 N.

(a) Predict the reading on each of the five scales.

(b) Your teacher will set up the masses and scales so that you can check
your predictions. Explain any differences between your predictions and
your observations.

(a)

(b)

L

9.8 N

M

9.8 N

(c)

N

O

P

9.8 N

9.8 N

Figure 4
Predicting spring scale readings

(a)

(b)

I   J   K

direction of motion of bus

Figure 3
(a) A pendulum-style accelerometer in a
stationary bus
(b) Three possible orientations of the
accelerometer

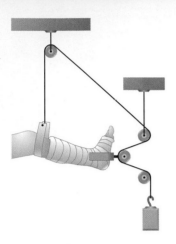

Figure 1
Designing a traction system that prevents leg motion requires an understanding of forces and the components of forces. In this case, the tibia (small lower leg bone) is stabilized by the traction cord attached to a weight and strung through a pulley system.

force $(\vec{F})$ a push or a pull

force of gravity $(\vec{F}_g)$ force of attraction between all objects

normal force $(\vec{F}_N)$ force perpendicular to the surfaces of objects in contact

tension $(\vec{F}_T)$ force exerted by materials, such as ropes, fibres, springs, and cables, that can be stretched

A **force** is a push or a pull. Forces act on objects, and can result in the acceleration, compression, stretching, or twisting of objects. Forces can also act to stabilize an object. For example, when a person fractures a leg, any motion of the leg can hinder the healing of the bone. To reduce this problem, the leg can be placed in a traction system, like that shown in **Figure 1**. A traction system stabilizes the broken limb and prevents unnecessary motion of its broken parts.

To analyze the forces that are acting on the leg shown in **Figure 1**, several background concepts must be understood. In this section, we will use the following questions to introduce the concepts:

- What are the main types of forces that you experience in everyday situations involving objects at rest or in motion, and how are these forces measured?
- How can you use diagrams to mathematically analyze the forces acting on a body or an object?
- What is the net force, or the resultant force, and how can it be calculated?

Common Forces

When you hold a textbook in your hand, you feel Earth's force of gravity pulling downward on the book. The **force of gravity** is the force of attraction between all objects. It is an action-at-a-distance force, which means that contact between the objects is not required. Gravity exists because matter exists. However, the force of gravity is extremely small unless at least one of the objects is very large. For example, the force of gravity between a 1.0-kg ball and Earth at Earth's surface is 9.8 N, but the force of gravity between two 1.0-kg balls separated by a distance of 1.0 m is only 6.7×10^{-11} N, a negligible amount.

The force of gravity on an object, like a book in your hand, acts downward, toward Earth's centre. However, to keep the book stationary in your hand, there must be an upward force acting on it. That force, called the **normal force**, is the force perpendicular to the two surfaces in contact. As you can see in **Figure 2**, the normal force acts vertically upward when the contact surfaces are horizontal.

Another common force, **tension**, is the force exerted by materials that can be stretched (e.g., ropes, strings, springs, fibres, cables, and rubber bands). The more the material is stretched, like the spring scale shown in **Figure 3**, the greater the tension in the material.

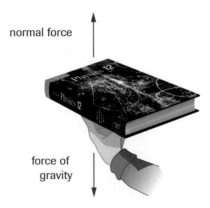

normal force

force of gravity

Figure 2
For a book held stationary in your hand, Earth's force of gravity acts downward. Your hand exerts a normal force upward on the book.

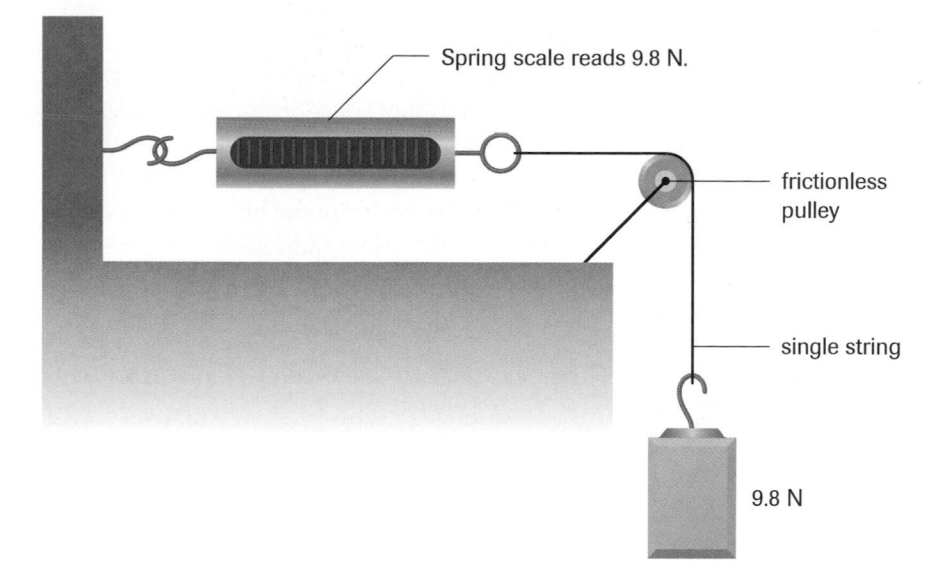

Figure 4
Since tension is constant along a single string, the tension in the horizontal part of this string has the same magnitude as the tension in the vertical part of the string.

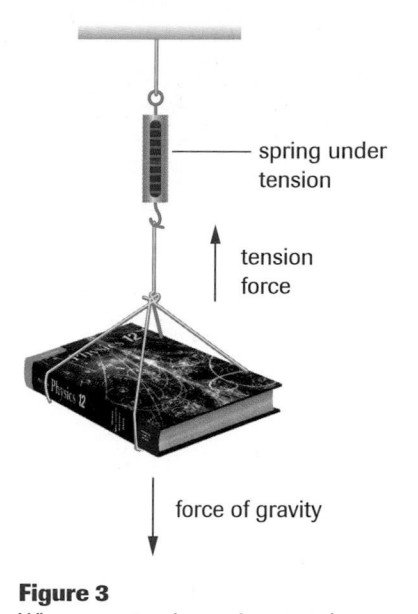

Figure 3
When an extension spring stretches, the tension increases to bring the spring back to its original state. The greater the downward force of gravity on the book, the greater the upward tension in the spring.

An important characteristic of the tension force in a material is that it has the same magnitude everywhere along the length of the material. This is true even if the direction of the force changes, as when a rope or string hangs over a pulley (**Figure 4**).

Another common force is **friction**—the force that resists motion or attempted motion between objects in contact. Friction always acts in the direction opposite to the direction of motion. For example, if you exert a force on your textbook causing it to move eastward across your desk, the force of friction acting on the book is westward. **Static friction** is the force that tends to prevent a stationary object from starting to move. **Kinetic friction** is the force that acts against an object's motion. **Air resistance** is friction that involves an object moving through air; it becomes noticeable at high speeds.

Finally, because there are several possible names for various pushes, pulls, thrusts, and so on, we will use the general term *applied force* for any contact force that does not fit any of the previously described categories.

We will use consistent symbols for the common forces as summarized in **Table 1**. Notice that because force is a vector quantity, we use an arrow above each symbol.

friction ($\vec{F}_f$) force that resists motion or attempted motion between objects in contact; acts in direction opposite to motion or attempted motion

static friction ($\vec{F}_S$) force that tends to prevent a stationary object from starting to move

kinetic friction ($\vec{F}_K$) force that acts against an object's motion

air resistance frictional force that opposes an object's motion through air

Table 1 Common Forces

Force	Symbol
gravity	$\vec{F}_g$
normal	$\vec{F}_N$
tension	$\vec{F}_T$
friction	$\vec{F}_f$
kinetic friction	$\vec{F}_K$
static friction	$\vec{F}_S$
air resistance	$\vec{F}_{air}$
applied force	$\vec{F}_{app}$

▶ **Practice**

Understanding Concepts

1. Summarize the common forces by completing a table with the following headings: Name of Force, Type of Force, and Example in Daily Life. (Indicate either action-at-a-distance or contact force under Type of Force.)

2. Refer to the traction system shown in **Figure 1**. Assuming that the tension in the cord just above the mass has a magnitude of 18 N, do you expect the tension in the vertical cord above the leg to be less than 18 N, equal to 18 N, or greater than 18 N? Give your reasons.

3. Mechanical and structural engineers say, "You can't push a rope." Rephrase this statement using more formal physics terminology.

Drawing Free-Body Diagrams

A convenient way to analyze situations involving forces is to use diagrams. A **free-body diagram** (FBD) is a diagram of a single object that shows only the forces acting on that object; no other objects are shown in the FBD. The object itself can be represented by a dot or drawn as a small sketch. The directions and the approximate magnitudes of the forces are drawn on the diagram as arrows facing away from the object. A coordinate system is shown in the FBD, with the $+x$ and $+y$ directions indicated.

In solving word problems, especially complex ones, it is sometimes helpful to sketch a diagram of the system, called a *system diagram*, before drawing an FBD.

Figure 5
The FBD of the ball in Sample Problem 1

> ► **SAMPLE** problem **1**
>
> You toss a ball vertically upward. Draw an FBD of the ball just before it leaves your hand.
>
> **Solution**
> Only two forces act on the ball (**Figure 5**). Gravity acts downward. The normal force applied by your hand (we may call this the applied force, since it comes from you) acts upward. Since there are no horizontal components of forces in this situation, our FBD shows a $+y$ direction, but no $+x$ direction.

> ► **SAMPLE** problem **2**
>
> A child is pushing with a horizontal force against a chair that remains stationary. Draw a system diagram of the overall situation and an FBD of the chair.
>
> **Solution**
> The system diagram in **Figure 6(a)** shows the four forces acting on the chair: gravity, the normal force, the applied force (the push delivered by the child), and the force of static friction. The $+x$ direction is chosen in the direction of the attempted motion. **Figure 6(b)** is the corresponding FBD, showing these same four forces.

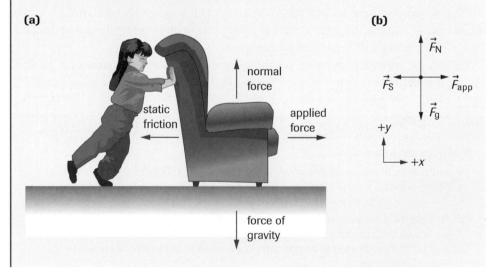

Figure 6
(a) The forces acting on the chair
(b) The FBD of the stationary chair

▶ **SAMPLE** problem **3**

A child pulls a sleigh up a snow-covered hill at a constant velocity with a force parallel to the hillside. Draw a system diagram of the overall situation and an FBD of the sleigh.

Solution

The system diagram of **Figure 7(a)** shows the four forces acting on the sleigh: gravity, tension in the rope, kinetic friction, and the normal force. The $+x$ direction is the direction of motion and the $+y$ direction is perpendicular to that motion. **Figure 7(b)** is the corresponding FBD, including the components of the force of gravity.

(a)

(b)

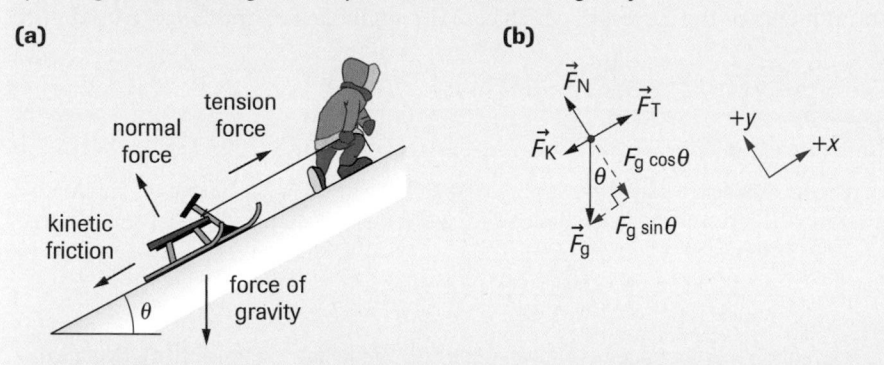

> **LEARNING TIP**
>
> **Components of Forces**
> Whenever there is a force in an FBD that is not parallel to either the $+x$ direction or the $+y$ direction, draw and label the components of that force, as in **Figure 7(b)**. Appendix A discusses vector components.

Figure 7
(a) The forces acting on the sleigh
(b) The FBD of the sleigh

▶ **Practice**

Understanding Concepts

4. Draw an FBD for objects A, B, C, and D.
   (a) A hot dog (object A) sits on a table.
   (b) A length of railway track (B) is being raised by a cable connected to a crane.
   (c) A pencil (C) has just begun falling from a desk to the floor. Air resistance is negligible.
   (d) A stove (D) is being pulled up a ramp into a delivery truck by a cable parallel to the ramp. The ramp is at an angle of 18° above the horizontal.

5. You throw a ball vertically upward from your hand. Air resistance is negligible. Draw an FBD of the ball (a) shortly after it leaves your hand, (b) when it is at the top of its motion, and (c) as it is falling back down.

6. Draw an FBD of the ball from question 5 as it falls back down, assuming there is a force of friction caused by air resistance.

7. The tourist in **Figure 8** is pulling a loaded suitcase at a constant velocity to the right with a force applied to the handle at an angle θ above the horizontal. A small force of friction resists the motion.
   (a) Draw an FBD of the suitcase, labelling the components of the appropriate forces. Choose the direction of motion to be the $+x$ direction.
   (b) Draw an FBD of the suitcase, labelling the components of the appropriate forces. Choose the $+x$ direction as the direction in which the handle is pointing.
   (c) Which choice of $+x$ is more convenient? Why? (*Hint:* Did you show the components of all the forces in your FBDs?)

Applying Inquiry Skills

8. You are watching a skydiver whose parachute is open and whose instantaneous height above ground level is indicated by digits on an electronic screen. The skydiver has reached terminal speed. (For this question, assume the skydiver and the parachute together act as one body.)
   (a) Draw a system diagram and an FBD for the situation.
   (b) Describe how you would estimate the force of air resistance acting on the skydiver and parachute. Include any assumptions and calculations.

Figure 8
For question 7

Analyzing Forces on Stationary Objects

net force $(\Sigma \vec{F})$ the sum of all forces acting on an object

When analyzing a problem involving forces acting on an object, you must find the sum of all the forces acting on that object. The sum of all forces acting on an object has a variety of names, including net force, resultant force, total force, or sum of the forces; in this text, we will use the term **net force**. The symbol for net force is $\Sigma \vec{F}$, where the Greek letter sigma (Σ) serves as a reminder to add, or "sum," all the forces.

Determining the sum of all the forces is straightforward if all the forces are linear or perpendicular to each other, but it is somewhat more complex if some forces are at angles other that 90°. In two-dimensional situations, it is often convenient to analyze the components of the forces, in which case the symbols ΣF_x and ΣF_y are used instead of $\Sigma \vec{F}$.

> ## LEARNING TIP
>
> **Net Force Symbols**
> The net force can have a variety of symbols, such as $\vec{F}_{net}$, $\vec{F}_R$ (for resultant force), $\vec{F}_{total}$, $\vec{F}_{sum}$, and the symbol used in this text, $\Sigma \vec{F}$.

▶ SAMPLE problem 4

In hitting a volleyball, a player applies an average force of 9.9 N [33° above the horizontal] for 5.0 ms. The force of gravity on the ball is 2.6 N [down]. Determine the net force on the ball as it is being struck.

Solution

The relevant given information is shown in the FBD of the ball in **Figure 9(a)**. (Notice that the time interval of 5.0 ms is not shown because it is not needed for this solution.) The net force on the ball is the vector sum $\vec{F}_g + \vec{F}_{app}$. We calculate the net force by taking components with the $+x$ and $+y$ directions as in **Figure 9(b)**.

First, we take components of $\vec{F}_{app}$:

$$F_{app,x} = (9.9\text{ N})(\cos 33°) \qquad F_{app,y} = (9.9\text{ N})(\sin 33°)$$
$$F_{app,x} = 8.3\text{ N} \qquad\qquad F_{app,y} = 5.4\text{ N}$$

Next, we take components of $\vec{F}_g$:

$$F_{gx} = 0.0\text{ N} \qquad\qquad F_{gy} = -2.6\text{ N}$$

We add the components to determine the net force:

$$\Sigma F_x = F_{app,x} + F_{gx} \qquad \Sigma F_y = F_{app,y} + F_{gy}$$
$$= 8.3\text{ N} + 0.0\text{ N} \qquad\quad = 5.4\text{ N} + (-2.6\text{ N})$$
$$\Sigma F_x = 8.3\text{ N} \qquad\qquad \Sigma F_y = 2.8\text{ N}$$

Figure 9(c) shows how we determine the magnitude of the net force:

$$|\Sigma \vec{F}| = \sqrt{(8.3\text{ N})^2 + (2.8\text{ N})^2}$$
$$|\Sigma \vec{F}| = 8.8\text{ N}$$

The direction of $\Sigma \vec{F}$ is given by the angle ϕ in the diagram:

$$\phi = \tan^{-1}\frac{2.8\text{ N}}{8.3\text{ N}}$$
$$\phi = 19°$$

The net force on the ball is 8.8 N [19° above the horizontal].

(a)

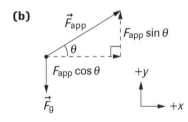

$|\vec{F}_{app}| = 9.9$ N
33°
$|\vec{F}_g| = 2.6$ N

(b)

$\vec{F}_{app}$
$F_{app}\sin\theta$
θ
$F_{app}\cos\theta$
$+y$
$\vec{F}_g$
$+x$

(c)

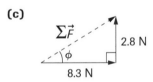

$\Sigma\vec{F}$
2.8 N
ϕ
8.3 N

Figure 9
(a) FBD of the ball
(b) The components of the forces
(c) The net force

The boat in **Figure 10** is secured to a lakeside pier with two horizontal ropes. A wind is blowing offshore. The tensions in the ropes are $\vec{F}_1 = 48$ N [16° N of E] and $\vec{F}_2 = 48$ N [16° S of E].

(a) Use a vector scale diagram to determine the sum of the tension forces in the two ropes.

(b) Assuming that the net horizontal force on the boat is zero, determine the force of the wind on the boat.

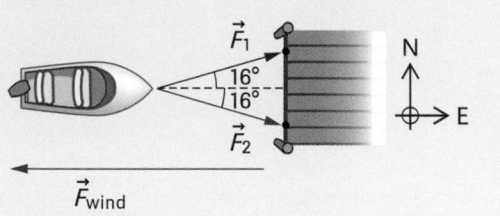

Figure 10
The horizontal forces acting on the boat

LEARNING *TIP*

Adding Force Vectors
As you know from Chapter 1 and Appendix A, this text uses three methods of adding vectors. For understanding concepts, using vector scale diagrams is highly recommended. For high accuracy and relatively quick solutions, trigonometry is an excellent method, but the laws of cosines and sines can be applied easily only to the addition (or subtraction) of two vectors. The component technique is highly accurate and appropriate for the addition (or subtraction) of any number of vectors.

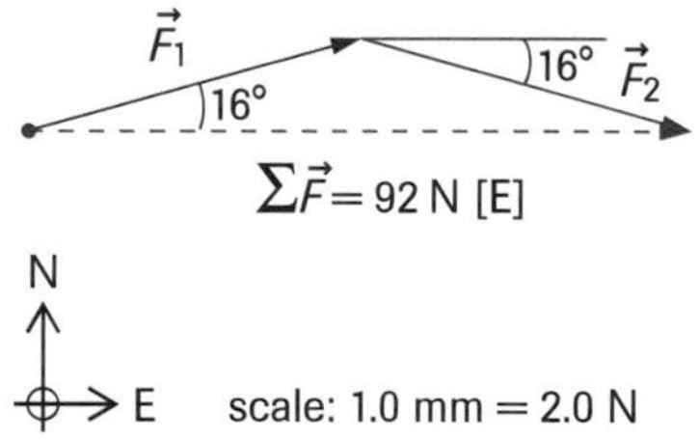

Solution

(a) $\vec{F}_1 = 48$ N [16° N of E]
$\vec{F}_2 = 48$ N [16° S of E]
$\vec{F}_1 + \vec{F}_2 = ?$

This vector addition is shown in **Figure 11**. Measurement with a ruler indicates that the sum of the tensions in the ropes is 92 N [E].

(b) Using the symbol $\vec{F}_{wind}$ for the force of the wind on the boat, we know that:

$\sum \vec{F} = 0$
$\vec{F}_1 + \vec{F}_2 = 92$ N [E]

$\sum \vec{F} = \vec{F}_1 + \vec{F}_2 + \vec{F}_{wind}$
$\vec{F}_{wind} = \sum \vec{F} - (\vec{F}_1 + \vec{F}_2)$
$= 0.0$ N $- 92$ N [E]
$\vec{F}_{wind} = 92$ N [W]

The force of the wind on the boat is 92 N [W].

$\sum \vec{F} = 92$ N [E]

scale: 1.0 mm = 2.0 N

Figure 11
Vector scale diagram showing the sum of the tensions for Sample Problem 5

▶ **Practice**

Understanding Concepts

9. Determine the net force on objects E, F, and G.
   (a) At a particular instant, a soaring bird (E) is subject to an upward lift of 3.74 N, a downward gravitational force of 3.27 N, and a horizontal air resistance force of 0.354 N.
   (b) A long-jump contestant (F) experiences at the instant of landing a gravitational force of 538 N [down] and a force, applied by the ground to the feet, of 6382 N [28.3° above the horizontal].
   (c) In a football game, a quarterback (G), hit simultaneously by two linebackers, experiences horizontal forces of 412 N [27.0° W of N] and 478 N [36.0° N of E]. (Consider only the horizontal forces and neglect friction. Note that we can ignore the vertical forces because they are equal in magnitude, but opposite in direction.)

Answers

9. (a) 0.59 N [53° above the horizontal]
   (b) 6.15×10^3 N [23.9° above the horizontal]
   (c) 678 N [17.1° E of N]

10. Solve Sample Problem 5(a) using (a) components and (b) trigonometry.

11. A crate is being dragged across a horizontal icy sidewalk by two people pulling horizontally on cords (**Figure 12**). The net horizontal force on the crate is 56 N [16° S of E]. The tension in cord 1 is 27 N [E]. If friction is negligible, determine the tension in cord 2.

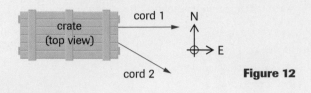

Figure 12

SUMMARY *Forces and Free-Body Diagrams*

- We commonly deal with Earth's force of gravity, the normal force, tension forces, and friction forces.

- Static friction tends to prevent a stationary object from starting to move; kinetic friction acts against an object's motion. Air resistance acts against an object moving through air.

- The free-body diagram (FBD) of an object shows all the forces acting on that object. It is an indispensable tool in helping to solve problems involving forces.

- The net force $\Sigma \vec{F}$ is the vector sum of all the forces acting on an object.

▶ *Section 2.1 Questions*

Understanding Concepts

1. You push your ruler westward at a constant speed across your desk by applying a force at an angle of 25° above the horizontal.
   (a) Name all the forces acting on the ruler and state which ones are contact forces.
   (b) What fundamental force is responsible for the contact forces?
   (c) Draw an FBD of the ruler in this situation. Where appropriate, include the components of forces.

2. Draw an FBD for objects H, I, J, and K.
   (a) a cup (H) hanging from a hook
   (b) a person (I) standing in an elevator that is moving downward
   (c) a curling rock (J) sliding freely in a straight line on a rink
   (d) a crate (K) being dragged across a floor, with significant friction, by a person pulling on a rope at an angle of 23° above the horizontal

3. The force of gravity on a textbook is 18 N [down].
   (a) What is the net force on the book if it is held stationary in your hand?
   (b) Neglecting air resistance, what is the net force acting on the book if you suddenly remove your hand?

4. At one particular instant in its flight, a ball experiences a gravitational force $\vec{F}_g = 1.5$ N [down] and an air resistance force $\vec{F}_{air} = 0.50$ N [32° above the horizontal]. Calculate the net force on the ball.

5. Given the following force vectors, $\vec{F}_A = 3.6$ N [28° W of S], $\vec{F}_B = 4.3$ N [15° N of W], and $\vec{F}_C = 2.1$ N [24° E of S], determine
   (a) $\vec{F}_A + \vec{F}_B + \vec{F}_C$, using a vector scale diagram
   (b) $\vec{F}_A + \vec{F}_B + \vec{F}_C$, using components
   (c) $\vec{F}_A - \vec{F}_B$, using a vector scale diagram
   (d) $\vec{F}_A - \vec{F}_B$, using trigonometry

6. Given $\vec{F}_1 = 36$ N [25° N of E] and $\vec{F}_2 = 42$ N [15° E of S], determine the force $\vec{F}_3$ that must be added to the sum of $\vec{F}_1 + \vec{F}_2$ to produce a net force of zero.

You are riding on a roller coaster with the safety harness snugly over your shoulders. Suddenly, an applied force causes the coaster to accelerate forward and you feel the back of the seat pressing hard against you. When the ride nears its end and a braking force causes the coaster to come to a quick stop, you feel as if you are being pressed forward against the harness. In this section, we will explore the origins of the forces that you experience on a roller coaster ride and those in other everyday situations.

The study of forces and the effects they have on the velocities of objects is called **dynamics**, from the Greek word *dynamis*, which means power. Three important principles related to dynamics are attributed to Sir Isaac Newton (**Figure 1**) and are called Newton's laws of motion.

dynamics the study of forces and the effects they have on motion

Newton's First Law of Motion

Picture a briefcase resting horizontally on the overhead shelf of a commuter train travelling at a constant velocity. As the train starts to slow down, you notice that the briefcase slides forward (relative to the train). What is happening?

It is instructive to learn how scientists analyzed this type of motion in the past. In ancient times, people who studied dynamics believed that an object moves with a constant velocity only when a constant external net force is applied. When Renaissance scientists, such as Galileo, began experimenting with dynamics, they verified that an object maintains a constant velocity when the net force acting on it is zero. **Figure 2** shows an example of each of these two points of view.

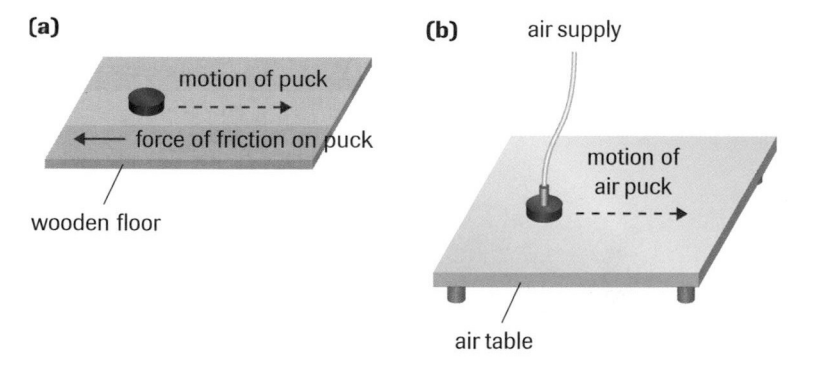

(a)
motion of puck
force of friction on puck
wooden floor

(b) air supply
motion of air puck
air table

Figure 2
(a) A puck sliding along the floor soon comes to rest. Scientists prior to Galileo believed that an object needed a net force to maintain constant velocity. We now know that the only net force acting on the puck in this case is friction.
(b) An air-hockey puck that slides along a surface with negligible friction maintains a constant velocity. This verifies Galileo's view that an object moving with constant velocity keeps moving at that velocity if the net force is zero.

Newton summarized Galileo's ideas about objects at rest and objects moving with constant velocity in his *first law of motion*.

> **Newton's First Law of Motion**
> If the net force acting on an object is zero, that object maintains its state of rest or constant velocity.

Figure 1
Isaac Newton, born in 1642, was perhaps the greatest of all mathematical physicists. In 1687, he published the book *Mathematical Principles of Natural Philosophy*, usually referred to as the *Principia*. In it, he described the works of other scientists as well as his own studies, including what are now called his three laws of motion and the law of universal gravitation. The concepts presented in his book represent a great leap forward in the world's understanding of the past, present, and future of the universe. Newton also contributed greatly to the studies of light, optics, and calculus. Although he died in 1727 at the age of 85, most of his great ideas were formulated by the age of 25.

inertia the property of matter that causes an object to resist changes to its motion

This law has important implications. An external net force is required to change an object's velocity; internal forces have no effect on an object's motion. For example, pushing on the dashboard of a car does not change the car's velocity. To cause a change in velocity—in other words, to cause acceleration—the net force acting on an object cannot be zero.

A common way to interpret this law is to say that an object at rest or moving with a constant velocity tends to maintain its state of rest or constant velocity unless acted upon by an external net force. The ability of an object to resist changes to its motion is a fundamental property of all matter called *inertia*. **Inertia** tends to keep a stationary object at rest or a moving object in motion in a straight line at a constant speed. Thus, the first law of motion is often called the *law of inertia*.

Examples of the law of inertia are common in everyday life. If you are standing on a stationary bus and it starts to accelerate forward, you tend to stay where you are initially, which means that you will start to fall backward relative to the accelerating bus. **Figure 3** shows another example of inertia.

Consider the inertia of an object in motion. One example is the briefcase on the overhead shelf in the commuter train. Another example occurs when a car slows down quickly; the people in the car tend to continue moving forward, possibly crashing their heads into the windshield if they are not wearing a seat belt. Wearing a seat belt properly helps to reduce the serious injuries that can occur in this situation. A seat belt also helps prevent injuries that can occur when an airbag deploys in a front-end collision. The operation of one type of seat belt is shown in **Figure 4**.

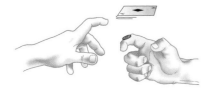

Figure 3
If a coin is balanced on a horizontal playing card on a finger and the card is flicked away, the coin, because of its inertia, will remain at rest on the finger.

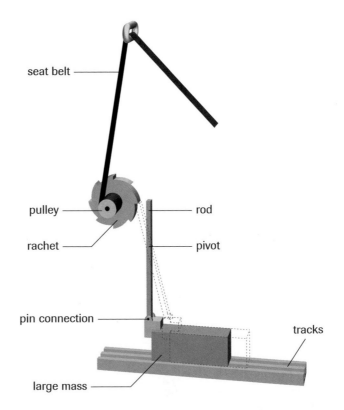

Figure 4
The operation of the seat belt shown here relies on the principle of inertia. Normally the ratchet turns freely, allowing the seat belt to wind or unwind whenever the passenger moves. With the car moving forward (to the right in this diagram), then slowing abruptly, the large mass on the track continues to move forward because of inertia. This causes the rod to turn on its pivot, locking the ratchet wheel and keeping the belt firmly in place.

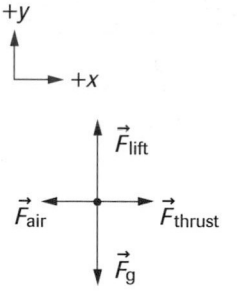

Figure 5
The FBD of the aircraft in
Sample Problem 1

> ▶ **SAMPLE** problem **1**

A 12-passenger jet aircraft of mass 1.6×10^4 kg is travelling at constant velocity of
850 km/h [E] while maintaining a constant altitude. What is the net force acting on
the aircraft?

Solution
According to Newton's first law, the net force on the aircraft must be zero because it is
moving with a constant velocity. **Figure 5** is an FBD of the aircraft. The vector sum of all
the forces is zero.

> ▶ **SAMPLE** problem **2**

You exert a force of 45 N [up] on your backpack, causing it to move upward with a constant velocity. Determine the force of gravity on the pack.

Solution
The FBD of the pack (**Figure 6**) shows that two forces act on the pack: the applied force
($\vec{F}_{app}$) that you exert and the force of gravity ($\vec{F}_g$) that Earth exerts. Since the pack is
moving at a constant velocity, the net force must, by the law of inertia, be zero. So the
upward and downward forces have the same magnitude, and $\vec{F}_g$ = 45 N [down].

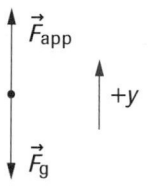

Figure 6
The FBD of the backpack in
Sample Problem 2

Any object that has zero net force acting on it is in a state of equilibrium. In this sense,
equilibrium is the property of an object experiencing no acceleration. The object can
be at rest (static equilibrium) or moving at a constant velocity (dynamic equilibrium).
In analyzing the forces on objects in equilibrium, it is convenient to consider the components of the force vectors. In other words, the condition for equilibrium, $\Sigma\vec{F} = 0$, can
be written as $\Sigma F_x = 0$ and $\Sigma F_y = 0$.

equilibrium property of an object
experiencing no acceleration

> ▶ **SAMPLE** problem **3**

The traction system of **Figure 7** stabilizes a broken tibia. Determine the force of the tibia
on the pulley. Neglect friction.

Solution
The FBD of the pulley (P) is shown in **Figure 8**. Since there is only one cord, we know
there must be only one tension, which is 18 N throughout the cord. The net force on the
pulley consists of both the horizontal (x) and vertical (y) components. We will use $\vec{F}_{tibia}$ as
the symbol for the force of the tibia on the pulley.

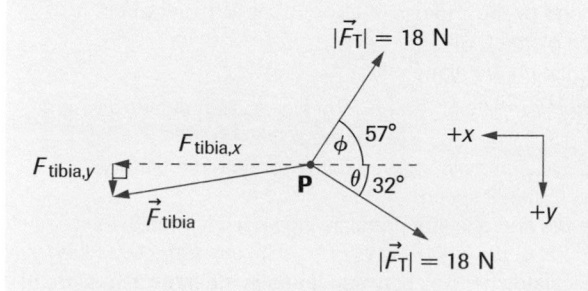

Figure 8
The FBD of the pulley (P)

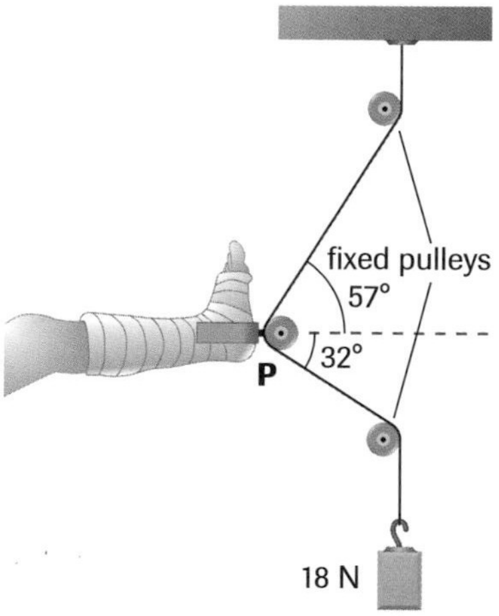

Figure 7
The system diagram of a leg in
traction for Sample Problem 3

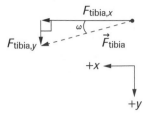

Figure 9
The force on the leg for Sample Problem 3

Horizontally:

$$\sum F_x = 0$$
$$F_{tibia,x} - F_T \cos \phi - F_T \cos \theta = 0$$
$$F_{tibia,x} = F_T (\cos \phi + \cos \theta)$$
$$= (18 \text{ N})(\cos 57° + \cos 32°)$$
$$F_{tibia,x} = 25 \text{ N}$$

Vertically:

$$\sum F_y = 0$$
$$F_{tibia,y} - F_T \sin \phi + F_T \sin \theta = 0$$
$$F_{tibia,y} = F_T (\sin \phi - \sin \theta)$$
$$= (18 \text{ N})(\sin 57° - \sin 32°)$$
$$F_{tibia,y} = 5.6 \text{ N}$$

From **Figure 9**, we can calculate the magnitude of the force:

$$|\vec{F}_{tibia}| = \sqrt{(25 \text{ N})^2 + (5.6 \text{ N})^2}$$
$$|\vec{F}_{tibia}| = 26 \text{ N}$$

We now determine the angle:

$$\omega = \tan^{-1} \frac{F_{tibia,y}}{F_{tibia,x}}$$
$$= \tan^{-1} \frac{5.6 \text{ N}}{25 \text{ N}}$$
$$\omega = 13°$$

The force of the tibia on the pulley is 26 N [13° below the horizontal].

In Activity 2.2.1, in the Lab Activities section at the end of this chapter, you will predict the force or forces needed for static equilibrium in a specific situation and check your predictions experimentally. Various methods can be used to accomplish this, including using a force table or a force board. ⊙▮

◉ ACTIVITY 2.2.1

Static Equilibrium of Forces (p. 112)

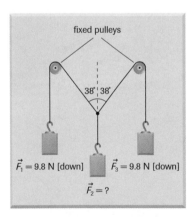

The above diagram shows a possible setup for a vertical force board. (You may prefer to modify the setup, however, using a force table instead of a force board, as suggested for this activity.) In this vertical force board, there are three different forces, each acting on a different string. If two of the forces are known, the third force can be determined. Describe how you would determine the unknown force $\vec{F}_2$.

▶ *Practice*

Understanding Concepts

1. Assume the 8-passenger Learjet shown in **Figure 10** has a force of gravity of 6.6×10^4 N [down] acting on it as it travels at a constant velocity of 6.4×10^2 km/h [W]. If the forward thrust provided by the engines is 1.3×10^4 N [W], determine
   (a) the upward lift force on the plane
   (b) the force due to air resistance on the plane

2. Choose which of the objects in *italics* are not examples of Newton's first law, giving a reason in each case:
   (a) A cat-food *can* moves at a constant velocity on a conveyor belt in a factory.
   (b) A *skydiver* falls vertically at terminal speed.
   (c) A rubber *stopper* is tied to the end of a string and swings back and forth as a pendulum.
   (d) A *shopper* stands on an escalator, halfway between floors in a department store, and rises at a constant speed.
   (e) A *ball* travels with projectile motion after leaving a pitcher's hand.

3. A child is trying to push a large desk across a wooden floor. The child is exerting a horizontal force of magnitude 38 N, but the desk is not moving. What is the magnitude of the force of friction acting on the desk?

4. A snowboarder is travelling at a high speed down a smooth snow-covered hill. The board suddenly reaches a rough patch, encountering significant friction. Use Newton's first law to describe and explain what is likely to happen to the snowboarder.

5. You are sitting on a bus that is travelling at a constant velocity of 55 km/h [N]. You toss a tennis ball straight upward and it reaches a height just above the level of your eyes. Will the ball collide with you? Explain your answer.

6. The following sets of forces are acting on a common point. Determine the additional force needed to maintain static equilibrium.
   (a) 265 N [E]; 122 N [W]
   (b) 32 N [N]; 44 N [E]
   (c) 6.5 N [25° E of N]; 4.5 N [W]; 3.9 N [15° N of E]

7. A single clothesline is attached to two poles 10.0 m apart. A pulley holding a mass $\left(|\vec{F}_g| = 294 \text{ N} \right)$ rolls to the middle of the line and comes to rest there. The middle of the line is 0.40 m below each end. Determine the magnitude of the tension in the clothesline.

Applying Inquiry Skills

8. (a) Describe how you could use a piece of paper, a coin, and your desk to demonstrate the law of inertia for an object initially at rest.
   (b) Describe how you could safely demonstrate, using objects of your choosing, the law of inertia for an object initially in motion.

Making Connections

9. Explain the danger of stowing heavy objects in the rear window space of a car.

Answers

6. (a) 143 N [W]
   (b) 54 N [36° S of W]
   (c) 7.2 N [16° W of S]

7. 1.8×10^3 N

Figure 10
The Bombardier Learjet® 45, built by the Canadian firm Bombardier Inc., is one of the first executive jets designed entirely on computer.

Newton's Second Law of Motion

Speculate on how the magnitudes of the accelerations compare in each of the following cases:

- You apply an equal net force to each of two boxes initially at rest on a horizontal set of low-friction rollers. One box has a mass that is double the mass of the other box.

- Two identical boxes with the same mass are initially at rest on a horizontal set of low-friction rollers. You apply a net force to one box that is twice as large in magnitude as the force you apply to the other box.

In the first case, it is the less massive box that experiences the larger acceleration. In the second case, it is the box to which the greater force is applied that experiences the larger acceleration. It is obvious that an object's acceleration depends on both the object's mass and the net force applied.

To show mathematically how the acceleration of an object depends on the net force and the object's mass, we can analyze the results of an ideal controlled experiment. (The experiment is "ideal" because the force of friction is so small that it can be neglected. This can be achieved, for instance, by using an air puck on an air table.) **Table 1** gives data from the experiment.

Table 1 Experimental Data

Mass (kg)	Net Force (N [fwd])	Average Acceleration (m/s² [fwd])
1.0	1.0	1.0
1.0	2.0	2.0
1.0	3.0	3.0
2.0	3.0	1.5
3.0	3.0	1.0

As you can see in **Table 1**, as the net force increases for a constant mass, the acceleration increases proportionally, and as the mass increases with a constant force, the acceleration decreases proportionally. This relationship is the basis for Newton's *second law of motion*.

> ### Newton's Second Law of Motion
>
> If the external net force on an object is not zero, the object accelerates in the direction of the net force. The acceleration is directly proportional to the net force and inversely proportional to the object's mass.

Newton's first law involves situations in which the net force acting on an object is zero, so that no acceleration occurs. His second law includes situations in which the net force is nonzero, so that acceleration occurs in the direction of the net force.

To write the second law in equation form, we begin with the proportionality statements stated in the law: $\vec{a} \propto \Sigma \vec{F}$ (with a constant mass) and $\vec{a} \propto \dfrac{1}{m}$ (with a constant net force). Combining these statements, we obtain

$$\vec{a} \propto \frac{\Sigma \vec{F}}{m}$$

Converting this to an equation requires a constant of proportionality, k. Thus,

$$\vec{a} = \frac{k \Sigma \vec{F}}{m}$$

If the appropriate units are chosen for the variables, then $k = 1$ and

$$\vec{a} = \frac{\Sigma \vec{F}}{m}$$

Or, equivalently,

$$\Sigma \vec{F} = m\vec{a}$$

For the components, the corresponding relationships are:

$$\Sigma F_x = ma_x \quad \text{and} \quad \Sigma F_y = ma_y$$

We can now define the SI unit of force. The newton (N) is the magnitude of the net force required to give a 1-kg object an acceleration of magnitude 1 m/s². By substituting into the equation $\Sigma \vec{F} = m\vec{a}$, we see that

$$1 \text{ N} = 1 \text{ kg}\left(\frac{\text{m}}{\text{s}^2}\right) \quad \text{or} \quad 1 \text{ N} = 1 \text{ kg·m/s}^2$$

DID YOU KNOW ?

Limitations of the Second Law

Newton's second law applies to all macroscopic objects—cars, bikes, people, rockets, planets, etc. The analysis of the motion of and forces on macroscopic objects is called *Newtonian mechanics*. The second law, however, does not apply to atomic and subatomic particles, such as electrons and quarks, where speeds are extremely high or the frame of reference is accelerating. In this microscopic realm, a different mathematical analysis, called *quantum mechanics*, applies.

▶ SAMPLE problem 4

The mass of a hot-air balloon, including the passengers, is 9.0×10^2 kg. The force of gravity on the balloon is 8.8×10^3 N [down]. The density of the air inside the balloon is adjusted by adjusting the heat output of the burner to give a buoyant force on the balloon of 9.9×10^3 N [up]. Determine the vertical acceleration of the balloon.

Solution

$m = 9.0 \times 10^2$ kg $\qquad F_{app} = |\vec{F}_{app}| = 9.9 \times 10^3$ N

$F_g = |\vec{F}_g| = 8.8 \times 10^3$ N $\qquad a_y = ?$

Figure 11 is an FBD of the balloon.

$$\sum F_y = ma_y$$

$$a_y = \frac{\sum F_y}{m}$$

$$= \frac{F_{app} - F_g}{m}$$

$$= \frac{9.9 \times 10^3 \text{ N} - 8.8 \times 10^3 \text{ N}}{9.0 \times 10^2 \text{ kg}}$$

$$= \frac{1.1 \times 10^3 \text{ kg·m/s}^2}{9.0 \times 10^2 \text{ kg}}$$

$$a_y = 1.2 \text{ m/s}^2$$

The acceleration of the balloon is 1.2 m/s^2 [up].

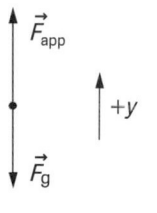

Figure 11
The FBD of the balloon shows the vertical forces as vectors. When only components are considered, the vector notation is omitted.

How does Newton's second law relate to his first law? According to the second law, $\vec{a} = \frac{\sum \vec{F}}{m}$, if the net force is zero, the acceleration must be zero, which implies that the velocity is constant (and could be zero). This agrees with the first law statement. It is evident that the first law is simply a special case of the second law, where $\sum \vec{F} = 0$.

> ### ▶ *Practice*

Understanding Concepts

10. A horizontal force is applied to a hockey puck of mass 0.16 kg initially at rest on the ice. The resulting acceleration of the puck has a magnitude of 32 m/s^2. What is the magnitude of the force? Neglect friction.

11. A fire truck with a mass of 2.95×10^4 kg experiences a net force of 2.42×10^4 N [fwd]. Determine the acceleration of the truck.

12. Derive an equation for the constant net force acting on an object in terms of the object's mass, its initial velocity, its final velocity, and the time interval during which the net force is applied.

13. A 7.27-kg bowling ball, travelling at 5.78 m/s [W], strikes a lone pin straight on. The collision lasts for 1.2 ms and causes the ball's velocity to become 4.61 m/s [W] just after the collision. Determine the net force (assumed to be constant) on the ball during the collision.

Applying Inquiry Skills

14. Describe how you would use an elastic band, three small carts with low-friction wheels, and a smooth horizontal surface to safely demonstrate Newton's second law. (Your demonstration need not involve taking numerical data.) Obtain teacher approval if you wish to try your demonstration.

Making Connections

15. Mining operations in outer space will require unique innovations if they are carried out where there is a very low force of gravity, such as on asteroids or the moons of various planets. One plan is to develop a device that will push particles with the same constant force, separating them according to the accelerations they achieve. Research "mining methods in zero-g" to learn more about this application of Newton's second law. Describe what you discover.

 www.science.nelson.com

Answers

10. 5.1 N

11. 0.820 m/s^2 [fwd]

13. 7.1×10^3 N [E]

Weight and Earth's Gravitational Field

We can apply Newton's second law to understand the scientific meaning of weight. The **weight** of an object is equal to the force of gravity acting on an object. Notice that this definition is different from *mass*, which is the quantity of matter. From the second law:

$$\text{weight} = \vec{F}_g = m\vec{g}$$

For example, the weight of a 5.5-kg turkey is

$$\vec{F}_g = m\vec{g} = (5.5 \text{ kg})(9.8 \text{ N/kg [down]}) = 54 \text{ N [down]}$$

Near Earth, weight results from Earth's relatively large force of attraction on other bodies around it. The space surrounding an object in which a force exists is called a **force field**. The gravitational force field surrounding Earth extends from Earth's surface far into space. At Earth's surface, the amount of force per unit mass, called the **gravitational field strength**, is 9.8 N/kg [down] (to two significant digits). This value is a vector quantity directed toward Earth's centre and is given the symbol $\vec{g}$. Notice that the gravitational field strength has the same value as the average acceleration due to gravity at Earth's surface, although for convenience the units are written differently. The two values are interchangeable and they have the same symbol, $\vec{g}$.

Earth's gravitational field strength, and thus the weight of objects on Earth's surface, varies slightly depending on various factors, which will be explored in Unit 2.

weight the force of gravity on an object

force field space surrounding an object in which a force exists

gravitational field strength $(\vec{g})$ amount of force per unit mass

> ▶ *Practice*

Understanding Concepts

16. Determine, from the indicated masses, the magnitude of the weight (in newtons) for each of the following stationary objects on Earth's surface:
    (a) a horseshoe (2.4 kg)
    (b) an open-pit coal-mining machine (1.3 Gg)
    (c) a table tennis ball (2.50 g) (Assume $|\vec{g}| = 9.80$ N/kg.)
    (d) a speck of dust (1.81 μg) (Assume $|\vec{g}| = 9.80$ N/kg.)
    (e) you

17. Determine the mass of each of the following objects, assuming that the object is stationary in a gravitational field of 9.80 N/kg [down]:
    (a) a field hockey ball with a weight of 1.53 N [down]
    (b) cargo attaining the 1.16 MN [down] weight limit of a C-5 Galaxy cargo plane

18. What is the weight of a 76-kg astronaut on a planet where the gravitational field strength is 3.7 N/kg [down]?

Applying Inquiry Skills

19. Show that the units N/kg and m/s^2 are equivalent.

Answers

16. (a) 24 N
    (b) 1.3×10^7 N
    (c) 2.45×10^{-2} N
    (d) 1.77×10^{-8} N
17. (a) 1.56×10^{-1} kg
    (b) 1.18×10^5 kg
18. 2.8×10^2 N [down]

Newton's Third Law of Motion

When a balloon is inflated and released, air rushing from the open nozzle causes the balloon to fly off in the opposite direction (**Figure 12(a)**). Evidently, when the balloon exerts a force on the air in one direction, the air exerts a force on the balloon in the opposite direction. This is illustrated in **Figure 12(b)** where vertical forces are not shown because they are so small.

(a)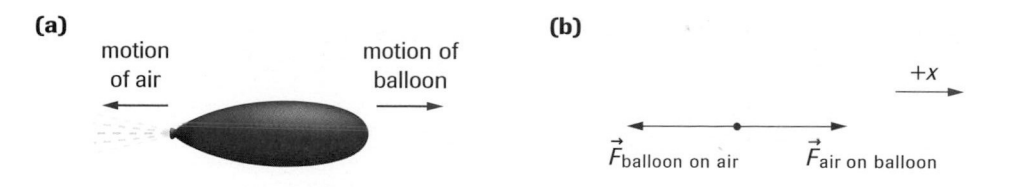

motion of air

motion of balloon

(b)

$+x$

$\vec{F}_{\text{balloon on air}}$ $\vec{F}_{\text{air on balloon}}$

Figure 12
(a) When an inflated balloon is released, air bursts out in one direction and the balloon reacts in the opposite direction.
(b) Two simultaneous forces acting on different objects

This example brings us to Newton's *third law of motion*, commonly called the *action–reaction law*, which considers forces that act in pairs on two objects. Notice that this differs from the first and second laws where only one object at a time was considered.

Newton's Third Law of Motion
For every action force, there is a simultaneous reaction force equal in magnitude but opposite in direction.

The third law can be used to explain situations where a force is exerted on one object by a second object. To illustrate how this law applies to the motion of people and vehicles, consider the following examples, which are also illustrated in **Figure 13**.

- When a motorcycle accelerates forward, the tires exert a backward action force on the road and the road exerts a forward reaction force on the tires. These forces are static friction between the tires and the road.

- When you walk, your feet exert an action force downward and backward on the floor, while the floor exerts a reaction force upward and forward on your feet.

- When you row a boat, the oar exerts an action force backward on the water and the water exerts a reaction force forward on the oar attached to the boat.

LEARNING TIP

Naming Action–Reaction Pairs
In the examples of action-reactions pairs shown in **Figure 13**, one force is called the action force and the other is called the reaction force. These two forces act on different objects. Since both forces occur simultaneously, it does not matter which is called the action force and which is called the reaction force. The names can be interchanged with no effect on the description.

(a)

direction of motion - - - - - - - - ➤

force of tire on road (action force)

force of road on tire (reaction force)

road

(b)

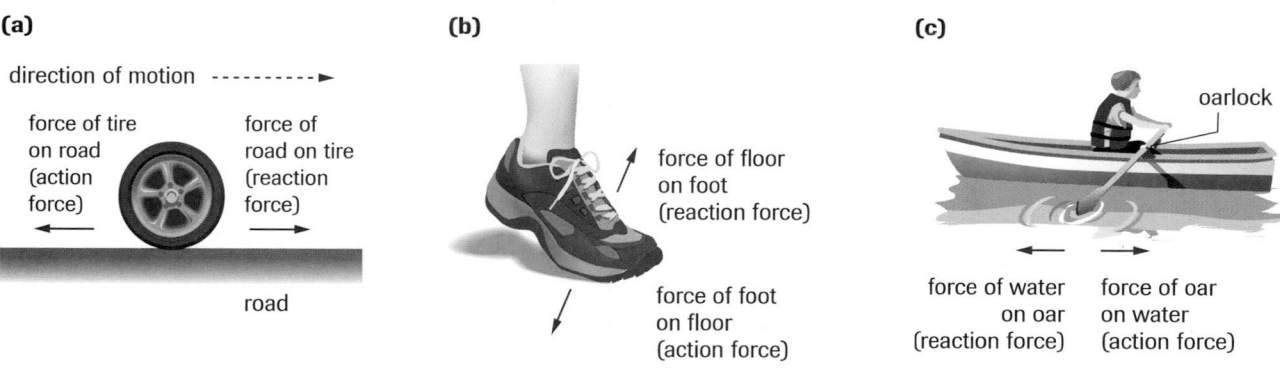

force of floor on foot (reaction force)

force of foot on floor (action force)

(c)

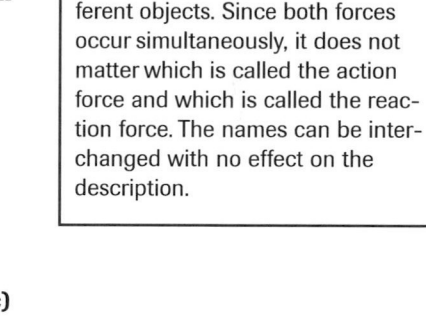

oarlock

force of water on oar (reaction force)

force of oar on water (action force)

Figure 13
Illustrations of Newton's third law of motion
(a) A tire accelerates on a road.
(b) A foot moves on a floor.
(c) Oars propel a boat.

▶ **SAMPLE** problem **5**

A softball player sliding into third base experiences the force of friction. Describe the action-reaction pair of forces in this situation.

Solution
We arbitrarily designate the action force to be the force of the ground on the player (in a direction opposite to the player's sliding motion). Given this choice, the reaction force is the force exerted by the player on the ground (in the direction of the player's sliding motion).

Understanding Concepts

20. Explain the motion of each of the following objects in *italics* using the third law of motion. Describe the action and reaction forces, and their directions.
    (a) A *rocket* being used to put a communications satellite into orbit has just left the launch pad.
    (b) A rescue *helicopter* hovers above a stranded victim on a rooftop beside a flooded river.
    (c) An inflated *balloon* is released from your hand and travels eastward for a brief time interval.

21. You are holding a pencil horizontally in your hand.
    (a) Draw a system diagram of this situation, showing all the action-reaction pairs of forces associated with the pencil.
    (b) Explain, with the help of an FBD, why the pencil is not accelerating.

Applying Inquiry Skills

22. Describe how you would safely demonstrate Newton's third law to students in elementary school using toys.

SUMMARY *Newton's Laws of Motion*

- Dynamics is the study of forces and the effects the forces have on the velocities of objects.

- The three laws of motion and the SI unit of force are named after Sir Isaac Newton.

- Newton's first law of motion (also called the law of inertia) states: If the net force acting on an object is zero, the object maintains its state of rest or constant velocity.

- Inertia is the property of matter that tends to keep an object at rest or in motion.

- An object is in equilibrium if the net force acting on it is zero, which means the object is either at rest or is moving at a constant velocity.

- Newton's second law of motion states: If the external net force on an object is not zero, the object accelerates in the direction of the net force. The acceleration is directly proportional to the net force and inversely proportional to the object's mass. The second law can be written in equation form as $\vec{a} = \dfrac{\Sigma \vec{F}}{m}$ (equivalently, $\Sigma \vec{F} = m\vec{a}$).

- Both the first and second laws deal with a single object; the third law deals with two objects.

- The SI unit of force is the newton (N): $1 \text{ N} = 1 \text{ kg·m/s}^2$.

- The weight of an object is the force of gravity acting on it in Earth's gravitational field. The magnitude of the gravitational field at Earth's surface is 9.8 N/kg, which is equivalent to 9.8 m/s^2.

- Newton's third law of motion (also called the action-reaction law) states: For every action force, there is a simultaneous force equal in magnitude, but opposite in direction.

> **Section 2.2** *Questions*

Understanding Concepts

1. A mallard duck of mass 2.3 kg is flying at a constant velocity of 29 m/s [15° below the horizontal]. What is the net force acting on the duck?

2. A 1.9-kg carton of juice is resting on a refrigerator shelf. Determine the normal force acting on the carton.

3. An electrical utility worker with a mass of 67 kg, standing in a cherry picker, is lowered at a constant velocity of 85 cm/s [down]. Determine the normal force exerted by the cherry picker on the worker.

4. Magnetic forces act on the electron beams in television tubes. If a magnetic force of magnitude 3.20×10^{-15} N is exerted on an electron ($m_e = 9.11 \times 10^{-31}$ kg), determine the magnitude of the resulting acceleration. (The mass of an electron is so low that gravitational forces are negligible.)

5. A karate expert shatters a brick with a bare hand. The expert has a mass of 65 kg, of which 0.65 kg is the mass of the hand. The velocity of the hand changes from 13 m/s [down] to zero in a time interval of 3.0 ms. The acceleration of the hand is constant.
   (a) Determine the acceleration of the hand
   (b) Determine the net force acting on the hand. What object exerts this force on the hand?
   (c) Determine the ratio of the magnitude of the net force acting on the hand to the magnitude of the expert's weight.

6. In target archery, the magnitude of the maximum draw force applied by a particular bow is 1.24×10^2 N. If this force gives the arrow an acceleration of magnitude 4.43×10^3 m/s², what is the mass, in grams, of the arrow?

7. The magnitude of the gravitational field strength on Venus is 8.9 N/kg.
   (a) Calculate the magnitude of your weight on the surface of Venus.
   (b) By what percentage would the magnitude of your weight change if you moved to Venus?

8. One force is given for each of the following situations. Identify the other force in the action-reaction pair, and indicate the name of the force, its direction, the object that exerts it, and the object on which it is exerted:
   (a) A chef exerts a force on a baking pan to pull it out of an oven.
   (b) The Sun exerts a gravitational force on Saturn.

(c) A swimmer's hands exert a backward force on the water.
(d) Earth exerts a gravitational force on a watermelon.
(e) An upward force of air resistance is exerted on a falling hailstone.

9. Two identical bags of gumballs, each of mass 0.200 kg, are suspended as shown in **Figure 14**. Determine the reading on the spring scale.

Figure 14

Applying Inquiry Skills

10. (a) Hold a calculator in your hand and estimate its mass in grams. Convert your estimate to kilograms.
    (b) Determine the weight of the calculator from your mass estimate.
    (c) Determine the weight of the calculator from its mass as measured on a balance.
    (d) Determine the percent error in your estimate in (b).

Making Connections

11. An astronaut in the International Space Station obtains a measurement of personal body mass from an "inertial device," capable of exerting a measured force. The display on the device shows that a net force of 87 N [fwd] gives the astronaut an acceleration of 1.5 m/s² [fwd] from rest for 1.2 s.
    (a) Why is the astronaut unable to measure personal body mass on an ordinary scale, such as a bathroom scale?
    (b) What is the mass of the astronaut?
    (c) How far did the astronaut move during the 1.2-s time interval?
    (d) Research how an inertial device works. Write a brief description of what you discover.

GO   www.science.nelson.com

12. Research the career of Isaac Newton. Report on some of his major accomplishments as well as his eccentricities.

When riders in a roller coaster are pulled toward the top of the first and highest hill, they are putting faith in the calculations used to determine the strength of the cable pulling on the coaster. The design engineers must analyze the relationship between the tension in the cable and the forces of gravity and friction acting on the coaster cars and all the passengers. This is just one example of a situation in which forces are analyzed. In this section you will expand your problem-solving skills as you apply Newton's three laws of motion to a variety of situations.

Solving Problems in a Systematic Way

Newton's laws of motion can be used to solve a variety of problems. One approach to solving most problems involves following a series of steps.

Step 1. Read the problem carefully and check the definitions of any unfamiliar words.

Step 2. Draw a system diagram. Label all relevant information, including any numerical quantities given. (For simple situations, you can omit this step.)

Step 3. Draw an FBD of the object (or group of objects) and label all the forces. Choose the $+x$ and $+y$ directions. (Try to choose one of these directions as the direction of the acceleration.)

Step 4. Calculate and label the x- and y-components of all the forces on the FBD.

Step 5. Write the second-law equation(s), $\Sigma F_x = ma_x$ and/or $\Sigma F_y = ma_y$, and substitute for the variables on both sides of the equation(s).

Step 6. Repeat steps 3 to 5 for any other objects as required.

Step 7. Solve the resulting equation(s) algebraically.

Step 8. Check to see if your answers have appropriate units, a reasonable magnitude, a logical direction (if required), and the correct number of significant digits.

▶ **SAMPLE** problem **1**

A contractor is pushing a stove across a kitchen floor with a constant velocity of 18 cm/s [fwd]. The contractor is exerting a constant horizontal force of 85 N [fwd]. The force of gravity on the stove is 447 N [down].

(a) Determine the normal force ($\vec{F}_N$) and the force of friction ($\vec{F}_f$) acting on the stove.

(b) Determine the total force applied by the floor ($\vec{F}_{floor}$) on the stove.

Solution

$\vec{F}_{app} = 85 \text{ N [fwd]}$

$\vec{F}_g = 447 \text{ N [down]}$

$\vec{v} = 18 \text{ cm/s [fwd]}$

(a) $\vec{F}_N = ?$
$\vec{F}_f = ?$

We can omit the system diagram (step 2) because this problem involves the motion of a single object in a simple, one-dimensional situation. We begin by drawing an FBD of the stove, as in **Figure 1(a)**.

Since the stove is moving at a constant velocity, $a_x = 0$ and $\sum F_x = 0$. Since the stove has no motion in the vertical direction, $a_y = 0$ and $\sum F_y = 0$. To solve for the normal force, we substitute using the vertical components of the forces:

$$\sum F_y = ma_y = 0$$
$$F_N + (-F_g) = 0$$
$$\therefore F_N = F_g = 447 \text{ N}$$

Since the direction of the normal force is upward, the final value is 447 N [up].

To determine the force of friction, we substitute using the horizontal components of the forces.

$$\sum F_x = ma_x = 0$$
$$F_{app} + (-F_f) = 0$$
$$\therefore F_{app} = F_f = 85 \text{ N}$$

The friction is 85 N [backward].

(b) $\vec{F}_{floor} = ?$

As shown in **Figure 1(b)**, the force applied by the floor on the stove has two components. We determine the magnitude of the required force as follows:

$$|\vec{F}_{floor}| = \sqrt{(F_N)^2 + (F_f)^2}$$
$$= \sqrt{(447 \text{ N})^2 + (85 \text{ N})^2}$$
$$|\vec{F}_{floor}| = 455 \text{ N}$$

We determine the direction of the force from trigonometry:

$$\phi = \tan^{-1}\frac{F_N}{F_f}$$
$$= \tan^{-1}\frac{447 \text{ N}}{85 \text{ N}}$$
$$\phi = 79°$$

The force of the floor on the stove is 4.6×10^2 N [79° above the horizontal].

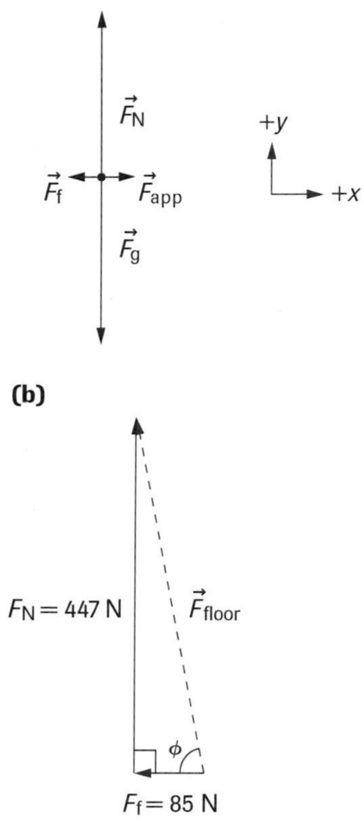

(a)

(b)

$F_N = 447$ N $\vec{F}_{floor}$

$F_f = 85$ N

Figure 1
(a) FBD of the stove
(b) Force exerted by the floor on the stove

LEARNING *TIP*

Using Components
Notice that when using components, vector notation is omitted. Remember that the symbol F_g represents the *magnitude* of the force $\vec{F}_g$ and is positive. If the $+y$ direction is chosen to be upward, then the y-component of the force of gravity is negative and is written $-F_g$.

▶ *SAMPLE* problem 2

Sleds A and B are connected by a horizontal rope, with A in front of B. Sled A is pulled forward by means of a horizontal rope with a tension of magnitude 29.0 N. The masses of A and B are 6.7 kg and 5.6 kg, respectively. The magnitudes of friction on A and B are 9.0 N and 8.0 N, respectively. Calculate the magnitude of

(a) the acceleration of the two-sled system

(b) the tension in the rope connecting the sleds

Solution

We begin by drawing a system diagram and labelling the pertinent information, as in **Figure 2**.

$\vec{F}_{T1}$ = 29.0 N $\quad\quad$ F_{fA} = 9.0 N

m_A = 6.7 kg $\quad\quad$ F_{fB} = 8.0 N

m_B = 5.6 kg

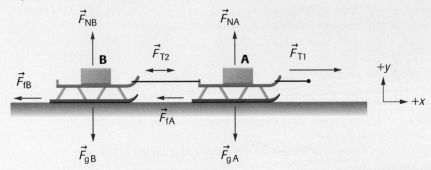

Figure 2
System diagram of sleds A and B for Sample Problem 2

(a) To determine the magnitude of the acceleration of the two-sled system, we note that the tension in the front rope, $\vec{F}_{T1}$, determines the acceleration of the entire system. **Figure 3** is the FBD of the system.

Horizontally for the system:

Applying Newton's second law:

$$\sum F_{system,x} = m_{system}a_{system,x}$$

$$a_x = \frac{\sum F_x}{m}$$

$$= \frac{F_{T1} + (-F_{f,total})}{m_A + m_B}$$

$$= \frac{29.0 \text{ N} - (9.0 \text{ N} + 8.0 \text{ N})}{(6.7 \text{ kg} + 5.6 \text{ kg})}$$

$$a_x = 0.98 \text{ m/s}^2$$

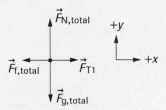

Figure 3
FBD of the two-sled system

The magnitude of the acceleration is 0.98 m/s².

(b) To determine the magnitude of the tension in the second rope, $\vec{F}_{T2}$, we analyze the forces that are acting only on sled B. **Figure 4** is the FBD of sled B. Knowing that the magnitude of the acceleration of sled B is the same as the acceleration of the system (i.e., 0.98 m/s²), we can apply the second-law equation to the horizontal components of the motion:

$$\sum F_{Bx} = m_B a_{Bx}$$
$$F_{T2} - F_{fB} = m_B a_{Bx}$$
$$F_{T2} = F_{fB} + m_B a_{Bx}$$
$$= 8.0 \text{ N} + (5.6 \text{ kg})(0.98 \text{ m/s}^2)$$
$$F_{T2} = 13 \text{ N}$$

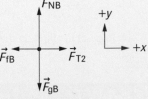

Figure 4
FBD of sled B

The magnitude of the tension in the connecting ropes is 13 N. We would have obtained the same value by drawing an FBD for sled A instead, since the tension force applied by the connecting rope to A is equal in magnitude, although opposite in direction, to the tension force applied by the connecting rope to B. The value of 13 N seems reasonable, since the tension must be large enough not only to overcome the friction of 8.0 N, but also to cause acceleration.

LEARNING TIP

Multiple Ropes

In Sample Problem 2, there are two sleds and two ropes. However, if there were three or more objects and three or more ropes, you would need to calculate the tensions in those ropes. You would first find the acceleration of the system, and then go to the last object and work your way step by step to the first object. These types of problems can also be solved by setting up and solving simultaneous equations. For example, Sample Problem 2 can be solved by setting up a second-law equation in the horizontal plane for each object. These two equations have two unknowns (the acceleration and the tension in the connecting rope). The simultaneous equations can then be solved for the unknowns.

▶ **SAMPLE** problem **3**

You attach a loonie (m_L = 6.99 g) and a dime (m_D = 2.09 g) to the ends of a thread. You put the thread over a smooth horizontal bar and pull the thread taut. Finally, you release your hands, letting the loonie drop and the dime rise. Friction between the thread and the bar is negligible, and the magnitude of $\vec{g}$ is 9.80 m/s². Determine the magnitude of

(a) the acceleration of the coins

(b) the tension in the thread

Solution

We begin by drawing the system diagram (**Figure 5(a)**), including as much information as possible. Since the loonie has more mass than the dime, the system of coins and thread will accelerate counterclockwise over the bar. We choose the direction of the acceleration as the positive direction for each coin: downward for the loonie and upward for the dime. Because there is only one thread, there is only one tension, $\vec{F}_T$.

(a) To determine the magnitude of the acceleration of the coins, we analyze the FBDs of the two coins separately (**Figures 5(b)** and **(c)**). The second-law equation with y-components in the coordinate system for the loonie yields the following:

$$\Sigma F_y = ma_y$$
$$F_{gL} - F_T = m_L a_y$$

Both F_T and a_y are unknown. Next, we apply the second-law equation with y-components in the coordinate system for the dime:

$$F_T - F_{gD} = m_D a_y$$

If we add the two equations, we find that one of the unknowns, F_T, disappears.

$$F_{gL} - F_{gD} = m_L a_y + m_D a_y$$
$$F_{gL} - F_{gD} = a_y(m_L + m_D)$$
$$a_y = \frac{F_{gL} - F_{gD}}{m_L + m_D}$$
$$= \frac{m_L g - m_D g}{m_L + m_D}$$
$$= \frac{(m_L - m_D)g}{m_L + m_D}$$
$$= \frac{(6.99 \times 10^{-3}\ \text{kg} - 2.09 \times 10^{-3}\ \text{kg})(9.80\ \text{m/s}^2)}{(6.99 \times 10^{-3}\ \text{kg}) + (2.09 \times 10^{-3}\ \text{kg})}$$
$$a_y = 5.29\ \text{m/s}^2$$

The magnitude of the acceleration is 5.29 m/s².

(b) To determine the magnitude of the tension, we can substitute the acceleration into either of the two second-law equations. Using the second-law equation for the dime:

$$F_T = F_{gD} + m_D a_y$$
$$= m_D g + m_D a_y$$
$$= m_D (g + a_y)$$
$$= (2.09 \times 10^{-3}\ \text{kg})(9.80\ \text{m/s}^2 + 5.29\ \text{m/s}^2)$$
$$F_T = 3.15 \times 10^{-2}\ \text{N}$$

The magnitude of the tension in the thread is 3.15×10^{-2} N.

(a)

direction of acceleration

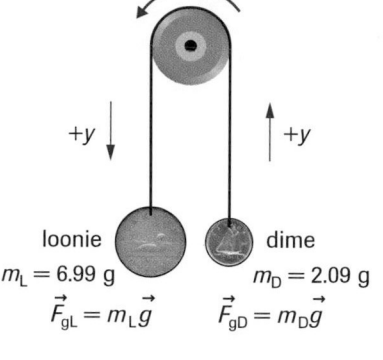

$+y$ $+y$

loonie   dime
$m_L = 6.99$ g $m_D = 2.09$ g
$\vec{F}_{gL} = m_L \vec{g}$ $\vec{F}_{gD} = m_D \vec{g}$

(b)   **(c)**

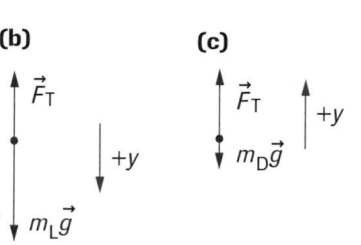

Figure 5
(a) The system diagram for the coins in Sample Problem 3
(b) The FBD of the loonie
(c) The FBD of the dime

LEARNING TIP

Directions in Pulley Problems
When you solve a problem that involves at least one pulley, choose a general positive direction for the entire system of objects. You should then assign a $+x$ or $+y$ direction for each object so that it is in the general positive direction. For example, the system of objects below will tend to accelerate in a clockwise direction. The positive direction will be upward for mass A, to the right for mass B, and downward for mass C.

direction of acceleration

Understanding Concepts

Answers

1. 35 g
2. (a) 2.74×10^3 N [up]
   (b) 35 kg
3. (a) 1.55 m/s²
   (b) 295 N
4. 1.2 kg
5. (a) 4.8 m/s²
   (b) 19 N
6. (a) 194 N
   (b) 2.4 N
   (c) 0.79 m/s
   (d) 2.9 N
7. (a) 6.2×10^2 N
   (b) 2.0 m/s²
8. (b) $mg - F_A \sin \theta$
   (c) $F_A \cos \theta$

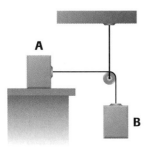

Figure 6
For question 5

1. You apply a force of 0.35 N [up] to lift a fork. The resulting acceleration of the fork is 0.15 m/s² [up]. Determine the mass of the fork in grams.

2. A hot-air balloon experiences an acceleration of 1.10 m/s² [down]. The total mass of the balloon, the basket, and the contents of the basket is 315 kg.
   (a) What is the upward (buoyant) force on the system?
   (b) The balloonist wishes to change the acceleration to zero. There is no fuel left to heat the air in the balloon. Determine the mass of the ballast that must be discarded overboard. (Neglect air resistance.)

3. A tree house has a vertical "fire pole" of smooth metal, designed for quick exits. A child of mass 35.7 kg slides down the pole with constant acceleration, starting from rest. The pole is 3.10 m high. The journey to the ground takes 2.00 s.
   (a) What is the magnitude of the downward acceleration of the child?
   (b) What is the magnitude of the upward force of friction exerted by the pole on the child?

4. When an external net force is applied to a particular mass m, an acceleration of magnitude "a" results. When the mass is increased by 2.0 kg and the same net force is applied, the acceleration is $0.37a$. Determine the mass, m.

5. Blocks A and B are connected by a string passing over an essentially friction-less pulley, as in **Figure 6**. When the blocks are in motion, Block A experiences a force of kinetic friction of magnitude 5.7 N. If $m_A = 2.7$ kg and $m_B = 3.7$ kg, calculate the magnitude of
   (a) the acceleration of the blocks
   (b) the tension in the string

6. A boy pushes a lawn mower ($m = 17.9$ kg) starting from rest across a horizontal lawn by applying a force of 32.9 N straight along the handle, which is inclined at an angle of 35.1° above the horizontal. The magnitude of the mower's acceleration is 1.37 m/s², which lasts for 0.58 s, after which the mower moves at a constant velocity. Determine the magnitude of
   (a) the normal force on the mower
   (b) the frictional force on the mower
   (c) the maximum velocity of the mower
   (d) the force applied by the boy needed to maintain the constant velocity

7. A skier ($m = 65$ kg) glides with negligible friction down a hill covered with hard-packed snow. If the hill is inclined at an angle of 12° above the horizontal, determine the magnitude of
   (a) the normal force on the skier
   (b) the skier's acceleration (*Hint:* Remember to choose the $+x$ direction as the direction of the acceleration, which in this case is downward, parallel to the hillside.)

Applying Inquiry Skills

8. Groups of physics students are each given a force scale (to measure an applied force of magnitude F_A), an electronic balance (to measure the mass, m), a rectangular wooden block with a hook at one end, a protractor, and a piece of string. Each group must determine the force of kinetic friction acting on the block as it is pulled with a constant velocity along a horizontal lab bench. However, the applied force must be at an angle θ above the horizontal.
   (a) Draw a system diagram and an FBD of the block for this investigation.
   (b) Derive an equation for the magnitude of the normal force on the block in terms of the given parameters F_A, g, m, and θ.
   (c) Derive an equation for the magnitude of friction on the block in terms of F_A and θ.

Making Connections

9. A physics student of mass 55.3 kg is standing on a weigh scale in an elevator. The scale shows the magnitude of the upward normal force (in newtons) on the student.
   (a) Determine the reading on the scale when the elevator has an acceleration of 1.08 m/s² [up].
   (b) The force calculated in (a) can be called the "apparent weight." How does the student's apparent weight in this case compare with the true weight? What happens to the apparent weight when the elevator is undergoing downward acceleration? undergoing free fall?
   (c) To check your answers in (b), determine the student's apparent weight when the elevator has first a downward acceleration of 1.08 m/s², then a downward acceleration of 9.80 m/s².
   (d) The term "weightless" is used to describe a person in free fall. Why is this term used? Is the term valid from the physics point of view? Explain your answer.
   (e) Repeat (a) when the elevator has a constant velocity of 1.08 m/s [up].

Answers

9. (a) 602 N
   (c) 482 N; 0 N
   (e) 542 N

Applying Newton's Third Law of Motion

Newton's third law of motion, the action–reaction law, always relates to two objects. When drawing a system diagram of action–reaction pairs of forces, both objects can be placed in the same diagram. However, when solving problems related to only one of objects, an FBD must be drawn for that object.

▶ **SAMPLE** problem **4**

An indoor skating rink is the venue for a family fun day. In one event, children on skates position themselves along a blue line facing one end of the rink. Behind each child, a parent, also on skates, prepares to push horizontally to see who can push their child the farthest. In this competition, a certain mother has a mass of 61 kg, and her daughter a mass of 19 kg. Both skaters experience negligible friction as long as their skates point straight ahead. At the starting bell, the mother pushes the child with a constant applied force of magnitude 56 N for 0.83 s. Determine the magnitude of

(a) the daughter's acceleration

(b) the mother's acceleration

(c) the maximum velocity of the daughter

Solution

Figure 7(a) is the system diagram. **Figures 7(b)** and **(c)** are the respective FBDs of the daughter and the mother. From Newton's third law of motion, it is evident that if the force of the mother on the daughter is 56 N in one direction, the force of the daughter on the mother is 56 N in the opposite direction.

(a)

(b) $\vec{F}_{ND}$ $\vec{F}_{app,D}$ $\vec{F}_{gD}$ $+y$ $+x$

(c) $\vec{F}_{NM}$ $\vec{F}_{app,M}$ $\vec{F}_{gM}$ $+y$ $+x$

Figure 7
(a) The system diagram for the mother-daughter pair in Sample Problem 4
(b) The FBD of the daughter
(c) The FBD of the mother

(a) Use the second-law equation for the daughter's horizontal motion:

$\sum F_{Dx} = 56\ N$

$m_D = 19\ kg$

$a_{Dx} = ?$

$$a_{Dx} = \frac{\sum F_{Dx}}{m_D}$$

$$= \frac{56\ N}{19\ kg}$$

$$a_{Dx} = 2.9\ m/s^2$$

The magnitude of the daughter's acceleration is 2.9 m/s².

(b) Use the second-law equation for the mother's horizontal motion:

$\sum F_{Mx} = 56\ N$

$m_M = 61\ kg$

$a_{Mx} = ?$

$$a_{Mx} = \frac{\sum F_{Mx}}{m_M}$$

$$= \frac{56\ N}{61\ kg}$$

$$a_{Mx} = 0.92\ m/s^2$$

The magnitude of the mother's acceleration is 0.92 m/s².

(c) $v_i = 0$

$a = 2.9\ m/s^2$

$\Delta t = 0.83\ s$

$v_f = ?$

$$v_f = v_i + a\Delta t$$

$$= 0 + (2.9\ m/s^2)(0.83\ s)$$

$$v_f = 2.4\ m/s$$

The magnitude of the maximum velocity of the daughter is 2.4 m/s.

▶ Practice

Understanding Concepts

Answers

10. (a) 1.0×10^4 N [fwd]

    (b) 2.0×10^4 N [fwd]

11. (a) 1.8 kg

    (b) 0.37 N

10. A train consisting of two cars pulled by a locomotive experiences an acceleration of 0.33 m/s² [fwd]. Friction is negligible. Each car has a mass of 3.1×10^4 kg.
    (a) Determine the force exerted by the first car on the second car.
    (b) Determine the force exerted by the locomotive on the first car.

11. Two books are resting side by side, in contact, on a desk. An applied horizontal force of 0.58 N causes the books to move together with an acceleration of 0.21 m/s² horizontally. The mass of the book to which the force is applied directly is 1.0 kg. Neglecting friction, determine
    (a) the mass of the other book
    (b) the magnitude of the force exerted by one book on the other

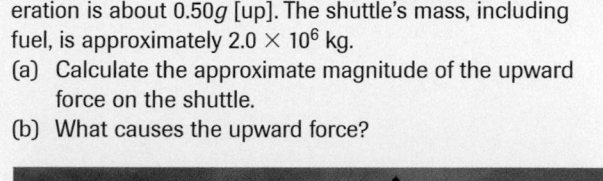

SUMMARY   *Applying Newton's Laws of Motion*

- It is wise to develop a general strategy that helps solve the great variety of types of problems involving forces, no matter how different each problem may at first appear.

- The skill of drawing an FBD for each object in a given problem is vital.

- For motion in two dimensions, it is almost always convenient to analyze the perpendicular components of the forces separately and then bring the concepts together.

▶ **Section 2.3** *Questions*

Understanding Concepts

1. A basketball is thrown so that it experiences projectile motion as it travels toward the basket. Air resistance is negligible. Draw an FBD of the ball (a) as it is rising, (b) as it arrives at the top of its flight, and (c) as it moves downward.

2. A shark, of mass 95 kg, is swimming with a constant velocity of 7.2 m/s [32° above the horizontal]. What is the net force acting on the shark?

3. **Figure 8** shows three masses (5.00 kg, 2.00 kg, and 1.00 kg) hung by threads.
   (a) Draw an FBD for the bottom mass. Determine the magnitude of the tension in the lowest thread.
   (b) Repeat (a) for the middle mass and the tension in the middle thread.
   (c) Repeat (a) for the top mass and the tension in the highest thread.

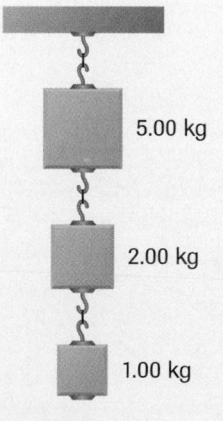

5.00 kg

2.00 kg

1.00 kg

Figure 8

4. Just after a space shuttle is launched (**Figure 9**), its acceleration is about $0.50g$ [up]. The shuttle's mass, including fuel, is approximately 2.0×10^6 kg.
   (a) Calculate the approximate magnitude of the upward force on the shuttle.
   (b) What causes the upward force?

Figure 9
The space shuttle *Endeavour* is launched carrying astronauts to the International Space Station.

5. Two boxes, of masses $m_1 = 35$ kg and $m_2 = 45$ kg, are hung vertically from opposite ends of a rope passing over a rigid horizontal metal rod. The system starts moving from rest. Assuming that friction between the rod and the rope is negligible, determine the magnitude of
   (a) the acceleration of the boxes
   (b) the tension in the rope
   (c) the magnitude of each box's displacement after 0.50 s

6. Two blocks are held in place by three ropes connected at point P, as shown in **Figure 10**. The magnitude of the force of static friction on block A is 1.8 N. The magnitude of the force of gravity on blocks A and B is 6.7 N and 2.5 N, respectively.
   (a) Draw an FBD for block B. Determine the magnitude of the tension in the vertical rope.
   (b) Draw an FBD for block A. Determine the magnitudes of the tension in the horizontal rope and of the normal force acting on block A.
   (c) Draw an FBD of point P. Calculate the tension (the magnitude and the angle θ) in the third rope.

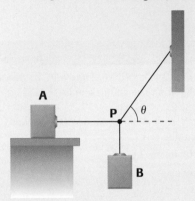

Figure 10

7. A store clerk pulls three carts connected with two horizontal cords (**Figure 11**) to move products from the storage room to the display shelves. The masses of the loaded carts are: $m_1 = 15.0$ kg; $m_2 = 13.2$ kg; and $m_3 = 16.1$ kg. Friction is negligible. A third cord, which pulls on cart 1 and is at an angle of 21.0° above the horizontal, has a tension of magnitude 35.3 N. Determine the magnitude of
   (a) the acceleration of the carts
   (b) the tension in the last cord
   (c) the tension in the middle cord

Figure 11

8. A hotel guest starts to pull an armchair across a horizontal floor by exerting a force of 91 N [15° above the horizontal]. The normal force exerted by the floor on the chair is 221 N [up]. The acceleration of the chair is 0.076 m/s² [fwd].
   (a) Determine the mass of the chair.
   (b) Determine the magnitude of the friction force on the chair.

9. A child on a toboggan slides down a hill with an acceleration of magnitude 1.5 m/s². If friction is negligible, what is the angle between the hill and the horizontal?

10. Blocks X and Y, of masses $m_X = 5.12$ kg and $m_Y = 3.22$ kg, are connected by a fishing line passing over an essentially frictionless pulley (**Figure 12**).
    (a) Show that block X slides up the incline with a positive acceleration. Determine the magnitude of that acceleration. Friction is negligible.
    (b) Determine the magnitude of the tension in the fishing line.

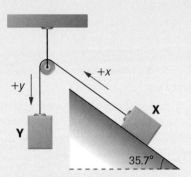

Figure 12

11. A figure skater of mass $m = 56$ kg pushes horizontally for 0.75 s with a constant force against the boards at the side of a skating rink. Having started from rest, the skater reaches a maximum speed of 75 cm/s. Neglecting friction, determine the magnitude of
    (a) the (constant) acceleration
    (b) the force exerted by the skater on the boards
    (c) the force exerted by the boards on the skater
    (d) the displacement of the skater from the boards after 1.50 s

Applying Inquiry Skills

12. (a) A constant net force is applied to various masses. Draw a graph of the magnitude of the resulting acceleration as a function of mass.
    (b) A variable net force is applied to a constant mass. Draw a graph of the resulting acceleration as a function of the net force.

Making Connections

13. Discuss the physics principles illustrated by the following statement: "In front-end collisions, airbag deployment can pose extreme danger if the passenger is not wearing a seat belt or if the passenger is a small child."

In Section 2.1, we looked at the definition of frictional forces, which include static friction and kinetic friction. In this section, we apply Newton's first law of motion, in which $\Sigma \vec{F} = 0$, and his second law, in which $\Sigma \vec{F} = m\vec{a}$, to situations involving friction. We will also consider situations in which one object slides over another and situations that involve air resistance and other forces of fluid friction. We will discover that analyzing friction has numerous practical applications, such as designing a nonstick frying pan, spinning a ball to curve its path in sports activities, maximizing the speed of skis, and maximizing the acceleration of racing cars.

There are some instances where scientists and engineers search for ways to increase friction. For example, an airport runway must be designed so that when it is wet, the friction between the airplane tires and the runway is almost as great as in dry conditions. Rock climbers (like the one shown in the introduction to this chapter) use footwear and gloves that provide the largest possible friction.

In other instances, reducing friction is the main objective. If you were responsible for designing an artificial limb, such as the hand shown in **Figure 1**, you would want to minimize the friction between the moving parts. Car manufacturers face a similar challenge as they try to maximize the efficiency of engines by minimizing the friction in the moving parts.

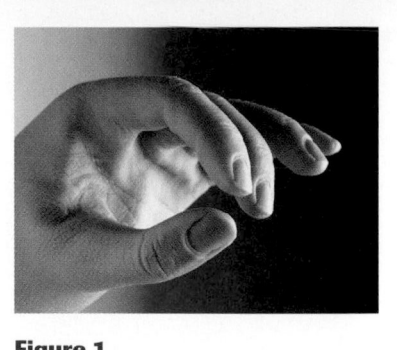

Figure 1
Artificial hands are designed to operate with as little friction as possible. How much friction do you feel within your hand when you wrap your fingers around a pen?

▶ **Practice**

Understanding Concepts

1. List examples (other than those given here) of situations in which it would be advantageous to have (a) increased friction and (b) decreased friction.

Coefficients of Friction

Consider what happens when you pull or push a box of bottled water across a countertop. Static friction acts on the stationary box and prevents it from starting to move. Once the box is in motion, kinetic friction acts to oppose the motion. For example, if you use a force meter or a spring scale to pull horizontally with an ever-increasing force on a stationary object, you will notice that the force increases steadily until, suddenly, the object starts moving. Then, if you keep the object moving at a constant velocity, you will notice that the applied force remains constant because there is no acceleration ($\Sigma \vec{F} = m\vec{a} = 0$). The magnitude of the force needed to start a stationary object moving is the *maximum static friction*, $F_{S,max}$. The magnitude of the force needed to keep the object moving at a constant velocity is the *kinetic friction*, F_K. The results of such an experiment are depicted in **Figure 2**.

The magnitudes of the forces of static and kinetic friction depend on the surfaces in contact with each other. For example, a fried egg in a nonstick frying pan experiences little friction, whereas a sleigh pulled across a concrete sidewalk experiences a lot of friction. The magnitude of the force of friction also depends on the normal force between the objects, which is logical when you consider the situations shown in **Figure 3**.

The coefficient of friction is a number that indicates the ratio of the magnitude of the force of friction between two surfaces to the normal force between those surfaces. The value for the coefficient of friction depends on the nature of the two surfaces in contact and the type of friction—static or kinetic. The **coefficient of static friction**, μ_S, is the ratio

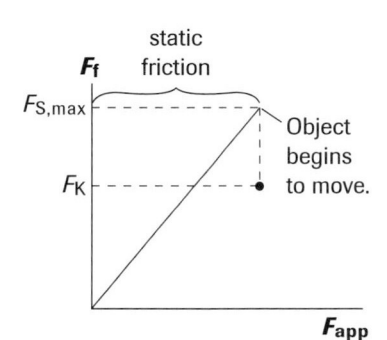

Figure 2
This graph depicts the magnitude of friction as a function of the magnitude of the applied force on an object up to the instant the object begins to move. The magnitude of kinetic friction is usually less than the maximum static friction.

coefficient of static friction (μ_S) the ratio of the magnitude of the maximum static friction to the magnitude of the normal force

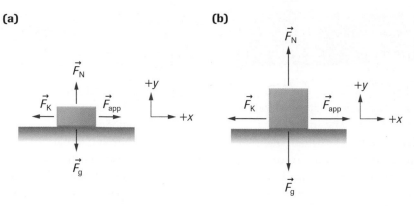

(a)

(b)

Figure 3
The greater the mass of an object, the greater is the normal force exerted on the object by the underlying surface, and the greater is the applied force needed to keep the object moving.
(a) If the mass is small, the normal force on it is small and so is the applied force needed to overcome kinetic friction.
(b) If the mass doubles, the normal force doubles and so does the applied force needed to overcome kinetic friction.

coefficient of kinetic friction
(μ_K) the ratio of the magnitude of the kinetic friction to the magnitude of the normal force

of the magnitude of the maximum static friction to the magnitude of the normal force. The **coefficient of kinetic friction**, μ_K, is the ratio of the magnitude of the kinetic friction to the magnitude of the normal force. The corresponding equations are

$$\mu_S = \frac{F_{S,max}}{F_N} \quad \text{and} \quad \mu_K = \frac{F_K}{F_N}$$

Determining μ_S and μ_K for given substances is done empirically, or through experimentation. Results of such experiments may differ from one laboratory to another, even with careful measurements and sophisticated equipment. For example, if several scientists at different locations in Canada measure the coefficient of kinetic friction between wood and dry snow, the wood and snow samples would vary; therefore, the coefficient values would not be consistent. The approximate coefficients of friction for several common pairs of surfaces are listed in **Table 1**.

Table 1 Approximate Coefficients of Friction of Some Common Materials

Materials	μ_S	μ_K
rubber on concrete (dry)	1.1	1.0
rubber on asphalt (dry)	1.1	1.0
steel on steel (dry)	0.60	0.40
steel on steel (greasy)	0.12	0.05
leather on rock (dry)	1.0	0.8
ice on ice	0.1	0.03
steel on ice	0.1	0.01
rubber on ice	?	0.005
wood on dry snow	0.22	0.18
wood on wet snow	0.14	0.10
Teflon® on Teflon	0.04	0.04
near-frictionless carbon, NFC (in air)	?	0.02 to 0.06
synovial joints in humans	0.01	0.003

SAMPLE problem 1

A crate of fish of mass 18.0 kg rests on the floor of a parked delivery truck. The coefficients of friction between the crate and the floor are $\mu_S = 0.450$ and $\mu_K = 0.410$. The local value of gravitational acceleration is, to three significant figures, 9.80 m/s^2. What are the force of friction and the acceleration (a) if a horizontal force of 75.0 N [E] is applied to the crate, and (b) if a horizontal force of 95.0 N [E] is applied?

Solution

Figure 4 shows both the system diagram and the FBD for this situation.

(a) $m = 18.0$ kg $\quad \mu_S = 0.450$

$\vec{F}_{app} = 75.0$ N [E] $\quad |\vec{g}| = 9.80$ N/kg

To determine whether the crate will accelerate or remain stationary, we find the maximum static friction. We first determine the normal force, using the equation for the second law in the vertical direction:

$$\begin{aligned} \sum F_y &= ma_y = 0 \\ F_N + (-mg) &= 0 \\ F_N &= mg \\ &= (18.0\text{ kg})(9.80\text{ N/kg}) \\ F_N &= 176\text{ N} \end{aligned}$$

We can now determine the magnitude of the maximum static friction:

$$\begin{aligned} F_{S,max} &= \mu_S F_N \\ &= (0.450)(176\text{ N}) \\ F_{S,max} &= 79.4\text{ N} \end{aligned}$$

Since the applied force is 75.0 N [E], the static friction (a reaction force to the applied force) must be 75.0 N [W], which is less than the magnitude of the maximum static friction. Consequently, the crate remains at rest.

(b) In this case, the magnitude of the applied force is greater than the magnitude of the maximum static friction. Since the crate is, therefore, in motion, we must consider the kinetic friction:

$\vec{F}_{app} = 95.0$ N [E]

$F_N = 176$ N

$\mu_K = 0.410$

$$\begin{aligned} F_K &= \mu_K F_N \\ &= (0.410)(176\text{ N}) \\ F_K &= 72.3\text{ N} \end{aligned}$$

To determine the acceleration of the crate, we apply the second-law equation in the horizontal direction:

$$\begin{aligned} \sum F_x &= ma_x \\ F_{app} + (-F_K) &= ma_x \\ a_x &= \frac{F_{app} + (-F_K)}{m} \\ &= \frac{95.0\text{ N} - 72.3\text{ N}}{18.0\text{ kg}} \\ a_x &= 1.26\text{ m/s}^2 \end{aligned}$$

Since the applied force is eastward, the acceleration of the crate is 1.26 m/s^2 [E].

(a)

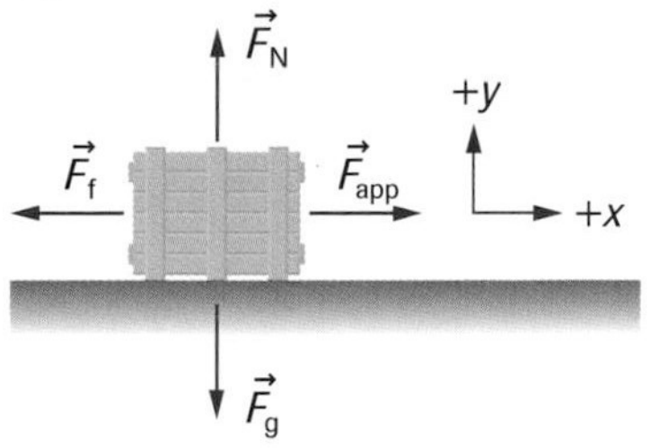

(b)

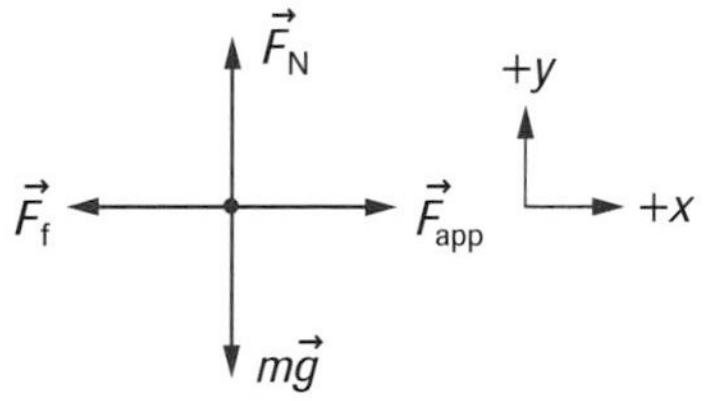

Figure 4
For Sample Problem 1
(a) System diagram for the crate
(b) FBD for the crate

In a lab practical test, students are asked to determine the coefficient of static friction between the back of their calculator and the cover of their (closed) textbook. The only permitted measuring instrument is a ruler. The students realize that, having placed the calculator on the book, they can very slowly raise one end of the book until the instant the calculator begins to slide, and can then take the measurements for "rise" and "run," indicated in **Figure 5**. Show how to calculate the coefficient of static friction from a measurement of 12 cm for rise and 25 cm for run.

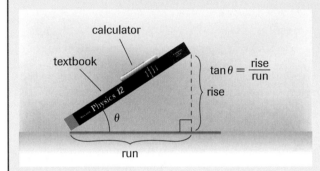

Figure 5
The system diagram for a calculator on a book

Solution
We begin by showing, as in **Figure 6(a)**, that the angle between the component of the force of gravity perpendicular to the book's surface equals the angle of the book above the horizontal.

Next, we derive an expression for the normal force:

$$\Sigma F_y = ma_y = 0$$
$$F_N - mg \cos \theta = 0$$
$$F_N = mg \cos \theta$$

Finally, we analyze the forces along the x-axis and substitute the expression for the normal force. **Figure 6(b)** shows the FBD of the calculator.

$$\Sigma F_x = ma_x = 0$$
$$mg \sin \theta - F_{S,max} = 0$$
$$mg \sin \theta = F_{S,max} \text{ where } F_{S,max} = \mu_S F_N$$
$$mg \sin \theta = \mu_S F_N$$
$$\mu_S = \frac{mg \sin \theta}{F_N}$$
$$= \frac{mg \sin \theta}{mg \cos \theta}$$
$$= \frac{\sin \theta}{\cos \theta}$$
$$= \tan \theta$$
$$= \frac{12 \text{ cm}}{25 \text{ cm}}$$
$$\mu_S = 0.48$$

The coefficient of static friction is 0.48.

(a)

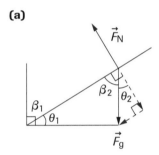

$\theta_1 + \beta_1 = 90°$
$\theta_2 + \beta_2 = 90°$
$\beta_1 = \beta_2$ (from the Z pattern)
Therefore, $\theta_1 = \theta_2$
($= \theta$, the angle in the problem)

(b)

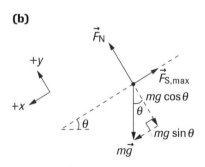

Figure 6
(a) Proof of angular equality
(b) The FBD of the calculator

It is relatively easy to determine the coefficient of static friction experimentally. Experiments can also be conducted to determine the coefficient of kinetic friction. Investigation 2.4.1, in the Lab Activities section at the end of this chapter, gives you the opportunity to measure both of these coefficients of friction.

▶ **TRY THIS** activity *Observing Triboluminescence*

Triboluminescence (from the Greek *tribein,* "to rub") is the production of light by friction. You can observe triboluminescence by crushing some crystals of hard candy, such as a WintOGreen Lifesaver®. Darken the room completely, allow your eyes to adapt, then crush the candy with pliers.

✋ **Wear goggles when crushing the candy.**

▶ **Practice**

Understanding Concepts

2. A car accelerates southward due to a frictional force between the road and the tires.
   (a) In what direction is the frictional force of the road on the tires? Why does that force exist?
   (b) Is the frictional force static or kinetic? Explain your answer.

3. The coefficients of friction between a 23-kg exercise mat and the gym floor are $\mu_S = 0.43$ and $\mu_K = 0.36$.
   (a) Determine the magnitude of the minimum horizontal force needed to start the mat moving.
   (b) Once the mat is moving, what magnitude of horizontal force will keep it moving at a constant velocity?

4. A musician applies a horizontal force of 17 N [W] to an instrument case of mass 5.1 kg. The case slides across a table with an acceleration of 0.39 m/s² [W]. What is the coefficient of kinetic friction between the case and the table?

5. A small box is resting on a larger box sitting on a horizontal surface. When a horizontal force is applied to the larger box, both boxes accelerate together. The small box does not slip on the larger box.
   (a) Draw an FBD of the small box during its acceleration.
   (b) What force causes the small box to accelerate horizontally?
   (c) If the acceleration of the pair of boxes has a magnitude of 2.5 m/s², determine the smallest coefficient of friction between the boxes that will prevent slippage.

6. Draw an FBD for the larger box in question 5 when it is accelerating.

7. An adult is pulling two small children in a sleigh over level snow. The sleigh and children have a total mass of 47 kg. The sleigh rope makes an angle of 23° with the horizontal. The coefficient of kinetic friction between the sleigh and the snow is 0.11. Calculate the magnitude of the tension in the rope needed to keep the sleigh moving at a constant velocity. (*Hint:* The normal force is not equal in magnitude to the force of gravity.)

Applying Inquiry Skills

8. (a) Describe how you would perform an experiment to determine the coefficient of kinetic friction between your shoes and a wooden board, using only a metre stick to take measurements.
   (b) Describe likely sources of random and systematic error in this experiment.

⚛ **INVESTIGATION 2.4.1**

Measuring Coefficients of Friction (p. 113)
What adjustments to the experiment described in Sample Problem 2 would you make to determine the coefficient of kinetic friction? Your answer will help you prepare for this investigation.

Answers

3. (a) 97 N
   (b) 81 N
4. 0.30
5. (c) 0.26
7. 53 N

DID YOU KNOW **?**

Low-Friction Materials
Scientists have found ways of producing materials with very low coefficients of friction. Teflon®, a compound of fluorine and carbon developed in 1938, experiences extremely weak electrical forces from molecules such as those in foods, so it makes an excellent coating for frying pans. (To make the coating stick to the pan, the Teflon is blasted into tiny holes in the metal.) Since Teflon does not interact with body fluids, it is also useful in surgical implants.

Fluid Friction and Bernoulli's Principle

A **fluid** is a substance that flows and takes the shape of its container. Both liquids and gases are fluids, with water and air being common examples. Fluids in relative motion are an important and practical part of our lives. One type of fluid motion occurs when a fluid, such as water or natural gas, moves through a pipe or a channel (motion of a fluid relative to the object). The other type of fluid motion occurs when an object, such as a golf ball, moves through air, water, or some other fluid (motion of an object relative to the fluid).

Newton's laws of motion can be applied to analyze relative fluid motion. Such analysis allows us to explore the factors that affect air resistance, as well as to learn how to research and reduce turbulence, and to control the motion of objects moving through fluids or the motion of fluids moving through objects.

As a fluid flows, the cohesive forces between molecules cause internal friction, or **viscosity**. A fluid with a high viscosity, such as liquid honey, has a high internal resistance and does not flow readily. A fluid with a low viscosity, such as water, has low internal resistance and flows easily. Viscosity depends not only on the nature of the fluid, but also on the fluid's temperature: as the temperature increases, the viscosity of a liquid generally decreases and the viscosity of a gas generally increases.

fluid substance that flows and takes the shape of its container

viscosity internal friction between molecules caused by cohesive forces

laminar flow stable flow of a viscous fluid where adjacent layers of a fluid slide smoothly over one another

> ▶ **TRY THIS** activity **Oil Viscosity**
>
> Observe the effect of temperature changes on the viscosity of various grades of motor oil (e.g., SAE 20, SAE 50, and SAE 10W-40) in stoppered test tubes provided by your teacher. Make sure that each tube has a small air space near the stopper. Record the time it takes for an air bubble to travel through the oil in a test tube that has been placed in a cold-water bath. Compare your results with the time it takes for a bubble to travel through the oil in a test tube that has been placed in a bath of water from the hot-water tap.
>
> ✋ **Wear gloves and goggles to handle the oil. Exercise care when using hot water from the tap.**

As a fluid flows, the fluid particles interact with their surroundings and experience external friction. For example, as water flows through a pipe, the water molecules closest to the walls of the pipe experience a frictional resistance that reduces their speed to nearly zero. Measurements show that the water speed varies from a minimum at the wall of the pipe to a maximum at the centre of the pipe. If the speed of a fluid is slow and the adjacent layers flow smoothly over one another, the flow is called a **laminar flow** (**Figure 7(a)**). Laminar flow can also occur when a fluid such as air passes around a smooth object (**Figure 7(b)**).

(a)

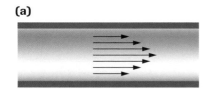

(b)

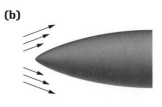

Figure 7
Laminar flow in fluids. The length of each vector represents the magnitude of the fluid velocity at that point.
(a) Water in a pipe
(b) Air around a cone

In most situations involving moving fluids, laminar flow is difficult to achieve. As the fluid flows through or past an object, the flow becomes irregular, resulting, for example, in whirls called *eddies* (**Figure 8**). Eddies are an example of **turbulence**, which resists the fluid's motion. A fluid undergoing turbulence loses kinetic energy as some of the energy is converted into thermal energy and sound energy. The likelihood of turbulence increases as the velocity of the fluid relative to its surroundings increases.

turbulence irregular fluid motion

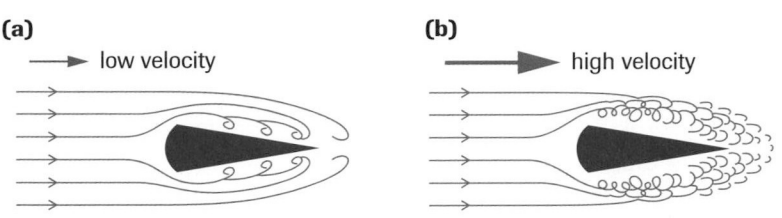

(a) ⟶ low velocity

(b) ⟶ high velocity

Figure 8
The turbulence caused by eddies increases as the fluid velocity increases.
(a) Low turbulence at a low velocity
(b) Higher turbulence at a high velocity

Turbulence in tubes or pipes can be reduced in various ways. For example, in London, UK, small amounts of liquid plastic are injected into the sewage system. The plastic particles mix with the sewage particles, reducing the liquid's viscosity and adhesion to the sewer pipe and walls, and thereby making it easier for the pumps to transfer the sewage. A similar method can be used to reduce the turbulence of water ejected from a fire-hose nozzle, allowing the water-jet to stream farther. This is advantageous, especially in fighting fires in tall buildings. In the human body, liquid plastic can be added to the bloodstream of a person with blood-flow restrictions. Doing this helps reduce turbulence in the blood and lessens the chances of a blood stoppage.

Turbulence around an object moving through a fluid is a problem observed both in nature and in the transportation industry. **Streamlining** is the process of reducing turbulence by altering the design of an object, such as a car body or an airplane. To aid their designs, designers have found it useful to study fish, birds, and other animals that move quickly in the water or air, and provide excellent examples of streamlining. The transportation industry in particular devotes much research trying to improve the streamlining of cars, trucks, motorcycles, trains, boats, submarines, airplanes, spacecraft, and other vehicles. Streamlining often enhances the appearance of a vehicle, but more importantly it improves safety and reduces fuel consumption.

Streamlining is an experimental science and the best way to research it is in large wind tunnels and water tanks. **Figure 9** shows a wind tunnel design used to investigate the

DID YOU *KNOW* ❓

Urban Wind Gusts
Wind turbulence can be a problem in a district with multiple high towers. Tall buildings direct fast-moving air from near the top, where the winds are greatest, toward the bottom. At street level, gusts of wind can have a devastating effect on an unsuspecting pedestrian. To help overcome this problem, engineers fine-tune their designs after running wind-tunnel tests on models of a proposed structure and its surroundings.

streamlining process of reducing turbulence by altering the design of an object

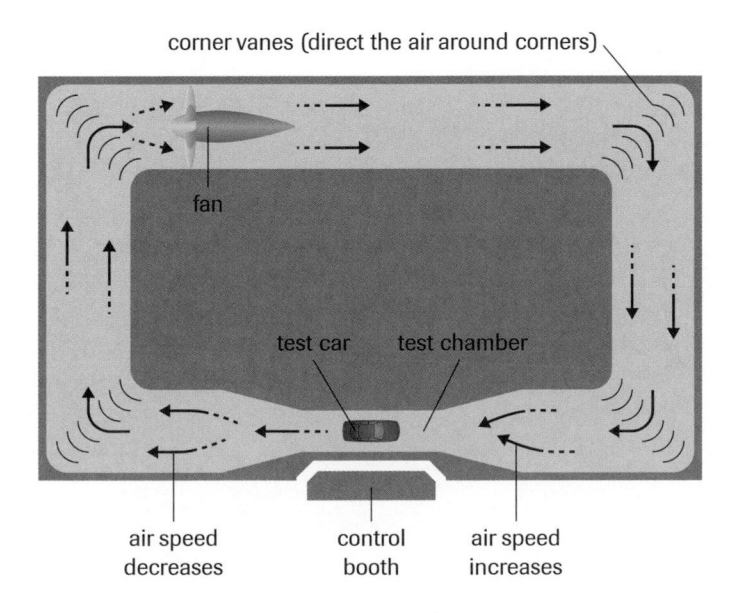

corner vanes (direct the air around corners)

fan

test car   test chamber

air speed decreases   control booth   air speed increases

Figure 9
A typical wind tunnel for analyzing the streamlining of automobiles

streamlining of automobiles. A fan directs air along the tunnel, around two corners, and then through the smaller tunnel. As the air moves into the smaller tunnel it accelerates, reaching speeds up to 100 km/h, and flows past the automobile being tested. It then returns to the fan to be recirculated. Researchers view the action from behind an adjacent glass wall and analyze the turbulence around the automobile. Pressure-sensitive beams, electronic sensors, drops of coloured water, small flags, and plumes of smoke are among the means of detecting turbulence.

Researchers have found interesting ways of reducing the turbulence that limits the speed of submarines travelling underwater. For example, to reduce the adhesion of water particles to a submarine's hull, compressed air is forced out from a thin layer between the hull and its porous outer skin. Millions of air bubbles then pass along the submarine, preventing adhesion and thus reducing the turbulence. Turbulence around a submarine can also be reduced by taking some of the water the submarine is passing through and expelling it under pressure from the rear. (What law of motion is applied here?) A third method of turbulence reduction for submarines, which at first seems surprising, applies a principle evolved by sharks. It has long been assumed that the best means of reducing turbulence is to have perfectly smooth surfaces and hidden joints. However sharks, which are obviously well adapted to moving through water with reduced fluid friction, have tiny grooves in their skin that are parallel to the flow of water. Similarly, a thin plastic coating with fine grooves applied to the surface of a submarine can reduce turbulence and increase the maximum speed (see **Figure 10**). Some of the innovations in submarine design can also be adapted to ships and boats, as well as to airplanes.

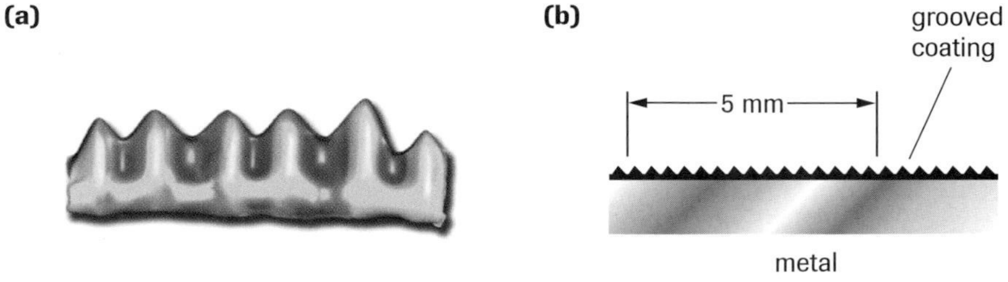

Figure 10
Using grooves to improve streamlining
(a) A patch of shark skin, shown here magnified to about 3000 times its actual size, contains grooves parallel to the water flow.
(b) A thin plastic coating with three grooves per millimetre reduces the drag of a metal surface in water.

(a)

(b)

grooved coating

|← 5 mm →|

metal

The speed of a moving fluid has an effect on the pressure exerted by the fluid. Consider water flowing under pressure through a pipe having the shape illustrated in **Figure 11**. As the water flows from the wide section to the narrow section, its speed increases. This effect is seen in a river that flows slowly at its wider regions, but speeds up when it passes through a narrow gorge.

The water flow in **Figure 11** accelerates as the water molecules travel from region A into region B. Acceleration is caused by an unbalanced force, but what is its source in this case? The answer lies in the pressure difference between the two regions. The pressure (or force per unit area) must be greater in region A than in region B to accelerate the water molecules as they pass into region B.

These concepts were analyzed in detail by Swiss scientist Daniel Bernoulli (1700–1782). His conclusions became known as *Bernoulli's principle*.

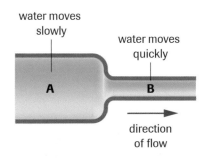

Figure 11
The flow speed depends on the diameter of the pipe.

Bernoulli's Principle

Where the speed of a fluid is low, the pressure is high.
Where the speed of the same fluid is high, the pressure is low.

Throwing a curve in baseball is also an application of Bernoulli's principle. In **Figure 12(a)**, a ball is thrown forward, which means that, relative to the ball, the air is moving backward. When the ball is thrown with a clockwise spin, the air near the ball's surface is dragged along with the ball (**Figure 12(b)**). To the left of the moving ball, the speed of the air is slow, so the pressure is high. The ball is forced to curve to the right, following the path shown in **Figure 12(c)**.

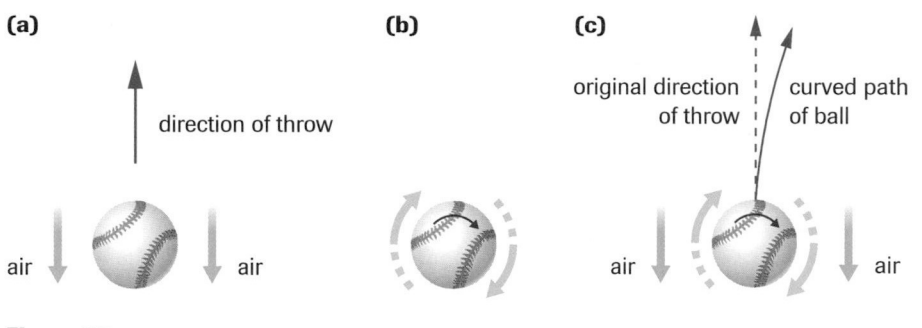

(a) direction of throw

air   air

(b)

(c) original direction of throw | curved path of ball

air   air

Figure 12
Bernoulli's principle explains curve balls as viewed from above.
(a) A ball thrown without spin is undeflected.
(b) Air is dragged around the surface of a spinning ball.
(c) Since the flow speed around a spinning ball is not equal on both sides, the pressure is not equal. The ball is deflected in the direction of lower pressure.

▶ **TRY THIS** activity   *How Will the Cans Move?*

Predict what will happen when you blow air between the two empty beverage cans arranged as shown in **Figure 13**. Verify your prediction experimentally and explain your results.

empty cans

drinking straws

air flow

Figure 13
What happens when you blow air between the cans?

▶ **Practice**

Understanding Concepts

10. List four liquids, other than those mentioned in the text, in order of increasing viscosity.

11. Describe what you think is meant by the following phrases:
  (a) As slow as molasses in January. (Molasses is the syrup made from sugar cane.)
  (b) Blood runs thicker than water.

12. Compare the speeds of the top and bottom of the bulge where the syrup leaves the jar (**Figure 14**). How does this pattern relate to laminar flow?

13. Identify design features commonly used to reduce drag in
  (a) the cabs of heavy trucks
  (b) launch rockets
  (c) sport motorcycles
  (d) locomotives

14. Explain the following observations in terms of Bernoulli's principle.
  (a) As a convertible car with its top up cruises along a highway, the top bulges upward.
  (b) A fire in a fireplace draws better when wind is blowing over the chimney than when the air is calm.

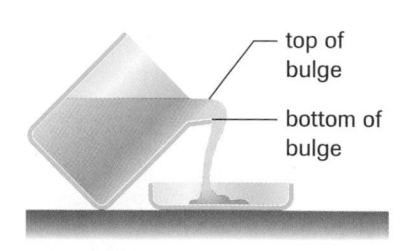

top of bulge

bottom of bulge

Figure 14
For question 12

Figure 15
For question 15

15. A baseball (viewed from above) is thrown in the direction indicated by the dashes in **Figure 15**. If the ball is spinning counterclockwise, determine the approximate direction of the path of the ball. Use diagrams in your explanation.

Applying Inquiry Skills

16. Describe how you would perform an experiment to measure the linear speed of water leaving a horizontal hose of known nozzle diameter. (*Hint:* Show that if you collect a measured volume of water for a certain amount of time, then divide that value by the area of the nozzle, you obtain the speed. You can see that this reasoning is plausible by considering units: $(cm^3/s)/cm^2 = cm/s$.) If possible, try the experiment.

Making Connections

17. Burrowing animals, such as prairie dogs and gophers, require air circulation in their burrows. To set the air into motion, these creatures give their burrow a front entrance and a back entrance, piling dirt up to make one entrance higher than the other. Draw a cross-section sketch of this burrow design and explain how it promotes air circulation.

SUMMARY *Exploring Frictional Forces*

- As the force applied to an object increases, the static friction opposing the force increases until the maximum static friction is reached, at which instant the object begins to move. After that instant, kinetic friction opposes the motion.
- The coefficients of static friction and kinetic friction are the ratios, respectively, of the magnitude of the static friction force and the kinetic friction force to the normal force between an object and the surface with which it is in contact. These coefficients have no units.
- Internal friction in a fluid is called viscosity and depends on the nature and temperature of the fluid.
- Laminar flow of a fluid occurs when the layers of the fluid flow smoothly over one another.
- The irregular flow of a fluid is called turbulence; this problem can be reduced by streamlining.
- Bernoulli's principle states: Where the speed of a fluid is low, the pressure is high, and where the speed of the same fluid is high, the pressure is low. Among the illustrations of this principle is the throwing of curve balls in baseball.

▶ *Section 2.4 Questions*

Understanding Concepts

1. When you rub your hands together vigorously, the temperature of the skin rises. Why?

2. A team of horses at a winter carnival is starting to pull a loaded sleigh with wooden runners along a horizontal trail covered in dry snow. The total mass of the sleigh, including its passengers, is 2.1×10^3 kg. The horses apply a force of 5.3×10^3 N [horizontally]. Determine the magnitude of (a) the frictional force and (b) the acceleration of the sled. (*Hint:* Look up the appropriate coefficient of friction in **Table 1**.)

3. Two skiers, A and B, each of mass *m*, are skiing down a snow-covered hill that makes an angle ϕ above the horizontal. A is moving with constant velocity. B is accelerating.
   (a) Derive an equation for the coefficient of kinetic friction experienced by A, in terms of the angle ϕ.
   (b) Derive an equation for the magnitude of the acceleration experienced by B, in terms of g, ϕ, and μ_K.
   (c) What effect would a change in the mass of skier B have on the magnitude of the acceleration? Explain your answer.

4. A race car is accelerating on a level track. The coefficient of static friction between the tires and the track is 0.88. The tires are not slipping.
   (a) Draw an FBD of the car.
   (b) Determine the maximum possible magnitude of acceleration if the car is to travel without slipping.

5. A steel ball reaches a terminal speed when falling in glycerine. Will the terminal speed be greater if the glycerine is at 20°C or at 60°C? Explain.

6. Why are pumping stations required at regular intervals along the cross-Canada natural gas pipeline?

7. **Figure 16** shows a *venturi flowmeter*, used to measure the speed of gas flowing through a tube. How does its design illustrate Bernoulli's principle?

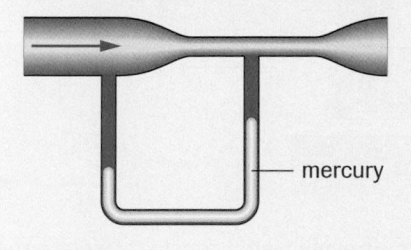

Figure 16
A venturi flowmeter

Applying Inquiry Skills

8. (a) With your hand facing palm downward, slide your fingers across the cover of your textbook. Estimate the coefficient of kinetic friction between your fingers and the cover.
   (b) Turn your hand over and repeat the procedure with your fingernails.
   (c) Devise and carry out an experiment (using a ruler for measurements) to determine values for the coefficients in (a) and (b). Compare your estimated and calculated values.
   (d) Describe what you could do to improve your skill in estimating coefficients of friction.

9. Predict, with an explanation, what will happen when a person blows through the horizontal straw in **Figure 17**. Verify your prediction experimentally with teacher approval. Relate your explanation to the design principle of a paint sprayer.

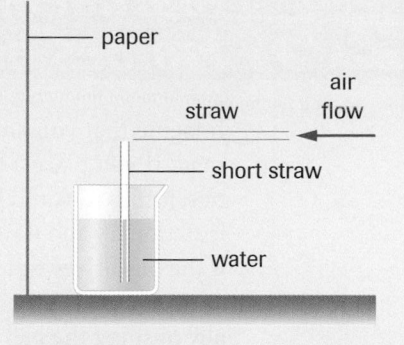

Figure 17

Making Connections

10. In 1896, Carl E. Johansson of Sweden produced the first *gauge blocks* (also called "Jo blocks" in his honour) for quality control in manufacturing. Since the blocks have extremely smooth sides, the coefficient of static friction is high. The blocks thus stick together upon contact. (You have likely noticed a similar strong bonding when microscope slides stick together.) Research the topic of gauge blocks, describing their properties and uses.

 www.science.nelson.com

11. What are the meanings of the terms "slice" and "hook" in golf? What causes slices and hooks? What can you do to prevent them?

 www.science.nelson.com

12. Running-shoe designs have changed with advances in technology. Research how the soles of running shoes have evolved, writing a few sentences on your findings.

 www.science.nelson.com

13. The near-frictionless carbon (NFC) listed in **Table 1** is a new, ultra-hard carbon film with a coefficient of kinetic friction of only about 0.001 in an environment of nitrogen or argon. Although the coefficient is greater in an ordinary environment of air, the friction remains low enough to give this amazing material many applications. Research the advantages and uses of NFC, and write a report on what you discover.

 www.science.nelson.com

2.5 Inertial and Noninertial Frames of Reference

Imagine that you are travelling on a bus at a constant speed along a straight, smooth road. If you place a ball on the floor of the bus, it stays at rest relative to you and the bus, just as it would if you placed it on the classroom floor (**Figure 1**). Initially, the ball is stationary and it remains that way because there is no net force acting on it. However, if the bus driver suddenly applies the brakes, the ball appears to accelerate forward relative to the bus, even though there is still no net force acting on it. (There is no force actually pushing the ball forward.)

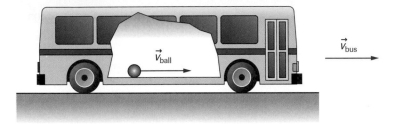

Figure 1
The bus and the ball move at a constant velocity. Relative to the bus, the ball is at rest.

inertial frame of reference a frame in which the law of inertia is valid

noninertial frame of reference a frame in which the law of inertia is not valid

Relative to your classroom, or relative to a bus travelling at a constant velocity, the ball stays at rest if there is no net force acting on it; in other words, the ball obeys Newton's first law of motion, the law of inertia. Therefore, we call your classroom or the bus moving at a constant velocity an inertial frame of reference. A frame of reference (defined in Chapter 1) is an object, such as a room, a bus, or even an atom, relative to which the positions, velocities, accelerations, etc., of other objects can be measured. An **inertial frame of reference** is a frame in which the law of inertia and other physics laws are valid. Any frame moving at a constant velocity relative to the first frame is also an inertial frame.

When the brakes are applied to the bus, the bus undergoes acceleration. Thus, it is a **noninertial frame of reference**, one in which the law of inertia does not hold. Although the ball accelerates toward the front of the bus when the brakes are applied, there is no net force causing that acceleration. The reason there appears to be a net force on the ball is that we are observing the motion from the accelerated frame of reference inside the bus (a noninertial frame). The situation is much easier to explain if we consider it from an inertial frame, such as the road. Relative to the road, when the brakes are applied to the bus, the ball tends to continue to move forward at a constant velocity, as explained by the law of inertia. Since the bus is slowing down and the ball is not, the ball accelerates toward the front, relative to the bus (**Figure 2**).

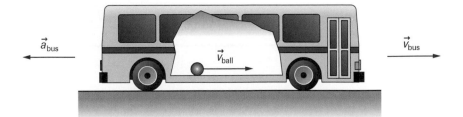

Figure 2
When the brakes are applied, the bus slows down, but the ball tends to continue moving forward at a constant velocity relative to the ground. Thus, relative to the bus, the ball accelerates forward.

To explain the ball's observed motion in the bus, we have to invent a force toward the front of the bus. This **fictitious force** is an invented force that we can use to explain observed motion in an accelerating frame of reference. In the case of the ball, the fictitious force is in the opposite direction to the acceleration of the noninertial frame itself.

fictitious force an invented force used to explain motion in an accelerating frame of reference

---

▶ **SAMPLE** problem **1**

Draw an FBD for the ball shown in (a) **Figure 1** and (b) **Figure 2**. Indicate the fictitious force in (b) relative to the frame of reference of the bus.

Solution

Figure 3 shows the required diagrams. We use the symbol $\vec{F}_{fict}$ to represent the fictitious force.

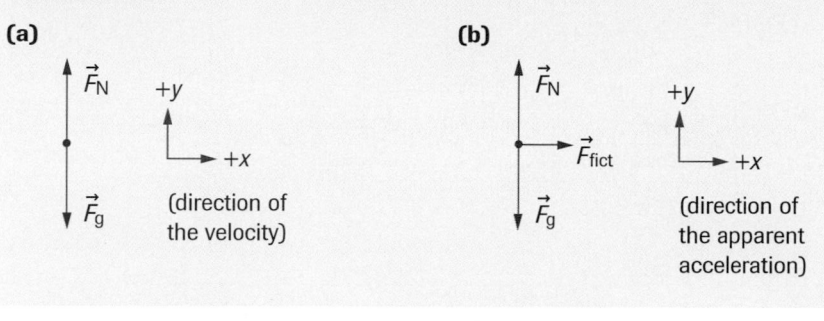

(a)   **(b)**

Figure 3
(a) The FBD in a fixed frame of reference. The $+x$ direction is chosen to be the direction of the velocity.
(b) The FBD in the accelerating frame of reference. The $+x$ direction is chosen to be the direction of the apparent acceleration due to the fictitious force $\vec{F}_{fict}$ relative to the frame of reference of the bus.

▶ **SAMPLE** problem **2**

A teacher suspends a small rubber stopper from the roof of a bus, as in **Figure 3(a)** from the chapter opener. The suspending cord makes an angle of 8.5° from the vertical as the bus is accelerating forward. Determine the magnitude of the acceleration of the bus.

Solution

To solve this problem, we will look at the situation from Earth's frame of reference because it is an inertial frame. We begin by drawing the system diagram and the FBD in that frame, as shown in **Figure 4**.

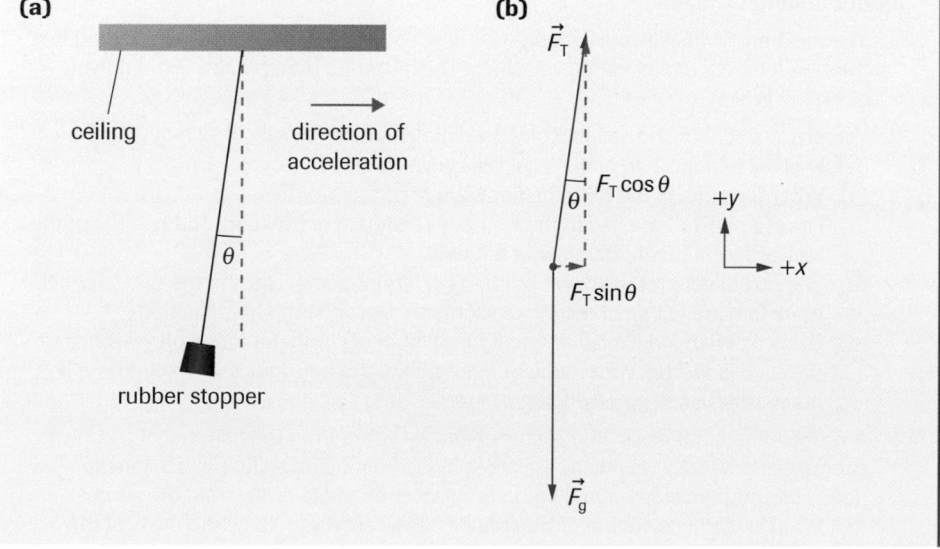

(a)   **(b)**

LEARNING TIP

Fictitious Forces
Fictitious forces are sometimes called pseudoforces or inertial forces. Fictitious forces are not needed in an inertial frame of reference.

Figure 4
(a) System diagram of improvised rubber-stopper accelerometer
(b) FBD of accelerometer bob

It is the horizontal component of the tension that causes the acceleration. Since both it and the horizontal acceleration are unknowns, we must use two equations. We start with the vertical components:

$$\sum F_y = ma_y = 0$$
$$F_T \cos \theta - F_g = 0$$
$$F_T \cos \theta = F_g \text{ where } F_g = mg$$
$$F_T = \frac{mg}{\cos \theta}$$

This expression for F_T can now be substituted into the equation for the horizontal components:

$$\sum F_x = ma_x$$
$$F_T \sin \theta = ma_x$$
$$a_x = (F_T)\left(\frac{\sin \theta}{m}\right)$$
$$= \left(\frac{mg}{\cos \theta}\right)\left(\frac{\sin \theta}{m}\right)$$
$$= g\left(\frac{\sin \theta}{\cos \theta}\right)$$
$$= g \tan \theta$$
$$= (9.8 \text{ m/s}^2)(\tan 8.5°)$$
$$a_x = 1.5 \text{ m/s}^2$$

The magnitude of the acceleration is 1.5 m/s².

We have so far considered inertial and noninertial frames of reference for linear motion. Comparing these frames of reference when the acceleration involves changing direction, such as when you are in a car following a curve on a highway, is presented in Chapter 3.

Answers

3. (a) 2.3 m/s² [E]
   (b) 0.25 N

▶ Practice

Understanding Concepts

1. You push an air-hockey puck along a surface with negligible friction while riding in a truck as it moves at a constant velocity in Earth's frame of reference. What do you observe? Why?

2. You are in a school bus initially travelling at a constant velocity of 12 m/s [E]. You gently place a tennis ball in the aisle beside your seat.
   (a) What happens to the ball's motion? Why?
   (b) Draw an FBD of the ball in the frame of reference of the road, and an FBD of the ball in the frame of reference of the bus.
   (c) The bus driver presses down on the accelerator pedal, causing the bus to accelerate forward with a constant acceleration. Describe the ball's motion.
   (d) Draw an FBD and explain the ball's motion in (c) from the frame of reference of the road, and from your frame of reference in the bus. Indicate which frame is noninertial, labelling any fictitious forces.

3. A rubber stopper of mass 25 g is suspended by string from the handrail of a subway car travelling directly westward. As the subway train nears a station, it begins to slow down, causing the stopper and string to hang at an angle of 13° from the vertical.
   (a) What is the acceleration of the train? Is it necessary to know the mass of the stopper? Why or why not?
   (b) Determine the magnitude of the tension in the string. Is it necessary to know the mass of the stopper? Why or why not?

SUMMARY **Inertial and Noninertial Frames of Reference**

- An inertial frame of reference is one in which the law of inertia (Newton's first law of motion) holds.

- An accelerating frame of reference is a noninertial frame where the law of inertia does not hold.

- In a noninertial frame of reference, fictitious forces are often invented to account for observations.

▶ **Section 2.5 Questions**

Understanding Concepts

1. What phrases can you think of that mean the same as "noninertial frame of reference"?

2. You are a passenger in a vehicle heading north. You are holding a horizontal accelerometer like the one shown in **Figure 5**.
   (a) How will you hold the accelerometer so that it can indicate the acceleration?
   (b) Describe what happens to the beads in the accelerometer when the vehicle
       (i) is at rest
       (ii) is accelerating northward
       (iii) is moving with a constant velocity
       (iv) begins to slow down while moving northward
   (c) Draw an FBD of the beads for an instant at which the vehicle is travelling with a constant acceleration northward, from the frame of reference of the road.
   (d) Repeat (c) from your frame of reference in the vehicle.
   (e) If the beads are at an angle of 11° from the vertical, what is the magnitude of the acceleration of the vehicle?
   (f) Determine the magnitude of the normal force acting on the middle bead, which has a mass of 2.2 g.

Applying Inquiry Skills

3. An ornament hangs from the interior rear-view mirror of your car. You plan to use this ornament as a pendulum-style accelerometer to determine the acceleration of the car as it is speeding up in a straight line.
   (a) Draw a system diagram, an FBD of the ornament from the frame of reference of the road, and an FBD of the ornament from the frame of reference of the car.
   (b) Describe how you would determine the acceleration, indicating what measurement(s) you would take and what calculations you would perform. Explain your calculations by referring to one of the two FBDs from part (a).

Making Connections

4. You are a passenger in a car stopped at an intersection. Although the stoplight is red and the driver's foot is still firmly on the brake, you suddenly feel as if the car is moving backward.
   (a) Explain your feeling. (*Hint:* Think about the motion of the car next to you.)
   (b) How could the sensation you feel be applied to the design of an amusement ride in which the riders remain stationary, but have the sensations of motion?

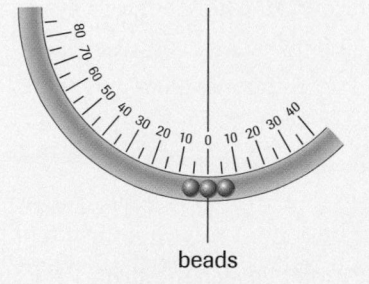

beads

Figure 5
A typical horizontal accelerometer

⦿ **ACTIVITY 2.2.1**

Static Equilibrium of Forces

In this activity, you will use components of vectors to analyze the condition required for static equilibrium of forces. Although the instructions are given for a vertical force board (**Figure 1**), you can adapt them to a horizontal force board or to a horizontal arrangement of force scales attached at a common point.

(a)

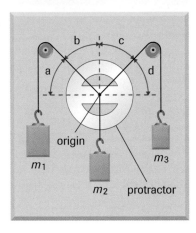

(b)

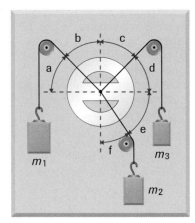

Figure 1
Using a vertical force board
(a) For steps 1 and 2, the string supporting m_2 is vertical.
(b) For steps 3 and 4, the string supporting m_2 is at an angle to the vertical.

Materials
vertical force board (or a support surface)
3 small pulleys
3 hangers plus masses (100-g, 200-g, and 500-g)
string
circular protractor

✋ **Do not use masses greater than 500 g.**
Place a pad or a box at the base of the board in case a string breaks. Do not use wire.

Procedure

1. Arrange the force board so that three different masses (m_1, m_2, and m_3) hang and remain at rest from three pieces of string tied together at a common origin, as in **Figure 1(a)**. Place the protractor so that its origin lines up with the origin of the strings. Draw a diagram of the system and label all angles and masses. Calculate the vertical components of the tensions in the obliquely directed strings attached to m_1 and m_3, and then compare their sum with the force produced by m_2. Determine the horizontal components of the tension in the sloping strings and compare them.

2. Vary the values and angles of m_1 and m_3, keeping the string supporting m_2 vertical, and repeat step 1.

3. Hold the third pulley against the string attached to m_2 so that the string is no longer vertical (see **Figure 1(b)**). Determine the vertical components of the three tension forces, and determine the vector sum of the components. Determine the horizontal components of the three forces and their vector sum.

4. Repeat step 3 for different values and angles of the forces.

Analysis

(a) State the condition for static equilibrium of forces.

(b) How does friction between the strings and the pulleys affect the results of this activity?

Evaluation

(c) Describe ways in which the accuracy of your measurements in this activity could be improved.

INVESTIGATION 2.4.1

Measuring Coefficients of Friction

Inquiry Skills

● Questioning	● Planning	● Analyzing
● Hypothesizing	● Conducting	● Evaluating
● Predicting	● Recording	● Communicating

The coefficients of static and kinetic friction can be determined experimentally on a horizontal surface by exerting a horizontal force, using a force-measuring instrument such as a force meter or force scale. But a less sophisticated method, the subject of this self-directed investigation, involves objects on an inclined plane, as shown in **Figure 1** and described in Sample Problem 2 in Section 2.4.

Figure 1
Do you think the coefficients of static and kinetic friction of a rubber shoe on wood change with different tread patterns?

Question

(a) Make up an appropriate question for this investigation.

Hypothesis/Prediction

(b) Write a hypothesis and a prediction for this investigation.

Experimental Design

Design your experiment together with your partners. The materials list may give you some ideas.

(c) Write up the steps in your plan and outline your safety considerations. Obtain your teacher's approval before beginning.

(d) Carry out the experiment and complete the experimental report.

Materials

metre stick
inclined plane(s)
several examples of materials that you want to test

Analysis

(e) Make up your own analysis questions and answer them based on your observations and calculations.

Evaluation

(f) Describe the most likely sources of random and systematic error, whether from human or from other sources, in your investigation. How might these errors be reduced?

Synthesis

(g) Describe how you would verify or refute the following statement with a mathematical proof and an experimental proof: "The coefficient of kinetic friction between an inclined plane and an object sliding down it at a constant speed is independent of the mass of the object."

Key Expectations

- define and describe the concepts and units related to the study of forces (e.g., inertial and noninertial frames of reference) (2.1, 2.2, 2.4, 2.5)

- distinguish between accelerating (noninertial) and nonaccelerating (inertial) frames of reference; predict velocity and acceleration in various situations (2.5)

- determine the net force acting on an object and the resulting acceleration by analyzing experimental data using vectors, graphs, trigonometry, and the resolution of vectors into components (2.2, 2.4)

- analyze and predict, in quantitative terms, and explain the acceleration of objects in one and two dimensions (2.2, 2.3, 2.4, 2.5)

- analyze the principles of the forces that cause acceleration and describe how the motion of human beings, objects, and vehicles can be influenced by modifying such factors as air pressure and frictional forces (e.g., analyze the physics of throwing a baseball; analyze the frictional forces acting on objects and explain how the control of these forces has been used to modify the design of objects) (2.2, 2.3, 2.4)

Key Terms

force

force of gravity

normal force

tension

friction

static friction

kinetic friction

air resistance

free-body diagram (FBD)

net force

dynamics

Newton's first law of motion

inertia

equilibrium (of forces)

Newton's second law of motion

weight

force field

gravitational field strength

Newton's third law of motion

coefficients of friction (static and kinetic)

fluid

viscosity

laminar flow

turbulence

streamlining

Bernoulli's principle

inertial frame of reference

noninertial frame of reference

fictitious force

Key Equations

- $\vec{a} = \dfrac{\sum \vec{F}}{m}$ (2.2)

- $\vec{F_g} = m\vec{g}$ (2.2)

- $\sum F_x = ma_x$ (2.2)

- $\sum F_y = ma_y$ (2.2)

- $F_f = \mu F_N$ (2.4)

- $\mu_S = \dfrac{F_{S,max}}{F_N}$ (2.4)

- $\mu_K = \dfrac{F_K}{F_N}$ (2.4)

▶ *MAKE* a summary

Draw a large diagram of a snow-covered hill shaped like the one shown in **Figure 1**. On one side of the hill, a child is pulling on a rope attached to a sleigh with the rope parallel to the hillside. On the other side of the hill, the child is on the sleigh and moving down the hill (not shown in the diagram). There is friction between the snow and the sleigh. At point E near the bottom of the hill, the sleigh stops when it hits a snowbank, and the child falls forward into the snow. Draw FBDs, as appropriate, of the child, the sleigh, or the child-sleigh system at each of the five points A through E. Show all the forces and components of forces. Add any notes that will help you summarize the key expectations, key terms, and key equations presented in this chapter.

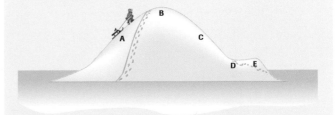

Figure 1
You can use a diagram of a snow-covered hill to summarize the concepts presented in this chapter.

Write numbers 1 to 11 in your notebook. Indicate beside each number whether the corresponding statement is true (T) or false (F). If it is false, write a corrected version, correcting just the part of the statement that is printed in *italics*. Assume air resistance to be negligible in each case.

1. When a ball is rising upward after you toss it vertically, *the net force on the ball is equal to the force of gravity on the ball.*

2. You pull horizontally on a rope, attached firmly to a hook on the wall, with a force of magnitude 16 N. If you pull horizontally with a force of the same magnitude on a string held firmly by a friend, *the magnitude of the tension in the string is 32 N.*

3. A grocery cart, at rest on a level floor, experiences a normal force of magnitude 155 N. You push on the cart handle with a force directed at an angle of 25° below the horizontal. *The magnitude of the normal force is now less than 155 N.*

4. Snow conditions are identical throughout the ski valley in **Figure 1.** The coefficient of kinetic friction between a skier's skis and the snow is 0.18 when the skier is travelling down the one side of the valley. As the skier moves up the other side of the valley, *the coefficient of kinetic friction exceeds 0.18 because gravity is acting against the skier's motion.*

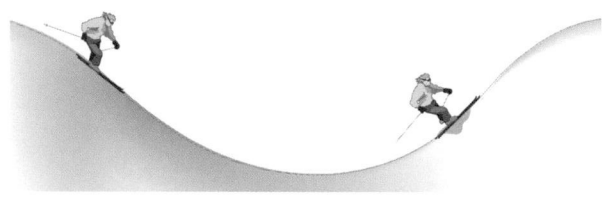

Figure 1

5. *It is impossible for an object to be travelling eastward while experiencing a westward net force.*

6. *It is possible for the sum of three vector forces of equal magnitude to be zero.*

7. *Static friction is always greater than kinetic friction.*

8. *One possible SI unit of weight is the kilogram.*

9. When you are standing at rest on the floor, *there are two action-reaction pairs of forces involved.*

10. *Viscosity and air resistance are both types of friction involving fluids.*

11. *Fictitious forces must be invented to explain observations whenever the chosen frame of reference is in motion.*

Write numbers 12 to 21 in your notebook. Beside each number, write the letter corresponding to the best choice.

12. A person of mass 65 kg is ascending on an escalator at a constant velocity of 2.5 m/s [22° above the horizontal]. The magnitude of the net force acting on the person is
    (a) 0 N
    (b) 6.4×10^2 N
    (c) 5.9×10^2 N
    (d) 2.4×10^2 N
    (e) 1.6×10^2 N

13. On a windy day, a quarterback throws a football into the wind. After the football has left the quarterback's hand and is moving through the air, the correct list of the force(s) acting on the football is
    (a) a force from the throw and the downward force of gravity
    (b) a force from the throw, a force exerted by the air, and the downward force of gravity
    (c) a force exerted by the air and a force from the throw
    (d) a force exerted by the air and the downward force of gravity
    (e) the downward force of gravity

14. A skier of mass m is sliding down a snowy slope that is inclined at an angle ϕ above the horizontal. The magnitude of the normal force on the skier is
    (a) $mg \tan \phi$
    (b) $mg \cos \phi$
    (c) $mg \sin \phi$
    (d) mg
    (e) zero

15. A soft-drink can is resting on a table. If Earth's force of gravity on the can is the action force, the reaction force is
    (a) an upward normal force exerted by the table on the can
    (b) a downward gravitational force exerted by Earth on the table
    (c) a downward normal force exerted on the table by the can
    (d) an upward force of gravity on Earth by the can
    (e) none of these

16. The coefficients of friction between a box of mass 9.5 kg and the horizontal floor beneath it are $\mu_S = 0.65$ and $\mu_K = 0.49$. The box is stationary. The magnitude of the minimum horizontal force that would suffice to set the box into motion is
    (a) 93 N
    (b) 61 N
    (c) 46 N
    (d) 6.2 N
    (e) 4.7 N

For questions 17 to 21, refer to **Figure 2**.

17. During the time interval that the spring acts on the double cart, the force exerted by the double cart on the single cart is
    (a) 2.0 N [W]
    (b) 0.0 N
    (c) 2.0 N [E]
    (d) 4.0 N [W]
    (e) 4.0 N [E]

18. During the spring interaction, the net force acting on the single cart is
    (a) 4.0 N [W]
    (b) 2.0 N [W]
    (c) 2.0 N [E]
    (d) 4.0 N [W]
    (e) zero

19. During the interaction, the acceleration of the double cart is
    (a) 0.33 m/s^2 [E]
    (b) 1.0 m/s^2 [E]
    (c) 3.0 m/s^2 [E]
    (d) 0.50 m/s^2 [E]
    (e) 2.0 m/s^2 [E]

20. The velocity of the double cart exactly 0.20 s after the compression spring is released is
    (a) 0.25 cm/s [E]
    (b) 1.0 cm/s [E]
    (c) 4.0 cm/s [E]
    (d) zero
    (e) less than 0.25 cm/s [E], but greater than zero

21. After the spring interaction is complete and the carts are separated, the net force acting on the single cart is
    (a) 19.6 N [down]
    (b) 2.0 N [W]
    (c) 19.6 N [up]
    (d) the vector sum of 19.6 N [down] and 2.0 N [W]
    (e) zero

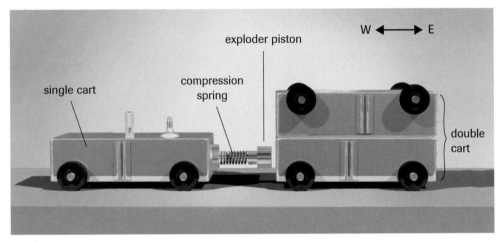

Figure 2
For questions 17 to 21. Two dynamics carts, one a single cart of mass 1.0 kg, the other a double cart of mass 2.0 kg, each with essentially frictionless wheels, are in contact and at rest. The compression spring on the single cart is suddenly released, causing the cart to exert an average force of 2.0 N [E] on the double cart for 0.50 s.

Understanding Concepts

1. Why must an object at rest have either no force or a minimum of two forces acting on it?

2. Whiplash injuries are common in automobile accidents where the victim's car is struck from behind. Explain how such accidents illustrate Newton's laws of motion, and how the laws can be applied in the development of safer car seat designs.

3. If you get to your feet in a canoe and move toward the front, the canoe moves in the opposite direction. Explain why.

4. How would you determine the mass of an object in interstellar space, where the force of gravity approaches zero?

5. In a disaster film, an elevator full of people falls freely when the cable snaps. The film depicts the people pressed upward against the ceiling. Is this good physics? Why or why not?

6. In the amusement park ride in **Figure 1**, cars and passengers slide down the incline before going around vertical loops. The incline is at an angle of 36° to the horizontal. If friction is negligible, what is the magnitude of the acceleration of the cars down the incline?

Figure 1

7. Two veggieburger patties, in contact with each other, are being pushed across a grill. The masses of the burgers are 113 g and 139 g. Friction is negligible. The applied horizontal force of magnitude 5.38×10^{-2} N is exerted on the more massive burger. Determine (a) the magnitude of the acceleration of the two-burger system, and (b) the magnitude of the force exerted by each of the two burgers on the other.

8. Three blocks, of masses $m_1 = 26$ kg, $m_2 = 38$ kg, and $m_3 = 41$ kg, are connected by two strings over two pulleys, as in **Figure 2**. Friction is negligible. Determine (a) the magnitude of the acceleration of the blocks, and (b) the magnitude of the tension in each of the two strings.

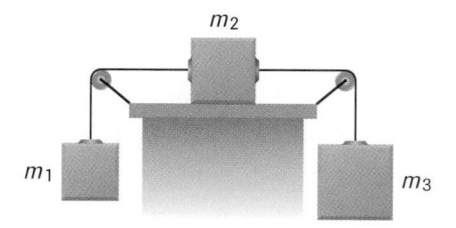

Figure 2

9. A mountain climber of mass 67.5 kg is using a rope to hang horizontally against a vertical cliff, as in **Figure 3**. The tension in the rope is 729 N [27.0° below the horizontal]. Determine the force exerted by the cliff on the climber's feet.

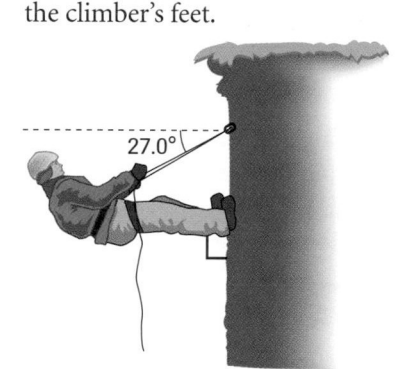

Figure 3

10. A child is pulling a wagon of mass 7.38 kg up a hill inclined at an angle of 14.3° to the horizontal. The child applies a force parallel to the hill. The acceleration of the wagon is 6.45 cm/s² up the hill. Friction is negligible. Determine the magnitude of (a) the force applied by the child, and (b) the normal force on the wagon.

11. Which is more likely to break when loaded with wet laundry—a clothesline with a significant sag, or a clothesline with almost no sag? Use diagrams to explain why.

12. In most sports, athletic shoes should have a high coefficient of friction, so that the person wearing the shoe can stop and turn quickly. In which sports would this be a disadvantage?

13. Why do people take very short steps on slippery surfaces?

14. A student is pushing horizontally on a table ($m = 16$ kg) to move it across a horizontal floor. The coefficient of kinetic friction between the table and the floor is 0.61.
    (a) Determine the magnitude of the applied force needed to keep the table moving at constant velocity.
    (b) If the applied force were 109 N and the table were to start from rest, how long would the table take to travel 75 cm?

15. A rope exerts a force of magnitude 21 N, at an angle 31° above the horizontal, on a box at rest on a horizontal floor. The coefficients of friction between the box and the floor are $\mu_S = 0.55$ and $\mu_K = 0.50$. The box remains at rest. Determine the smallest possible mass of the box.

16. A skier on a slope inclined at 4.7° to the horizontal pushes on ski poles and starts down the slope. The initial speed is 2.7 m/s. The coefficient of kinetic friction between skis and snow is 0.11. Determine how far the skier will slide before coming to rest.

17. A passenger is standing without slipping in a forward-accelerating train. The coefficient of static friction between feet and floor is 0.47.
    (a) Draw an FBD for the passenger in Earth's frame of reference.
    (b) Draw an FBD for the passenger in the train's frame of reference.
    (c) Determine the maximum required acceleration of the train relative to the track if the passenger is not to slip.

18. You throw a baseball eastward. The ball has a fast clockwise spin when viewed from above. In which direction does the ball tend to swerve? Show your reasoning.

19. It takes 30.0 s to fill a 2.00-L container with water from a hose with constant radius 1.00 cm. The hose is held horizontally. Determine the speed of the water being ejected from the hose.

Applying Inquiry Skills

20. A varying net force is applied to a loaded wagon. **Table 1** gives the resulting accelerations. Plot a graph of the data. Use the information on the graph to determine the mass of the wagon.

Table 1 Data for Question 20

Net Force (N [fwd])	0	10.0	20.0	30.0	40.0	50.0
Acceleration (m/s² [fwd])	0	0.370	0.741	1.11	1.48	1.85

21. The apparatus in **Figure 4** determines the coefficient of static friction between two surfaces. The force sensor measures the minimum horizontal force, $\vec{F}_{app}$, needed to prevent the object from sliding down the vertical slope.
    (a) Draw an FBD of the object against the wall. Use this FBD to derive an expression for the coefficient of static friction in terms of m, g, and $\vec{F}_{app}$.
    (b) Design and carry out an investigation to determine the coefficient of static friction between two appropriate surfaces. Use the technique sketched in **Figure 4** and two other techniques. Compare the results, describing the advantages and disadvantages of each technique.

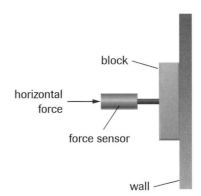

block

horizontal force

force sensor

wall

Figure 4

22. Obtain a piece of paper about 10 cm by 20 cm and fold it into the shape of an airplane wing, as in **Figure 5(a)**. Tape the ends together. Hold the middle of the wing with a pencil, as in **Figure 5(b)**, blowing across the wing as indicated. Repeat the procedure for the situation shown in **Figure 5(c)**. Explain what you observe.

Making Connections

23. High-speed movies reveal that the time interval during which a golf club is in contact with a golf ball is typically 1.0 ms, and that the speed of the ball when it leaves the club is about 65 m/s. The mass of a golf ball is 45 g.

(a)

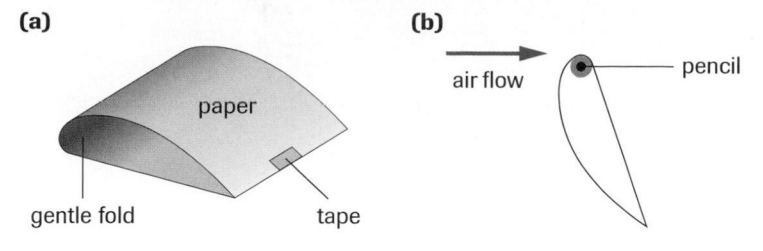

gentle fold   tape

(b)

air flow ——→   ●—— pencil

(c)

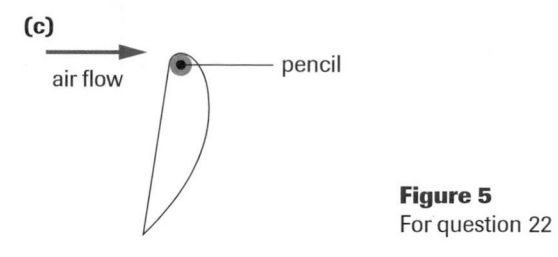

air flow ——→   ●—— pencil

Figure 5
For question 22

(a) Determine the magnitude of the average force exerted by the club on the ball. (For this calculation, you can neglect the force of gravity.)

(b) Why is it reasonable to neglect the force of gravity in calculating the average force exerted by the club?

(c) What does the term "high-speed movies" mean?

Extension

24. You are a gymnast of mass 72 kg, initially hanging at rest from a bar. You let go of the bar and fall vertically 92 cm to the floor below. Upon landing, you bend your knees, bringing yourself to rest over a distance of 35 cm. The floor exerts a constant force on your body as you slow down. Determine (a) your speed at impact, and (b) the magnitude of the force the floor exerts on you as you slow down.

25. A box of mass $m = 22$ kg is at rest on a ramp inclined at 45° to the horizontal. The coefficients of friction between the box and the ramp are $\mu_S = 0.78$ and $\mu_K = 0.65$.
    (a) Determine the magnitude of the largest force that can be applied upward, parallel to the ramp, if the box is to remain at rest.
    (b) Determine the magnitude of the smallest force that can be applied onto the top of the box, perpendicular to the ramp, if the box is to remain at rest.

26. In the oscilloscope shown in **Figure 6**, an electron beam is deflected by an electric force produced by charged metal plates AD and BC. In the region ABCD, each electron experiences a uniform downward electric force of 3.20×10^{-15} N. Each electron enters the electric field along the illustrated axis, halfway between A and B, with a velocity of 2.25×10^7 m/s

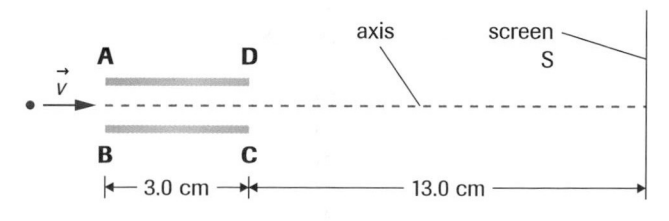

Figure 6

parallel to the plates. The electric force is zero outside ABCD. The mass of an electron is 9.11×10^{-31} kg. The gravitational force can be neglected during the short time interval an electron travels to the fluorescent screen, S. Determine how far an electron is below the axis of entry when it hits the screen.

27. Tarzan ($m = 100$ kg) holds one end of an ideal vine (infinitely strong, completely flexible, but having zero mass). The vine runs horizontally to the edge of a cliff, then vertically to where Jane ($m = 50$ kg) is hanging on, above a river filled with hungry crocodiles. A sudden sleet storm has removed all friction. Assuming that Tarzan hangs on, what is his acceleration toward the cliff edge?

● Sir Isaac Newton Contest Question

28. Two blocks are in contact on a frictionless table. A horizontal force is applied to one block as shown in **Figure 7**. If $m_1 = 2.0$ kg, $m_2 = 1.0$ kg, and $|\vec{F}| = 3.0$ N, find the force of contact between the two blocks.

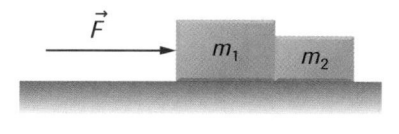

Figure 7

● Sir Isaac Newton Contest Question

29. A 2.0-kg chicken rests at point C on a slack clothesline ACB as shown in **Figure 8**. C represents chicken, not centre—real problems don't have to be symmetrical, you know! CA and CB slope up from the horizontal at 30° and 45°, respectively. What minimum breaking strength must the line have to ensure the continuing support of the bird?

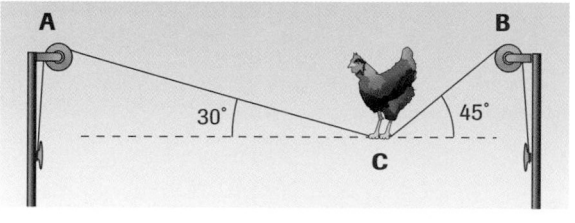

Figure 8

● Sir Isaac Newton Contest Question

chapter

3

Circular Motion

In this chapter, you will be able to

- define and describe the concepts and SI units related to the dynamics of circular motion
- analyze and predict, in quantitative terms, and explain uniform circular motion in the horizontal and vertical planes, with reference to the forces involved
- distinguish between noninertial (accelerating) and inertial (nonaccelerating) frames of reference, and calculate the velocity and acceleration of objects in uniform circular motion
- describe Newton's law of universal gravitation and apply it quantitatively
- investigate experimentally and analyze relationships among variables involved in uniform circular motion
- describe technological devices based on concepts and principles related to circular motion
- analyze the forces involved in circular motion and describe how the circular motions of human beings, objects, and vehicles can be influenced by modifying certain factors

At an amusement park, riders on a Ferris wheel experience circular motion as they move around the centre point of the ride. Usually their speeds are slow enough that they don't feel pushed into their seats. However, on a fast-moving loop-the-loop roller coaster (**Figure 1**), riders experience motion on circles of varying radii for brief periods of time, sometimes feeling large forces pushing on them. Those forces would be even greater (and much more dangerous) if the loops had constant radii. But the loops have smaller radii at the top than at the sides, for reasons that you will explore in this chapter.

In this chapter, you will explore circular motion and associated forces in different situations, answering questions such as:

- What forces are involved when figure skating pairs do the spiral?
- How could artificial gravity be created on future space flights for humans to Mars?
- Why are expressway ramps banked at an angle to the horizontal?
- What principles explain the operation of a centrifuge?

This chapter builds on what you learned in Chapters 1 and 2, especially regarding motion and forces in two dimensions. Your skill in drawing free-body diagrams (FBDs) and solving problems will be developed further, and you will have opportunities to investigate the forces and accelerations of circular motion.

REFLECT on your learning

1. **Figure 2** shows a truck negotiating a curve, with the path of the truck in the horizontal plane. The curve is banked at an angle ϕ from the horizontal.
   (a) Draw an FBD of the truck.
   (b) What is the magnitude of the normal force acting on the truck?
   (c) In what direction is the net force acting on the truck?

2. **Figure 3** shows a typical student accelerometer, for use as a force meter in analyzing circular motion. You hold the accelerometer upright at an amusement park, while on a horizontal ride roating counterclockwise as viewed from above. You are near the outer edge of the ride, and are at this particular instant facing northward.
   (a) Draw a system diagram of the accelerometer in the (noninertial) reference frame of your body, and an FBD of the middle bead of the accelerometer in that frame.
   (b) Draw system diagrams of the accelerometer in the reference frame of your body, showing what would happen to the beads
      (i) if the ride were to rotate faster, with your distance from the centre the same
      (ii) if you were closer to the centre at the original rate of the ride's rotation

3. (a) You are a space-flight architect. What design would you use to create artificial gravity on interplanetary space flights?
   (b) What designs have authors of science-fiction books and film scripts used?

Figure 1
Although a loop-the-loop roller coaster looks scary, the forces it exerts on riders are carefully controlled.

Figure 2
For question 1

Figure 3
For question 2

beads

▶ **TRY THIS** *activity*   *A Challenge*

The device shown in **Figure 4** has one small marble on either side of the barrier. Consider, in a brainstorming session with a small group of your classmates, how you would get both marbles into the holes near the top of the curve. Test your ideas, one at a time, in your group until you succeed.

(a) Describe your successful idea.

(b) Describe at least one other device that operates on a similar principle.

Figure 4
How could you make a similar device using common materials, such as beads or marbles?

When figure skating pairs perform the spiral, the woman travels in a circular path around the man (**Figure 1**). In doing so, she is constantly changing direction, which means she is undergoing acceleration. In this section, we will analyze the factors influencing that acceleration and relate our analysis to other applications that involve motion in a circular path.

Imagine you have attached a rubber stopper to the end of a string and are whirling the stopper around your head in a horizontal circle. If both the speed of the stopper and the radius of its path remain constant, the stopper has **uniform circular motion**. **Figure 2** shows the position and velocity vectors at various positions during the motion of the stopper. Uniform circular motion also occurs if only part of the circle (an arc) is covered.

Figure 1
In performing the spiral, the female skater undergoes circular motion.

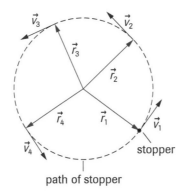

path of stopper

Figure 2
In uniform circular motion, the speed of the object remains constant, but the velocity vector changes because its direction changes. The radius of the path also remains constant. Notice that the instantaneous position vector (also called the radius vector) is perpendicular to the velocity vector and the velocity vectors are tangent to the circle.

uniform circular motion motion that occurs when an object has constant speed and constant radius

centripetal acceleration instantaneous acceleration directed toward the centre of the circle

Uniform circular motion occurs for the individual parts of any object spinning at a constant rate, for example, electric fans and motors, lawn mower blades, wheels (from the point of view of the centre of the wheel), and rotating rides at amusement parks. Circular or almost circular motion can also occur for objects or particles in orbits around other objects. For example, to analyze the motion of a planet orbiting the Sun, a satellite around Earth, or an electron around a nucleus, we make the assumption that the motion is uniform circular motion even though the paths are often ellipses rather than circles.

As you learned in Chapter 1, an object travelling at a constant speed is undergoing acceleration if the direction of the velocity is changing. This is certainly true for uniform circular motion. The type of acceleration that occurs in uniform circular motion is called **centripetal acceleration**.

Centripetal acceleration is an instantaneous acceleration. Investigation 3.1.1 in the Lab Activities section at the end of this chapter will help you to better understand the related concepts. In this investigation, you will perform a controlled experiment to explore the factors that affect centripetal acceleration and the force that causes it. 🔬∎

⚛ **INVESTIGATION 3.1.1**

Analyzing Uniform Circular Motion (p. 152)
If you are whirling a rubber stopper, attached to a string, around your head, the tension in the string (a force you can measure) keeps the stopper travelling in a circle. How do you think the force depends on such factors as the mass of the stopper, the frequency with which you are whirling the stopper, and the distance between your hand and the stopper? You will explore these relationships in a controlled experiment at the end of this chapter.

▶ **Practice**

Understanding Concepts

1. (a) What does "uniform" mean in the expression "uniform circular motion"?
   (b) Give some examples of uniform circular motion, other than those in the text.

2. How can a car moving at a constant speed be accelerating at the same time?

The Direction of Centripetal Acceleration

Recall that the defining equation for instantaneous acceleration is $\vec{a} = \lim\limits_{\Delta t \to 0} \dfrac{\Delta \vec{v}}{\Delta t}$. To apply this equation to uniform circular motion, we draw vector diagrams and perform vector subtractions. **Figure 3** shows what happens to $\Delta \vec{v}$ as Δt decreases. As the time interval approaches zero, the direction of the change of velocity $\Delta \vec{v}$ comes closer to pointing toward the centre of the circle. From the defining equation for instantaneous acceleration, you can see that the direction of the acceleration is the same as the direction of the change of velocity. We conclude that *the direction of the centripetal acceleration is toward the centre of the circle*. Notice that the centripetal acceleration and the instantaneous velocity are perpendicular to each other.

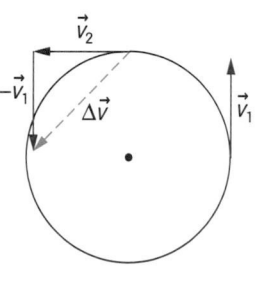 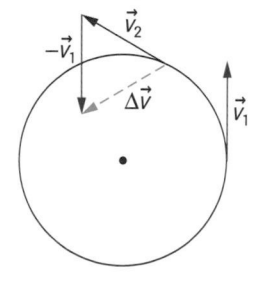 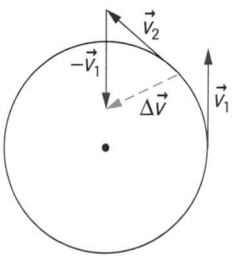 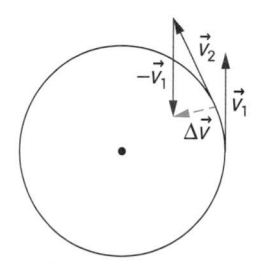

Figure 3
As the time interval between $\vec{v}_1$ and $\vec{v}_2$ is made shorter and shorter, $\Delta \vec{v}$ comes closer and closer to pointing toward the centre of the circle. In the diagram on the far right, Δt is very small and the $\Delta \vec{v}$ vector is nearly perpendicular to the instantaneous velocity vector $\vec{v}_2$.

> **Practice**

Understanding Concepts

3. A sports car moves through a horizontal circular arc at a constant speed.
   (a) What is the direction of the instantaneous acceleration at every point in the arc?
   (b) Draw a sketch showing the directions of the instantaneous velocity and instantaneous acceleration at two different positions.

4. If the direction of an object moving with uniform circular motion is reversed, what happens to the direction of the centripetal acceleration?

The Magnitude of Centripetal Acceleration

We can derive an equation for the magnitude of the centripetal acceleration in terms of the instantaneous speed and the radius of the circle. **Figure 4(a)** shows a particle in uniform circular motion as it moves from an initial position $\vec{r}_1$ to a subsequent position $\vec{r}_2$; its corresponding velocities are $\vec{v}_1$ and $\vec{v}_2$. Since we have uniform circular motion, $|\vec{v}_1| = |\vec{v}_2|$. The change in position is $\Delta \vec{r}$ and the change in velocity is $\Delta \vec{v}$. Both of these quantities involve a vector subtraction as shown in **Figures 4(b)** and **(c)**. Both triangles are isosceles because $|\vec{r}_1| = |\vec{r}_2|$ and $|\vec{v}_1| = |\vec{v}_2|$. Since $\vec{v}_1 \perp \vec{r}_1$ and $\vec{v}_2 \perp \vec{r}_2$, the two triangles are similar. Therefore, the following equation can be written:

$$\frac{|\Delta \vec{v}|}{|\vec{v}|} = \frac{|\Delta \vec{r}|}{|\vec{r}|} \quad \text{where} \quad |\vec{v}| = |\vec{v}_1| = |\vec{v}_2| \text{ and } |\vec{r}| = |\vec{r}_1| = |\vec{r}_2|$$

$$\text{or } |\Delta \vec{v}| = \frac{|\vec{v}| \times |\Delta \vec{r}|}{|\vec{r}|}$$

Now, the magnitude of the centripetal acceleration $\vec{a}_c$ is

$$|\vec{a}_c| = \lim\limits_{\Delta t \to 0} \frac{|\Delta \vec{v}|}{\Delta t}$$

(a)

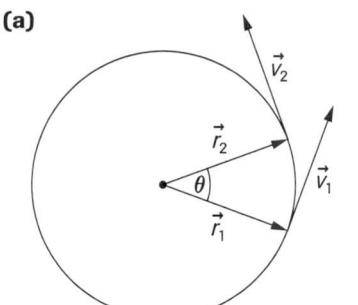

(b)

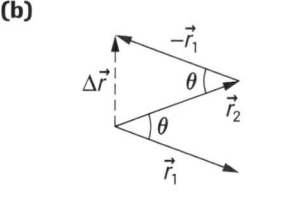

(c)

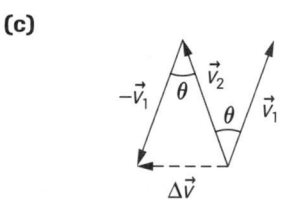

Figure 4
Derivation of the equation for the magnitude of the centripetal acceleration
(a) The position and velocity vectors
(b) The change of position
(c) The change of velocity

We can divide both sides of the $\left|\Delta\vec{v}\right|$ equation by Δt to obtain

$$\frac{\left|\Delta\vec{v}\right|}{\Delta t} = \frac{\left|\vec{v}\right|}{\left|\vec{r}\right|} \times \frac{\left|\Delta\vec{r}\right|}{\Delta t}$$

Therefore, $\left|\vec{a}_c\right| = \lim\limits_{\Delta t \to 0} \left(\dfrac{\left|\vec{v}\right|}{\left|\vec{r}\right|} \times \dfrac{\left|\Delta\vec{r}\right|}{\Delta t} \right)$

Now the magnitude of the instantaneous velocity is

$$\left|\vec{v}\right| = \lim\limits_{\Delta t \to 0} \frac{\left|\Delta\vec{r}\right|}{\Delta t}$$

Therefore, $\left|\vec{a}_c\right| = \dfrac{\left|\vec{v}\right|}{\left|\vec{r}\right|} \times \left|\vec{v}\right|$

Hence, the magnitude of the centripetal acceleration is

$$a_c = \frac{v^2}{r}$$

where a_c is the centripetal acceleration, v is the speed of the object undergoing uniform circular motion, and r is the radius of the circle or arc.

The equation $a_c = \dfrac{v^2}{r}$ makes sense because as the speed of an object in circular motion increases at a constant radius, the direction of the velocity changes more quickly requiring a larger acceleration; as the radius becomes larger (at a constant speed), the direction changes more slowly, meaning a smaller acceleration.

▶ **SAMPLE** problem **1**

A child on a merry-go-round is 4.4 m from the centre of the ride, travelling at a constant speed of 1.8 m/s. Determine the magnitude of the child's centripetal acceleration.

Solution

$v = 1.8$ m/s

$r = 4.4$ m

$a_c = ?$

$$a_c = \frac{v^2}{r}$$

$$= \frac{(1.8 \text{ m/s})^2}{4.4 \text{ m}}$$

$$a_c = 0.74 \text{ m/s}^2$$

The child's centripetal acceleration has a magnitude of 0.74 m/s².

For objects undergoing uniform circular motion, often the speed is not known, but the radius and the period (the time for one complete trip around the circle) are known. To determine the centripetal acceleration from this information, we know that the speed is constant and equals the distance travelled ($2\pi r$) divided by the period of revolution (T):

$$v = \frac{2\pi r}{T}$$

Substituting this expression into the centripetal acceleration equation $a_c = \dfrac{v^2}{r}$, we obtain

$$a_c = \frac{4\pi^2 r}{T^2}$$

For high rates of revolution, it is common to state the frequency rather than period. The frequency f is the number of revolutions per second, or the reciprocal of the period. It is measured in cycles per second or hertz (Hz), but may be stated mathematically as s^{-1}. Since $f = \dfrac{1}{T}$, the equation for centripetal acceleration can be written as:

$$a_c = 4\pi^2 r f^2$$

We now have three equations for determining the magnitude of the centripetal acceleration:

$$a_c = \frac{v^2}{r} = \frac{4\pi^2 r}{T^2} = 4\pi^2 r f^2$$

Remember that the direction of the centripetal acceleration is always toward the centre of the circle.

▶ **SAMPLE** problem **2**

Find the magnitude and direction of the centripetal acceleration of a piece of lettuce on the inside of a rotating salad spinner. The spinner has a diameter of 19.4 cm and is rotating at 780 rpm (revolutions per minute). The rotation is clockwise as viewed from above. At the instant of inspection, the lettuce is moving eastward.

Solution

$f = (780 \text{ rev/min})(1 \text{ min/60 s}) = 13 \text{ Hz} = 13 \text{ s}^{-1}$

$r = \dfrac{19.4 \text{ cm}}{2} = 9.7 \text{ cm} = 9.7 \times 10^{-2} \text{ m}$

$\vec{a}_c = ?$

$\begin{aligned} a_c &= 4\pi^2 r f^2 \\ &= 4\pi^2 (9.7 \times 10^{-2} \text{ m})(13 \text{ s}^{-1})^2 \\ a_c &= 6.5 \times 10^2 \text{ m/s}^2 \end{aligned}$

Figure 5 shows that since the lettuce is moving eastward, the direction of its centripetal acceleration must be southward (i.e., toward the centre of the circle). The centripetal acceleration is thus $6.5 \times 10^2 \text{ m/s}^2$ [S].

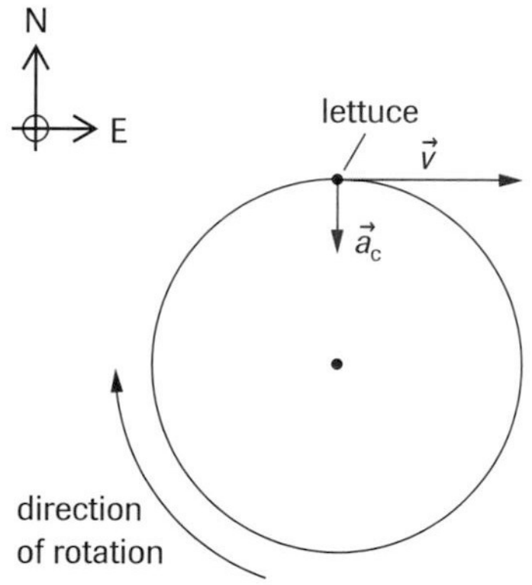

Figure 5
Piece of lettuce undergoing uniform circular motion for Sample Problem 2

▶ **SAMPLE** problem **3**

Determine the frequency and period of rotation of an electric fan if a spot at the end of one fan blade is 15 cm from the centre and has a centripetal acceleration of magnitude $2.37 \times 10^3 \text{ m/s}^2$.

Solution

$a_c = 2.37 \times 10^3 \text{ m/s}^2 \qquad f = ?$

$r = 15 \text{ cm} = 0.15 \text{ m} \qquad T = ?$

$$a_c = 4\pi^2 r f^2$$

$$f^2 = \frac{a_c}{4\pi^2 r}$$

$$f = \pm\sqrt{\frac{a_c}{4\pi^2 r}}$$

$$= \pm\sqrt{\frac{2.37 \times 10^3 \text{ m/s}^2}{4\pi^2(0.15 \text{ m})}}$$

$$= \pm 2.0 \times 10^1 \text{ s}^{-1}$$

$$f = 2.0 \times 10^1 \text{ Hz} \quad \text{(rejecting a negative frequency as meaningless)}$$

The frequency of rotation of the electric fan is 2.0×10^1 Hz.

$$T = \frac{1}{f}$$

$$= \frac{1}{2.0 \times 10^1 \text{ Hz}}$$

$$= \frac{1}{2.0 \times 10^1 \text{ s}^{-1}}$$

$$T = 5.0 \times 10^{-2} \text{ s}$$

The period of rotation of the fan is 5.0×10^{-2} s.

▶ Practice

Understanding Concepts

5. **Figure 6** shows a particle undergoing uniform circular motion at a speed of 4.0 m/s.
   (a) State the direction of the velocity vector, the acceleration vector, and the radius vector at the instant shown.
   (b) Calculate the magnitude of the centripetal acceleration.

6. You are whirling a ball on the end of a string in a horizontal circle around your head. What is the effect on the magnitude of the centripetal acceleration of the ball if
   (a) the speed of the ball remains constant, but the radius of the circle doubles?
   (b) the radius of the circle remains constant, but the speed doubles?

7. At a distance of 25 km from the eye of a hurricane, the wind is moving at 180 km/h in a circle. What is the magnitude of the centripetal acceleration, in metres per second squared, of the particles that make up the wind?

8. Calculate the magnitude of the centripetal acceleration in the following situations:
   (a) An electron is moving around a nucleus with a speed of 2.18×10^6 m/s. The diameter of the electron's orbit is 1.06×10^{-10} m.
   (b) A cowhand is about to lasso a calf with a rope that is undergoing uniform circular motion. The time for one complete revolution of the rope is 1.2 s. The end of the rope is 4.3 m from the centre of the circle.
   (c) A coin is placed flat on a vinyl record, turning at $33\frac{1}{3}$ rpm. The coin is 13 cm from the centre of the record.

9. A ball on a string, moving in a horizontal circle of radius 2.0 m, undergoes a centripetal acceleration of magnitude 15 m/s^2. What is the speed of the ball?

10. Mercury orbits the Sun in an approximately circular path, at an average distance of 5.79×10^{10} m, with a centripetal acceleration of magnitude 4.0×10^{-2} m/s^2. What is its period of revolution around the Sun, in seconds? in "Earth" days?

Applying Inquiry Skills

11. Graph the relationship between the magnitude of centripetal acceleration and
    (a) the speed of an object in uniform circular motion (with a constant radius)
    (b) the radius of a circle (at a constant speed)
    (c) the radius of rotation (at a constant frequency)

Answers

5. (b) 2.0×10^1 m/s^2

7. 0.10 m/s^2

8. (a) 8.97×10^{22} m/s^2
   (b) 1.2×10^2 m/s^2
   (c) 1.6 m/s^2

9. 5.5 m/s

10. 7.6×10^6 s or 88 d

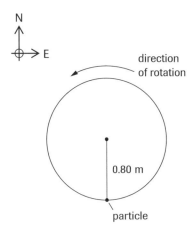

Figure 6
For question 5

 **SUMMARY** *Uniform Circular Motion*

- Uniform circular motion is motion at a constant speed in a circle or part of a circle with a constant radius.
- Centripetal acceleration is the acceleration toward the centre of the circular path of an object travelling in a circle or part of a circle.
- Vector subtractions of position and velocity vectors can be used to derive the equations for centripetal acceleration.

▶ **Section 3.1** *Questions*

Understanding Concepts

1. Describe examples of uniform circular motion that can occur
   (a) in a kitchen
   (b) in a repair workshop
   (c) in situations in which there is less than a complete circle

2. Two balls at the ends of two strings are moving at the same speed in horizontal circular paths. One string is three times as long as the other. Compare the magnitudes of the two centripetal accelerations.

3. Calculate the magnitude of the centripetal acceleration in each of the following situations:
   (a) A satellite is travelling at 7.77×10^3 m/s in a circular orbit of radius 6.57×10^6 m from the centre of Earth.
   (b) A motorcycle is racing at 25 m/s on a track with a constant radius of curvature of 1.2×10^2 m.

4. (a) What is the magnitude of centripetal acceleration due to the daily rotation of an object at Earth's equator? The equatorial radius is 6.38×10^6 m.
   (b) How does this acceleration affect a person's weight at the equator?

5. Patrons on an amusement park ride called the Rotor stand with their backs against the wall of a rotating cylinder while the floor drops away beneath them. To keep from sliding downward, they require a centripetal acceleration in excess of about 25 m/s². The Rotor has a diameter of 5.0 m. What is the minimum frequency for its rotation? (The vertical force required to support the rider's weight is supplied by static friction with the wall.)

6. A car, travelling at 25 m/s around a circular curve, has a centripetal acceleration of magnitude 8.3 m/s². What is the radius of the curve?

7. The Moon, which revolves around Earth with a period of about 27.3 d in a nearly circular orbit, has a centripetal acceleration of magnitude 2.7×10^{-3} m/s². What is the average distance from Earth to the Moon?

Applying Inquiry Skills

8. You are asked to design a controlled experiment to verify the mathematical relationships between centripetal acceleration and other relevant variables.
   (a) Describe how you would conduct the experiment.
   (b) What are the most likely sources of random and systematic error in your experiment? How does your experiment help keep these sources of error within reasonable bounds?

Making Connections

9. A biophysicist seeks to separate subcellular particles with an analytic ultracentrifuge. The biophysicist must determine the magnitude of the centripetal acceleration provided by the centrifuge at various speeds and radii.
   (a) Calculate the magnitude of the centripetal acceleration at 8.4 cm from the centre of the centrifuge when it is spinning at 6.0×10^4 rpm. Express your answer in terms of g.
   (b) What are some other uses of centrifuges?

How would you design a highway turn in which northbound traffic would go around a curve and become westbound, as in **Figure 1(a)**? Which design shown in **Figure 1(b)** is preferable?

Figure 1
(a) A car travelling around a curve undergoes centripetal acceleration since the curve is an arc with radius *r*.
(b) Would the best design of a highway turn have a flat curve or a banked curve?

(a)

(b)

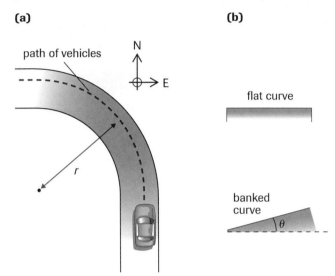

Cars negotiating curves on highways provide an example of circular motion. You learned in Section 3.1 that an object travelling at a constant speed in a circle or an arc experiences centripetal acceleration toward the centre of the circle. According to Newton's second law of motion, centripetal acceleration is the result of a net force acting in the direction of the acceleration (toward the centre of the circle) and perpendicular to the instantaneous velocity vector.

It is important to note that this net force is no different from other forces that cause acceleration: it might be gravity, friction, tension, a normal force, or a combination of two or more forces. For example, if we consider Earth travelling in a circular orbit around the Sun, the net force is the force of gravity that keeps Earth in its circular path.

We can combine the second-law equation for the magnitude of the net force, $\Sigma F = ma$, with the equation for centripetal acceleration, $a_c = \dfrac{v^2}{r}$:

$$\Sigma F = \frac{mv^2}{r}$$

where ΣF is the magnitude of the net force that causes the circular motion, m is the mass of the object in uniform circular motion, v is the speed of the object, and r is the radius of the circle or arc.

The equations for centripetal acceleration involving the period and frequency of circular motion can also be combined with the second-law equation. Thus, there are three common ways of writing the equation:

$$\Sigma F = \frac{mv^2}{r} = \frac{4\pi^2 mr}{T^2} = 4\pi^2 mrf^2$$

▶ **SAMPLE** problem **1**

A car of mass 1.1×10^3 kg negotiates a level curve at a constant speed of 22 m/s. The curve has a radius of 85 m, as shown in **Figure 2**.

(a) Draw an FBD of the car and name the force that provides the centripetal acceleration.

(b) Determine the magnitude of the force named in (a) that must be exerted to keep the car from skidding sideways.

(c) Determine the minimum coefficient of static friction needed to keep the car on the road.

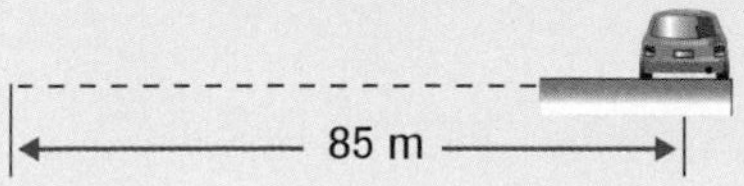

Figure 2
The radius of the curve is 85 m.

85 m

Solution

(a) **Figure 3** is the required FBD. The only horizontal force keeping the car going toward the centre of the arc is the force of static friction ($\vec{F}_S$) of the road on the wheels perpendicular to the car's instantaneous velocity. (Notice that the forces parallel to the car's instantaneous velocity are not shown in the FBD. These forces act in a plane perpendicular to the page; they are equal in magnitude, but opposite in direction because the car is moving at a constant speed.)

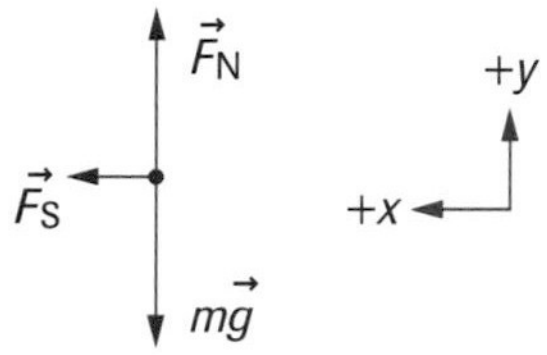

(b) $m = 1.1 \times 10^3$ kg

$v = 22$ m/s

$r = 85$ m

$F_S = ?$

$$F_S = \frac{mv^2}{r}$$

$$= \frac{(1.1 \times 10^3 \text{ kg})(22 \text{ m/s})^2}{85 \text{ m}}$$

$$F_S = 6.3 \times 10^3 \text{ N}$$

The magnitude of the static friction force is 6.3×10^3 N.

(c) $g = 9.8$ N/kg

We know from part (b) that the static friction is 6.3×10^3 N and from **Figure 3** that $F_N = mg$. To determine the minimum coefficient of static friction, we use the ratio of the maximum value of static friction to the normal force:

$$\mu_S = \frac{F_{S,max}}{F_N}$$

$$= \frac{6.3 \times 10^3 \text{ N}}{(1.1 \times 10^3 \text{ kg})(9.8 \text{ N/kg})}$$

$$\mu_S = 0.58$$

The minimum coefficient of static friction needed is 0.58. This value is easily achieved on paved and concrete highways in dry or rainy weather. However, snow and ice make the coefficient of static friction less than 0.58, allowing a car travelling at 22 m/s to slide off the road.

Figure 3
The FBD of the car on a level curve

A car of mass 1.1×10^3 kg travels around a frictionless, banked curve of radius 85 m. The banking is at an angle of 19° to the horizontal, as shown in **Figure 4**.

(a) What force provides the centripetal acceleration?

(b) What constant speed must the car maintain to travel safely around the curve?

(c) How does the required speed for a more massive vehicle, such as a truck, compare with the speed required for this car?

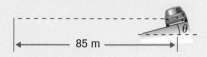

← 85 m →

Figure 4
The radius of the curve is 85 m.

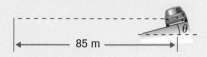

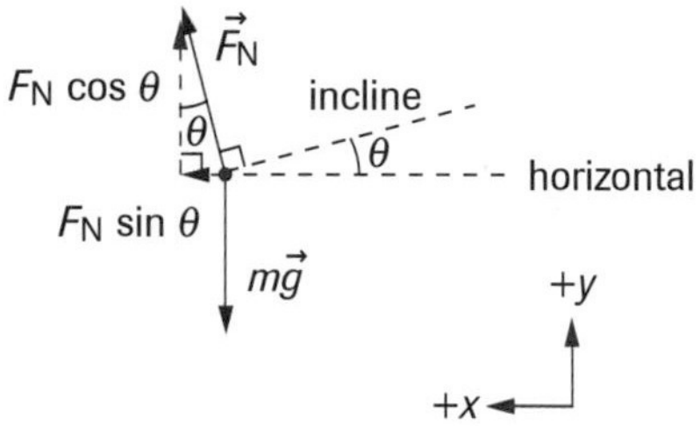

Figure 5
The FBD of the car on a banked curve

Solution

(a) From the FBD shown in **Figure 5**, you can see that the cause of the centripetal acceleration, which acts toward the centre of the circle, is the horizontal component of the normal force, $F_N \sin \theta$. Thus, the horizontal acceleration, a_x, is equivalent to the centripetal acceleration, a_c. (Notice that the FBD resembles the FBD of a skier going downhill, but the analysis is quite different.)

(b) $m = 1.1 \times 10^3$ kg

$r = 85$ m

$\theta = 19°$

$v = ?$

We take the vertical components of the forces:

$$\Sigma F_y = 0$$
$$F_N \cos \theta - mg = 0$$
$$F_N = \frac{mg}{\cos \theta}$$

Next, we take the horizontal components of the forces:

$$\Sigma F_x = ma_c$$
$$F_N \sin \theta = ma_c$$
$$\frac{mg}{\cos \theta} \sin \theta = ma_c$$
$$mg \tan \theta = \frac{mv^2}{r}$$
$$v^2 = gr \tan \theta$$
$$v = \pm\sqrt{gr \tan \theta}$$
$$= \pm\sqrt{(9.8 \text{ m/s}^2)(85 \text{ m})(\tan 19°)}$$
$$v = \pm 17 \text{ m/s}$$

We choose the positive square root, since v cannot be negative. The speed needed to travel safely around the frictionless curve is 17 m/s. If the car travels faster than 17 m/s, it will slide up the banking; if it travels slower than 17 m/s, it will slide downward.

(c) The speed required for a more massive vehicle is the same (17 m/s) because the mass does not affect the calculations. One way of proving this is to point to our expression $v^2 = gr \tan \theta$: v depends on g, r, and θ but is independent of m.

▶ **SAMPLE** problem 3

A 3.5-kg steel ball in a structural engineering lab swings on the end of a rigid steel rod at a constant speed in a vertical circle of radius 1.2 m, at a frequency of 1.0 Hz, as in **Figure 6**. Calculate the magnitude of the tension in the rod due to the mass at the top (A) and the bottom (B) positions.

Solution

$m = 3.5$ kg

$r = 1.2$ m

$f = 1.0$ Hz

$F_T = ?$

In both FBDs in **Figure 7**, the tension in the rod is directed toward the centre of the circle. At position A, the weight, mg, of the ball acts together with the tension to cause the centripetal acceleration. At position B, the tension must be greater than at A because the tension and the ball's weight are in opposite directions and the net force must be toward the centre of the circle. In each case, $+y$ is the direction in which the centripetal acceleration is occurring.

At position A:

$$\Sigma F_y = ma_c$$
$$F_T + mg = 4\pi^2 mrf^2$$
$$F_T = 4\pi^2 mrf^2 - mg$$
$$= 4\pi^2(3.5 \text{ kg})(1.2 \text{ m})(1.0 \text{ Hz})^2 - (3.5 \text{ kg})(9.8 \text{ N/kg})$$
$$F_T = 1.3 \times 10^2 \text{ N}$$

When the ball is moving at the top of the circle, the magnitude of the tension is 1.3×10^2 N.

At position B:

$$\Sigma F_y = ma_c$$
$$F_T - mg = 4\pi^2 mrf^2$$
$$F_T = 4\pi^2 mrf^2 + mg$$
$$= 4\pi^2(3.5 \text{ kg})(1.2 \text{ m})(1.0 \text{ Hz})^2 + (3.5 \text{ kg})(9.8 \text{ N/kg})$$
$$F_T = 2.0 \times 10^2 \text{ N}$$

When the ball is moving at the bottom of the circle, the magnitude of the tension is 2.0×10^2 N.

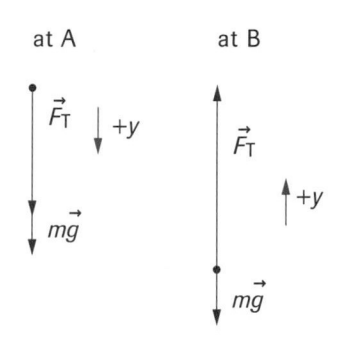

Figure 6
The system diagram for the steel ball and the rod in Sample Problem 3

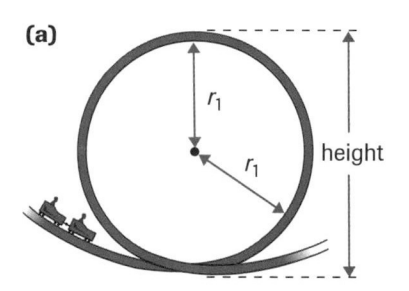

Figure 7
The FBDs at positions A and B

(a)

(b)

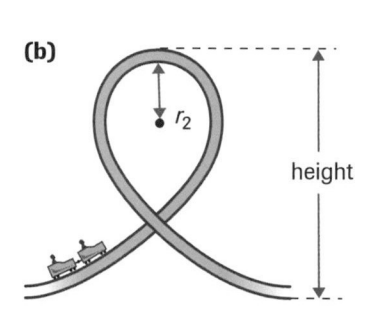

Figure 8
Two different loop designs used in roller coasters
(a) The circular loop used almost a century ago
(b) The clothoid loop used in today's looping coasters

Case Study *The Physics of the Looping Roller Coaster*

The first loop-the-loop roller coaster, built in the early part of the 20th century, consisted of a circular loop as illustrated in **Figure 8(a)**. With this design, however, the coaster had to be so fast that many people were injured on the ride and the design was soon abandoned.

Today's looping coasters have a much different design: a curve with a radius that starts off large, but becomes smaller at the top of the loop. This shape, called a *clothoid loop*, is illustrated in **Figure 8(b)**.

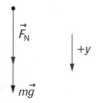

Figure 9
The FBD of the rider at the top of a roller-coaster loop

We can apply physics principles to compare the two designs. We will assume that in both designs, the magnitude of the normal force felt by a rider of mass m at the top of the loop is double his or her own weight, mg. (This means that the normal force has a magnitude of $2mg$.) This assumption allows us to calculate how fast each coaster must travel to achieve the same force on the rider.

Figure 9 shows the FBD of a rider at the top of the loop. The magnitude of the net force acting on the rider at that instant, ΣF, can be used to determine an expression for the speed of the coaster. Note that in this case study, we will use the subscript "old" to represent the older, circular loop and the subscript "new" to represent the newer, clothoid loop. We will also estimate that the ratio of the radius in the old design to the radius in the new design is 2.0 : 1.0.

$$\Sigma F = ma_c$$
$$F_N + mg = \frac{mv^2}{r}$$
$$2mg + mg = \frac{mv^2}{r}$$
$$3g = \frac{v^2}{r}$$
$$v^2 = 3gr$$
$$v = \sqrt{3gr} \quad \text{(rejecting the negative square root as meaningless)}$$

Next, we find the ratio of the speeds of the two designs required to satisfy these conditions:

$$r_{old} = 2.0r_{new}$$

$$\frac{v_{old}}{v_{new}} = \sqrt{\frac{3gr_{old}}{3gr_{new}}}$$

$$= \sqrt{\frac{r_{old}}{r_{new}}}$$

$$= \sqrt{\frac{2.0r_{new}}{r_{new}}}$$

$$= \sqrt{2.0}$$

$$v_{old} = 1.4v_{new}$$

Thus, the speed of the roller coaster of the older design had to be 1.4 times as fast as the roller coaster of the new design to have the same force act on the riders, even though the heights of the two loops are equal.

> **Practice**

Understanding Concepts

Answers

1. (a) 19 m/s; 68 km/h
   (b) 95 km/h

1. (a) Determine the speed required by a coaster that would cause a rider to experience a normal force of $2mg$ at the top of a clothoid loop where the radius is 12 m. Express your answer both in metres per second and in kilometres per hour.
   (b) How fast would a coaster on a circular loop of the same height have to travel to create the same normal force? Express your answer in kilometres per hour.

So far in our discussion of forces and circular motion, we have seen that centripetal acceleration can be caused by a variety of forces or combinations of forces: static friction (in Sample Problem 1); the horizontal component of a normal force (in Sample Problem 2); gravity (Earth orbiting the Sun); gravity and a tension force (in Sample Problem 3); and gravity and a normal force (in the Case Study). The net force that causes centripetal acceleration is called the **centripetal force**. Notice that centripetal force is *not* a separate force of nature; rather it is a net force that can be a single force (such as gravity) or a combination of forces (such as gravity and a normal force).

centripetal force net force that causes centripetal acceleration

▶ **Practice**

Understanding Concepts

2. Draw an FBD of the object in *italics,* and name the force or forces causing the centripetal acceleration for each of the following situations:

   (a) The *Moon* is in an approximately circular orbit around Earth.

   (b) An *electron* travels in a circular orbit around a nucleus in a simplified model of a hydrogen atom.

   (c) A *snowboarder* slides over the top of a bump that has the shape of a circular arc.

3. The orbit of Uranus around the Sun is nearly a circle of radius 2.87×10^{12} m. The speed of Uranus is approximately constant at 6.80×10^3 m/s. The mass of Uranus is 8.80×10^{25} kg.

   (a) Name the force that causes the centripetal acceleration.

   (b) Determine the magnitude of this force.

   (c) Calculate the orbital period of Uranus, both in seconds and in Earth years.

4. A bird of mass 0.211 kg pulls out of a dive, the bottom of which can be considered to be a circular arc with a radius of 25.6 m. At the bottom of the arc, the bird's speed is a constant 21.7 m/s. Determine the magnitude of the upward lift on the bird's wings at the bottom of the arc.

5. A highway curve in the horizontal plane is banked so that vehicles can proceed safely even if the road is slippery. Determine the proper banking angle for a car travelling at 97 km/h on a curve of radius 450 m.

6. A 2.00-kg stone attached to a rope 4.00 m long is whirled in a circle horizontally on a frictionless surface, completing 5.00 revolutions in 2.00 s. Calculate the magnitude of tension in the rope.

7. A plane is flying in a vertical loop of radius 1.50 km. At what speed is the plane flying at the top of the loop if the vertical force exerted by the air on the plane is zero at this point? State your answer both in metres per second and in kilometres per hour.

8. An 82-kg pilot flying a stunt airplane pulls out of a dive at a constant speed of 540 km/h.

   (a) What is the minimum radius of the plane's circular path if the pilot's acceleration at the lowest point is not to exceed $7.0g$?

   (b) What force is applied on the pilot by the plane seat at the lowest point in the pullout?

Applying Inquiry Skills

9. You saw in Sample Problem 3 that when an object is kept in circular motion in the vertical plane by a tension force, the tension needed is greater at the bottom of the circle than at the top.

   (a) Explain in your own words why this is so.

   (b) Describe how you could safely demonstrate the variation in tension, using a one-hole rubber stopper and a piece of string.

Answers

3. (b) 1.42×10^{21} N

   (c) 2.65×10^9 s; 84.1 a

4. 5.95 N

5. 9.3°

6. 1.97×10^3 N

7. 121 m/s or 436 km/h

8. (a) 3.3×10^2 m

   (b) 6.4×10^3 N

Rotating Frames of Reference

We saw in Section 2.5 that an accelerating frame of reference is a noninertial frame in which Newton's law of inertia does not hold. Since an object in circular motion is accelerating, any motion observed *from that object* must exhibit properties of a noninertial frame of reference. Consider, for example, the forces you feel when you are the passenger in a car during a left turn. You feel as if your right shoulder is being pushed against the passenger-side door. From Earth's frame of reference (the inertial frame), this force that you feel can be explained by Newton's first law of motion: you tend to maintain your initial velocity (in both magnitude and direction). When the car you are riding in goes left, you tend to go straight, but the car door pushes on you and causes you to go in a circular path along with the car. Thus, there is a centripetal force to the left on your body, as depicted in **Figure 10(a)**. The corresponding FBD (as seen from the side) is shown in **Figure 10(b)**.

Figure 10
(a) The top view of a passenger in a car from Earth's frame of reference as the car makes a left turn
(b) The side-view FBD of the passenger

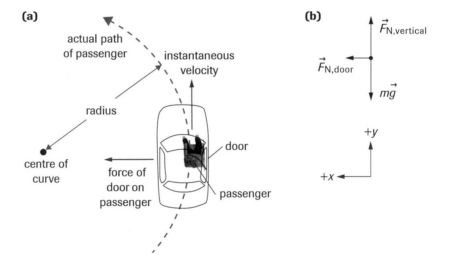

centrifugal force fictitious force in a rotating (accelerating) frame of reference

Consider the same situation from the accelerating frame of reference of the car. You feel as if something is pushing you toward the outside of the circle. This force away from the centre is a fictitious force called the **centrifugal force**. This situation, and the corresponding FBD involving the centrifugal force, are shown in **Figure 11**. Since the passenger is stationary (and remains so) in the rotating frame, the sum of the forces in that frame is zero.

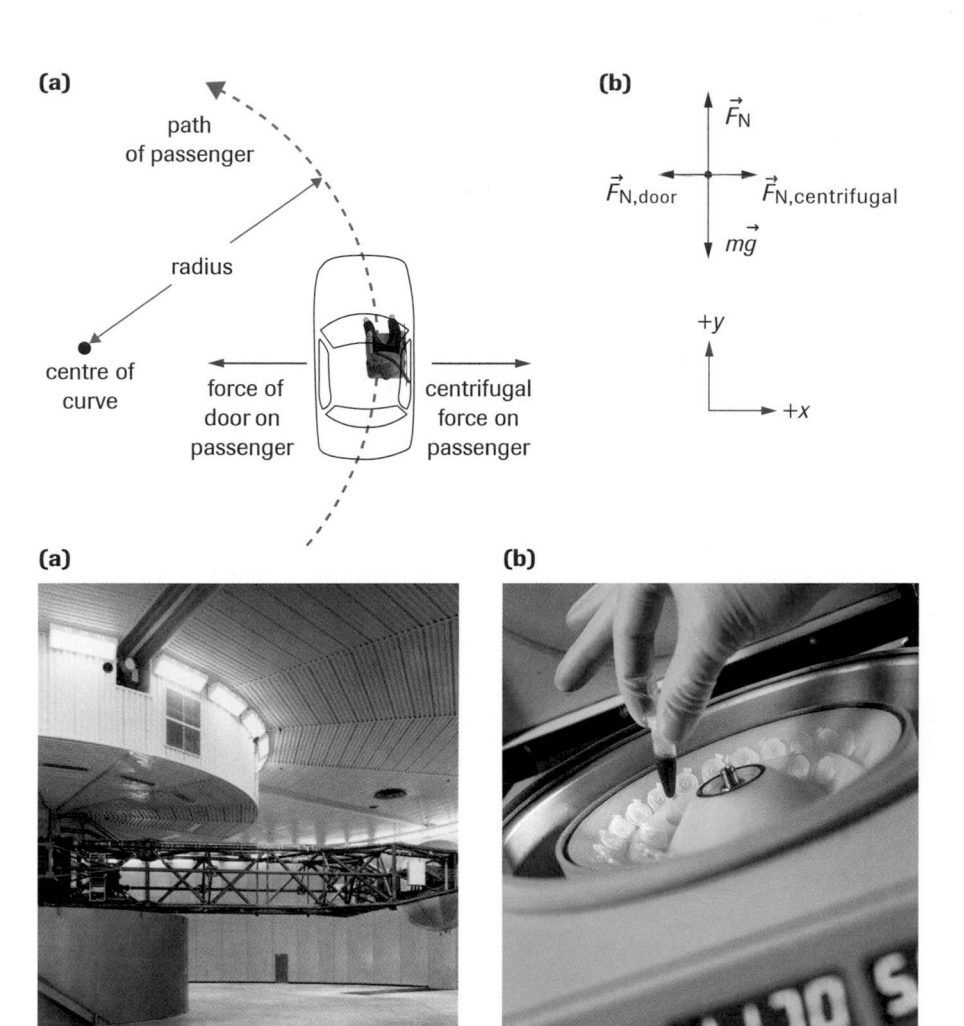

(a)

path
of passenger

radius

centre of
curve

force of
door on
passenger

centrifugal
force on
passenger

(b)

$\vec{F}_N$

$\vec{F}_{N,door}$ $\vec{F}_{N,centrifugal}$

$\vec{mg}$

$+y$

$+x$

Figure 11
(a) Top view of a passenger from
the car's frame of reference as
the car makes a left turn
(b) The side-view FBD of the passenger, showing the fictitious
force in the accelerating frame
of reference

(a) **(b)**

Figure 12
(a) This centrifuge located at the Manned Spacecraft Center in Huston, Texas, swings a
three-person gondola to create *g*-forces experienced by astronauts during liftoff and
re-entry conditions.
(b) A medical centrifuge used to separate blood for testing purposes

centrifuge rapidly-rotating device
used for separating substances and
training astronauts

A practical application of centrifugal force is the **centrifuge**, a rapidly-rotating device
used for such applications as separating substances in solution according to their densities and training astronauts. **Figure 12** shows some applications of a centrifuge.

Figure 13 shows the operation of a typical centrifuge. Test tubes containing samples
are rotated at high frequencies; some centrifuges have frequencies higher than 1100 Hz.
A dense cell or molecule near the top of a tube at position A tends to continue moving
at a constant speed in a straight line (if we neglect fluid friction due to the surrounding
liquid). This motion carries the cell toward the bottom of the tube at position B. Relative
to the rotating tube, the cell is moving away from the centre of the circle and is settling
out. Relative to Earth's frame of reference, the cell is following Newton's first law of
motion as the tube experiences an acceleration toward the centre of the centrifuge.

Another rotating noninertial frame of reference is Earth's surface. As Earth rotates
daily on its axis, the effects of the centrifugal acceleration on objects at the surface are
very small; nonetheless, they do exist. For example, if you were to drop a ball at the
equator, the ball would fall straight toward Earth's centre because of the force of gravity.
However, relative to Earth's rotating frame of reference, there is also a centrifugal force

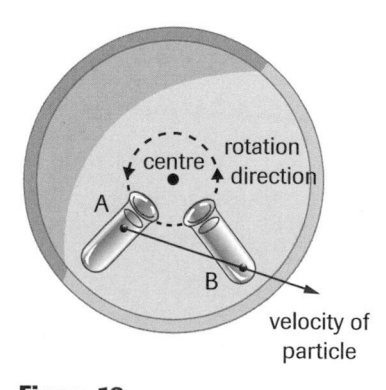

rotation
direction

centre

A

B

velocity of
particle

Figure 13
As the centrifuge rotates, a particle
at position A tends to continue
moving at a constant velocity, thus
settling to the bottom of the tube.

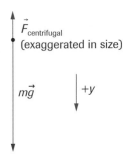

$\vec{F}_{centrifugal}$
(exaggerated in size)

$m\vec{g}$ $\qquad$ $+y$

Figure 14
A ball dropped at the equator experiences not only the force of gravity, but also a small centrifugal force. This FBD of the ball is in Earth's rotating frame of reference.

Figure 15
A Foucault pendulum at the North Pole for the Try This Activity

Answers

13. (d) 35°
    (e) 5.4×10^{-2} N

Coriolis force fictitious force that acts perpendicular to the velocity of an object in a rotating frame of reference

directed away from Earth's centre. (This is Newton's first law of motion in action; you feel a similar, though much greater effect when travelling at a high speed over the hill of a roller coaster track.) Thus, the net force on the ball in Earth's rotating frame is less than the force of gravity in a nonrotating frame of reference. This is illustrated in the FBD of the ball in **Figure 14**. The acceleration of the ball at the equator is about 0.34% less than the acceleration due to gravity alone. The magnitude of the centrifugal force is a maximum at the equator, and decreases to zero at the Poles.

A detailed analysis of the motion of particles in a rotating frame of reference would show that another fictitious force is involved. This force, perpendicular to the velocity of the particle or object *in the rotating frame*, is called the **Coriolis force**. It is named after the French mathematician Gaspard Gustave de Coriolis (1792–1843). Notice that this fictitious force acts on objects that are in motion relative to the rotating frame.

For most objects moving at Earth's surface, the effect of the Coriolis force is not noticeable. However, for objects that move very quickly or for a very long time, the effect is important. For example, the Coriolis force is responsible for the rotation of many weather patterns, such as the low-pressure systems that rotate counterclockwise in the Northern Hemisphere and clockwise in the Southern Hemisphere.

▶ **TRY THIS** activity   *The Foucault Pendulum*

In 1851, Jean Foucault, a French physicist, set up a pendulum to illustrate that Earth is a rotating frame of reference. The Foucault pendulum consists of a heavy bob suspended on a long wire; Foucault used a 28-kg bob attached to a 67-m wire. However, you can use a much smaller pendulum with a globe to model a Foucault pendulum.

(a) How would you use a globe and a simple pendulum to illustrate the behaviour of a Foucault pendulum swinging at the North Pole, as in **Figure 15**? Describe what you would observe at that location.
(b) How does the observed behaviour of a Foucault pendulum at the equator differ from the observed behaviour at your latitude?
(c) If possible, set up a demonstration of your answer to (a).

▶ **Practice**

Understanding Concepts

12. You are standing on a slowly rotating merry-go-round, turning counterclockwise as viewed from above. Draw an FBD for your body and explain your motion
    (a) in Earth's frame of reference (assumed to have negligible rotation)
    (b) in the frame of reference of the merry-go-round

13. When you stand on the merry-go-round in question 12, you hold a string from which is suspended a rubber stopper of mass 45 g. You are 2.9 m from the centre of the merry-go-round. You take 4.1 s to complete one revolution.
    (a) Draw a system diagram, showing the situation at the instant you are moving due east.
    (b) Draw an FBD of the stopper in Earth's frame of reference for a person looking eastward from behind you.
    (c) Draw an FBD of the stopper in your frame of reference.
    (d) What angle does the string make with the vertical?
    (e) What is the magnitude of the tension in the string?

14. (a) Show that the acceleration of an object dropped at the equator is about 0.34% less than the acceleration due to gravity alone.
    (b) What is the difference between your weight at the equator (in newtons) and your weight (from acceleration due to gravity alone)?

Applying Inquiry Skills

15. You take a horizontal accelerometer (the type with three small beads in transparent tubing, as in **Figure 3** in the introduction to this chapter) onto an amusement-park ride rotating in the horizontal plane to determine your centripetal acceleration (**Figure 16**). The mass of the central bead in the accelerometer is 1.1 g. The ride rotates clockwise as viewed from above, at a frequency of 0.45 Hz. You are 4.5 m from the centre.

Figure 16
As this ride begins, it rotates in the horizontal plane, allowing a rider to use a horizontal accelerometer to measure the acceleration.

(a) How would you hold the accelerometer to obtain the reading?
(b) What is the magnitude of your centripetal acceleration?
(c) At what angle from the vertical is the central bead in the accelerometer?
(d) Determine the magnitude of the normal force exerted by the accelerometer on the bead.

Making Connections

16. Research the origin and design of Foucault pendulums. Where is the Foucault pendulum closest to your home? (*Hint:* Science centres and university astronomy or physics departments may have a demonstration pendulum in operation.)

 www.science.nelson.com

Answers
15. (b) 36 m/s^2
(c) 75°
(d) 4.1 × 10^{-2} N

SUMMARY *Analyzing Forces in Circular Motion*

- The net force acting on an object in uniform circular motion acts toward the centre of the circle. (This force is sometimes called the centripetal force, although it is always just gravity, the normal force, or another force that you know already.)

- The magnitude of the net force can be calculated by combining Newton's second-law equation with the equations for centripetal acceleration.

- The frame of reference of an object moving in a circle is a noninertial frame of reference.

- Centrifugal force is a fictitious force used to explain the forces observed in a rotating frame of reference.

- Centrifuges apply the principles of Newton's first law of motion and centrifugal force.

- The Coriolis force is a fictitious force used to explain particles moving in a rotating frame of reference.

Understanding Concepts

1. Which of the two designs in **Figure 1(b)** at the beginning of this section is better? Why?

2. A 1.00-kg stone is attached to one end of a 1.00-m string, of breaking strength 5.00×10^2 N, and is whirled in a horizontal circle on a frictionless tabletop. The other end of the string is kept fixed. Find the maximum speed the stone can attain without breaking the string.

3. A 0.20-kg ball on the end of a string is rotated in a horizontal circle of radius 10.0 m. The ball completes 10 rotations in 5.0 s. What is the magnitude of the tension in the string?

4. In the Bohr-Rutherford model of the hydrogen atom, the electron, of mass 9.1×10^{-31} kg, revolves around the nucleus. The radius of the orbit is 5.3×10^{-11} m and the period of revolution of the electron around the nucleus is 1.5×10^{-16} s.
   (a) Find the magnitude of the acceleration of the electron.
   (b) Find the magnitude of the electric force acting on the electron.

5. A 1.12-m string pendulum has a bob of mass 0.200 kg.
   (a) What is the magnitude of the tension in the string when the pendulum is at rest?
   (b) What is the magnitude of the tension at the bottom of the swing if the pendulum is moving at 1.20 m/s?

6. When you whirl a small rubber stopper on a cord in a vertical circle, you find a critical speed at the top for which the tension in the cord is zero. At this speed, the force of gravity on the object is itself sufficient to supply the necessary centripetal force.
   (a) How slowly can you swing a 15-g stopper like this so that it will just follow a circle with a radius of 1.5 m?
   (b) How will your answer change if the mass of the stopper doubles?

7. An object of mass 0.030 kg is whirled in a vertical circle of radius 1.3 m at a constant speed of 6.0 m/s. Calculate the maximum and minimum tensions in the string.

8. A child is standing on a slowly rotating ride in a park. The ride operator makes the statement that in Earth's frame of reference, the child remains at the same distance from the centre of the ride because there is no net force acting on him. Do you agree with this statement? Explain your answer.

Applying Inquiry Skills

9. You are on a loop-the-loop roller coaster at the inside top of a loop that has a radius of curvature of 15 m. The force you feel on your seat is 2.0 times as great as your normal weight. You are holding a vertical accelerometer, consisting of a small metal bob attached to a sensitive spring (**Figure 17**).
   (a) Name the forces that act toward the centre of the circle.
   (b) Determine the speed of the coaster at the top of the loop.

(c) Name the forces contributing to the centripetal force on the bob of the accelerometer.
(d) If the accelerometer is calibrated as in **Figure 17**, what reading will you observe at the top of the loop? (*Hint:* Draw an FBD of the accelerometer bob when it is inverted in Earth's frame of reference at the top of the ride. Assume two significant digits.)
(e) What are the most likely sources of random and systematic error in trying to use a vertical accelerometer on a roller coaster?

Making Connections

10. Very rapid circular motion, particularly of machinery, presents a serious safety hazard. Give three examples of such hazards—one from your home, one from an ordinary car, and one from the workplace of a friend or family member. For each hazard, describe the underlying physics and propose appropriate safety measures.

11. Centrifuges are used for separating out components in many mixtures. Describe two applications of centrifuges from one of the following areas: the clinical analysis of blood, laboratory investigations of DNA and proteins, the preparation of dairy products, and sample analyses in geology.

 www.science.nelson.com

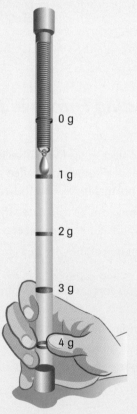

Figure 17
This vertical accelerometer is calibrated in such a way that when it is at rest, the scale reads "1g" at the bottom of the bob.

0 g
1 g
2 g
3 g
4 g

People have always enjoyed viewing stars and planets on clear, dark nights (**Figure 1**). It is not only the beauty and variety of objects in the sky that is so fascinating, but also the search for answers to questions related to the patterns and motions of those objects.

Until the late 1700s, Jupiter and Saturn were the only outer planets identified in our solar system because they were visible to the naked eye. Combined with the inner planets (Mercury, Venus, Earth, and Mars), the solar system was believed to consist of the Sun and six planets, as well as other smaller bodies such as moons. Then in 1781, British astronomer William Herschel (1738–1822), after making careful observations on what other astronomers thought was a star, announced that the "star" appeared to move relative to the background stars over a long period. This wandering star turned out to be the seventh planet, which Herschel named Uranus, after the Greek god of the sky and ruler of the universe. Astronomers studied the motion of Uranus over many years and discovered that its path was not quite as smooth as expected. Some distant hidden object appeared to be "tugging" on Uranus causing a slightly uneven orbit. Using detailed mathematical analysis, they predicted where this hidden object should be, searched for it for many years, and in 1846 discovered Neptune (**Figure 2**). Neptune is so far from the Sun that it takes almost 165 Earth years to complete one orbit; in other words, it will soon complete its first orbit since being discovered.

The force that keeps the planets in their orbits around the Sun and our Moon in its orbit around Earth is the same force tugging on Uranus to perturb its motion—the force of gravity. This force exists everywhere in the universe where matter exists. Sir Isaac Newton first analyzed the effects of gravity throughout the universe. Neptune was discovered by applying Newton's analysis of gravity.

Figure 2
Neptune, the most distant of the gas giant planets, was named after the Roman god of water. Although earthbound telescopes disclose little detail, photographs taken by the space probe *Voyager 2* in 1989 reveal bright blue and white clouds, and a dark area that may be a large storm.

Newton's Law of Universal Gravitation

In his *Principia*, published in 1687, Newton described how he used known data about objects in the solar system, notably the Moon's orbit around Earth, to discover the factors that affect the force of gravity throughout the universe. The relationships involved are summarized in his *law of universal gravitation*.

LEARNING TIP

Perturbations
In physics, a perturbation is a slight alteration in the action of a system that is caused by a secondary influence. Perturbations occur in the orbits of planets, moons, comets, and other heavenly bodies. When astronomers analyze the perturbations in the orbits of heavenly bodies, they search for the secondary influence and sometimes discover another body too small to find by chance.

Newton's Law of Universal Gravitation

The force of gravitational attraction between any two objects is directly proportional to the product of the masses of the objects, and inversely proportional to the square of the distance between their centres.

To express this law in equation form, we use the following symbols for the magnitudes of the variables involved: F_G is the force of gravitational attraction between any two objects; m_1 is the mass of one object; m_2 is the mass of a second object; and r is the distance *between the centres* of the two objects, which are assumed to be spherical.

Newton discovered the following proportionalities:

If m_2 and r are constant, $F_G \propto m_1$ (direct variation).

If m_1 and r are constant, $F_G \propto m_2$ (direct variation).

If m_1 and m_2 are constant, $F_G \propto \dfrac{1}{r^2}$ (inverse square variation).

Combining these statements, we obtain a joint variation:

$$F_G \propto \frac{m_1 m_2}{r^2}$$

Finally, we can write the equation for the law of universal gravitation:

$$F_G = \frac{Gm_1 m_2}{r^2}$$

where G is the universal gravitation constant.

In applying the law of universal gravitation, it is important to consider the following observations:

- There are two equal, but opposite forces present. For example, Earth pulls on you and you pull on Earth with a force of equal magnitude.

- For the force of attraction to be noticeable, at least one of the objects must be very large.

- The inverse square relationship between F_G and r means that the force of attraction diminishes rapidly as the two objects move apart. On the other hand, there is no value of r, no matter how large, that would reduce the force of attraction to zero. Every object in the universe exerts a force of attraction on every other object.

- The equation for the law of universal gravitation applies only to two spherical objects (such as Earth and the Sun), to two objects whose sizes are much smaller than their separation distance (for example, you and a friend separated by 1.0 km), or to a small object and a very large sphere (such as you and Earth).

▶ SAMPLE problem 1

Earth's gravitational pull on a spacecraft some distance away is 1.2×10^2 N in magnitude. What will the magnitude of the force of gravity be on a second spacecraft with 1.5 times the mass of the first spacecraft, at a distance from Earth's centre that is 0.45 times as great?

Solution

Let m_E represent the mass of Earth, and the subscripts 1 and 2 represent the first and second spacecraft, respectively.

$F_1 = 1.2 \times 10^2$ N

$m_2 = 1.5m_1$

$r_2 = 0.45r_1$

$F_2 = ?$

By ratio and proportion:

$$\frac{F_2}{F_1} = \frac{\left(\dfrac{Gm_E m_2}{r_2^2}\right)}{\left(\dfrac{Gm_E m_1}{r_1^2}\right)}$$

$$F_2 = F_1\left(\frac{m_2}{r_2^2}\right)\left(\frac{r_1^2}{m_1}\right)$$

$$= F_1\left(\frac{1.5m_1}{(0.45r_1)^2}\right)\left(\frac{r_1^2}{m_1}\right)$$

$$= 1.2 \times 10^2 \text{ N}\left(\frac{1.5}{(0.45)^2}\right)$$

$$F_2 = 8.9 \times 10^2 \text{ N}$$

The force of gravity on the spacecraft is 8.9×10^2 N in magnitude.

▶ Practice

Understanding Concepts

1. Relate Newton's third law of motion to his law of universal gravitation.

2. What is the direction of the gravitational force of attraction of object A on object B?

3. The magnitude of the force of gravitational attraction between two uniform spherical masses is 36 N. What would the magnitude of the force be if one mass were doubled, and the distance between the objects tripled?

4. Mars has a radius and mass 0.54 and 0.11 times the radius and mass of Earth. If the force of gravity on your body is 6.0×10^2 N in magnitude on Earth, what would it be on Mars?

5. The magnitude of the force of gravity between two uniform spherical masses is 14 N when their centres are 8.5 m apart. When the distance between the masses is changed, the force becomes 58 N. How far apart are the centres of the masses?

Applying Inquiry Skills

6. Sketch a graph showing the relationship between the magnitude of the gravitational force and the distance separating the centres of two uniform spherical objects.

Making Connections

7. In the past, Pluto has been known as the ninth planet in the solar system. Recently, however, it has been suggested that Pluto should be classified as a body other than a planet. Research and write a brief report on Pluto's discovery, and also the reasons for the recent controversy over Pluto's planetary status.

 www.science.nelson.com

Answers

3. 8.0 N

4. 2.3×10^2 N

5. 4.2 m

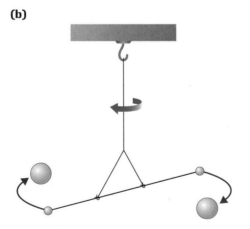

Determining the Universal Gravitation Constant

The numerical value of the universal gravitation constant G is extremely small; experimental determination of the value did not occur until more than a century after Newton
formulated his law of universal gravitation. In 1798, British scientist Henry Cavendish
(1731–1810), using the apparatus illustrated in **Figure 3**, succeeded in measuring the
gravitational attraction between two small spheres that hung on a rod approximately
2 m long and two larger spheres mounted independently. Using this equipment, he
derived a value of G that is fairly close to today's accepted value of 6.67×10^{-11} N·m²/kg².
His experiment showed that gravitational force exists even for relatively small objects and,
by establishing the value of the constant of proportionality G, he made it possible to
use the law of universal gravitation in calculations. Cavendish's experimental determination of G was a great scientific triumph. Astronomers believe that its magnitude may
influence the rate at which the universe is expanding.

(a)

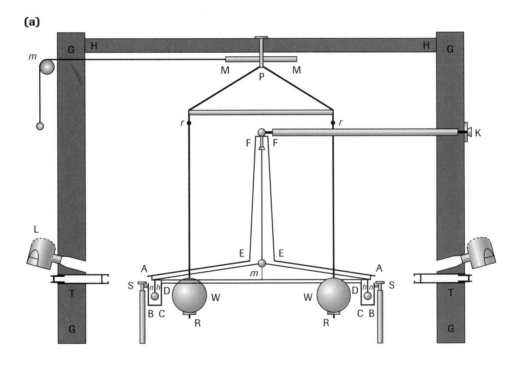

(b)

Figure 3
Cavendish's experimental setup
(a) This sketch of the apparatus
appeared in his original paper. The
device is mounted in a large case G,
with outside controls to move the
masses and adjust the horizontal
rod. Scales near the end of the rod
are illuminated by lamps L and
observed through the telescope T.
(b) A simplified view of the apparatus

> ### *SAMPLE* problem 2

Determine the magnitude of the force of attraction between two uniform metal balls, of mass 4.00 kg, used in women's shot-putting, when the centres are separated by 45.0 cm.

Solution

$G = 6.67 \times 10^{-11}$ N·m²/kg² $r = 0.450$ m

$m_1 = m_2 = 4.00$ kg $F_G = ?$

$$F_G = \frac{Gm_1m_2}{r^2}$$

$$= \frac{(6.67 \times 10^{-11} \text{ N·m}^2/\text{kg}^2)(4.00 \text{ kg})(4.00 \text{ kg})}{(0.450 \text{ m})^2}$$

$$F_G = 5.27 \times 10^{-9} \text{ N}$$

The magnitude of the force of attraction is 5.27×10^{-9} N, an extremely small value.

> ### Practice

Understanding Concepts

8. What is the magnitude of the force of gravitational attraction between two 1.8×10^8-kg spherical oil tanks with their centres 94 m apart?

9. A 50.0-kg student stands 6.38×10^6 m from Earth's centre. The mass of Earth is 5.98×10^{24} kg. What is the magnitude of the force of gravity on the student?

10. Jupiter has a mass of 1.90×10^{27} kg and a radius of 7.15×10^7 m. Calculate the magnitude of the acceleration due to gravity on Jupiter.

11. A space vehicle, of mass 555 kg, experiences a gravitational pull from Earth of 255 N. The mass of Earth is 5.98×10^{24} kg. How far is the vehicle (a) from the centre of Earth and (b) above the surface of Earth?

12. Four masses are located on a plane, as in **Figure 4**. What is the magnitude of the net gravitational force on m_1 due to the other three masses?

Making Connections

13. The mass of Earth can be calculated by applying the fact that an object's weight is equal to the force of gravity between Earth and the object. The radius of Earth is 6.38×10^6 m.
    (a) Determine the mass of Earth.
    (b) At what stage in the historical development of science would physicists first have been able to calculate Earth's mass accurately? Explain your answer.
    (c) What effect on society is evident now that we accurately know Earth's mass?

Answers

8. 2.4×10^2 N

9. 4.90×10^2 N

10. 24.8 m/s²

11. (a) 2.95×10^7 m

    (b) 2.31×10^7 m

12. 6.8 N

13. (a) 5.98×10^{24} kg

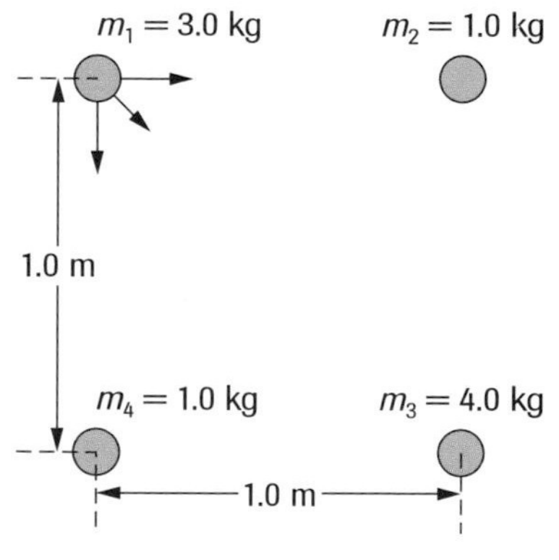

Figure 4
For question 12

> ### SUMMARY   *Universal Gravitation*

- Newton's law of universal gravitation states that the force of gravitational attraction between any two objects is directly proportional to the product of the masses of the objects and inversely proportional to the square of the distance between their centres.

- The universal gravitation constant, $G = 6.67 \times 10^{-11}$ N·m²/kg², was first determined experimentally by Henry Cavendish in 1798.

- The law of universal gravitation is applied in analyzing the motions of bodies in the universe, such as planets in the solar system. (This analysis can lead to the discovery of other celestial bodies.)

Understanding Concepts

1. Do you agree with the statement, "There is no location anywhere in the universe where a body can exist with no force acting on it"? Explain.

2. The force of attraction between masses m_1 and m_2 is 26 N in magnitude. What will the magnitude of the force become if m_2 is tripled, and the distance between m_2 and m_1 is halved?

3. You are an astronaut. At what altitude above the surface of Earth is your weight one-half your weight on the surface? Express your answer as a multiple of Earth's radius r_E.

4. Calculate the magnitude of the gravitational attraction between a proton of mass 1.67×10^{-27} kg and an electron of mass 9.11×10^{-31} kg if they are 5.0×10^{-11} m apart (as they are in a hydrogen atom).

5. Uniform spheres A, B, and C have the following masses and centre-to-centre separations: $m_A = 55$ kg, $m_B = 75$ kg, $m_C = 95$ kg; $r_{AB} = 0.68$ m, $r_{BC} = 0.95$ m. If the only forces acting on B are the forces of gravity due to A and C, determine the net force acting on B with the spheres arranged as in **Figures 5(a)** and **(b)**.

(a)

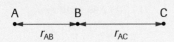

(b)

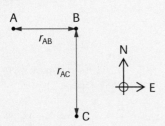

Figure 5

6. At a certain point between Earth and the Moon, the net gravitational force exerted on an object by Earth and the Moon is zero. The Earth-Moon centre-to-centre separation is 3.84×10^5 km. The mass of the Moon is 1.2% the mass of Earth.
   (a) Where is this point located? Are there any other such points? (*Hint:* Apply the quadratic formula after setting up the related equations.)

(b) What is the physical meaning of the root of the quadratic equation whose value exceeds the Earth-Moon distance? (An FBD of the object in this circumstance will enhance your answer.)

Applying Inquiry Skills

7. Using **Figure 6**, you can illustrate what happens to the magnitude of the gravitational force of attraction on an object as it recedes from Earth. Make a larger version of the graph and complete it for the force of gravity acting on you as you move from the surface of Earth to 7.0 Earth radii from the centre of Earth.

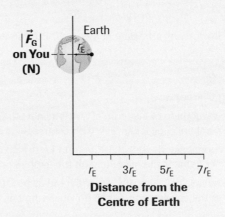

Figure 6

Making Connections

8. A geosynchronous satellite must remain at the same location above Earth's equator as it orbits Earth.
   (a) What period of revolution must a geosynchronous satellite have?
   (b) Set up an equation to express the distance of the satellite from the centre of Earth in terms of the universal gravitation constant, the mass of Earth, and the period of revolution around Earth.
   (c) Determine the value of the distance required in (b). (Refer to Appendix C for data.)
   (d) Why must the satellite remain in a fixed location (relative to an observer on Earth's surface)?
   (e) Research the implications of having too many geosynchronous satellites in the space available above the equator. Summarize your findings in a brief report.

 www.science.nelson.com

A **satellite** is an object or a body that revolves around another object, which is usually much larger in mass. Natural satellites include the planets, which revolve around the Sun, and moons that revolve around the planets, such as Earth's Moon. Artificial satellites are human-made objects that travel in orbits around Earth or another body in the solar system.

A common example of an artificial satellite is the network of 24 satellites that make up the Global Positioning System, or GPS. This system is used to determine the position of an object on Earth's surface to within 15 m of its true position. The boat shown in **Figure 1** has a computer-controlled GPS receiver that detects signals from each of three satellites. These signals help to determine the distance between the boat and the satellite, using the speed of the signal and the time it takes for the signal to reach the boat.

satellite object or body that revolves around another body

space station an artificial satellite that can support a human crew and remains in orbit around Earth for long periods

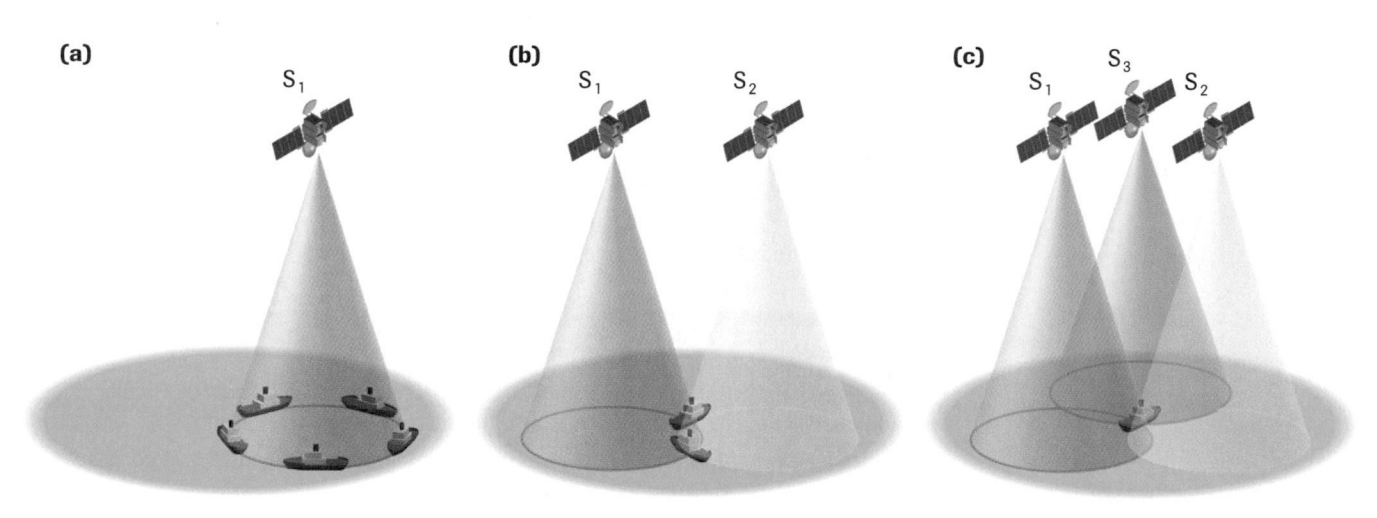

(a) **(b)** **(c)**

Figure 1
GPS satellites can determine the location of an object, in this case a boat.
(a) With one satellite, the location is known to be somewhere along the circumference of a circle.
(b) With two satellites consulted simultaneously, the location is found to be at one of two intersection spots.
(c) With three satellites consulted simultaneously, the intersection of three circles gives the exact location of the boat.

Another example of an artificial satellite is a **space station**, a spacecraft in which people live and work. Currently, the only space station in operation is the International Space Station, or ISS. Like satellites travelling with uniform circular motion, the ISS travels in an orbit of approximately fixed radius. The ISS is a permanent orbiting laboratory in which research projects, including testing how humans react to space travel, are conducted. In the future, the knowledge gained from this research will be applied to design and operate a spacecraft that can transport people great distances to some destination in the solar system, such as Mars.

Satellites in Circular Orbit

When Isaac Newton developed his idea of universal gravitation, he surmised that the same force that pulled an apple downward as it fell from a tree was responsible for keeping the Moon in its orbit around Earth. But there is a big difference: the Moon does not hit the ground. The Moon travels at the appropriate speed that keeps it at approximately the same distance, called the orbital radius, from Earth's centre. As the Moon circles Earth, it is undergoing constant free fall toward Earth; all artificial satellites in circular motion around Earth undergo the same motion. A satellite pulled by the force of gravity toward Earth follows a curved path. Since Earth's surface is curved, the

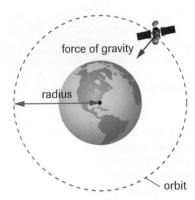

Figure 2
A satellite in a circular orbit around Earth experiences constant free fall as its path follows the curvature of Earth's surface.

Figure 3
The Hubble Space Telescope (HST) being deployed from the cargo bay of a space shuttle

satellite falls downward at the same rate as Earth's curvature. If the orbiting, free-falling satellite has the proper speed for its orbital radius as it falls toward Earth, it will never land (**Figure 2**).

To analyze the motion of a satellite in uniform circular motion, we combine Newton's law of universal gravitation with the equation for centripetal acceleration involving the satellite's speed. Using the magnitudes of the forces only, we have:

$$\sum F = \frac{Gm_S m_E}{r^2} = \frac{m_S v^2}{r}$$

where G is the universal gravitation constant, m_S is the mass of the satellite, m_E is the mass of Earth, v is the speed of the satellite, and r is the distance from the centre of Earth to the satellite. Solving for the speed of the satellite and using only the positive square root:

$$v = \sqrt{\frac{Gm_E}{r}}$$

This equation indicates that for a satellite to maintain an orbit of radius r, its speed must be constant. Since the Moon's orbital radius is approximately constant, its speed is also approximately constant. A typical artificial satellite with a constant orbital radius is a geosynchronous satellite used for communication. Such a satellite is placed in a 24-hour orbit above the equator so that the satellite's period of revolution coincides with Earth's daily period of rotation.

The equations for centripetal acceleration in terms of the orbital period and frequency can also be applied to analyze the motion of a satellite in uniform circular motion depending on the information given in a problem.

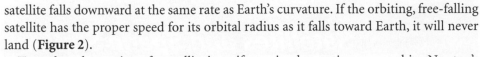

▶ **SAMPLE problem 1**

The Hubble Space Telescope (HST), shown in **Figure 3**, follows an essentially circular orbit, at an average altitude of 598 km above the surface of Earth.

(a) Determine the speed needed by the HST to maintain its orbit. Express the speed both in metres per second and in kilometres per hour.

(b) What is the orbital period of the HST?

Solution

(a) $G = 6.67 \times 10^{-11} \text{ N·m}^2/\text{kg}^2$ $\qquad r = 6.38 \times 10^6 \text{ m} + 5.98 \times 10^5 \text{ m} = 6.98 \times 10^6 \text{ m}$

$m_E = 5.98 \times 10^{24} \text{ kg}$ $\qquad v = ?$

Since gravity causes the centripetal acceleration,

$$\frac{Gm_S m_E}{r^2} = \frac{m_S v^2}{r}$$

Solving for v:

$$v = \sqrt{\frac{Gm_E}{r}}$$

$$= \sqrt{\frac{(6.67 \times 10^{-11} \text{ N·m}^2/\text{kg}^2)(5.98 \times 10^{24} \text{ kg})}{6.98 \times 10^6 \text{ m}}}$$

$$= 7.56 \times 10^3 \text{ m/s}$$

$$v = 2.72 \times 10^4 \text{ km/h}$$

The required speed of the HST is 7.56×10^3 m/s, or 2.72×10^4 km/h.

(b) $v = 2.72 \times 10^4$ km/h

$d = 2\pi r = 2\pi (6.98 \times 10^3 \text{ km})$

$T = ?$

$$T = \frac{2\pi r}{v}$$

$$= \frac{2\pi (6.98 \times 10^3 \text{ km})}{2.72 \times 10^4 \text{ km/h}}$$

$$T = 1.61 \text{ h}$$

The orbital period of the HST is 1.61 h.

▶ *Practice*

Understanding Concepts

1. (a) As the altitude of an Earth satellite in circular orbit increases, does the speed of the satellite increase, decrease, or remain the same? Why?
   (b) Check your answer by comparing the speed of the HST (discussed in Sample Problem 1) with the speed of the Moon. The orbital radius of the Moon is 3.84×10^5 km.

2. The ISS follows an orbit that is, on average, 450 km above the surface of Earth. Determine (a) the speed of ISS and (b) the time for one orbit.

3. Derive an expression for the radius of a satellite's orbit around Earth in terms of the period of revolution, the universal gravitation constant, and Earth's mass.

4. Satellite-broadcast television is an alternative to cable. A "digital TV" satellite follows a geosynchronous orbit.
   (a) State the period of revolution of the satellite in seconds.
   (b) Determine the altitude of the orbit above the surface of Earth.

Applying Inquiry Skills

5. Sketch graphs showing the relationship between the speed of a satellite in uniform circular motion and
   (a) the mass of the body around which the satellite is orbiting
   (b) the orbital radius

Making Connections

6. Astronomers have identified a black hole at the centre of galaxy M87 (**Figure 4**). From the properties of the light observed, they have measured material at a distance of 5.7×10^{17} m from the centre of the black hole, travelling at an estimated speed of 7.5×10^5 m/s.

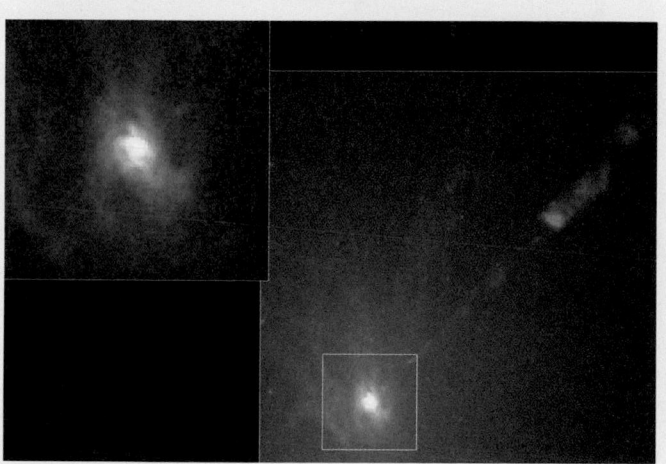

Answers

1. (b) $v_M = 1.02 \times 10^3$ m/s

2. (a) 7.64×10^3 m/s
   (b) 1.56 h

3. $r = \sqrt[3]{\dfrac{T^2 G m_E}{4\pi^2}}$

4. (a) 8.64×10^4 s
   (b) 3.59×10^4 km

6. (a) 4.8×10^{39} kg
   (b) $2.4 \times 10^9 {:} 1$

Figure 4
This image of the centre of galaxy M87 was obtained by the HST. The square identifies the area at the core of the galaxy where a black hole is believed to exist.

apparent weight the net force exerted on an accelerating object in a noninertial frame of reference

Figure 5

(a) The reading on a bathroom scale is equal to the magnitude of your weight, *mg*.

(b) The reading on the bathroom scale becomes less than *mg* if you weigh yourself on an elevator accelerating downward.

(c) The reading is zero in vertical free fall at an amusement park.

(d) An astronaut in orbit is in free fall, so the reading on the scale is zero.

Apparent Weight and Artificial Gravity

When you stand on a bathroom scale, you feel a normal force pushing upward on your body. That normal force makes you aware of your weight, which has a magnitude of *mg*. If you were standing on that same scale in an elevator accelerating downward, the normal force pushing up on you would be less, so the weight you would feel would be less than *mg*. This force, called the **apparent weight**, is the net force exerted on an accelerating object in its noninertial frame of reference. If you were standing on that same scale on a free-falling amusement park ride, there would be no normal force and the scale would read zero. If you were to travel on the ISS, you would be in constant free fall, so there would be no normal force acting on you. **Figure 5** illustrates these four situations.

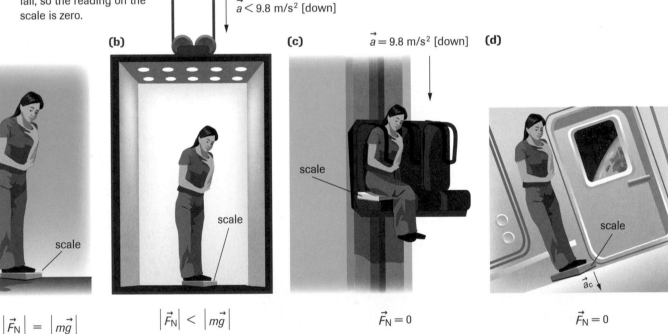

$\vec{a} < 9.8$ m/s² [down]

$\vec{a} = 9.8$ m/s² [down]

(a) **(b)** **(c)** **(d)**

scale scale scale scale

$\vec{a_c}$

$\left|\vec{F_N}\right| = \left|m\vec{g}\right|$ $\left|\vec{F_N}\right| < \left|m\vec{g}\right|$ $\vec{F_N} = 0$ $\vec{F_N} = 0$

Have you ever noticed how astronauts and other objects in orbiting spacecraft appear to be floating (**Figure 6**)? This condition arises as the spacecraft and everything in it undergo constant free fall. The apparent weight of all the objects is zero. (This condition of constant free fall has been given various names, including zero gravity, microgravity, and weightlessness. These terms will be avoided in this text because they are misleading.)

Since humans first became space travellers approximately four decades ago, researchers have investigated the effects of constant free fall on the human body. The absence of forces against the muscles causes the muscles to become smaller and the bones to become brittle as they lose calcium. Excess body fluids gather in the upper regions of the body causing the heart and blood vessels to swell, making the astronauts' faces look puffy and their legs look thinner. This imbalance of fluids also affects the kidneys, resulting in excess urination.

Today, vigorous exercise programs on space flights help astronauts reduce these negative effects on their bodies. Even with such precautions, however, the effects of constant free fall would be disastrous over the long periods needed to travel to other parts of the solar system, such as Mars. The most practical solution to this problem is to design interplanetary spacecrafts that have **artificial gravity**, where the apparent weight of an object is similar to its weight on Earth.

One way to produce artificial gravity during long space flights is to have the spacecraft constantly rotating (**Figure 7**). Adjusting the rate of rotation of the spacecraft to the appropriate frequency allows the astronauts' apparent weight to equal the magnitude of their Earth-bound weight.

Physics teachers often use water in a bucket swung quickly (and safely!) in a loop to simulate artificial gravity. You can perform a similar simulation in Activity 3.4.1 in the Lab Activities section at the end of this chapter.

Figure 6
Canadian astronaut Julie Payette in free fall during duties on the space shuttle *Discovery* in 1999.

artificial gravity situation in which the apparent weight of an object is similar to its weight on Earth

ACTIVITY 3.4.1

Simulating Artificial Gravity (p. 154)
You can use a ball inside a bucket swung quickly in a vertical circle to simulate the situation in which an astronaut moves with uniform circular motion on the interior wall of a rotating space station. How does this model differ from the real-life rotating space station?

DID YOU KNOW?

Early Space Stations
The former Soviet Union and the United States operated experimental space stations intermittently from the 1970s onward. The most famous and long-lasting station before the ISS was the Soviet (later Russian) *Mir*, launched in 1986 and decommissioned in 2001.

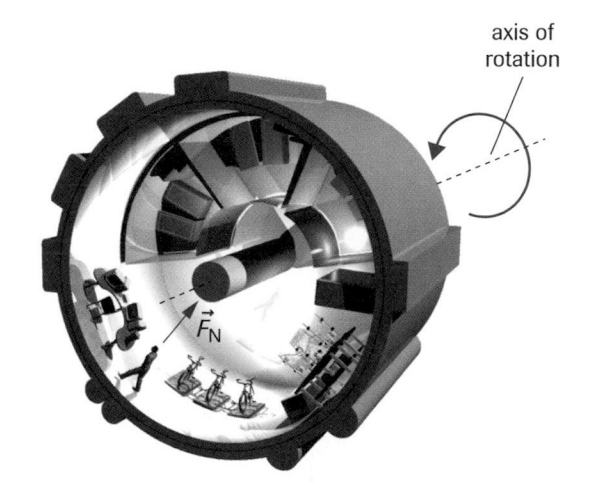

Figure 7
Any object on the inside surface of a rotating spacecraft experiences a normal force toward the centre of the craft. This normal force causes the centripetal acceleration of the objects in circular motion.

> **SAMPLE problem 2**

You are an astronaut on a rotating space station. Your station has an inside diameter of 3.0 km.

(a) Draw a system diagram and an FBD of your body as you stand on the interior surface of the station.

(b) Determine the speed you need to have if your apparent weight is to be equal in magnitude to your Earth-bound weight.

(c) Determine your frequency of rotation, both in hertz and in revolutions per minute.

(a)

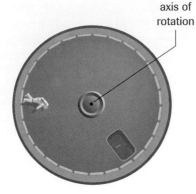

axis of rotation

(b)

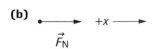

$\vec{F}_N$ $+x \longrightarrow$

Figure 8
(a) The system diagram of the astronaut and the space station for Sample Problem 2
(b) The FBD of the astronaut

Solution

(a) **Figure 8** contains the required diagrams.

(b) The centripetal acceleration is caused by the normal force of the inside surface of the station on your body. Your weight on Earth is *mg*.

$r = 1.5 \text{ km} = 1.5 \times 10^3 \text{ m}$

$v = ?$

$$\sum F = ma_x$$
$$F_N = ma_c$$
$$F_N = \frac{mv^2}{r}$$
$$mg = \frac{mv^2}{r}$$
$$v^2 = gr$$
$$v = \sqrt{gr}$$
$$= \sqrt{(9.8 \text{ m/s}^2)(1.5 \times 10^3 \text{ m})}$$
$$v = 1.2 \times 10^2 \text{ m/s}$$

Your speed must be 1.2×10^2 m/s.

(c) $v = 1.2 \times 10^2 \text{ m/s}$

$f = ?$

$$v = \frac{2\pi r}{T}$$
$$f = \frac{1}{T}$$
$$v = 2\pi r f$$
$$f = \frac{v}{2\pi r}$$
$$= \frac{1.2 \times 10^2 \text{ m/s}}{2\pi(1.5 \times 10^3 \text{ m})}$$
$$f = 1.3 \times 10^{-2} \text{ Hz, or 0.77 rpm}$$

Your frequency of rotation is 1.3×10^{-2} Hz, or 0.77 rpm.

▶ *Practice*

Understanding Concepts

7. Determine the magnitude of the apparent weight of a 56-kg student standing in an elevator when the elevator is experiencing an acceleration of (a) 3.2 m/s² downward and (b) 3.2 m/s² upward.

8. Describe why astronauts appear to float around the ISS even though the gravitational pull exerted on them by Earth is still relatively high.

9. The ISS travels at an altitude of 450 km above the surface of Earth.
   (a) Determine the magnitude of the gravitational force on a 64-kg astronaut at that altitude.
   (b) What percentage of the astronaut's Earth-bound weight is the force in (a)?

10. A cylindrical spacecraft travelling to Mars has an interior diameter of 3.24 km. The craft rotates around its axis at the rate required to give astronauts along the interior wall an apparent weight equal in magnitude to their Earth-bound weight. Determine (a) the speed of the astronauts relative to the centre of the spacecraft and (b) the period of rotation of the spacecraft.

Answers

7. (a) 3.7×10^2 N
  (b) 7.3×10^2 N

9. (a) 5.5×10^2 N
  (b) 87%

10. (a) 126 m/s
   (b) 80.8 s

Applying Inquiry Skills

11. You are an astronaut on a mission to Mars. You want to determine whether the frequency of rotation of your spacecraft is providing an apparent weight equal in magnitude to your Earth-bound weight. What experiment(s) could you perform?

Making Connections

12. Astronauts on a rotating spacecraft travelling to Mars, like present-day astronauts on the nonrotating ISS, need to minimize problems with muscles, bones, and body fluids. In what ways would an exercise program for astronauts bound for Mars resemble, and in what ways would it differ from, an exercise program for astronauts on the ISS?

SUMMARY *Satellites and Space Stations*

- Satellites can be natural (such as moons of planets) or artificial (such as the Hubble Space Telescope).

- The speed of a satellite in uniform circular motion around a central body is a function of the mass of that central body and the radius of the orbit. The speed is constant for a given radius.

- Any interplanetary space travel for humans in the future must involve artificial gravity aboard a spacecraft.

▶ *Section 3.4* *Questions*

Understanding Concepts

1. Describe a situation in which a space station is a satellite and a situation in which a space station is not a satellite.

2. Arrange the following satellites in decreasing order of speed: the Moon, the ISS, a geosynchronous satellite, and a weather-watch satellite. (Weather-watch satellites are closer to Earth than the ISS.)

3. The Moon's mass is 1.23% of Earth's mass and its radius is 27.2% of Earth's radius. Determine the ratio of the speed of an artificial satellite in orbit around Earth to the speed of a similar satellite in orbit around the Moon, assuming that the orbital radii are the same.

4. Mars travels around the Sun in 1.88 Earth years in an approximately circular orbit with a radius of 2.28×10^8 km. Determine (a) the orbital speed of Mars (relative to the Sun) and (b) the mass of the Sun.

5. Each satellite in the Global Positioning System travels at 1.05×10^4 km/h. Determine, in kilometres, each satellite's (a) orbital radius and (b) distance from the surface of Earth. (Refer to Appendix C for data.)

6. As a spacecraft of diameter 2.8 km approaches Mars, the astronauts want to experience what their Mars-bound weight will be. What should (a) the period and (b) the frequency of rotation be to simulate an acceleration due to gravity of magnitude 3.8 m/s²?

Applying Inquiry Skills

7. (a) Choose a toy that involves motion and describe how you think its operation on the ISS would differ from its operation on Earth.

   (b) Research which toys have been taken into space for physics experiments. Describe some results of these experiments.

    www.science.nelson.com

Making Connections

8. Although Earth's orbit around the Sun is not perfectly circular, it can still be analyzed by applying the principles and equations of circular motion. Consider that Earth's orbital speed is slightly greater during our winters than during our summers.

   (a) In which month, June or December, is Earth closer to the Sun?

   (b) Does your answer to (a) explain why June in the Northern Hemisphere is so much warmer than December? Why or why not?

INVESTIGATION 3.1.1

Analyzing Uniform Circular Motion

Inquiry Skills

○ Questioning	○ Planning	● Analyzing
● Hypothesizing	● Conducting	● Evaluating
● Predicting	● Recording	● Communicating

We have noted that the velocity of an object in circular motion at a constant speed is constantly changing in direction. Consequently, the object is undergoing acceleration directed toward the centre of the circle. The apparatus shown in **Figure 1** is designed for you to gather data as a rubber stopper travels with uniform circular motion. The apparatus consists of a hollow tube that can be held vertically in your hand and twirled around, causing the rubber stopper at the end of the string to revolve horizontally. The string to which the stopper is attached hangs through the tube and supports various masses. The force of gravity acting on these masses provides the tension force needed to keep the stopper moving along a circle.

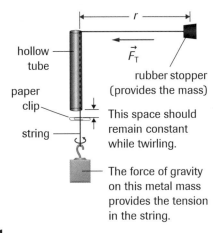

Figure 1
A rubber stopper twirled in the horizontal plane at a constant speed with a constant radius experiences uniform circular motion.

LEARNING TIP

Data Analysis
Investigation 3.1.1 is a controlled experiment in which three independent sets of data are analyzed to determine three different proportionality statements. An overall relationship can then be determined by combining the statements. Any one of the following methods can be used for the analysis:

- proportioning
- plotting of graphs to obtain straight lines
- log-log graphing
- using a graphing calculator

Appendix A discusses these methods.

Question

What is the relationship between the frequency of revolution of an object in uniform circular motion and

- the magnitude of the force causing the circular motion?
- the radius of the circular path?
- the mass of the object?

Hypothesis/Prediction

(a) State what you think is the relationship between the frequency of revolution and each variable named in the Question. Give a reason in each case.

(b) Sketch three graphs to illustrate your answers to (a).

Materials

For each group of three or four students:
a reinforced glass tube with smooth ends
1.5 m of fishing line or strong, smooth string
three one-holed rubber stoppers of equal size
metal masses (50 g, 100 g, and 200 g)
small paper clip or masking tape
electronic or triple-beam balance
metre stick

For each student, depending on the method of data analysis chosen:
linear graph paper (optional)
log-log graph paper (optional)
graphing calculator (optional)

 Appoint a spotter, responsible for keeping the working area clear of other students.

Wear impact-resistant safety goggles.

Procedure

1. Prepare a data table. You will need to have three sets of values when varying the tension force, three sets when varying the radius, and three sets when varying the mass.

INVESTIGATION 3.1.1 *continued*

2. Measure and record the mass, in kilograms, of each rubber stopper.

3. With one rubber stopper attached securely to one end of the string, hang a 200-g mass on the other end of the string and begin twirling the stopper around your head. Practise twirling the stopper in such a way that its path remains horizontal and at a constant radius. Do not proceed to the next step until you have gained proficiency in twirling the stopper at a constant speed.

4. Use the following method to control a constant radius of 75 cm: attach a paper clip or a small piece of masking tape 1 cm below the bottom of the tube when $r = 75$ cm. With this radius, a constant mass of one rubber stopper, and a tension force of 1.96 N (caused by the 200-g mass), twirl the stopper at a constant speed and measure the time for 20 complete cycles. Repeat this measurement until you think you have a good average value. Calculate the frequency of revolution. Enter your data in your data table.

5. Repeat step 4 using a tension force of 1.47 N, then 0.98 N, placing the appropriate mass on the end of the string both times.

6. With the mass constant at one rubber stopper and the tension force constant at 0.98 N, measure the time for 20 complete cycles when $r = 60$ cm and $r = 45$ cm. Repeat any measurements for accuracy. Calculate the frequencies and tabulate the data.

7. With a constant radius of 75 cm and a constant tension force of 1.96 N, add a second rubber stopper and measure the time for 20 complete cycles. Add a third rubber stopper and repeat the procedure. Calculate the frequencies and tabulate the data.

Analysis

(c) Use graphing techniques to determine the relationship (proportionality statement) between the frequency of revolution and each of the following:
  • the magnitude of the tension force (varied in steps 4 and 5)
  • the radius of the circle (varied in step 6)
  • the mass of the object in motion (varied in step 7)

(d) Combine the three results from (c) to obtain an equation for the frequency in terms of the tension, the radius, and the mass. Check your equation using your data points.

(e) The following relationship gives the magnitude of the net force causing the acceleration of an object in uniform circular motion:

$$\sum F = 4\pi^2 mrf^2$$

Rearrange this equation to isolate the frequency. Compare this result with the equation you derived in (d). Indicate the likely causes for any discrepancies.

(f) Draw an FBD of the mass in circular motion in this investigation. Be realistic here: Is the tension force on the stopper truly horizontal?

Evaluation

(g) For the greatest accuracy in this investigation, the tension force acting on the stopper should be horizontal. In this context, what happens to the accuracy as the frequency of revolution of the stopper increases (with other variables held constant)?

(h) Describe the sources of random, systematic, and human error in this investigation, as well as ways you tried to minimize them.

Synthesis

(i) Explain how this investigation illustrates all three of Newton's laws of motion.

ACTIVITY 3.4.1

Simulating Artificial Gravity

You can use a ball in a bucket moving with uniform circular motion to simulate the forces felt by an astronaut in a rotating space station (**Figure 1**).

Materials

For each group of three or four students:
plastic bucket with a strong handle
a tennis ball
metre stick
stopwatch

Perform this activity outdoors, far away from any windows or bystanders.

Procedure

1. Use a metre stick to measure the distance from the base of the bucket to the shoulder (i.e., the centre of revolution) of the person who will be performing the whirling.

2. Place the tennis ball into the bucket. Have the person responsible for whirling swing the bucket back and forth, until ready to swing it in complete vertical loops at a fairly high, constant speed. Have another group member, standing a safe distance away, use the stopwatch to determine the time for five complete revolutions of the bucket while it is moving at a constant speed.

3. Swing the bucket at the minimum speed needed to keep the ball inside. Determine the time for five complete revolutions of the bucket while it is moving at this speed.

Analysis

(a) Draw a system diagram and an FBD for the ball at the top of its loop in step 2.

(b) Estimate the speed of the bucket at the top of the loop in step 2, showing your calculations. From this estimate, calculate the magnitude of the centripetal acceleration of the ball at the top of the loop.

(c) Determine the approximate ratio of the apparent weight of the ball at the top of the loop to its regular Earth-bound weight.

(d) Repeat (a), (b), and (c) for step 3.

Evaluation

(e) Describe the strengths and weaknesses of this model of artificial gravity.

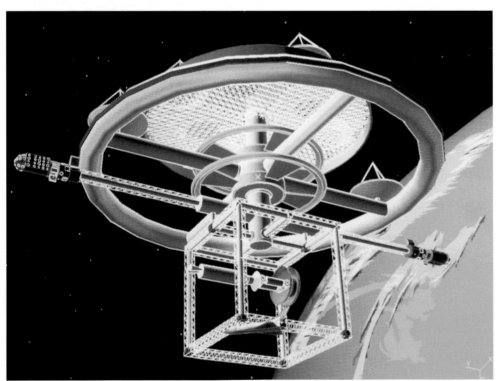

Figure 1
An artist's conception of a future space station

There are many different types of careers that involve the study of forces and motion. Find out more about the careers described below or about some other interesting career in forces and motion.

Commercial Airline Pilot

To become a commercial airline pilot, you must obtain an under-graduate degree, then a private pilot's license. You should also have a good working knowledge of trigonometry, vectors, and other math and physics principles. You must attend flight school for three to four years of in-flight training, and must then pass another examination set by Transport Canada. Commercial airline pilots work for major carriers such as Air Transat, Air Canada, and WestJet, and for small charter companies. Becoming a private pilot typically takes one or two years. About 45 hours of in-flight training are required before you can take the Transport Canada examination.

Certified Prostheticist

Prostheticists use a wide variety of tools—computers, hammers, saws, sanders, lathes, milling machines—and materials—plastic bandages, sculpting supplies, paints—to supply arms and legs, fingers, and toes for amputees. After obtaining an undergraduate degree in kinesiology, human kinetics, biology, or a related field, a prostheticist must study for two more years at a community college, take a two-year internship, and write national examinations for certification to the clinical pro-gram. Experienced medical technicians may also be admitted to the two-year pro-gram. Some community colleges offer a technical program for high-school graduates. High-school physics and mathematics are essential.

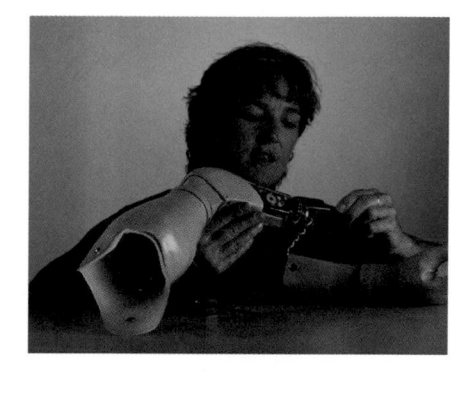

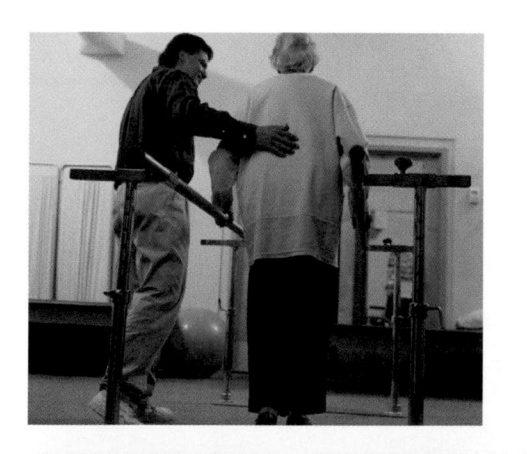

Physiotherapist

A physiotherapist must graduate from high school with a strong science back-ground, including physics and biology, then take a four-year bachelor's degree in science. Physiotherapists are healthcare professionals qualified to assist patients with physical conditions that cause pain and prevent or hamper mobility. Physiotherapists primarily work with their hands but also use an array of tools, including ultrasound equipment and lasers. Physiotherapists work both in hos-pitals and in private clinics. Strong interpersonal skills are essential.

► **Practice**

Making Connections

1. Identify several careers that require knowledge about forces and motion. Select a career you are interested in from the list you made or from the careers described above. Imagine that you have been employed in your chosen career for five years and that you are applying to work on a new project of interest.
   (a) Describe the project. It should be related to some of the new things you learned in this unit. Explain how the concepts from this unit are applied in the project.

   (b) Create a résumé listing your credentials and explaining why you are qualified to work on the project. Include in your résumé
   • your educational background: what university degree or diploma program you graduated with, which educational institute you attended, post-graduate training (if any)
   • your skills
   • your duties in previous positions
   • your salary expectations

   www.science.nelson.com

Key Expectations

- define and describe concepts and SI units related to the dynamics of circular motion (3.1, 3.2, 3.3, 3.4)

- analyze and predict, in quantitative terms, and explain uniform circular motion in the horizontal and vertical planes with reference to the forces involved (3.2)

- distinguish between noninertial (accelerating) and inertial (nonaccelerating) frames of reference, and calculate velocity and acceleration of objects in uniform circular motion (3.2, 3.4)

- describe Newton's law of universal gravitation, apply it quantitatively, and use it to explain the motion of planets and satellites (3.3, 3.4)

- investigate, through experimentation, the relationships among centripetal acceleration, radius of orbit, and frequency and period of an object in uniform circular motion, and analyze the relationships in quantitative terms (3.1)

- describe technological devices that are based on the concepts and principles of circular motion (e.g., explain, using scientific concepts and principles, how a centrifuge separates the components of a mixture and why the clothoid loop is used in the design of looping roller coasters) (3.2, 3.4)

- analyze the principles of dynamics and describe, with reference to these principles, how the motion of human beings, objects, and vehicles can be influenced by modifying certain factors (e.g., analyze artificial gravity in long-range spacecraft) (3.2, 3.4)

Key Terms

uniform circular motion	Newton's law of universal gravitation
centripetal acceleration	satellite
centripetal force	space station
centrifugal force	apparent weight
centrifuge	artificial gravity
Coriolis force	

Key Equations

- $a_c = \dfrac{v^2}{r} = \dfrac{4\pi^2 r}{T^2} = 4\pi^2 r f^2$ (3.1)

- $\sum F = \dfrac{mv^2}{r} = \dfrac{4\pi^2 mr}{T^2} = 4\pi^2 mr f^2$ (3.2)

- $F_G = \dfrac{Gm_1 m_2}{r^2}$ (3.3)

▶ *MAKE* a summary

Draw and label several FBDs to illustrate the key expectations, key terms, key equations, concepts, and applications presented in this chapter. Objects for which you can draw FBDs include

- a passenger near the outside perimeter of a merry-go-round (show both the inertial and noninertial frames of reference)

- a horizontal accelerometer held by a passenger on a merry-go-round

- a rubber stopper on the end of a string being twirled in a vertical circle (draw at least three FBDs)

- a car travelling around a banked curve as viewed from the rear of the car

- a geosynchronous satellite in orbit around Earth

- an astronaut walking along the inside wall of a large rotating space station

- a physics student using a vertical accelerometer at various locations on the ride shown in **Figure 1**

Figure 1
A vertical accelerometer can be used to determine the accelerations experienced by the riders at various locations on this coaster.

Write numbers 1 to 11 in your notebook. Indicate beside each number whether the corresonding statement is true (T) or false (F). If it is false, write a corrected version.

1. A body in uniform circular motion experiences acceleration that is constant in magnitude.

2. Centripetal acceleration is in a direction tangential to the path of the object in motion.

3. At a constant speed, the centripetal acceleration of an object in uniform circular motion is inversely proportional to the orbital radius, yet, at a constant period of revolution, the centripetal acceleration is directly proportional to the orbital radius.

4. The centrifugal force on an object in uniform circular motion is, as required by Newton's first law of motion, directed toward the centre of the circle.

5. Centripetal force is a fundamental force of nature that applies to all objects, both natural and human-made, in circular motion.

6. It is possible for static friction to be the sole force producing centripetal acceleration in a moving object.

7. The centripetal and centrifugal forces are an action-reaction pair of forces for an object in uniform circular motion.

8. Perturbations in the orbits of planets or other heavenly bodies can be used to locate additional such bodies.

9. The magnitude of your weight, as calculated from $F = mg$, yields a much smaller value than the magnitude of the force of gravity between you and Earth, as calculated from $F_G = \dfrac{Gmm_E}{r^2}$.

10. The International Space Station is an example of an artificial satellite.

11. As the radius of the orbit of a satellite in uniform circular motion around a central body increases, the speed of the satellite decreases.

Write numbers 12 to 23 in your notebook. Beside each number, write the letter corresponding to the best choice.

12. You are whirling a rubber stopper of mass m, attached to a string, in a vertical circle at a high constant speed. At the top of the circle, the net force that causes acceleration is
    (a) horizontal and greater in magnitude than mg
    (b) horizontal and lower in magnitude than mg
    (c) vertically downward and greater in magnitude than mg
    (d) vertically downward and lower in magnitude than mg
    (e) vertical and equal in magnitude to mg

13. At the bottom of the circle for this same rubber stopper, the net force that causes acceleration is
    (a) horizontal and greater in magnitude than mg
    (b) horizontal and lower in magnitude than mg
    (c) vertically upward and greater in magnitude than mg
    (d) vertically upward and lower in magnitude than mg
    (e) vertical and equal in magnitude to mg

14. You now reduce the speed of this stopper, so that the stopper barely makes it over the top of the circle. When the stopper is at its highest point, the net force toward the centre of the circle is
    (a) horizontal, and greater in magnitude than mg
    (b) horizontal, and lower in magnitude than mg
    (c) vertically downward, and greater in magnitude than mg
    (d) vertically downward, and lower in magnitude than mg
    (e) vertical, and equal in magnitude to mg

15. You are a passenger in a car making a right turn on level ground. The direction of the instantaneous velocity is north. The direction of the centrifugal force you feel is
    (a) west
    (b) northwest
    (c) north
    (d) northeast
    (e) east

16. When the tip of the minute hand on a clock face is moving past the 4:00 o'clock position, the vector in **Figure 1(a)** that gives the direction of the acceleration of the tip is
    (a) vector 4
    (b) vector 7
    (c) vector 1
    (d) vector 6
    (e) vector 10

17. When the child on the swing in **Figure 1(b)** reaches the lowest position on the swing, the vector in **Figure 1(a)** that gives the direction of the centripetal force is
    (a) vector 4
    (b) vector 10
    (c) vector 12
    (d) vector 6
    (e) vector 8

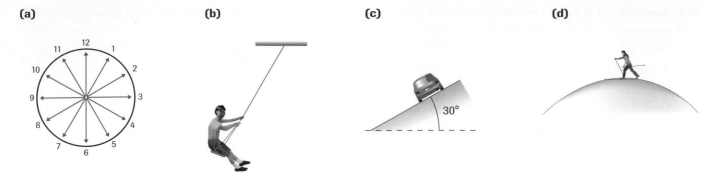

(a) **(b)** **(c)** **(d)**

Figure 1
For questions 16 to 19

18. In **Figure 1(c)**, the car is travelling at a constant speed around a banked curve. The direction of the normal force acting on the car and the direction of the centripetal acceleration of the car are the same as the directions, in **Figure 1(a)**, of
   (a) vector 12 and vector 6, respectively
   (b) vector 11 and vector 7, respectively
   (c) vector 11 and vector 8, respectively
   (d) vector 11 and vector 9, respectively
   (e) vector 11 and vector 11, respectively

19. At the instant shown in **Figure 1(d)**, the skier is travelling over a frictionless, circular hump. The direction of the skier's instantaneous velocity and the direction of the net force acting on the skier are the same as the directions, in **Figure 1(a)**, of
   (a) vector 9 and vector 9, respectively
   (b) vector 9 and vector 6, respectively
   (c) vector 10 and vector 7, respectively
   (d) vector 8 and vector 5, respectively
   (e) vector 8 and vector 12, respectively

20. Choose the graph in **Figure 2** that most accurately represents the variation in the net force toward the centre of the circle on an object in uniform circular motion, as a function of the mass of the object.

21. Choose the graph in **Figure 2** that most accurately represents the variation in the gravitational force of attraction between two uniform spheres, as a function of their centre-to-centre separation.

22. Choose the graph in **Figure 2** that most accurately represents the variation in the centripetal acceleration of an object in uniform circular motion, as a function of the speed of the object at a constant radius.

23. Choose the graph in **Figure 2** that most accurately represents the variation in the speed of a moon undergoing uniform circular motion around a planet, as a function of the mass of the planet.

(a) **(b)** **(c)** **(d)** **(e)**

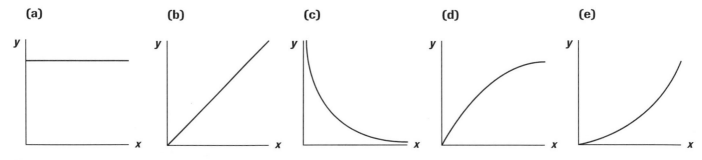

Figure 2
For questions 20 to 23

An interactive version of the quiz is available online.   NEL
GO   www.science.nelson.com

Understanding Concepts

1. Is centripetal acceleration an instantaneous acceleration, an average acceleration, both, or neither? Explain.

2. Do all points along the minute hand of a clock experience the same centripetal acceleration? Explain.

3. If the speed of a particle in circular motion is increasing, is the net acceleration of the particle still directed toward the centre of the circle? Use a diagram to explain your answer.

4. A civil engineer has calculated that the magnitude of the maximum centripetal acceleration of a car on a certain horizontal curve is 4.4 m/s². What is the minimum radius of this curve for a car travelling at 25 m/s?

5. For the clock shown in **Figure 1**, calculate the magnitude of the centripetal acceleration of the tip of the second hand, the minute hand, and the hour hand.

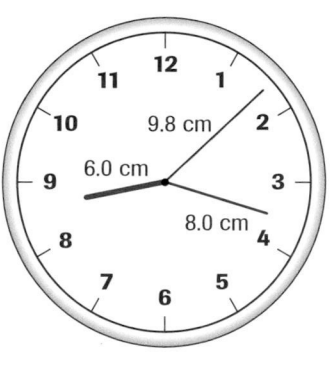

Figure 1

6. A chicken is cooking on the rotating turntable of a microwave oven. The end of the drumstick, which is 16 cm from the centre of rotation, experiences a centripetal acceleration of magnitude 0.22 m/s². Determine the period of rotation of the plate.

7. For each of the following situations, draw an FBD and name the force(s) causing the centripetal acceleration:
   (a) A truck travels, without sliding, around an unbanked curve on a highway.
   (b) A bus travels around a banked curve at the optimal speed for the banking angle.
   (c) A planet travels in an essentially circular orbit around the Sun.
   (d) A communications satellite travels in a circular orbit around Earth.

8. A wet towel, of mass 0.65 kg, travels in a horizontal circle of radius 26 cm in the spin cycle of a washing machine. The frequency of rotation is 4.6 Hz.
   (a) Name the force causing the centripetal acceleration. What object exerts that force?
   (b) What is the speed of the towel?
   (c) Determine the magnitude of the centripetal force on the towel.

9. Neptune travels in a nearly circular orbit, of diameter 9.0×10^{12} m, around the Sun. The mass of Neptune is 1.0×10^{26} kg. The gravitational force of attraction between Neptune and the Sun has a magnitude of 6.8×10^{20} N.
   (a) What is the speed of Neptune?
   (b) Determine Neptune's period of revolution around the Sun in Earth years.

10. Points A through E in **Figure 2** represent a piece of cement experiencing centripetal acceleration in the vertical plane inside a rotating cement mixer. The mixer itself is in uniform circular motion. For each of the points A through E, draw an FBD of the piece of cement at that point, and state what forces cause the centripetal acceleration.

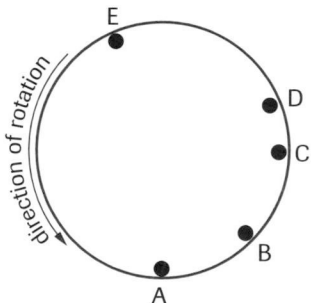

Figure 2

11. A 45.7-kg boy on a swing moves in a circular arc of radius 3.80 m. At the lowest position, the child's speed reaches 2.78 m/s. Determine the magnitude of the tension in each of the two vertical support chains.

12. A sport utility vehicle, of mass 2.1×10^3 kg, travels in the horizontal plane around an unbanked curve of radius 275 m at a speed of 26 m/s, without sliding.
   (a) Determine the minimum coefficient of static friction between the tires and the road.
   (b) How would your answer in (a) be affected if the mass of the vehicle were greater because of the presence of heavy cargo?
   (c) How would your answer in (a) be affected if the curve were sharper (i.e., if its radius were smaller)?

13. A ball, of mass 0.23 kg, is attached securely to a string, then whirled at a constant speed in a vertical circle of radius 75 cm.
    (a) Draw FBDs of the ball at the top and the bottom of the circle.
    (b) Determine the magnitude of the tension in the string at the locations in (a) for which the speed of the ball is 3.6 m/s.
    (c) Calculate the minimum speed of the ball at the top of the path if it is to follow a complete circle.

14. In which of the following situations would it *not* be possible to determine the gravitational force of attraction from the equation $F_G = \dfrac{Gm_A m_B}{r^2}$, if in each case the masses and the radius r are provided?
    (a) Saturn and one of Saturn's moons
    (b) two friends hugging
    (c) a ball moving in a parabola through the air and Earth
    (d) two textbooks standing together on a bookshelf

15. A spherical meteor approaches Earth from a great distance. By what factor does the force between Earth and the meteor increase when the distance between the centres of the two bodies decreases by a factor of 3.9?

16. At a certain distance above Earth's surface, the gravitational force on a certain object is only 2.8% of its value at Earth's surface. Determine this distance, expressing it as a multiple of Earth's radius, r_E.

17. Determine the magnitude of the gravitational force between two bowling balls, each of mass 1.62 kg, if the centres are separated by 64.5 cm.

18. The orbit of Venus is approximately circular. The masses of the Sun and Venus are 1.99×10^{30} kg and 4.83×10^{24} kg, respectively. The Sun-Venus distance is 1.08×10^8 km. Determine the centripetal acceleration of Venus.

19. Given the data in **Figure 3**, calculate the net gravitational force on the Moon due to the gravitational forces exerted by Earth and the Sun.

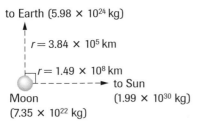

to Earth (5.98×10^{24} kg)

$r = 3.84 \times 10^5$ km

$r = 1.49 \times 10^8$ km

to Sun

Moon   (1.99×10^{30} kg)
(7.35×10^{22} kg)

Figure 3

20. The *Canadarm2* is the robotic arm, designed and built in Canada, that services the ISS in its orbit 4.50×10^2 km above the surface of Earth. Although the mass of this arm is 1.80×10^3 kg, it can move masses as large as 1.16×10^5 kg on the ISS.
    (a) Determine the magnitude of the force of gravity acting on the maximum load for the arm.
    (b) If the arm had to move such a large mass here on the surface of Earth, it would break. Why does it not break in space?

Applying Inquiry Skills

21. Suppose that you have determined the results in **Table 1** while performing an investigation. Determine the new value for the centripetal force.

Table 1 Data for Question 21

Before	After
mass = 1 ball	mass = 3 balls
radius = 0.75 m	radius = 1.50 m
frequency = 1.5 Hz	frequency = 3.0 Hz
centripetal force = 8.0 units	centripetal force = ? units

22. A conical pendulum consists of a mass (the pendulum bob) that travels in a circle on the end of a string, tracing out a cone as in **Figure 4**. For the pendulum shown, $m = 1.50$ kg, $L = 1.15$ m, and $\theta = 27.5°$.

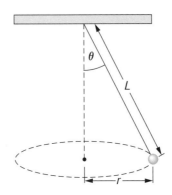

Figure 4
A conical pendulum

    (a) Describe how you would investigate what factors affect the frequency of revolution of the pendulum.
    (b) Draw an FBD of the bob at the instant shown. What force causes the centripetal acceleration?

(c) Calculate the speed of the bob.

(d) Determine the frequency of the bob.

23. How would the device in **Figure 4** of the Chapter 3 introductory Try This Activity have to be modified to make it work aboard the ISS? Explain your answer.

Making Connections

24. In April 2001, an automobile race on a 2.4-km oval racetrack in Fort Worth, Texas, was cancelled because of complaints of danger by the drivers. At the high speeds involved, the drivers experienced forces nearly twice as great as the forces on most racetracks. Find out why the racetrack was so dangerous and why the race was cancelled. Explain the physics of the situation, referring to the banking angle of the track and the net forces on the drivers.

 www.science.nelson.com

Extension

25. Obtain the value of *g* at the surface of Earth using the motion of the Moon. Assume that the Moon's period around Earth is 27 d 8 h and that the radius of its orbit is 60.1 times the radius (6.38×10^6 m) of Earth.

26. Snoopy, in hot pursuit of the Red Baron, is flying his vintage warplane in a "loop-the-loop" path. His instruments tell him that the plane is level (at the bottom of the loop) and travelling at a speed of 180 km/h. He is sitting on a set of bathroom scales. He notes that the scales show four times his normal weight. What is the radius of the loop, in metres?

   ● Sir Isaac Newton Contest Question

27. Your favourite physics teacher who is late for class attempts to swing from the roof of a 24-m high building to the bottom of an identical building using a 24-m rope as shown in **Figure 5**. She starts from rest with the rope horizontal, but the rope will break if the tension force in it is twice the weight of the teacher. How high is the swinging physicist above level when the rope breaks? (*Hint:* Apply the law of conservation of energy.)

   ● Sir Isaac Newton Contest Question

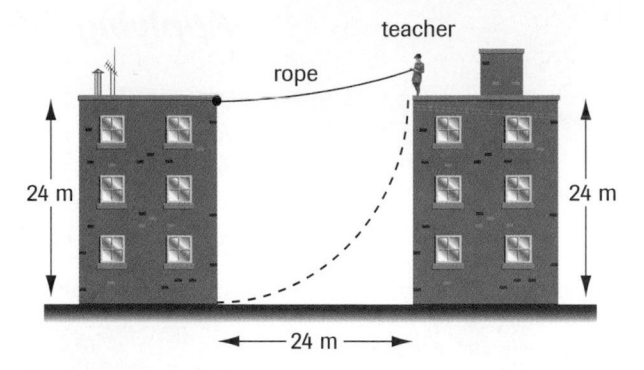

Figure 5

28. A baseball player works out by slugging a baseball in an Olympic stadium. The ball hangs from a long, light vertical rod that is free to pivot about its upper end (P), as shown in **Figure 6(a)**. The ball starts off with a large horizontal velocity, but the rod pulls it up in a big vertical circle and it coasts slowly over the top as shown. If we look at the ball on the way down, after the rod has swung through 270°, which of the vector arrows shown in **Figure 6(b)** gives the correct direction for the acceleration of the ball? Ignore air resistance and friction at the pivot.

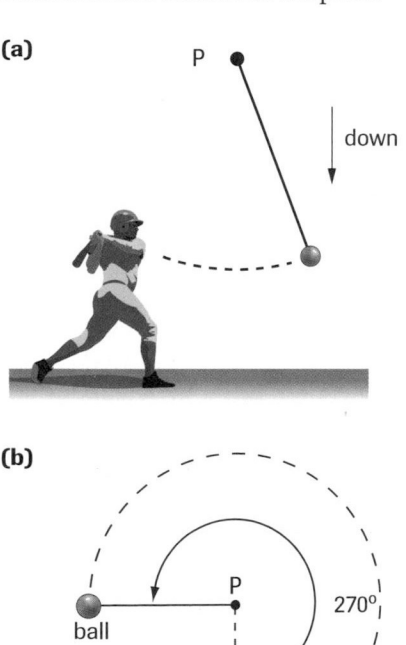

Figure 6

   ● Sir Isaac Newton Contest Question

PERFORMANCE TASK

Applying Principles of Motion and Forces

▶ **Criteria**

Process

- Choose appropriate apparatus and materials to build the coaster model or the toys OR choose appropriate research tools, such as books, magazines, the Internet, and experts in the field.

- Apply physics principles to the design, construction, testing, and modification of the roller coaster or the toys OR carry out the research, synthesizing the information with appropriate organization and sufficient detail.

- Evaluate the design, construction, testing, and modification process OR analyze the physical principles of the centrifuges.

- Evaluate the research reporting process (Option 3).

Product

- Demonstrate an understanding of the related physics principles, laws, and theories.

- Use terms, symbols, equations, and SI units correctly.

- Prepare a suitable technological task portfolio with notes, diagrams, safety considerations, tests, modifications, and analysis (Options 1 and 2) OR prepare an appropriate research portfolio in print and/or audiovisual format (Option 3).

- Create a working model of an original looping roller coaster or an original toy with operating instructions (Options 1 and 2) OR prepare a formal report and a live or videotaped presentation (Option 3).

Unit 1 deals with motion and forces in one and two dimensions. In this performance task, you will create or analyze a device that involves motion and forces. The motion can be linear or circular. Your chosen forces can be of any kind—including the force of gravity, the normal force, tension, the force of static friction, the force of kinetic friction, air resistance, etc. **Figure 1** shows a few devices that fit these criteria.

Figure 1
The ideas presented in Unit 1 are applied in the design and operation of roller coasters, toys involving friction and air resistance, and centrifuges.

The first looping roller coaster, called the "Flip-Flap," was built in 1888. The ride, lasting just ten seconds, took a circular loop so rapidly that neck and back injuries were common. Years later, roller coasters with the clothoid loop design (Section 3.3) were developed. The evolution of the roller coaster illustrates the process of technological development: a need is identified; a product is designed, constructed, and tested to meet that need; problems are identified, which may create a new need; and modifications are made to the product to solve the problems or to accommodate the new need.

For this task, you will follow this process of technological development to build a model roller coaster (Option 1) or an original toy (Option 2). You will analyze your final product with the physics principles we have examined in Unit 1.

You will research and analyze centrifuges for Option 3. Centrifuges are used in many ways. Focus on a few applications of particular interest to you. In researching centrifuges, find a variety of sources of information, from printed matter and the Internet to local enterprises and people who work with and/or use centrifuges. You can then synthesize the information you discover in your final communication product.

Basic safety and design rules should be discussed before brainstorming for your task begins. For example, any tools used to construct the models in Options 1 and 2 must be used safely, and the tests of any device should be carried out in a safe and proper way.

You are expected to demonstrate an understanding of the relationships between forces and motions discussed in this text. Further, you will apply skills of inquiry and communication which you have developed not only in physics, but in your other science studies.

The Task
Choose one of the following:

Option 1: A Model Roller Coaster
Your task is to apply physics principles to design, build, test, modify, and analyze a model of a looping coaster that will take a marble or a small ball bearing from the top of the coaster to the bottom. Your design of this gravity ride will depend on the dimensions and construction materials suggested by your teacher. Before starting the task, decide what criteria can be used to evaluate the model, and whether there will be a model coaster competition.

Option 2: Toys That Apply Physics Principles
Your task is to apply physics principles to design, build, test, modify, and analyze two models of an original toy that involves friction and/or air resistance. Look carefully at existing toys that require friction and/or air resistance to operate. After observing what currently exists, think of an original toy. You should build two models of your design to demonstrate how changing the friction or air resistance leads to a change in the toy's action.

Option 3: Centrifuges
Your task is to research the application of centrifuges for medical, forensic, and industrial purposes, and for testing and training humans. As an extension, you can research and compare the use of centrifuges in space with Earth-bound centrifuges. You will use scientific concepts and principles to explain the operation and advantages of centrifuges.

Analysis
Your analysis should include answers to the following questions:

Options 1 and 2
(a) What are the physics principles applied to the design and/or use of the roller coaster model or the toys?

(b) What criteria can be used to evaluate the success of your device?

(c) What safety precautions did you observe in constructing and testing your device?

(d) How did you test your device to identify necessary improvements?

(e) How can the process you used in performing this task be applied in the real world?

(f) List problems that you encountered during the creation of the model coaster or toys, and explain how you solved them.

(g) Create your own analysis questions and answer them.

Option 3
(h) What are the physics principles applied to the design and use of centrifuges?

(i) What are the principal uses of centrifuges, and who are the principal users?

(j) How is the design of a centrifuge affected by its purpose?

(k) How common and costly are centrifuges?

(l) What impact have centrifuges had on individual users and society at large?

(m) What careers are related to the manufacture and use of centrifuges?

(n) What research (including research related to space science) is being carried out to improve the design and use of centrifuges?

(o) Create your own analysis questions and answer them.

Evaluation
Your evaluation will depend on the option you choose.

Options 1 and 2
(p) How does your design compare with the designs of other students or groups?

(q) Draw a flow chart of the process you used in working on this task. How do the steps compare to the steps in a typical laboratory investigation in this unit?

(r) If you were to begin this task again, what would you modify to ensure a better process and a better final product?

Option 3
(s) Evaluate the resources you used in your research.

(t) If you were to embark on a similar task with a different goal, what changes to the process would you make to ensure successful research and an appropriate means of communicating what you find?

Write numbers 1 to 12 in your notebook. Indicate beside each number whether the corresponding statement is true (T) or false (F). If it is false, write a corrected version.

For questions 1 to 6, consider a ball of mass *m*, thrown at an angle above the horizontal and undergoing projectile motion under negligible air resistance.

1. The time for the ball to rise equals the time for the ball to fall to the same horizontal level.

2. The net force on the ball at the top of its flight is zero.

3. The acceleration of the ball on the way up equals the acceleration on the way down.

4. After leaving your hand and before landing, the speed of the ball is at a minimum at the top of its trajectory.

5. The magnitude of the horizontal component of the velocity of the ball just before impact exceeds the magnitude of the horizontal component of the velocity just after the ball leaves your hand.

6. The magnitude of the acceleration of the ball at the top of its trajectory equals the ratio of the weight of the ball to its mass.

For questions 7 to 12, assume that you are twirling a small rubber stopper of mass *m* (at a constant speed *v*) tied to a string in a vertical circle as shown in **Figure 1**.

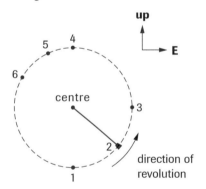

Figure 1
For questions 7 to 12

7. At position 3, the direction of the instantaneous acceleration is westward and the direction of the instantaneous velocity is upward.

8. The vector quantity $\frac{\Delta \vec{v}}{\Delta t}$ is closest to the instantaneous acceleration as the stopper moves from position 6 to position 1.

9. The magnitude of the tension in the string at position 1 exceeds the magnitude of the tension at position 4 by an amount equal to *mg*.

10. At position 5, the force that causes the stopper to accelerate toward the centre of the circle is the sum of the force of tension in the string and a component of the force of gravity on the stopper.

11. If you release the ball at the instant it reaches position 1, the instantaneous velocity of the stopper just after the release will have a small upward component and a large eastward component.

12. For a constant radius and frequency of revolution of the stopper, the magnitude of the centripetal acceleration is directly proportional to *m*.

Write numbers 13 to 24 in your notebook. Beside each number, write the letter corresponding to the best choice.

Questions 13 to 18 relate to the situation in **Figure 2**, in which a child on a toboggan (a system of total mass *m*) accelerates down a hill of length *L* inclined at an angle *θ* to the horizontal in a time interval Δ*t*. The +*x* and +*y* directions are labelled on the diagram. Assume that friction is negligible unless indicated.

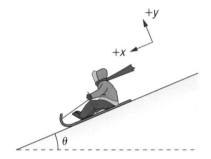

Figure 2
For questions 13 to 18

13. The magnitude of the child's acceleration down the hill is

(a) $\frac{g}{\sin \theta}$ (c) $g \sin \theta$ (e) $g \tan \theta$

(b) $\frac{g}{\cos \theta}$ (d) $g \cos \theta$

14. The magnitude of the child's average velocity is

(a) $\sqrt{2gL}$ (c) $\sqrt{2gL \sin \theta}$ (e) $\sqrt{\frac{gL \sin \theta}{2}}$

(b) $\sqrt{\frac{gL}{2}}$ (d) $\sqrt{gL \sin \theta}$

15. The magnitude of the force exerted by the toboggan on the hill is

(a) *mg* (c) *mg* sin *θ* (e) −*mg* sin *θ*
(b) *mg* cos *θ* (d) *mg* tan *θ*

16. If the child starts from rest and accelerates uniformly down the hill, the time required to reach the bottom of the hill is

(a) *Lg* sin *θ* (c) $\sqrt{2Lg \sin \theta}$ (e) $\sqrt{\frac{2L}{g \sin \theta}}$

(b) 2*Lg* sin *θ* (d) $\frac{2L}{g \sin \theta}$

17. If $\vec{v}_{av}$ is the average velocity and $\vec{v}$ is the instantaneous velocity, then at the halfway point in the journey down the hill
(a) $|\vec{v}_{av}| = |\vec{v}|$
(b) $|\vec{v}_{av}| > |\vec{v}|$
(c) $|\vec{v}_{av}| < |\vec{v}|$
(d) $|\vec{v}_{av}|$ and $|\vec{v}|$ can be compared only if we are given numerical data.
(e) $\vec{v}_{av}$ and $\vec{v}$ cannot be meaningfully compared, since the object in question is on an inclined plane .

18. If the situation in **Figure 2** is changed so that there is a coefficient of kinetic friction μ_K between the toboggan and the hill, then the magnitude of the child's acceleration down the hill is
(a) $g(\sin\theta - \mu_K\cos\theta)$
(d) $g(\mu_K\cos\theta - \sin\theta)$
(b) $g(\sin\theta + \mu_K\cos\theta)$
(e) none of these
(c) $\dfrac{g\sin\theta}{\mu_K\cos\theta}$

19. A car of mass m collides head-on with a truck of mass $5m$. If $\vec{F}_{C\rightarrow T}$ and $\vec{F}_{T\rightarrow C}$ are the forces respectively exerted during the collision on the car by the truck and on the truck by the car, then
(a) $|\vec{F}_{T\rightarrow C}| > |\vec{F}_{C\rightarrow T}|$
(b) $|\vec{F}_{T\rightarrow C}| < |\vec{F}_{C\rightarrow T}|$
(c) $|\vec{F}_{T\rightarrow C}| = |\vec{F}_{C\rightarrow T}|$
(d) $|\vec{F}_{T\rightarrow C}| = 0$
(e) $\vec{F}_{C\rightarrow T}$ and $\vec{F}_{T\rightarrow C}$ cancel because they are in opposite directions

20. A monkey throws a walnut from a tree, giving the walnut an initial velocity of 2.5 m/s [down]. Air resistance is negligible. After being released, the walnut experiences an acceleration of
(a) 9.8 m/s² [up]
(b) 9.8 m/s² [down]
(c) less than 9.8 m/s² [down]
(d) more than 9.8 m/s² [down]
(e) zero

21. A rocket of mass m is at a distance $3r_E$ from Earth's centre when its engines are fired to move it to a distance $6r_E$ from Earth's centre. Upon reaching its destination, its new mass is $\dfrac{m}{2}$ since fuel is consumed in the burn. The ratio of Earth's gravitational force on the rocket at the first location to the gravitational force on the rocket at the second location is
(a) 8:1 (b) 4:1 (c) 2:1 (d) 1:4 (e) 1:8

22. Which of the following is a list of all the forces that act on a satellite in circular orbit around Earth?
(a) the force due to the satellite's motion and the force of gravity toward Earth
(b) the force due to the satellite's motion, the centrifugal force, and the force of gravity toward Earth
(c) the centrifugal force and the force of gravity toward Earth
(d) the centripetal force and the force of gravity toward Earth
(e) the force of gravity toward Earth

23. A stunt airplane flies in a vertical circular loop of radius r at a constant speed. When the airplane is at the top of the loop, the pilot experiences an apparent weight of zero. The speed of the airplane is
(a) $2gr$
(c) $\dfrac{g}{r}$
(e) $\sqrt{\dfrac{g}{r}}$
(b) gr
(d) $\sqrt{gr}$

24. A 9.5-kg box is initially stationary on a horizontal table. The coefficient of kinetic friction between the table and the box is 0.49. The coefficient of static friction is 0.65. The magnitude of the minimum force needed to set the box into motion is
(a) 4.7 N
(c) 93 N
(e) 46 N
(b) 6.2 N
(d) 61 N

Write the numbers 25 to 40 in your notebook. Beside each number, place the word, number, phrase, or equation that completes the sentence(s).

25. State the number of significant digits in each measurement or answer of the operation:
(a) 0.0501 N ___?___
(b) 3.00×10^5 km/s ___?___
(c) 25.989 m + 25.98 m + 25.9 m + 25 m ___?___
(d) 65.98 m ÷ 11.5 s ÷ 2.0 s ___?___

26. Convert the following measurements:
(a) 109 km/h = ___?___ m/s
(b) 7.16×10^4 km/min = ___?___ m/s
(c) 3.4 mm/s² = ___?___ m/s²
(d) 5.7 cm/(ms)² = ___?___ m/s²
(e) 4.62×10^{-3} (km/h)/s = ___?___ m/s²

27. A windsock indicates ___?___ .

28. The three principal controls a car has for regulating acceleration are ___?___ , ___?___ , and ___?___ .

29. You are facing southward when suddenly a snowball passes in front of your eyes from left to right. The snowball was thrown from some distance away with an initial horizontal velocity. The direction of the instantaneous velocity is now __?__. The direction of the instantaneous acceleration is now __?__.

30. If the direction of an object undergoing uniform circular motion is suddenly reversed, the direction of the centripetal acceleration is __?__.

31. If $\vec{v}_{LM}$ is 26 m/s [71° W of S], then $\vec{v}_{ML}$ is __?__.

32. __?__ $= \vec{v}_{CD} + \vec{v}_{DE}$

33. The horizontal acceleration of a projectile is __?__.

34. The acceleration of an object falling (vertically) through the air at terminal speed is __?__.

35. Using L, M, and T for the dimensions of length, mass, and time, respectively, then
    (a) the dimensions of the slope of a line on a velocity-time graph are __?__
    (b) the dimensions of the area under the line on an acceleration-time graph are __?__
    (c) the dimensions of weight are __?__
    (d) the dimensions of the universal gravitation constant are __?__
    (e) the dimensions of gravitational field strength are __?__
    (f) the dimensions of a coefficient of static friction are __?__
    (g) the dimensions of frequency are __?__
    (h) the dimensions of the slope of a line on an acceleration-force graph are __?__

36. The law of inertia is also known as __?__.

37. As the speed of a flowing river increases, the pressure of the flowing water __?__.

38. An accelerating frame of reference is also known as __?__. In such a frame, we must invent __?__ to explain an observed acceleration. If the frame is rotating, the invented force is called __?__.

39. A passenger of mass m is standing on an elevator that has an acceleration of magnitude a. The normal force acting on the passenger has a magnitude of __?__ if the acceleration is upward, and __?__ if the acceleration is downward.

40. On the surface of the Moon, your __?__ would be the same as on the surface of Earth, but your __?__ would be reduced by a factor of __?__.

Write the numbers 41 to 46 in your notebook. Beside each number, place the letter that matches the best choice. Use the choices listed below.

(a) directly proportional to
(b) inversely proportional to
(c) proportional to the square of
(d) inversely proportional to the square of
(e) proportional to the square root of
(f) inversely proportional to the square root of
(g) independent of

41. For an object moving at a constant velocity, the time interval needed to cover a certain displacement is __?__ the velocity.

42. When a ball is undergoing projectile motion, the horizontal motion is __?__ the vertical motion.

43. For a car that starts from rest and undergoes constant acceleration, the time interval to cover a certain displacement is __?__ the displacement.

44. On the surface of Earth, your weight is __?__ the mass of Earth.

45. For an object that remains stationary on a horizontal surface, the magnitude of the static friction is __?__ the magnitude of the horizontal force applied to the object.

46. For an object undergoing uniform circular motion with a constant radius, the magnitude of the centripetal acceleration is __?__ the speed. The force that causes the centripetal acceleration is __?__ the period of revolution of the object.

Understanding Concepts

1. Choosing the positive direction of a one-dimensional motion as south, describe the motion of a runner with
   (a) a positive velocity and a positive acceleration
   (b) a positive velocity and a negative acceleration
   (c) a negative velocity and a negative acceleration
   (d) a negative velocity and a positive acceleration

2. State the conditions under which
   (a) average speed exceeds instantaneous speed
   (b) average speed is less than instantaneous speed
   (c) average speed equals instantaneous speed

3. Can a component of a vector have a magnitude greater than the magnitude of the vector? Explain.

4. Describe the motion represented by each graph in **Figure 1**.

(a)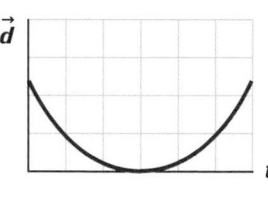

(b)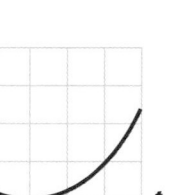

(c)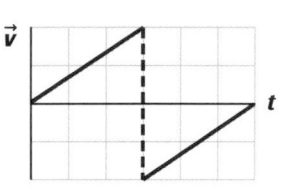

(d)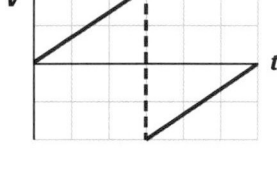

Figure 1

5. Would a parachute work on the Moon? Explain your answer.

6. A square is inscribed in a circle as shown in **Figure 2**. One person walks from X to Y along the edge of the square. A second person walks along the circumference. Each person reaches B after 48 s. Calculate
   (a) each person's average speed
   (b) each person's average velocity

7. Compare the horizontal ranges of projectiles launched with identical velocities on Earth and on the Moon.

8. The following objects are dropped from a rooftop: a pencil, a Ping-Pong ball, a piece of paper, and a feather. On a single speed-time graph, sketch the curve for each object, assuming that the objects reach the ground in the order given.

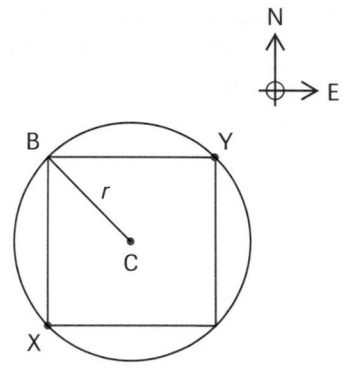

$r = 12$ m

Figure 2
For question 6

9. A car of mass 1.2×10^3 kg travels initially at 42 km/h on the entrance ramp of an expressway, then accelerates uniformly to 105 km/h in 21 s.
   (a) How far, in kilometres, does the car travel in this interval?
   (b) Determine the magnitude of the car's average acceleration, in kilometres per hour per second.
   (c) Calculate the magnitude of the average force needed to cause this acceleration.

10. A billiard ball travels 0.44 m [S] from its original position, bounces off another ball and travels 0.88 m [N], then bounces off the edge of the billiard table, coming to rest 0.12 m from that edge. The entire motion is one-dimensional and takes 2.4 s. Calculate
    (a) average speed of the ball
    (b) the final position of the ball
    (c) the average velocity of the ball

11. A 12-hour clock mounted on a vertical wall has a second hand with a tip that is 14 cm from the centre of the clock.
    (a) What is the average speed of the tip of the second hand?
    (b) Determine the instantaneous velocity of the tip when it passes the 6:00 o'clock position and the 10:00 o'clock position.
    (c) Find the average velocity of the tip between the 1:00 o'clock position and the 5:00 o'clock position.

12. A train is travelling at 23 m/s [E] when it enters a curved portion of the track and experiences an average acceleration of 0.15 m/s² [S] for 95 s. Determine the velocity of the train after this acceleration.

13. A projectile lands at the same elevation from which it is launched. At what position(s) in its flight is the speed of the projectile greatest? least?

14. An inflated balloon is released and immediately moves eastward. Explain what causes this motion.

15. In running a 100-m sprint in 10 s, an Olympic-class athlete accelerates to a speed of about 8.0 m/s in the first 2.0 s. Determine the magnitude of the average horizontal force on a 63-kg runner during this interval. What exerts the force?

16. At a certain distance above the surface of Earth, the gravitational force on an object is reduced to 18% of its value at Earth's surface. Determine this distance and express it as a multiple of Earth's radius, r_E.

17. A trapeze artist balances in the middle of a tightrope 14.2 m in length. The middle of the rope is 2.3 m below the two secured ends. If the artist's weight is 6.3×10^2 N [down], determine the magnitude of the tension in the rope.

18. If the speed of a particle in circular motion is decreasing, is the particle's acceleration still toward the centre of the circle? Use a diagram to explain your answer.

19. The magnitude of the maximum centripetal acceleration of a car on a certain horizontal curve is 4.49 m/s^2. For a car travelling at 22 m/s, determine the minimum radius of curvature of this curve.

20. Mars travels in a nearly circular orbit of radius 2.28×10^{11} m around the Sun. The mass of Mars is 6.27×10^{23} kg. The gravitational force of attraction between Mars and the Sun has a magnitude of 1.63×10^{21} N.
    (a) What is the speed of Mars?
    (b) Determine the period of revolution of Mars around the Sun in Earth years.

21. A ride at an amusement park rotates, with circular motion, in the vertical plane 72 times during the 3.0 min of maximum rotation rate. Passengers on the ride are 6.3 m from the centre of the ride. When viewed from the side of the ride so that it is rotating clockwise, determine the instantaneous velocity of a passenger at the following clock positions:
    (a) 3:00 o'clock
    (b) 6:00 o'clock
    (c) 7:00 o'clock

22. Determine the magnitude of the average acceleration during the time interval it takes each object described below to complete half a revolution around the central object.
    (a) A satellite takes 80.0 min to travel once around Earth, in an orbit of diameter 1.29×10^4 km.
    (b) The Moon travels once around Earth in 2.36×10^6 s, at an average speed of 1.02 km/s.

23. In pairs figure skating, a female of mass 55 kg spirals in a horizontal circle of radius 1.9 m around a male skater of mass 88 kg. The frequency of revolution is 0.88 Hz.
    (a) Determine the magnitude of the force causing the female skater to maintain her circular motion.
    (b) What is the magnitude of the horizontal force on the male skater?

24. An 18-g rubber stopper is suspended by a 45-cm string from the rear-view mirror of a car. As the car accelerates eastward, the string makes an angle of 5.1° with the vertical.
    (a) Draw an FBD of the stopper in Earth's frame of reference.
    (b) Draw an FBD of the stopper in the car's frame of reference.
    (c) Determine the acceleration of the car.

25. A homeowner drags a garbage can of mass 27 kg along a horizontal sidewalk at a constant speed of 1.8 m/s by applying a force of 1.12×10^2 N [27° above the horizontal]. What is the coefficient of kinetic friction between the garbage can and the sidewalk?

26. Box A ($m = 2.5$ kg) is connected by a rope that passes over a frictionless pulley to Box B ($m = 5.5$ kg), as shown in **Figure 3**. The coefficient of kinetic friction between the box and the ramp is 0.54. Determine the magnitude of the acceleration of the boxes.

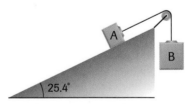

Figure 3

27. Determine the magnitude of the apparent weight of a 62-kg person in an elevator when the elevator is
    (a) accelerating at 2.5 m/s² [up]
    (b) accelerating at 2.5 m/s² [down]
    (c) moving with zero acceleration at 2.5 m/s [up]

Applying Inquiry Skills

28. A Ferris wheel at an amusement park close to your school somehow falls off its support and rolls along the ground.
    (a) Determine a reasonable estimate of the number of rotations the wheel would make, travelling in a straight line, to reach the closest capital city of a province other than your own. State all your assumptions and show all your calculations.
    (b) If you were at an amusement park, how would you use indirect measurements to determine the diameter of a Ferris wheel that cannot be accessed directly. Show a sample calculation.

29. Assuming that you have an accurate stopwatch, describe how you could calculate the average acceleration of a car in the distance from the starting position to the end of a straight 100-m stretch of track.

30. You are planning a controlled investigation in which you determine the effect of air resistance on falling objects.
    (a) What objects would you choose to test the effects of air resistance?
    (b) Describe what measurements you would make and how you would make them.
    (c) What safety precautions would you take in conducting your investigation?

31. Draw a sine curve for angles ranging from 0° to 180°. With reference to this curve, explain why there are two possible launch angles corresponding to any horizontal range for a projectile, with one exception. What is that exception?

32. Steel washers connected by a fishing line to a force sensor, labelled A in **Figure 4**, are kept hovering by a heavy U-shaped magnet suspended from a second force sensor, B. The force sensors are connected to a computer such that the force registered by A is negative and the force registered by B is positive.
    (a) If the force registered by A is −0.38 N, what is the force registered by B? Explain the physics principle on which your answer is based.
    (b) Sketch, on a single force-time graph, the dataset the computer program would generate as the force sensor B is slowly raised.

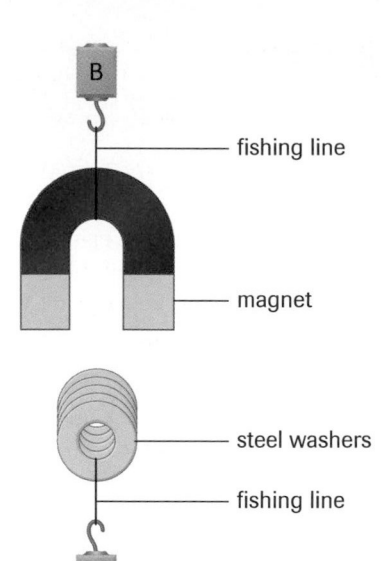

Figure 4

33. An experiment is performed in which a varying net force is applied to a dynamics cart; the resulting accelerations are shown in **Table 1**. Plot a graph of the data and use the information on the graph to determine the object's mass.

Table 1 Data for Question 33

Net Force (N [forward])	Acceleration (m/s² [forward])
0	0
1.0	0.29
2.0	0.54
3.0	0.83
4.0	1.10
5.0	1.42
6.0	1.69
7.0	1.89

34. After performing an investigation to determine how the frequency of a rubber stopper in uniform circular motion in the horizontal plane depends on the magnitude of the tension force acting on the stopper, the mass of the stopper, and the radius of the circle, you draw graphs to show the relationships. You are then asked to draw the corresponding graphs by replacing the frequency with the period of revolution as the dependent variable. Draw these graphs.

Making Connections

35. A pole vault jumper clears the crossbar set at a height of 6.0 m above the mat.
    (a) Determine the time interval for the first 45 cm on the way down.
    (b) Determine the time interval for the last 45 cm before reaching the mat.
    (c) Explain why the jumper appears to be in "slow motion" near the top of the jump.

36. A swimmer steps off the edge of a diving board and falls vertically downward into the water. Describe the velocities and accelerations of the swimmer from the initial position until impact.

37. If you drop a stone into a deep well and hear a splash 4.68 s after dropping the stone, how far down is the water level? Neglect air resistance and assume that the speed of the sound in air is 3.40×10^2 m/s.

38. A certain volleyball player can jump to a vertical height of 85 cm while spiking the volleyball.
    (a) How long is the player in the air?
    (b) What is the player's vertical take-off speed?

39. A person's terminal speed with an open parachute ranges from 5.0 m/s to 10.0 m/s. You are designing a training facility in which people practise landing at the same speeds they would when parachuting. What range of heights will you specify for the practice platforms?

40. Explain why an east-to-west trans-Canada airplane flight generally takes longer than a west-to-east flight.

41. Water moving horizontally at 2.0 m/s spills over a waterfall and falls 38 m into a pool below. How far out from the vertical wall of the waterfall could a walkway be built so that spectators stay dry?

42. A motorist's reaction time can be crucial in avoiding an accident. As you are driving with a velocity of 75.0 km/h [N], you suddenly realize that there is a stalled vehicle in your lane 48.0 m directly ahead. You react, applying the brakes to provide an acceleration of 4.80 m/s² [S]. If you manage to just avoid a collision, what is your reaction time?

43. **Figure 5** shows a time-exposure photograph in which the stars and planets visible appear to be travelling in circles around a central star (the North Star, Polaris).

Figure 5
The North Star is almost directly above Earth's North Pole.

(a) Explain the observed motion of the stars and planets in the photograph. (Include the concepts related to frames of reference.)
(b) How can you estimate how long the exposure time was?
(c) Would people in Australia be able to take this photograph or a similar one? Explain your answer.

44. In answering a newspaper reader's question, "Why does a shower curtain move inward while water is spraying downward?" a physicist replies, "The air being dragged downward by the water must be replaced by air from somewhere else."
    (a) With reference to the appropriate principle, provide a more technical explanation to the reader's question.
    (b) If you were answering the question in a newspaper article, what other examples or demonstrations could you describe to help the readers understand the situation?

45. In the exciting sport of kite surfing (**Figure 6**), a specially designed power kite propels the pilot across the water on kite boards. The pilot can rise high into the air for several seconds, performing amazing aerial stunts. Would you expect the power kite to be designed to have good streamlining? Explain your answer.

46. A remote-sensing satellite travels in a circular orbit at a constant speed of 8.2×10^3 m/s.
    (a) What is the speed of the satellite in kilometres per hour?
    (b) Determine the altitude in kilometres of the satellite above Earth's surface.
    (c) What is remote sensing? Give some practical uses of a remote-sensing satellite.

47. In the future, video games and simulations of sports activities will become more realistic, as designers become better able to apply the physics principles presented in this unit. Describe some ways in which these games and simulations could become more realistic.

48. In testing a model of a looping roller coaster, an engineer observes that the current design would result in a zero normal force acting on the passengers at the top of the loop.
    (a) If the radius of the loop is 2.1 m, what is the speed of the model coaster at the top of the loop?
    (b) Explain why and how the coaster design should be changed.

49. (a) Why will artificial gravity be needed on a space mission to Mars by humans?
    (b) Describe how artificial gravity could be created on such a mission.

Extension

50. In a basketball game, a ball leaves a player's hand 6.1 m downrange from the basket from a height of 1.2 m below the level of the basket. If the initial velocity of the ball is 7.8 m [55° above the horizontal] in line with the basket, will the player score a basket? If not, by how much will the ball miss the basket?

Figure 6
Kite surfing is a dangerous and physically demanding sport.

Energy and Momentum

Dr. Judith Irwin
Astrophysicist, Queen's University

Humans have looked at the night sky for thousands of years, but the science of astrophysics is a relatively young field. Today, astrophysicists such as Judith Irwin, carry out detailed observations, carefully reducing collected data until they can see some small part of the universe that no one has ever seen before. This spirit of discovery has led astrophysicists to examine the extremes of our physical universe, from the least dense regions in the so-called vacuum of space, to the densest objects known—black holes. Dr. Irwin's research involves understanding the dynamics of gases that are found in interstellar space between hot stars. Because gases are affected by the dynamics of objects nearby (like a supernova or an exploding star) the gases are swept up into an expanding shell around the explosion. Calculating the energy and momentum of this shell provides information on its evolution as it grows and expands into space.

While astrophysics is exploding with new research, it is still a vast unexplored canvas. Unravelling the secrets of celestial objects becomes ever more possible as technology—including such telescopes as the Very Large Array in New Mexico, the James Clerk Maxwell Telescope in Hawaii, and the Giant Metre-wave Radio Telescope in India—becomes more sophisticated and precise. Dr. Irwin and her Canadian colleagues are involved in several major international projects involving the "next generation" of telescopes.

▶ Overall Expectations

In this unit, you will be able to

- apply the concepts of work, energy, and momentum, and the laws of conservation of energy and momentum for objects moving in two dimensions, and explain them in qualitative and quantitative terms

- investigate the laws of conservation of momentum and of energy (including elastic and inelastic collisions) through experiments or simulations, and analyze and solve problems involving these laws with the aid of vectors, graphs, and free-body diagrams

- analyze and describe the application of the concepts of energy and momentum to the design and development of a wide range of collision and impact-absorbing devices used in everyday life

▸ **Prerequisites**

Concepts

- define terms and use them
  in context
- apply relationships involving
  uniform acceleration and
  Newton's laws of motion
- recognize different forms of
  energy
- describe examples of energy
  transformations

Skills

- analyze graphs
- analyze vectors
- manipulate algebraic
  equations
- apply basic trigonometric
  functions
- draw scale diagrams and
  free-body diagrams
- analyze dimensions of
  quantities
- use SI units
- perform controlled
  investigations
- communicate using written
  and mathematical formats
- manipulate computer
  software
- conduct research using
  printed resources and the
  Internet
- identify and analyze social
  issues related to the design
  of vehicles

Knowledge and Understanding

1. Name and briefly identify the different forms of energy associated with vehicles travelling on a mountain highway (**Figure 1**).

Figure 1
Several different forms of energy are involved in the movement of vehicles along this highway.

2. State at least one quantity that has the following SI base units:
   (a) kg　　　(b) $kg \cdot m^2/s^2$　　　(c) $kg \cdot m/s^2$　　　(d) $kg \cdot m^2/s^3$

3. In your answers to question 2, identify any derived units that have been named after a scientist and name the scientist.

4. You move a box of mass m from the floor to a shelf, as in **Figure 2**. On what does the work you do on the box depend? Be specific in your answer.

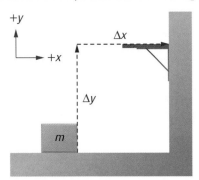

Figure 2
Does the work you do in raising the box depend on the values of Δy and Δx?

Inquiry and Communication

5. A basketball has a kinetic energy of 29.5 J before bouncing off the floor, and a kinetic energy of 25.1 J afterward.
   (a) Determine the percentage of the initial energy lost during the bounce.
   (b) Was that kinetic energy really lost? Explain your answer.

6. You pull a child on a sleigh up a hill inclined at an angle to the horizontal with a force parallel to the hillside (**Figure 3**).
   (a) What measurements would you need to make to determine the efficiency of the incline in this situation?
   (b) What conditions are required for the efficiency to be 100%?

7. Some people confuse conservation of energy with conserving energy. Clarify the meanings of these two expressions.

Making Connections

8. A school bus is involved in a collision.
   (a) What features of the bus help protect the passengers?
   (b) What features not currently incorporated in school buses would make the bus safer in a collision?
   (c) Why are the features you described in (b) not currently available on school buses?

9. (a) Describe the energy transformations that occur when a ski jumper goes from the base of a hill to the top, then moves down the hill and glides through the air (**Figure 4**), eventually landing on the hillside and coming to rest at the bottom of the hill.
   (b) What law of physics governs the energy transformations in (a)?
   (c) What safety precautions are implemented in this sport?

Math Skills

10. Write the proportionality statement relating the variables in *italics*, and sketch the corresponding graph for each of the following cases.
    (a) The *work* done by the net force on an object triples if the *displacement* of the object triples.
    (b) The *energy* stored in a rubber band increases by a factor of 4 if the *stretch* of the band doubles.
    (c) The *power* achieved by a person going up a flight of stairs increases by a factor of 2.5 if the *time interval* needed to climb the stairs decreases by a factor of 2.5.
    (d) Your *kinetic energy* depends on the square of your *speed* of motion.

11. State the *x*- and *y*-components of the forces shown in **Figure 5** in terms of the variables labelled on each diagram.

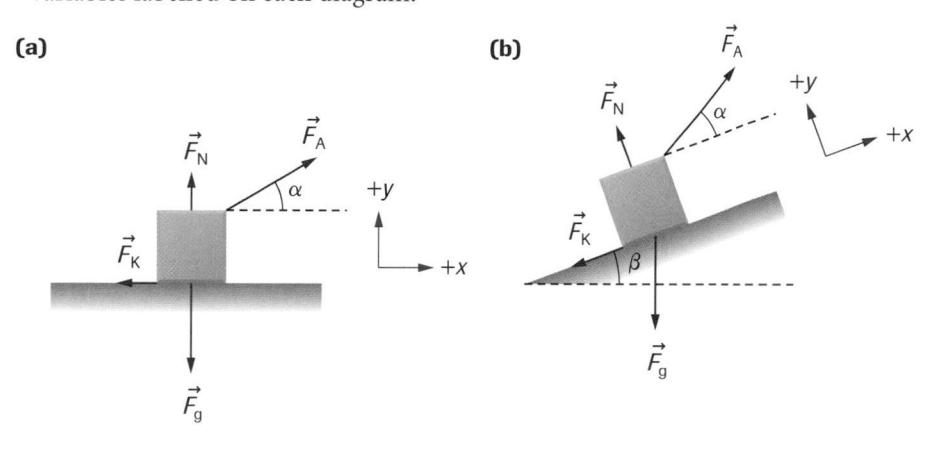

(a)

(b)

12. **Figure 6** shows a cone with the vertex labelled. Copy the diagram into your notebook, and then label the plane that cuts across the cone to illustrate
    (a) a circle   (b) an ellipse   (c) a parabola   (d) a hyperbola

Technical Skills and Safety

13. An air table is a useful device for studying the collisions between two air pucks. Although a level may be available to determine if the table is horizontal, another method can be used.
    (a) Describe how to use air pucks to determine whether the air table is level.
    (b) Why should you ensure that the table is level before determining the speeds of the air pucks before and after they collide?
    (c) What other major sources of error should be minimized in performing an investigation with an air table or other device that involves motion in two dimensions?

14. What safety precautions should be followed when using motion sensors, force sensors, and electrical equipment, such as an air table?

Figure 3
Efficiency relates output work or energy to input work or energy.

Figure 4
Safety is important in the exciting, but dangerous, sport of ski jumping.

Figure 5
(a) The object is moving on a horizontal surface.
(b) The object is moving up an inclined plane.

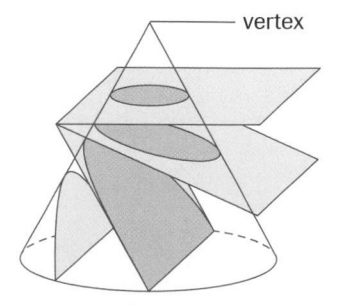

Figure 6
"Conic sections" can be drawn or cut on a cone to generate various geometric shapes.

Work and Energy

In this chapter, you will be able to

- analyze and explain situations involving work and energy
- define and describe concepts and units related to energy
- analyze situations involving the concepts of mechanical energy, thermal energy and its transfer (heat), and the law of conservation of energy
- design and conduct an experiment to verify the law of conservation of energy in a system involving several types of energy
- analyze and describe, using the law of conservation of energy, various practical applications of energy transformations
- state Hooke's law and analyze it in quantitative terms

Springs are used in bed mattresses, armchairs, door-closing units, pens, toys, exercise equipment, children's jumpers, trampolines, vehicles, and many other objects. Whenever a force is applied to a spring, the spring has elastic potential energy that is stored until the spring returns to its original shape. What forms of energy can be transformed into elastic potential energy? How can that energy be used for other functions? These are just a few of the questions you will learn to answer in this chapter.

On most vehicles, springs operate in conjunction with shock absorbers. Both devices serve to improve the safety and comfort of the occupants (**Figure 1**). As its name suggests, a shock absorber absorbs some of the shock that occurs when a vehicle encounters a bump or pothole in the road. As this is happening, energy of motion changes into elastic potential energy, which in turn changes back into energy of motion and thermal energy. The energy does not disappear—it simply changes form.

You may recall how energy is changed from one form into another, and how such energy transformations can be analyzed. In this chapter, you will extend your knowledge to analyze energy transformations in two-dimensional situations.

REFLECT on your learning

1. Some springs are compression springs. Others are extension springs. Explain the difference, giving several examples of each.

2. Although a bouncing ball obeys the law of conservation of energy, it reaches a lower height with each successive bounce. Explain this apparent discrepancy.

3. How does a grandfather clock use gravitational potential energy to keep time?

4. **Figure 2** shows identical carts being pushed along a smooth, horizontal surface with negligible friction. Force $\vec{F}_1$ has a horizontal component equal in magnitude to force $\vec{F}_2$.
   (a) If both carts are pushed the same distance forward, how does the work done on cart 1 compare with the work done on cart 2?
   (b) Would your answer to (a) change if the carts were replaced with boxes, assuming that the coefficient of kinetic friction between each box and the surface were equal? Explain your answer.
   (c) If $\vec{F}_2$ is less than the maximum static friction force between box 2 and the underlying surface, how much work does $\vec{F}_2$ do on the box?

5. The spring in a spring scale stretches when a force is applied to it. Assuming that the spring does not overstretch, sketch a graph to show how the amount of stretch depends on the magnitude of the force.

6. You are designing a shock absorber to be attached to the wheel of a motorcycle. What design features will you include? (Consider such issues as choice of materials, internal friction, and dimensions.)

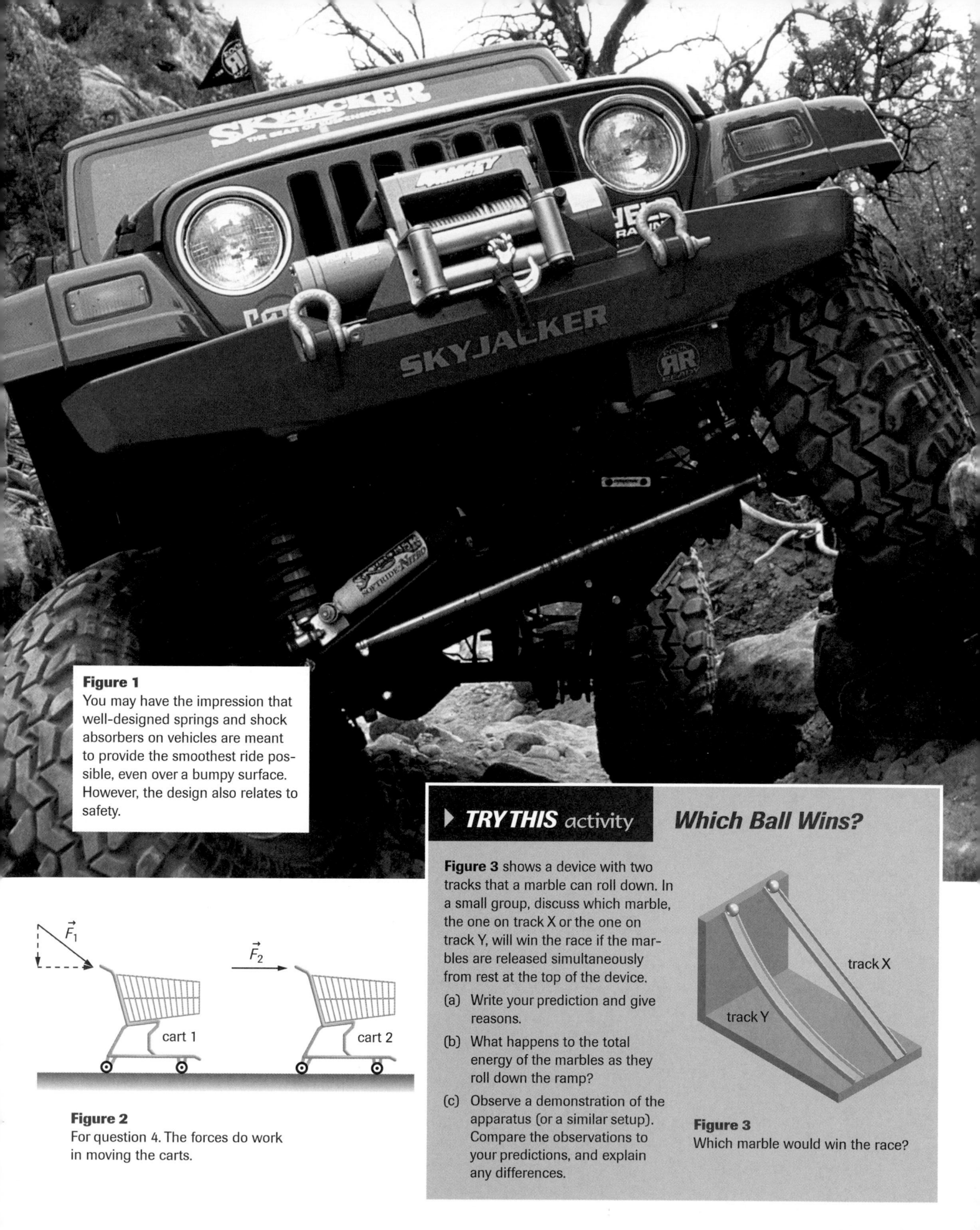

Figure 1
You may have the impression that well-designed springs and shock absorbers on vehicles are meant to provide the smoothest ride possible, even over a bumpy surface. However, the design also relates to safety.

Figure 2
For question 4. The forces do work in moving the carts.

cart 1

cart 2

▶ **TRY THIS** activity   *Which Ball Wins?*

Figure 3 shows a device with two tracks that a marble can roll down. In a small group, discuss which marble, the one on track X or the one on track Y, will win the race if the marbles are released simultaneously from rest at the top of the device.

(a) Write your prediction and give reasons.

(b) What happens to the total energy of the marbles as they roll down the ramp?

(c) Observe a demonstration of the apparatus (or a similar setup). Compare the observations to your predictions, and explain any differences.

track X

track Y

Figure 3
Which marble would win the race?

Work and Energy   **177**

work (W) the energy transferred to an object when a force acting on the object moves it through a distance

In everyday language, the term "work" has a variety of meanings. In physics, however, **work** is the energy transferred to an object when a force acting on the object moves it through a distance. For example, to raise your backpack from the floor to your desk, you must do work. The work you do in raising the backpack is directly proportional to the magnitude of the displacement and directly proportional to the magnitude of the applied force.

The force needed to raise the backpack and the displacement of the backpack are in the same direction. However, this is often not the case, as shown in **Figure 1** where the force is at some angle θ to the displacement. The component of the force that is parallel to the displacement, $F \cos \theta$, causes the object to undergo the displacement. The resulting mathematical relationship is the defining equation for work:

$$W = (F \cos \theta)\Delta d$$

where W is the work done on an object by a constant force $\vec{F}$, F is the magnitude of that force, θ is the angle between the force and the displacement, and Δd is the magnitude of the displacement.

(a)

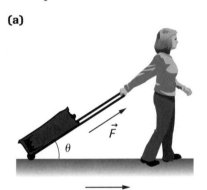

direction of the displacement

(b)

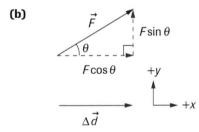

Figure 1
(a) Work can be done by a force that is at an angle to the displacement.
(b) The component of the force parallel to the displacement is $F \cos \theta$.

joule (J) SI derived unit for measuring forms of energy and work; equal to the work done when a force of 1 N displaces an object 1 m in the direction of the force

Work is a scalar quantity—it has no direction. Since force is measured in newtons and displacement in metres, the SI unit for work is the newton metre (N·m). The newton metre is called a **joule** (J) after James Prescott Joule (1818–1889), a British physicist who did pioneering research into the relationship between work and heat. Since the joule is a derived SI unit, it can be expressed in terms of metres, kilograms, and seconds: $1 \text{ J} = 1 \text{ kg·m}^2/\text{s}^2$.

> ▶ **SAMPLE** problem 1
>
> An emergency worker applies a force to push a patient horizontally for 2.44 m on a gurney with nearly frictionless wheels.
>
> (a) Determine the work done in pushing the gurney if the force applied is horizontal and of magnitude of 15.5 N.
>
> (b) Determine the work done if the force, of magnitude 15.5 N, is applied at an angle of 25.3° below the horizontal.
>
> (c) Describe the difference in the observed motion between (a) and (b).

Solution

(a) In this case, the force and the displacement are in the same direction.

$F = 15.5 \text{ N}$

$\theta = 0°$

$\Delta d = 2.44 \text{ m}$

$W = ?$

$$W = (F \cos \theta)\Delta d$$
$$= (15.5 \text{ N})(\cos 0°)(2.44 \text{ m})$$
$$= 37.8 \text{ N·m}$$
$$W = 37.8 \text{ J}$$

The work done is 37.8 J.

(b) $\theta = 25.3°$

$W = ?$

$$W = (F \cos \theta)\Delta d$$
$$= (15.5 \text{ N})(\cos 25.3°)(2.44 \text{ m})$$
$$W = 34.2 \text{ J}$$

The work done is 34.2 J.

(c) Since friction is negligible, the applied force causes an acceleration in the direction of the horizontal component. The greater amount of work accomplished in (a) must result in a greater speed after the gurney has moved 2.44 m. (This example relates to the concept of work changing into kinetic energy, which is presented in Section 4.2.)

In Sample Problem 1, the positive work done caused the speed of the gurney to increase. However, if the force acting on an object in motion is opposite in direction to the displacement, we say that negative work is done. If the only force acting on an object does negative work, the result is a decrease in the speed of the object.

> ▶ **SAMPLE** problem **2**

A snowboarder reaches the bottom of a hill, then glides to a stop in 16.4 m along a horizontal surface (**Figure 2**). The total mass of the board and its rider is 64.2 kg. The coefficient of kinetic friction between the snowboard and the snow is 0.106.

(a) Draw an FBD of the snowboarder as the board is gliding to a stop. Determine the magnitude of the kinetic friction.

(b) Calculate the work done by friction in bringing the board to a stop.

Solution

(a) The FBD of the snowboarder is shown in **Figure 3**.

$m = 64.2 \text{ kg}$

$g = |\vec{g}| = 9.80 \text{ N/kg}$

$\mu_K = 0.106$

$|\vec{F}_N| = |m\vec{g}|$ because $\Sigma \vec{F}_y = ma_y = 0$

$F_K = ?$

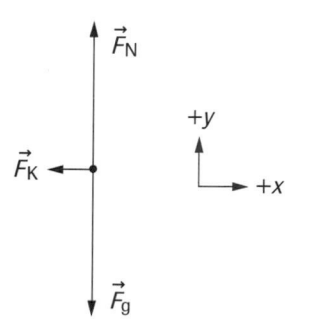

Figure 2
The system diagram of the snowboarder in Sample Problem 2

Figure 3
The FBD of the snowboarder in Sample Problem 2

Using the magnitudes of the forces (as described in Section 2.4):

$$F_K = \mu_K F_N$$
$$= (\mu_K)(mg)$$
$$= (0.106)(64.2 \text{ kg})(9.80 \text{ N/kg})$$
$$F_K = 66.7 \text{ N}$$

The magnitude of kinetic friction is 66.7 N.

(b) $F_K = 66.7$ N

$\Delta d = 16.4$ m

$\theta = 180°$

$$W = (F_K \cos \theta)\Delta d$$
$$= (66.7 \text{ N})(\cos 180°)(16.4 \text{ m})$$
$$W = -1.09 \times 10^3 \text{ J}$$

The work done by the kinetic friction is -1.09×10^3 J.

In Sample Problem 2, the work done by the kinetic friction is negative. In this case, the negative work caused a decrease in speed. Can negative work be done in other situations? Consider the work done in lowering an object at a constant speed.

> ▶ **SAMPLE** problem **3**

A store employee raises an 8.72-kg case of cola at a constant velocity from the floor to a shelf 1.72 m above the floor. Later, a customer lowers the case 1.05 m from the shelf to a cart at a constant velocity. (We can neglect the short periods of acceleration at the beginning and end of the raising and lowering of the case.) Determine the work done on the case

(a) by the employee as the case rises

(b) by gravity as the case rises

(c) by the customer as the case descends

Solution

(a) **Figure 4(a)** shows that the force needed to raise the case at constant velocity is equal in magnitude to the weight of the case, $|m\vec{g}|$.

$\theta = 0°$ $g = 9.80$ N/kg $W = ?$

$m = 8.72$ kg $\Delta d = 1.72$ m

$$W = (F \cos \theta)\Delta d$$
$$= (mg \cos \theta)\Delta d$$
$$= (8.72 \text{ kg})(9.80 \text{ N/kg})(\cos 0°)(1.72 \text{ m})$$
$$W = 1.47 \times 10^2 \text{ J}$$

The work done on the case by the employee is 1.47×10^2 J.

(b) Since the force of gravity is opposite in direction to the displacement, $\theta = 180°$.

$$W = (F \cos \theta)\Delta d$$
$$= (mg \cos \theta)\Delta d$$
$$= (8.72 \text{ kg})(9.80 \text{ N/kg})(\cos 180°)(1.72 \text{ m})$$
$$W = -1.47 \times 10^2 \text{ J}$$

The work done by gravity is -1.47×10^2 J.

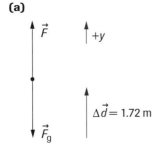

(a)

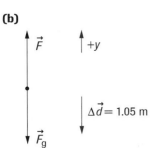

(b)

Figure 4
System diagrams and FBDs for Sample Problem 3
(a) Employee raising a case of cola
(b) Customer lowering a case of cola into a cart

(c) **Figure 4(b)** shows that the force needed to lower the case at constant velocity is upward while the displacement is downward.

$\theta = 180°$

$\Delta d = 1.05$ m

$$W = (F \cos \theta) \Delta d$$
$$= (mg \cos \theta) \Delta d$$
$$= (8.72 \text{ kg})(9.80 \text{ N/kg})(\cos 180°)(1.05 \text{ m})$$
$$W = -8.97 \times 10^1 \text{ J}$$

The work done on the case by the customer is -8.97×10^1 J.

.Notice that in Sample Problem 3, the work done on the case by an upward force as the case rises (at constant velocity) is positive, but the work done by a downward force (gravity) as the case rises is negative. Likewise, the work done on the case by an upward force as the case moves downward (at constant velocity) is negative. We can conclude that the equation $W = (F \cos \theta) \Delta d$ yields positive work when the force and displacement are in the same direction, and negative work when the force and displacement are in opposite directions. This conclusion also applies when considering the components of the forces involved.

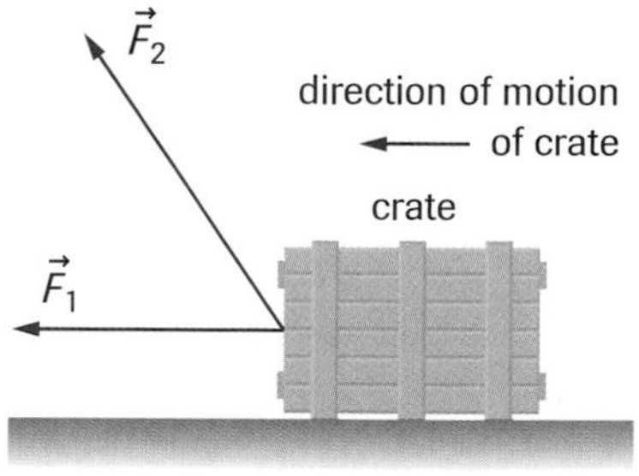

direction of motion
of crate

crate

scale: 1.0 cm = 5.0 N

Figure 5
For question 1

▶ *Practice*

Understanding Concepts

1. **Figure 5** shows a scale diagram of two applied forces, $\vec{F}_1$ and $\vec{F}_2$, acting on a crate and causing it to move horizontally. Which force does more work on the crate? Explain your reasoning.

2. Can the work done by the force of kinetic friction on an object ever be positive? If "yes," give an example. If "no," explain why not.

3. Can the work done by the force of Earth's gravity on an object ever be positive? If "yes," give an example. If "no," explain why not.

4. A 2.75-kg potted plant rests on the floor. Determine the work required to move the plant at a constant speed
   (a) to a shelf 1.37 m above the floor
   (b) along the shelf for 1.07 m where the coefficient of kinetic friction is 0.549

5. A loaded grocery cart of mass 24.5 kg is pushed along an aisle by an applied force of 14.2 N [22.5° below the horizontal]. How much work is done by the applied force if the aisle is 14.8 m long?

6. A tension force of 12.5 N [19.5° above the horizontal] does 225 J of work in pulling a toboggan along a smooth, horizontal surface. How far does the toboggan move?

7. **Figure 6** is a graph of the net horizontal forces acting on an object as a function of displacement along a horizontal surface.
   (a) Determine the area under the line up to a displacement of 2.0 m [E]. What does that area represent?
   (b) Determine the total area up to 6.0 m [E].
   (c) Describe a physical situation that could result in this graph.

Applying Inquiry Skills

8. How would you demonstrate, using a pen and a sheet of paper, that static friction can do positive work on a pen?

Answers

4. (a) 36.9 J
   (b) 15.8 J

5. 194 J

6. 19.1 m

7. (a) 8.0 J
   (b) 0.0 J

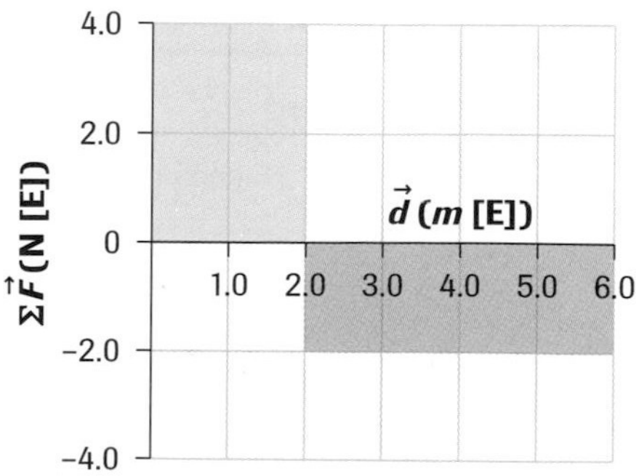

Figure 6
For question 7

Figure 7
As a volunteer carries a heavy sandbag toward the bank of a flooding river, the normal force on the sandbag is upward and the displacement is horizontal.

(a)

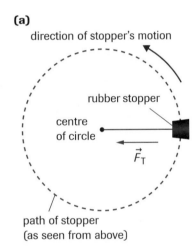

direction of stopper's motion

rubber stopper

centre of circle

$\vec{F}_T$

path of stopper
(as seen from above)

(b)

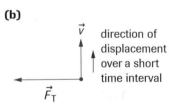

$\vec{v}$ direction of displacement over a short time interval

$\vec{F}_T$

($\vec{F}_g$ is ignored because it is very small compared to $\vec{F}_T$.)

Figure 8
(a) The situation for Sample Problem 4
(b) An instantaneous view of the force on the stopper, the velocity, and the direction of a small displacement

Zero Work

If you push against a tree, are you doing work? Since the force you apply does not move the tree, you do zero work on the tree. Whenever the magnitude of displacement Δd is zero, the work, $W = (F \cos \theta)\Delta d$, is also zero. No energy is transferred to the object.

Zero work due to zero displacement is just one way in which no work is done on an object. Consider a space probe that has travelled beyond the farthest planet in the solar system and is so far from any noticeable forces that the net force on it is negligible. Although the probe undergoes a displacement, since the force acting on it is zero the work done on the probe is zero. In this case, too, no energy is transferred to the object.

Finally, consider the third variable in the work equation, the angle θ between the force and the displacement. When the force and the displacement are perpendicular, cos 90° is zero. Thus, no work is done by the force on the object, even if the object moves, and no energy is transferred to the object. This can happen, for example, when you carry a heavy bag of sand (**Figure 7**): an upward force is exerted on the bag of sand to keep it from falling as you move horizontally. The normal force is perpendicular to the displacement, so the work done by that normal force on the bag of sand is zero. Can you think of other situations in which the force is perpendicular to the motion?

> ► **SAMPLE** problem 4

In performing a centripetal-acceleration investigation, you twirl a rubber stopper in a horizontal circle around your head. How much work is done on the stopper by the tension in the string in half a revolution?

Solution
Figure 8(a) shows the situation described. The force causing the centripetal acceleration is the tension $\vec{F}_T$. This force changes direction continually as the stopper travels in a circle. However, at any particular instant as shown in **Figure 8(b)**, the instantaneous velocity is perpendicular to the tension. Consequently, the displacement over a very short time interval is also at an angle of 90° to the tension force applied by the string to the stopper. Thus, for any short time interval during the rotation,

$$W = (F \cos \theta)\Delta d$$
$$= F(\cos 90°)\Delta d$$
$$W = 0.0 \text{ J}$$

Adding the work done over all the short time intervals in half a revolution yields 0.0 J. Therefore, the work done by the tension on the stopper is zero.

Using Sample Problem 4 as an example, we conclude that *the work done by any centripetal force acting on an object in circular motion is zero*. This applies because the orbit can be considered to be a series of individual small displacements perpendicular to the force, even though the force on the object in circular motion continually changes its direction.

> ► **Practice**

Understanding Concepts

9. Describe four different situations in a physics classroom or laboratory in which the equation $W = (F \cos \theta)\Delta d$ yields a zero result.

10. Describe, with the use of diagrams, a situation in which one component of a force does zero work while the other component does (a) positive work and (b) negative work.

SUMMARY ***Work Done by a Constant Force***

- Work is the energy transferred to an object when a force $\vec{F}$, acting on the object, moves it through a distance Δd.

- The SI unit of work is the joule (J).

- If the force causing an object to undergo a displacement is at an angle to the displacement, only the component of the force in the direction of the displacement does work on the object.

- Under certain conditions, zero work is done on an object even if the object experiences an applied force or is in motion.

▶ **Section 4.1** *Questions*

Understanding Concepts

1. In what ways is the everyday usage of the word "work" different from the physics usage? In what ways is it the same?

2. Is it possible for a centripetal force to do work on an object? Explain your answer.

3. Describe why you can get tired pushing on a wall even though you are not doing work on the wall.

4. Estimate the work you would do in climbing a vertical ladder equal in length to the height of your classroom.

5. **Figure 9** shows a girl and a boy each exerting a force to move a crate horizontally a distance of 13 m at a constant speed. The girl's applied force is 75 N [22° below the horizontal]. The tension in the rope pulled by the boy is 75 N [32° above the horizontal].
   (a) Determine the total work done by the girl and the boy on the crate.
   (b) How much work is done by the floor on the crate?

Figure 9

6. A child does 9.65×10^2 J of work in pulling a friend on a sleigh 45.3 m along a snowy horizontal surface (**Figure 10**). The force applied by the child is 24.1 N [parallel to the handle of the sleigh]. What angle relative to the snowy surface is the handle oriented?

Figure 10

7. A parent pulls a toboggan with three children at a constant velocity for 38 m along a horizontal snow-covered trail. The total mass of the children and the toboggan is 66 kg. The force the parent exerts is 58 N [18° above the horizontal].
   (a) Draw an FBD of the toboggan, and determine the magnitude of the normal force and the coefficient of kinetic friction.
   (b) Determine the work done on the toboggan by kinetic friction.
   (c) List three forces, or components of forces, that do zero work on the toboggan.
   (d) How much work does the parent do on the toboggan in pulling it the first 25 m?

Applying Inquiry Skills

8. Plot the cosine of an angle as a function of the angle (from 0° to 180°). Describe how the graph indicates when the work done on an object is positive, negative, or zero.

Making Connections

9. Describe the environmental effects that result from work done by friction.

Kinetic Energy and the Work-Energy Theorem

In Section 4.1, we learned how to calculate the amount of work done on an object when a force acts on the object as it moves through a displacement. But how is the object different as a result of having work done on it? Consider what happens when a net force causes a seaplane to accelerate as it covers a certain displacement (**Figure 1**). According to the defining equation of work, the total work done on the plane by the net force is $W_{\text{total}} = (\Sigma F)(\cos \theta)\Delta d$. In this case, the work done causes the speed of the plane to increase, thereby causing the energy of the plane to increase.

Specifically, the plane gains **kinetic energy** as its speed increases; in simple terms, kinetic energy is energy of motion. Kinetic energy depends on both the mass and the speed of the moving object. Since work is energy transferred to an object, if the work results in an increase in speed, the kinetic energy also increases.

Figure 2 illustrates a situation we will analyze mathematically.

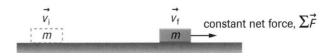

Figure 2
This situation can be used to derive an equation relating work and kinetic energy.

A constant net horizontal force is applied to an object, causing its speed to increase uniformly from v_i to v_f as it moves a distance Δd. The total work done by the net force is

$$W_{\text{total}} = \left(\Sigma F\right)(\cos \theta)\Delta d$$

Since $\theta = 0°$, then $\cos \theta = 1$, and we can simplify the equation:

$$W_{\text{total}} = \left(\Sigma F\right)\Delta d$$

From Newton's second law of motion,

$$\Sigma F = ma$$

where a is the acceleration. With a constant force, the acceleration is constant. We can rearrange the equation involving constant acceleration, $v_f^2 = v_i^2 + 2a\Delta d$ as

$$a = \frac{v_f^2 - v_i^2}{2\Delta d} \text{ and substitute for } a:$$

$$\Sigma F = m\left(\frac{v_f^2 - v_i^2}{2\Delta d}\right)$$

We now substitute this equation into the equation for total work:

$$W_{\text{total}} = m\left(\frac{v_f^2 - v_i^2}{2\Delta d}\right)\Delta d$$

$$W_{\text{total}} = \frac{1}{2}mv_f^2 - \frac{1}{2}mv_i^2$$

Our result shows that the total work done on an object equals the change in the quantity $\frac{1}{2}mv^2$. We define $\frac{1}{2}mv^2$ to be the kinetic energy E_K of the object.

Figure 1
As the propeller of a seaplane exerts a backward force on the air, the air exerts a forward force on the propeller. This force, applied as the plane moves forward by a displacement of magnitude Δd, does work on the plane.

kinetic energy (E_K) energy of motion

Kinetic Energy Equation

$$E_K = \frac{1}{2}mv^2$$

where E_K is the kinetic energy of the object in joules, m is the mass of the object in kilograms, and v is the speed of the object in metres per second. Note that kinetic energy is a scalar quantity.

We can summarize the relationship involving the total work and the kinetic energy as follows:

$$W_{total} = \frac{1}{2}mv_f^2 - \frac{1}{2}mv_i^2$$
$$= E_{Kf} - E_{Ki}$$
$$W_{total} = \Delta E_K$$

These relationships are the basis of the *work-energy theorem*.

Work-Energy Theorem

The total work done on an object equals the change in the object's kinetic energy, provided there is no change in any other form of energy (for example, gravitational potential energy).

Although this theorem was derived for one-dimensional motion involving a constant net force, it is also true for motion in two or three dimensions involving varying forces.

It is important to note that a change in the object's kinetic energy equals the work done by the net force $\Sigma \vec{F}$, which is the vector sum of all the forces. If the total work is positive, then the object's kinetic energy increases. If the total work is negative, then the object's kinetic energy decreases.

> **LEARNING TIP**
>
> **Comparing Force and Energy**
> There is no completely satisfactory definition of energy. However, the concept of energy can be more easily understood by comparing it with force: *force is the agent that causes change; energy is a measure of that change.* For example, when a net force causes the speed of an object to change, that change is manifested as a change in the kinetic energy of the object. Remember that the energy of an object is a measure of how much work that object can do.

▶ **SAMPLE** problem **1**

What total work, in megajoules, is required to cause a cargo plane of mass 4.55×10^5 kg to increase its speed in level flight from 105 m/s to 185 m/s?

Solution

$m = 4.55 \times 10^5$ kg $v_f = 185$ m/s

$v_i = 105$ m/s $W_{total} = ?$

$$W_{total} = \Delta E_K$$
$$= E_{Kf} - E_{Ki}$$
$$= \frac{1}{2}mv_f^2 - \frac{1}{2}mv_i^2$$
$$= \frac{1}{2}m\left(v_f^2 - v_i^2\right)$$
$$= \frac{1}{2}\left(4.55 \times 10^5 \text{ kg}\right)\left((185 \text{ m/s})^2 - (105 \text{ m/s})^2\right)$$
$$= 5.28 \times 10^9 \text{ J}\left(\frac{1 \text{ MJ}}{10^6 \text{ J}}\right)$$
$$W_{total} = 5.28 \times 10^3 \text{ MJ}$$

The total work required is 5.28×10^3 MJ.

A fire truck of mass 1.6×10^4 kg, travelling at some initial speed, has -2.9 MJ of work done on it, causing its speed to become 11 m/s. Determine the initial speed of the fire truck.

Solution

$m = 1.6 \times 10^4$ kg

$\Delta E_K = -2.9$ MJ $= -2.9 \times 10^6$ J

$v_f = 11$ m/s

$v_i = ?$

$$\Delta E_K = \frac{1}{2}m(v_f^2 - v_i^2)$$

$$2\Delta E_K = mv_f^2 - mv_i^2$$

$$mv_i^2 = mv_f^2 - 2\Delta E_K$$

$$v_i^2 = \frac{mv_f^2 - 2\Delta E_K}{m}$$

$$v_i = \pm\sqrt{\frac{mv_f^2 - 2\Delta E_K}{m}}$$

$$= \pm\sqrt{\frac{(1.6 \times 10^4 \text{ kg})(11 \text{ m/s})^2 - 2(-2.9 \times 10^6 \text{ J})}{1.6 \times 10^4 \text{ kg}}}$$

$$v_i = \pm 22 \text{ m/s}$$

We choose the positive root because speed is always positive. The initial speed is thus 22 m/s.

▶ **Practice**

Understanding Concepts

Answers

2. (a) 4

   (b) 9

   (c) 1.9

4. (a) 42 J

   (b) 2.1×10^3 N

5. 66 m/s

6. 1.38×10^4 m/s

1. Could a slow-moving truck have more kinetic energy than a fast-moving car? Explain your answer.

2. By what factor does a cyclist's kinetic energy increase if the cyclist's speed:
   (a) doubles
   (b) triples
   (c) increases by 37%

3. Calculate your kinetic energy when you are running at your maximum speed.

4. A 45-g golf ball leaves the tee with a speed of 43 m/s after a golf club strikes it.
   (a) Determine the work done by the club on the ball.
   (b) Determine the magnitude of the average force applied by the club to the ball, assuming that the force is parallel to the motion of the ball and acts over a distance of 2.0 cm.

5. A 27-g arrow is shot horizontally. The bowstring exerts an average force of 75 N on the arrow over a distance of 78 cm. Determine, using the work-energy theorem, the maximum speed reached by the arrow as it leaves the bow.

6. A deep-space probe of mass $4.55. \times 10^4$ kg is travelling at an initial speed of 1.22×10^4 m/s. The engines of the probe exert a force of magnitude 3.85×10^5 N over 2.45×10^6 m. Determine the probe's final speed. Assume that the decrease in mass of the probe (because of fuel being burned) is negligible.

7. A delivery person pulls a 20.8-kg box across the floor. The force exerted on the box is 95.6 N [35.0° above the horizontal]. The force of kinetic friction on the box has a magnitude of 75.5 N. The box starts from rest. Using the work-energy theorem, determine the speed of the box after being dragged 0.750 m.

8. A toboggan is initially moving at a constant velocity along a snowy horizontal surface where friction is negligible. When a pulling force is applied parallel to the ground over a certain distance, the kinetic energy increases by 47%. By what percentage would the kinetic energy have changed if the pulling force had been at an angle of 38° above the horizontal?

Applying Inquiry Skills

9. Use either unit analysis or dimensional analysis to show that kinetic energy and work are measured in the same units.

Making Connections

10. Many satellites move in elliptical orbits (**Figure 3**). Scientists must understand the energy changes that a satellite experiences in moving from the farthest position A to the nearest position B. A satellite of mass 6.85×10^3 kg has a speed of 2.81×10^3 m/s at position A, and speed of 8.38×10^3 m/s at position B. Determine the work done by Earth's gravity as the satellite moves
(a) from A to B
(b) from B to A

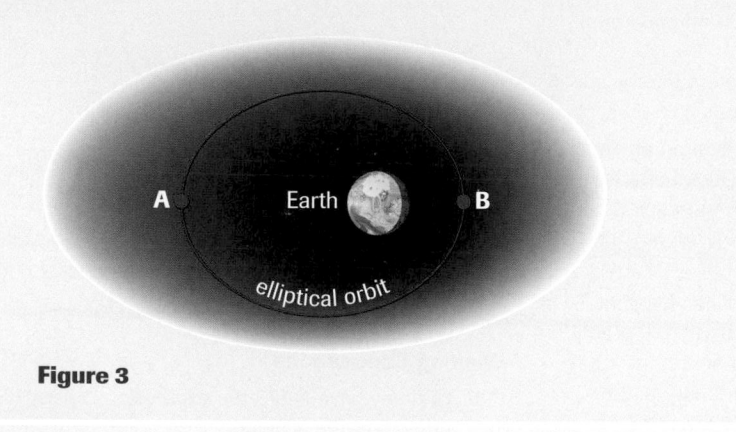

Figure 3

 **Kinetic Energy and the Work-Energy Theorem**

- Kinetic energy E_K is energy of motion. It is a scalar quantity, measured in joules (J).

- The work-energy theorem states that the total work done on an object equals the change in the object's kinetic energy, provided there is no change in any other form of energy.

Understanding Concepts

1. As a net external force acts on a certain object, the speed of the object doubles, and then doubles again. How does the work done by the net force in the first doubling compare with the work done in the second doubling? Justify your answer mathematically.

2. What is the kinetic energy of a car of mass 1.50×10^3 kg moving with a velocity of 18.0 m/s [E]?

3. (a) If the velocity of the car in question 2 increases by 15.0%, what is the new kinetic energy of the car?
   (b) By what percentage has the kinetic energy of the car increased?
   (c) How much work was done on the car to increase its kinetic energy?

4. A 55-kg sprinter has a kinetic energy of 3.3×10^3 J. What is the sprinter's speed?

5. A basketball moving with a speed of 12 m/s has a kinetic energy of 43 J. What is the mass of the ball?

6. A plate of mass 0.353 kg falls from rest from a table to the floor 89.3 cm below.
   (a) What is the work done by gravity on the plate during the fall?
   (b) Use the work-energy theorem to determine the speed of the plate just before it hits the floor.

7. A 61-kg skier, coasting down a hill that is at an angle of 23° to the horizontal, experiences a force of kinetic friction of magnitude 72 N. The skier's speed is 3.5 m/s near the top of the slope. Determine the speed after the skier has travelled 62 m downhill. Air resistance is negligible.

8. An ice skater of mass 55.2 kg falls and slides horizontally along the ice travelling 4.18 m before stopping. The coefficient of kinetic friction between the skater and the ice is 0.27. Determine, using the work-energy theorem, the skater's speed at the instant the slide begins.

Applying Inquiry Skills

9. The heaviest trucks in the world travel along relatively flat roads in Australia. A fully loaded "road-train" (**Figure 4**) has a mass of 5.0×10^2 t, while a typical car has a mass of about 1.2 t.

Figure 4
Australian "road-trains" are massive transport trucks comprised of three or more trailers hooked up together. The long, flat desert roads of central Australia make this an ideal form for transporting goods.

   (a) Prepare a table to compare the kinetic energies of these two vehicles travelling at ever-increasing speeds, up to a maximum of 40.0 m/s.
   (b) Prepare a single graph of kinetic energy as a function of speed, plotting the data for both vehicles on the same set of axes.
   (c) Based on your calculations and the graph, write conclusions about the masses, speeds, and kinetic energies of moving vehicles.

Making Connections

10. You may have heard the expression "Speed kills" in discussions of traffic accidents. From a physics perspective, a better expression might be "Kinetic energy kills."
    (a) When a traffic accident involving at least one moving vehicle occurs, the initial kinetic energy of the vehicle(s) must transform into something. Where do you think the energy goes?
    (b) Explain the expression "Kinetic energy kills."

Gravitational Potential Energy at Earth's Surface

A roller coaster, like the one in **Figure 1**, is called a "gravity ride" for a very good reason. Work is done on the coaster to raise it to the top of the first hill, which is the highest position in the ride. Once the coaster leaves that position, the only work that keeps the coaster moving is the work done by gravity. At the highest position, the coaster has the maximum *potential* to develop kinetic energy. The coaster has **gravitational potential energy** due to its elevation above Earth's surface.

To analyze gravitational potential energy mathematically, consider a situation in which a box of groceries is raised by an applied force to rollers at a higher level (**Figure 2**). Because gravity acts vertically, we will use Δy rather than Δd for the magnitude of the displacement. The force applied to the box to raise it is in the same direction as the displacement and has a magnitude equal to mg. The work done by the force on the box is

$$W = (F \cos \theta)\Delta y$$
$$= mg(\cos 0°)\Delta y$$
$$W = mg\Delta y$$

At the top of the rollers (the higher position), the box of groceries has gravitational potential energy relative to all lower positions. In other words, gravitational potential energy is a relative quantity in which the height of an object above some reference level must be known. Thus, the work done in increasing the elevation of an object is equal to the change in the gravitational potential energy:

$$\Delta E_g = mg\Delta y$$

where ΔE_g is the change in gravitational potential energy, in joules; m is the mass, in kilograms; g is the magnitude of the gravitational field constant in newtons per kilogram or metres per second squared; and Δy is the vertical component of the displacement, in metres.

There are a few important points to remember in using this equation:

- The equation determines the change in gravitational potential energy and does *not* determine an absolute value of gravitational potential energy. In practical problems involving the equation, Earth's surface is often used as a reference level of zero gravitational potential energy, although any other convenient arbitrary level may be chosen.

- The value of Δy is the vertical displacement of the object. This means that the horizontal path an object follows in changing its vertical height is not significant.

- The equation may only be used when Δy is small enough that g does not vary appreciably over Δy.

- Values of Δy (and ΔE_g) are positive if the displacement is upward, and negative if the displacement is downward.

Many of the situations in which this equation is applied involve objects that are thrown or lifted up away from Earth, or dropped toward Earth. In such cases, kinetic energy is converted into gravitational potential energy as the object moves upward, and gravitational potential energy is converted into kinetic energy after the object is released and falls downward. In both cases, if friction is negligible, the sum total of kinetic energy and gravitational potential energy remains constant.

gravitational potential energy
(E_g) the energy due to elevation above Earth's surface

Figure 1
In any "gravity ride," such as this roller coaster, the first hill is the highest. Can you explain why?

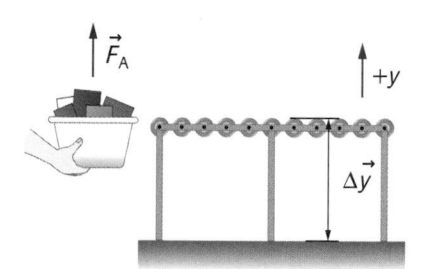

Figure 2
Work is done on the box of groceries to raise it from the floor to the top of the rollers.

When an object has gravitational potential energy relative to a lower position and the object is released, the force of gravity does work on the object, giving it kinetic energy, as specified by the work-energy theorem. For example, if you hold a basketball at shoulder height and then drop it, the ball has an initial velocity of zero, but a gravitational potential energy relative to the floor. When you release the ball, the force of gravity does work on the ball and the gravitational potential energy changes into kinetic energy. As a roller coaster leaves the highest hill, gravity does work on the coaster and gravitational potential energy changes into kinetic energy. The kinetic energy provides the coaster with enough speed to get up the next hill.

A diver, of mass 57.8 kg, climbs up a diving-board ladder and then walks to the edge of the board. He then steps off the board and falls vertically from rest to the water 3.00 m below. The situation is shown in **Figure 3**. Determine the diver's gravitational potential energy at the edge of the diving board, relative to the water.

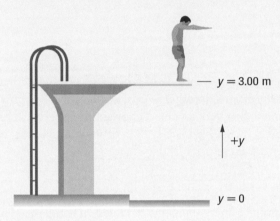

Figure 3

Solution

The $+y$ direction is upward. The reference position ($y = 0$) is the level of the water.

$m = 57.8$ kg

$g = 9.80$ m/s^2

$\Delta y = 3.00$ m

$\Delta E_g = ?$

$$\Delta E_g = mg\Delta y$$
$$= (57.8 \text{ kg})(9.80 \text{ m/s}^2)(3.00 \text{ m})$$
$$\Delta E_g = 1.70 \times 10^3 \text{ J}$$

The diver's gravitational potential energy relative to the water is 1.70×10^3 J.

LEARNING TIP

Choosing the Reference Position

Gravitational potential energy is a relative quantity—it is always measured with respect to some arbitrary position where $y = 0$. In many cases, you will have to choose the reference position. It is usually easiest to choose $y = 0$ to be the lowest possible position. This ensures that all y values and all gravitational potential energies are positive (or zero), and therefore easy to work with. Often it is the change in gravitational potential energy, which does not depend on the choice of $y = 0$, that is important. Strictly speaking, y is the height of the centre of mass of the object.

Notice that in Sample Problem 1, the diver would have the same gravitational potential energy relative to the water surface no matter where he stood along the horizontal diving board. Furthermore, his gravitational potential energy relative to the water surface does not depend on the path he took to reach the higher level. If he had been lifted by a crane and placed on the diving board, instead of climbing the ladder, his gravitational potential energy relative to the water surface would still be 1.70×10^3 J.

▶ *Practice*

Understanding Concepts

1. You lower your pen vertically by 25 cm, then you raise it vertically by 25 cm. During this motion, is the total work done by gravity positive, negative, or zero? Explain your answer.

2. What, relative to the ground, is the gravitational potential energy of a 62.5-kg visitor standing at the lookout level of Toronto's CN Tower, 346 m above the ground?

3. A 58.2-g tennis ball is dropped from rest vertically downward from a height of 1.55 m above the court surface.
   (a) Determine the gravitational potential energy of the ball relative to the court surface before it is dropped, and as it strikes the court surface.
   (b) How much work has the force of gravity done on the ball at the instant the ball strikes the court surface?
   (c) Relate the work done in (b) to the change in the kinetic energy from the release point to the court surface.

4. A 68.5-kg skier rides a 2.56-km ski lift from the base of a mountain to the top. The lift is at an angle of 13.9° to the horizontal. Determine the skier's gravitational potential energy at the top of the mountain relative to the base of the mountain.

5. A high jumper clears the pole at a height of 2.36 m, then falls safely back to the ground. The change in the jumper's gravitational potential energy from the pole to the ground is -1.65×10^3 J. Determine the jumper's mass.

6. On your desk you have N identical coins, each with a mass m. You stack the coins into a vertical pile to height y.
   (a) Approximately how much work, in terms of m, g, and y, must you do on the last coin to raise it from the desk to the top of the pile?
   (b) Approximately how much gravitational potential energy, in terms of m, g, N, and y, is stored in the entire pile?

Applying Inquiry Skills

7. Using unit analysis, express the units of gravitational potential energy in terms of base SI units. Compare the result to the SI base units of work and kinetic energy.

Making Connections

8. A barrel of oil contains about 6.1×10^9 J of chemical potential energy.
   (a) Determine to what height above the ground this energy could raise all the students in your school. State all your assumptions and show all your calculations.
   (b) How many joules of chemical potential energy are stored in each litre of oil? (*Hint:* You will have to determine how many litres there are in a barrel.)

 www.science.nelson.com

Answers

2. 2.12×10^5 J

3. (a) 0.884 J; 0.0 J
   (b) 0.884 J

4. 4.13×10^5 J

5. 71.3 kg

There are many practical applications of gravitational potential energy. For example, hydroelectric generating stations take advantage of the gravitational potential energy of water as it flows or falls from one level to a lower level. At many stations, huge dams store the water, allowing engineers to control the flow of water through pipes into turbines connected to the generators.

One of the major problems with building large dams is that the local ecology is drastically and permanently affected. Large artificial lakes created by dams flood previously dry areas, destroying plant life and animal habitat.

Bhutan, located east of Nepal and north of India (see **Figure 4**), has found a method of generating hydroelectricity without large dams. This small country, with a land area only about 85% that of Nova Scotia, is located in the Himalayan Mountain region. It has very strict environmental laws to protect its great forests, which cover more than 70% of its land. Careful environmental policy is evident in the design of the Chukha electrical generating station, which generates power at a rate of 360 MW. (By comparison, the two huge Robert Beck generating stations and the adjacent pumping-generating station at Niagara Falls generate 1800 MW.) The design of this generating station along the Wong Chu River is called a "run-of-the-river scheme," as shown in **Figure 5**. In this design, a small dam diverts some of the river's water flow into a large entrance tunnel, or *head race*, that is 6.0 km long. This tunnel, drilled through solid granite, is angled downward to the top of the generating station and takes advantage of the drop in elevation to convert the gravitational potential energy of the water into kinetic energy. After the water falls through the turbines at the generating station, it flows through an exit tunnel, or *tail race*, rejoining the river 1.0 km downstream.

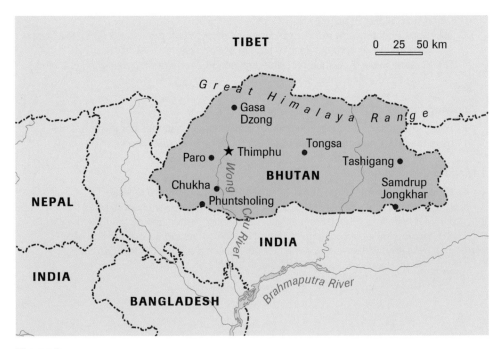

Figure 4
Bhutan is a land-locked nation with many mountain glaciers and rivers.

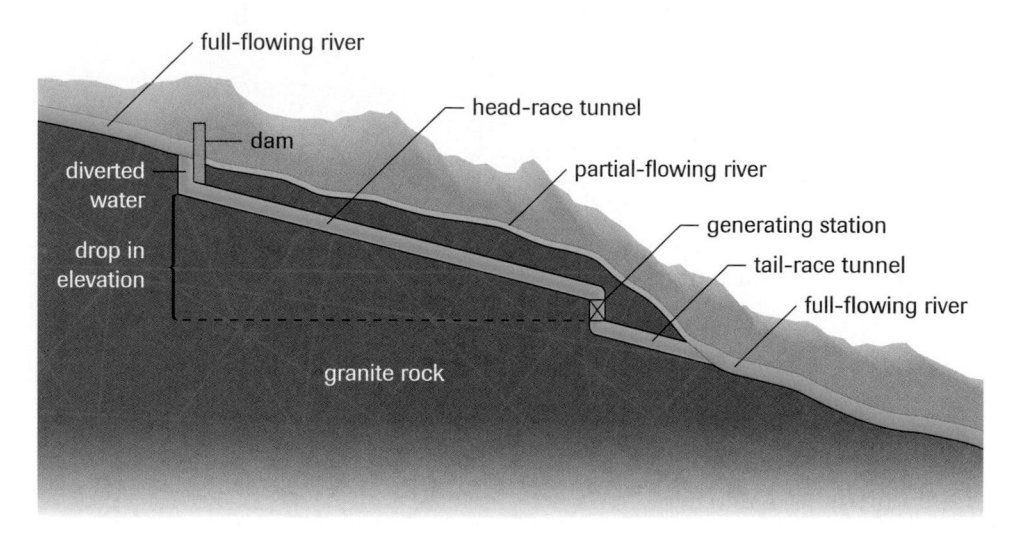

Figure 5
The basic design of the Chukha generating plant

Only about 5% of the electrical energy generated at the Chukha plant is used in Bhutan. The remainder is exported to India along 220-V transmission lines.

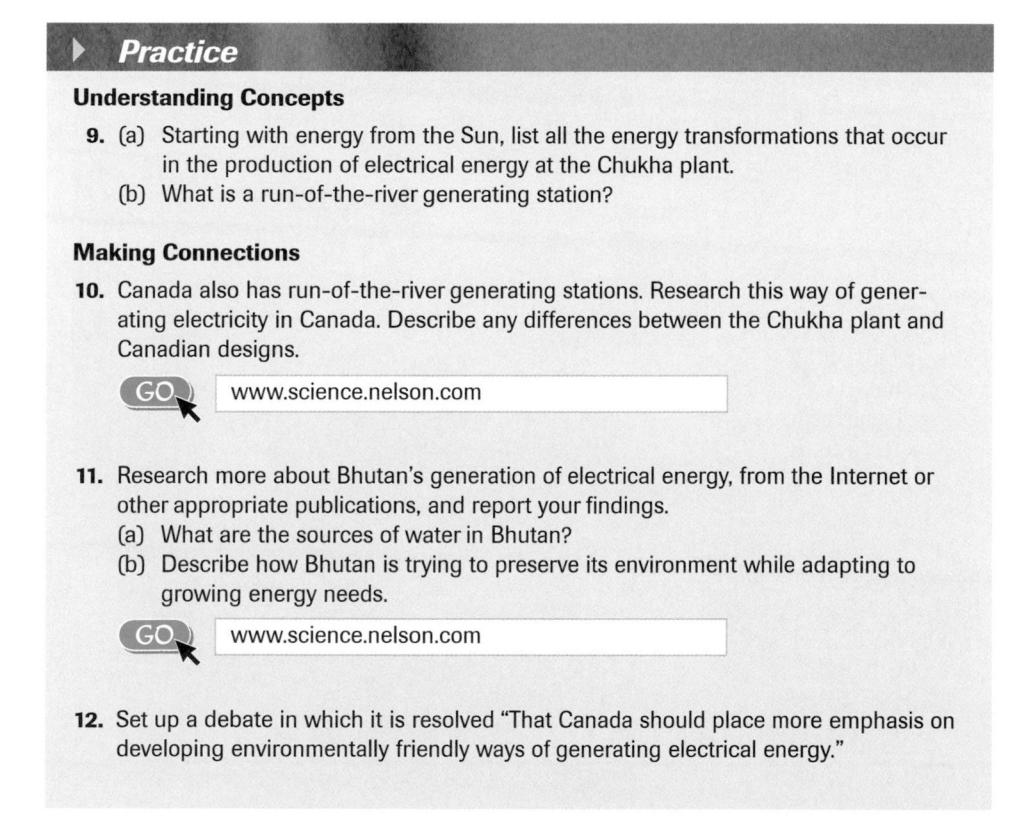

▶ *Practice*

Understanding Concepts

9. (a) Starting with energy from the Sun, list all the energy transformations that occur in the production of electrical energy at the Chukha plant.
   (b) What is a run-of-the-river generating station?

Making Connections

10. Canada also has run-of-the-river generating stations. Research this way of generating electricity in Canada. Describe any differences between the Chukha plant and Canadian designs.

    GO   www.science.nelson.com

11. Research more about Bhutan's generation of electrical energy, from the Internet or other appropriate publications, and report your findings.
    (a) What are the sources of water in Bhutan?
    (b) Describe how Bhutan is trying to preserve its environment while adapting to growing energy needs.

    GO   www.science.nelson.com

12. Set up a debate in which it is resolved "That Canada should place more emphasis on developing environmentally friendly ways of generating electrical energy."

SUMMARY Gravitational Potential Energy at Earth's Surface

- Gravitational potential energy is the energy possessed by an object due to its elevation above Earth's surface. It is a scalar quantity measured in joules (J).
- Gravitational potential energy is always stated relative to a reference level.
- The gravitational potential energy of an object depends on its mass, the gravitational field in which the object is located, and the object's height above a reference level.

▶ Section 4.3 Questions

Understanding Concepts

1. When a construction worker lifts a piece of wood from the ground, does the wood's gravitational potential energy increase or decrease?

2. An astronaut of mass 63 kg climbs a set of stairs with a total vertical rise of 3.4 m.
   (a) What is the astronaut's gravitational potential energy, relative to the bottom of the stairs, if the stairs are located on Earth?
   (b) Repeat (a) if the stairs are located on the Moon where $g = 1.6$ N/kg.

3. A pear of mass 125 g falls from a branch 3.50 m above the ground. What are the respective gravitational potential energies of the pear on the branch and on the ground
   (a) relative to the ground
   (b) relative to the branch

4. After being hit by a bat, a 0.15-kg baseball reaches a maximum height where its gravitational potential energy has increased by 22 J from the point where it was hit. What is the ball's maximum height (above the point where it was hit)?

5. A weightlifter, doing a biceps curl, lifts a 15-kg mass a vertical distance of 66 cm. Acceleration is negligible.
   (a) How much work is done by gravity on the mass?
   (b) How much work is done by the weightlifter on the mass?
   (c) By how much does the gravitational potential energy of the mass increase?

Applying Inquiry Skills

6. Plot, on a single graph, the gravitational potential energy of a 60.0-kg astronaut on Earth, on the Moon, and on Mars, as a function of the vertical elevation above the surface to a maximum height of 10.0 m. Your graph will have three distinct lines. (If necessary, refer to Appendix C for planetary data.)

Making Connections

7. Some Canadian hydroelectric generating facilities, similar to the one in **Figure 6**, convert the gravitational potential energy of water behind a dam into electrical energy.
   (a) Determine the gravitational potential energy relative to the turbines of a lake of volume 32.8 km³ with an average height of 23.1 m above the turbines. (The density of the water is 1.00×10^3 kg/m³.)
   (b) Compare your answer in (a) with the annual energy output of the Chukha plant in Bhutan, which is 1.14×10^{15} J.

Figure 6
The Revelstoke Dam and Generating Station sits on the Columbia River in British Columbia, 5 km north of the city of Revelstoke, B.C.

What does a computer have in common with a moving truck? What does the production of starlight have in common with a waterfall? In each case, energy is converted from one form into another form, while following an extremely important law of nature—the *law of conservation of energy.*

> **Law of Conservation of Energy**
>
> For an isolated system, energy can be converted into different forms, but cannot be created or destroyed.

The law of conservation of energy is an example of a conservation law that applies to an **isolated system**, which is a system of particles that is completely isolated from outside influences. As the particles of an isolated system move about and interact with one another, the total energy of the system remains constant with no energy flowing into or out of the system. An example of an isolated system is the system of your calculator sliding across your desk after your hand has stopped pushing it. The kinetic energy of the calculator is converted into other forms of energy, mainly thermal energy, and a small amount of sound energy as the particles of the desk and calculator rub against each other.

As far as we know, the law of conservation of energy cannot be violated. It is one of the fundamental principles in operation in the universe. When applied in physics, the law provides a very useful tool for analyzing a variety of problems.

As an example, consider a 50.0-kg swimmer falling (from rest) from a 3.00-m diving board under negligible air resistance. At the diving board, the swimmer has zero kinetic energy and maximum gravitational potential energy relative to the water surface below. Together, the kinetic energy and gravitational potential energy make up the swimmer's *mechanical energy.* When the swimmer is falling, the gravitational potential energy is converted into kinetic energy, but the total amount of mechanical energy remains constant. **Table 1** gives sample values for this example.

Table 1 Various Energies of a Falling Swimmer

Height (m)	Gravitational Potential Energy E_g (J)	Kinetic Energy E_K (J)	Total Mechanical Energy $E_T = E_g + E_K$ (J)
3.00	1.47×10^3	0.00	1.47×10^3
2.00	9.80×10^2	4.90×10^2	1.47×10^3
1.00	4.90×10^2	9.80×10^2	1.47×10^3
0.00	0.00	1.47×10^3	1.47×10^3

So far, the only forms of energy we have discussed in detail are gravitational potential energy and kinetic energy. The sum of these two energies is called the *total mechanical energy* E_T, where $E_T = E_g + E_K$. We will extend this equation in Section 4.5 to include other forms of energy, such as elastic potential energy.

isolated system a system of particles that is completely isolated from outside influences

A basketball player makes a free-throw shot at the basket. The basketball leaves the player's hand at a speed of 7.2 m/s from a height of 2.21 m above the floor. Determine the speed of the basketball as it goes through the hoop, 3.05 m above the floor. **Figure 1** shows the situation.

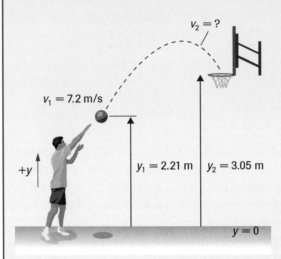

Figure 1

LEARNING TIP

Choosing Reference Levels
In Sample Problem 1, the floor was used as the reference level. A different reference level, such as the release position, would yield the same final answer. When you solve a problem involving gravitational potential energy, remember to choose a reference level and use that level throughout the problem.

Solution

According to the law of conservation of energy, the total energy of the basketball is constant as it travels through the air. Using the subscript 1 for the release position and 2 for the position where the basketball goes through the hoop, and taking the heights y_1 and y_2 relative to the floor,

$v_1 = 7.2$ m/s $\qquad g = 9.80$ m/s^2

$y_1 = 2.21$ m $\qquad v_2 = ?$

$y_2 = 3.05$ m

Applying the law of conservation of energy:

$$E_{T1} = E_{T2}$$

$$\frac{1}{2}mv_1{}^2 + mgy_1 = \frac{1}{2}mv_2{}^2 + mgy_2$$

$$mv_1{}^2 + 2mgy_1 = mv_2{}^2 + 2mgy_2$$

$$v_1{}^2 + 2gy_1 = v_2{}^2 + 2gy_2$$

$$v_2{}^2 = v_1{}^2 + 2gy_1 - 2gy_2$$

$$v_2{}^2 = v_1{}^2 + 2g(y_1 - y_2)$$

$$v_2 = \pm \sqrt{v_1{}^2 + 2g(y_1 - y_2)}$$

$$= \pm \sqrt{(7.2 \text{ m/s})^2 + 2(9.80 \text{ m/s}^2)(2.21 \text{ m} - 3.05 \text{ m})}$$

$$v_2 = \pm 5.9 \text{ m/s}$$

Only the positive square root applies since speed is always greater than zero. The speed of the basketball through the hoop is therefore 5.9 m/s. It is logical that this speed is less than the release speed because the ball is at a higher level; the gravitational potential energy of the ball is greater while its kinetic energy (and thus its speed) must be less.

The direction of the initial velocity and the parabolic path that the basketball follows are not important in solving Sample Problem 1. The kinetic and potential energies are scalar quantities, and do not involve a direction.

In general, we consider the work done by the net force as the amount of energy transformed from one form into another. The forms of energy involved depend on the nature of the net force. However, if the work done by the net force is positive, then the kinetic energy increases. Similarly, if the work done by the net force is negative, the kinetic energy decreases.

The law of conservation of energy can be applied to many practical situations. A common example is found in the operation of a "gravity clock," like the one in **Figure 2**. To explore this application and others, perform Activity 4.4.1 in the Lab Activities section at the end of this chapter. 🔍

▶ Practice

Understanding Concepts

1. A ball has an initial speed of 16 m/s. After a single external force acts on the ball, its speed is 11 m/s. Has the force done positive or negative work on the ball? Explain.

2. Two snowboarders start from rest at the same elevation at the top of a straight slope. They take different routes to the bottom, but end at the same lower elevation. If the energy lost due to friction and air resistance is identical for both snowboarders, how do their final speeds compare? Would your answer be different if the slope has dips and rises, instead of being straight?

3. Apply energy concepts to determine the maximum speed reached by a roller coaster at the bottom of the first hill, if the vertical drop from the top of the hill is 59.4 m, and the speed at the top of the hill is approximately zero. Friction and air resistance are negligible. Express your answer in metres per second and kilometres per hour.

4. A skier, moving at 9.7 m/s across the top of a mogul (a large bump), becomes airborne, and moves as a projectile under negligible air resistance. The skier lands on the downward side of the hill at an elevation 4.2 m below the top of the mogul. Use energy concepts to determine the skier's speed upon touching the hillside.

5. The highest waterfall in Canada is the Della Falls in British Columbia, with a change in elevation of 4.4×10^2 m. When the water has fallen 12% of its way to the bottom, its speed is 33 m/s. Neglecting air resistance and fluid friction, determine the speed of the water at the top of the waterfall.

6. A cyclist reaches the bottom of a gradual hill with a speed of 9.7 m/s—a speed great enough to coast up and over the next hill, 4.7 m high, without pedalling. Friction and air resistance are negligible. Find the speed at which the cyclist crests the hill.

7. A simple pendulum, 85.5 cm long, is held at rest so that its amplitude will be 24.5 cm as illustrated in **Figure 3**. Neglecting friction and air resistance, use energy concepts to determine the maximum speed of the pendulum bob after release.

Applying Inquiry Skills

8. A 5.00-kg rock is released from rest from a height of 8.00 m above the ground. Prepare a data table to indicate the kinetic energy, the gravitational potential energy, and the total mechanical energy of the rock at heights of 8.00 m, 6.00 m, 4.00 m, 2.00 m, and 0.00 m. Plot a single graph showing all three energies as a function of the height above the ground. (If possible, use a spreadsheet program to generate the graph.)

Making Connections

9. A wrecking ball used to knock over a wall provides an example of the law of conservation of energy. Describe how a wrecking ball is used and list the energy transformations that occur in its use.

🔍 ACTIVITY 4.4.1

Applying the Law of Conservation of Energy (p. 220)
Gravity clocks tend to be used more for decoration than for accurate timekeeping. They do, however, provide a good example of the application of the law of conservation of energy. Describe what you think are the energy transformations responsible for the operation of a gravity clock.

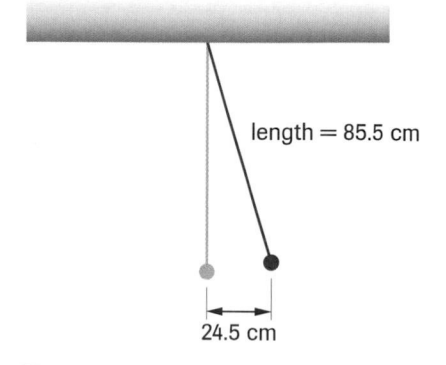

Figure 2
A gravity clock

Answers

3. 34.1 m/s; 123 km/h

4. 13 m/s

5. 5.0 m/s

6. 1.4 m/s

7. 0.838 m/s

length = 85.5 cm

24.5 cm

Figure 3
For question 7

Other Forms of Energy

Kinetic energy and gravitational potential energy are just two of the many forms of energy. **Table 2** lists several other forms of energy.

As the law of conservation of energy states, energy can be changed from one form to another. However, the efficiency of conversion is often not 100% because of friction. Friction causes kinetic energy to transform into **thermal energy**, or internal energy, which is associated with the motion of atoms and molecules. For example, picture a curling rock sliding along the ice in a straight line toward its target, covering a horizontal distance Δd (**Figure 4**). After the rock has left the player's hand, the only force that does work on the rock is the force of kinetic friction, $\vec{F}_K$. (Gravity and the normal force are both perpendicular to the displacement, and do no work on the rock.) Since the kinetic friction is in the opposite direction to the displacement, the angle θ between this force and the displacement is 180°. Since $\cos 180° = -1$, the work done by the kinetic friction is

$$W = (F_K \cos \theta)\Delta d$$
$$W = -F_K \Delta d$$

thermal energy (E_{th}) internal energy associated with the motion of atoms and molecules

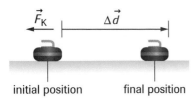

initial position   final position

Figure 4
As the speed of the curling rock along the ice decreases, kinetic energy is transformed into thermal energy.

Table 2   Common Forms of Energy

Form of Energy	Comment
electromagnetic	• carried by travelling oscillations called electromagnetic waves • includes light energy, radio waves, microwaves, infrared waves, ultraviolet waves, X rays, and gamma rays • travels in a vacuum at 3.00×10^8 m/s, the speed of light
electrical	• results from the passage of electrons, for example, along wires in appliances in your home
electric potential	• associated with electric force • changes as charges are moved
gravitational potential	• associated with the gravitational force • changes as masses are moved relative to each other
chemical potential	• stored in the chemical bonds that hold the atoms of molecules together
nuclear potential	• the stored energy in the nucleus of an atom • converts into other forms by rearranging the particles inside a nucleus, by fusing nuclei together (fusion), or by breaking nuclei apart (fission)
sound	• carried by longitudinal waves from molecule to molecule
elastic potential	• stored in objects that are stretched or compressed
thermal	• associated with the motion of atoms and molecules • for a monatomic gas such as helium, it is the total kinetic energy of all the atoms • for more complicated molecules and for atoms in solids, it is partly kinetic energy and partly electric potential energy • differs from heat, which is the transfer of energy due to a difference in temperatures

Since F_K and Δd are both positive (being the magnitudes of vectors), the work done by friction is negative. This means that friction is removing kinetic energy from the rock. However, because energy is always conserved, the kinetic energy is transformed into another form, in this case into thermal energy of the rock and the ice. As the rock slides along the ice, the atoms in the rock and the ice vibrate with increased energy. Both the rock and the ice warm up, with a small portion of the ice developing a thin layer of melted water.

Whenever kinetic friction does negative work to slow an object down, the magnitude of the work equals the thermal energy produced. Since kinetic friction is always oppo-site to the direction of the displacement, the work done by friction can be written as

$$W = -F_K \Delta d$$

Note that the magnitude of the work done by friction is $F_K \Delta d$. Thus, we can write

$$E_{th} = F_K \Delta d$$

where E_{th} is the thermal energy produced by kinetic friction, in joules; F_K is the magnitude of the kinetic friction, in newtons; and Δd is the magnitude of the displacement, in metres.

▶ **SAMPLE** problem **2**

After leaving a player's hand, a 19.9-kg curling rock slides in a straight line for 28.8 m, experiencing friction with a coefficient of kinetic friction of 0.105. The situation is shown in **Figure 5**.

(a) How much thermal energy is produced during the slide?

(b) Determine, using energy conservation, the rock's speed just as it left the player's hand.

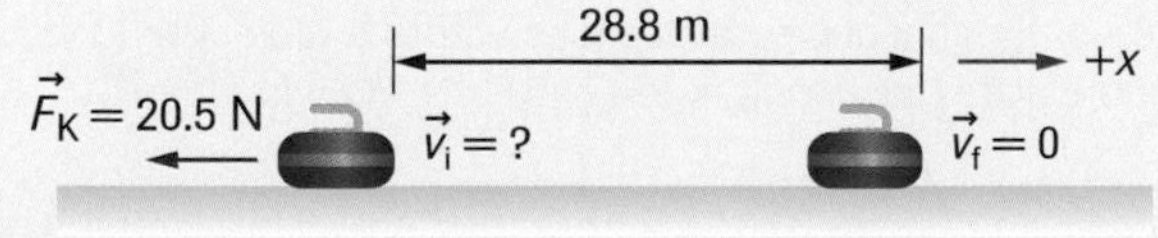

Figure 5
Using components to illustrate the rock's motion

Solution

(a) $\mu_K = 0.105$ $\qquad F_K = \mu_K F_N$

$\quad m = 19.9$ kg $\qquad F_N = mg$

$\quad \Delta d = 28.8$ m $\qquad E_{th} = ?$

$$\begin{aligned}
E_{th} &= F_K \Delta d \\
&= \mu_K F_N \Delta d \\
&= \mu_K mg \Delta d \\
&= (0.105)(19.9 \text{ kg})(9.80 \text{ N/kg})(28.8 \text{ m}) \\
E_{th} &= 5.90 \times 10^2 \text{ J}
\end{aligned}$$

The thermal energy produced is 5.90×10^2 J.

(b) According to the law of conservation of energy, the initial kinetic energy of the rock must equal the thermal energy produced during the slide, because there is no kinetic energy remaining at the end of the slide. (Gravitational potential energy is not considered because the ice surface is level.)

$$E_{th} = 5.90 \times 10^2 \, J$$
$$v_i = ?$$

$$E_{Ki} = E_{th}$$
$$\frac{mv_i^2}{2} = E_{th}$$
$$v_i^2 = \frac{2E_{th}}{m}$$
$$v_i = \pm \sqrt{\frac{2(5.90 \times 10^2 \, J)}{19.9 \, kg}}$$
$$v_i = \pm 7.70 \, m/s$$

We choose the positive root because speed is always positive. Thus, the rock's initial speed is 7.70 m/s.

▶ Practice

Understanding Concepts

10. (a) You push this book across a horizontal desk at a constant velocity. You are supplying some energy to the book. Into what form(s) does this energy go?
    (b) You push the same book with a larger force so that the book accelerates. Into what form(s) does the energy now go?

11. A force of kinetic friction, of magnitude 67 N, acts on a box as it slides across the floor. The magnitude of the box's displacement is 3.5 m.
    (a) What is the work done by friction on the box?
    (b) How much thermal energy is produced?

12. A plate produces 0.620 J of thermal energy as it slides across a table. The kinetic friction force acting on the plate has a magnitude of 0.83 N. How far does the plate slide?

13. A clerk pushes a filing cabinet of mass 22.0 kg across the floor by exerting a horizontal force of magnitude 98 N. The magnitude of the force of kinetic friction acting on the cabinet is 87 N. The cabinet starts from rest. Use the law of conservation of energy to determine the speed of the cabinet after it moves 1.2 m.

14. A pen of mass 0.057 kg slides across a horizontal desk. In sliding 25 cm, its speed decreases to 5.7 cm/s. The force of kinetic friction exerted on the pen by the desk has a magnitude of 0.15 N. Apply the law of conservation of energy to determine the initial speed of the pen.

Applying Inquiry Skills

15. (a) Describe how you would use the motion of a simple pendulum to verify the law of conservation of energy.
    (b) Describe sources of random and systematic error in your experiment.

Making Connections

16. Most of the thermal energy associated with operating a vehicle is produced by the combustion of fuel, although some is also produced by friction. Describe how the circulation systems in a car (the oil circulation system and the water-cooling system) relate to the thermal energy produced in a moving car.

Answers

11. (a) $-2.3 \times 10^2 \, J$
    (b) $2.3 \times 10^2 \, J$

12. 0.75 m

13. 1.1 m/s

14. 1.1 m/s

 **The Law of Conservation of Energy**

- The law of conservation of energy states that for an isolated system, energy can be converted into different forms, but cannot be created or destroyed.

- The work done on a moving object by kinetic friction results in the conversion of kinetic energy into thermal energy.

- The law of conservation of energy can be applied to solve a great variety of physics problems.

▶ **Section 4.4** *Questions*

Understanding Concepts

1. Why do roller-coaster rides always start by going uphill?

2. You crack an egg and drop the contents of mass 0.052 kg from rest 11 cm above a frying pan. Determine, relative to the frying pan ($y = 0$),
   (a) the initial gravitational potential energy of the egg's contents
   (b) the final gravitational potential energy of the egg's contents
   (c) the change in gravitational potential energy as the egg's contents fall
   (d) the kinetic energy and the speed of the egg's contents just before hitting the pan

3. A child throws a ball, which hits a vertical wall at a height of 1.2 m above the ball's release point. The speed of the ball at impact is 9.9 m/s. What was the initial speed of the ball? Use conservation of energy and ignore air resistance.

4. A river flows at a speed of 3.74 m/s upstream from a waterfall of vertical height 8.74 m. During each second, 7.12×10^4 kg of water pass over the waterfall.
   (a) What is the gravitational potential energy of this mass of water at the top of the waterfall, relative to the bottom?
   (b) If there is a complete conversion of gravitational potential energy into kinetic energy, what is the speed of the water at the bottom?

5. An acrobat, starting from rest, swings freely on a trapeze of length 3.7 m (**Figure 6**). If the initial angle of the trapeze is 48°, use the law of conservation of energy to determine
   (a) the acrobat's speed at the bottom of the swing
   (b) the maximum height, relative to the initial position, to which the acrobat can rise

6. A skier of mass 55.0 kg slides down a slope 11.7 m long, inclined at an angle ϕ to the horizontal. The magnitude of the kinetic friction is 41.5 N. The skier's initial speed is 65.7 cm/s and the speed at the bottom of the slope is 7.19 m/s. Determine the angle ϕ from the law of conservation of energy. Air resistance is negligible.

7. A skateboarder, initially at rest at the top edge of a vertical ramp half-pipe (**Figure 7**), travels down the pipe, reaching a speed of 6.8 m/s at the bottom of the pipe. Friction is negligible. Use the law of conservation of energy to find the radius of the half-pipe.

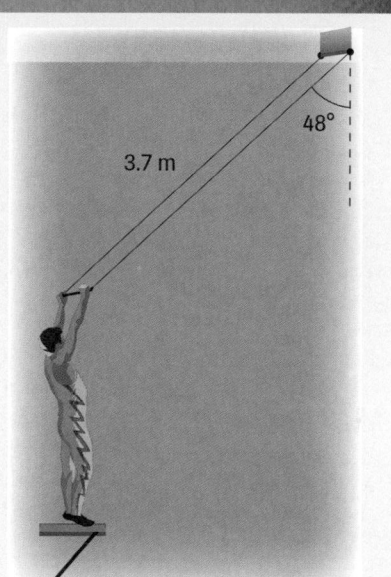

Figure 6
For question 5

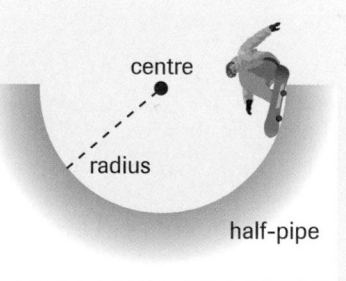

half-pipe

Figure 7
For question 7

8. A 55-g chalkboard eraser slides along the ledge at the bottom of the chalkboard. Its initial speed is 1.9 m/s. After sliding for 54 cm, it comes to rest.
   (a) Calculate, from the law of conservation of energy, the coefficient of kinetic friction between the eraser and the ledge.
   (b) Repeat the calculation using kinematics and force principles.
   (c) Into what form is the kinetic energy converted?

9. Brakes are applied to a car initially travelling at 85 km/h. The wheels lock and the car skids for 47 m before coming to a halt. The magnitude of the kinetic friction between the skidding car and the road is 7.4×10^3 N.
   (a) How much thermal energy is produced during the skid?
   (b) In what form was this thermal energy before the skid?
   (c) Use the law of conservation of energy to determine the mass of the car.
   (d) Determine the coefficient of kinetic friction between the tires and the road.

10. A box of apples of mass 22 kg slides 2.5 m down a ramp inclined at 44° to the horizontal. The force of friction on the box has a magnitude of 79 N. The box starts from rest.
    (a) Determine the work done by friction.
    (b) Determine the box's final kinetic energy. (*Hint:* Use the law of conservation of energy.)
    (c) Find the thermal energy produced.

Applying Inquiry Skills

11. The backward-looping roller coaster in **Figure 8** accelerates from the top of the lift by the station, travels through several vertical loops, and then moves part way up a second lift. At this stage, the coaster must be pulled up to the top of the second lift, where it is released to accelerate backward, returning the riders to the first lift and the station.
    (a) What physics principle(s) would you apply to determine the amount of thermal energy produced as the coaster travels from the top of the first lift to the position where it starts to be pulled up the second lift?
    (b) List the equations you would need to determine the amount of energy converted into thermal energy for the situation in (a).

(c) Describe how you would conduct measurements from the ground outside the ride to determine an estimate of the thermal energy mentioned in (a).

Making Connections

12. In medieval times, the weapon of choice for military engineers was a *trebuchet*, a mechanical device that converted gravitational potential energy of a large rock into kinetic energy. **Figure 9** shows the design of a gravity-powered trebuchet used to hurl projectiles at castle walls. Find out more about this device, and explain why it is a good illustration of the law of conservation of energy.

 www.science.nelson.com

Figure 9
A medieval trebuchet

Figure 8
A reversing ride is easy to analyze to determine energy losses due to friction.

Imagine that you are to design a cord that will be used for bungee jumping from a bridge to a river (**Figure 1**). Although the distance between the bridge and the river is constant, the masses of the jumpers vary. The cord should offer complete and consistent safety, while at the same time providing a good bounce to prolong the thrill of jumping.

Figure 1
How would you test the properties of a bungee cord?

How could you analyze the force exerted by an elastic device, such as a bungee cord? What happens when the energy is transformed, as a person attached to the cord bounces up and down? A situation that involves the force changing as the cord is squeezed or compressed is more complex that the situations that we have looked at so far.

Hooke's Law

The force exerted by an elastic device varies as the device is stretched or compressed. To analyze the force mathematically, consider a horizontal spring attached to a wall and resting on a surface with negligible friction (**Figure 2(a)**). The position at which the spring rests, $x = 0$, is the *equilibrium position*. If a force is applied to the spring, stretching the spring to the right of equilibrium, the spring pulls back to the left as shown in **Figure 2(b)**. Similarly, if a force is applied to compress the spring to the left of equilibrium, the spring pushes back to the right. In both cases, the direction of the force exerted by the spring is opposite to the direction of the force applied to the spring.

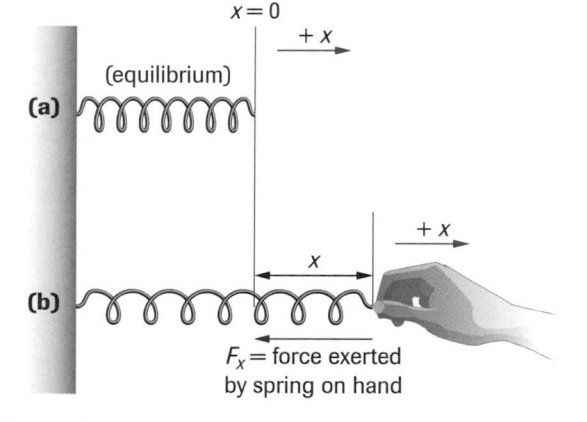

Figure 2
(a) A spring at its equilibrium position
(b) If the spring is stretched to the right, it exerts a force to the left: $F_x = -kx$.

Experiments with springs show that the magnitude of the force exerted by the spring is directly proportional to the distance the spring has moved from equilibrium. This relationship is known as **Hooke's law**, after Robert Hooke (1635–1703), who published his law and its corresponding equation in 1678. Any spring that obeys Hooke's law is called an **ideal spring** because it experiences no friction, either internal or external. Using *k* as the constant of proportionality, we can write Hooke's law for the force exerted *by* a spring in equation form, in this case with horizontal components to correspond to the situation in **Figure 2(b)**:

$$F_x = -kx$$

where F_x is the force exerted by the spring, *x* is the position of the spring relative to equilibrium, and *k* (the proportionality constant) is the **force constant** of the spring. Springs that require a large force to stretch or compress them have large *k* values.

According to Hooke's law, if $x > 0$, then $F_x < 0$. In other words, if the spring is stretched in the $+x$ direction, it pulls in the opposite direction. Similarly, if $x < 0$, then $F_x > 0$, which means that if the spring is compressed in the $-x$ direction, it pushes in the opposite direction.

Since $-kx$ indicates the force exerted *by* the spring, we can apply Newton's third law to find that $+kx$ is the force applied *to* the spring to stretch or compress it to position *x*. Thus, Hooke's law for the force applied *to* a spring is:

$$F_x = kx$$

Although we have been referring to springs, Hooke's law applies to any elastic device for which the magnitude of the force exerted by the device is directly proportional to the distance the device moves from equilibrium.

▶ **SAMPLE** problem **1**

A student stretches a spring horizontally a distance of 15 mm by applying a force of 0.18 N [E].

(a) Determine the force constant of the spring.

(b) What is the force exerted by the spring on the student?

Solution

(a) $F_x = 0.18$ N

$x = 15$ mm $= 0.015$ m

$k = ?$

Since the force is applied *to* the spring, we use the equation

$$F_x = kx$$

$$k = \frac{F_x}{x}$$

$$= \frac{0.18 \text{ N}}{0.015 \text{ m}}$$

$$k = 12 \text{ N/m}$$

The force constant is 12 N/m. (Notice the SI units of the force constant.)

(b) According to Newton's third law, if the force applied to the spring is 0.18 N [E], then the force exerted by the spring is 0.18 N [W].

▶ ***SAMPLE** problem 2*

A ball of mass 0.075 kg is hung from a vertical spring that is allowed to stretch slowly from its unstretched equilibrium position until it comes to a new equilibrium position 0.15 m below the initial one. **Figure 3(a)** is a system diagram of the situation, and **Figure 3(b)** is an FBD of the ball at its new equilibrium position.

(a) Determine the force constant of the spring.

(b) If the ball is returned to the spring's unstretched equilibrium position and then allowed to fall, what is the net force on the ball when it has dropped 0.071 m?

(c) Determine the acceleration of the ball at the position specified in (b).

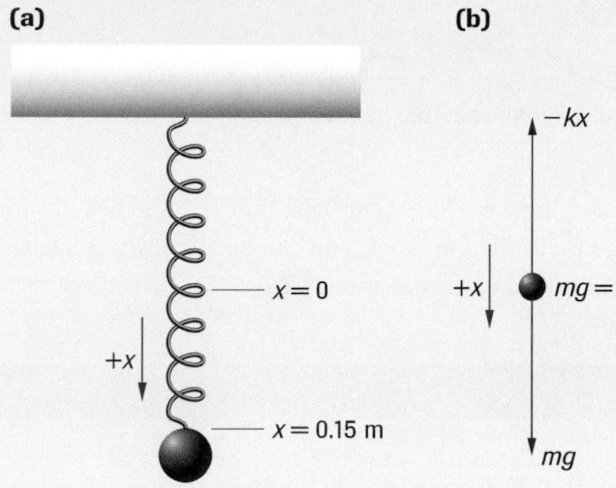

(a)   **(b)**

Figure 3
(a) The system diagram
(b) The FBD of the ball when the extension is 0.15 m

Solution

(a) We measure the extension x of the spring from its original unstretched position ($x = 0$) and choose $+x$ to be downward. Two vertical forces act on the ball: gravity and the upward force of the spring. At the new equilibrium position, the ball is stationary, so the net force acting on it is zero.

$m = 0.075$ kg

$x = 0.15$ m

$k = ?$

$$\sum F_x = 0$$
$$mg + (-kx) = 0$$
$$k = \frac{mg}{x}$$
$$= \frac{(0.075 \text{ kg})(9.8 \text{ N/kg})}{0.15 \text{ m}}$$
$$k = 4.9 \text{ N/m}$$

The force constant is 4.9 N/m.

(b) **Figure 4** is the FBD for the ball when $x = 0.071$ m. Considering the components of the forces in the vertical (x) direction:

$$\sum F_x = mg + (-kx)$$
$$= (0.075 \text{ kg})(9.8 \text{ N/kg}) - (4.9 \text{ N/m})(0.071 \text{ m})$$
$$\sum F_x = +0.39 \text{ N}$$

The net force is 0.39 N [down] when the ball has dropped to 0.071 m.

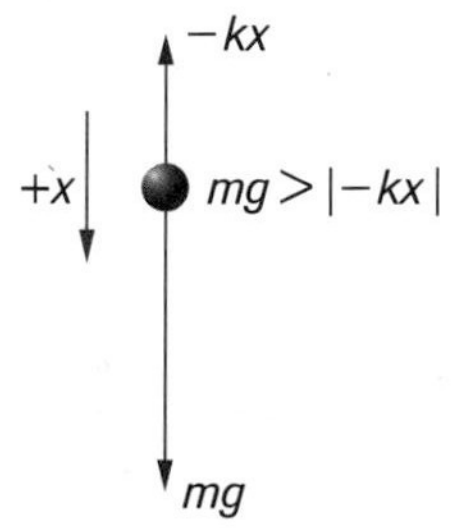

Figure 4
The FBD of the ball when the extension is 0.071 m

(c) $\sum F_y = 0.39$ N

$a_y = ?$

Applying Newton's second law:

$$\sum F_y = ma_y$$

$$a_y = \frac{\sum F_y}{m}$$

$$= \frac{0.39 \text{ N}}{0.075 \text{ kg}}$$

$$a_y = 5.2 \text{ m/s}^2$$

The acceleration is 5.2 m/s² [down] when the ball is at a spring extension of 0.071 m.

In our applications of Hooke's law, we have assumed that the springs are ideal. To discover how real springs compare to ideal springs, you can perform Investigation 4.5.1 in the Lab Activities section at the end of this chapter.

⟡ INVESTIGATION 4.5.1

Testing Real Springs (p. 220)
A graph of the force applied to an ideal extension spring suspended vertically yields a single straight line with a positive slope. How do you think a graph of the force applied to a real extension spring would compare?

Answers

3. (a) 4.0 N; 8.0 N

    (b) 4.0 N; 8.0 N

4. 6.4 N

▶ *Practice*

Understanding Concepts

1. Spring A has a force constant of 68 N/m. Spring B has a force constant of 48 N/m. Which spring is harder to stretch?

2. If you pull northward on a spring, in what direction does the spring exert a force on you?

3. An ideal spring has a force constant of 25 N/m.
    (a) What magnitude of force would the spring exert on you if you stretched it from equilibrium by 16 cm? by 32 cm?
    (b) What magnitude of force would you have to exert on the spring to compress it from equilibrium by 16 cm? by 32 cm?

4. **Figure 5** shows the design of a tire-pressure gauge. The force constant of the spring in the gauge is 3.2×10^2 N/m. Determine the magnitude of the force applied by the air in the tire if the spring is compressed by 2.0 cm. Assume the spring is ideal.

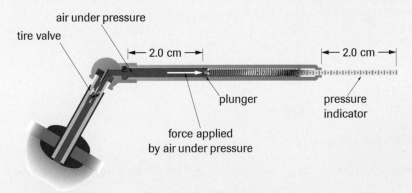

Figure 5
A pressure gauge indicates the force per unit area, a quantity measured in pascals, or newtons per square metre (1 Pa = 1 N/m²).

5. A 1.37-kg fish is hung from a vertical spring scale with a force constant of 5.20×10^2 N/m. The spring obeys Hooke's law.
   (a) By how much does the spring stretch if it stretches slowly to a new equilibrium position?
   (b) If the fish is attached to the unstretched spring scale and allowed to fall, what is the net force on the fish when it has fallen 1.59 cm?
   (c) Determine the acceleration of the fish after it has fallen 2.05 cm.

Applying Inquiry Skills

6. (a) Draw a graph of F_x as a function of x for an ideal spring, where F_x is the x-component of the force exerted *by* the spring *on* whatever is stretching (or compressing) it to position x. Include both positive and negative values of x.
   (b) Is the slope of your graph positive or negative?

Making Connections

7. Spring scales are designed to measure weight but are sometimes calibrated to indicate mass. You are given a spring scale with a force constant of 80.0 N/m.
   (a) Prepare a data table to indicate the stretch that would occur if masses of 1.00 kg, 2.00 kg, and on up to 8.00 kg were suspended from the scale at your location.
   (b) Draw a scale diagram to show the calibration of the scale if it is set up to measure
      (i) mass at your location
      (ii) weight at your location
   (c) If both springs in (b) were taken to the top of a high mountain, would they give the correct values? Explain.

Answers

5. (a) 0.0258 m

   (b) 5.16 N [down]

   (c) 2.02 m/s^2 [down]

Elastic Potential Energy

When an archer draws a bow, work is done on the limbs of the bow, giving them potential energy. The energy stored in objects that are stretched, compressed, bent, or twisted is called **elastic potential energy**. In the case of the bow, the stored energy can be transferred to the arrow, which gains kinetic energy as it leaves the bow.

To derive an equation for elastic potential energy, we consider the work done on an ideal spring in stretching or compressing it. Recall from Practice question 7 in Section 4.1 that the area under the line on a force-displacement graph indicates the work. For a constant force, the area is a rectangle. However, the force applied to an ideal spring depends on the displacement, so the area of the graph is a triangle (**Figure 6**). Since the area of a triangle is equal to $\frac{1}{2} bh$, we have:

$$W = \frac{1}{2}x(kx)$$

$$W = \frac{1}{2}kx^2$$

where W is the work, k is the force constant of the spring, and x is the amount of stretch or compression of the spring from the equilibrium position. Since this work has been transformed into elastic potential energy, we can rewrite the equation as

$$E_e = \frac{1}{2}kx^2$$

where E_e is the elastic potential energy.

elastic potential energy (E_e) the energy stored in an object that is stretched, compressed, bent, or twisted

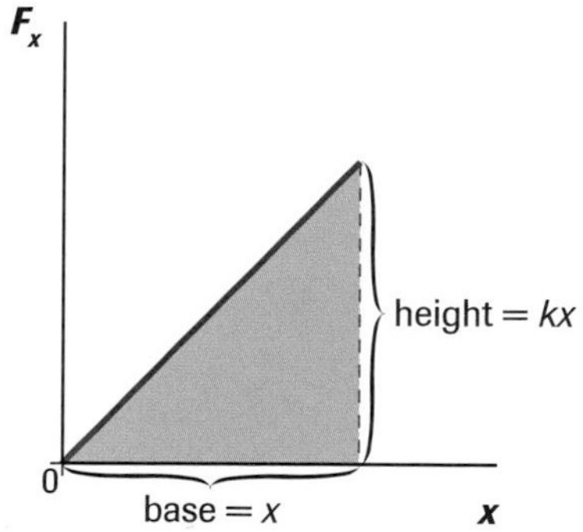

Figure 6
The magnitude of the force applied to a spring as a function of x

Elastic potential energy can be transformed into other forms of energy, such as the kinetic energy of an arrow shot by a bow, the sound energy of a guitar string, or the gravitational potential energy of a pole-vaulter at the top of the jump. As you can see from these examples, elastic potential energy can be stored in objects other than springs.

▶ SAMPLE problem 3

An apple of mass 0.10 kg is attached to a vertical spring with a force constant of 9.6 N/m. The apple is held so that the spring is at its unstretched equilibrium position, then it is allowed to fall. Neglect the mass of the spring and its kinetic energy.

(a) How much elastic potential energy is stored in the spring when the apple has fallen 11 cm?

(b) What is the speed of the apple when it has fallen 11 cm?

Solution

(a) We measure the extension x of the spring from its original unstretched position ($x = 0$) and choose $+x$ to be downward (**Figure 7**).

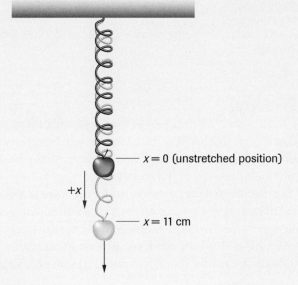

Figure 7

$x = 11 \text{ cm} = 0.11 \text{ m}$
$k = 9.6 \text{ N/m}$
$E_e = ?$

$$E_e = \frac{1}{2}kx^2$$

$$= \frac{1}{2}(9.6 \text{ N/m})(0.11 \text{ m})^2$$

$$E_e = 5.8 \times 10^{-2} \text{ J}$$

The elastic potential energy stored in the spring is 5.8×10^{-2} J.

(b) We use the prime symbol (') to represent the final condition of the apple. To apply the law of conservation of energy to determine v', we include the elastic potential energy.

$m = 0.10$ kg

$x = 0.11$ m   (for the gravitational potential energy of the apple at the initial position relative to the final position)

$v = 0$

$k = 9.6$ N/m

$g = 9.8$ m/s^2

$x' = 0.11$ m   (the extension of the spring when the apple is at the final position)

$E_K = E_e = 0$

$v' = ?$

$$E_T = E_T'$$
$$E_g + E_K + E_e = (E_g + E_K + E_e)'$$
$$E_g = (E_K + E_e)'$$
$$mgx = \frac{1}{2}mv'^2 + \frac{1}{2}kx'^2$$

$$\frac{1}{2}mv'^2 = mgx - \frac{1}{2}kx'^2$$

$$v' = \pm\sqrt{2gx - \frac{kx'^2}{m}}$$

$$= \pm\sqrt{2(9.8 \text{ m/s}^2)(0.11 \text{ m}) - \frac{(9.6 \text{ N/m})(0.11 \text{ m})^2}{0.10 \text{ kg}}}$$

$$v' = \pm 1.0 \text{ m/s}$$

We choose the positive root because speed is always positive. The speed of the apple is 1.0 m/s.

▶ *SAMPLE* problem 4

A group of students participating in an annual "Spring Wars Contest" is given a spring and the following challenge: Launch the spring so that it leaves a launching pad at an angle of 32.5° above the horizontal and strikes a target at the same elevation, a horizontal distance of 3.65 m away (**Figure 8**). Friction and air resistance are negligible.

(a) What measurements must the students make before they perform the calculations and launch their springs?

(b) Calculate the stretch needed for the spring to reach the target if the spring's mass is 15.4 g and its force constant is 28.5 N/m.

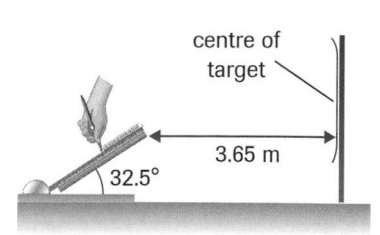

Figure 8
A student-designed launching pad for a spring

Solution

(a) As the spring is stretched, it gains elastic potential energy $E_e = \frac{1}{2}kx^2$.
According to the law of conservation of energy, when the spring is released, this energy is converted into kinetic energy ($E_K = \frac{1}{2}mv^2$). The spring then moves as a projectile, covering a horizontal range given by the projectile motion equation from Section 1.4, $\Delta x = \frac{v_i^2}{g}\sin 2\theta$. (Note that Δx is the horizontal range, which is not to be confused with the extension x of a spring.) The force constant and the mass of the spring must be measured experimentally. The other variables are either given or can be calculated.

(b) We begin by calculating the speed of a projectile needed to cover the horizontal range.

$$\Delta x = 3.65 \text{ m} \qquad \theta = 32.5°$$
$$g = 9.80 \text{ m/s}^2 \qquad v = ?$$

$$\Delta x = \frac{v^2}{g}\sin 2\theta$$

$$v^2 = \frac{g\Delta x}{\sin 2\theta}$$

$$v = \pm\sqrt{\frac{g\Delta x}{\sin 2\theta}}$$

$$= \pm\sqrt{\frac{(9.80 \text{ m/s}^2)(3.65 \text{ m})}{\sin 2(32.5°)}}$$

$$= \pm 6.28 \text{ m/s}$$

$$v = 6.28 \text{ m/s}$$

We choose the positive root because speed is always positive. Since the elastic potential energy changes into kinetic energy, we apply the law of conservation of energy equation to find the stretch x of the spring:

$$m = 15.4 \text{ g} = 0.0154 \text{ kg} \qquad v = 6.28 \text{ m/s}$$
$$k = 28.5 \text{ N/m} \qquad x = ?$$

$$E_e = E_K$$

$$\frac{1}{2}kx^2 = \frac{1}{2}mv^2$$

$$x^2 = \frac{mv^2}{k}$$

$$x = \pm\sqrt{\frac{mv^2}{k}}$$

$$= \pm\sqrt{\frac{(0.0154 \text{ kg})(6.28 \text{ m/s})^2}{28.5 \text{ N/m}}}$$

$$x = \pm 0.146 \text{ m}$$

The required stretch is 0.146 m, or 14.6 cm. (The negative root would apply to a compression spring.)

▶ **TRY THIS** activity   *Hitting the Target*

Using ideas from Sample Problem 4, design an adjustable launching pad for firing a spring (provided by your teacher) from any angle above the horizontal toward a target at least 3.00 m away and at the same vertical height as the spring. Determine the mass and force constant of your spring, and then calculate the stretch needed to launch the spring at a given angle to hit the target. If the spring is not "ideal," make adjustments to the launch so that your spring comes closer to the target.

 Perform this activity away from other people.
Wear safety goggles in case the spring misfires.

> ▶ *Practice*

Understanding Concepts

8. **Figure 9** is a graph of the force as a function of stretch for a certain spring.
   (a) Is the force applied *to* or *by* the spring? Explain your answer.
   (b) Determine the force constant of the spring.
   (c) Use the graph to determine the elastic potential energy stored in the spring after it has been stretched 35 cm.

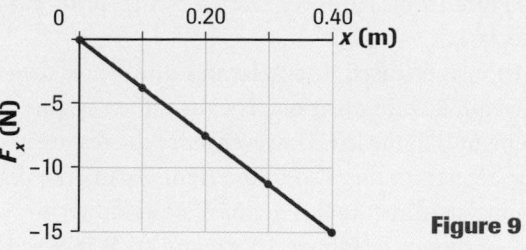

Figure 9

9. A spring has a force constant of 9.0×10^3 N/m. What is the elastic potential energy stored in the spring when it is (a) stretched 1.0 cm and (b) compressed 2.0 cm?

10. A child's toy shoots a rubber dart of mass 7.8 g, using a compressed spring with a force constant of 3.5×10^2 N/m. The spring is initially compressed 4.5 cm. All the elastic potential energy is converted into the kinetic energy of the dart.
    (a) What is the elastic potential energy of the spring?
    (b) What is the speed of the dart as it leaves the toy?

11. In a game, a small block is fired from a compressed spring up a plastic ramp into various holes for scoring. The mass of the block is 3.5×10^{-3} kg. The spring's force constant is 9.5 N/m. Friction is negligible.
    (a) If the block is to slide up the ramp through a vertical height of 5.7 cm, by how much must the spring be compressed?
    (b) If friction were not negligible, would your answer in (a) increase, decrease, or remain the same? Explain.

12. A 0.20-kg mass is hung from a vertical spring of force constant 55 N/m. When the spring is released from its unstretched equilibrium position, the mass is allowed to fall. Use the law of conservation of energy to determine
    (a) the speed of the mass after it falls 1.5 cm
    (b) the distance the mass will fall before reversing direction

13. A horizontal spring, of force constant 12 N/m, is mounted at the edge of a lab bench to shoot marbles at targets on the floor 93.0 cm below. A marble of mass 8.3×10^{-3} kg is shot from the spring, which is initially compressed a distance of 4.0 cm. How far does the marble travel horizontally before hitting the floor?

Applying Inquiry Skills

14. You are designing a toy that would allow your friends to bounce up and down when hanging (safely) onto a vertical spring.
    (a) What measurement(s) would you make to determine the approximate force constant the spring would need to allow a maximum stretch of 75 cm when a person was suspended at rest from it?
    (b) Estimate the approximate force constant for such a spring. Show your calculations.

Making Connections

15. Scientists analyze the muscles of a great variety of animals and insects. For example, when a flea jumps, the energy is provided not by muscles alone, but also by an elastic protein that has been compressed like a spring. If a flea of mass 2.0×10^2 μg jumps vertically to a height of 65 mm, and 75% of the energy comes from elastic potential energy stored in the protein, determine the initial quantity of elastic potential energy. Neglect energy losses due to air resistance.

Simple Harmonic Motion

When a mass on the end of a spring vibrates in line with the central axis of the spring, it undergoes *longitudinal vibration*. Consider the longitudinal vibration of a mass on a flat surface, connected to the end of a horizontal spring that can be stretched or compressed (**Figure 10(a)**). The mass is initially at its equilibrium or rest position ($x = 0$). A force is then applied to pull the mass to a maximum displacement, called the *amplitude A* (**Figure 10(b)**). If the mass is released at this stage, the force exerted by the spring accelerates it to the left, as in **Figure 10(c)**. The force exerted by the spring varies with the stretch x according to Hooke's law, $F_x = -kx$.

After the mass in **Figure 10(c)** is released, it accelerates until it reaches maximum speed as it passes through the equilibrium position. The mass then begins to compress the spring so that the displacement is to the left. However, since the restoring force of the spring is now to the right, the acceleration is also to the right. Again, the displacement and the acceleration are in opposite directions. The mass slows down and comes to a momentary stop at $x = -A$, as shown in **Figure 10(d)**, and then moves to the right through the equilibrium position at maximum speed, and reaches $x = A$ again.

Since we are neglecting friction both in the spring and between the mass and the surface, this back-and-forth motion continues indefinitely in **simple harmonic motion** (SHM). SHM is defined as a periodic vibratory motion in which the force (and the acceleration) is directly proportional to the displacement. Be careful not to confuse simple harmonic motion with other back-and-forth motions. For example, if basketball players are running back and forth across a gym during practice, their motion is not SHM, even though the time taken for each trip may be constant.

A convenient way to analyze SHM mathematically is to combine Hooke's law and Newton's second law with a *reference circle* (**Figure 11**). Imagine a mass attached to a horizontal spring, vibrating back and forth with SHM. At the same time, a handle pointing upward from a rotating disk revolves with uniform circular motion; the circular motion of the handle provides the reference circle. The frequency of revolution of the circular motion equals the frequency of vibration of the SHM, and the motions synchronize with one another. (Technically, we can say that the motions are in phase with one another.) Furthermore, the radius of the circle equals the amplitude of the SHM. A bright light source can be aimed from the side of the disk so that it casts a shadow of the upright handle onto the mass in SHM, and this shadow appears to have the same motion as the mass. This verifies that we can use equations from uniform circular motion to derive equations for SHM.

Recall that the magnitude of the acceleration of an object in uniform circular motion with a radius r and a period T is given by

$$a_c = \frac{4\pi^2 r}{T^2}$$

which we can rewrite as

$$T^2 = \frac{4\pi^2 r}{a_c} \quad \text{or} \quad T = 2\pi \sqrt{\frac{r}{a_c}}$$

Since $r = A$ for the reference circle in **Figure 11**,

$$T = 2\pi \sqrt{\frac{A}{a_c}}$$

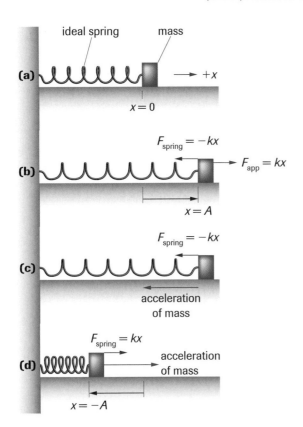

Figure 10
Using the longitudinal vibration of a mass-spring system to define simple harmonic motion (SHM)
(a) The equilibrium position
(b) The position of maximum stretch
(c) Releasing the mass
(d) The position of maximum compression

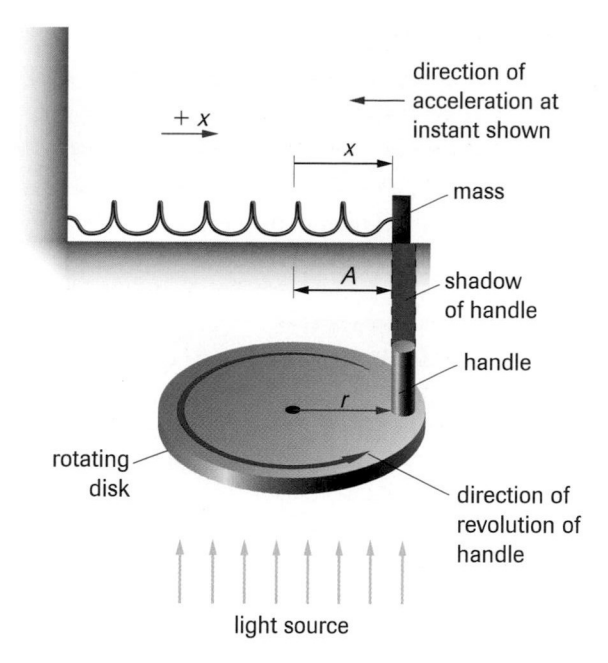

direction of
acceleration at
instant shown

$+ x$

x

mass

A

shadow
of handle

handle

r

rotating
disk

direction of
revolution of
handle

light source

Figure 11
A reference circle. The handle on the disk is revolving with uniform circular motion, at the same frequency as the mass on the end of the spring is undergoing SHM. As the light source causes a shadow of the handle to be superimposed on the mass, the motions appear to be identical when viewed from the side. We use the motion of the reference circle to derive equations for SHM.

This period is not only the period of revolution of any point on the reference circle, but it is also the period of the mass undergoing SHM, since this mass has the same motion as the shadow of the handle.

Although the handle on the reference circle is undergoing uniform circular acceleration, its shadow is undergoing the same acceleration as the mass attached to the spring. This acceleration is not constant, as can be shown by applying Hooke's law ($F_x = -kx$) and Newton's second law ($F_x = ma_x$). If we equate the right-hand sides of these equations, then $-kx = ma_x$, from which $a_x = \dfrac{-kx}{m}$. Thus, since k and m are constants, the acceleration of a mass (and the shadow of the handle) undergoing SHM is proportional to the displacement, x, from the equilibrium position. Furthermore, the acceleration is opposite to the direction of the displacement, as indicated by the negative sign.

The relationship between the displacement and the acceleration can be written as $\dfrac{-x}{a_x} = \dfrac{m}{k}$; that is, the ratio of the displacement to the acceleration is constant. But in the equation that we developed for the period of SHM, the ratio $\dfrac{A}{a_c}$ is one specific value of the more general ratio of $\dfrac{-x}{a_x}$. Thus, a general equation for the period of SHM is

$$T = 2\pi \sqrt{\dfrac{-x}{a_x}}$$

The equation always yields a positive value under the square root sign because x and a_x have opposite signs.

If we substitute $\dfrac{-x}{a_x} = \dfrac{m}{k}$, then

$$T = 2\pi \sqrt{\dfrac{m}{k}}$$

where T is the period in seconds, m is the mass in kilograms, and k is the force constant of the spring in newtons per metre.

Since the frequency is the reciprocal of the period,

$$f = \frac{1}{2\pi} \sqrt{\frac{k}{m}}$$

These equations for the SHM of a mass–spring system apply even if the motion is vertical. The horizontal motion was used in the derivations because we did not have to consider gravity.

▶ **SAMPLE** problem 5

A 0.45-kg mass is attached to a spring with a force constant of 1.4×10^2 N/m. The mass-spring system is placed horizontally, with the mass resting on a surface that has negligible friction. The mass is displaced 15 cm, and is then released. Determine the period and frequency of the SHM.

Solution

$m = 0.45$ kg

$k = 1.4 \times 10^2$ N/m

$A = 15$ cm $= 0.15$ m

$T = ?$

$f = ?$

$$T = 2\pi \sqrt{\frac{m}{k}}$$

$$= 2\pi \sqrt{\frac{0.45 \text{ kg}}{1.4 \times 10^2 \text{ N/m}}}$$

$$T = 0.36 \text{ s}$$

Now, $f = \frac{1}{T}$

$$= \frac{1}{0.36 \text{ s}}$$

$$f = 2.8 \text{ Hz}$$

The period and the frequency of the motion are 0.36 s and 2.8 Hz.

▶ **Practice**

Understanding Concepts

16. A vertical mass–spring system is bouncing up and down with SHM of amplitude A. Identify the location(s) at which
    (a) the magnitude of the displacement from the equilibrium position is at a maximum
    (b) the speed is at a maximum
    (c) the speed is at a minimum
    (d) the magnitude of the acceleration is at a maximum
    (e) the magnitude of the acceleration is at a minimum

17. Determine the period and frequency, in SI units, for the following:
    (a) a human eye blinks 12 times in 48 s
    (b) a compact disc rotates at a rate of 210 revolutions per minute
    (c) the A string on a guitar vibrates 2200 times in 5.0 s

Answers

17. (a) 4.0 s; 0.25 Hz
    (b) 0.29 s; 3.5 Hz
    (c) 2.3×10^{-3} s; 4.4×10^2 Hz

18. A 0.25-kg mass is attached to the end of a spring that is attached horizontally to a wall. When the mass is displaced 8.5 cm and then released, it undergoes SHM. The force constant of the spring is 1.4×10^2 N/m. The amplitude remains constant.
    (a) How far does the mass move in the first five cycles?
    (b) What is the period of vibration of the mass-spring system?

19. A 0.10-kg mass is attached to a spring and set into 2.5-Hz vibratory motion. What is the force constant of the spring?

20. What mass, hung from a spring of force constant 1.4×10^2 N/m, will give a mass-spring system a period of vibration of 0.85 s?

Applying Inquiry Skills

21. Show that $\sqrt{\dfrac{x}{a}}$ and $\sqrt{\dfrac{m}{k}}$ are dimensionally equivalent.

Making Connections

22. To build up the amplitude of vibration in a trampoline, you move up and down on the trampoline 6.0 times in 8.0 s without losing contact with the surface.
    (a) Estimate the force constant of the trampoline.
    (b) If you bounce into the air above the trampoline with a regular period of bouncing, are you undergoing SHM? Explain.

Answers

18. (a) 1.7×10^2 cm
    (b) 0.27 s
19. 25 N/m
20. 2.6 kg

Energy in Simple Harmonic Motion and Damped Harmonic Motion

We have seen that the elastic potential energy in an ideal spring when it is stretched or compressed a displacement x is $\dfrac{1}{2}kx^2$. Let us now look at the energy transformations in an ideal spring that undergoes SHM, as in **Figure 12**. The spring is first stretched to the right, to $x = A$, from its equilibrium position, then released. The elastic potential energy is at a maximum at $x = A$:

$$E_e = \frac{1}{2}kA^2$$

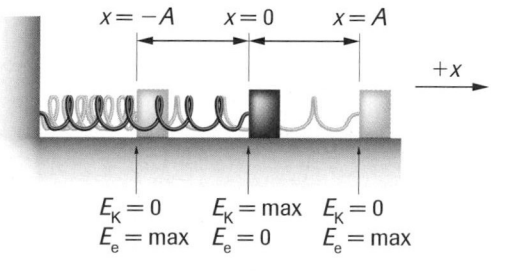

Figure 12
Mechanical energy in a mass–spring system

According to the law of conservation of energy, when the mass is released, the total energy E_T of the system is the sum of the elastic potential energy in the spring and the kinetic energy of the mass. Thus,

$$E_T = \frac{1}{2}kx^2 + \frac{1}{2}mv^2$$

where k is the spring constant, x is the displacement of the mass from the equilibrium position, m is the mass at the end of the spring, and v is the instantaneous speed of the mass. As we will now see, the conservation of mechanical energy can be used to solve problems involving SHM.

A 55-g box is attached to a horizontal spring of force constant 24 N/m. The spring is then compressed to a position $A = 8.6$ cm to the left of the equilibrium position. The box is released and undergoes SHM.

(a) What is the speed of the box when it is at position $x = 5.1$ cm from the equilibrium position?

(b) What is the maximum speed of the box?

Solution

(a) We use the prime symbol ($'$) to represent the final condition. We apply the law of conservation of mechanical energy at the two positions of the box, the initial position A and the final position x'.

$A = 8.6$ cm $= 0.086$ m

$m = 55$ g $= 0.055$ kg

$x' = 5.1$ cm $= 0.051$ m

$k = 24$ N/m

$v' = ?$

$$E_T = E_T'$$

$$E_e + E_K = E_e' + E_K'$$

$$\frac{kA^2}{2} + 0 = \frac{kx'^2}{2} + \frac{mv'^2}{2}$$

$$kA^2 = kx'^2 + mv'^2$$

$$v' = \sqrt{\frac{k}{m}(A^2 - x'^2)} \qquad \text{(discarding the negative root)}$$

$$= \sqrt{\frac{24 \text{ N/m}}{0.055 \text{ kg}}\left((0.086 \text{ m})^2 - (0.051 \text{ m})^2\right)}$$

$$v' = 1.4 \text{ m/s}$$

The speed of the box is 1.4 m/s.

(b) The maximum speed occurs when $x' = 0$.

$$v' = \sqrt{\frac{k}{m}(A^2 - x'^2)}$$

$$= \sqrt{\frac{24 \text{ N/m}}{0.055 \text{ kg}}(0.086 \text{ m})^2}$$

$$v' = 1.8 \text{ m/s}$$

The maximum speed of the box is 1.8 m/s.

damped harmonic motion periodic or repeated motion in which the amplitude of vibration and the energy decrease with time

In many practical situations involving a mass–spring system, it would be a disadvantage to have SHM. For example, if you were to step onto a bathroom scale to find your mass or weight, you would not want the spring in the scale to undergo SHM. You would expect the spring to settle down quickly and come to rest so you could observe the reading. This "settling down" is called *damping*. **Damped harmonic motion** is periodic or repeated motion in which the amplitude of vibration and thus the energy decrease with time. A typical displacement-time curve representing damped harmonic motion with a fairly long damping time is shown in **Figure 13**.

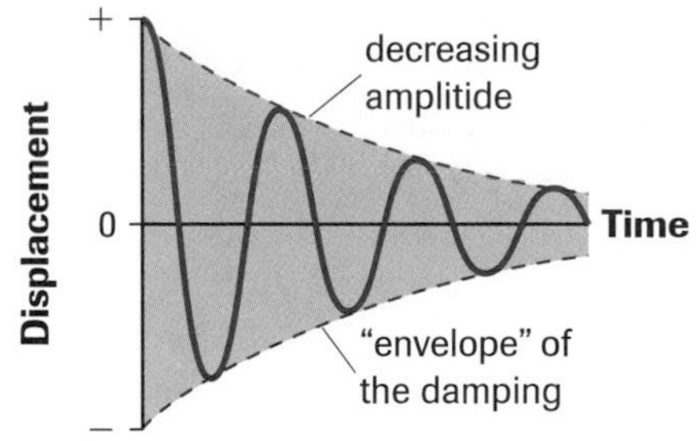

Figure 13
A displacement-time curve repre-senting damped harmonic motion. The overall outline of the curve is called the *envelope of the damping*.

One way to study the damping properties of a real spring is to set up a mass–spring system vertically, start the mass vibrating with an appropriate amplitude, and observe the vibrations. Investigation 4.5.2, in the Lab Activities section at the end of this chapter, gives you an opportunity for such a study. ⚛▮

A bathroom scale is one example of a device specifically designed for damping. Another example is the system of springs and shock absorbers in a car. When a wheel goes over a bump in the road, the wheel's spring and shock absorber are compressed easily, but they are designed to quickly stop bouncing up and down. The energy given to the spring and shock absorber is dissipated, or transformed into other types of energy. To find out more about the spring and shock absorbers on automobiles, you can perform Activity 4.5.1 in the Lab Activities section at the end of this chapter. 🔍▮

▶ *Practice*

Understanding Concepts

23. Figures **14(a)** and **(b)** show a mass–spring system undergoing SHM at maximum compression and maximum extension.
(a) At what length(s) of the spring is the speed of the mass at a minimum? What is that speed?
(b) At what length(s) of the spring is the speed of the mass at a maximum? What is that speed?
(c) What is the amplitude of the SHM?

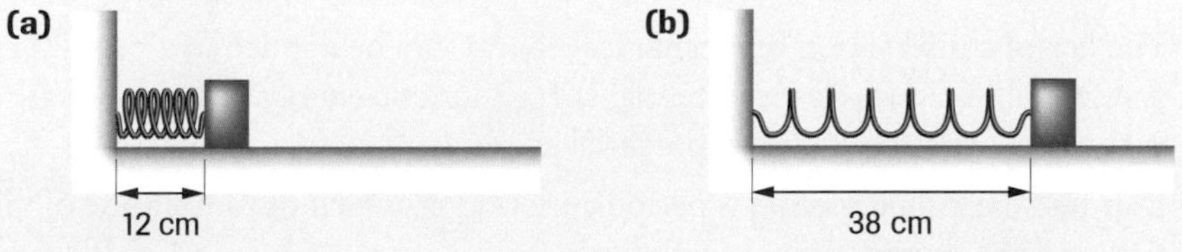

(a)

12 cm

(b)

38 cm

Figure 14

24. The maximum energy of a mass–spring system undergoing SHM is 5.64 J. The mass is 0.128 kg and the force constant is 244 N/m.
(a) What is the amplitude of the vibration?
(b) Use two different approaches to determine the maximum speed of the mass.
(c) Find the speed of the mass when it is 15.5 cm from the equilibrium position.

25. The amplitude of vibration of a mass on a spring experiencing SHM is 0.18 m. The mass is 58 g and the force constant is 36 N/m.
(a) Find the maximum energy of the system and the maximum speed of the mass.
(b) What amplitude of vibration would be required to double the maximum energy?
(c) What is the maximum speed of the mass at this new energy?

26. Prove that the maximum speed of a mass on a spring in SHM is given by $2\pi fA$.

⚛ **INVESTIGATION 4.5.2**

Analyzing Forces and Energies in a Mass–Spring System (p. 222)
If you were given a spring and appropriate measuring apparatus, you could determine the force con-stant of a spring. You could then apply the conservation of energy to predict the motion that will occur when a known mass, attached verti-cally to the end of the spring, is released from rest from the unstretched equilibrium position. What measurements would you need to make to determine the damping properties of the spring when the mass is set into vibration?

🔍 **ACTIVITY 4.5.1**

Achieving a Smooth and Safe Ride (p. 223)
Springs and shock absorbers on an automobile help create a smooth and safe ride for the occupants. What happens to the energy of vibration produced when the auto-mobile goes over a bump?

Answers
23. (a) 12 cm; 38 cm; zero
    (b) 25 cm; zero
    (c) 13 cm
24. (a) 0.215 m
    (b) 9.39 m/s
    (c) 6.51 m/s
25. (a) 0.58 J; 4.5 m/s
    (b) 0.25 m
    (c) 6.3 m/s

27. (a) Determine the dimensions of the expression $\sqrt{\dfrac{k}{m}\,(A^2 - x^2)}$.

    (b) Explain in words the meaning of this expression.

Making Connections

28. State whether each of the following devices is designed to have fast, medium, or slow damping. Give a reason for each answer.
    (a) the prongs of a tuning fork
    (b) the needle on an analog voltmeter
    (c) a guitar string
    (d) saloon doors (of the swinging type)
    (e) the string on an archer's bow after the arrow leaves the bow

SUMMARY — Elastic Potential Energy and Simple Harmonic Motion

- Hooke's law for an ideal spring states that the magnitude of the force exerted by or applied to a spring is directly proportional to the displacement the spring has moved from equilibrium.

- The constant of proportionality k in Hooke's law is the force constant of the spring, measured in newtons per metre.

- Elastic potential energy is the energy stored in objects that are stretched, compressed, twisted, or bent.

- The elastic potential energy stored in a spring is proportional to the force constant of the spring and to the square of the stretch or compression.

- Simple harmonic motion (SHM) is periodic vibratory motion such that the force (and thus the acceleration) is directly proportional to the displacement.

- A reference circle can be used to derive equations for the period and frequency of SHM.

- The law of conservation of mechanical energy can be applied to a mass–spring system and includes elastic potential energy, kinetic energy, and, in the case of vertical systems, gravitational potential energy.

- Damped harmonic motion is periodic motion in which the amplitude of vibration and the energy decrease with time.

▶ Section 4.5 Questions

Understanding Concepts

Note: For the following questions, unless otherwise stated, assume that all springs obey Hooke's law.

1. Two students pull equally hard on a horizontal spring attached firmly to a wall. They then detach the spring from the wall and pull horizontally on its ends. If they each pull equally hard, is the amount of stretch of the spring equal to, greater than, or less than the first stretch? Explain your answer. (*Hint:* Draw an FBD for the spring in each case.)

2. Is the amount of elastic potential energy stored in a spring greater when the spring is stretched 2.0 cm than when it is compressed by the same amount? Explain your answer.

3. What does "harmonic" mean in the term "simple harmonic motion?"

4. State the relationship, if any, between the following sets of variables. Where possible, write a mathematical variation (proportionality) statement based on the appropriate equation.
   (a) period and frequency
   (b) acceleration and displacement in SHM
   (c) period and the force constant for a mass on a spring in SHM
   (d) the maximum speed of a body in SHM and the amplitude of its motion

5. A student of mass 62 kg stands on an upholstered chair containing springs, each of force constant 2.4×10^3 N/m. If the student is supported equally by six springs, what is the compression of each spring?

6. What magnitude of force will stretch a spring of force constant 78 N/m by 2.3 cm from equilibrium?

7. The coiled spring in a hand exerciser compresses by 1.85 cm when a force of 85.5 N is applied. Determine the force needed to compress the spring by 4.95 cm.

8. A trailer of mass 97 kg is connected by a spring of force constant 2.2×10^3 N/m to an SUV. By how much does the spring stretch when the SUV causes the trailer to undergo an acceleration of magnitude 0.45 m/s^2?

9. A grapefruit of mass 289 g is attached to an unstretched vertical spring of force constant 18.7 N/m, and is allowed to fall.
   (a) Determine the net force and the acceleration on the grapefruit when it is 10.0 cm below the unstretched position and moving downward.
   (b) Air resistance will cause the grapefruit to come to rest at some equilibrium position. How far will the spring be stretched?

10. A bungee jumper of mass 64.5 kg (including safety gear) is standing on a platform 48.0 m above a river. The length of the unstretched bungee cord is 10.1 m. The force constant of the cord is 65.5 N/m. The jumper falls from rest and just touches the water at a speed of zero. The cord acts like an ideal spring. Use conservation of energy to determine the jumper's speed at a height of 12.5 m above the water on the first fall.

11. A toy car is attached to a horizontal spring. A force of 8.6 N exerted on the car causes the spring to stretch 9.4 cm.
    (a) What is the force constant of the spring?
    (b) What is the maximum energy of the toy-spring system?

12. If the maximum amplitude of vibration that a human eardrum can withstand is 1.0×10^{-7} m, and if the energy stored in the eardrum membrane is 1.0×10^{-13} J, determine the force constant of the eardrum.

13. A 22-kg crate slides from rest down a ramp inclined at 29° to the horizontal (**Figure 15**) onto a spring of force constant 8.9×10^2 N/m. The spring is compressed a distance of 0.30 m before the crate stops. Determine the total distance the crate slides along the ramp. Friction is negligible.

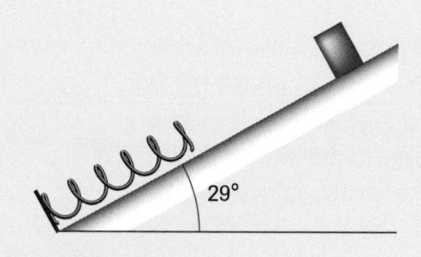

29°

Figure 15

14. A 0.20-kg ball attached to a vertical spring of force constant 28 N/m is released from rest from the unstretched equilibrium position of the spring. Determine how far the ball falls, under negligible air resistance, before being brought to a momentary stop by the spring.

Applying Inquiry Skills

15. **Figure 16** shows the energy relationships of a 0.12-kg mass undergoing SHM on a horizontal spring. The quantity x is the displacement from the equilibrium position.
    (a) Which line represents (i) the total energy, (ii) the kinetic energy, and (iii) the elastic potential energy?
    (b) What is the amplitude of the SHM?
    (c) What is the force constant of the spring?
    (d) What is the maximum speed of the mass?

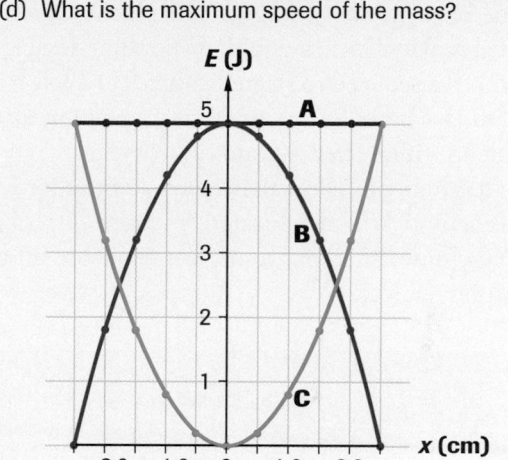

Figure 16

16. You are given a spring comprised of 24 coils that has a force constant of 24 N/m.
    (a) If this spring were cut into two equal pieces, would the force constant of each new spring be equal to, greater than, or less than 24 N/m? Explain.
    (b) With your teacher's permission, design and carry out an experiment to test your answer in (a). Explain what you discover.

Making Connections

17. The shock absorbers in the suspension system of a truck are in such poor condition that they have no effect on the behaviour of the springs attached to the axles. Each of the two identical springs attached to the rear axle supports 5.5×10^2 kg. After going over a severe bump, the rear end of the truck vibrates through six cycles in 3.5 s. Determine the force constant of each spring.

18. In designing components to be sent on board a satellite, engineers perform tests to ensure that the components can withstand accelerations with a magnitude as high as $25g$. In one test, the computer is attached securely to a frame that is vibrated back and forth in SHM with a frequency of 8.9 Hz. What is the minimum amplitude of vibration used in this test?

ACTIVITY 4.4.1

Applying the Law of Conservation of Energy

The gravity clock, originally called the pendulum clock, was first described by Galileo after he observed the regular period and frequency of suspended lamps in a cathedral. In 1656, the Dutch scientist Christian Huygens (1629–1695) built a pendulum clock that was accurate to within 10 s per day. Many design improvements were developed to increase the accuracy of keeping time using gravity clocks. The most sophisticated gravity clock, a double-pendulum design, was built in 1921. It used electromagnetic forces to allow a side pendulum to give input energy to the main pendulum, and was accurate to within a few seconds in five years.

In a small group, plan how the responsibilities for completing this activity will be allocated. To avoid duplicating topics, discuss how different groups can focus on different eras or features of clocks.

(a) Predict the energy transformations that occur during the operation of a simple gravity clock, and also for a more complex gravity clock.

(b) Use the Internet and other resources to research the design and operation of at least two or three different designs of gravity clocks. Record your notes for reference.

 www.science.nelson.com

(c) Choose a design (one not chosen by another group), and prepare a paper that summarizes your findings. Your paper can be a written report, a model with an accompanying explanation, a poster, or a Web site.

(d) Evaluate the resource(s) you used for this activity.

(e) Comment on your predictions in (a).

(f) Suggest ways in which the process your group used for completing this activity could be improved.

INVESTIGATION 4.5.1

Testing Real Springs

In this investigation, you will test real springs to determine under what conditions, if any, they obey Hooke's law. You will also explore what happens to the force constant of springs that are linked together.

Inquiry Skills

○ Questioning	● Planning	● Analyzing
● Hypothesizing	● Conducting	● Evaluating
● Predicting	● Recording	● Communicating

Questions

(i) What can be learned by graphing the forces applied by various masses to a spring as the spring undergoes stretching?

(ii) How does the force constant of two springs hung linearly compare with the individual force constants?

Hypothesis

(a) How do you expect a graph of F_x versus x for a real spring will compare with the corresponding graph for an ideal spring? Explain your reasoning.

(b) Hypothesize an answer to question (ii).

Prediction

(c) Sketch a graph to illustrate what you predict the relationship between F_x and x will be.

(d) Predict the equation that relates the total force constant, k_{total}, to the individual force constants, k_1 and k_2, of two springs joined together linearly.

Materials

For each group of three or four students:

support stand with clamp to which the spring can be attached

clamp to secure the support stand to the lab bench

string

3 extension springs of different stiffness

mass set (with masses from 50 g to 200 g for a sensitive spring, or 500 g to 2000 g for a stiff spring)

metre stick

graph paper

safety goggles

 **Do not allow the springs to overstretch.**

Make sure that the support stand is secure so that a mass cannot tip it over. Use the clamp.

Wear safety goggles.

Procedure

1. Use string to suspend the first spring from the clamp attached to the stand (**Figure 1**). Measure the amount that the spring stretches when various masses are hung from it and the mass-spring system reaches the equilibrium position. Tabulate your data.

2. Repeat step 1 with the other two springs.

3. Select two springs of different stiffness and suspend them (attached vertically in line with each other). Measure the amount that the double spring stretches when various masses are hung from it and the system reaches the equilibrium position. Tabulate your data.

Analysis

(e) Plot, on a single graph, the force applied to the spring versus the stretch of the spring, for each of the three springs tested in steps 1 and 2. Account for any part of each line that is not straight.

(f) Calculate and compare the slopes of the straight segments of the three lines on your graph in (e). What does each slope represent?

(g) Is extrapolation to a force of 50 N feasible for each of the springs graphed in (e)? Explain your answer.

(h) Derive an equation that relates the total force constant, k_{total}, to the individual force constants, k_1 and k_2, of the two springs you chose in step 3. (*Hint:* This is not a simple subtraction of the individual force constants.)

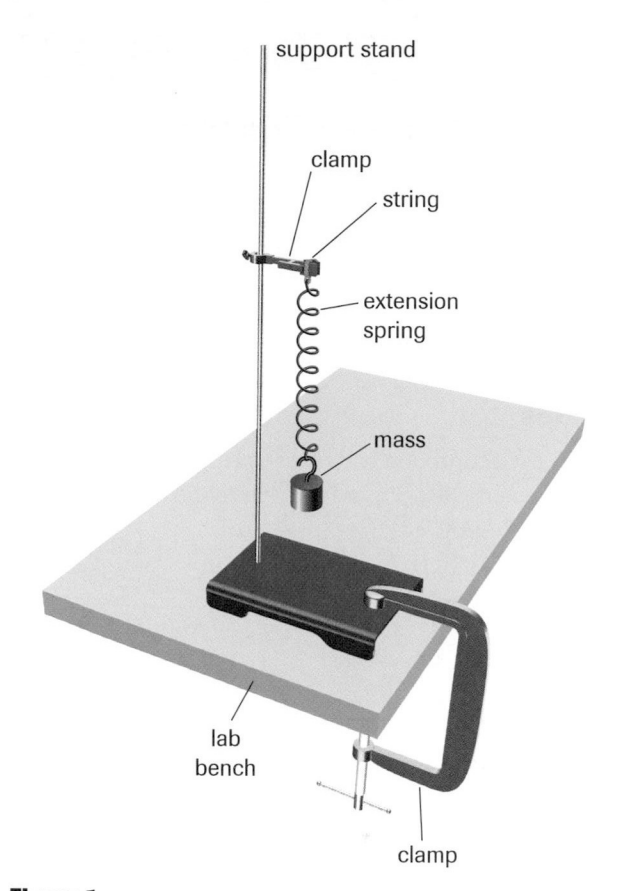

Figure 1
Setup for Investigation 4.5.1

Evaluation

(i) Comment on the accuracy of your hypotheses and predictions.

(j) Identify probable sources of random and systematic error in this investigation, and describe ways in which the errors can be minimized.

Synthesis

(k) Explain why applied force is plotted on the vertical axis of the graph even though it is the independent variable in this investigation.

(l) Describe the differences between a real spring and an ideal spring.

INVESTIGATION 4.5.2

Analyzing Forces and Energies in a Mass-Spring System

A mass-spring system can be used to analyze and synthesize several concepts presented in this chapter. In this investigation, you will explore how the law of conservation of energy relates to the SHM of a vertical mass-spring system.

Questions

(i) Does the action of a real mass-spring system suspended vertically, support or refute the law of conservation of energy?

(ii) What are the damping properties of a real mass-spring system that vibrates vertically?

Hypothesis

(a) Do you think a vibrating real spring undergoes SHM or damped harmonic motion? Give reasons for your answer.

(b) Hypothesize an answer to question (ii).

Prediction

(c) On a single graph, sketch each of the following energies as a function of the stretch of the vertical spring from the instant a mass is dropped from the highest (unstretched) position to the lowest position: gravitational potential energy, elastic potential energy, kinetic energy, and total energy.

(d) Sketch a graph of your prediction of the total energy of a vertically vibrating mass-spring system as a function of time.

Materials

For each group of three or four students:
support stand with clamp to which the spring can be attached
clamp to secure the support stand to the lab bench
string
extension spring
mass of appropriate size, depending on the spring (from 50 g to 200 g for a sensitive spring, or from 500 g to 2000 g for a stiff spring)
metre stick
stopwatch
graph paper
safety goggles

 Do not allow the spring to overstretch.
Make sure that the support stand is secure so that a mass cannot tip it over. Use the clamp.
Wear safety goggles.

Procedure

1. Design and carry out measurements to determine the force constant of the spring in newtons per metre. (If necessary, refer to Investigation 4.5.1.)

2. Obtain a mass approved by your instructor, and use string to suspend it from the unstretched spring. Determine the maximum stretch the spring undergoes when the mass is released and falls straight downward. Repeat this measurement until you are convinced that you have achieved the highest possible accuracy.

3. Using the same mass-spring system, allow the mass to drop from rest from the unstretched position, and to undergo vibratory motion as you determine the maximum vertical displacement for each of 10 cycles. Simultaneously, use the stopwatch to determine the time for the 10 complete cycles. Repeat the measurements to improve the accuracy.

Analysis

(e) Determine the gravitational potential energy, elastic potential energy, kinetic energy, and total energy at the top, middle, and bottom positions for the mass that you dropped from the unstretched spring in step 2. Tabulate the data, and then plot the data on a single graph, showing all the energies as a function of the displacement y. (If possible, use a spreadsheet program to tabulate the data and generate the corresponding graph.) Your graph should resemble **Figure 1**.

(f) Use the graph in (e) to determine the speed of the mass at the midpoint of the drop.

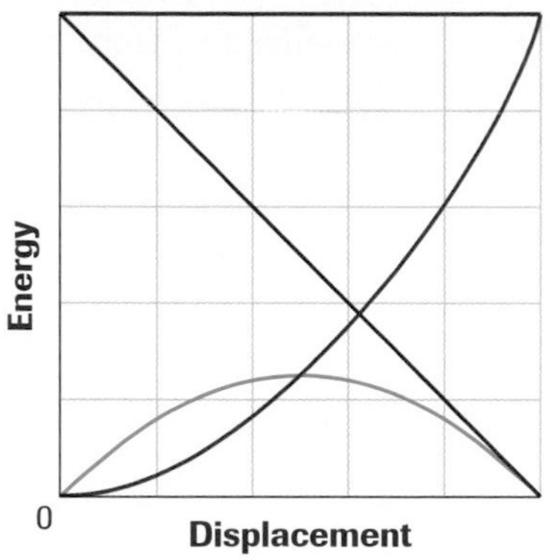

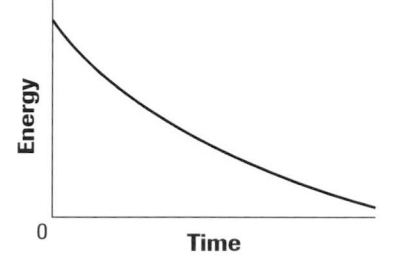

Figure 1
A typical energy-displacement graph for the first drop of a vertical mass-spring system

(g) Use the data collected in step 3 to determine the total energy of the mass at the beginning of each cycle, for 10 complete cycles. Plot the total energy as a function of time. (Your graph should resemble **Figure 2**.)

(h) Explain what happens to the energy that seems to disappear with each subsequent bounce of a vibrating mass-spring system.

(i) Answer questions (i) and (ii).

Evaluation

(j) Comment on the accuracy of your hypotheses and predictions.

(k) Identify the probable sources of random and systematic error in this investigation, and describe ways in which the errors can be minimized.

Synthesis

(l) Does a stiff spring undergo slower or faster damping than a less stiff spring of the same length?

Figure 2
A typical energy-time graph of a vibrating mass-spring system

○ ACTIVITY 4.5.1

Achieving a Smooth and Safe Ride

The suspension system of a car consists of a shock absorber and a stiff spring mechanism for each wheel. This system applies physics principles to help create a smooth and safe ride for the occupants.

(a) Hypothesize about the energy conversions that take place in the suspension system of a car.

(b) Research the design features of an effective suspension system. Record notes for reference.

 www.science.nelson.com

(c) Describe the design and operation of a modern version of a suspension system, and analyze the energy conversions that take place when the system is operating. In your description and analysis, show that you understand SHM, damped harmonic motion, and the law of conservation of energy.

(d) Explain why the newer, low-friction designs last longer than earlier designs, and offer better performance and safety when cornering.

(e) Evaluate the resource(s) you used for this activity.

(f) Comment on your hypothesis in (a).

Key Expectations

- define and describe the concepts and units related to energy (e.g., work-energy theorem, gravitational potential energy, elastic potential energy, thermal energy and its transfer [heat], open and closed energy systems, and simple harmonic motion) (4.1, 4.2, 4.3, 4.4, 4.5)

- analyze situations involving the concepts of mechanical energy, thermal energy and its transfer (heat), and the law of conservation of energy (4.4)

- analyze and explain common situations involving work and energy (4.1, 4.2, 4.3, 4.4, 4.5)

- state Hooke's law and analyze it in quantitative terms (4.5)

- design and conduct an experiment to verify the law of conservation of energy in a system involving several types of energy (4.5)

- analyze and describe, using the law of conservation of energy, various applications of energy transformations (e.g., analyze and describe the operation of a shock absorber, and analyze the energy transformations that take place; research and explain the operation of a gravity clock) (4.4, 4.5)

Key Terms

work

joule

kinetic energy

work-energy theorem

gravitational potential energy

law of conservation of energy

isolated system

Hooke's law

ideal spring

force constant

elastic potential energy

simple harmonic motion

damped harmonic motion

Key Equations

- $W = (F \cos \theta)\Delta d$ (4.1)

- $E_K = \dfrac{1}{2} mv^2$ (4.2)

- $W_{total} = \Delta E_K$ assuming no change in any (4.2) other form of energy

- $\Delta E_g = mg\Delta y$ (4.3)

- $E_{th} = F_K \Delta d$ (4.4)

- $F_x = \pm kx$ (4.5)

- $E_e = \dfrac{1}{2} kx^2$ (4.5)

- $T = 2\pi \sqrt{\dfrac{m}{k}}$ (4.5)

▶ MAKE a summary

Launching an extension spring so that it travels through the air toward an intended target (**Figure 1**) provides the context for a summary of this chapter. Imagine that you are given the following materials:

- a spring of unknown mass and unknown force constant
- a ruler
- a mass scale
- a set of launch parameters (the distance to the target, the launch angle, and the height the target is above or below the launching pad)

Use the following questions as a guideline for summarizing the concepts presented in this chapter:

1. Describe how you would make sure that the spring lands as close to the target as possible. Show typical calculations.

2. Show how you would determine the maximum height of the spring. Include typical calculations.

3. How would friction within the spring, friction on the launching pad, and air resistance affect your calculations?

4. List the energy transformations involved in the sequence of events starting with the work you must do in stretching the spring and ending after the spring hits the floor near the target and slides to a stop.

5. What would you observe if the same spring were set up to demonstrate SHM and/or damped harmonic motion?

6. How can the concepts and equations related to springs be applied in practical situations?

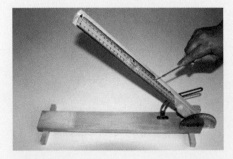

Figure 1
If the spring is stretched the appropriate amount and then launched from the launching pad, it will travel as a projectile and strike the target several metres away.

Write numbers 1 to 9 in your notebook. Indicate beside each number whether the corresponding statement is true (T) or false (F). If it is false, write a corrected version.

1. If friction is negligible, the work done on a pen in raising it 25 cm is the same whether the pen is raised along a vertical path or along a path inclined at some angle θ to the horizontal.

2. As you walk along a horizontal floor carrying a backpack at a constant height above the floor, the work done by gravity on the backpack is negative.

3. Extending the situation in question 2, you come to a complete stop to talk to a friend. As you are in the process of slowing down to stop, the work you do on the backpack is zero.

4. An eraser falls from rest from a desktop to the floor. As it falls, its kinetic energy increases in proportion to the square of its speed, and its gravitational potential energy decreases in proportion to the square of the distance fallen.

5. A ball bouncing off a floor never reaches the same height from which it was dropped (from rest). This does not refute the law of conservation of energy, because the ball and the floor do not belong to the same isolated system.

6. Thermal energy is the same as internal energy, whereas heat is the transfer of energy from a warmer object to a cooler one.

7. In a horizontal mass-spring system undergoing SHM, the maximum speed of the mass occurs when the elastic potential energy is at a minimum.

8. In a vertical mass-spring system undergoing SHM, the maximum speed of the mass occurs when the elastic potential energy is at a minimum.

9. A long damping time would be appropriate for a bathroom scale, but inappropriate for a child's "jolly-jumper" toy.

Write numbers 10 to 16 in your notebook. Beside each number, write the letter correspondng to the best choice.

For questions 10 to 15, choose the graph in **Figure 1** that best represents the relationship between the described variables.

10. The y-variable is the work done by a spring; x is the spring's stretch.

11. The y-variable is the kinetic energy of an object; x is the object's speed.

12. The y-variable is the period of vibration of an object undergoing SHM; x is the frequency of vibration.

13. The y-variable is the frequency of vibration of an object undergoing SHM in a mass-spring system; x is the force constant of the spring.

14. The y-variable is the period squared of an object undergoing SHM in a mass-spring system; x is the force constant of the spring.

15. The y-variable is the period squared of an object undergoing SHM in a mass-spring system; x is the reciprocal of the force constant of the spring.

16. A child pulls a sleigh up the incline in **Figure 2**. The work done by gravity on the sleigh during this motion is

  (a) $mgL \cos \theta$
  (b) $mgL \sin \theta$
  (c) $-mgL \cos \theta$
  (d) $-mgL \sin \theta$
  (e) none of these

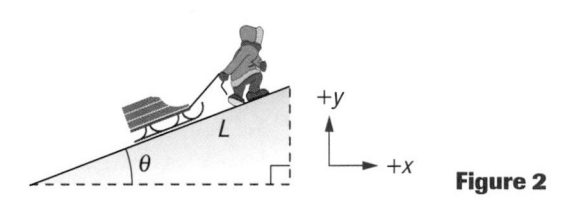

Figure 2

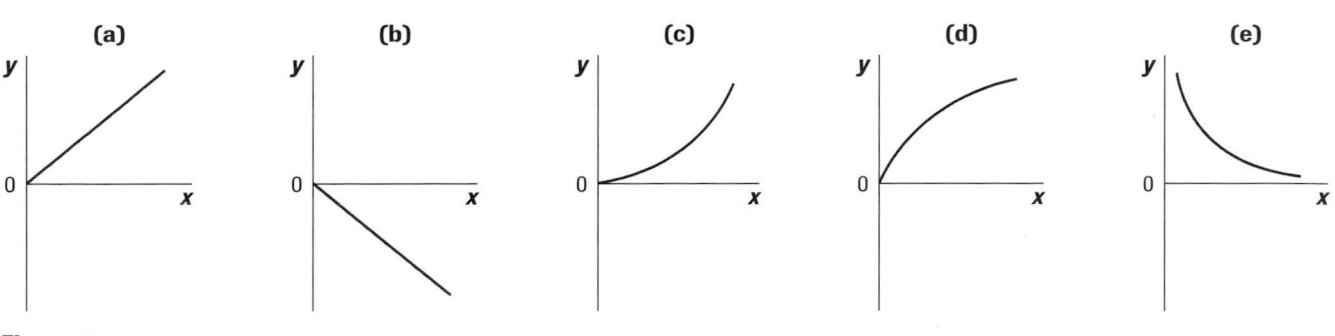

| (a) | (b) | (c) | (d) | (e) |

Figure 1
The first variable in questions 10 to 15 corresponds to the y-variable on one of these graphs; the second variable corresponds to the x-variable.

NEL   An interactive version of the quiz is available online.   Work and Energy **225**

GO www.science.nelson.com

Understanding Concepts

1. In each of the following situations, indicate whether the work done on object X by force $\vec{F}$ is positive, negative, or zero.
   (a) A golfer, walking at constant velocity, carries a golf bag X horizontally by exerting an upward force $\vec{F}$ on it.
   (b) A student exerts a force $\vec{F}$ on a book X as the book is lowered at constant velocity toward the floor.
   (c) The force of gravity $\vec{F}$ acts on a hot-air balloon X moving vertically upward.
   (d) A normal force $\vec{F}$ is exerted by a road on a car X accelerating away from an intersection.
   (e) In a simple model of the atom, an electron X travels in a circular orbit as a result of the electrical force $\vec{F}$ toward the nucleus.
   (f) A tension $\vec{F}$ acts on a mass X attached to a string. The mass is swinging as a pendulum.

2. A force is applied to an object, which undergoes a displacement. What can you conclude if the work done on the object by the force is zero?

3. Can the normal force on an object ever do work on the object? Explain your answer.

4. A swimmer is trying to swim upstream in a river with a constant flow of water, but remains stationary relative to the shore.
   (a) Is any work being done on the swimmer? Explain.
   (b) If the swimmer stops swimming and floats with the water flow, is any work done on the swimmer? Explain.

5. A nonzero net external force acts on a particle. Is this enough information to conclude that there is a change
   (a) to the particle's velocity?
   (b) to the particle's speed?
   (c) to the particle's kinetic energy?

   Justify each answer.

6. Do you agree or disagree with the statement: "If friction and air resistance can be neglected, the speed of a falling body does not depend on the mass of the body or the path it takes." Justify your answer.

7. Give examples in which the damping of vibrations is
   (a) useful and (b) not useful.

8. Do you think it is possible to have any isolated harmonic motion that is not damped? ("Isolated" means there is no external influence.) If "yes," give at least one example. If "no," explain why not.

9. A soccer ball of mass 0.425 kg is kicked on a parabolic trajectory so that its maximum height is 11.8 m above the ground. What work does gravity do on the ball (a) on the way up and (b) on the way down?

10. A gardener pushes a lawnmower by exerting a constant force of magnitude 9.3 N. If this force does 87 J of work on the lawnmower while pushing it 11 m across level ground, what is the angle between the applied force and the horizontal?

11. A 25.6-kg child pulls a 4.81-kg toboggan up a hill inclined at 25.7° to the horizontal. The vertical height of the hill is 27.3 m. Friction is negligible.
    (a) Determine how much work the child must do on the toboggan to pull it at constant velocity up the hill.
    (b) Repeat (a) if the vertical height is still 27.3 m, but the angle is 19.6°. What general conclusion can you make?
    (c) The child now slides down the hill on the toboggan. Determine the total work on the child and toboggan during the slide.

12. A 73-kg skier coasts up a hill inclined at 9.3° to the horizontal. Friction is negligible. Use the work-energy theorem to determine how far along the hill the skier slides before stopping, if the initial speed at the bottom is 4.2 m/s.

13. What is the original speed of an object if its kinetic energy increases by 50.0% when its speed increases by 2.00 m/s?

14. Assume that the Great Pyramid of Cheops in Egypt (**Figure 1**) has a mass of 7.0×10^9 kg and that its centre of mass is 36 m above the ground.
    (a) Determine the gravitational potential energy of the pyramid relative to the ground on which it was built.
    (b) Assume that each person worked on building the pyramid 40 days each year and was able to do 5×10^6 J of work each day in raising stone blocks. If the efficiency of each worker in moving the blocks was 20% and the pyramid took 20 years to complete, how many workers were involved?

15. In a biceps curl, a weightlifter lifts a mass of 45 kg a vertical distance of 66 cm. Acceleration is negligible.
    (a) How much work is done by gravity on the mass?
    (b) How much work is done by the weightlifter on the mass?
    (c) By how much does the gravitational potential energy of the mass increase?

Figure 1
The Great Pyramid of Cheops was the largest pyramid ever built. (for question 14)

16. A seagull drops a 47-g seashell, initially at rest, from the roof of a cabin.
    (a) If air resistance is negligible, what is the seashell's speed when it has fallen 4.3 m? Use the law of conservation of energy.
    (b) If air resistance were included, would your answer to (a) increase, decrease, or remain the same?

17. A stick is thrown from a cliff 27 m high with an initial velocity of 18 m/s at an angle of 37° above the horizontal.
    (a) Use the law of conservation of energy to determine the speed of the stick just before it hits the ground.
    (b) Repeat (a) with an angle of 37° below the horizontal.

18. A gardener exerts a force of 1.5×10^2 N [22° below the horizontal] in pushing a large 18-kg box of flower seeds a distance of 1.6 m. The coefficient of kinetic friction between the box and the floor is 0.55.
    (a) Use Newton's laws to determine the magnitudes of the normal force and the force of friction on the box.
    (b) Use the law of conservation of energy to determine the final speed of the box if it starts from rest.
    (c) How much thermal energy is produced?

19. A 1.2×10^3-kg space probe, travelling initially at a speed of 9.5×10^3 m/s through deep space, fires its engines that produce a force of magnitude 9.2×10^4 N over a distance of 86 km. Determine the final speed of the probe.

20. A gymnast springs vertically from a trampoline, leaving the trampoline at a height of 1.15 m from the ground, and reaching a maximum height of 4.75 m from the ground. Determine the speed with which the gymnast leaves the trampoline. (Ignore air resistance and apply energy concepts.)

21. **Figure 2** is a graph of the horizontal component of the force exerted by a person moving a table in a straight line across a horizontal floor. How much work does the person do on the table as the table moves 6.0 m?

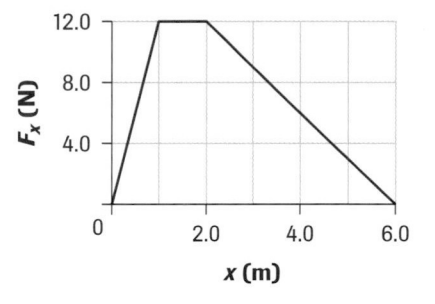

Figure 2

22. A spring is stretched 0.418 m from equilibrium by a force of magnitude 1.00×10^2 N.
    (a) What is the force constant of the spring?
    (b) What is the magnitude of force required to stretch the spring 0.150 m from equilibrium?
    (c) How much work must be done on the spring to stretch it 0.150 m from equilibrium and to compress it 0.300 m from equilibrium?

23. A student uses a compressed spring of force constant 22 N/m to shoot a 7.5×10^{-3}-kg eraser across a desk. The magnitude of the force of friction on the eraser is 4.2×10^{-2} N. How far along the horizontal desk will the eraser slide if the spring is initially compressed 3.5 cm? Use the law of conservation of energy.

24. A block attached to a horizontal spring of force constant 75 N/m undergoes SHM with an amplitude of 0.15 m. If the speed of the mass is 1.7 m/s when the displacement is 0.12 m from the equilibrium position, what is the mass of the block?

25. A mass of 0.42 kg, attached to a horizontal spring of force constant 38 N/m, undergoes SHM without friction at an amplitude of 5.3 cm.
    (a) What is the maximum energy of the mass-spring system?
    (b) Determine the maximum speed of the mass using energy concepts.
    (c) What is the speed of the mass when the displacement is 4.0 cm?
    (d) Determine the sum of the system's kinetic energy and elastic potential energy when the displacement is 4.0 cm. Compare your result with your answer in (a).

Applying Inquiry Skills

26. (a) Use actual measurements to determine how much work you would have to do to stack five of these physics texts one on top of the other, if they are originally lying flat on the table.
    (b) Identify sources of random and systematic error in your measurements.

27. A force sensor is used to push a box along a horizontal surface at a constant velocity. If the sensor is connected to a graphing calculator, what information would the calculator have to generate to indicate the amount of work done by the force applied by the sensor to the box?

28. The end of a diving board exhibits damped harmonic motion after a diver jumps off. At the instant the diver leaves the board ($t = 0$), the end of the board is at its highest position, $y = 26$ cm above the equilibrium position. The period of vibration of the end of the board is 0.40 s. The amplitude becomes negligible after 6 cycles. Draw a graph showing the approximate displacement as a function of time for this motion. (Include the envelope of the damping.)

29. Farm tractors often produce vibrations that are irritating to the person riding in them. You are hired by a manufacturer to design a tractor seat that will reduce the vibrations transmitted to the person sitting in the seat to a minimum. Describe ways of accomplishing your goal. (Consider concepts presented in this chapter, such as damping and the law of conservation of energy.)

Making Connections

30. On extremely windy or cold days, certain roller-coaster rides are shut down. Why?

31. Two identical balls, A and B, are released from rest on inclines that have the same vertical drop and the same horizontal distance from one end to the other. The inclines differ in detail as illustrated in **Figure 3**. (Note that very little energy is lost due to rolling friction.)
    (a) Which ball arrives at the end first? Explain your answer.
    (b) Racing cyclists apply this principle on inclined oval tracks. Explain how.

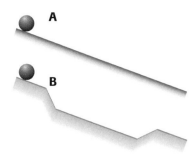

Figure 3

Extension

32. **Figure 4** shows a partial profile of a roller-coaster ride. Friction and air resistance are negligible. Determine the speed of the coaster at position C if the speed at the top of the highest hill is (a) zero and (b) 5.00 m/s.

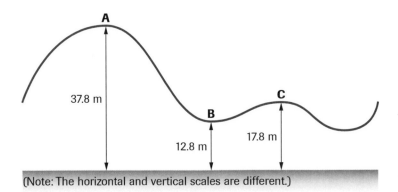

(Note: The horizontal and vertical scales are different.)

Figure 4

33. (a) Why, in question 32, was it unnecessary to specify the mass of the coaster?
    (b) Compare the increase in speeds in the two situations. Is the difference surprising? Why or why not?

34. A helicopter of mass m has an acceleration of magnitude 0.12 g upward.
    (a) Determine the force required to cause this acceleration.
    (b) How much work is done by this force in moving the helicopter a distance Δy upward?

35. A 1.5-kg steel mass is dropped onto a vertical compression spring of force constant 2.1×10^3 N/m, from a height of 0.37 m above the top of the spring. Find, from energy considerations, the maximum distance the spring is compressed.

36. A stretched elastic band of mass 0.55 g is released so that its initial velocity is horizontal, and its initial position is 95 cm above the floor. What was the elastic potential energy stored in the stretched band if, when it lands, it has a horizontal displacement of 3.7 m from the initial position under negligible air resistance?

37. A skier swoops down a hill and over a ramp as in **Figure 5**. She starts from rest at a height of 16 m, leaves the 9.0-m ramp at an angle of 45°, and just clears the hedge on her way down, making an angle of 30° with the vertical as she does. Assuming that there is no friction, and that she is small compared to the dimensions of the problem, solve for H, the height of the hedge in metres.

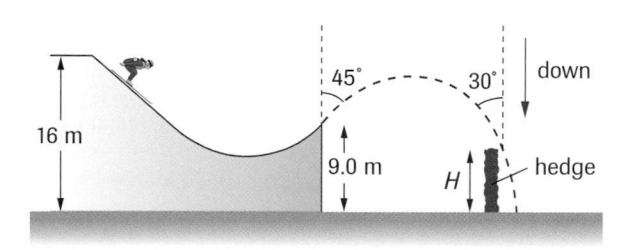

Figure 5

Sir Isaac Newton Contest Question

38. An athlete throws a basketball through a hoop as in **Figure 6**. The ball leaves his hands at a height of 2.5 m with a speed of 9.0 m/s. Calculate the speed of the ball when it "swishes" through the hoop. The hoop is at a height of 3.0 m and it is 5.0 m along the court from the basketball player.

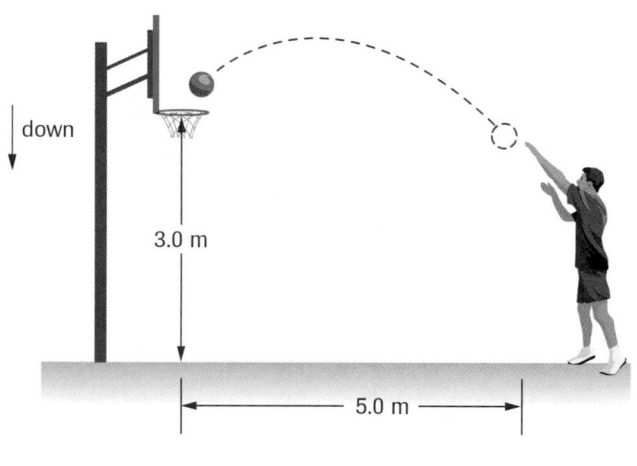

Figure 6

Sir Isaac Newton Contest Question

39. A space shuttle lands on a distant planet where the gravitational acceleration is 2.0. (We don't know the local units of length and time, but they are consistent throughout this problem.) The shuttle coasts along a level, frictionless plane (**Figure 7**) with a speed of 6.0 (position 1). It then coasts up a frictionless ramp of height 5.0 and angle 30° (position 2). After a brief ballistic flight, it lands a distance S from the ramp (position 3). Solve for S in local units of length. Assume the shuttle is small compared to the local length unit and that all atmospheric effects are negligible.

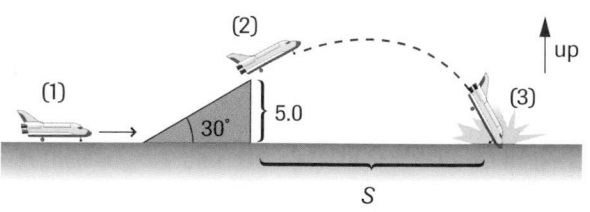

Figure 7

Sir Isaac Newton Contest Question

Momentum and Collisions

In this chapter, you will be able to

- define and describe the concepts and units related to momentum (momentum, impulse, elastic collisions, and inelastic collisions)

- analyze, with the aid of vector diagrams, the linear momentum of a collection of objects, and quantitatively apply the law of conservation of linear momentum

- analyze situations involving the concepts of mechanical energy, thermal energy and its transfer (heat), and the laws of conservation of momentum and energy

- distinguish between elastic and inelastic collisions

- investigate the laws of conservation of momentum and energy in one and two dimensions by carrying out experiments or simulations and the necessary analytical procedures

- analyze and describe practical applications of momentum conservation, applying the law of conservation of momentum

- identify and analyze social issues that relate to the development of vehicles

Collisions occur all the time. Air molecules continually collide with each other and with objects near them, such as your eardrums. Hockey sticks and pucks, and tennis rackets and tennis balls collide. Hailstones collide with car roofs. A train engine attached to a set of railway cars collides with the cars and then pulls them away. Energetic particles from the Sun undergo collisions with molecules in Earth's atmosphere to produce the northern and southern lights (*aurora borealis* and *aurora australis*). Even entire galaxies collide. To understand collisions and apply the knowledge to the world around us, we need to understand the concept of momentum and the law of conservation of momentum.

The knowledge gained in studying collisions can be applied to many situations that involve safety issues. In sports activities, helmets and other protective gear reduce concussions and other injuries that occur as a result of collisions. In transportation, vehicle airbags are designed to reduce injuries that occur in collisions. Crash barriers are incorporated into highway designs to reduce damage to vehicles and injuries to the vehicle's occupants (**Figure 1**).

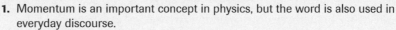

REFLECT on your learning

1. Momentum is an important concept in physics, but the word is also used in everyday discourse.
   (a) Explain the everyday meaning of the expression "Our soccer team appears to be gaining momentum."
   (b) How do you think the physics meaning of "gaining momentum" differs from the everyday meaning?

2. For each of the following situations involving objects A and B, state whether the magnitude of the momentum of A is greater than, less than, or equal to the magnitude of the momentum of B.
   (a) Car A is at rest; an identical car B is in motion.
   (b) Cyclist A is moving at moderate speed; a cyclist of equal mass B, riding an identical bicycle, is moving at a high speed.
   (c) A large truck A is moving at the same speed as car B.

3. In sports activities in which a ball is struck by a device, such as a golf club, a baseball bat, a tennis racket, etc., "follow-through" is an advantage.
   (a) What is meant by the phrase "follow-through?" Why is it an advantage?
   (b) What variable do you think affects follow-through in sports activities?

4. **Figure 2** is a graph of the force applied by a cue to a billiard ball as a function of time.
   (a) What technique could you use to determine the approximate area between the curved line and the time axis?
   (b) Use unit analysis or dimensional analysis to determine what quantity the area under the line on the graph could represent. (*Hint:* Convert newtons to base SI units.)

5. If you were designing a new car, would you design it so that it was highly elastic and would bounce off other cars in a collision, or would you design it so that it had flexible components that would become crunched in a crash? Give reasons.

Figure 2

For question 4. The force applied by a cue as it collides with a billiard ball is not constant.

$\uparrow F$ (N)

0   t (s)

▶ TRY THIS activity

Predicting the Bounces

In this simple activity, you will offer a prediction and hypothesis about the bounce of a ball, and will then test your ideas by observation. With no preliminary class or group discussion, your teacher will pass ball A around the class, followed by ball B, to allow each student to decide whether ball A's bounce will be higher than, lower than, or equal to ball B's bounce, assuming that both are dropped from rest from the same height above the floor.

(a) Write your prediction.

(b) Discuss the situation with other students and then write your hypothesis explaining how you think ball A compares with B.

(c) Drop balls A and B to test the predictions made by you and your classmates. Assess your prediction and hypothesis.

(d) Link your observations in this activity to the law of conservation of energy as applied to collisions on highways or in sports activities.

✋ Do not throw the balls. The bounce can be dangerous.

Figure 1

Which design would offer better protection to the occupants of a car if the car crashed into these barriers?

In bobsleigh racing (**Figure 1**), also called bobsled racing, team members push as hard as they can on the bobsleigh in the start zone, then jump in to race it at the fastest speed possible down an icy, curved course over 1.2 km long. The two-person bobsleigh has a mass of about 220 kg and requires a large force to achieve a high velocity. When the competitors jump into the bobsleigh, the total mass can be as high as 390 kg.

The quantities of mass and velocity combine to give an object **linear momentum**. The linear momentum of a moving object is the product of the object's mass and (instantaneous) velocity:

$$\vec{p} = m\vec{v}$$

where $\vec{p}$ is the linear momentum of the object in kilogram metres per second, m is its mass in kilograms, and $\vec{v}$ is its velocity in metres per second. The direction of the linear momentum is the same as the direction of the velocity.

Linear momentum depends on both the mass and the velocity of an object. For any given mass, the linear momentum is directly proportional to the velocity, and for any given velocity, the linear momentum is directly proportional to the mass. A truck has more linear momentum than a car travelling at the same speed, but a fast-moving car may have the same linear momentum as a slow-moving truck.

Linear momentum is a vector quantity, being the product of a scalar (mass) and a vector (velocity). We will often consider the components of linear momentum:

$p_x = mv_x$

$p_y = mv_y$

In most of our discussions, we will omit the word "linear" to describe the type of momentum that involves a mass moving linearly. Another type of momentum, called *angular momentum*, is possessed by a rotating object, such as a spinning figure skater. (Angular momentum is not presented in detail in this text.)

Figure 1
The start zone of a bobsleigh race is about 15 m long. The racers must exert as large a force as possible on the bobsleigh over that distance to increase its velocity and give it as much momentum as possible.

linear momentum ($\vec{p}$) the product of the mass of a moving object and its velocity; a vector quantity

---

▶ **SAMPLE problem 1**

Determine the momentum of a Pacific leatherback turtle of mass 8.6×10^2 kg, swimming at a velocity of 1.3 m/s [forward]. (The Pacific leatherback turtle is the world's largest species of turtle.)

Solution

$m = 8.6 \times 10^2$ kg

$\vec{v} = 1.3$ m/s [forward]

$\vec{p} = ?$

$\qquad \vec{p} = m\vec{v}$

$\qquad\quad = (8.6 \times 10^2 \text{ kg})(1.3 \text{ m/s [forward]})$

$\qquad \vec{p} = 1.1 \times 10^3$ kg·m/s [forward]

The momentum of the turtle is 1.1×10^3 kg·m/s [forward].

Understanding Concepts

1. Calculate the momentum of each of the following:
   (a) a 7.0×10^3-kg African elephant running at 7.9 m/s [E]
   (b) a 19-kg mute swan flying at 26 m/s [S]
   (c) an electron of mass 9.1×10^{-31} kg moving at 1.0×10^7 m/s [forward]

2. A personal watercraft and its rider have a combined mass of 405 kg, and a momentum of 5.02×10^3 kg·m/s [W]. Determine the velocity of the craft.

3. A bullet travelling at 9.0×10^2 m/s [W] has a momentum of 4.5 kg·m/s [W]. What is its mass?

4. (a) By estimating your top running speed, estimate the magnitude of your momentum when you are running at this speed.
   (b) How fast would a typical compact car have to be moving to reach the same momentum? State your assumptions and show your calculations.

Answers

1. (a) 5.5×10^4 kg·m/s [E]
   (b) 4.9×10^2 kg·m/s [S]
   (c) 9.1×10^{-24} kg·m/s [forward]

2. 12.4 m/s [W]

3. 5.0×10^{-3} kg, or 5.0 g

Impulse and Change in Momentum

Consider the factors that cause the momentum of the bobsleigh shown in **Figure 1** to build in the start zone from zero to the maximum possible value. The force applied by the team is an obvious factor: the greater the force applied, the greater is the final momentum. The other factor is the time interval over which the force is applied: the greater the time interval, the greater is the final momentum. To analyze these relationships, we refer to Newton's second law of motion.

Newton's second law states that an object acted upon by an external net force accelerates in the direction of the net force; the relationship between the object's mass, acceleration, and the net force acting on it is expressed by the equation $\sum \vec{F} = m\vec{a}$. We can derive an equation to express an object's change in momentum in terms of the net force (assumed to be constant) and the time interval starting with this equation:

$$\sum \vec{F} = m\vec{a}$$

$$\sum \vec{F} = m\left(\frac{\vec{v}_f - \vec{v}_i}{\Delta t}\right)$$

$$\sum \vec{F}\Delta t = m(\vec{v}_f - \vec{v}_i)$$

$$\sum \vec{F}\Delta t = \vec{p}_f - \vec{p}_i$$

Since the vector subtraction $\vec{p}_f - \vec{p}_i = \Delta \vec{p}$, we have:

$$\sum \vec{F}\Delta t = \Delta \vec{p}$$

The product $\sum \vec{F}\Delta t$ is called the **impulse**, which is *equal to the change in momentum*. The SI unit of impulse is the newton second (N·s), and the direction of the impulse is the same as the direction of the change in momentum.

You can apply the concepts implied in the equation $\sum \vec{F}\Delta t = \Delta \vec{p}$ in your daily activities. For example, catching a ball with your bare hands will hurt depending on the force $\sum \vec{F}$ of the ball. Since the ball always approaches you at the same speed, its change in momentum as you stop it is always the same: $\Delta \vec{p} = m(\vec{v}_f - \vec{v}_i) = m(0 - \vec{v}_i)$. Thus, if you allow your hands to move with the ball as you catch it, Δt will be larger, $\sum \vec{F}$ will be smaller, and your hands will hurt less.

impulse the product $\sum \vec{F}\Delta t$, equal to the object's change in momentum

High-Speed Particles
The familiar form of Newton's second law of motion, $\sum \vec{F} = m\vec{a}$, does not apply to tiny particles, such as electrons, when their speeds approach the speed of light. However, the more general form, $\sum \vec{F} = \dfrac{\Delta \vec{p}}{\Delta t}$, does apply even at these high speeds.

The relationship between impulse and change in momentum can be stated for components:

$$\sum F_x \Delta t = \Delta p_x$$
$$\sum F_y \Delta t = \Delta p_y$$

The form of Newton's second law of motion that we are familiar with is $\sum \vec{F} = m\vec{a}$, but by rearranging $\sum \vec{F} \Delta t = \Delta \vec{p}$, we can express Newton's second law as

$$\sum \vec{F} = \dfrac{\Delta \vec{p}}{\Delta t}$$

This equation indicates that *the net force on an object equals the rate of change of the object's momentum.* This form of the second law is actually more general than $\sum \vec{F} = m\vec{a}$ because it lets us handle situations in which the mass changes. In fact, it is the way in which Newton originally stated his second law. In terms of *x*- and *y*-components, we can write this equation as

$$\sum F_x = \dfrac{\Delta p_x}{\Delta t} \quad \text{and} \quad \sum F_y = \dfrac{\Delta p_y}{\Delta t}$$

In deriving the equation $\sum \vec{F} \Delta t = \Delta \vec{p}$, we assumed that the acceleration of the object is constant, and thus the net force on the object is constant. However, in many situations, the force applied to an object changes nonlinearly during its time of application. The equation $\sum \vec{F} \Delta t = \Delta \vec{p}$ still applies, provided the net force $\sum \vec{F}$ is equal to the *average force* acting on the object over the time interval Δt.

To understand the term "average force," consider **Figure 2(a)**, which shows the typical shape of a graph of the magnitude of the force as a function of time during a collision or other interaction of time interval Δt. The graph could represent, for example, the force acting on a soccer ball as a player kicks it. The area between the curved line and the time axis represents the impulse given to the object. (You can verify this by considering that the unit of the area, the newton second (N·s), represents impulse.) The *average force* is the constant force that would yield the same impulse as the changing force does in the same time interval. On a force-time graph, the average force is the constant force, shown as the straight line in **Figure 2(b)**, that would yield the same area as the curved line in the same time interval.

LEARNING TIP

Finding the Areas on Graphs
Estimating the average force on a force-time graph involving a nonconstant force is one way of determining the impulse (i.e., the area) on an object. Another way is to draw a grid system on the graph as in **Figure 2(c)** and count the small rectangles of known area. A third way involves applying integral calculus, a topic left for more advanced physics courses.

(a)

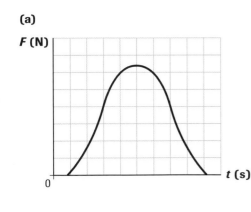

(b)

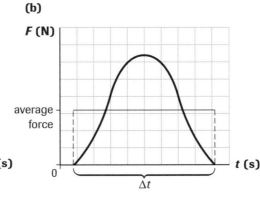

(c)

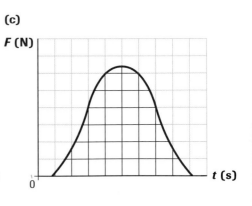

Figure 2
(a) The magnitude of the force acting on an object during a typical collision
(b) The average force, acting over Δt, gives the same area as the area under the curve in (a).
(c) Estimating the area under the curve by counting squares of known area on a superimposed grid

▶ **SAMPLE** problem 2

A baseball of mass 0.152 kg, travelling horizontally at 37.5 m/s [E], collides with a baseball bat. The collision lasts for 1.15 ms. Immediately after the collision, the baseball travels horizontally at 49.5 m/s [W] (**Figure 3**).

(a) Determine the initial momentum of the baseball.

(b) What is the average force applied by the bat to the baseball?

(c) Determine the ratio of the magnitude of this force to the magnitude of the force of gravity on the baseball.

Solution

(a) $m = 0.152$ kg

$\vec{v}_i = 37.5$ m/s [E]

$\vec{p}_i = ?$

$$\vec{p}_i = m\vec{v}_i$$
$$= (0.152 \text{ kg})(37.5 \text{ m/s [E]})$$
$$\vec{p}_i = 5.70 \text{ kg·m/s [E]}$$

The initial momentum is 5.70 kg·m/s [E].

(b) $m = 0.152$ kg

$\Delta t = 1.15$ ms $= 1.15 \times 10^{-3}$ s

$\vec{v}_i = 37.5$ m/s [E]

$\vec{v}_f = 49.5$ m/s [W]

$\Sigma\vec{F} = ?$

$$\Sigma\vec{F} = \frac{\Delta\vec{p}}{\Delta t}$$
$$= \frac{m(\vec{v}_f - \vec{v}_i)}{\Delta t}$$
$$= \frac{(0.152 \text{ kg})(49.5 \text{ m/s [W]} - 37.5 \text{ m/s [E]})}{1.15 \times 10^{-3} \text{ s}}$$
$$= \frac{(0.152 \text{ kg})(49.5 \text{ m/s [W]} + 37.5 \text{ m/s [W]})}{1.15 \times 10^{-3} \text{ s}}$$

$$\Sigma\vec{F} = 1.15 \times 10^4 \text{ N [W]}$$

The average force is 1.15×10^4 N [W].

(c) Determine the magnitude of the force of gravity on the ball:

$$F_g = mg$$
$$= (0.152 \text{ kg})(9.80 \text{ N/kg})$$
$$F_g = 1.49 \text{ N}$$

We can now calculate the required ratio:

$$\frac{1.15 \times 10^4 \text{ N}}{1.49 \text{ N}} = 7.72 \times 10^3$$

The ratio of forces is $7.72 \times 10^3 : 1$.

W ◄————► E

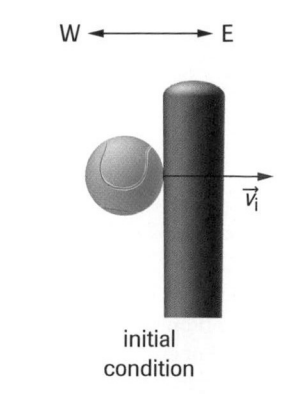

initial
condition

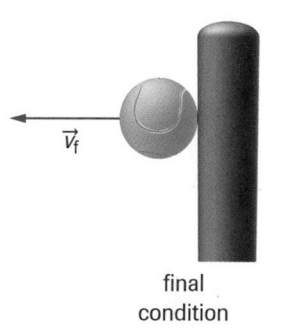

final
condition

Figure 3
The situation for Sample Problem 2

In Sample Problem 2(c), the magnitude of the average force exerted by the bat on the baseball is almost 8000 times larger than the magnitude of the force of gravity. In general, the forces between objects involved in collisions tend to be much larger than other forces, such as gravity. We can therefore usually ignore other forces when analyzing collisions.

To analyze the effect on impulse of a "follow-through" in sports activities, we will look at a specific example of a typical collision between a tennis ball and a racket.

▶ SAMPLE problem 3

A 57-g tennis ball is thrown upward and then struck just as it comes to rest at the top of its motion. The racket exerts an average horizontal force of magnitude 4.2×10^2 N on the tennis ball.

(a) Determine the speed of the ball after the collision if the average force is exerted on the ball for 4.5 ms.

(b) Repeat the calculation, assuming a time interval of 5.3 ms.

(c) Explain the meaning and advantage of follow-through in this example.

Solution

(a) Since this is a one-dimensional problem, we can use components.

$$m = 57\,g = 0.057\,kg \qquad\qquad v_{ix} = 0$$
$$\sum F_x = 4.2 \times 10^2\,N \qquad\qquad v_{fx} = ?$$
$$\Delta t = 4.5\,ms = 4.5 \times 10^{-3}\,s$$

$$\sum F_x \Delta t = \Delta p_x$$
$$\sum F_x \Delta t = m(v_{fx} - v_{ix})$$
$$\sum F_x \Delta t = mv_{fx} - mv_{ix}$$
$$mv_{fx} = \sum F_x \Delta t + mv_{ix}$$
$$v_{fx} = \frac{\sum F_x \Delta t}{m} + v_{ix}$$
$$= \frac{(4.2 \times 10^2\,N)(4.5 \times 10^{-3}\,s)}{0.057\,kg} + 0$$
$$v_{fx} = 33\,m/s$$

The speed of the tennis ball after the collision is 33 m/s.

(b) $$m = 57\,g = 0.057\,kg \qquad\qquad v_{ix} = 0$$
$$\sum F_x = 4.2 \times 10^2\,N \qquad\qquad v_{fx} = ?$$
$$\Delta t = 5.3\,ms = 5.3 \times 10^{-3}\,s$$

We use the same equation for v_{fx} as was derived in part (a):

$$v_{fx} = \frac{\sum F_x \Delta t}{m} + v_{ix}$$
$$= \frac{(4.2 \times 10^2\,N)(5.3 \times 10^{-3}\,s)}{0.057\,kg} + 0$$
$$v_{fx} = 39\,m/s$$

The speed of the tennis ball after the collision is 39 m/s.

(c) The racket in (b) exerts the same average force as in (a) but over a longer time interval. The additional time interval of 0.8 ms is possible only if the player follows through in swinging the racket. The advantage of follow-through is that the final speed of the tennis ball after the collision is greater even though the average force on the ball is the same.

▶ *Practice*

Understanding Concepts

5. Show that the units of impulse and change in momentum are equivalent.

6. A snowball of mass 65 g falls vertically toward the ground where it breaks apart and comes to rest. Its speed just before hitting the ground is 3.8 m/s. Determine
   (a) the momentum of the snowball before hitting the ground
   (b) the momentum of the snowball after hitting the ground
   (c) the change in momentum

7. A truck's initial momentum is 5.8×10^4 kg·m/s [W]. An average force of 4.8×10^3 N [W] increases the truck's momentum for the next 3.5 s.
   (a) What is the impulse on the truck over this time interval?
   (b) What is the final momentum of the truck?

8. A 0.27-kg volleyball, with an initial velocity of 2.7 m/s horizontally, hits a net, stops, and then drops to the ground. The average force exerted on the volleyball by the net is 33 N [W]. How long, in milliseconds, is the ball in contact with the net?

9. In its approach to an airport runway, an airplane of mass 1.24×10^5 kg has a velocity of 75.5 m/s [11.1° below the horizontal]. Determine the horizontal and vertical components of its momentum.

Applying Inquiry Skills

10. Determine the impulse imparted during the interaction represented in each graph in **Figure 4**.

Making Connections

11. In boxing matches in the nineteenth century, boxers fought with bare hands. Today's boxers use padded gloves.
    (a) How do gloves help protect a boxer's head (and brain) from injury?
    (b) Boxers often "roll with the punch." Use physics principles to explain how this manoeuvre helps protect them.

Answers

6. (a) 0.25 kg·m/s [down]
   (b) zero
   (c) 0.25 kg·m/s [up]
7. (a) 1.7×10^4 N·s [W]
   (b) 7.5×10^4 kg·m/s [W]
8. 22 ms
9. 9.19×10^6 kg·m/s;
   1.80×10^6 kg·m/s
10. (a) 1.0 N·s [E]
    (b) about 4.0 N·s [S]

(a)

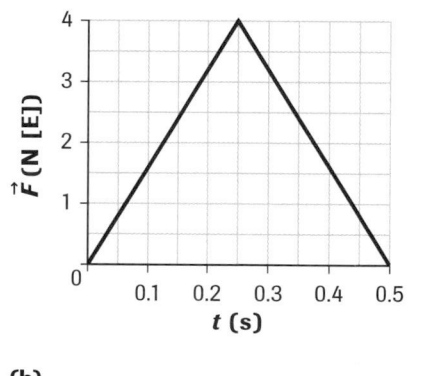

(b)

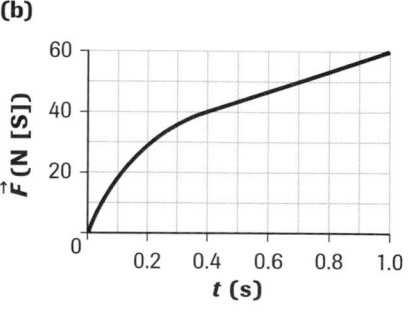

Figure 4
For question 10

SUMMARY *Momentum and Impulse*

- The linear momentum of an object is the product of the object's mass and velocity. It is a vector quantity whose SI base units are kg·m/s.

- The impulse given to an object is the product of the average net force acting on the object and the time interval over which that force acts. It is a vector quantity whose SI base units are N·s.

- The impulse given to an object equals the change in momentum experienced by the object.

Understanding Concepts

1. State Newton's second law as it was originally proposed by Newton, as a relationship between momentum and force. Write an equation expressing this relationship.

2. What is the property of the forces for which the concept of impulse proves most helpful when analyzing the changes in motion that occur as a result of the force?

3. Determine the impulse exerted in each of the following cases:
   (a) An average force of 24 N [E] is applied to a dynamics cart for 3.2 s.
   (b) A hockey stick exerts an average force of 1.2×10^2 N [forward] on a puck during the 9.1 ms they are in contact.
   (c) Earth pulls down on a 12-kg rock during the 3.0 s it takes the rock to fall from a cliff.
   (d) A toy car crashes into a brick wall, experiencing the changing force shown on the force-time graph in **Figure 5**.

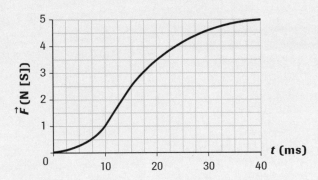

Figure 5

4. What velocity will a 41-kg child sitting on a 21-kg wagon acquire if pushed from rest by an average force of 75 N [W] for 2.0 s?

5. What average force will stop a 1.1×10^3-kg car in 1.5 s, if the car is initially moving at 22 m/s [E]?

6. A billiard ball of mass 0.17 kg rolls toward the right-hand cushion of a billiard table at 2.1 m/s, then rebounds straight back at 1.8 m/s.
   (a) What is the change in momentum of the ball as a result of hitting the cushion?
   (b) What impulse does the cushion give to the ball?

7. A 0.16-kg hockey puck is sliding along a smooth, flat section of ice at 18 m/s when it encounters some snow. After 2.5 s of sliding through the snow, it returns to smooth ice, continuing at a speed of 11 m/s.
   (a) What is the change in the momentum of the puck?
   (b) What impulse does the snow exert on the puck?
   (c) What average frictional force does the snow exert on the puck?

8. A frictionless disk of mass 0.50 kg is moving in a straight line across an air table at a speed of 2.4 m/s [E] when it bumps into an elastic band stretched between two fixed posts. The elastic band exerts an average opposing force of 1.4 N [W] on the disk for 1.5 s. What is the final velocity of the disk?

9. A 2.0-kg skateboard is rolling across a smooth, flat floor when a child kicks it, causing it to speed up to 4.5 m/s [N], in 0.50 s, without changing direction. The average force exerted by the child on the skateboard is 6.0 N [N]. What is the initial velocity of the skateboard?

10. A 0.61-kg basketball is thrown vertically downward. Just before it hits the floor, its speed is 9.6 m/s. It then rebounds upward with a speed of 8.5 m/s just as it leaves the floor. The basketball is in contact with the floor for 6.5 ms.
    (a) Determine the basketball's change in momentum.
    (b) Determine the average force exerted on the basketball by the floor. (Apply an equation involving the change in momentum.)

11. Explain why the force of gravity can be ignored during the collision between the basketball and the floor in question 10.

Applying Inquiry Skills

12. Describe an experiment you would perform to determine which of four or five athletes have good follow-through when they are striking a ball (or a puck) with a tennis racket, golf club, baseball bat, or hockey stick. Assume that you are allowed to use sophisticated apparatus, such as a digital camera or a video camera, and a stroboscopic light source. Draw sketches to compare photographic images of a good follow-through with a weak follow-through.

Making Connections

13. Experience has taught you that when you land upright on the ground after a jump, you feel less pain if you bend your knees as you are landing than if you land with your knees locked. Explain why bending your knees helps alleviate pain and injury.

14. A collision analyst applies physics principles to reconstruct what happened at automobile crashes. Assume that during a head-on crash between two cars, the cars came to a stop, and a large component of a plastic bumper broke off one car and skidded along the highway shoulder leaving skid marks.
    (a) What information could the analyst gather from the bumper component and from the skid marks it produced? What measurements would be needed to estimate the speed of the cars just before the collision, and how would they be used?
    (b) Find out more about how traffic collision analysts apply physics and math in their investigations using the Internet or other suitable publications. Report your findings in a paper, highlighting connections with momentum.

 www.science.nelson.com

Imagine standing at rest on skates on essentially frictionless ice, and throwing a basketball forward (**Figure 1**). As the ball moves in one direction, you move in the opposite direction at a much lower speed. This situation can be explained using Newton's third law: you exert a forward force on the ball as it exerts a backward force on you. We can also explain the situation using the *law of conservation of linear momentum.*

> **Law of Conservation of Linear Momentum**
>
> If the net force acting on a system of interacting objects is zero, then the linear momentum of the system before the interaction equals the linear momentum of the system after the interaction.

The system comprised of you (on skates) and the basketball has zero momentum before you throw the ball. Thus, the momentum of the system after the ball is thrown must also equal zero. Therefore, the momentum of the ball forward must be balanced by your momentum in the opposite direction.

During the seventeenth century, scientists including Newton discovered that the total momentum of colliding objects before and after a collision remains constant. To analyze the conditions under which this is true, we can study a simple collision between two gliders on a frictionless air track. It is useful to imagine a boundary around the gliders to focus our attention on the two-glider system. This system and its boundary are shown in **Figure 2(a)**.

Figure 1
As a person on skates throws a basketball forward, the force exerted by the skater on the ball is equal in magnitude, but opposite in direction to the force of the ball on the skater. Friction between the skates and the ice is assumed to be negligible. Thus, the net force on the system is zero and the linear momentum of this system is conserved.

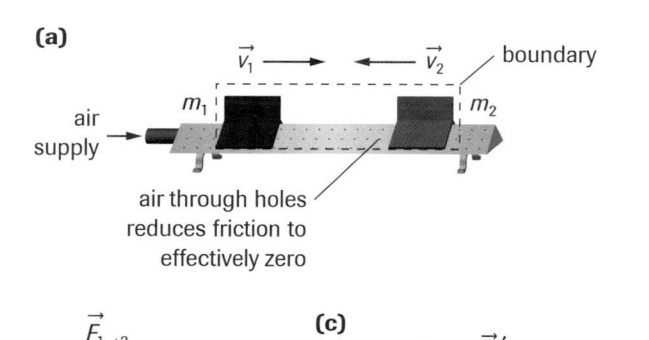

Figure 2
(a) Two gliders on an air track will soon collide.
(b) The collision is in progress.
(c) After colliding the gliders move apart.

Before the two gliders collide, the total momentum of the system is the vector sum of the momentum of each glider:

$$\vec{p}_{total} = m_1\vec{v}_1 + m_2\vec{v}_2$$

where $\vec{p}_{total}$ is the total momentum, m_1 is the mass and $\vec{v}_1$ is the velocity of one glider, and m_2 is the mass and $\vec{v}_2$ is the velocity of the other glider.

When the two gliders collide, each exerts a force on the other as in **Figure 2(b)**. According to Newton's third law of motion, the two forces are equal in magnitude, but opposite in direction:

$$\vec{F}_{2 \rightarrow 1} = -\vec{F}_{1 \rightarrow 2}$$

where $\vec{F}_{2 \rightarrow 1}$ is the force glider 2 exerts on glider 1, and $\vec{F}_{1 \rightarrow 2}$ is the force glider 1 exerts on glider 2. Thus, the net force acting on the two-glider system is zero:

$$\vec{F}_{2 \rightarrow 1} + \vec{F}_{1 \rightarrow 2} = 0$$

Note that the vertical forces—gravity and the upward force exerted by the air—also add to zero. Therefore, the net force on the system is zero.

The forces exerted by the gliders on each other cause each glider to accelerate according to Newton's second law of motion, $\sum \vec{F} = m\vec{a}$. Starting with the equation involving the forces we have:

$$\vec{F}_{2 \rightarrow 1} = -\vec{F}_{1 \rightarrow 2}$$
$$m_1 \vec{a}_1 = -m_2 \vec{a}_2$$
$$m_1 \frac{\Delta \vec{v}_1}{\Delta t_1} = -m_2 \frac{\Delta \vec{v}_2}{\Delta t_2}$$

We know that $\Delta t_1 = \Delta t_2$ because the force $\vec{F}_{1 \rightarrow 2}$ acts only as long as the force $\vec{F}_{2 \rightarrow 1}$ acts; that is, $\vec{F}_{1 \rightarrow 2}$ and $\vec{F}_{2 \rightarrow 1}$ act only as long as the gliders are in contact with each other. Thus,

$$m_1 \Delta \vec{v}_1 = -m_2 \Delta \vec{v}_2$$

This equation summarizes the law of conservation of (linear) momentum for two colliding objects. It states that *during an interaction between two objects on which the total net force is zero, the change in momentum of object 1 ($\Delta \vec{p}_1$) is equal in magnitude but opposite in direction to the change in momentum of object 2 ($\Delta \vec{p}_2$)*. Thus,

$$\Delta \vec{p}_1 = -\Delta \vec{p}_2$$

Let us now consider the glider system before and after the collision (**Figure 2(c)**). We will use the prime symbol ($'$) to represent the final velocities:

$$m_1 \Delta \vec{v}_1 = -m_2 \Delta \vec{v}_2$$
$$m_1 (\vec{v}_1' - \vec{v}_1) = -m_2 (\vec{v}_2' - \vec{v}_2)$$
$$m_1 \vec{v}_1' - m_1 \vec{v}_1 = -m_2 \vec{v}_2' + m_2 \vec{v}_2$$
$$m_1 \vec{v}_1 + m_2 \vec{v}_2 = m_1 \vec{v}_1' + m_2 \vec{v}_2'$$

This equation represents another way of summarizing the law of conservation of (linear) momentum. It states that *the total momentum of the system before the collision equals the total momentum of the system after the collision*. Thus,

$$\vec{p}_{\text{system}} = \vec{p}_{\text{system}}'$$

It is important to remember that momentum is a vector quantity; thus, any additions or subtractions in these conservation of momentum equations are vector additions or vector subtractions. These equations also apply to the conservation of momentum in two dimensions, which we will discuss in Section 5.4. Note that the equations written for components are:

$$m_1 \Delta v_{1x} = -m_2 \Delta v_{2x}$$
$$m_1 \Delta v_{1y} = -m_2 \Delta v_{2y}$$
$$m_1 v_{1x} + m_2 v_{2x} = m_1 v_{1x}' + m_2 v_{2x}'$$
$$m_1 v_{1y} + m_2 v_{2y} = m_1 v_{1y}' + m_2 v_{2y}'$$

LEARNING TIP

Interactions and Collisions
A collision between two or more objects in a system can also be called an *interaction*. However, there are interactions that are not collisions, although they obey the law of conservation of momentum. Examples include a person throwing a ball, an octopus ejecting water in one direction to propel itself in the opposite direction, and fireworks exploding into several pieces.

LEARNING TIP

Systems with More than Two Objects
The equation that relates the total momentum of the system before and after a collision can be applied to interactions involving more than two objects. For example, if three figure skaters, initially at rest in a huddle, push away from each other, the initial momentum of the system is zero and the vector sum of the skaters' momentums after the interaction is also zero.

▶ **SAMPLE** problem **1**

A vacationer of mass 75 kg is standing on a stationary raft of mass 55 kg. The vacationer then walks toward one end of the raft at a speed of 2.3 m/s relative to the water. What are the magnitude and direction of the resulting velocity of the raft relative to the water? Neglect fluid friction between the raft and the water.

Solution

In problems involving conservation of momentum, it is useful to draw diagrams that show the initial and final situations (**Figure 3**).

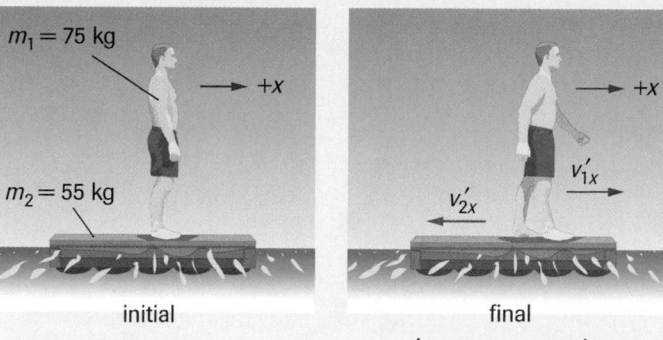

initial
$$v_{1x} = v_{2x} = 0$$

final
$$v_1' = 2.3 \text{ m/s} \qquad v_2' = ?$$

Figure 3
The initial and final situations

A coordinate system is then chosen; we will arbitrarily select the $+x$ direction to lie in the direction of the vacationer's final velocity. Since there is no net force acting on the system of the raft and person, we can apply the law of conservation of momentum:

$$m_1 v_{1x} + m_2 v_{2x} = m_1 v_{1x}' + m_2 v_{2x}'$$

where the subscript 1 refers to the person and the subscript 2 refers to the raft. Since this is a one-dimensional problem, we can omit the x subscripts:

$$m_1 v_1 + m_2 v_2 = m_1 v_1' + m_2 v_2'$$

Note that the v's in the equation represent velocity components and can have positive, zero, or negative values. They do not represent the magnitudes of the velocities, which must be nonnegative.

In this problem, $v_1 = v_2 = 0$, since the vacationer and the raft are initially stationary. Therefore, we can write:

$$0 = m_1 v_1' + m_2 v_2'$$

$$v_2' = \frac{-m_1 v_1'}{m_2}$$

$$= \frac{-(75 \text{ kg})(2.3 \text{ m/s})}{55 \text{ kg}}$$

$$v_2' = -3.1 \text{ m/s}$$

The final velocity of the raft is 3.1 m/s in the opposite direction to the vacationer's velocity (as the negative sign indicates).

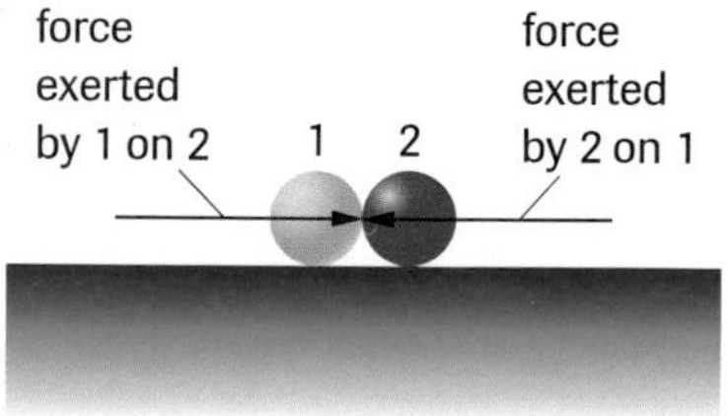

Conservation of momentum can be applied to many collisions. For example, in the collision of two billiard balls on a table (**Figure 4**), the force exerted on the first ball by the second is equal in magnitude, but opposite in direction to the force exerted on the second ball by the first. The net force on the system is zero and, therefore, the momentum of the system is conserved. (In this case, we can ignore any friction because it is very small compared to the forces exerted by the billiard balls on each other. Vertically there is no acceleration and, thus, there is no net vertical force.)

force exerted by 1 on 2   1   2   force exerted by 2 on 1

Figure 4
Two billiard balls colliding: the momentum of the system is conserved.

An important application of conservation of momentum is rocket propulsion, both on Earth and in the "vacuum" of outer space. As the rocket thruster exerts an action force on the hot gases ejected backward, the gases exert a reaction force equal in magnitude on the spacecraft, causing it to accelerate forward. Since the spacecraft and ejected gases form an isolated system, the change in momentum of the gases is equal in magnitude to the change in momentum of the spacecraft. As the thruster continues to fire its engines, its fuel supply becomes smaller, so there is a decrease in the mass of the spacecraft and remaining fuel. Although the conservation of momentum applies, the mathematical analysis of this changing-mass system is left for calculus-based physics texts.

▶ **SAMPLE** problem **2**

During a football game, a fullback of mass 108 kg, running at a speed of 9.1 m/s, is tackled head-on by a defensive back of mass 91 kg, running at a speed of 6.3 m/s. What is the speed of this pair just after the collision?

Solution
Figure 5 shows the initial and final diagrams. We choose the +x-axis as the direction of the initial velocity of the fullback. Therefore, the initial velocity of the defensive back is negative.

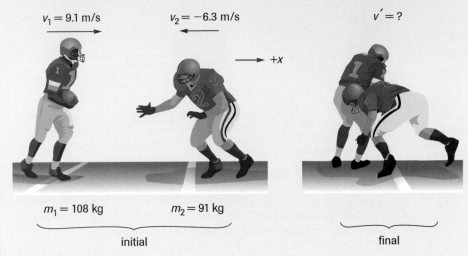

Figure 5
The initial and final situations

During the collision, there is no net force on the two-player system. (The horizontal force exerted between the players is much larger than friction, which can therefore be neglected. In the vertical direction, there is no acceleration because there is no vertical net force.) Therefore, the momentum of this system is conserved. Thus,

$$m_1 v_1 + m_2 v_2 = m_1 v_1' + m_2 v_2'$$

where the subscript 1 refers to the fullback and the subscript 2 refers to the defensive back. Remember that v represents a velocity component, not a velocity magnitude.

Since the two players have the same final velocity:

$$v_1' = v_2' = v'$$
$$m_1 v_1 + m_2 v_2 = (m_1 + m_2)v'$$
$$v' = \frac{m_1 v_1 + m_2 v_2}{m_1 + m_2}$$
$$= \frac{(108 \text{ kg})(9.1 \text{ m/s}) + (91 \text{ kg})(-6.3 \text{ m/s})}{(108 \text{ kg} + 91 \text{ kg})}$$
$$v' = +2.1 \text{ m/s}$$

The final velocity of the players is 2.1 m/s in the direction of the initial velocity of the fullback (as the positive sign indicates).

It is a misconception to think that momentum is conserved in *all* collisions. There are many collisions in which the net force on the colliding objects is not zero and, therefore, momentum is not conserved. For example, if a person jumps from a ladder to a wooden deck, the momentum of the person–deck system is not conserved because there is a large normal force exerted by the deck supports and the ground during the collision. In other words, the deck is not free to move, so $\Delta \vec{p}_{jumper}$ does not equal $-\Delta \vec{p}_{deck}$. However, if we change the boundary of the system to include Earth, momentum would be conserved because $\Delta \vec{p}_{jumper} = -\Delta \vec{p}_{Earth}$. Since the mass of Earth is very large compared to the mass of the person, Earth's change in velocity when the person lands is, of course, too small to measure. The person–Earth system is isolated, but the person–deck system is not.

Experiments can be performed to determine if momentum is conserved in a variety of collisions. However, much more can be learned about the collisions if energy is also analyzed. For greater accuracy, these experiments should involve collisions of objects that are isolated from external forces, as presented in Investigation 5.2.1 in the Lab Activities section at the end of this chapter. ◈▮

INVESTIGATION 5.2.1

Analyzing One-Dimensional Collisions (p. 260)
Different types of apparatus, including gliders on air tracks with motion and force sensors to collect data, can be used to create and analyze one-dimensional collisions. How do you think the challenge of isolating two colliding objects will affect the degree to which momentum and energy are conserved?

▶ Practice

Understanding Concepts

1. What condition(s) must be met for the total momentum of a system to be conserved?

2. State whether you agree or disagree with the following statement: "The law of conservation of momentum for a system on which the net force is zero is equivalent to Newton's first law of motion." Give a reason for your answer.

3. You drop a 59.8-g hairbrush toward Earth (mass 5.98×10^{24} kg).
   (a) What is the direction of the gravitational force exerted by Earth on the hairbrush?
   (b) What is the direction of the gravitational force exerted by the hairbrush on Earth?
   (c) How do the forces in (a) and (b) compare in magnitude?
   (d) What is the net force on the system consisting of Earth and the hairbrush?
   (e) What can you conclude about the momentum of this system?
   (f) If we consider Earth and the hairbrush to be initially stationary, how does Earth move as the hairbrush falls down?
   (g) If the hairbrush reaches a speed of 10 m/s when it hits Earth (initially stationary), what is Earth's speed at this time?

4. A 45-kg student stands on a stationary 33-kg raft. The student then walks with a velocity of 1.9 m/s [E] relative to the water. What is the resulting velocity of the raft, relative to the water, if fluid friction is negligible.

5. Two ice skaters, initially stationary, push each other so that they move in opposite directions. One skater of mass of 56.9 kg has a speed of 3.28 m/s. What is the mass of the other skater if her speed is 3.69 m/s? Neglect friction.

6. A stationary 35-kg artillery shell accidentally explodes, sending two fragments of mass 11 kg and 24 kg in opposite directions. The speed of the 11-kg fragment is 95 m/s. What is the speed of the other fragment?

7. A railway car of mass 1.37×10^4 kg, rolling at 20.0 km/h [N], collides with another railway car of mass 1.12×10^4 kg, also initially rolling north, but moving more slowly. After the collision, the coupled cars have a velocity of 18.3 km/h [N]. What is the initial velocity of the second car?

8. A 0.045-kg golf ball is hit with a driver. The head of the driver has a mass of 0.15 kg, and travels at a speed of 56 m/s before the collision. The ball has a speed of 67 m/s as it leaves the clubface. What is the speed of the head of the driver immediately after the collision?

Applying Inquiry Skills

9. The graph in **Figure 6** shows velocity as a function of time for a system of two carts that undergo an experimental collision on a horizontal, frictionless surface. The mass of cart A is 0.40 kg. The mass of cart B is 0.80 kg.

Answers

3. (g) 1×10^{-25} m/s
4. 2.6 m/s [W]
5. 50.6 kg
6. 44 m/s
7. 16.2 km/h [N]
8. 36 m/s
9. (b) 0.24 kg·m/s [E]
   (c) 0.10 m/s [W]

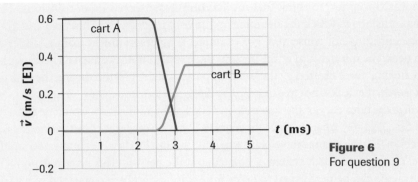

Figure 6
For question 9

(a) If you were conducting this experiment, describe what you would observe based on the graph.
(b) Determine the momentum of the system of carts before the collision.
(c) Assuming momentum is conserved, determine the velocity of cart A after the collision is complete.
(d) Copy the graph into your notebook, and complete the line for cart A. Superimpose lines that you think you would obtain in an experiment in which friction is not quite zero.

Making Connections

10. During a space walk, an astronaut becomes stranded a short distance from the spacecraft. Explain how the astronaut could solve the problem by applying conservation of momentum to return safely to the spacecraft. State any assumptions needed for your solution to work.

SUMMARY | *Conservation of Momentum in One Dimension*

- The law of conservation of linear momentum states that if the net force acting on a system is zero, then the momentum of the system is conserved.

- During an interaction between two objects in a system on which the total net force is zero, the change in momentum of one object is equal in magnitude, but opposite in direction, to the change in momentum of the other object.

- For any collision involving a system on which the total net force is zero, the total momentum before the collision equals the total momentum after the collision.

Understanding Concepts

1. A bowling ball (B) moving at high speed is about to collide with a single stationary pin (P) (**Figure 7**). The mass of the ball is more than four times greater than the mass of the pin. For the short time interval in which the collision occurs, state whether each of the following statements is true or false. If the statement is false, write a corrected version.
   (a) The magnitude of the force exerted by B on P is greater than the magnitude of the force exerted by P on B.
   (b) The magnitude of the change in velocity of B equals the magnitude of the change in velocity of P.

Figure 7
The bowling ball has a greater mass than the pin.

(c) The time interval of the collision for B equals the time interval of the collision for P.

(d) The magnitude of the change in momentum of B is less than the magnitude of the change in momentum of P.

2. Can individual objects in a system have nonzero momentum while the momentum of the entire system is zero? If "yes," give an example. If "no," explain why not.

3. In which of the following situations is the momentum conserved for the system of objects A and B?

(a) A vacationer A stands in a stationary raft B; the vacationer then walks in the raft. (Neglect fluid friction.)

(b) A freely rolling railway car A strikes a stationary railway car B.

(c) A veggie burger A is dropped vertically into a frying pan B and comes to rest.

4. In 1920, a prominent newspaper wrote the following about Robert Goddard, a pioneer of rocket ship development: "Professor Goddard does not know the relationship of action to reaction, and of the need to have something better than a vacuum against which to react. Of course, he only seems to lack the knowledge ladled out daily in high schools." Explain why the newspaper was wrong (as it itself admitted years later).

5. A 57-kg factory worker takes a ride on a large, freely rolling 27-kg cart. The worker initially stands still on the cart, and they both move at a speed of 3.2 m/s relative to the floor. The worker then walks on the cart in the same direction as the cart is moving. The worker's speed is now 3.8 m/s relative to the floor. What are the magnitude and direction of the final velocity of the cart?

6. A hiker of mass 65 kg is standing on a stationary raft of mass 35 kg. He is carrying a 19-kg backpack, which he throws horizontally. The resulting velocity of the hiker and the raft is 1.1 m/s [S] relative to the water. What is the velocity with which the hiker threw the backpack, relative to the water?

7. Two automobiles collide. One automobile of mass 1.13×10^3 kg is initially travelling at 25.7 m/s [E]. The other automobile of mass 1.25×10^3 kg has an initial velocity of 13.8 m/s [W]. The vehicles become attached during the collision. What is their common velocity immediately after the collision?

8. (a) Determine the magnitude and direction of the change in momentum for each automobile in question 7.

(b) How are these two quantities related?

(c) What is the total change in momentum of the two-automobile system?

9. A stationary quarterback is tackled by an 89-kg linebacker travelling with an initial speed of 5.2 m/s. As the two players move together after the collision, they have a speed of 2.7 m/s. What is the mass of the quarterback?

10. Two balls roll directly toward each other. The 0.25-kg ball has a speed of 1.7 m/s; the 0.18-kg ball has a speed of 2.5 m/s. After the collision, the 0.25-kg ball has reversed its direction and has a speed of 0.10 m/s. What is the magnitude and direction of the velocity of the 0.18-kg ball after the collision?

Applying Inquiry Skills

11. You are given two dynamics carts of masses m_1 and m_2, with nearly frictionless wheels. The carts are touching each other and are initially at rest. Cart 1 has an internal spring mechanism that is initially compressed (**Figure 8**). The spring is suddenly released, driving the carts apart. Describe an experimental procedure that you could use to test conservation of momentum for this "exploding" system. Include a list of apparatus you would need, safety precautions you would follow, and measurements you would take.

Making Connections

12. On a two-lane highway where the posted speed limit is 80 km/h, a car of mass m_C and an SUV of mass m_S have a head-on collision. The collision analyst observes that both vehicles came to a stop at the location of the initial impact. Researching the mass of the vehicles, the analyst found that $m_S = 2m_C$. Both drivers survived the collision and each claimed to be travelling at the legal speed limit when the collision occurred.

(a) It is obvious that the analyst cannot believe both drivers. Use numerical data to explain why.

(b) If both vehicles had been travelling at the legal speed limit before the collision, how would the accident scene have been different? (Assume that the collision was still head-on.)

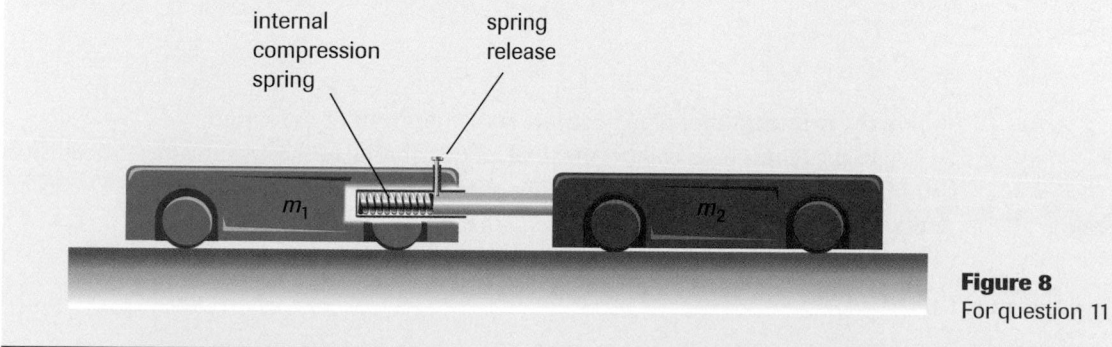

internal compression spring

spring release

m_1

m_2

Figure 8
For question 11

If you have inspected the structure of a safety helmet, such as a hockey or bicycle helmet, you may have noticed that the inside is made of relatively soft material designed to fit tightly around the head (**Figure 1**). A hockey helmet protects a player's head during a collision, whether with another player, the ice, or the goal post. For example, if a player without a helmet trips and slides head-first into a goal post, the contact with the post affects only a small area of the head, which must absorb a considerable amount of the player's kinetic energy. This of course is extremely dangerous. With a properly-fitted helmet, on the other hand, the force of the impact is spread out over a much larger surface area, so that any one spot would have to absorb only a fraction of the energy absorbed without the helmet. (The padding in the helmet also increases the time interval of the collision, reducing the force applied to the helmet as the collision causes the player to come to a stop.) In this section, we will explore the relationship of energy to various types of collisions.

Experiments in which different sets of balls are thrown toward each other so that they collide head-on can be used to illustrate different types of collisions (**Figure 2**). The experimental observations vary greatly depending on the type of balls selected. When two superballs collide, they bounce off each other at high speed; tennis balls bounce off each other with moderate speed; and putty balls (of similar mass) stick together and have negligible speed after the collision. In each collision, momentum is conserved. To understand the differences between the collisions, we must consider the kinetic energy of each system.

Figure 1
A hockey helmet is designed to spread the force and energy of a collision over as large an area as possible.

Figure 2
(a) Collision of two superballs
(b) Collision of two tennis balls
(c) Collision of two balls made of soft putty

In the superball collision, the total kinetic energy of the system before the collision is equal to the total kinetic energy of the system after the collision. This type of collision is called an **elastic collision**. For a system undergoing an elastic collision,

$$E_K' = E_K$$
$$\vec{p}' = \vec{p}$$

where the prime symbol represents the final condition of the system.

When the tennis balls collide, the total kinetic energy of the system after the collision is not equal to the total kinetic energy of the system before the collision. This is an **inelastic collision**. For a system undergoing an inelastic collision,

$$E_K' \neq E_K$$
$$\vec{p}' = \vec{p}$$

elastic collision a collision in which the total kinetic energy after the collision equals the total kinetic energy before the collision

inelastic collision a collision in which the total kinetic energy after the collision is different from the total kinetic energy before the collision

When two objects stick together during a collision, as is the case with the putty balls, we have a **completely inelastic collision**. The decrease in total kinetic energy in a completely inelastic collision is the maximum possible. For a system undergoing a completely inelastic collision,

$$E_K' < E_K$$
$$\vec{p}' = \vec{p}$$

Note that in a completely inelastic collision, the objects stick together and thus have the same final velocity.

It is important to realize that we compare the kinetic energies of the colliding objects *before* and *after* the collision, not during the collision. Consider two gliders of equal mass with springs attached approaching each other at the same speed (**Figure 3**). Just before the gliders collide, their speeds and kinetic energies are at a maximum, but in the middle of the collision, their speeds and kinetic energies are zero. The kinetic energy is transformed into elastic potential energy stored in the springs. This potential energy is at a maximum when the kinetic energy is at a minimum. After the elastic collision, when the springs no longer touch, the elastic potential energy drops back to zero and the kinetic energies return to their original values.

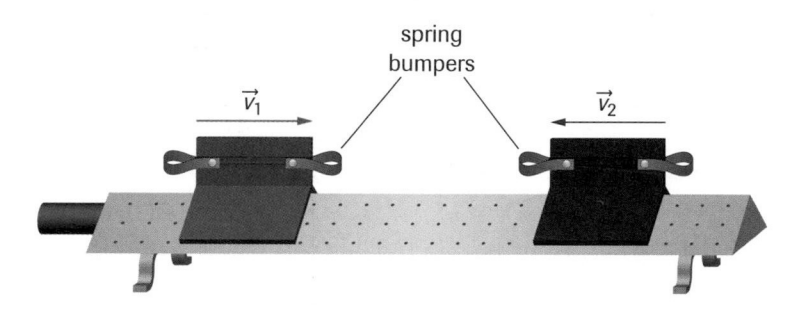

spring bumpers

$\vec{v}_1$ $\vec{v}_2$

Figure 4 is a graph of the mechanical energy of the system of gliders and springs. At any instant in this elastic collision, the sum of the elastic potential energy and the kinetic energy of the system remains constant, even though the kinetic energy does not return to its initial value until after the collision is complete.

In practice, it is almost impossible to have a truly elastic collision between two macroscopic objects, such as gliders with springs or superballs. There is always some small amount of kinetic energy transformed into other forms. For instance, when superballs collide, thermal energy and sound energy are produced. However, in this text we will treat certain collisions between macroscopic objects as being elastic, and we will ignore the small amount of kinetic energy that is lost. Collisions involving molecules, atoms, and subatomic particles, on the other hand, can be perfectly elastic.

After an inelastic collision or a completely inelastic collision, the total final kinetic energy of the system is not equal to the initial kinetic energy of the system. Usually the final kinetic energy is less than the initial kinetic energy unless the collision is explosive. Since energy is conserved, the lost kinetic energy must be transformed into other forms of energy. For example, when two putty balls collide, the putty balls become warmer because the kinetic energy has been transformed into thermal energy. Depending on the properties of the colliding objects, the kinetic energy could be transformed into sound energy, elastic potential energy, thermal energy, or another form of energy.

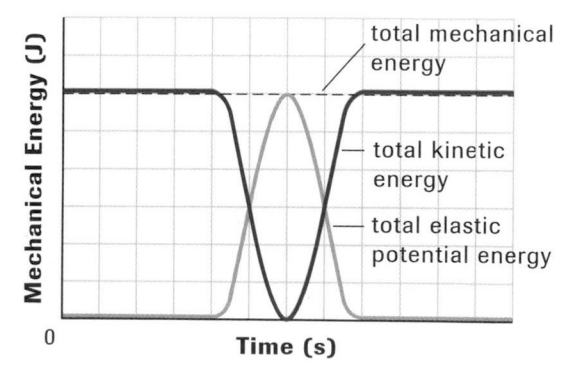

Figure 4
Mechanical energy in an elastic collision as a function of time

LEARNING TIP

Inelastic Collisions
In most inelastic collisions, for example, between two tennis balls, the total final kinetic energy of the system is less than the total initial kinetic energy of the system. However, in some inelastic collisions, such as a collision that initiates an explosion, kinetic energy is produced, giving a total final kinetic energy of the system greater than the initial kinetic energy of the system.

completely inelastic collision a collision in which there is a maximum decrease in kinetic energy after the collision since the objects stick together and move at the same velocity

Figure 3
When gliders with springs collide, the duration of the collision is greater than without the springs, making it easier to observe what happens to the energies of the gliders as they collide.

In the early history of the solar system, there were many completely inelastic collisions between relatively large objects, such as the Moon and chunks of rock (**Figure 5**). Such collisions produced the craters on the Moon's surface. Similar collisions created craters on Earth, although most have been destroyed in erosion by rain and wind. However, some relatively recent craters still exist, such as the famous Barringer Crater in Arizona, which is believed to be about 50 000 years old (**Figure 6**). This crater, with a diameter of 1.6 km and a depth of 180 m, resulted when a large meteorite collided with Earth.

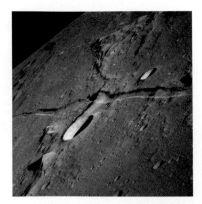

Figure 5
Craters on the Moon are the result of completely inelastic collisions with large rocks.

Figure 6
Analyzing impact craters, such as the Barringer Crater, helps scientists understand more about the history of the solar system. The meteorite that created this crater was about 45 m in diameter, but it was travelling at about 65 000 km/h (relative to Earth) when it collided.

▶ TRY THIS activity   *Newton's Cradle*

Figure 7 shows a Newton's cradle. Each sphere has the same mass m. If the raised sphere is released, it will move, and just before it collides with the stationary spheres, its momentum has a magnitude of mv.

(a) Is it true that momentum can be conserved, no matter how many spheres fly outward after the initial collision? Why or why not?
(b) Is it true that kinetic energy can be conserved, no matter how many spheres fly outward after the initial collision? Why or why not?
(c) Based on your calculations, predict what will happen when a single sphere hits the stationary spheres. Test your prediction by trying the demonstration.
(d) Predict what will happen when two spheres, and also when three spheres, strike the stationary spheres. Test your predictions.

▶ Practice

Understanding Concepts

1. In a completely inelastic collision between two objects, under what condition(s) will all of the original kinetic energy be transformed into other forms of energy?

2. In a certain collision between two cars, the cars end up sticking together. Can we conclude that the collision is completely inelastic? Explain.

3. Use physics principles to explain why head-on vehicle collisions are usually more dangerous than other types of collisions.

Applying Inquiry Skills

4. Describe how you would use the elasticity of a ball when you squeeze it to predict how well it will bounce off a hard floor. Test your answer experimentally.

5. Draw a graph similar to the one in **Figure 4**, illustrating mechanical energy as a function of time for
   (a) an inelastic collision
   (b) a completely inelastic collision

Making Connections

6. A safety helmet spreads the force of an impact over as large an area as possible; the soft interior also changes the time interval of a collision.
   (a) Why is the impact force reduced for a helmet with a soft interior versus a hard interior?
   (b) How is safety reduced if the helmet does not fit properly?
   (c) Once a helmet has been involved in a collision, it should be replaced. Why?

7. If you were designing a passenger train, would you favour a design with a rigid frame or a flexible frame? Why?

Figure 7
Newton's cradle

Solving Collision Problems

In solving problems involving collisions, it is important to distinguish between elastic, inelastic, and completely inelastic collisions. For all collisions involving two objects on which the net force is zero, momentum is conserved:

$$mv_1 + mv_2 = mv_1' + mv_2'$$

where m_1 and m_2 are the masses of the colliding objects, v_1 and v_2 are the velocities before the collision, and v_1' and v_2' are the velocities after the collision. (Remember that vector notation is omitted because the collisions are in one dimension.) If the collision is inelastic, this is the only equation that can be used. In the case of a completely inelastic collision, the objects stick together and their final velocities are equal $v_1' = v_2'$.

For an elastic collision (which will be stated clearly in the problem), the total kinetic energy before the collision equals the total kinetic energy after the collision:

$$\frac{1}{2}mv_1{}^2 + \frac{1}{2}mv_2{}^2 = \frac{1}{2}mv_1'{}^2 + \frac{1}{2}mv_2'{}^2$$

We can combine this equation with the equation for conservation of momentum to solve problems that involve elastic collisions.

▶ ***SAMPLE* problem *1***

A billiard ball with mass m and initial speed v_1, undergoes a head-on elastic collision with another billiard ball, initially stationary, with the same mass m. What are the final speeds of the two balls?

Solution

Figure 8 shows the initial and final diagrams. We choose the $+x$-axis as the direction of motion of the initially moving ball (ball 1). Since the problem states that the collision is elastic, we know that the total initial kinetic energy equals the total final kinetic energy. Momentum is conserved in this collision. We can thus write two equations, one for kinetic energy and one for momentum:

$$\frac{1}{2}mv_1{}^2 + \frac{1}{2}mv_2{}^2 = \frac{1}{2}mv_1'{}^2 + \frac{1}{2}mv_2'{}^2$$
$$mv_1 + mv_2 = mv_1' + mv_2'$$

where the subscript 1 refers to the initially moving ball and the subscript 2 refers to the initially stationary ball. Note that the v's represent velocity components (not velocity magnitudes) and can be positive or negative. Since the masses are equal, they cancel:

$$v_1{}^2 + v_2{}^2 = v_1'{}^2 + v_2'{}^2$$
$$v_1 + v_2 = v_1' + v_2'$$

Since ball 2 is initially stationary, $v_2 = 0$, and we can write:

$$v_1{}^2 = v_1'{}^2 + v_2'{}^2$$
$$v_1 = v_1' + v_2'$$

We now have two equations and two unknowns, so we rearrange the latter equation to solve for v_1':

$$v_1' = v_1 - v_2'$$

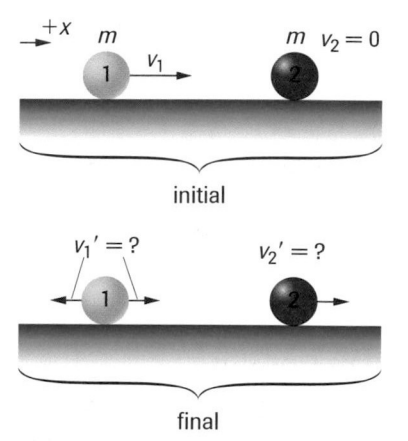

Figure 8
The situations before and after the collision for Sample Problem 1

Substituting for v_1':

$$v_1^2 = (v_1 - v_2')^2 + v_2'^2$$
$$= v_1^2 - 2v_1v_2' + v_2'^2 + v_2'^2$$
$$0 = -2v_1v_2' + 2v_2'^2$$
$$0 = -v_2'(v_1 - v_2')$$

Therefore, either $v_2' = 0$ (which is not an appropriate solution since it means that no collision occurred) or $v_1 - v_2' = 0$. Thus, we can conclude that $v_2' = v_1$. Substituting this value into the equation $v_1 = v_1' + v_2'$:

$$v_1 = v_1' + v_1$$
$$v_1' = 0$$

Therefore, ball 1, which was initially moving, is at rest after the collision ($v_1' = 0$); ball 2, which was initially stationary, has the same speed after the collision that ball 1 had before the collision ($v_2' = v_1$). Note that this conclusion is not valid for all elastic collisions in which one object is initially stationary—the colliding objects must have the same mass.

▶ SAMPLE problem 2

A child rolls a superball of mass 2.5×10^{-2} kg along a table at a speed of 2.3 m/s to collide head-on with a smaller stationary superball of mass 2.0×10^{-2} kg. The collision is elastic. Determine the velocity of each ball after the collision.

Solution

$$m_1 = 2.5 \times 10^{-2} \text{ kg} \qquad v_1' = ?$$
$$m_2 = 2.0 \times 10^{-2} \text{ kg} \qquad v_2' = ?$$
$$v_1 = 2.3 \text{ m/s}$$

Figure 9 shows diagrams of the situation. We choose the $+x$ axis as the direction of the initial velocity of the larger ball. Since the collision is elastic, both kinetic energy and momentum are conserved:

$$\frac{1}{2}m_1v_1^2 + \frac{1}{2}m_2v_2^2 = \frac{1}{2}m_1v_1'^2 + \frac{1}{2}m_2v_2'^2$$
$$m_1v_1 + m_2v_2 = m_1v_1' + m_2v_2'$$

where the subscript 1 refers to the larger ball and the subscript 2 refers to the smaller ball. Since ball 2 is initially stationary, $v_2 = 0$. Substituting into both equations and multiplying the kinetic energy equation by 2, we have:

$$m_1v_1^2 = m_1v_1'^2 + m_2v_2'^2$$
$$m_1v_1 = m_1v_1' + m_2v_2'$$

We can rearrange the second equation to solve for v_1' in terms of v_2':

$$v_1' = v_1 - \frac{m_2}{m_1}v_2'$$
$$= 2.3 \text{ m/s} - \left(\frac{2.0 \times 10^{-2} \text{ kg}}{2.5 \times 10^{-2} \text{ kg}}\right)v_2'$$
$$v_1' = 2.3 \text{ m/s} - 0.80 \, v_2'$$

which we can then substitute into the first equation and solve for v_2'. However, before substituting for v_1', we can substitute known numbers into the first equation:

$$m_1v_1^2 = m_1v_1'^2 + m_2v_2'^2$$
$$(2.5 \times 10^{-2} \text{ kg})(2.3 \text{ m/s})^2 = (2.5 \times 10^{-2} \text{ kg})v_1'^2 + (2.0 \times 10^{-2} \text{ kg})v_2'^2$$

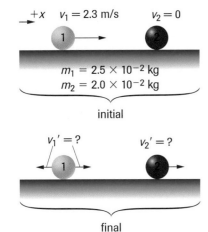

$+x$ $v_1 = 2.3$ m/s $v_2 = 0$

$m_1 = 2.5 \times 10^{-2}$ kg
$m_2 = 2.0 \times 10^{-2}$ kg

initial

$v_1' = ?$ $v_2' = ?$

final

Figure 9
The situations before and after the collision for Sample Problem 2

Multiplying by 10^2 to eliminate each 10^{-2}, we have:

$$(2.5 \text{ kg})(2.3 \text{ m/s})^2 = (2.5 \text{ kg})v_1'^2 + (2.0 \text{ kg})v_2'^2$$
$$13.2 \text{ kg·m}^2/\text{s}^2 = (2.5 \text{ kg})v_1'^2 + (2.0 \text{ kg})v_2'^2$$

Now, substituting the expression for v_1':

$$13.2 \text{ kg·m}^2/\text{s}^2 = (2.5 \text{ kg})(2.3 \text{ m/s} - 0.80v_2')^2 + (2.0 \text{ kg})v_2'^2$$
$$13.2 \text{ kg·m}^2/\text{s}^2 = (2.5 \text{ kg})(5.29 \text{ m}^2/\text{s}^2 - 3.68 \text{ m/s}v_2' + 0.64v_2'^2) + (2.0 \text{ kg})v_2'^2$$
$$13.2 \text{ kg·m}^2/\text{s}^2 = 13.2 \text{ kg·m}^2/\text{s}^2 - 9.2 \text{ kg·m/s } v_2' + 1.6 \text{ kg } v_2'^2 + 2.0 \text{ kg } v_2'^2$$
$$0 = -9.2 \text{ kg·m/s } v_2' + 3.6 \text{ kg } v_2'^2$$
$$0 = (-9.2 \text{ kg·m/s} + 3.6 \text{ kg } v_2')v_2'$$

Thus, $\qquad 0 = -9.2 \text{ kg·m/s} + 3.6 \text{ kg } v_2' \quad$ or $\quad v_2' = 0$

Since $v_2' = 0$ corresponds to no collision, we must have:

$$0 = -9.2 \text{ kg·m/s} + 3.6 \text{ kg } v_2'$$
$$v_2' = +2.6 \text{ m/s}$$

We can now substitute this value for v_2' to solve for v_1':

$$v_1' = 2.3 \text{ m/s} - 0.80v_2'$$
$$= 2.3 \text{ m/s} - 0.80(2.6 \text{ m/s})$$
$$v_1' = +0.3 \text{ m/s}$$

Thus, after the collision, both balls are moving in the $+x$ direction (the same direction as the larger ball was originally moving). The speeds are 2.6 m/s and 0.3 m/s for the smaller and larger balls, respectively.

The collisions analyzed so far in this chapter have been one-dimensional. Most collisions, however, involve two- or three-dimensional situations. By performing an investigation to study two-dimensional collisions, you will find the theory and mathematical analysis of such collisions much easier to understand. To explore two-dimensional collisions further, perform Investigation 5.3.1 in the Lab Activities section at the end of this chapter. ⚛️▮

⚛️ INVESTIGATION 5.3.1

Analyzing Two-Dimensional Collisions (p. 262)

There are various ways of creating collisions in the laboratory in which the objects collide with a crisp, clear bang, or the objects stick together and have a common final velocity. What problems would you anticipate having to overcome in analyzing two-dimensional collisions between pucks on a horizontal air table?

▶ *Practice*

Understanding Concepts

8. A small truck and a large truck have the same kinetic energies. Which truck has the greater momentum? Justify your answer.

9. (a) Can an object have kinetic energy, but no momentum? Can an object have momentum, but no kinetic energy? Explain.
   (b) Repeat (a) for an isolated system of two interacting objects.

10. During a friendly snowball fight, two snowballs, each of mass 0.15 kg, collide in mid-air in a completely inelastic collision. Just before the collision, both balls are travelling horizontally, one ball with a velocity of 22 m/s [N] and the other 22 m/s [S]. What is the velocity of each ball after the collision?

11. A proton travelling with an initial speed of 815 m/s collides head-on with a stationary proton in an elastic collision. What is the velocity of each proton after the collision? Show your work.

Answers

10. 0 m/s

11. 0 m/s; 815 m/s in the direction of initial velocity

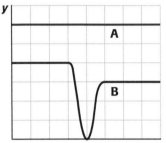

Figure 10
For question 15

12. A truck of mass 1.3×10^4 kg, travelling at 9.0×10^1 km/h [N], collides with a car of mass 1.1×10^3 kg, travelling at 3.0×10^1 km/h [N]. If the collision is completely inelastic, what are the magnitude and direction of the velocity of the vehicles immediately after the collision?

13. Calculate the total kinetic energy before and after the collision described in question 12. Determine the decrease in kinetic energy during the collision.

14. A nitrogen molecule of mass 4.65×10^{-26} kg in the air undergoes a head-on elastic collision with a stationary oxygen molecule of mass 5.31×10^{-26} kg. After the collision, the nitrogen molecule has reversed its direction and has a speed of 34.1 m/s, while the oxygen molecule is travelling at 4.81×10^2 m/s in the original direction of the nitrogen molecule. What is the initial speed of the nitrogen molecule?

Applying Inquiry Skills

15. An experiment is performed in which two low-friction carts on an air track approach each other and collide. The motions of the carts are monitored by sensors connected to a computer that generates the graphs in **Figure 10**.
    (a) One line on the graph represents the total momentum of the two-cart system, and the other represents the total kinetic energy. Which line is which? How can you tell?
    (b) What type of collision occurred in the experiment? How can you tell?

Making Connections

16. In some situations, riot police use rubber bullets to control demonstrators. In designing these bullets, tests are carried out in labs to compare the collisions involving rubber bullets and lead bullets striking a target.
    (a) In these tests, one type of bullet has an elastic collision with the test target, while the other type has an almost completely inelastic collision with the test target. Which bullet has the elastic collision and which has the almost completely inelastic collision?
    (b) Using the subscripts R for the rubber bullet, L for the lead bullet, and T for the target, develop equations for the magnitude of the momentum transferred to the target after being struck by the rubber bullet and the lead bullet. Assume both bullets to have the same masses and initial speeds. Express your answers in terms of the magnitudes of the initial momentum of the bullet and the final momentum of the bullet. Which bullet transfers the larger magnitude of momentum to the target?
    (c) Explain why rubber bullets are preferred in riot control.

SUMMARY   *Elastic and Inelastic Collisions*

- In all elastic, inelastic, and completely inelastic collisions involving an isolated system, the momentum is conserved.

- In an elastic collision, the total kinetic energy after the collision equals the total kinetic energy before the collision.

- In an inelastic collision, the total kinetic energy after the collision is different from the total kinetic energy before the collision.

- In a completely inelastic collision, the objects stick together and move with the same velocity, and the decrease in total kinetic energy is at a maximum.

- Elastic collisions can be analyzed by applying both the conservation of kinetic energy and the conservation of momentum simultaneously.

Section 5.3 Questions

Understanding Concepts

1. A moving object collides with a stationary object.
   (a) Is it possible for both objects to be at rest after the collision? If "yes," give an example. If "no," explain why not.
   (b) Is it possible for only one object to be at rest after the collision? If "yes," give an example. If "no," explain why not.

2. A wet snowball of mass m, travelling at a speed v, strikes a tree. It sticks to the tree and stops. Does this example violate the law of conservation of momentum? Explain.

3. Two particles have the same kinetic energies. Are their momentums necessarily equal? Explain.

4. A 22-g superball rolls with a speed of 3.5 m/s toward another stationary 27-g superball. The balls have a head-on elastic collision. What are the magnitude and direction of the velocity of each ball after the collision?

5. An object of mass m has an elastic collision with another object initially at rest, and continues to move in the original direction but with one-third its original speed. What is the mass of the other object in terms of m?

6. A 66-kg skier, initially at rest, slides down a hill 25 m high, then has a completely inelastic collision with a stationary 72-kg skier. Friction is negligible. What is the speed of each skier immediately after the collision?

Applying Inquiry Skills

7. **Figure 11(a)** shows a ballistics pendulum used to determine speeds of bullets before the advent of modern electronic timing. A bullet is shot horizontally into a block of wood suspended by two strings. The bullet remains embedded in the wood, and the wood and bullet together swing upward.
   (a) Explain why the *horizontal* momentum of the bullet-wood system is conserved during the collision, even though the strings exert tension forces on the wood.

   (b) If the bullet and wood have masses of m and M, respectively, and the bullet has an initial speed of v, derive an algebraic expression for the speed of the bullet and wood immediately after the collision, before they swing upward, in terms of m, M, and v.
   (c) As the bullet and wood swing up, what law of nature can be used to relate the maximum vertical height to the speed just after the collision?
   (d) Use your answers to (b) and (c) to derive an expression for the maximum vertical height h in terms of m, M, v, and g.
   (e) Rearrange your expression in (d) so that if h is a known quantity, v can be calculated.
   (f) If a bullet of mass 8.7 g hits a block of wood of mass 5.212 kg, and the bullet and wood swing up to a maximum height of 6.2 cm, what is the initial speed of the bullet?
   (g) **Figure 11(b)** shows a modern ballistics pendulum used for student experimentation. Describe some of the sources of random and systematic error that should be minimized in determining the speed of the ball fired from the spring-loaded triggering mechanism.

Making Connections

8. Decades ago, cars were designed to be as rigid as possible. Modern cars, however, are designed with "crumple zones" that collapse upon impact. Explain the advantage of this design.

9. Chunks of material from space, both large and small, collide with Earth. Research the sizes of these materials and the frequencies of the collisions, as well as some of the well-known collisions scientists have studied. Some famous impact sites are Sudbury, Ontario; Chicxulub, Mexico; and Tunguska, Russia. Write a brief report summarizing what you discover.

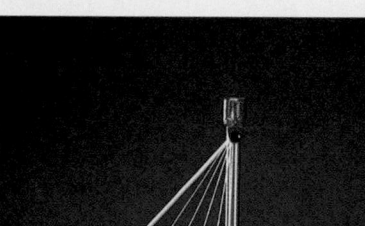 www.science.nelson.com

(a)

(b)

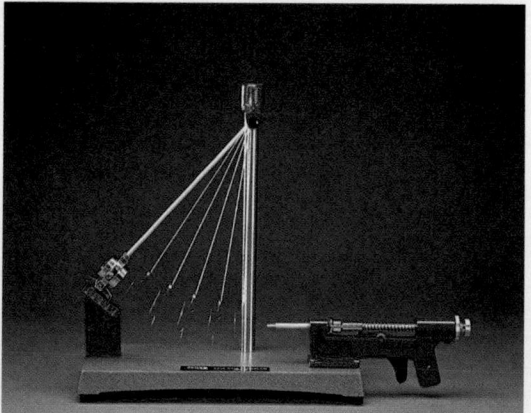

Figure 11
Ballistics pendulums (for question 7)

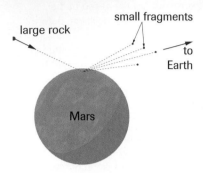

Figure 1
The two-dimensional nature of the collision between a rock and the surface of Mars

How could a chunk of rock from Antarctica provide a basis for research into the possibility that life once existed on Mars? The answer lies in a two-dimensional collision that occurred about 15 million years ago, when a large high-speed rock crashed into Mars at a glancing angle (**Figure 1**). Some of the kinetic energy of the rock was converted into thermal energy, melting some of the surface rock and trapping bubbles from the atmosphere in material that splashed off the surface, cooled, and flew off into space. Eventually a chunk of that surface material from Mars became the rock that landed in Antarctica. Researchers discovered that the rock's dissolved gases were the same as those identified by probes landing on Mars. Further research identified possible materials that may be associated with microscopic life forms.

In the previous section, we examined the conservation of momentum in one-dimensional collisions, such as the recoil of a raft when a person walks on it or the head-on collisions of automobiles. For momentum to be conserved, the net force on the system must be zero. The forces exerted by the objects on each other are equal in magnitude but opposite in direction (from Newton's third law) and add to zero. If other forces on the system also add to zero or are so small as to be negligible, then the net force on the system will be zero.

The same reasoning applies to two-dimensional situations, such as the collision between pucks on an air table with negligible friction (see Investigation 5.3.1). Since both the net force and momentum are vector quantities, when we say that momentum is conserved, we mean that both the magnitude and direction of the momentum vector do not change. Alternatively, in two dimensions, we can state that both the x- and y-components of the momentum do not change.

The law of conservation of momentum applies to any situation in which a system is subject to a net force of zero. It applies to collisions between all sorts of objects; it also applies to interactions that are not collisions, such as the ejection of gases from a rocket thruster to control the spacecraft's motion.

► SAMPLE problem 1

A 38-kg child is standing on a 43-kg raft that is drifting with a velocity of 1.1 m/s [N] relative to the water. The child then walks on the raft with a net velocity of 0.71 m/s [E] relative to the water. Fluid friction between the raft and water is negligible. Determine the resulting velocity of the raft relative to the water.

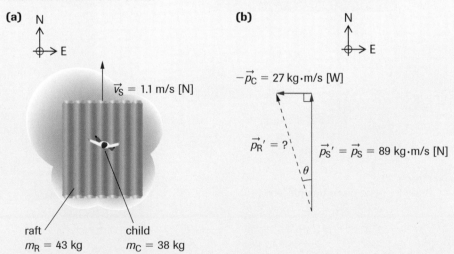

Figure 2
(a) The basic situation
(b) Determining the final momentum of the raft

Solution

Figure 2(a) shows the situation. Since there is no net force acting on the system, momentum is conserved. Thus,

$$\vec{p}_S = \vec{p}_S'$$

where the subscript S represents the system. Finding the initial momentum of the system:

$m_S = 38 \text{ kg} + 43 \text{ kg} = 81 \text{ kg}$
$\vec{v}_S = 1.1 \text{ m/s [N]}$
$\vec{p}_S = ?$

$$\begin{aligned} \vec{p}_S &= m_S \vec{v}_S \\ &= (81 \text{ kg})(1.1 \text{ m/s [N]}) \\ \vec{p}_S &= 89 \text{ kg·m/s [N]} \end{aligned}$$

The final momentum of the system is equal to the vector addition of the child (indicated by subscript C) and the raft (indicated by subscript R):

$$\vec{p}_S' = \vec{p}_C' + \vec{p}_R'$$

Determine $\vec{p}_C'$:

$m_C = 38 \text{ kg}$
$\vec{v}_C' = 0.71 \text{ m/s [E]}$
$\vec{p}_C' = ?$

$$\begin{aligned} \vec{p}_C' &= m_C \vec{v}_C' \\ &= (38 \text{ kg})(0.71 \text{ m/s [E]}) \\ \vec{p}_C' &= 27 \text{ kg·m/s [E]} \end{aligned}$$

Since $\vec{p}_S = \vec{p}_S'$, we can now solve for $\vec{p}_R'$:

$$\begin{aligned} \vec{p}_R' &= \vec{p}_S' - \vec{p}_C' \\ \vec{p}_R' &= \vec{p}_S' + (-\vec{p}_C') \end{aligned}$$

Figure 2(b) shows the vector subtraction. Using the law of Pythagoras, we find:

$$\begin{aligned} |\vec{p}_R'|^2 &= |\vec{p}_S'|^2 + |\vec{p}_C'|^2 \\ |\vec{p}_R'| &= \sqrt{(89 \text{ kg·m/s})^2 + (27 \text{ kg·m/s})^2} \\ |\vec{p}_R'| &= 93 \text{ kg·m/s} \end{aligned}$$

The angle θ can now be found:

$$\theta = \tan^{-1} \frac{27 \text{ kg·m/s}}{89 \text{ kg·m/s}}$$

$$\theta = 17°$$

Thus, the direction of the raft's final momentum and final velocity is 17° W of N.

Finally, we solve for the final velocity of the raft:

$$\begin{aligned} \vec{p}_R' &= m_R \vec{v}_R' \\ \vec{v}_R' &= \frac{\vec{p}_R'}{m_R} \\ &= \frac{93 \text{ kg·m/s [17° W of N]}}{43 \text{ kg}} \\ \vec{v}_R' &= 2.2 \text{ m/s [17° W of N]} \end{aligned}$$

The resulting velocity of the raft relative to the water is 2.2 m/s [17° W of N].

DID YOU KNOW ?

Bike Helmets
Studies have shown that wearing a bike helmet reduces the risk of death or injury in an accident by more than 80%.

In a game of marbles, a collision occurs between two marbles of equal mass m. One marble is initially at rest; after the collision, the marble acquires a velocity of 1.10 m/s at an angle of $\theta = 40.0°$ from the original direction of motion of the other marble, which has a speed of 1.36 m/s after the collision. What is the initial speed of the moving marble?

(a)

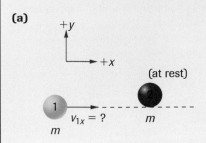

(b)

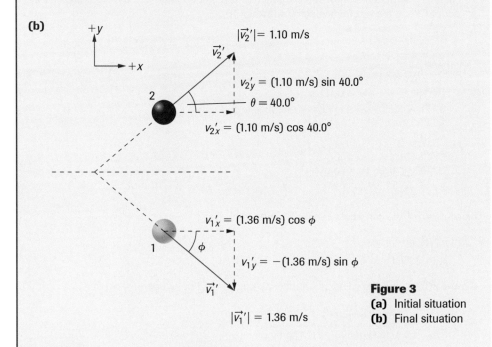

Figure 3
(a) Initial situation
(b) Final situation

Solution

Figure 3(a) shows the initial situation. Since the momentum is conserved,

$$\vec{p} = \vec{p}'$$
$$m_1\vec{v}_1 + m_2\vec{v}_2 = m_1\vec{v}_1' + m_2\vec{v}_2'$$

Since $m_1 = m_2$ and $\vec{v}_2 = 0$, we can simplify:

$$\vec{v}_1 = \vec{v}_1' + \vec{v}_2'$$

The components used to perform this vector addition are shown in **Figure 3(b)**, with the chosen directions of $+x$ rightward and $+y$ upward. Since we do not know the direction of $\vec{v}_1'$, we use components to analyze the situation and solve for the angle ϕ. Applying conservation of momentum to the y-components:

$$v_{1y} = v_{1y}' + v_{2y}'$$

$$0 = -1.36 \text{ m/s} \sin \phi + 1.10 \text{ m/s} \sin \theta$$

$$\sin \phi = \frac{1.10 \text{ m/s} \sin \theta}{1.36 \text{ m/s}}$$

$$\sin \phi = \frac{1.10 \text{ m/s} \sin 40.0°}{1.36 \text{ m/s}}$$

$$\phi = 31.3°$$

Applying conservation of momentum to the x-components:

$$v_{1x} = v_{1x}' + v_{2x}'$$

$$= 1.36 \text{ m/s} \cos \phi + 1.10 \text{ m/s} \cos \theta$$

$$= 1.36 \text{ m/s} \cos 31.3° + 1.10 \text{ m/s} \cos 40.0°$$

$$v_{1x} = 2.00 \text{ m/s}$$

The initial speed of the moving marble is 2.00 m/s.

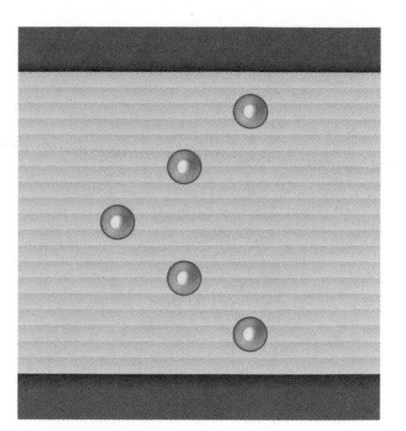

Figure 4
A 5-pin bowling setup is much easier to analyze than a 10-pin setup! (for question 1)

▶ Practice

Understanding Concepts

1. Bowling involves numerous collisions that are essentially two-dimensional. Copy the 5-pin setup in **Figure 4** and complete the diagram to show where a bowling ball could be aimed to cause a "strike" (i.e., a hit in which all the pins are knocked down).

2. A 52-kg student is standing on a 26-kg cart that is free to move in any direction. Initially, the cart is moving with a velocity of 1.2 m/s [S] relative to the floor. The student then walks on the cart and has a net velocity of 1.0 m/s [W] relative to the floor.
   (a) Use a vector scale diagram to determine the approximate final velocity of the cart.
   (b) Use components to determine the approximate final velocity of the cart.

3. Two automobiles collide at an intersection. One car of mass 1.4×10^3 kg is travelling at 45 km/h [S]; the other car of mass 1.3×10^3 kg is travelling at 39 km/h [E]. If the cars have a completely inelastic collision, what is their velocity just after the collision?

4. Two balls of equal mass m undergo a collision. One ball is initially stationary. After the collision, the velocities of the balls make angles of 31.1° and 48.9° relative to the original direction of motion of the moving ball.
   (a) Draw a diagram showing the initial and final situations. If you are uncertain about the final directions of motion, remember that momentum is conserved.
   (b) If the initial speed of the moving ball is 2.25 m/s, what are the speeds of the balls after the collision?
   (c) Repeat (b) using a vector scale diagram.
   (d) Is this collision elastic? Justify your answer.

5. A nucleus, initially at rest, decays radioactively, leaving a residual nucleus. In the process, it emits two particles horizontally: an electron with momentum 9.0×10^{-21} kg·m/s [E] and a neutrino with momentum 4.8×10^{-21} kg·m/s [S].
   (a) In what direction does the residual nucleus move?
   (b) What is the magnitude of its momentum?
   (c) If the mass of the residual nucleus is 3.6×10^{-25} kg, what is its recoil velocity?

Answers

2. 4.1 m/s [61° S of E]

3. 3.0×10^1 km/h [51° S of E]

4. (b) 1.18 m/s at 48.9°;
   1.72 m/s at 31.1°

   (d) no

5. (a) 28° N of W

   (b) 1.0×10^{-20} kg·m/s

   (c) 2.8×10^4 m/s [28° N of W]

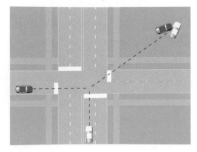

Figure 5
For question 6

Applying Inquiry Skills

6. The police report of an accident between two identical cars at an icy intersection contains the diagram shown in **Figure 5**.
   (a) Which car was travelling faster at the moment of impact? How can you tell?
   (b) What measurements could be made directly on the diagram to help an investigator determine the details of the collision?

Making Connections

7. Choose a sport or recreational activity in which participants wear protective equipment.
   (a) Describe the design and function of the protective equipment.
   (b) Based on the scientific concepts and principles you have studied thus far, explain how the equipment accomplishes its intended functions.
   (c) Using the Internet or other appropriate publications, research your chosen protective equipment. Use what you discover to enhance your answer in (b).

   GO www.science.nelson.com

SUMMARY

Conservation of Momentum in Two Dimensions

- Collisions in two dimensions are analyzed using the same principles as collisions in one dimension: conservation of momentum for all collisions for which the net force on the system is zero, and both conservation of momentum and conservation of kinetic energy if the collision is elastic.

▶ Section 5.4 *Questions*

Understanding Concepts

1. **Figure 6** shows an arrangement of billiard balls, all of equal mass. The balls travel in straight lines and do not spin. Draw a similar, but larger, diagram in your notebook and show the approximate direction that ball 1 must travel to get ball 3 into the end pocket if
   (a) ball 1 collides with ball 2 (in a combination shot)
   (b) ball 1 undergoes a single reflection off the side of the table and then collides with ball 3

2. A neutron of mass 1.7×10^{-27} kg, travelling at 2.7 km/s, hits a stationary lithium nucleus of mass 1.2×10^{-26} kg. After the collision, the velocity of the lithium nucleus is 0.40 km/s at 54° to the original direction of motion of the neutron. If the speed of the neutron after the collision is 2.5 km/s, in what direction is the neutron now travelling?

3. Two ice skaters undergo a collision, after which their arms are intertwined and they have a common velocity of 0.85 m/s [27° S of E]. Before the collision, one skater of mass 71 kg had a velocity of 2.3 m/s [12° N of E], while the other skater had a velocity of 1.9 m/s [52° S of W]. What is the mass of the second skater?

Figure 6
For question 1

4. A steel ball of mass 0.50 kg, moving with a velocity of 2.0 m/s [E], strikes a second ball of mass 0.30 kg, initially at rest. The collision is a glancing one, causing the moving ball to have a velocity of 1.5 m/s [30° N of E] after the collision. Determine the velocity of the second ball after the collision.

Applying Inquiry Skills

5. Figure 7 shows the results of a collision between two pucks on a nearly frictionless air table. The mass of puck A is 0.32 kg, and the dots were produced by a sparking device every 0.50 s.

(a) Trace the diagram onto a separate piece of paper and determine the mass of puck B. (*Hint:* Determine which equation applies, and then draw the vectors on your diagram.)

(b) Determine the amount of kinetic energy lost in the collision.

(c) Name the type of collision that occurred.

(d) Identify the most likely sources of error in determining the mass of puck B.

Making Connections

6. Today's consumers are well aware that safety features are important in automobiles. For an automobile of your choice, analyze the design, the operation of the vehicle in a collision or other emergency, and the economic and social costs and benefits of its safety features. Use the following questions as a guideline:

(a) What social and economic issues do you think are important in automobile safety, from an individual point of view, as well as society's point of view?

(b) For the automobile you have chosen to analyze, what safety features do you think are essential?

(c) What safety features are lacking that you think would be beneficial to the driver and passengers?

(d) Considering your answers in (a), (b), and (c), perform a cost-benefit analysis of developing safety devices in automobiles. Write concluding remarks.

GO www.science.nelson.com

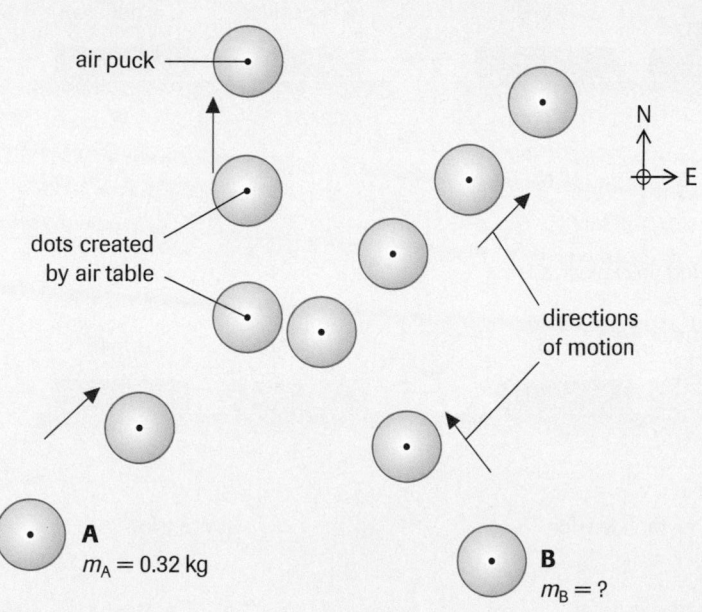

air puck

dots created by air table

directions of motion

N

E

A
$m_A = 0.32$ kg

B
$m_B = ?$

Figure 7
For question 5

INVESTIGATION 5.2.1

Analyzing One-Dimensional Collisions

Inquiry Skills

○ Questioning ● Planning ● Analyzing
● Hypothesizing ● Conducting ● Evaluating
● Predicting ● Recording ● Communicating

The basic concept of testing collisions to determine if momentum and kinetic energy are conserved is simple. Since momentum and kinetic energy involve only two variables (mass and velocity), the main measurements you must make involve the masses and velocities of the colliding objects. However, momentum and kinetic energy are very different quantities because one is a vector and the other is a scalar. It is important to remember this difference as you complete your data collection and analysis in this investigation.

Question

What can be learned from comparing the total momentum and total kinetic energy of a two-mass system involving collisions in one dimension before, during, and after the collisions?

Prediction

(a) For Categories I, II, and III in **Figure 1**, predict how the total momentum of the two-cart system before the collision will compare with the total momentum during and after the collision.

Category I: Carts experiencing repulsive forces during the collision

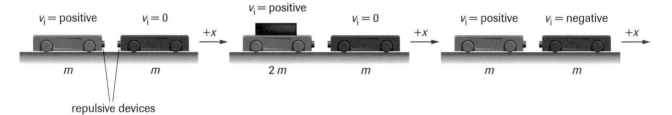

Category II: Carts that are initially stationary experiencing an explosive force

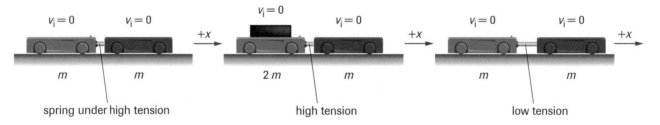

Category III: Carts experiencing adhesive forces during the collision

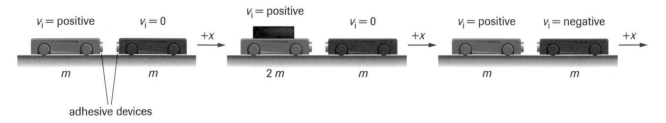

Category IV: Determining an unknown mass

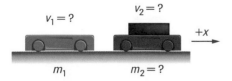

Figure 1
Possible collisions to analyze in Investigation 5.2.1

⚛ INVESTIGATION 5.2.1 *continued*

(b) For Categories I, II, and III, predict how the total kinetic energy of the two-cart system before the collision will compare with the total kinetic energy during and after the collision.

Hypothesis

(c) Describe how you will determine the unknown mass in the Category IV collision. Write a hypothesis to explain why your method should work.

Materials

The class will need at least one of each of the following items:
two low-friction carts or gliders
dynamics track compatible with the carts or gliders
a stopper at each end of the dynamics track
a level
cart accessories, such as magnetic or spring bumpers, to allow the carts to repel each other
cart accessories, such as Velcro® bumpers, to allow the carts to stick to each other
cart plunger accessory to cause the stationary carts to explode apart
extra mass (e.g., 0.25 kg if each cart is of mass 0.25 kg)
mass scale
device for measuring the speed of each cart, such as a ticker-tape timer or a bi-directional motion sensor linked to a computer
unknown masses (for the Category IV collision)

 Use only low velocities in this investigation.

Keep the carts and their accessories away from the motion sensors.

Provide stops at each end of the track to prevent the carts from falling off.

Follow instructions from your teacher when using electric equipment.

Procedure

1. In conjunction with the other groups in the class, choose which collisions your group will perform and analyze from the categories shown in **Figure 1**. Set up a data table similar to **Table 1** to summarize the measurements and calculations for each collision analyzed by the entire class.

2. Measure and record the masses involved in the collisions you will be creating.

3. Set up the dynamics track. Use a level to determine if it needs to be adjusted. If necessary, adjust one end of the track.

4. Set up the data-collecting apparatus so that the motion of the carts before, during, and after the collision can be observed. (If the data are collected by motion sensors linked to a computer, set up the software so that it will analyze as many of these variables as possible: position, velocity, acceleration, force, momentum, and kinetic energy.)

5. Using relatively low velocities, create the first collision your group will analyze. Perform the measurements and calculations to complete each row in your data table. Repeat the collision and data collection for accuracy. Then repeat for the other collisions you have chosen. Share your data with other groups so that all the collisions in Categories I, II, and III are completed.

6. If the computer program generates a graph or other data *during* the collisions, record those data for all the collisions analyzed.

7. Your teacher will set up the apparatus for you to perform the Category IV collision in which you will determine the unknown mass of one cart.

Analysis

(d) For each collision in Categories I, II, and III, how did the total final momentum of the system compare with the total initial momentum of the system?

Table 1 Data for Investigation 5.2.1

| Collision | Before the Collision | | | | After the Collision | | | | Total $\vec{p}$ (kg·m/s) | | Total E_K (J) | | Loss in E_K (%) |
	m_1 (kg)	$\vec{v}_1$ (m/s)	m_2 (kg)	$\vec{v}_2$ (m/s)	m_1 (kg)	$\vec{v}_1{}'$ (m/s)	m_2 (kg)	$\vec{v}_2{}'$ (m/s)	before	after	before	after	
I (a)	?	?	?	?	?	?	?	?	?	?	?	?	?

(e) For each collision in Categories I, II, and III, how did the total final kinetic energy of the system compare with the total initial kinetic energy of the system? Determine the percentage of the kinetic energy lost in each case in Categories I and III, and enter the data in your table.

(f) Based on your answers in (e), classify each collision as elastic, inelastic, or completely inelastic. For each collision, describe what happened to the lost kinetic energy or state the source of added kinetic energy.

(g) If you collected data *during* the collisions, describe what you learned by analyzing the data.

(h) Calculate the unknown mass in the Category IV collision. What principle did you apply to determine the unknown mass? Obtain the true mass from your teacher and calculate the percent error in your calculated value of the mass.

Evaluation

(i) Comment on the accuracy of your predictions and hypothesis.

(j) List the sources of random, systematic, and human errors in this investigation, and describe ways your group used to try to minimize them.

Synthesis

(k) In some collisions in this investigation, the total momentum was zero before, during, and after the collision (or interaction), yet the total kinetic energy did not remain constant. Use this observation to explain why it is important to distinguish between scalar and vector quantities when analyzing conservation of momentum and conservation of energy.

(l) How could the results of this investigation be applied to determine the mass of a sealed refuse bag on board the International Space Station? (Everything in the station is under constant free fall.)

(m) Adjustable friction pads are available as cart accessories. How would using these pads have affected the results of the collisions in this investigation? (With your teacher's permission, you may be able to perform a collision to test your answer.)

INVESTIGATION 5.3.1

Analyzing Two-Dimensional Collisions

Inquiry Skills		
○ Questioning	● Planning	● Analyzing
● Hypothesizing	● Conducting	● Evaluating
● Predicting	● Recording	● Communicating

This investigation explores two-dimensional collisions to determine whether total momentum and total kinetic energy are conserved. The vector nature of momentum is crucial in performing calculations involving collisions in two dimensions. Although vector scale diagrams are recommended for the analysis of the collisions you will study, you may choose components or trigonometry to analyze the collisions.

Question

What can be learned by comparing the total momentums and total kinetic energies of objects colliding in two dimensions before and after the collision?

Prediction

(a) For the Category I collisions shown in **Figure 1**, predict how the total momentum and total kinetic energy of the system before the collision will compare with the total values after the collision.

(b) For the Category II collisions, predict how the change in momentum of puck 1 will compare with the change in momentum of puck 2.

Hypothesis

(c) Write a hypothesis to explain what you anticipate you will observe in the collision in Category III.

(d) Describe how you will find the unknown mass in the Category IV collision and write a hypothesis to explain why your method should work.

INVESTIGATION 5.3.1 *continued*

Figure 1
Possible collisions to analyze in Investigation 5.3.1

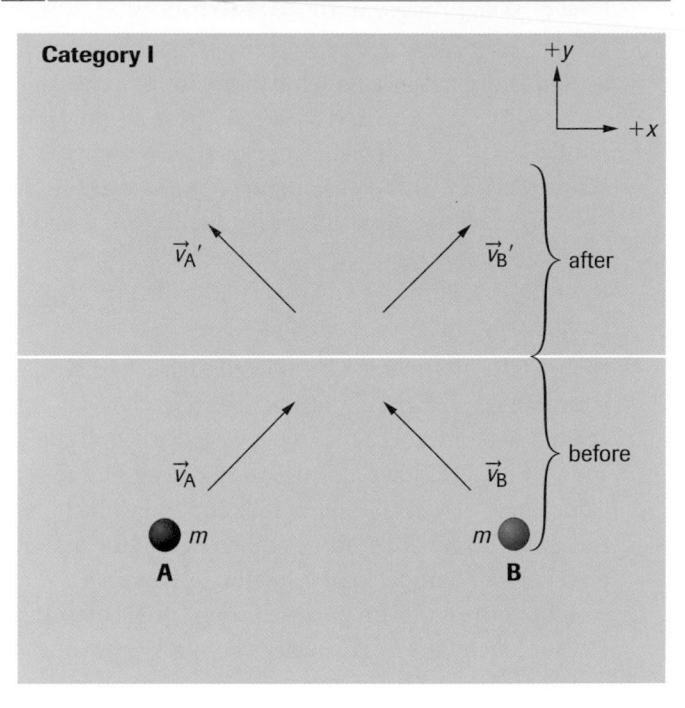

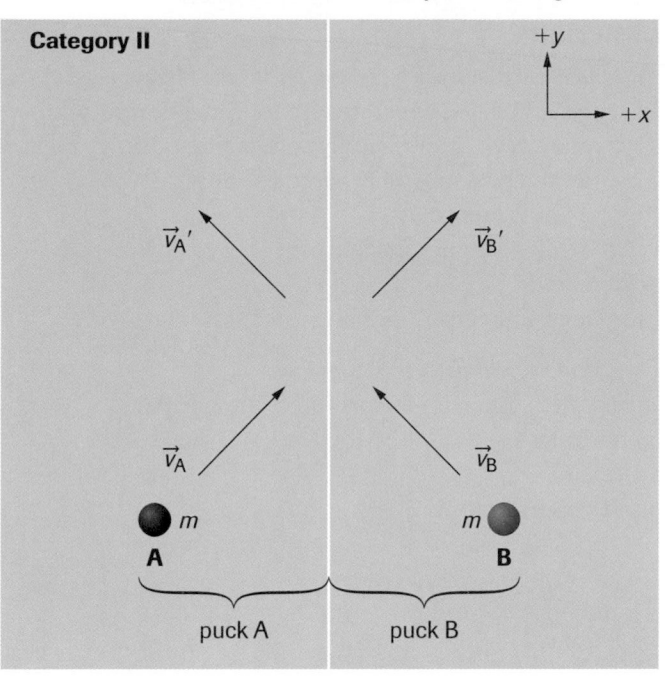

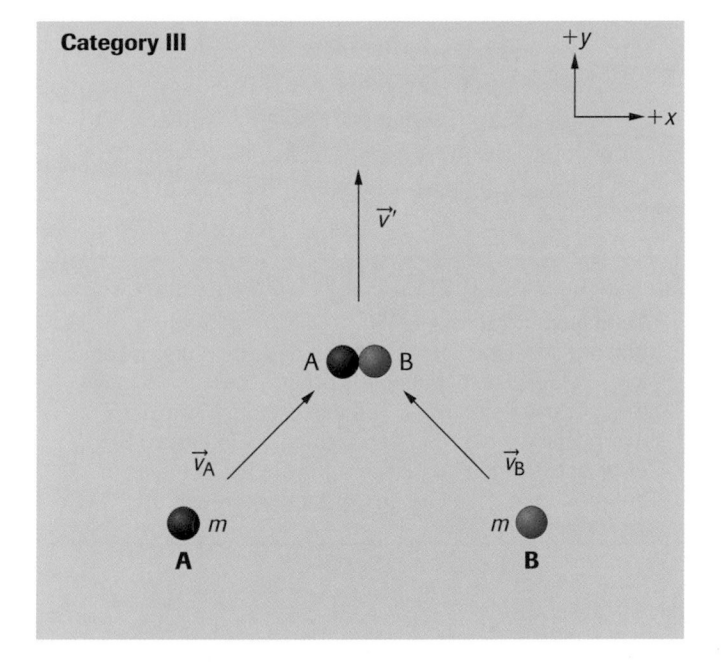

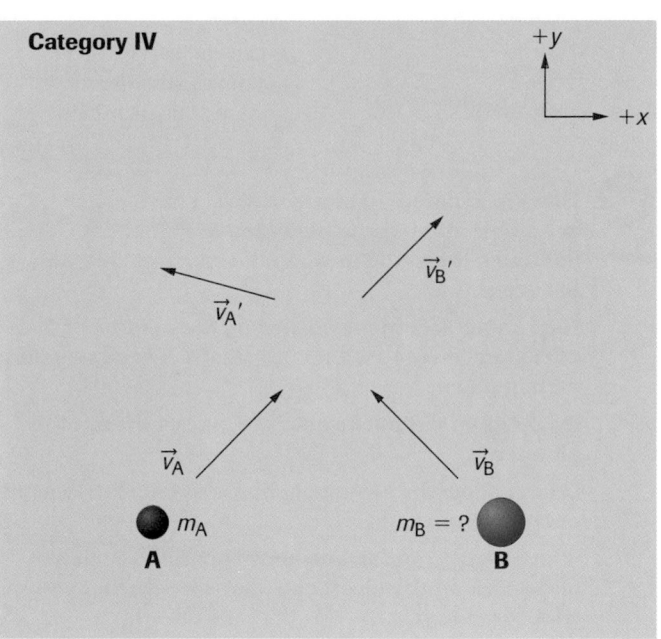

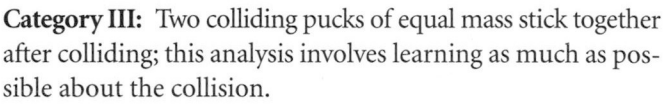

Category I: The total momentum before the collision is compared to the total momentum after the collision; this analysis involves a *vector addition*. Choose either (a) steel pucks, or (b) magnetic pucks.

Category II: The change in momentum of one puck is compared to the change in momentum of the other puck; this analysis involves a *vector subtraction*. Choose either (a) steel pucks, or (b) magnetic pucks.

Category III: Two colliding pucks of equal mass stick together after colliding; this analysis involves learning as much as possible about the collision.

Category IV: Determining an unknown mass: you must choose between vector addition and vector subtraction to solve this problem.

Materials

The entire class will need at least one of the following setups:
air table and related apparatus (spark generator, air pump, activating switch, electrically conducting carbon paper, pair of pucks, connecting wires and hoses)
circular level (**Figure 2**)
Velcro® adhesive puck collars
extra mass
two puck launchers (optional)

Each student will need the following:
at least two sheets of newsprint recording paper
metric ruler
protractor
plastic triangles (optional)

Figure 2
A circular level is used to determine whether a horizontal plane is level.

 There is a danger of electrocution. Leave the spark generator off until you are ready to gather data. Do not touch the air table when the spark generator is activated.

Turn on the electricity only when the centres of the pucks are in contact with the electrically conducting carbon paper.

Do not drop the pucks onto the glass surface of the air table.

Do not allow the air-supply hoses to become twisted or entangled.

If an air-supply hose becomes separated from its puck, turn off the electricity immediately, and inform your teacher.

Use only low-speed collisions.

Procedure

1. Use the circular level to be sure that the surface of the air table is level. Adjust the support legs accordingly.

2. In a group of three or four students, turn on the air pump (but *not* the spark generator) and practise creating Category I and Category II collisions in a way that ensures that the external force (from your hands or the puck launchers) is removed as soon as possible. When you have developed an appropriate level of skill, proceed to the next step.

3. Set the spark generator to an appropriate period, such as 50 ms, and have each member of your group create a Category I collision and a Category II collision. Do not touch the air table when the spark generator is activated. After each collision, turn the spark generator off. Label the puck numbers and directions, and record the period of sparking on the back of the recording paper. Begin your analysis while the remaining groups complete this step.

4. After all the groups have completed steps 2 and 3, your teacher will install the Velcro® collar tightly around each puck. Practise the Category III collision so that the pucks have a common velocity after the collision. (This requires great skill and some luck; however, you can learn just as much even if the pucks do not have identical final velocities.) Have each member of your group create a Category III collision. Do not touch the air table when the spark generator is activated.

5. After all the groups have completed step 4, your teacher will tell you the mass of one puck and add an extra mass to the other puck. Have each member of your group create a Category IV collision. Do not touch the air table when the spark generator is activated.

LEARNING *TIP*

Transferring Vectors
When performing vector addition or vector subtraction in a vector scale diagram, it is often necessary to move a vector parallel to itself. You can do this by moving two rulers in a step-by-step fashion, as in **Figure 3(a)**, or by positioning two plastic right-angled triangles appropriately, as in **Figure 3(b)**.

Analysis

(e) Write out the conservation-of-momentum equation you intend to use for each of the four categories of collision. Ask your teacher to check the equation before you apply it to the data sheets obtained.

(f) Starting with the Category I collision, mark off four appropriate displacement vectors, one sample of which is shown in **Figure 4**. In this sample, the time interval during which the displacement occurred is $5 \times 20 \text{ ms} = 100 \text{ ms}$, or 0.10 s, assuming two significant digits. Avoid the dots near the actual collision,

(a)

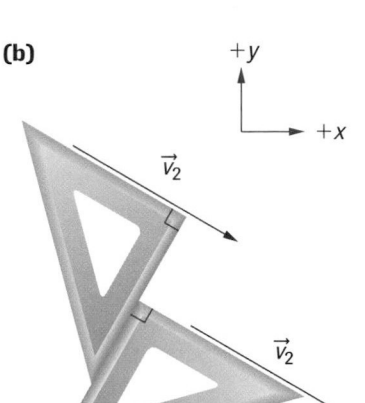

(b)

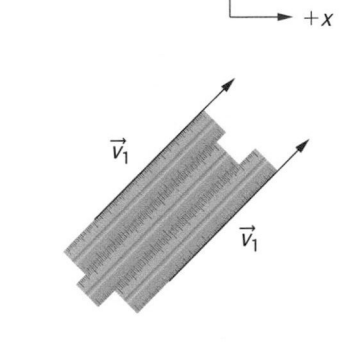

+y
→+x

Avoid dots
during collision.

direction
of puck

$\vec{d}_1$

$\Delta t = 0.10$ s

$t = 20$ ms

Avoid dots
during impulse.

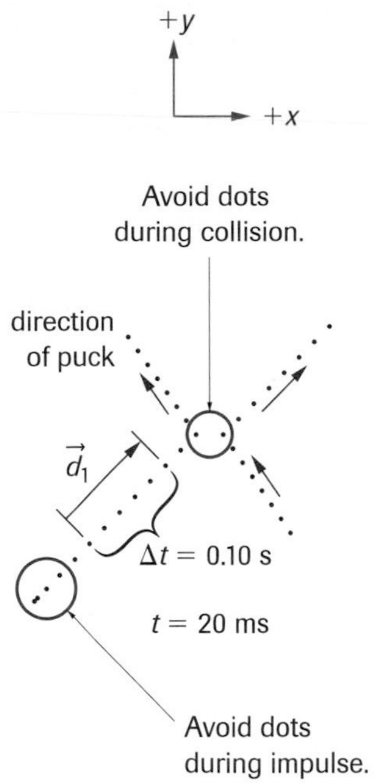

Figure 4
Sample displacement vector
for the Category I collision

Figure 3
Moving a vector to a
new position
(a) using rulers
(b) using plastic triangles

and avoid the dots produced when any external
force from your hand was applied to the pucks.
Working directly on the recording paper, draw all
the vectors and use them to determine whether total
momentum and kinetic energy are conserved.

(g) Repeat (f) for the Category II collision.

(h) Analyze the Category III collision showing as much as
you can about momentum and kinetic energy.

(i) You know the mass of one puck in the Category IV
collision. Perform the measurements and calculations
needed to determine the total unknown mass of the
second puck. If your teacher indicates what that mass
is, calculate your percent error. Show all the work on
the recording sheet.

(j) Classify each collision you analyzed as elastic, inelastic,
or completely inelastic. For each type of collision,
describe what happened to the lost kinetic energy.

Evaluation

(k) Comment on the accuracy of your predictions and
hypotheses.

(l) List the sources of random, systematic, and human
errors in this investigation, and describe ways you
tried to minimize them.

Synthesis

(m) One way of testing conservation of momentum is to
analyze the momentum of the "system." For which
category or categories of collision does this apply?

(n) Another way of testing conservation of momentum is
to analyze the momentum of each individual puck.
For which category or categories of collision does this
apply?

(o) Why is it wise to avoid the dots right where the collision occurred or while the pucks were being pushed?

(p) Based on your observations in this investigation, is it
better to have rubber barriers or steel barriers along
the edge of a car-racing track? Explain your reasoning.

Key Expectations

- define and describe the concepts and units related to momentum (momentum, impulse, elastic collisions, inelastic collisions) (5.1, 5.2, 5.3)

- analyze, with the aid of vector diagrams, the linear momentum of a collection of objects, and apply quantitatively the law of conservation of linear momentum (5.2, 5.3, 5.4)

- analyze situations involving the concepts of mechanical energy, thermal energy and its transfer (heat), and the laws of conservation of momentum and energy (5.2, 5.3)

- distinguish between elastic and inelastic collisions (5.3, 5.5)

- investigate the laws of conservation of momentum and energy in one and two dimensions by carrying out experiments or simulations and the necessary analytical procedures (e.g., use vector diagrams to determine whether the collisions of pucks on an air table are elastic or inelastic) (5.2, 5.3, 5.5)

- analyze and describe, using the concept of the law of conservation of momentum, practical applications of momentum conservation (e.g., analyze and explain, using scientific concepts and principles, the design of protective equipment developed for recreational and sports activities) (5.2, 5.3, 5.4)

- identify and analyze social issues that relate to the development of vehicles (e.g., analyze, using your own criteria, the economic and social costs and benefits of safety devices in automobiles) (5.4)

Key Terms

linear momentum

impulse

law of conservation of linear momentum

elastic collision

inelastic collision

completely inelastic collision

Key Equations

- $\vec{p} = m\vec{v}$ (5.1)
- $\sum \vec{F}\Delta t = \Delta \vec{p}$ (5.1)
- $m_1 \Delta \vec{v}_1 = -m_2 \Delta \vec{v}_2$ (5.2)
- $m_1 \vec{v}_1 + m_2 \vec{v}_2 = m_1 \vec{v}_1' + m_2 \vec{v}_2'$ (5.2)
- $\frac{1}{2}mv_1^2 + \frac{1}{2}mv_2^2 = \frac{1}{2}mv_1'^2 + \frac{1}{2}mv_2'^2$ (5.3)

  for elastic collisions only

▶ *MAKE* a summary

Draw and label diagrams to show the following situations:

- an elastic collision in one dimension
- an inelastic collision in one dimension
- a completely inelastic collision in one dimension
- an elastic collision in two dimensions

Incorporate as many key expectations, key terms, and key equations as possible.

How can the laws of conservation of momentum and energy be applied to analyzing fireworks displays?

Write numbers 1 to 10 in your notebook. Indicate beside each number whether the corresponding statement is true (T) or false (F). If it is false, write a corrected version.

1. The impulse you give to a child on a swing to start the child moving is equal in magnitude, but opposite in direction, to the child's change in momentum.

2. Newton's second law of motion can be written both as $\sum \vec{F} = m\vec{a}$ and $\sum \vec{F} = \dfrac{\Delta \vec{p}}{\Delta t}$.

3. If you have developed your follow-through skills when playing tennis, you have increased the force you are able to apply as you swing the racket.

For questions 4 to 6, refer to **Figure 1**.

4. The total momentum before the collision is positive, and the total momentum after the collision is negative.

5. For this collision, if the change in momentum of glider 1 is -1.4 kg·m/s [W], then the change in momentum of glider 2 is 1.4 kg·m/s [W].

6. At the exact midpoint of the collision, both the kinetic energy and the momentum of the system are zero.

7. If a small car of mass m_S and speed v_S has a momentum equal in magnitude to a large car of mass m_B and speed v_B, then the two cars have equal kinetic energies.

8. When a snowball hits a tree and sticks entirely to the tree, momentum of the snowball is not conserved because the collision is completely inelastic.

9. Elastic collisions are more likely to occur between atoms and molecules than between macroscopic objects.

10. In an interaction involving an isolated system, it is impossible for the final kinetic energy to be greater than the initial kinetic energy.

Write numbers 11 to 22 in your notebook. Beside each number, write the letter corresponding to the best choice.

11. Using L, M, and T for the dimensions of length, mass, and time, respectively, the dimensions of impulse are
    (a) $\dfrac{LT}{M}$ (b) $\dfrac{L}{TM}$ (c) $\dfrac{ML^2}{T^2}$ (d) $\dfrac{ML}{T^2}$ (e) $\dfrac{ML}{T}$

12. If an arrow's speed and mass are both doubled, then its momentum and kinetic energy are respectively increased by factors of
    (a) 2 and 2   (d) 4 and 8
    (b) 2 and 4   (e) 8 and 8
    (c) 4 and 4

13. The area under the line on a force-time graph indicates
    (a) the impulse
    (b) the change in momentum
    (c) the product of the average force and the time interval during which that force is applied
    (d) all of these
    (e) none of these

14. When you catch a fast-moving baseball, your hand hurts less if you move it in the same direction as the ball because
    (a) the change in momentum in the ball is less
    (b) the change in kinetic energy of the ball is less
    (c) the time interval of the interaction is less
    (d) the time interval of the interaction is greater
    (e) the impulse on the ball is greater

15. The force applied by an apple hitting the ground depends on
    (a) whether or not the apple bounces
    (b) the time interval of the impact with the ground
    (c) the apple's maximum speed just before impact
    (d) the air resistance acting on the apple as it falls
    (e) all of these

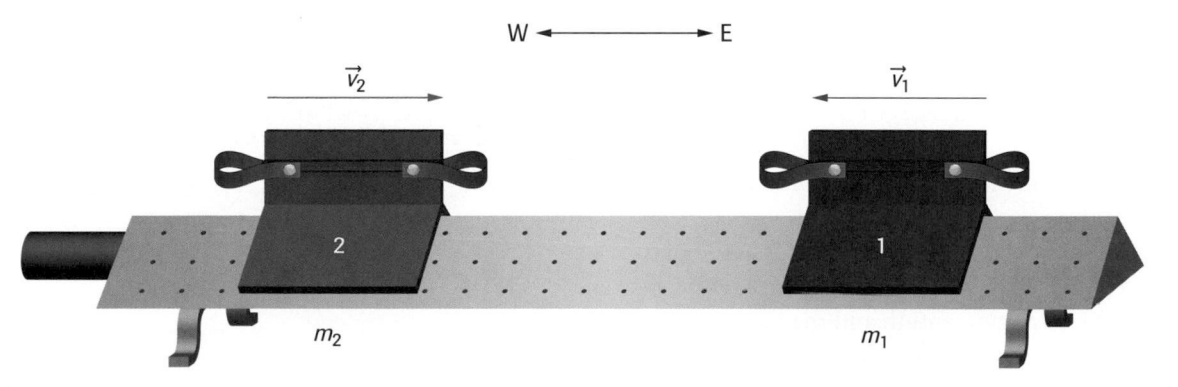

Figure 1
In this isolated system, two gliders ($m_1 = m_2$) on an air track move toward each other at equal speed, collide, and then move away from each other at equal speed. (for questions 4 to 6)

16. In an inelastic collision involving two interacting objects, the final kinetic energy of the system
    (a) can be equal to the initial kinetic energy of the system
    (b) is always less than or equal to the initial kinetic energy of the system
    (c) is always greater than or equal to the initial kinetic energy of the system
    (d) is always less than the initial kinetic energy of the system
    (e) can be greater than the initial kinetic energy of the system

17. When you are jogging and you increase your kinetic energy by a factor of 2, then your momentum
    (a) changes by a factor of $\frac{1}{2}$
    (b) increases by a factor of $\sqrt{2}$
    (c) increases by a factor of 2
    (d) increases by a factor of 4
    (e) increases by an amount that cannot be determined with the information given

18. A rubber bullet R and a metal bullet M of equal mass strike a test target T with the same speed. The metal bullet penetrates the target and comes to rest inside it, while the rubber bullet bounces off the target. Which statement is true?
    (a) M and R exert the same impulse on T.
    (b) M exerts a greater impulse on T than R does.
    (c) R exerts a greater impulse on T than M does.
    (d) The magnitudes of the change in momentum of M and R are equal.
    (e) none of these

19. Two protons approach one another in a straight line with equal speeds. Eventually, they repel, and move apart with equal speeds in the same straight line. At the instant of minimum separation between the particles
    (a) the total momentum of the interacting particles is zero, but the total energy of the system remains constant
    (b) both the total momentum and the total energy are zero
    (c) the total momentum of the system is at the maximum value, but the total energy is zero
    (d) both the total momentum and the total energy of the system are at their maximum values
    (e) both the total momentum and the total energy of the system are reduced, but not to zero

20. A ball bounces off the edge of a pool table as in **Figure 2**. The speeds before and after the bounce are essentially equal. Which of the five vectors in **Figure 2** represent the direction of the impulse by the table on the ball?

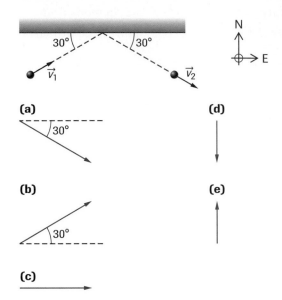

Figure 2

21. A glider of mass m travels leftward on a frictionless air track with a speed v. It collides head-on in a completely inelastic collision with a glider that has twice its mass and half its speed moving to the right. After the collision, the combined speed of the glider system is
    (a) 0
    (b) $\frac{v}{3}$
    (c) $\frac{v}{2}$
    (d) $2v$
    (e) v

22. A baseball of mass m leaves a pitching machine of mass M (where M includes the mass of the ball m) with a speed v. The recoil speed of the machine after shooting the baseball is
    (a) $\frac{2mv}{(M - m)}$
    (b) $\frac{mv}{M}$
    (c) $\frac{mv}{(M + m)}$
    (d) $\frac{mv}{(M - m)}$
    (e) 0

An interactive version of the quiz is available online. NEL

www.science.nelson.com

Understanding Concepts

1. Is it possible for an object to receive a larger impulse from a small force than from a large force? Explain.

2. When a meteoroid collides with the Moon, surface material at the impact site melts. Explain why.

3. A falling rock gains momentum as its speed increases. Does this observation contradict the law of conservation of momentum? Explain your answer.

4. A piece of putty is dropped vertically onto a floor, where it sticks. A rubber ball of the same mass is dropped from the same height onto the floor and rebounds to almost its initial height. For which of these objects is the magnitude of the change of momentum greater during the collision with the floor? Explain your answer.

5. A football kickoff receiver catches the ball and is about to be tackled head-on by one of two possible opponents. If the two opponents have different masses ($m_1 > m_2$), but equal momentums ($\vec{p}_1 = \vec{p}_2$), which opponent would the receiver be wise to avoid: $\vec{p}_1 = m_1\vec{v}_1$ or $\vec{p}_2 = m_2\vec{v}_2$? Explain why.

6. Give an example of a collision in which the momentum of the system of the colliding objects is not conserved. Explain why momentum is not conserved in this collision, but is conserved in other situations.

7. A boat of mass 1.3×10^2 kg has a velocity of 8.7 m/s [44° E of N]. Determine the northward and eastward components of its momentum.

8. A car of mass 1.1×10^3 kg is travelling in a direction 22° N of E. The eastward component of its momentum is 2.6×10^4 kg·m/s. What is the speed of the car?

9. A car of mass 1.2×10^3 kg travelling at 53 km/h [W] collides with a telephone pole and comes to rest. The duration of the collision is 55 ms. What is the average force exerted on the car by the pole?

10. A 59-g tennis ball is thrown upward, and is hit just as it comes to rest at the top of its motion. It is in contact with the racket for 5.1 ms. The average force exerted on the ball by the racket is 324 N horizontally.
    (a) What is the impulse on the ball?
    (b) What is the velocity of the ball just as it leaves the racket?

11. A child places a spring of negligible mass between two toy cars of masses 112 g and 154 g (**Figure 1**). She compresses the spring and ties the cars together with a piece of string. When she cuts the string, the spring

is released and the cars move in opposite directions. The 112-g car has speed of 1.38 m/s. What is the speed of the other car?

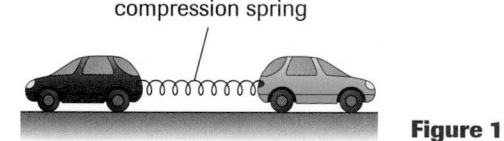

compression spring

Figure 1

12. A proton of mass 1.67×10^{-27} kg is travelling with an initial speed of 1.57 km/s when it collides head-on with a stationary alpha particle of mass 6.64×10^{-27} kg. The proton rebounds with a speed of 0.893 km/s. What is the speed of the alpha particle?

13. Two rocks in space collide. One rock has a mass of 2.67 kg, and travels at an initial velocity of 1.70×10^2 m/s toward Jupiter; the other rock has a mass of 5.83 kg. After the collision, the rocks are both moving toward Jupiter with speeds of 185 m/s for the less massive rock and 183 m/s for the more massive rock. What is the initial velocity of the more massive rock?

14. Sets of objects made of various materials undergo head-on collisions. Each set consists of two masses ($m_1 = 2.0$ kg and $m_2 = 4.0$ kg). Given the following initial and final velocities, identify the collisions as elastic, inelastic, or completely inelastic.
    (a) $v_{1i} = 6.0$ m/s; $v_{2i} = 0$; $v_{1f} = v_{2f} = 2.0$ m/s
    (b) $v_{1i} = 24$ m/s; $v_{2i} = 0$; $v_{1f} = -4.0$ m/s; $v_{2f} = 14$ m/s
    (c) $v_{1i} = 12$ m/s; $v_{2i} = 0$; $v_{1f} = -4.0$ m/s; $v_{2f} = 8.0$ m/s

15. Two carts equipped with spring bumpers on an air track have an elastic collision. The 253-g cart has an initial velocity of 1.80 m/s [N]. The 232-g cart is initially stationary. What is the velocity of each cart after the collision?

16. Two hockey pucks of equal mass undergo a collision on a hockey rink. One puck is initially at rest, while the other is moving with a speed of 5.4 m/s. After the collision, the velocities of the pucks make angles of 33° and 46° relative to the original velocity of the moving puck.
    (a) Draw a diagram showing the initial and final situations. Make sure that the geometry of your diagram is such that momentum is conserved.
    (b) Determine the speed of each puck after the collision.

17. Two subatomic particles collide. Initially, the more massive particle (A) is at rest and the less massive particle (B) is moving. After the collision, the velocities

of A and B make angles of 67.8° and 30.0°, respectively, to the original direction of B's motion. The ratio of the final speeds of the particles $\frac{v_B}{v_A}$ is 3.30. What is the ratio of the masses of the particles $\frac{m_B}{m_A}$?

18. Two rolling golf balls of the same mass collide. The velocity of one ball is initially 2.70 m/s [E]. After the collision, the velocities of the balls are 2.49 m/s [62.8° N of W] and 2.37 m/s [69.2° S of E]. What are the magnitude and direction of the unknown initial velocity?

19. A 0.25-kg ball is attached to a 26-cm piece of string (**Figure 2**). The ball is first raised so that the string is taut and horizontal, then the ball is released so that, at the bottom of its swing, it undergoes an elastic head-on collision with a 0.21-kg ball that is free to roll along a horizontal table.
    (a) What is the speed of the swinging ball just before the collision?
    (b) What is the speed of the 0.21-kg ball just after the collision?

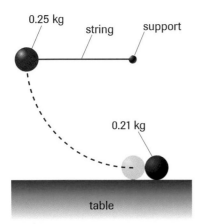

0.25 kg
string
support
0.21 kg
table

Figure 2

20. A large ball of modelling clay of mass 4.5×10^2 g is rolled on a tabletop so that it collides with a stationary small wooden box of mass 7.9×10^2 g. The collision is completely inelastic, and the ball and box then slide on the table for a distance of 5.1 cm. If the speed of the ball is 2.2 m/s just before the collision, determine
    (a) the speed of the ball and box just after the collision
    (b) the magnitude of the friction force acting on the ball and box

21. Two spacecrafts from different nations have linked in space and are coasting with their engines off, heading directly toward Mars. The spacecrafts are thrust apart by the use of large springs. Spacecraft 1, of mass 1.9×10^4 kg, then has a velocity of 3.5×10^3 km/h at 5.1° to its original direction (**Figure 3**), and spacecraft 2, of mass 1.7×10^4 kg, has a velocity of 3.4×10^3 km/h at 5.9° to its original direction. Determine the original speed of the spacecrafts when they were linked together.

22. During the testing of a fireworks device, an engineer records the data shown in **Table 1** when the device, initially at rest, explodes under controlled conditions into three components that spread out horizontally. Determine the unknown quantity.

Table 1 Data for Question 22

Component	1	2	3
Mass	2.0 kg	3.0 kg	4.0 kg
Final Velocity	1.5 m/s [N]	2.5 m/s [E]	?

Applying Inquiry Skills

23. A number of objects with different masses have the same speed. Sketch the shape of the graph of the magnitude of momentum versus mass for these objects.

24. A variety of objects of different masses are moving at different speeds, but the momentum of each object has the same magnitude. Sketch the shape of the graph of speed vs. mass for these objects.

25. **Figure 4** shows a device used to test the "coefficient of restitution" of spherical objects that are made from a variety of materials, such as brass, plastic, steel, wood, rubber, and aluminum.
    (a) Determine what is meant by the term "coefficient of restitution." How would this device help you determine the coefficient of restitution for spheres made of various materials?
    (b) With your teacher's approval, use either this device or some other method to determine the coefficient of restitution of various spheres.

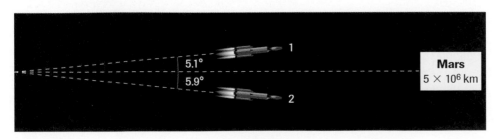

1
5.1°
5.9°
2
Mars
5×10^6 km

Figure 3
For question 21

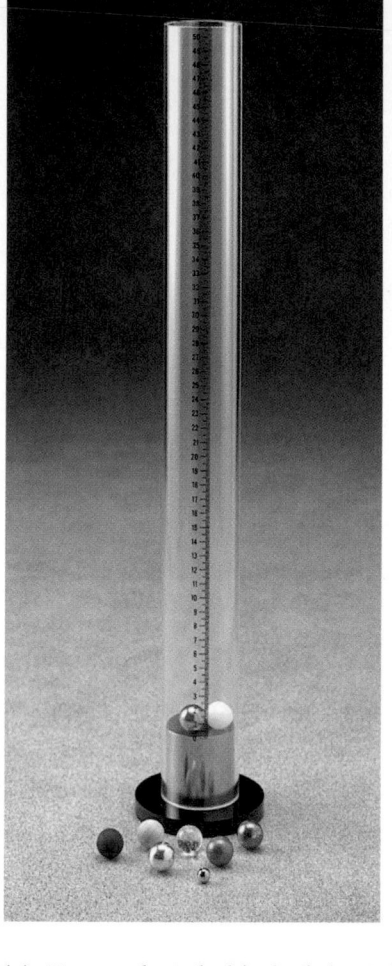

Figure 4
For question 25

26. (a) Two students hold a bed sheet almost vertically to create a "landing pad" for a raw egg tossed at high speed toward the middle of the sheet. Even at a very high speed, the egg does not break. Explain why. (*Caution:* If you try this, perform the experiment outside, and make sure the egg hits near the centre and does not fall to the ground after the collision.)

    (b) How would you apply the concept presented in (a) to rescue operations? What experiments could you perform (without using any living creatures) to determine the maximum height a person could fall and be caught without injury?

Making Connections

27. From the point of view of transportation safety, is it better to have a telephone pole that collapses (crumples), or one that remains sturdy when a vehicle crashes into it? Explain why.

28. Safety research engineers use high-speed photography to help them analyze test crashes. Compare and con-

trast the use of high-speed photography with the methods you used to analyze collisions in Investigation 5.2.1 and Investigation 5.3.1.

29. On a navy aircraft carrier, an arrester hook is used to help stop a high-speed aircraft on the relatively short landing strip. Research the Internet or other appropriate publications to find out how this device successfully converts the kinetic energy of the aircraft into other forms of energy. Describe what you discover.

  www.science.nelson.com

30. A space shuttle, used to transport equipment and astronauts to and from the International Space Station, has an "ablation shield" on the front. This shield is needed to protect the shuttle from collisions with objects. Research the Internet or other appropriate publications to find out what the shuttle might collide with, and how the ablation shield helps to reduce the damage to the craft.

 www.science.nelson.com

Extension

31. An object of mass m_1 and initial velocity v_{1i} undergoes a head-on elastic collision with a stationary object of mass m_2.
    (a) In terms of m_1, m_2, and v_{1i}, determine the final velocity of each mass. (*Hint:* You will need two equations to solve for the two unknowns.)
    (b) Determine the final velocity of each mass if $m_1 = m_2$ (for example, two billiard balls collide).
    (c) Determine the final velocity of each mass if $m_1 >> m_2$ (for example, a bowling ball hits a superball).
    (d) Determine the final velocity of each mass if $m_1 << m_2$ (for example, a superball hits a bowling ball).

32. A 1.0×10^3-kg plane is trying to make a forced landing on the deck of a 2.0×10^3-kg barge at rest on the surface of a calm sea. The only frictional force to consider is between the plane's wheels and the deck; this braking force is constant and is equal to one-quarter of the plane's weight. What must the minimum length of the barge be for the plane to stop safely on deck, if the plane touches down just at the rear end of the deck with a velocity of 5.0×10^1 m/s toward the front of the barge?

🍎 Sir Isaac Newton Contest Question

6

Gravitation and Celestial Mechanics

In this chapter, you will be able to

- analyze the factors affecting the motion of isolated celestial objects and calculate the gravitational potential energy for each system
- analyze isolated planetary and satellite motion, and describe the motion in terms of the forms of energy and energy transformations that occur

When we view the planets and stars on clear nights away from bright city lights, or look at images of the night sky obtained by telescopes, we realize that there are many questions we can ask about our universe. What causes the stars in a galaxy (**Figure 1**) to be grouped together? What keeps the planets and their moons in our solar system moving in our galaxy? The answers to these and other questions relate to gravitation. The force of gravity is responsible for the existence of galaxies, stars, planets, and moons, as well as for the patterns of their motion.

When we analyzed the motion of planets and satellites in previous chapters, we treated their orbits as circular. In some cases, this is a close approximation, but to understand celestial motion in detail, we must analyze the noncircular properties of many orbits. The discovery of these types of orbits by astronomer Johannes Kepler is an amazing story of determination and careful analysis.

In this chapter, you will also apply what you have learned to analyze energy transformations required to launch a spacecraft from Earth's surface that will travel in an orbit around Earth or to launch a spacecraft on an interplanetary mission.

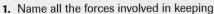

💡 REFLECT on your learning ▼

1. Name all the forces involved in keeping
   (a) the rings of Saturn in their orbit around Saturn
   (b) the Hubble Space Telescope in a stable orbit around Earth

2. Two space probes of masses m and $2m$ are carried into space aboard two rockets.
   (a) For the probes to escape from Earth's pull of gravity, how do you think the minimum speed required by the probe of mass m compares to the minimum speed required by the probe of mass $2m$? Give a reason.
   (b) For the probes to escape from Earth's gravity, how do you think the minimum kinetic energy by the probe of mass m compares to the minimum kinetic energy required by the probe of mass $2m$? Give a reason.

3. Speculate on the meaning of the following statement: "If r is the distance from the centre of a main body (such as Earth) to an object (such as a space probe), we will find as we analyze the gravitational potential energy of the probe, that as $r \rightarrow \infty$, $E_g \rightarrow 0$."

4. A space probe is launched from Earth's surface.
   (a) Sketch a graph of the magnitude of the force of gravity F_g of Earth on the space probe as a function of the distance r between Earth's centre and the probe, assuming the mass of the probe is constant.
   (b) On the same graph, use a broken line to sketch the force on the probe assuming its mass decreases gradually as it burns fuel to propel itself away from Earth.

5. An intriguing result of the study of gravitation and celestial motion is the discovery of black holes in the universe. Briefly describe what you know about black holes.

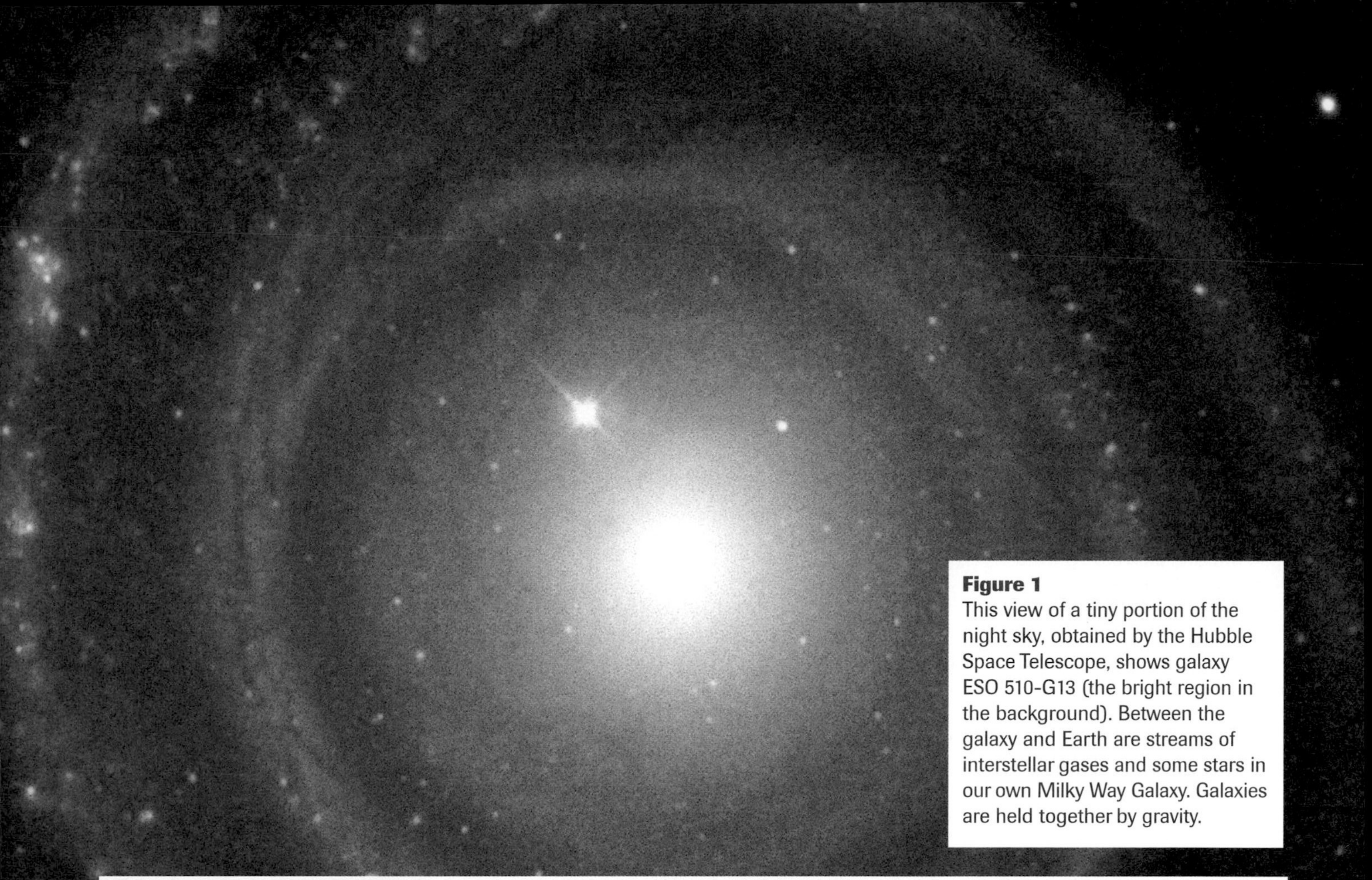

Figure 1
This view of a tiny portion of the night sky, obtained by the Hubble Space Telescope, shows galaxy ESO 510-G13 (the bright region in the background). Between the galaxy and Earth are streams of interstellar gases and some stars in our own Milky Way Galaxy. Galaxies are held together by gravity.

▶ **TRY THIS** activity   *Drawing and Comparing Ellipses*

An *ellipse* is defined as a closed curve such that the sum of the distances from any point P to two other fixed points, the *foci* F_1 and F_2, is a constant: $PF_1 + PF_2$ equals a constant. **Figure 2** shows an ellipse. A circle is a special case of an ellipse for which the two foci are at the same position. Ellipses have different elongations as indicated by a quantity called *eccentricity* (e), shown in the diagram to be $e = \dfrac{c}{a}$; for a circle, $e = 0$ and for a long, thin ellipse $e \rightarrow 1$.

For this activity, each group of three or four students needs a pencil, a ruler, a piece of string tied to create a loop of length 40 cm, two tacks, and a piece of cardboard at least 40 cm by

40 cm. With the foci located 10 cm apart, attach the ends of the string to the tacks, hold the string taut with the pencil held against it, and draw an ellipse around the tacks. Note that the sum of the distances from any point on the curve to the two foci (tacks) is a constant (the length of that part of the string). On the reverse side of the cardboard, draw a second ellipse with a distance of 15 cm between the foci.

(a) Label the major and minor axes for each ellipse. Compare the eccentricities of your two ellipses.

(b) Planets travel in ellipses. What must be at one focus of the ellipse of each planet? What is at one focus of the elliptical orbit of the Moon?

Store the cardboard with the ellipses in a safe place so that you can use it for further study in this chapter.

✋ **Exercise care with the tacks, and remove them after you have drawn the ellipses.**

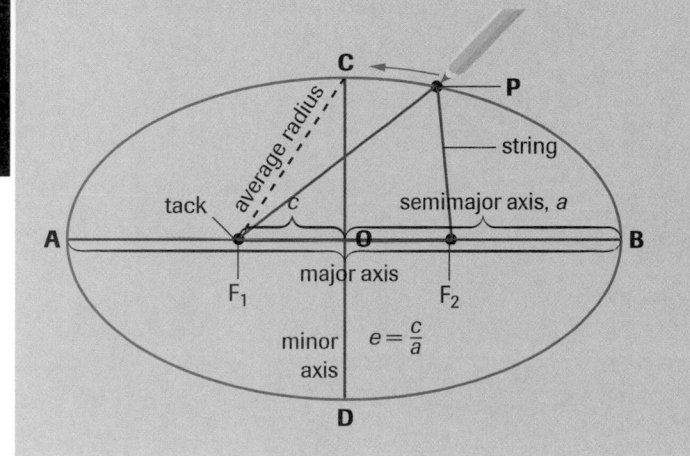

Figure 2
An ellipse. The line AB is the *major axis* of the ellipse; CD is the *minor axis*. The distance AO or OB is the length a of the *semimajor axis*. The eccentricity is defined as $\dfrac{c}{a}$, where c is the distance OF_1 or OF_2 from a focus to the centre of the ellipse.

gravitational field exists in the space surrounding an object in which the force of gravity exists

Humans have a natural curiosity about how Earth and the solar system formed billions of years ago, and whether or not we are alone in the universe. The search for answers to these questions begins with an understanding of *gravity*, the force of attraction between all objects with mass in the universe.

Concepts and equations related to gravity have been introduced earlier in the text. In this section, we will build on the concepts most directly related to planetary and satellite motion.

A *force field* exists in the space surrounding an object in which a force is exerted on objects. Thus, a **gravitational field** exists in the space surrounding an object in which the force of gravity is exerted on objects. The strength of the gravitational field is directly proportional to the mass of the central body and inversely proportional to the square of the distance from the centre of that body. To understand this relationship, we combine the law of universal gravitation and Newton's second law of motion, as illustrated in **Figure 1**.

From the law of universal gravitation,

$$F_G = \frac{GMm}{r^2}$$

where F_G is the magnitude of the force of gravity, G is the universal gravitation constant, m is the mass of a body influenced by the gravitational field of the central body of mass M, and r is the distance between the centres of the two bodies. (Remember that this law applies to spherical bodies, which is basically what we are considering in this topic of celestial mechanics.)

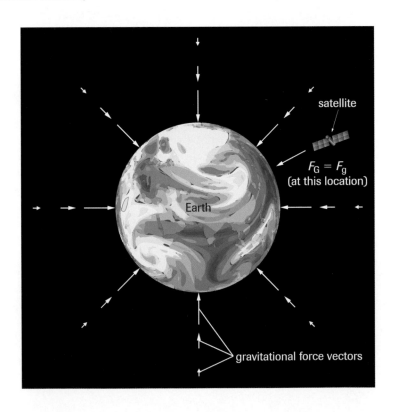

Figure 1

The magnitudes of the force vectors surrounding Earth show how the strength of the gravitational field diminishes inversely as the square of the distance to Earth's centre. To derive the equation for the gravitational field strength in terms of the mass of the central body (Earth in this case), we equate the magnitudes of the forces F_G and F_g.

From Newton's second law,

$$F_g = mg$$

where F_g is the magnitude of the force of gravity acting on a body of mass m and g is the magnitude of the gravitational field strength. At any specific location, F_g and F_G are equal, so we have:

$$F_g = F_G$$
$$mg = \frac{GMm}{r^2}$$
$$g = \frac{GM}{r^2}$$

LEARNING *TIP*

Units of *g*
Recall that the magnitude of g at Earth's surface is 9.8 N/kg, which is equivalent to the magnitude of the acceleration due to gravity (9.8 m/s²). In all calculations involving forces and energies in this topic, it is important to remember to use the SI base units of metres (m), kilograms (kg), and seconds (s).

▶ SAMPLE problem 1

Determine the mass of Earth using the magnitude of the gravitational field strength at the surface of the Earth, the distance r between Earth's surface and its centre (6.38×10^6 m), and the universal gravitation constant.

Solution

$g = 9.80$ N/kg $G = 6.67 \times 10^{-11}$ N·m²/kg²

$r = 6.38 \times 10^6$ m $M = ?$

$$g = \frac{GM}{r^2}$$

$$M = \frac{gr^2}{G}$$

$$= \frac{(9.80 \text{ N/kg})(6.38 \times 10^6 \text{ m})^2}{6.67 \times 10^{-11} \text{ N·m}^2/\text{kg}^2}$$

$$M = 5.98 \times 10^{24} \text{ kg}$$

The mass of Earth is 5.98×10^{24} kg.

Notice that the relation $g = \dfrac{GM}{r^2}$ is valid not only for objects on Earth's surface, but also for objects above Earth's surface. For objects above Earth's surface, r represents the distance from an object to Earth's centre and, except for objects close to Earth's surface, g is not 9.80 N/kg. The magnitude of the gravitational field strength g decreases with increasing distance r from Earth's centre according to $g = \dfrac{GM}{r^2}$. We can also use the same equation for other planets and stars by substituting the appropriate mass M.

▶ SAMPLE problem 2

(a) Calculate the magnitude of the gravitational field strength on the surface of Mars.

(b) What is the ratio of the magnitude of the gravitational field strength on the surface of Mars to that on the surface of Earth?

Solution

Appendix C contains the required data.

(a) $G = 6.67 \times 10^{-11}$ N·m²/kg² $r = 3.40 \times 10^6$ m

  $M = 6.37 \times 10^{23}$ kg $g = ?$

Table 1 Magnitude of the Gravitational Field Strength of Planets Relative to Earth's Value ($g = 9.80$ N/kg)

Planet	Surface Gravity (Earth = 1.00)
Mercury	0.375
Venus	0.898
Earth	1.00
Mars	0.375
Jupiter	2.53
Saturn	1.06
Uranus	0.914
Neptune	1.14
Pluto	0.067

$$g = \frac{GM}{r^2}$$

$$= \frac{(6.67 \times 10^{-11} \text{ N·m}^2/\text{kg}^2)(6.37 \times 10^{23} \text{ kg})}{(3.40 \times 10^6 \text{ m})^2}$$

$$g = 3.68 \text{ N/kg}$$

The magnitude of the gravitational field strength on the surface of Mars is 3.68 N/kg.

(b) The required ratio is:

$$\frac{g_{Mars}}{g_{Earth}} = \frac{3.68 \text{ N/kg}}{9.80 \text{ N/kg}} = 0.375:100$$

The ratio of the magnitudes of the gravitational field strengths is 0.375:100. This means that the gravitational field strength on the surface of Mars is 37.5% of the gravitational field strength on the surface of Earth.

The magnitude of the gravitational field strength on the surface of Mars is only 0.375 of that on the surface of Earth. The corresponding values for all the planets in the solar system are listed in **Table 1**.

Answers

2. (a) 1.99×10^{20} N [toward Earth's centre]

   (b) 1.99×10^{20} N [toward the Moon's centre]

3. (a) $\dfrac{g}{4}$

   (b) $\dfrac{g}{16}$

   (c) $\dfrac{g}{27}$

4. $4.0g$

5. (a) 7.3×10^{22} kg

6. (a) 5.42×10^{-9} N

   (b) 4.83×10^{-3} N

▶ **Practice**

Understanding Concepts

Refer to Appendix C for required data.

1. What keeps the International Space Station and other satellites in their orbits around Earth?

2. Determine the magnitude and direction of the gravitational force exerted (a) on the Moon by Earth and (b) on Earth by the Moon.

3. If we represent the magnitude of Earth's surface gravitational field strength as $1g$, what are the magnitudes of the gravitational field strengths (in terms of g) at the following distances above Earth's surface: (a) 1.0 Earth radii, (b) 3.0 Earth radii, and (c) 4.2 Earth radii?

4. If a planet has the same mass as Earth, but a radius only 0.50 times the radius of Earth, what is the magnitude of the planet's surface gravitational field strength as a multiple of Earth's surface g?

5. The Moon has a surface gravitational field strength of magnitude 1.6 N/kg.
   (a) What is the mass of the Moon? (*Hint:* The Moon's radius is in the appendix.)
   (b) What would be the magnitude of your weight if you were on the Moon?

6. The magnitude of the total gravitational field strength at a point in interstellar space is 5.42×10^{-9} N/kg. What is the magnitude of the gravitational force at this point on an object (a) of mass 1.00 kg and (b) of mass 8.91×10^5 kg?

Applying Inquiry Skills

7. A space probe orbits Jupiter, gathering data and sending the data to Earth by electromagnetic waves. The probe then travels away from Jupiter toward Saturn.
   (a) As the probe gets farther away from Jupiter (in an assumed straight-line motion), sketch the shape of the graph of the magnitude of the force of Jupiter on the probe as a function of the distance between the centres of the two bodies.
   (b) Repeat (a) for the magnitude of the force of the probe on Jupiter.

Making Connections

8. If the density of Earth were much greater than its actual value, but its radius was the same, what would be the effect on
   (a) Earth's surface gravitational field strength?
   (b) the evolution of human bone structure?
   (c) some other aspects of nature or human activity? (Use your imagination.)

SUMMARY   *Gravitational Fields*

- A gravitational field exists in the space surrounding an object in which the force of gravity is exerted on objects.

- The magnitude of the gravitational field strength surrounding a planet or other body (assumed to be spherical) is directly proportional to the mass of the central body, and inversely proportional to the square of the distance to the centre of the body.

- The law of universal gravitation applies to all bodies in the solar system, from the Sun to planets, moons, and artificial satellites.

▶ Section 6.1 Questions

Understanding Concepts

Refer to Appendix C for required data.

1. How does the weight of a space probe change as it travels from Earth to the Moon? Is there any location at which the weight is zero? Does its mass change? Explain.

2. A satellite of mass 225 kg is located 8.62×10^6 m above Earth's surface.
   (a) Determine the magnitude and direction of the gravitational force on the satellite.
   (b) Determine the magnitude and direction of the resulting acceleration of the satellite.

3. Determine the magnitude and direction of the gravitational field strength at a point in space 7.4×10^7 m from the centre of Earth.

4. A 6.2×10^2-kg satellite above Earth's surface experiences a gravitational field strength of magnitude 4.5 N/kg.
   (a) Knowing the gravitational field strength at Earth's surface and Earth's radius, how far above Earth's surface is the satellite? (Use ratio and proportion.)
   (b) Determine the magnitude of the gravitational force on the satellite.

5. Calculate the magnitude of Neptune's surface gravitational field strength, and compare your answer to the value in **Table 1**.

6. A 456-kg satellite in circular orbit around Earth has a speed of 3.9 km/s and is 2.5×10^7 m from Earth's centre.
   (a) Determine the magnitude and direction of the acceleration of the satellite.
   (b) Determine the magnitude and direction of the gravitational force on the satellite.

7. (a) On the surface of Titan, a moon of Saturn, the gravitational field strength has a magnitude of 1.3 N/kg. Titan's mass is 1.3×10^{23} kg. What is the radius of Titan in kilometres?
   (b) What is the magnitude of the force of gravity on a 0.181-kg rock on Titan?

8. Given that Earth's surface gravitational field strength has a magnitude of 9.80 N/kg, determine the distance (as a multiple of Earth's radius r_E) above Earth's surface at which the magnitude of the field strength is 3.20 N/kg.

Applying Inquiry Skills

9. Use free-body diagrams of a 1.0-kg mass at increasingly large distances from Earth to illustrate that the strength of the gravitational field is inversely proportional to the square of the distance from Earth's centre.

Making Connections

10. Based solely on the data in **Table 1**, speculate on at least one reason why some astronomers argue that Pluto should not be classified as a planet.

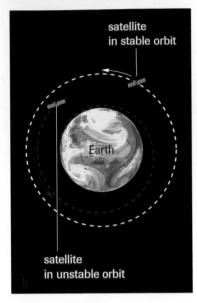

satellite
in stable orbit

Earth

satellite
in unstable orbit

Figure 1
Comparing stable and unstable orbits of an artificial satellite. If a satellite is far enough from Earth's surface that atmospheric friction is negligible, then the firing of booster rockets is unnecessary.

Periodically we hear of "space junk" that falls through Earth's atmosphere, leaving streaks of light as friction causes it to vaporize. This "junk" falls toward Earth when its orbit becomes unstable, yet when it was in proper working order, it remained in a stable orbit around Earth (**Figure 1**). To maintain a stable orbit, a satellite or other space vehicle must maintain a required speed for a particular radius of orbit. This requires a periodic firing of the small booster rockets on the vehicle to counteract the friction of the thin atmosphere. When the Russian space station Mir was no longer needed, its booster rockets were not fired, which resulted in a gradual loss of speed because of friction. Without the correct speed to continue in a curved path that follows Earth's curvature, Mir's orbit became unstable and it was pulled down to Earth by gravity. After 15 years in service, Mir re-entered Earth's atmosphere on March 23, 2001.

We saw in Section 3.4 that for a satellite to maintain a stable circular orbit around Earth, it must maintain a specific speed v that depends on the mass of Earth and the radius of the satellite's orbit. The mathematical relationship derived for circular motion was summarized in the equation

$$v = \sqrt{\frac{Gm_E}{r}}$$

where G is the universal gravitation constant, m_E is the mass of Earth, v is the speed of the satellite, and r is the distance from the centre of Earth to the satellite.

This equation is not restricted to objects in orbit around Earth. We can rewrite the equation for any central body of mass M around which a body is in orbit. Thus, in general,

$$v = \sqrt{\frac{GM}{r}}$$

> ▶ **SAMPLE** problem **1**
>
> Determine the speeds of the second and third planets from the Sun. Refer to Appendix C for the required data.
>
> **Solution**
> We will use the subscript V to represent Venus (the second planet), the subscript E to represent Earth (the third planet), and the subscript S to represent the Sun.
>
> $G = 6.67 \times 10^{-11}$ N·m²/kg²
> $M_S = 1.99 \times 10^{30}$ kg
> $r_V = 1.08 \times 10^{11}$ m
> $r_E = 1.49 \times 10^{11}$ m
> $v_V = ?$
> $v_E = ?$
>
> $$v_V = \sqrt{\frac{GM_S}{r_V}}$$
>
> $$= \sqrt{\frac{(6.67 \times 10^{-11} \text{ N·m}^2/\text{kg}^2)(1.99 \times 10^{30} \text{ kg})}{1.08 \times 10^{11} \text{ m}}}$$
>
> $v_V = 3.51 \times 10^4$ m/s

$$v_E = \sqrt{\frac{GM_S}{r_E}}$$

$$= \sqrt{\frac{(6.67 \times 10^{-11} \text{ N·m}^2/\text{kg}^2)(1.99 \times 10^{30} \text{ kg})}{1.49 \times 10^{11} \text{ m}}}$$

$$v_E = 2.98 \times 10^4 \text{ m/s}$$

Venus travels at a speed of 3.51×10^4 m/s and Earth travels more slowly at a speed of 2.98×10^4 m/s around the Sun.

> ### ▶ *Practice*

Understanding Concepts

Refer to Appendix C for required data.

1. Why does the Moon, which is attracted by gravity toward Earth, not fall into Earth?

2. Why does the gravitational force on a space probe in a circular orbit around a planet not change the speed of the probe?

3. A satellite is in circular orbit 525 km above the surface of Earth. Determine the satellite's (a) speed and (b) period of revolution.

4. A satellite can travel in a circular orbit very close to the Moon's surface because there is no air resistance. Determine the speed of such a satellite, assuming the orbital radius is equal to the Moon's radius.

Applying Inquiry Skills

5. (a) Write a proportionality statement indicating the relationship between the speed of a natural or artificial satellite around a central body and the radius of the satellite's orbit.
   (b) Sketch a graph of that relationship.

Making Connections

6. Space junk is becoming a greater problem as more human-made objects are abandoned in their orbits around Earth. Research this problem using the Internet or other appropriate publications, and write a brief summary of what you discover.

(GO) www.science.nelson.com

Answers

3. (a) 7.60×10^3 m/s
   (b) 5.71×10^3 s (or 1.59 h)
4. 1.68×10^3 m/s

Kepler's Laws of Planetary Motion

Centuries before telescopes were invented, astronomers made detailed observations of the night sky and discovered impressive and detailed mathematical relationships. Prior to the seventeenth century, scientists continued to believe that Earth was at or very near the centre of the universe, with the Sun and the other known planets (Mercury, Venus, Mars, Jupiter, and Saturn) travelling in orbits around Earth. Using Earth as the frame of reference, the "geocentric model" of the universe was explained by introducing complicated motions (**Figure 2**).

The detailed observations and analysis needed to invent these complex orbits were amazingly accurate and allowed scientists to predict such celestial events as solar and lunar eclipses. However, the causes of the motions were poorly understood. Then in 1543, Polish astronomer Nicolas Copernicus (1473–1543) published a book in which he proposed the "heliocentric model" of the solar system in which the planets revolve around the Sun. He deduced that the planets closer to the Sun have a higher speed than those

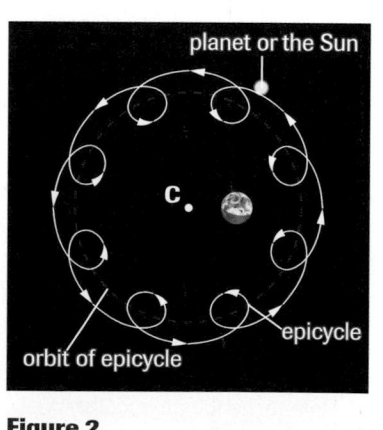

Figure 2
Using Earth as the frame of reference, the motion of the Sun and the other planets is an orbit called an *epicycle*, which itself is in an orbit around point C, located away from Earth.

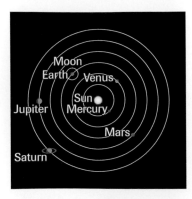

Figure 3
Using the Sun as the frame of reference, the motions of the planets were modelled as simple circles around the Sun, and the Moon was modelled as a circle around Earth.

Figure 4
This large instrument, called a *quadrant*, was so precise that Tycho could measure the angular position of a star to the closest $\frac{1}{1000}$ of a degree.

farther away, which agrees with the orbital speed calculations given by $v = \sqrt{\dfrac{GM}{r}}$.

Using the Sun's frame of reference, the motions of the planets suddenly appeared very simple (**Figure 3**).

Although Copernicus was at the forefront of the scientific revolution, his explanation of the orbits of the planets did not account for slight irregularities observed over long periods. The orbits were not exactly circles. More analysis was needed to find the true shapes of the orbits.

The next influential astronomer was Danish astronomer Tycho Brahe (1546–1601), usually called Tycho. He was hired in Denmark as a "court astronomer" to the king. For 20 years, he carried out countless naked-eye observations using unusually large instruments (**Figure 4**), accumulating the most complete and accurate observations yet made. However, after annoying those around him, he lost the king's support and in 1597, he moved from Denmark to Prague. There he spent the last years of his life analyzing his data. In 1600, shortly before his death, he hired a brilliant young mathematician to assist in the analysis. That mathematician was Johannes Kepler (1571–1630).

Kepler, who was born and educated in Germany, moved to Prague and spent much of the next 25 years painstakingly analyzing Tycho's great volume of planetary motion data. His objective was to find the orbital shape of the motions of the planets that best fit the data. Working mainly with the orbit of Mars, for which Tycho's records were most complete, Kepler finally discovered that the only shape that fit all the data was the ellipse. He then developed three related conclusions to explain the true orbits of planets. (We now know that these conclusions also apply to the motion of any body orbiting another body, such as the Moon or a satellite orbiting Earth.) These three relationships are called *Kepler's laws of planetary motion*.

Kepler's First Law of Planetary Motion
Each planet moves around the Sun in an orbit that is an ellipse, with the Sun at one focus of the ellipse.

Figure 5 illustrates Kepler's first law. Although this law states correctly that the planetary orbits are ellipses, for most of the planets the ellipses are not very elongated. In fact, if you were to draw a scale diagram of the orbits of the planets (except for Mercury and Pluto), they would look much like circles. For example, the distance from Earth to the Sun varies by only about 3% during its annual motion about the Sun.

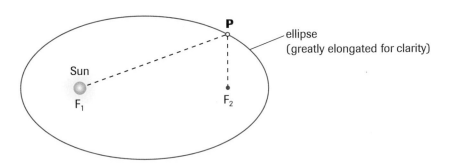

Figure 5
The orbit of a planet is an ellipse with the Sun at one focus. Based on the definition of an ellipse, for any point P, the distance $PF_1 + PF_2$ is a constant.

Even before Kepler had established that the orbit of Mars is an ellipse, he had determined that Mars speeds up as it approaches the Sun and slows down as it moves away. *Kepler's second law of planetary motion* states the relationship precisely:

> **Kepler's Second Law of Planetary Motion**
> The straight line joining a planet and the Sun sweeps out equal areas in space in equal intervals of time.

Figure 6 illustrates Kepler's second law. The statement that equal areas are swept out in equal time intervals is equivalent to saying that each planet moves most rapidly when closest to the Sun and least rapidly when farthest from the Sun. Earth is closest to the Sun around January 4, and so is farthest from the Sun around July 5.

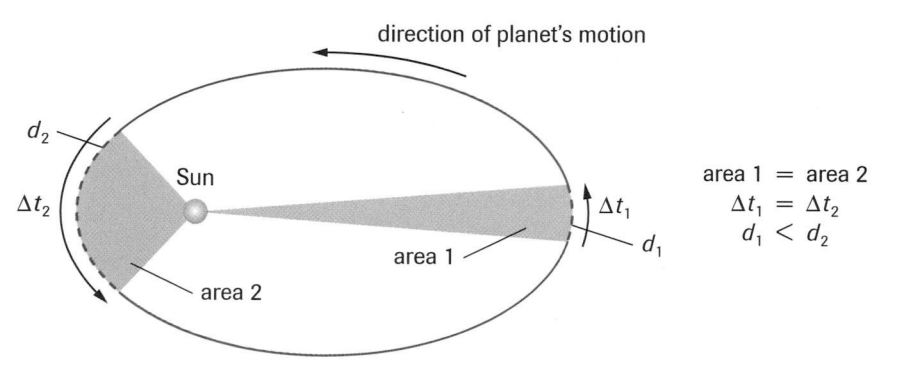

Figure 6
This ellipse is elongated to better illustrate the idea of equal areas swept out in equal time intervals.

Kepler's third law of planetary motion gives the relationship between the period T of a planet's orbit (i.e., the time taken for each revolution about the Sun) and the average distance r from the Sun:

> **Kepler's Third Law of Planetary Motion**
> The cube of the average radius r of a planet's orbit is directly proportional to the square of the period T of the planet's orbit.

Writing Kepler's third law mathematically, we have:

$$r^3 \propto T^2$$
$$r^3 = C_S T^2$$
or $\quad C_S = \dfrac{r^3}{T^2}$

where C_S is the constant of proportionality for the Sun for Kepler's third law. In SI units, C_S is stated in metres cubed per seconds squared (m^3/s^2).

DID YOU KNOW ?

Earth's Changing Seasons
Our seasons occur because Earth's axis of rotation is at an angle of about 23.5° to the plane of Earth's orbit around the Sun. As a result, the North Pole faces somewhat away from the Sun during the months close to December, giving rise to winter in the Northern Hemisphere. At the same time, the South Pole faces somewhat toward the Sun, producing summer in the Southern Hemisphere. In months close to June, the North Pole points slightly toward the Sun and the South Pole points away from it, reversing the seasons.

▶ **SAMPLE problem 2**

The average radius of orbit of Earth about the Sun is 1.495×10^8 km. The period of revolution is 365.26 days.

(a) Determine the constant C_S to four significant digits.

(b) An asteroid has a period of revolution around the Sun of 8.1×10^7 s. What is the average radius of its orbit?

Solution

(a) $r_E = 1.495 \times 10^8$ km $= 1.495 \times 10^{11}$ m
$T_E = 365.26$ days $= 3.156 \times 10^7$ s
$C_S = ?$

$$C_S = \frac{r^3}{T_E^2}$$

$$= \frac{(1.495 \times 10^{11}\ m)^3}{(3.156 \times 10^7\ s)^2}$$

$$C_S = 3.355 \times 10^{18}\ m^3/s^2$$

The Sun's constant is $3.355 \times 10^{18}\ m^3/s^2$.

(b) We can apply the Sun's constant found in (a) to this situation.

$$C_S = 3.355 \times 10^{18}\ m^3/s^2$$

$$T = 8.1 \times 10^7\ s$$

$$r = ?$$

$$\frac{r^3}{T^2} = C_S$$

$$r = \sqrt[3]{C_S T^2}$$

$$= \sqrt[3]{(3.355 \times 10^{18}\ m^3/s^2)(8.1 \times 10^7\ s)^2}$$

$$r = 2.8 \times 10^{11}\ m$$

The average radius of the asteroid's orbit is 2.8×10^{11} m.

Kepler's findings were highly controversial because they contradicted the geocentric model of the solar system supported by the Roman Catholic Church. Indeed, in 1616, the Church issued a decree labelling the heliocentric hypothesis as "false and absurd." (This decree was made largely because Galileo supported the heliocentric hypothesis.)

Kepler's third law equation is all the more amazing when we observe that many years later, the same relationship could be obtained by applying Newton's law of universal gravitation to the circular motion of one celestial body travelling around another. We begin by equating the magnitude of the gravitational force to the product of the mass and the centripetal acceleration for a planet moving around the Sun: $\frac{GM_S m_{planet}}{r^2} = \frac{m_{planet}v^2}{r}$.

From which $v = \sqrt{\dfrac{GM_S}{r}}$

Since $T = \dfrac{2\pi r}{v}$

$$T = \frac{2\pi r}{\sqrt{\dfrac{GM_S}{r}}}$$

$$T^2 = \frac{4\pi^2 r^2}{\left(\dfrac{GM_S}{r}\right)}$$

$$= 4\pi^2 r^2\left(\frac{r}{GM_S}\right)$$

$$T^2 = \frac{4\pi^2 r^3}{GM_S}$$

$$\frac{r^3}{T^2} = \frac{GM_S}{4\pi^2}$$

$$C_S = \frac{GM_S}{4\pi^2} \quad \text{for the Sun, or in general}$$

$$C = \frac{GM}{4\pi^2} = \frac{r^3}{T^2}$$

We have proven that the constant for the Sun depends only on the mass of the Sun. This relationship, however, applies to any central body about which other bodies orbit. For example, the constant for Earth C_E depends on the mass of Earth M_E and applies to the Moon or to any artificial satellite in orbit around Earth:

$$C_E = \frac{GM_E}{4\pi^2} = \frac{r_{Moon}^3}{T_{Moon}^2}$$

Today's astronomers use sophisticated Earth-bound and orbiting telescopes to gather accurate data of the motions of celestial bodies, as well as advanced computing and simulation programs to analyze the data. But astronomers will always admire the accuracy and unending hard work of the Renaissance astronomers, especially Tycho and Kepler.

> **Practice**

Understanding Concepts

7. If the solar system were considered to be an isolated system, which model (geocentric or heliocentric) is the noninertial frame of reference? Explain your answer.

8. Why did Tycho not gather any data from the planets beyond Saturn?

9. Between March 21 and September 21, there are three days more than between September 21 and March 21. These two dates are the spring and fall equinoxes when the days and nights are of equal length. Between the equinoxes, Earth moves 180° around its orbit with respect to the Sun. Using Kepler's laws, explain how you can determine the part of the year during which the Earth is closer to the Sun.

10. Using the planetary data in Appendix C, calculate the ratio $\frac{r^3}{T^2}$ for each planet, and verify Kepler's third law by confirming that $r^3 \propto T^2$.

11. (a) What is the average value (in SI base units) of the constant of proportionality in $r^3 \propto T^2$ that you found in question 10?
    (b) Use your answer in (a) to determine the mass of the Sun.

12. (a) Use the data of the Moon's motion (refer to Appendix C) to determine Kepler's third-law constant C_E to three significant digits for objects orbiting Earth.
    (b) If a satellite is to have a circular orbit about Earth ($m_E = 5.98 \times 10^{24}$ kg) with a period of 4.0 h, how far, in kilometres, above the centre of Earth must it be? What must be its speed?

Applying Inquiry Skills

13. Go back to the ellipses you drew in the Try This Activity at the beginning of Chapter 6 and label one focus on each ellipse the "Sun." As accurately as possible, draw diagrams to illustrate Kepler's second law of planetary motion. Verify that a planet travels faster when it is closer to the Sun. (Your diagram for each ellipse will resemble **Figure 6**; you can use approximate distances along the arcs to compare the speeds.)

Making Connections

14. Astronomers have announced newly discovered solar systems far beyond our solar system. To determine the mass of a distant star, they analyze the motion of a planet around that star.
    (a) Derive an equation for the mass of a central body, around which another body revolves in an orbit of known period and average radius.
    (b) If a planet in a distant solar system cannot be observed directly, its effect on the central star might be observed and used to determine the radius of the planet's orbit. Describe how this is possible for a "main-sequence star" whose mass can be estimated by its luminosity. (Assume there is a single large-mass planet in orbit around the star and that the star has an observable wobble.)

LEARNING TIP

More about Kepler's Third-Law Constant
The constant of proportionality C is defined in this text as the ratio of r^3 to T^2, which is equal to the ratio $\frac{GM}{4\pi^2}$ and is measured in metres cubed per second squared. The constant could also be written as the ratio of T^2 to r^3, or $\frac{4\pi^2}{GM}$ and is measured in seconds squared per metre cubed. This latter case is found in some references.

Answers

11. (a) 3.36×10^{18} m³/s²
    (b) 1.99×10^{30} kg
12. (a) 1.02×10^{13} m³/s²
    (b) 1.3×10^4 km; 5.6×10^3 m/s
14. (a) $M = \dfrac{4\pi^2 r^3}{GT^2}$

SUMMARY   *Orbits and Kepler's Laws*

- The orbits of planets are most easily approximated as circles even though they are ellipses.
- Kepler's first law of planetary motion states that each planet moves around the Sun in an orbit that is an ellipse, with the Sun at one focus of the ellipse.
- Kepler's second law of planetary motion states that the straight line joining a planet and the Sun sweeps out equal areas in space in equal intervals of time.
- Kepler's third law of planetary motion states that the cube of the average radius r of a planet's orbit is directly proportional to the square of the period T of the planet's orbit.

▶ *Section 6.2* *Questions*

Understanding Concepts

Refer to Appendix C for required data.

1. Apply one of Kepler's laws to explain why we are able to observe comets close to Earth for only small time intervals compared to their orbital periods. (*Hint:* A comet's elliptical orbit is very elongated.)

2. Earth is closest to the Sun about January 4 and farthest from the Sun about July 5. Use Kepler's second law to determine on which of these dates Earth is travelling most rapidly and least rapidly.

3. A nonrotating frame of reference placed at the centre of the Sun is very nearly an inertial frame of reference. Why is it not exactly an inertial frame of reference?

4. An asteroid has a mean radius of orbit around the Sun of 4.8×10^{11} m. What is its orbital period?

5. If a small planet were discovered with an orbital period twice that of Earth, how many times farther from the Sun is this planet located?

6. A spy satellite is located one Earth radius above Earth's surface. What is its period of revolution, in hours?

7. Mars has two moons, Phobos and Deimos (Greek for "Fear" and "Panic," companions of Mars, the god of war). Deimos has a period of 30 h 18 min and an average distance from the centre of Mars of 2.3×10^4 km. The period of Phobos is 7 h 39 min. What is the average distance of Phobos from the centre of Mars?

Applying Inquiry Skills

8. Show that the SI base units of $\sqrt{\dfrac{GM}{r}}$ are metres per second.

9. Sketch the shape of a graph of r^3 as a function of T^2 for planets orbiting the Sun. What does the slope of the line on the graph indicate?

Making Connections

10. Galileo was the first person to see any of Jupiter's moons.
    (a) Relate this important event to the works of Tycho and Kepler by researching when Galileo first discovered that Jupiter had moons and how this discovery came to pass.
    (b) After discovering these moons, what would Galileo need to know to calculate Jupiter's mass?
    (c) Would Galileo have been able to determine Jupiter's mass when he first saw the moons, or would that calculation have had to wait for awhile? (*Hint:* Kepler's first two laws were published in 1609.)

Gravitational Potential Energy in General 6.3

To explore such concepts as how much energy a space probe needs to escape from Earth's gravity, we must expand on the topic of gravitational potential energy, which we examined in Section 4.3 for objects at Earth's surface. To calculate the change in gravitational potential energy for a mass that undergoes a vertical displacement near Earth's surface, we developed the following equation:

$$\Delta E_g = mg\Delta y$$

where ΔE_g is the change in gravitational potential energy, m is the mass, g is the magnitude of the gravitational field constant, and Δy is the vertical displacement. This equation is accurate provided that the magnitude of the gravitational field strength g remains reasonably constant during Δy. This means that we can be fairly accurate for vertical displacements of a few hundred kilometres but inaccurate for vertical displacements beyond that.

The more general problem, however, is to develop an expression for the gravitational potential energy of a system of any two masses a finite distance apart. Recall that the law of universal gravitation is given by

$$F_G = \frac{GMm}{r^2}$$

where F_G is the magnitude of the force of gravitational attraction between any two objects, M is the mass of one object, m is the mass of the second object, and r is the distance between the centres of the two spherical objects (**Figure 1**). To increase the separation of the two masses from r_1 to r_2 requires work to be done to overcome their force of attraction, just as in stretching a spring. As a result of this work being done, the gravitational potential energy of the system increases. Notice that the work done to change the separation from r_1 to r_2 is equal to the change in gravitational potential energy from r_1 to r_2. This applies to an isolated system in which the law of conservation of energy holds.

However, recall that the work done by a varying force is equal to the area under the force-displacement graph for the interval. The force-separation graph, with the shaded area representing the work done to increase the separation from r_1 to r_2, is shown in **Figure 2**.

You may not recognize this area as a well-known geometric shape, and you have no simple equation to determine its area. The mathematics for an inverse square relationship involves calculus and is beyond the scope of this book. However, instead of using the arithmetic average of F_1 and F_2, we can use the geometric average $\sqrt{F_1 F_2}$, to produce an accurate result. Thus, to determine the area under the force-separation graph from r_1 to r_2:

$$\text{area} = \sqrt{F_1 F_2}\,(r_2 - r_1)$$

$$= \sqrt{\left(\frac{GMm}{r_1^2}\right)\left(\frac{GMm}{r_2^2}\right)}\,(r_2 - r_1)$$

$$= \frac{GMm}{r_1 r_2}\,(r_2 - r_1)$$

$$\text{area} = \frac{GMm}{r_1} - \frac{GMm}{r_2}$$

This area represents the work done in changing the separation of the two masses from r_1 to r_2 and is an expression for the resulting change in gravitational potential energy.

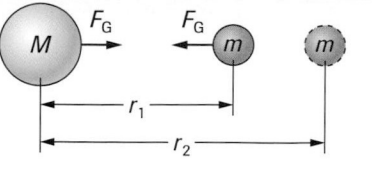

Figure 1
The two masses, M and m, are moved from a separation r_1 to a separation r_2 by a force that just overcomes the gravitational attraction between the masses at every point along the path. The masses are at rest at both positions.

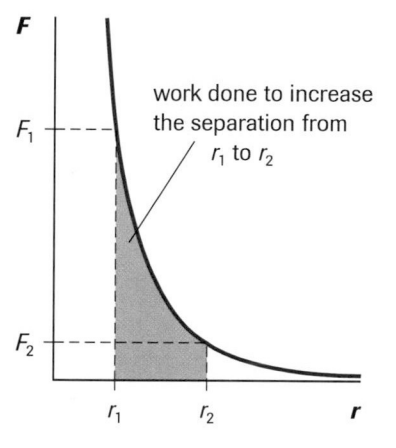

Figure 2
In this force-separation graph, the area under the curve for the interval r_1 to r_2 is equal to the work done in increasing the separation of the two masses.

LEARNING TIP

Energy of a System
The equation for the gravitational potential energy between two masses gives the potential energy of the system, such as an Earth-satellite system. Despite this fact, we often say that the potential energy is associated with only the smaller object, in this case the satellite.

Thus, $\Delta E_g = E_2 - E_1$

$$\Delta E_g = \frac{GMm}{r_1} - \frac{GMm}{r_2}$$

$$\Delta E_g = \left(-\frac{GMm}{r_2}\right) - \left(-\frac{GMm}{r_1}\right)$$

where ΔE_g is the change in gravitational potential energy in joules. The term involving r_1 is changed to negative, which places the term involving r_2 first. Thus, the first term in the expression depends only on r_2 and the second term only on r_1. As $r_2 \to \infty$, $E_{g2} \to 0$. Since m is now outside the gravitational field of M, the expression simplifies to

$$\Delta E_g = 0 - E_{g1}$$

$$= -\left(-\frac{GMm}{r_1}\right)$$

Thus, $\Delta E_g = \dfrac{GMm}{r_1}$ or $E_g = -\dfrac{GMm}{r}$

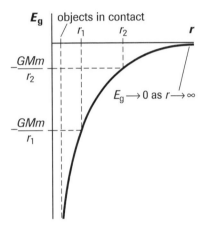

Figure 3
A graph of gravitational potential energy E_g as a function of r for two masses M and m

Note that r is the distance between the centres of two objects and that the expression is not valid at points inside either object. As with the law of universal gravitation, objects must be spherical or far enough apart that they can be considered as small particles.

The equation for E_g always produces a negative value. As r increases—that is, as the masses get farther apart—E_g increases by becoming less negative. Also, as $r \to \infty$, $E_g \to 0$. The zero value of gravitational potential energy between two masses occurs when they are infinitely far apart; this is a reasonable assumption since the point at which $r = \infty$ is the only point when the masses will have no gravitational attraction force between them. A graph of E_g as a function of r for two masses is shown in **Figure 3**.

We can show that the equation for the change in gravitational potential energy at Earth's surface is just a special case of the general situation. Near Earth's surface

$r_1 = r_E$ and $r_2 = r_E + \Delta y$
so that $r_1 r_2 \approx r_E^2$ (because $\Delta y << r_E$ close to the surface of Earth)
and $\Delta y = r_2 - r_1$

Thus, $\Delta E_g = \left(-\dfrac{GMm}{r_2}\right) - \left(-\dfrac{GMm}{r_1}\right)$

$\qquad = \dfrac{GMm}{r_1 r_2}(r_2 - r_1)$

$\Delta E_g \approx \dfrac{GMm\Delta y}{r_E^2}$

However, from the law of universal gravitation,

$$F_G = \frac{GMm}{r_E^2} = mg$$

Therefore, $\Delta E_g \approx mg\Delta y$ for a mass near the surface of Earth.

▶ **SAMPLE** problem **1**

What is the change in gravitational potential energy of a 64.5-kg astronaut, lifted from Earth's surface into a circular orbit of altitude 4.40×10^2 km?

Solution

$G = 6.67 \times 10^{-11}$ N·m²/kg²　　　$m = 64.5$ kg

$M_E = 5.98 \times 10^{24}$ kg　　　$r_E = 6.38 \times 10^6$ m

$$r_2 = r_E + 4.40 \times 10^2 \text{ km}$$
$$= 6.38 \times 10^6 \text{ m} + 4.40 \times 10^5 \text{ m}$$
$$r_2 = 6.82 \times 10^6 \text{ m}$$

On Earth's surface,

$$E_{g1} = -\frac{GM_E m}{r_E}$$

$$= -\frac{(6.67 \times 10^{-11} \text{ N·m}^2/\text{kg}^2)(5.98 \times 10^{24} \text{ kg})(64.5 \text{ kg})}{6.38 \times 10^6 \text{ m}}$$

$$E_{g1} = -4.03 \times 10^9 \text{ J}$$

In orbit,

$$E_{g2} = -\frac{GM_E m}{r_2}$$

$$= -\frac{(6.67 \times 10^{-11} \text{ N·m}^2/\text{kg}^2)(5.98 \times 10^{24} \text{ kg})(64.5 \text{ kg})}{6.82 \times 10^6 \text{ m}}$$

$$E_{g2} = -3.77 \times 10^9 \text{ J}$$

$$\Delta E_g = E_{g2} - E_{g1}$$
$$= (-3.77 \times 10^9 \text{ J}) - (-4.03 \times 10^9 \text{ J})$$
$$\Delta E_g = 2.6 \times 10^8 \text{ J}$$

The change in gravitational potential energy is 2.6×10^8 J.

Notice that even though the values for the astronaut's gravitational potential energy are negative at both positions, the change in E_g, when the astronaut's distance from Earth increases, is positive, indicating an increase in gravitational potential energy. Note also that, even for an altitude of 4.40×10^2 km, the approximation assuming a constant value of g is quite good.

$$\Delta E_g \approx mg\Delta y$$
$$= (64.5 \text{ kg})(9.80 \text{ N/kg})(4.40 \times 10^5 \text{ m})$$
$$\Delta E_g \approx 2.8 \times 10^8 \text{ J}$$

▶ Practice

Understanding Concepts

1. Determine the gravitational potential energy of the Earth–Moon system, given that the average distance between their centres is 3.84×10^5 km, and the mass of the Moon is 0.0123 times the mass of Earth.

2. (a) Calculate the change in gravitational potential energy for a 1.0-kg mass lifted 1.0×10^2 km above the surface of Earth.
   (b) What percentage error would have been made in using the equation $\Delta E_g = mg\Delta y$ and taking the value of g at Earth's surface?
   (c) What does this tell you about the need for the more exact treatment in most normal Earth-bound problems?

3. With what initial speed must an object be projected vertically upward from the surface of Earth to rise to a maximum height equal to Earth's radius? (Neglect air resistance.) Apply energy conservation.

Answers

1. -7.64×10^{28} J

2. (a) 1.0×10^6 J
   (b) 2%

3. 7.91×10^3 m/s

LEARNING TIP

"Apo" and "Peri"
The prefix "apo" means away from and "geo" represents Earth, so apogee refers to the point in a satellite's elliptical orbit farthest from Earth. Furthermore, since "helios" represents the Sun, aphelion refers to the point in a planet's elliptical orbit farthest from the Sun. The prefix "peri" means around, so perihelion refers to the point in a planet's orbit closest to the Sun. What does perigee mean?

---

4. The distance from the Sun to Earth varies from 1.47×10^{11} m at perihelion (closest approach) to 1.52×10^{11} m at aphelion (farthest distance away).
   (a) What is the maximum change in the gravitational potential energy of Earth during one orbit of the Sun?
   (b) At what point in its orbit is Earth moving the fastest? What is its maximum change in kinetic energy during one orbit? (Think about energy conservation.)

Making Connections

5. A satellite of mass 5.00×10^2 kg is in a circular orbit of radius $2r_E$ around Earth. Then it is moved to a circular orbit of radius $3r_E$.
   (a) Determine the satellite's gravitational potential energy in each orbit.
   (b) Determine the change in gravitational potential energy from the first orbit to the second orbit.
   (c) Determine the work done in moving the satellite from the first orbit to the second orbit. Apply energy conservation.

Escape from a Gravitational Field

We have seen that any two masses have a gravitational potential energy of $E_g = -\dfrac{GMm}{r}$ at a separation distance r. The negative value of this potential energy is characteristic of a *potential well*, a name derived from the shape of the graph of the gravitational potential energy as a function of separation distance (**Figure 4**).

For example, a rocket at rest on Earth's surface has the value of E_g, given by point A on the graph in **Figure 4**. Since the kinetic energy E_K of the rocket is zero, its total energy E_T would also be represented by point A, and the rocket would not leave the ground. However, suppose the rocket is launched at a speed such that its kinetic energy is represented by the distance AB on the graph. Now its total energy $E_T = E_g + E_K$ is represented by point B, and the rocket begins to rise. As its altitude increases, E_g increases

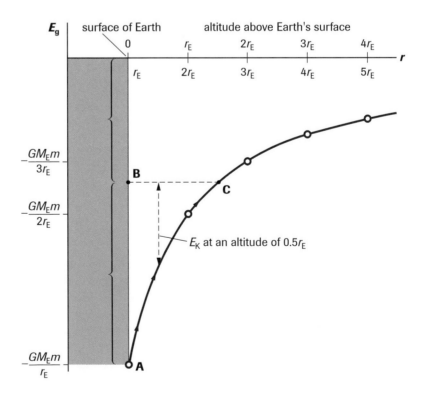

Figure 4
This graph of the gravitational potential energy as a function of the altitude above Earth's surface illustrates Earth's potential well.

along the curve AC and E_T remains constant along the line BC. The kinetic energy decreases and, at any point, is given by the length of the vertical line from the curve to the horizontal line BC. When the rocket reaches an altitude corresponding to point C, E_K has decreased to zero, and the rocket can go no higher. Instead, it falls back down, with E_K and E_g governed by the same constraints as on the upward trip.

It is an interesting exercise to determine what minimum speed this rocket would have to be given at Earth's surface to "escape" the potential well of Earth. To "escape," the rocket's initial kinetic energy must just equal the depth of the potential well at Earth's surface, thereby making its total energy zero. This also means the rocket must reach an infinite distance, where $E_g = 0$, before coming to rest. At this infinite distance, the gravitational force is zero and hence the rocket remains at rest there.

$$E_T = E_K + E_g = 0$$
$$E_K = -E_g$$
$$\frac{1}{2}mv^2 = -\left(-\frac{GM_E m}{r_E}\right)$$
$$v = \sqrt{\frac{2GM_E}{r_E}}$$
$$= \sqrt{\frac{2(6.67 \times 10^{-11} \text{ N·m}^2/\text{kg}^2)(5.98 \times 10^{24} \text{ kg})}{6.38 \times 10^6 \text{ m}}}$$

$$v = 1.12 \times 10^4 \text{ m/s, or } 11.2 \text{ km/s}$$

This speed is called the **escape speed**, which is the minimum speed needed to project a mass m from the surface of mass M to just escape the gravitational force of M (with a final speed of zero). The **escape energy** is the kinetic energy needed to give an object its escape speed. A rocket launched from Earth with a speed greater than the escape speed moves away from Earth, losing E_K and gaining E_g as it does so. Since its E_K is greater than the depth of its gravitational potential well at any point, its total energy will always be positive. This rocket will reach an infinite separation distance from Earth with some E_K left. For a launch speed less than the escape speed, the rocket will come to rest at some finite distance and then fall back to Earth.

In practice, a space vehicle does not achieve its highest speed upon launch. Its speed increases after launch as its rocket engines continue to be fired. If a satellite is launched from the cargo hold of an orbiting space shuttle, it is already travelling at the speed of the shuttle (about 8×10^3 m/s), so the small rocket engines on the satellite need to supply a relatively small amount of energy to propel the satellite into its higher orbit.

A rocket whose total energy is negative will not be able to escape from Earth's potential well and is "bound" to Earth. The **binding energy** of any mass is the amount of additional kinetic energy it needs to just escape (with a final speed of zero) to an infinite distance away. For a rocket of mass m at rest on Earth's surface (of mass M_E), the total energy is equal to the gravitational potential energy:

$$E_T = E_K + E_g$$
$$= 0 + \left(-\frac{GM_E m}{r_E}\right)$$
$$E_T = -\frac{GM_E m}{r_E}$$

Thus, the binding energy must be $\dfrac{GM_E m}{r_E}$ to give the rocket enough energy to escape.

escape speed the minimum speed needed to project a mass m from the surface of mass M to just escape the gravitational force of M

escape energy the minimum kinetic energy needed to project a mass m from the surface of mass M to just escape the gravitational force of M

binding energy the amount of additional kinetic energy needed by a mass m to just escape from a mass M

An example of a bound object is a satellite moving in a circular orbit of radius r in the potential well of Earth. The net force (of magnitude ΣF) necessary to sustain the circular orbit is provided by the force of gravitational attraction between the satellite and Earth. Using the magnitudes of the forces, for a satellite of mass m and orbital speed v:

$$\Sigma F = F_G$$

$$\frac{mv^2}{r} = \frac{GM_Em}{r^2}$$

$$mv^2 = \frac{GM_Em}{r}$$

The total energy of the satellite is constant and is given by:

$$E_T = E_K + E_g$$

$$E_T = \frac{1}{2}mv^2 - \frac{GM_Em}{r}$$

Substituting $mv^2 = \dfrac{GM_Em}{r}$ into the equation:

$$E_T = \frac{1}{2}\frac{GM_Em}{r} - \frac{GM_Em}{r}$$

$$= -\frac{1}{2}\frac{GM_Em}{r}$$

$$E_T = \frac{1}{2}E_g$$

This is a very significant result. The total energy of a satellite in circular orbit is negative and is equal to one-half the value of the gravitational potential energy at the separation corresponding to the radius of its orbit. **Figure 5** shows the potential well for Earth and the position of this orbiting satellite in the well. This satellite is bound to Earth and its binding energy is $\dfrac{1}{2}\dfrac{GM_Em}{r}$.

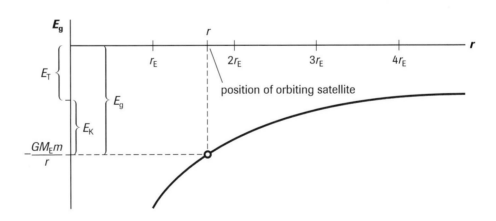

Figure 5
The gravitational potential energy of a satellite in Earth's potential well

In summary, the total energy of any object in Earth's gravitational field is composed of kinetic energy and gravitational potential energy. The graphs shown in **Figure 6** illustrate the three general cases possible for such an object.

Case 1: $E_T = 0$, object just escapes

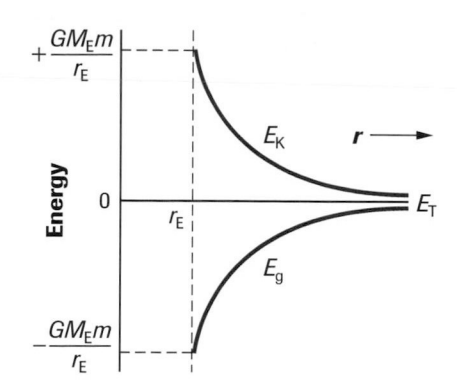

Case 2: $E_T > 0$, object escapes with a speed > 0 as $r \to \infty$

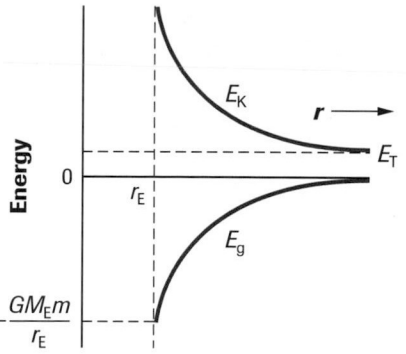

Case 3: $E_T < 0$, object is bound to Earth

Figure 6
Comparing the energies of the same object given different amounts of kinetic energy at Earth's surface

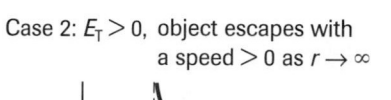

SAMPLE problem 2

A 5.00×10^2-kg communications satellite is to be placed into a circular geosynchronous orbit around Earth. (A geosynchronous satellite remains in the same relative position above Earth because it has a period of 24.0 h, the same as that of Earth's rotation on its axis.)

(a) What is the radius of the satellite's orbit?

(b) What is the gravitational potential energy of the satellite when it is attached to its launch rocket, at rest on Earth's surface?

(c) What is the total energy of the satellite when it is in geosynchronous orbit?

(d) How much work must the launch rocket do on the satellite to place it into orbit?

(e) Once in orbit, how much additional energy would the satellite require to escape from Earth's potential well?

Solution

(a) $G = 6.67 \times 10^{-11}$ N·m²/kg²

$T = 24.0$ h $= 8.64 \times 10^4$ s

$M_E = 5.98 \times 10^{24}$ kg

As for any satellite:

$$\Sigma F = F_G$$

$$\frac{4\pi^2 mr}{T^2} = \frac{GM_E m}{r^2}$$

$$r = \sqrt[3]{\frac{GM_E T^2}{4\pi^2}}$$

$$= \sqrt[3]{\frac{(6.67 \times 10^{-11} \text{ N·m}^2/\text{kg}^2)(5.98 \times 10^{24} \text{ kg})(8.64 \times 10^4 \text{ s})^2}{4\pi^2}}$$

$$r = 4.22 \times 10^7 \text{ m}$$

The radius of the satellite's orbit is 4.22×10^7 m. This radius represents an altitude of 3.58×10^4 km above Earth's surface.

(b) $r_E = 6.38 \times 10^6$ m

$m = 5.00 \times 10^2$ kg

At the surface of Earth,

$$E_g = -\frac{GM_E m}{r_E}$$

$$= -\frac{(6.67 \times 10^{-11}\ \text{N·m}^2/\text{kg}^2)(5.98 \times 10^{24}\ \text{kg})(5.00 \times 10^2\ \text{kg})}{6.38 \times 10^6\ \text{m}}$$

$$E_g = -3.13 \times 10^{10}\ \text{J}$$

The gravitational potential energy of the satellite when it is attached to its launch rocket at rest on Earth's surface is -3.13×10^{10} J.

(c) $r = 4.22 \times 10^7$ m

The total energy of a satellite in circular orbit, bound to Earth, is given by:

$$E_T = E_K + E_g$$

$$= \frac{1}{2}mv^2 - \frac{GM_E m}{r}$$

$$= -\frac{1}{2}\frac{GM_E m}{r} \quad \text{(based on the theory related to \textbf{Figure 5})}$$

$$= -\frac{1}{2}\frac{(6.67 \times 10^{-11}\ \text{N·m}^2/\text{kg}^2)(5.98 \times 10^{24}\ \text{kg})(5.00 \times 10^2\ \text{kg})}{4.22 \times 10^7\ \text{m}}$$

$$E_T = -2.36 \times 10^9\ \text{J}$$

The total energy of the satellite when in geosynchronous orbit is -2.36×10^9 J.

(d)
$$W = \Delta E = E_T\ (\text{in orbit}) - E_T\ (\text{on Earth})$$
$$= -2.36 \times 10^9\ \text{J} - (-3.13 \times 10^{10}\ \text{J})$$
$$W = 2.89 \times 10^{10}\ \text{J}$$

The launch rocket must do 2.89×10^{10} J of work on the satellite to place it into orbit.

(e) To escape Earth's potential well, the total energy of the satellite must be zero or greater. In orbit, $E_T = -2.36 \times 10^9$ J. Therefore, to escape Earth's potential well, the satellite must acquire at least 2.36×10^9 J of additional energy.

black hole a very dense body in space with a gravitational field so strong that nothing can escape from it

event horizon the surface of a black hole

singularity the dense centre of a black hole

Schwartzschild radius the distance from the centre of the singularity to the event horizon

 LAB EXERCISE 6.3.1

Graphical Analysis of Energies (p. 295)
A detailed analysis of the energies involved in launching a space vehicle and its payload from another body must be carried out before the mission is undertaken. How can graphing be used to analyze the energy data related to a spacecraft launch?

An important goal of future space missions will be to mine minerals on distant bodies, such as moons and asteroids, in the solar system. Once the minerals are mined, some will be used for manufacturing on the moon or asteroid, while others will be brought back to Earth or to the International Space Station for research and manufacturing. You can learn about the energies associated with this application by performing Lab Exercise 6.3.1 in the Lab Activities section at the end of this chapter.

Among the most interesting objects in the universe are extremely dense bodies that form at the end of a massive star's life. A **black hole** is a small, very dense body with a gravitational field so strong that nothing can escape from it. Even light cannot be radiated away from its surface, which explains the object's name.

The surface of a black hole is called its **event horizon** because no "event" can be observed from outside this surface. Inside the event horizon, at the very core of the black hole, is an unbelievably dense centre called a **singularity**. The distance from the centre of the singularity to the event horizon is the **Schwartzschild radius**, named after German astronomer Karl Schwartzschild (1873–1916), who was the first person to solve Einstein's equations of general relativity.

Since the speed of light c is 3.00×10^8 m/s, we can use that value in the equation for escape speed to determine the Schwartzschild radius of a black hole of known mass.

As an example, assume that a certain black hole results from the collapse of a star that has a mass 28 times the Sun's mass. Since the minimum escape speed is $v_e = c$, we have

$$\frac{mv_e^2}{2} = \frac{GMm}{r}$$

$$v_e^2 = \frac{2GM}{r}$$

$$r = \frac{2GM}{v_e^2}$$

$$= \frac{2GM}{c^2}$$

$$= \frac{2(6.67 \times 10^{-11} \ \text{N·m}^2/\text{kg}^2)(28 \times 1.99 \times 10^{30} \ \text{kg})}{(3.00 \times 10^8 \ \text{m/s})^2}$$

$$= 8.26 \times 10^4 \ \text{m}$$

$$r = 82.6 \ \text{km}$$

Since light cannot escape from a black hole, the only way a black hole can be detected is indirectly. Material that is close enough to the black hole gets sucked in, and as it does so, the material emits X rays that can be detected and analyzed.

The celestial mechanics analyzed in this chapter is not a complete picture. You will learn more about high-speed and high-energy particles when you study Einstein's special theory of relativity in Chapter 11.

▶ **Practice**

Understanding Concepts

6. Does the escape speed of a space probe depend on its mass? Why or why not?

7. Jupiter's mass is 318 times that of Earth, and its radius is 10.9 times that of Earth. Determine the ratio of the escape speed from Jupiter to the escape speed from Earth.

8. The Moon is a satellite of mass 7.35×10^{22} kg, with an average distance of 3.84×10^8 m from the centre of Earth.
   (a) What is the gravitational potential energy of the Moon–Earth system?
   (b) What is the Moon's kinetic energy and speed in circular orbit?
   (c) What is the Moon's binding energy to Earth?

9. What is the total energy needed to place a 2.0×10^3-kg satellite into circular Earth orbit at an altitude of 5.0×10^2 km?

10. How much additional energy would have to be supplied to the satellite in question 9 once it was in orbit, to allow it to escape from Earth's gravitational field?

11. Consider a geosynchronous satellite with an orbital period of 24 h.
    (a) What is the satellite's speed in orbit?
    (b) What speed must the satellite reach during launch to attain the geosynchronous orbit? (Assume all fuel is burned in a short period. Neglect air resistance.)

12. Determine the Schwarztschild radius, in kilometres, of a black hole of mass 4.00 times the Sun's mass.

Applying Inquiry Skills

13. Sketch the general shape of the potential wells of both Earth and the Moon on a single graph. Label the axes and use colour coding to distinguish the line for Earth from the line for the Moon.

Making Connections

14. (a) Calculate the binding energy of a 65.0-kg person on Earth's surface.
    (b) How much kinetic energy would this person require to just escape from the gravitational field of Earth?
    (c) How much work is required to raise this person by 1.00 m at Earth's surface?
    (d) Explain why one of NASA's objectives in designing launches into space is to minimize the mass of the payload (including the astronauts).

Answers

7. 5.40 : 1

8. (a) -7.63×10^{28} J
   (b) 3.82×10^{28} J; 1.02×10^3 m/s
   (c) 3.82×10^{28} J

9. 6.7×10^{10} J

10. 5.80×10^{10} J

11. (a) 3.1×10^3 m/s
    (b) 1.1×10^4 m/s

12. 11.8 km

14. (a) 4.06×10^9 J
    (b) 4.06×10^9 J
    (c) 6.37×10^2 J

SUMMARY — Gravitational Potential Energy in General

- The gravitational potential energy of a system of two (spherical) masses is directly proportional to the product of their masses, and inversely proportional to the distance between their centres.

- A gravitational potential energy of zero is assigned to an isolated system of two masses that are so far apart (i.e., their separation is approaching infinity) that the force of gravity between them has dropped to zero.

- The change in gravitational potential energy very close to Earth's surface is a special case of gravitational potential energy in general.

- Escape speed is the minimum speed needed to project a mass m from the surface of mass M to just escape the gravitational force of M.

- Escape energy is the minimum kinetic energy needed to project a mass m from the surface of mass M to just escape the gravitational force of M.

- Binding energy is the amount of additional kinetic energy needed by a mass m to just escape from a mass M.

► Section 6.3 Questions

Understanding Concepts

1. How does the escape energy of a 1500-kg rocket compare to that of a 500-kg rocket, both initially at rest on Earth?

2. Do you agree or disagree with the statement, "No satellite can orbit Earth in less than about 80 min"? Give reasons. (*Hint:* The greater the altitude of an Earth satellite, the longer it takes to complete one orbit.)

3. A space shuttle ejects a 1.2×10^3-kg booster tank so that the tank is momentarily at rest, relative to Earth, at an altitude of 2.0×10^3 km. Neglect atmospheric effects.
   (a) How much work is done on the booster tank by the force of gravity in returning it to Earth's surface?
   (b) Determine the impact speed of the booster tank.

4. A space vehicle, launched as a lunar probe, arrives above most of Earth's atmosphere. At this point, its kinetic energy is 5.0×10^9 J and its gravitational potential energy is -6.4×10^9 J. What is its binding energy?

5. An artificial Earth satellite, of mass 2.00×10^3 kg, has an elliptical orbit with an average altitude of 4.00×10^2 km.
   (a) What is its average gravitational potential energy while in orbit?
   (b) What is its average kinetic energy while in orbit?
   (c) What is its total energy while in orbit?
   (d) If its perigee (closest position) is 2.80×10^2 km, what is its speed at perigee?

6. A 5.00×10^2-kg satellite is in circular orbit 2.00×10^2 km above Earth's surface. Calculate
   (a) the gravitational potential energy of the satellite
   (b) the kinetic energy of the satellite
   (c) the binding energy of the satellite
   (d) the percentage increase in launching energy required for the satellite to escape from Earth

7. (a) Calculate the escape speed from the surface of the Sun: mass = 1.99×10^{30} kg, radius = 6.96×10^8 m.
   (b) What speed would an object leaving Earth need to escape from our solar system?

8. The mass of the Moon is 7.35×10^{22} kg, and its radius is 1.74×10^6 m. With what speed must an object be projected from the its surface to reach an altitude equal to its radius?

9. A black hole has a Schwartzschild radius of 15.4 km. What is the mass of the black hole in terms of the Sun's mass?

Applying Inquiry Skills

10. Mars is a planet that could be visited by humans in the future.
    (a) Generate a graph of Mars' potential well (using data from Appendix C) for a spacecraft of mass 2.0×10^3 kg that is launched from Mars. Draw the graph up to $5r_M$.
    (b) On your graph, draw
        (i) the line for the kinetic energy needed for the craft to just escape from Mars
        (ii) the line of the total energy from Mars' surface to $5r_M$

11. (a) What is the theoretical Schwartzschild radius of a black hole whose mass is equal to the mass of Earth. Express your answer in millimetres.
    (b) What does your answer imply about the density of a black hole?

Making Connections

12. How would the amount of fuel required to send a spacecraft from Earth to the Moon compare with the amount needed to send the same spacecraft from the Moon back to Earth? Explain. (Numerical values are not required.)

Graphical Analysis of Energies

Inquiry Skills

○ Questioning ○ Planning ● Analyzing
○ Hypothesizing ● Conducting ● Evaluating
○ Predicting ● Recording ○ Communicating

This lab exercise explores a small example of the types of calculations and analysis that could be involved in planning a space mission to mine minerals on Europa (**Figure 1**), a moon of Jupiter.

Figure 1
Jupiter and four of its planet-size moons, photographed by *Voyager I*. Reddish Io (upper left) is nearest Jupiter, then Europa (centre), Ganymede, and Callisto.

Table 1 Data for a Space Vehicle Leaving Europa

r (m)	E_g (J)	r (Mm)	E_g (GJ)
1.6×10^6	-3.0×10^9	?	?
3.2×10^6	-1.5×10^9	?	?
4.8×10^6	-1.0×10^9	?	?
6.4×10^6	-7.5×10^8	?	?
8.0×10^6	-6.0×10^8	?	?
9.6×10^6	-5.0×10^8	?	?
1.12×10^6	-4.3×10^8	?	?
1.28×10^7	-3.8×10^8	?	?
1.44×10^7	-3.3×10^8	?	?
1.60×10^7	-3.0×10^8	?	?

Question

What graphs are useful in analyzing the energy data of an isolated spacecraft-moon system?

Evidence

Table 1 gives the gravitational potential energy data of a space vehicle (total mass, including the payload, is 1.5×10^5 kg) launched from the surface of Europa (mass is 4.8×10^{20} kg). In this table, r is the distance from Europa's centre to the space vehicle.

Note: The instructions for this lab exercise are written for a spreadsheet program, but can also be followed by using regular graphing techniques.

Procedure

1. Copy **Table 1** into your notebook. Complete the final two columns to express the distance r from Europa's centre, in megametres (Mm) and the gravitational potential energy E_g, in gigajoules (GJ).

2. Enter the equation for gravitational potential energy into the spreadsheet program, and then plot a graph of the gravitational potential energy of the space vehicle as a function of the distance from the centre of Europa.

3. Enter the equation for the binding energy into the spreadsheet program, and then plot a graph of the binding energy at each position listed in **Table 1**. Plot these values on your graph.

4. Assuming that the space vehicle just escapes the gravitational pull of Europa, enter the equation for the kinetic energy of the space vehicle into the spreadsheet program, and then plot a graph of these data on your graph.

5. Assuming that the space vehicle has 1.0×10^9 J of energy after it has escaped from the gravitational pull of Europa, enter the equation for the kinetic energy required by the space vehicle at each position, and then plot the data on your graph.

Analysis

(a) Answer the question.

Evaluation

(b) Describe the advantages and disadvantages of the spreadsheet program in this application.

Synthesis

(c) Why are energy considerations important in planning future space missions?

There are many different types of careers that involve the study of energy and momentum. Find out more about the careers described below or about some other interesting career in energy and momentum.

Astrophysicist

Using the theories and techniques of physics and astronomy, an astrophysicist studies extra-terrestrial phenomena to obtain a greater understanding of our universe. Normally, astrophysicists must obtain a Ph.D. in astrophysics and have several years of postdoctoral research experience before they can be employed at a university or a research facility; however, some may enter research facilities at the undergraduate or masters level. Research institutes such as the Herzberg Institute at the National Research Council in Victoria, space programs like NASA or the Canadian Space Agency, and observatories and museums are the principal employers of astrophysicists. Astrophysicists use many tools including optical and radio telescopes and computers.

Forensic Scientist

A forensic scientist with a background in physics may work, for example, in the area of accident reconstruction to determine the cause of death or injury in automobile crashes. A strong high-school science and mathematics background is necessary. Some forensic scientists will enter the field with a four-year bachelor of science degree in forensic science while others will come to the profession with a four-year bachelor of science from other fields. Forensic scientists will typically work in government- or university-funded centres for forensic science, or for RCMP, provincial, or municipal police laboratories.

Sports Equipment Designer

While there are no rigid educational criteria for becoming a sports-equipment designer, a common route into the field is the four-year bachelor's in engineering, particularly in mechanical engineering or materials science. Entry into such degree programs requires high marks in mathematics and physics. To become a designer of bicycles for instance, it is necessary to have knowledge of physics, mechanical design, the manufacturing process, and an understanding of the relative strengths and weaknesses of the materials being used. Tools include Computer Assisted Design (CAD) workstations, and shop tools such as lathes and milling machines for the preparation of three-dimensional prototypes. Designers typically work for manufacturers in the private sector.

▶ **Practice**

Making Connections

1. Identify several careers that require knowledge about energy and momentum. Select a career you are interested in from the list you made or from the careers described above. Imagine that you have been employed in your chosen career for five years and that you are applying to work on a new project of interest.
   (a) Describe the project. It should be related to some of the new things you learned in this unit. Explain how the concepts from this unit are applied in the project.

(b) Create a résumé listing your credentials and explaining why you are qualified to work on the project. Include in your résumé
   • your educational background: what university degree or diploma program you graduated with, which educational institute you attended, post-graduate training (if any)
   • your skills
   • your duties in previous positions
   • your salary expectations

 www.science.nelson.com

Key Expectations

- analyze the factors affecting the motion of isolated celestial objects and calculate the gravitational potential energy for each system (6.1, 6.2, 6.3)

- analyze isolated planetary and satellite motion, and describe the motion in terms of the forms of energy and energy transformations that occur (e.g., calculate the energy required to propel a spacecraft from Earth's surface out of Earth's gravitational field, and describe the energy transformations that take place; calculate the kinetic energy and gravitational potential energy of a satellite in a stable orbit around a planet) (6.1, 6.2, 6.3)

Key Terms

gravitational field

Kepler's laws of planetary motion

escape speed

escape energy

binding energy

black hole

event horizon

singularity

Schwartzschild radius

Key Equations

- $g = \dfrac{GM}{r^2}$ (6.1)

- $v = \sqrt{\dfrac{GM}{r}}$ (6.2)

- $C_S = \dfrac{r^3}{T^2}$ for the Sun (6.2)

- $C_S = \dfrac{GM_S}{4\pi^2}$ for the Sun (6.2)

- $C = \dfrac{GM}{4\pi^2} = \dfrac{r^3}{T^2}$ in general (6.2)

- $E_g = -\dfrac{GMm}{r}$ (6.3)

- $\Delta E_g = \left(-\dfrac{GMm}{r_2}\right) - \left(-\dfrac{GMm}{r_1}\right)$ (6.3)

- $v = \sqrt{\dfrac{2GM}{r}}$ escape speed (6.3)

▸ **MAKE** a summary

Draw an Earth-Moon system diagram. Add a geosynchronous satellite (**Figure 1**) on the side of Earth opposite the Moon. Beyond the geosynchronous satellite, add a space probe, moving away from Earth, that has just enough energy to escape Earth's gravitational attraction. Show as many key expectations, key terms, and key equations as possible on your diagram.

Figure 1

Write numbers 1 to 10 in your notebook. Indicate beside each number whether the corresponding statement is true (T) or false (F). If it is false, write a corrected version.

1. At a particular location, the gravitational field around a celestial body depends only on the mass of the body.

2. If both the radius and mass of a planet were to double, the magnitude of the gravitational field strength at its surface would become half as great.

3. The speed of a satellite in a stable circular orbit around Earth is independent of the mass of the satellite.

4. In the Sun's frame of reference, the Moon's orbit around Earth appears as an epicycle.

5. In a typical high-school physics investigation, the "Evidence" is to the "Analysis" as Kepler's work was to Tycho Brahe's work.

6. In **Figure 1**, where the path distances d_1 and d_2 are equal, the speeds along those path segments are equal.

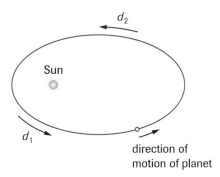

Figure 1

7. When calculating Kepler's third-law constant for Earth, the value is larger for the Moon than for an Earth-bound satellite because the Moon is much farther away.

8. The gravitational potential energy of the Earth-Moon system is inversely proportional to the square of the distance between the centres of the two bodies.

9. As a space probe travels away from Earth, its change in gravitational potential energy is positive, even though its gravitational potential energy is negative.

10. As you are working on this problem, your escape energy is greater than your binding energy.

Write numbers 11 to 26 in your notebook. Beside each number, write the letter corresponding to the best choice.

For questions 11 to 19, refer to **Figure 2**.

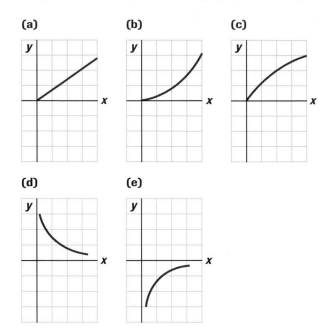

Figure 2
The first variable named in each of questions 11 to 19 corresponds to the *y*-variable on one of these graphs; the second variable named corresponds to the *x*-variable.

11. The *y*-variable is the magnitude of the gravitational field strength at a point above a planet's surface; *x* is the planet's mass.

12. The *y*-variable is the magnitude of the gravitational field strength at a point above a planet's surface; *x* is the distance to the centre of the planet.

13. The *y*-variable is the speed of a satellite in a stable circular orbit around a planet; *x* is the mass of the planet.

14. The *y*-variable is the speed of a satellite in a stable circular orbit around a planet; *x* is the distance to the centre of the planet.

15. The *y*-variable is the area swept out by a line joining a planet to the Sun; *x* is the time interval during which that line is swept out.

16. The *y*-variable is the average radius of a planet's orbit; *x* is the period of revolution of the planet's motion around the Sun.

17. The *y*-variable is the cube of the average radius of a planet's orbit; *x* is the square of the period of revolution of the planet's motion around the Sun.

18. The *y*-variable is the kinetic energy of a space probe that was given enough energy to escape Earth's gravitational field; *x* is the distance from Earth's centre.

19. The *y*-variable is the gravitational potential energy of a space probe that was given enough energy to escape Earth's gravitational field; *x* is the distance from Earth's centre.

20. The law that allows us to determine Earth's mass is
    (a) Kepler's first law of planetary motion
    (b) Kepler's second law of planetary motion
    (c) Kepler's third law of planetary motion
    (d) Newton's law of universal gravitation
    (e) Newton's second law of motion

21. If the distance between a spacecraft and Saturn increases by a factor of three, the magnitude of Saturn's gravitational field strength at the position of the spacecraft
    (a) decreases by a factor of $\sqrt{3}$
    (b) increases by a factor of $\sqrt{3}$
    (c) decreases by a factor of 9
    (d) increases by a factor of 9
    (e) decreases by a factor of 3

22. Satellite S_1 is moving around Earth in a circular orbit of radius four times as large as the radius of the orbit of satellite S_2. The speed of S_1, v_1, in terms of v_2 equals
    (a) $16v_2$
    (b) v_2
    (c) $2v_2$
    (d) $0.5v_2$
    (e) none of these

23. If the mass of the Sun were to become half its current value, with Earth maintaining its same orbit, the time interval of one Earth year would
    (a) remain the same
    (b) decrease by a factor of $\sqrt{2}$
    (c) increase by a factor of $\sqrt{2}$
    (d) increase by a factor of 2
    (e) decrease by a factor of 2

24. A satellite in geosynchronous orbit has a period of revolution of
    (a) 1.5 h
    (b) 1.0 h
    (c) 24 h
    (d) 365.26 d
    (e) none of these

25. **Figure 3** shows the path of a comet around the Sun. The speeds at the four positions shown are v_A, v_B, v_C, and v_D. Which statement is true?
    (a) $v_A > v_B = v_D > v_C$
    (b) $v_A < v_B = v_D < v_C$
    (c) $v_A > v_B > v_C > v_D$
    (d) $v_A < v_B < v_C < v_D$
    (e) none of these

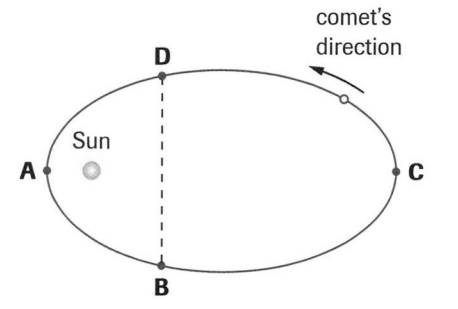

Figure 3

26. A certain planet has Earth's mass, but only one-quarter its diameter. The escape speed from this planet in terms of Earth's escape speed v_E is
    (a) v_E
    (b) $\dfrac{1}{2}v_E$
    (c) $\dfrac{1}{4}v_E$
    (d) $4v_E$
    (e) $2v_E$

Understanding Concepts

1. If a rocket is given a great enough speed to escape from Earth, could it also escape from the Sun and, hence, the solar system? What happens to the artificial Earth satellites that are sent to explore the space around distant planets, such as Neptune?

2. Assuming that a rocket is aimed above the horizon, does it matter which way it is aimed for it to escape from Earth? (Neglect air resistance.)

3. Determine the elevation in kilometres above the surface of Uranus where the gravitational field strength has a magnitude of 1.0 N/kg.

4. Ganymede, one of Jupiter's moons discovered by Galileo in 1610, has a mass of 1.48×10^{23} kg. What is the magnitude of Ganymede's gravitational field strength at a point in space 5.55×10^3 km from its centre?

5. Determine the total gravitational field strength (magnitude and direction) of the Earth and Moon at the location of the spacecraft in **Figure 1**.

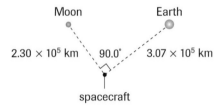

Moon   Earth

2.30×10^5 km   90.0° 3.07×10^5 km

spacecraft   **Figure 1**

6. Mercury has both a surface gravitational field strength and a diameter 0.38 times the corresponding Earth values. Determine Mercury's mass.

7. A satellite in a circular orbit around Earth has a speed of 7.15×10^3 m/s. Determine, in terms of Earth's radius,
   (a) the distance the satellite is from Earth's centre
   (b) the altitude of the satellite

8. Tethys, one of Saturn's moons, travels in a circular orbit at a speed of 1.1×10^4 m/s. Calculate
   (a) the orbital radius in kilometres
   (b) the orbital period in Earth days

9. Using the mass of the Sun and the period of revolution of Venus around the Sun, determine the average Sun-Venus distance.

10. A 4.60-kg rocket is launched directly upward from Earth at 9.00 km/s.
    (a) What altitude above Earth's surface does the rocket reach?
    (b) What is the rocket's binding energy at that altitude?

11. Titan, a moon of Saturn discovered by Christian Huygens in 1655, has a mass of 1.35×10^{23} kg and a radius of 2.58×10^3 km. For a 2.34×10^3-kg rocket, determine
    (a) the escape speed from Titan's surface
    (b) the escape energy of the rocket

12. A rocket ship of mass 1.00×10^4 kg is located 1.00×10^{10} m from Earth's centre.
    (a) Determine its gravitational potential energy at this point, considering only Earth.
    (b) How much kinetic energy must it have at this location to be capable of escaping from Earth's gravitational field?
    (c) What is its escape speed from Earth at this position?

13. Calculate the gravitational potential energy of the Sun-Earth system.

14. Determine the escape speeds from
    (a) Mercury
    (b) Earth's Moon

15. A *neutron star* results from the death of a star about 10 times as massive as the Sun. Composed of tightly packed neutrons, it is small and extremely dense.
    (a) Determine the escape speed from a neutron star of diameter 17 km and mass 3.4×10^{30} kg.
    (b) Express your answer as a percentage of the speed of light.

16. A solar-system planet has a diameter of 5.06×10^4 km and an escape speed of 24 km/s.
    (a) Determine the mass of the planet.
    (b) Name the planet.

17. A proton of mass 1.67×10^{-27} kg is travelling away from the Sun. At a point in space 1.4×10^9 m from the Sun's centre, the proton's speed is 3.5×10^5 m/s.
    (a) Determine the proton's speed when it is 2.8×10^9 m from the Sun's centre.
    (b) Will the proton escape from the Sun? Explain why or why not.

18. Explain this statement: "A black hole is blacker than a piece of black paper."

19. Determine the Schwartzschild radius of a black hole equal to the mass of the entire Milky Way galaxy (1.1×10^{11} times the mass of the Sun).

Applying Inquiry Skills

20. **Table 1** provides data concerning some of the moons of Uranus.

Table 1 Data of Several Moons of the Planet Uranus for Question 20

Moon	Discovery	$r_{average}$ (km)	T (Earth days)	C_U (m³/s²)
Ophelia	*Voyager 2* (1986)	5.38×10^4	0.375	?
Desdemona	*Voyager 2* (1986)	6.27×10^4	0.475	?
Juliet	*Voyager 2* (1986)	6.44×10^4	0.492	?
Portia	*Voyager 2* (1986)	6.61×10^4	0.512	?
Rosalind	*Voyager 2* (1986)	6.99×10^4	?	?
Belinda	*Voyager 2* (1986)	?	0.621	?
Titania	Herschel (1787)	4.36×10^5	?	?
Oberon	Herschel (1787)	?	13.46	?

(a) Copy the table into your notebook. Determine Kepler's third-law constant C_U for Uranus using the data for the first four moons.
(b) Find the average of the C_U values of your calculations in (a).
(c) Use another method to determine C_U. Do the values agree?
(d) Complete the missing information for the last four moons listed.
(e) Explain why some of the moons were discovered so much earlier than others.

21. It is beneficial to develop skill in analyzing a situation to determine if the given information or the answer to a question makes sense. Consider the following problem: Determine the radius of the orbit of a satellite travelling around Earth with a period of revolution of 65 min.
(a) Do you think this problem makes sense? Why or why not?
(b) Calculate a numerical answer to the problem.
(c) Does the numerical answer make sense? Why or why not?
(d) Why would this skill be valuable to a research physicist?

22. **Figure 2** shows the energy relationships for a rocket launched from Earth's surface.
(a) Determine the rocket's mass.
(b) What is the escape energy of the rocket (to three significant digits)?
(c) Determine the launch speed given to the rocket.
(d) What will the rocket's speed be at a very large distance from Earth.

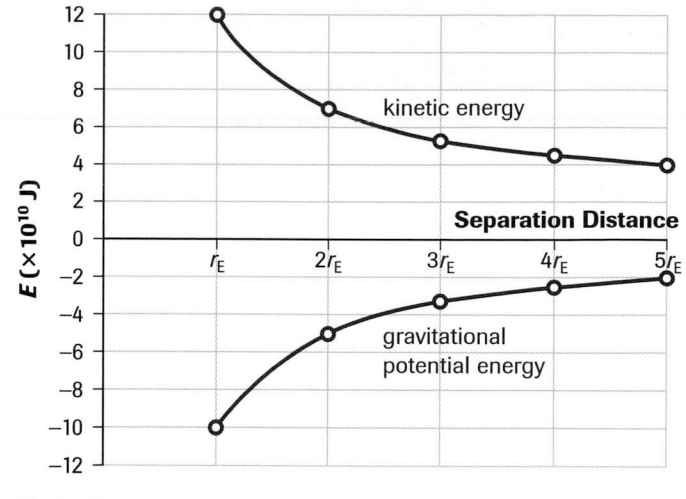

Figure 2

Making Connections

23. When the *Apollo 13* spacecraft was about halfway to the Moon, it developed problems in the oxygen system. Rather than turning the craft around and returning directly to Earth, mission control decided that the craft should proceed to the Moon before returning to Earth.
(a) Explain the physics principles involved in this decision.
(b) Describe at least one major risk of this decision.

Extension

24. Two remote planets consist of identical material, but one has a radius twice as large as the other. If the shortest possible period for a low-altitude satellite orbiting the smaller planet is 40 min, what is the shortest possible period for a similar low-altitude satellite orbiting the larger one? Give your answer in minutes.

  ⏺ Sir Isaac Newton Contest Question

25. A certain *double star* consists of two identical stars, each of mass 3.0×10^{30} kg, separated by a distance of 2.0×10^{11} m between their centres. How long does it take to complete one cycle? Give your answer in seconds.

  ⏺ Sir Isaac Newton Contest Question

26. We owe our lives to the energy reaching us from the Sun. At a particular planet, the solar energy flux E (the amount of energy from the Sun arriving per square metre per second) depends on the distance from the Sun to the planet. If T is the period of that planet in its journey around the Sun, that is, the length of its year, calculate how E depends on T.

  ⏺ Sir Isaac Newton Contest Question

PERFORMANCE TASK

Safety in Transportation and Sports

Safety is a very important issue in transportation, and also in sports and recreational activities (**Figure 1**). Safety features in cars include seat belts, front airbags, side airbags, children's car seats, energy-absorbing bumpers, antilock brakes, nonshattering glass, and improved tire design. Helmets, facemasks, goggles, kneepads, elbow pads, shoulder pads, gloves, oxygen supply equipment, life jackets, body suits, and specialized footwear are just some of the safety equipment used in sports and recreational activities.

Figure 1
Safety features in transportation and recreation

In this performance task, you will apply the concepts related to energy, momentum, collisions, and springs to the use and design of safety equipment. You can choose one of three options. For the option you choose, you are expected to display an understanding of the concepts and principles presented in Chapters 4, 5, and 6.

Task

Choose one of the following options:

Option 1: Protective Equipment in Sports and Recreational Activities

Your task is to research the design and use of protective equipment in sports and recreational activities. You can choose one sport or activity and analyze the associated equipment, or you can choose one piece of equipment and analyze its use in various sports and activities. You will apply scientific concepts and principles to explain the need for and advantage of the protective equipment you choose to analyze.

Process
- Choose appropriate research tools, such as books, magazines, the Internet, and experts in the field of safety equipment OR choose appropriate apparatus and materials for the egg-drop container (for Option 3).
- Research safety equipment and synthesize the information with appropriate organization and sufficient detail OR apply physics principles to the design, construction, testing, and modification of the egg-drop container (for Option 3).
- Analyze the physics principles of the safety equipment OR evaluate the design, construction, testing, and modification process of the egg-drop container.
- Evaluate the research reporting process (for Options 1 and 2).

Product
- Demonstrate an understanding of the related physics principles, laws, and theories.
- Use terms, symbols, equations, and SI units correctly.
- Prepare an appropriate research portfolio in print and/or audiovisual format (for Options 1 and 2) OR prepare a suitable technological task portfolio with notes, diagrams, safety considerations, tests, modifications, and analysis (for Option 3).
- Prepare a report and a live or videotaped presentation (for Options 1 and 2) OR create an egg-drop container that bounces when dropped from a height above the floor (for Option 3).

Option 2: Vehicle Safety Features

Your task is to identify social issues, such as a cost-benefit analysis, requiring or arising from the development of safety features for vehicles, to research information about the issues you have identified, and to create a communication product to synthesize your analysis of the issues.

Option 3: The Bouncing Egg

Your task is to develop criteria to specify the design of a bouncing "egg-drop" container made with springs. The container will be dropped from a predetermined height, such as 1.0 m, to the floor. You will analyze the effectiveness of the container (how well the egg is protected) while achieving the largest number of clear bounces. You will analyze the initial design of the container and make modifications to improve the container. You will describe practical applications of your final design and of the process you used to create the product.

For this option, safety and design rules should be discussed before brainstorming begins. For example, any tools used to construct the device must be used safely, and tests of the device should be carried out in a safe and proper manner. Notice that this option involves testing and modification, which are part of the technology design process.

Analysis

Your analysis will depend on the option you choose. You should include answers to the following questions:

Options 1 and 2

(a) What physics principles are applied to the design and use of your chosen safety device?

(b) What are the advantages and disadvantages of your chosen safety device?

(c) How is the design of your chosen safety device affected by its function?

(d) How common and costly is your chosen safety device?

(e) What impact has your safety device had on individual users and on society in general?

(f) What careers are related to the manufacture and use of your safety device?

(g) What research is being carried out to improve the design and use of your safety device?

(h) Create and answer your own analysis questions.

Option 3

(i) What physics principles are applied in designing your container?

(j) What criteria can be used to evaluate the success of your design?

(k) What safety measures were followed in constructing and testing your container?

(l) How did you test your container to determine how to improve it?

(m) How can your design of the container be applied to the design of real shock-absorbing devices?

(n) List problems you encountered during the creation of the container. How did you solve them?

(o) Create and answer your own analysis questions.

Evaluation

Your evaluation will depend on the option you choose.

Options 1 and 2

(p) Evaluate the resources you used during your research.

(q) If you were to embark on a similar task with a different goal, what changes would you make to the process to ensure that you were successful in your research and in communicating that research?

Option 3

(r) How does your design compare with the design of other students or groups?

(s) Draw a flow chart of the process you used in working on this task. How do the steps in your flow chart compare with the steps you would follow in a typical investigation in this unit?

(t) If you were to begin this task again, what would you modify to ensure a better process and a better final product?

Write numbers 1 to 14 in your notebook. Indicate beside each number whether the corresponding statement is true (T) or false (F). If it is false, write a corrected version.

1. One joule is one newton metre squared per second squared.

2. The force constant of a spring can be said to measure the "stiffness" of the spring.

3. Two boxes are being moved on level terrain, one on Earth, the other on the Moon. If the displacement and coefficient of kinetic friction are the same, then the thermal energy produced by the kinetic friction would also be the same.

4. Impulse and momentum are the same quantity because their base SI units are equivalent.

5. Two figure skaters, initially stationary, push away from each other. Just after this interaction, the total momentum of this system is zero.

6. The only type of collision in which momentum is not conserved is a completely inelastic collision.

7. The gravitational field strength at a location in the Sun's gravitational field is inversely proportional to the distance between that location and the Sun's centre.

8. The work done by the force of Earth's gravity acting on a satellite in circular motion around Earth is positive because the satellite is always accelerating toward Earth.

9. In the heliocentric model, Earth is at the centre of the universe and all other celestial bodies revolve around it.

10. The Sun is located at the centre of a planet's orbit.

11. The speed of a satellite in elliptical orbit around Earth is independent of the satellite's position in its orbit.

12. A black hole has an extremely strong magnetic field.

13. A black hole is a celestial body with an escape speed equal to or greater than the speed of light.

14. X rays and gamma rays can escape from a black hole, even though visible light cannot.

Write numbers 15 to 28 in your notebook. Beside each number, write the letter corresponding to the best choice.

15. If you were to climb a ladder that was your height, the work you would do against the force of gravity is approximately
    (a) 10^1 J   (d) 10^4 J
    (b) 10^2 J   (e) 10^5 J
    (c) 10^3 J

For questions 16 to 18, refer to **Figure 1**, in which a toboggan is pulled up a hill of length L at a constant velocity.

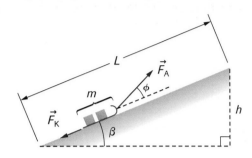

Figure 1
For questions
16, 17, and 18

16. The magnitude of the normal force of the hillside acting on the toboggan is
    (a) $mg \cos \beta$
    (b) $F_A \sin \phi$
    (c) $mg \cos \beta - F_A \sin \phi$
    (d) $mg \cos \beta + F_A \sin \phi$
    (e) $-(mg \cos \beta + F_A \sin \phi)$

17. The magnitude of the applied force $\vec{F}_A$ is
    (a) $\dfrac{(F_K + mg \sin \beta)}{\cos \phi}$
    (b) $\dfrac{(F_K - mg \sin \beta)}{\sin \phi}$
    (c) $\dfrac{(F_K - mg \sin \beta)}{\cos \phi}$
    (d) $F_K + F_N$
    (e) $F_K + F_N - mg$

18. The work done by the applied force in moving the toboggan the length of the hill, L, is
    (a) $F_A L$
    (b) $F_K L$
    (c) $(F_A - F_K)L$
    (d) $\dfrac{F_A \cos \phi h}{\sin \beta}$
    (e) none of these

19. A satellite in a circular orbit of radius r around Mars experiences a force of gravity of magnitude F exerted by Mars. The work done by this force on the satellite as it travels halfway around its orbit is
    (a) $2F\pi r$ (b) $\dfrac{F\pi r}{2}$ (c) Fr (d) $F\pi r$ (e) zero

20. A motorcycle of mass of m, with a driver of mass $\dfrac{m}{5}$, is travelling at speed v. Later, it is travelling with the same driver, as well as a passenger of mass $\dfrac{m}{5}$, at a speed $0.80v$. The motorcycle's new kinetic energy is
    (a) equal to the initial kinetic energy
    (b) greater than the initial kinetic energy by a factor of 0.75
    (c) less than the initial kinetic energy by a factor of 0.75
    (d) greater than the initial kinetic energy by a factor of 1.3
    (e) less than the initial kinetic energy by a factor of 1.3

21. Three stones are thrown with identical initial speeds from the top of a cliff into the water below (**Figure 2**). Air resistance is negligible. The speeds with which stones 1, 2, and 3 strike the water are
    (a) $v_1 = v_3 > v_2$ (d) $v_3 > v_2 > v_1$
    (b) $v_2 > v_1 = v_3$ (e) $v_1 = v_2 = v_3$
    (c) $v_1 > v_2 > v_3$

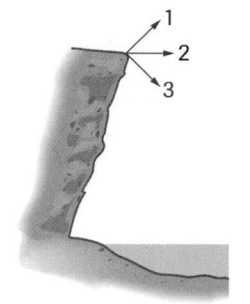

Figure 2

22. The contact times in collisions between a baseball and a baseball bat are typically a few
    (a) seconds   (d) milliseconds
    (b) nanoseconds   (e) kiloseconds
    (c) microseconds

23. A billiard ball, moving with speed v, collides head-on with a stationary ball of the same mass. After the collision, the billiard ball that was initially moving is at rest. The speed of the other ball in terms of v is
    (a) $\dfrac{v}{2}$ (b) 0   (c) v (d) $2v$ (e) $\dfrac{3v}{4}$

Questions 24 to 26 relate to **Figure 3**.

24. If the escape speeds of the rockets are v_F, v_G, and v_H, then
    (a) $v_F = v_G = v_H$
    (b) $v_F > v_G > v_H$
    (c) $v_F < v_G < v_H$
    (d) $v_F = v_G$, but v_H has no defined escape speed
    (e) the speeds cannot be compared with the information given

25. In the situation of **Figure 3**, which of the following statements is true?
    (a) H will rise to an altitude of $2r_E$ above Earth's surface and remain there.
    (b) F and G will escape and have zero speed after escaping.
    (c) Only F will escape, but it will have zero speed after escaping.
    (d) Only F will escape and it will have a nonzero speed after escaping.
    (e) none of these

26. If the escape energies of the rockets are E_F, E_G, and E_H, then
    (a) $E_F = E_G = E_H$
    (b) $E_F > E_G > E_H$
    (c) $E_F < E_G < E_H$
    (d) $E_F = E_G$, but E_H has no defined escape energy
    (e) the energies cannot be compared with the information given

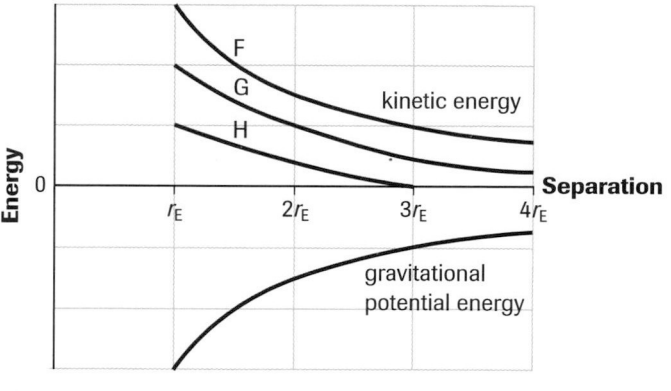

Figure 3
This graph shows the kinetic energy given to three rockets (F, G, and H) of equal mass as they are launched from Earth's surface. (for questions 24, 25, and 26)

27. If the distance between a spacecraft and Jupiter increases by a factor of 4, the magnitude of Jupiter's gravitational field at the position of the spacecraft
    (a) increases by a factor of 4
    (b) decreases by a factor of 4
    (c) increases by a factor of 16
    (d) decreases by a factor of 16
    (e) decreases by a factor of 2

28. If the Sun's mass were 8 times its current value, and Earth's period of revolution around the Sun retained its current value, then the average distance from Earth to the Sun, in terms of its current value, r, would be
    (a) $8r$ (c) $\dfrac{r}{2}$ (e) none of these
    (b) $\dfrac{r}{8}$ (d) $2r$

Write numbers 29 to 35 in your notebook. Beside each number place the word, phrase, or equation that completes the sentence.

29. (a) ___?___ first used a telescope to observe the moons of a distant planet.
    (b) ___?___ first proposed that the orbits of planets are ellipses.
    (c) The SI unit of energy is named after ___?___.

NEL   An interactive version of the quiz is available online.
GO www.science.nelson.com

Energy and Momentum   **305**

(d) ___?___ provided the data used to derive the laws of planetary motion.

(e) ___?___ first analyzed the relationship between the force applied to a spring and the spring's stretch or compression.

(f) The radius of a black hole is named after ___?___.

30. (a) The area under a force-displacement graph represents ___?___.

(b) The slope of a line on a force-stretch graph represents ___?___.

(c) The area under the line on a force-time graph represents ___?___.

(d) The slope of a line on a momentum-time graph represents ___?___.

(e) The area under the line on a kinetic friction-displacement graph represents ___?___.

(f) The slope of the line on a graph of r^3 versus T^2, for a satellite in orbit around Earth, represents ___?___.

31. A collision in which the two objects stick together is called a(n) ___?___ collision. In an elastic collision, the total kinetic energy after the collision ___?___ the total kinetic energy before the collision. A collision in which the decrease in kinetic energy is the maximum possible is called a(n) ___?___.

32. The eccentricity of a circle is ___?___.

33. At the centre of a black hole is a region called ___?___. The distance from the centre of this region to the event horizon is called the ___?___.

34. **Figure 4(a)** represents the motion of a truck with positions separated by equal time intervals of 5.0 s. Choose the graph in **Figure 4(b)** that best represents

(a) the truck's momentum

(b) the truck's kinetic energy

35. Write the following terms in a column: impulse; law of conservation of momentum; kinetic energy; thermal energy; elastic potential energy; escape speed; gravitational potential energy; Kepler's third-law constant; and frequency of a mass-spring system in SHM. Beside each term, write the letter of the following mathematical relationships that best defines the quantity.

(a) $\dfrac{GM}{4\pi^2}$ (f) $m\vec{v}$ (j) $F_K \Delta d$

(b) $-\dfrac{GMm}{r}$ (g) $m_1 \Delta \vec{v}_1 = -m_2 \Delta \vec{v}_2$ (k) $\dfrac{1}{2}kx^2$

(c) $\sqrt{\dfrac{GM}{r}}$ (h) $\dfrac{1}{2}mv^2$ (l) $\pm kx$

(d) $\sqrt{\dfrac{2GM}{r}}$ (i) $(F\cos\theta)\Delta d$ (m) $\dfrac{1}{2\pi}\sqrt{\dfrac{k}{m}}$

(e) $\sum\vec{F}\Delta t$

(a)

$\vec{v}_i = 0$ ... $\vec{v}_f = 0$

(b)
A

B
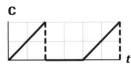

C
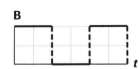

D
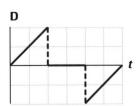

E
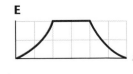

F
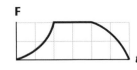

G
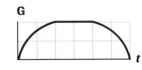

H
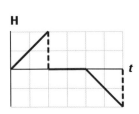

Figure 4
For question 34
(a) The motion of a truck
(b) Possible graphs related to momentum and energy of the truck

Understanding Concepts

1. Describe three situations in which a force is exerted on an object, and yet no work is done.

2. It is often possible to do work in pushing an object without transferring any energy to the object. What happens to the energy associated with the work done in this case?

3. A baseball and a shot used in shot put have the same kinetic energy. Which has the greater momentum? Why?

4. Two loaded toboggans of unequal mass reach the bottom of a hill with the same initial kinetic energy and are sliding across a flat, level ice surface in the same direction. If each is subjected to the same retarding force, how will their stopping distances compare?

5. Two dynamics carts are moving in a straight line toward each other. The ensuing collision is cushioned by a spring between them. During the collision, there is a point where both carts are momentarily at rest. Where has all the kinetic energy that the carts possessed before the collision gone?

6. List several common devices that can store elastic potential energy when temporarily deformed.

7. Why would car bumpers mounted on springs that obey Hooke's law prove impractical?

8. Draw a sketch to show how two springs with different lengths and spring constants cars might be combined to have the force-stretch graph in **Figure 1**.

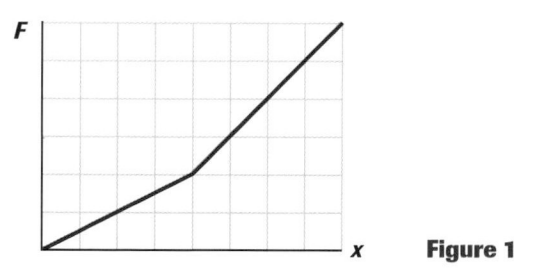

Figure 1

9. From what height must a 1.5×10^3-kg pile driver fall to drive a pile 0.50 m into the ground against an opposing force of average magnitude 3.5×10^5 N?

10. A 10.0-kg block is pushed from rest along a horizontal, frictionless surface with a horizontal force given by the graph in **Figure 2**.
   (a) How much work is done in moving the block the first 2.00 m?
   (b) What is the block's kinetic energy after it has moved 3.00 m?
   (c) What is its velocity at the 3.00 m mark?

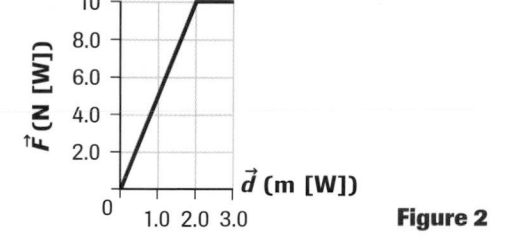

Figure 2

11. A force that increases gradually from 0 to 1.00×10^2 N [E] at a rate of 10.0 N/s [E] does 1.25×10^4 J of work on an object, accelerating it from rest to a velocity of 50.0 m/s [E] on a horizontal, frictionless surface.
   (a) What is the mass of the object?
   (b) What constant force, acting over 5.00 m, would give the object the same final velocity?

12. What is the magnitude of the momentum of a 5.0-kg sled with a kinetic energy of 5.0×10^2 J?

13. A linear elastic spring can be compressed 0.10 m by an applied force of magnitude 5.0 N. A 4.5-kg crate of apples, moving at 2.0 m/s, collides with this spring, as shown in **Figure 3**. What will be the maximum compression of the spring?

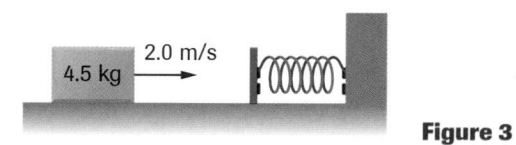

Figure 3

14. A spring bumper, with a force-compression relationship given by $F = (50.0 \text{ N/m})x$, is compressed 2.00 cm.
   (a) What elastic potential energy is stored in the spring at this compression?
   (b) The spring is compressed further to 6.00 cm. What is the change in elastic potential energy?
   (c) A 0.400-kg cart is placed against the compressed spring on a horizontal, frictionless plane. The system is released. With what speed does the cart leave the spring?

15. A small moving object collides with a larger stationary object. Does the magnitude of the force exerted by the small object depend on whether the small object bounces off the larger object or sticks to it? (Assume that the collision takes the same amount of time in either case.) Explain your answer. Relate this situation to the use of rubber bullets by riot police.

16. For what types of forces does the concept of impulse prove most helpful in analyzing the changes in motion that occur as a result of the force?

17. A hose discharges 78 kg of water each minute, with a speed of 24 m/s. The water, travelling horizontally, hits a vertical wall and is stopped. Neglecting any splash back, what is the magnitude of the average force exerted by the water on the wall?

18. A 9.5-kg dog is standing on a stationary wagon. It then walks forward on the wagon at a speed of 1.2 m/s, and the wagon moves backward at a speed of 3.0 m/s (both speeds relative to the ground). Friction is negligible. What is the mass of the wagon?

19. A 2.4-kg dynamics cart with a linear elastic spring attached to its front end is moving at 1.5 m/s [W] when it collides head-on with a stationary 3.6-kg cart.
    (a) Calculate the total energy of the system before the collision.
    (b) What is the velocity of each cart at minimum separation?
    (c) Calculate the change in total kinetic energy of the system at minimum separation.
    (d) If the maximum compression of the spring during the collision is 12 cm, what is its force constant?

20. Two trolleys, of mass 1.2 kg and 4.8 kg, are at rest with a compressed spring between them. A string holds the carts together. When the string is cut, the trolleys spring apart. If the force constant of the spring is 2.4×10^3 N/m, by how much must the spring have been compressed so that the 4.8-kg cart moves at 2.0 m/s?

21. A 25-kg object moving to the right with a velocity of 3.0 m/s collides with a 15-kg object moving to the left at 6.0 m/s. Find the velocity of the 25-kg object after the collision if
    (a) the 15-kg object continues to move to the left, but at only 0.30 m/s
    (b) the 15-kg object rebounds to the right at 0.45 m/s
    (c) the 15-kg object sticks together with the 25-kg object

22. An experimental rocket sled on a level, frictionless track has a mass of 1.4×10^4 kg. It propels itself by expelling gases from its rocket engines at a rate of 10 kg/s, at an exhaust speed of 2.5×10^4 m/s relative to the rocket. For how many seconds must the engines burn if the sled is to acquire a speed of 5.0×10^1 m/s starting from rest? You may ignore the small decrease in mass of the sled and the small speed of the rocket compared to the exhaust gas.

23. A 2.3-kg bird, flying horizontally at 18 m/s [E], collides with a bird flying at 19 m/s [W]. The collision is completely inelastic. After the collision, the two birds tumble together at 3.1 m/s [E]. Determine the mass of the second bird.

24. Two nuclei undergo a head-on elastic collision. One nucleus of mass m is initially stationary. The other nucleus has an initial velocity v and a final velocity of $-\frac{v}{5}$. Determine the mass of the second nucleus in terms of m.

25. A 2.0×10^3-kg car travelling at 2.4×10^1 m/s [E] enters an icy intersection and collides with a 3.6×10^3-kg truck travelling at 1.0×10^1 m/s [S]. If they become coupled together in the collision, what is their velocity immediately after impact?

26. A truck of mass 2.3×10^4 kg travelling at 15 m/s [51° S of W] collides with a second truck of mass 1.2×10^4 kg. The collision is completely inelastic. The trucks have a common velocity of 11 m/s [35° S of W] after the collision.
    (a) Determine the initial velocity of the less massive truck.
    (b) What percentage of the initial kinetic energy is lost in the collision between the trucks?

27. In a hockey game, an 82-kg player moving at 8.3 m/s [N] and a 95-kg player moving at 6.7 m/s [25° W of N] simultaneously collide with a stationary opposition player of mass 85 kg. If the players remain together after the collision, what is their common velocity?

28. Comets orbit the Sun in an elliptical path of high eccentricity. Are you more likely to see a comet when it is moving at its fastest or at its slowest? Explain your answer with the help of a sketch based on Kepler's second law.

29. What changes would have to be made in the speed of a space vehicle to enable it to increase or decrease the size of its circular orbit around Earth?

30. Does a spacecraft always need a speed of 11.2 km/s to escape from Earth? If not, what is the true meaning of "escape speed?"

31. A satellite is in a circular orbit 655 km above Earth's surface. Determine the magnitude of the gravitational acceleration at this height.

32. What is the magnitude of the surface gravitational acceleration (as a multiple of Earth's surface g) of a planet having a mass 0.25 times that of Earth and a radius 0.60 times that of Earth?

33. Determine the gravitational field of the Sun at the position of Earth.

34. An asteroid is travelling in a circular orbit around the Sun midway between the orbits of Mars and Jupiter. Determine, to three significant digits,
    (a) the period of the asteroid's orbit in Earth years
    (b) the asteroid's speed

35. Scientists want to place a satellite in a circular orbit around Neptune with an orbital period of 24.0 h.
    (a) Determine Kepler's third-law constant for Neptune using Neptune's mass.
    (b) What distance from Neptune's centre must the satellite be to maintain its circular orbit?
    (c) What is the altitude of this orbit in kilometres?

36. Io, a moon of Jupiter discovered by Galileo, has an orbital period of 1.77 Earth days and an average distance from Jupiter's centre of 4.22×10^8 m. Determine Jupiter's mass.

37. Because of Mercury's close proximity to the Sun, its primordial atmosphere was heated to a sufficiently high temperature that it evaporated off the surface of the planet, escaping the planet's gravitational grasp. Assume that the mass of a typical molecule was 5.32×10^{-26} kg.
    (a) With what minimum speed must the atmospheric molecules have been moving on Mercury's surface to have escaped?
    (b) If a molecule took up orbit around Mercury at an altitude above the surface equivalent to Mercury's radius, what would be its speed in orbit?
    (c) What speed would the molecule need at launch from the surface to achieve the orbit calculated in (b)?
    (d) What would the molecule's binding energy be in this orbit?

38. (a) Determine the Schwartzschild radius of a black hole that is 85 times as massive as Jupiter.
    (b) What is the escape speed from this celestial body?

Applying Inquiry Skills

39. A heavy lab cart with a spring mounted on its front end collides elastically head-on with a stationary, lighter cart on a level, frictionless surface. Sketch a graph of the kinetic energy of each cart as a function of distance between the two carts, showing the intervals before, during, and after the collision. Sketch a graph of the total energy throughout.

40. Sketch the general shape of the graph of force versus separation for each of the following collisions:
    (a) A billiard ball bounces off a cushion, leaving at the same speed as it approached.

(b) A tin can collides with a brick wall and is slightly dented before bouncing off at a slower speed.
(c) A ball of soft putty is thrown at a wall and sticks to it in the collision.

41. The apparatus in **Figure 4(a)** is used to study the action of two identical extension springs linked to an air puck of mass 0.55 kg on a horizontal air table. The spark timer is set at 0.020 s. After the puck is displaced in the $+y$ direction and then released, the paper beneath the puck records the data in **Figure 4(b)**.
    (a) Use the information in the diagram to determine the spring constant of the springs. (Assume that when the puck is at its maximum displacement from the equilibrium position, the elastic potential energy is stored in one spring only.)
    (b) Would you obtain more accurate results if you pulled the paper quickly or slowly? Explain your answer.
    (c) If you were to perform a similar experiment in class, what are the most probable sources of error you would need to minimize?
    (d) What safety precautions are required in performing this type of experiment?

(a)

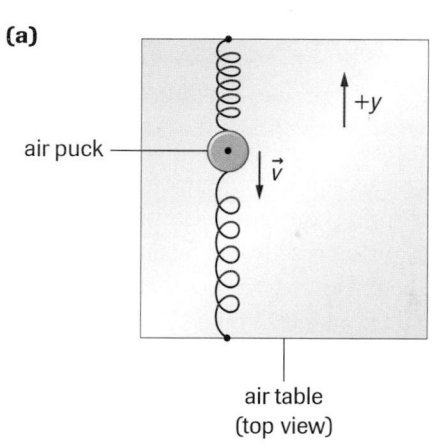

air puck

$+y$

$\vec{v}$

air table
(top view)

(b)

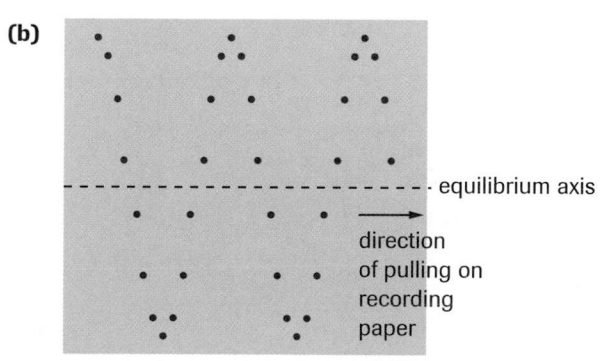

equilibrium axis

direction of pulling on recording paper

Figure 4
(a) Each tension spring is stretched 5.0 cm when the puck is in its equilibrium position.
(b) Recorded data for the experiment

42. The vertical accelerometer shown in **Figure 5** contains a small lead weight attached to a spring that obeys Hooke's law. To calibrate the accelerometer spring, you are given two lead weights, each of mass *m*, and other apparatus.
    (a) List the measurements and apparatus you would need to calibrate the accelerometer.
    (b) Describe a situation in the classroom in which you would observe the reading shown on the accelerometer.
    (c) Describe various possible situations at an amusement park in which you would observe the reading shown on the accelerometer.

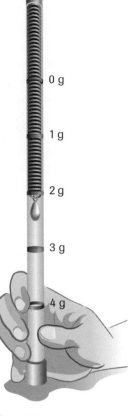

Figure 5

43. An exploder piston is set to maximum compression on the dynamics cart shown in **Figure 6**. The cart's mass is 0.88 kg. The spring constant of the piston is 36 N/m. Just after the piston is activated by the trigger on the cart, a motion sensor determines that the speed of the cart leaving the wall is 0.22 m/s. The cart rolls along the horizontal surface, coming to rest in 2.5 m.

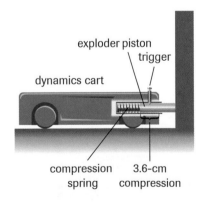

exploder piston

trigger

dynamics cart

compression spring   3.6-cm compression   **Figure 6**

(a) Determine the maximum elastic potential energy in the spring and the maximum kinetic energy of the cart after it starts moving. What happened to the remaining elastic potential energy?
(b) Determine the average kinetic friction that acts on the cart from the position where it leaves the wall to its stopping position.
(c) Describe the most probable sources of random and systematic error in taking measurements during this type of experiment.

Making Connections

44. (a) Describe ways in which you can reduce the jarring forces on your legs when you are jogging.
    (b) What is the advantage of reducing the jarring?

45. (a) Explain the physics principles behind the use of front-seat airbags that inflate during an automobile collision (**Figure 7**).
    (b) Describe similar instances in which physics principles are applied to increase safety.

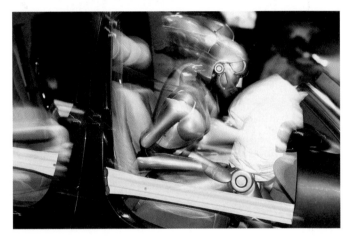

Figure 7

46. By looking at distant galaxies, astronomers have concluded that our solar system is circling the centre of our galaxy. The hub of this galaxy is located about 2.7×10^{20} m from the Sun. The Sun circles the centre about every 200 million years. We assume that the Sun is attracted by a large number of stars at the hub of our galaxy, and that the Sun is kept in orbit by the gravitational attraction of these stars.
    (a) Calculate the total mass of the stars at the hub of our galaxy.
    (b) Calculate the approximate number of stars that are the size of our Sun (2.0×10^{30} kg).

Extension

47. A 2.5-kg ball travelling at 2.3 m/s to the right collides head-on elastically with a stationary ball of mass 2.0 kg. Find the velocity of each ball after the collision. (*Hint:* Determine the number of equations you need by counting the unknowns.)

48. A bullet of mass 4.0 g, moving horizontally with a velocity of 5.0×10^2 m/s [N], strikes a wooden block of mass 2.0 kg that is initially at rest on a rough, horizontal surface. The bullet passes through the block in a negligible interval, emerging with a velocity of 1.0×10^2 m/s [N], and causing the block to slide 0.40 m along the surface before coming to rest.
    (a) With what velocity does the wooden block move just after the bullet exits?
    (b) What is the maximum kinetic energy of the block?
    (c) What is the average frictional force stopping the block?
    (d) What is the decrease in kinetic energy of the bullet?
    (e) Explain why the decrease in kinetic energy of the bullet and the maximum kinetic energy of the block are not equal. What happened to this missing energy?

49. A 1.0-Mg plane is trying to make a forced landing on the deck of a 2.0-Mg barge at rest on the surface of a calm sea. The only significant frictional force is between the wheels and the deck. This braking force is constant, and equal in magnitude to one-quarter of the plane's weight. What must the minimum length of the barge be so that the plane can stop safely on deck if the plane touches down at the rear end of the deck with a velocity of 5.0×10^1 m/s toward the front of the barge?

50. Astronauts on board the International Space Station measure their mass by determining the period of a special chair that vibrates on springs. The chair is calibrated by attaching known masses, setting the chair vibrating, and then measuring the period. **Table 1** gives the possible calibration data.
    (a) Determine the combined spring constant of the chair springs and the mass of the empty chair. (*Hint:* You can use graphing techniques to determine these values. A spreadsheet program is helpful.)
    (b) If you were to be set vibrating in the chair, what frequency of vibration would you observe?

(c) Determine the mass loss of a crewmember who measures a period of vibration of the chair of 2.01 s at the start of a 3-month mission and 1.98 s at the end.

Table 1 The Period of the Chair on Springs for Attached Masses

Mass (kg)	0.00	14.1	23.9	33.8	45.0	56.1	67.1
Period (s)	0.901	1.25	1.44	1.61	1.79	1.94	2.09

51. **Table 2** lists the orbital eccentricities of the solar system planets.
    (a) Which planet has the most circular orbit, and which has the most elongated orbit?
    (b) Draw a scale diagram of the major axis of Mercury's orbit. Label the Sun at one focus and label the distances c and a (two of the variables described in the Try This Activity at the beginning of this chapter). Mark the perihelion and aphelion locations of Mercury's orbit.
    (c) Repeat (b) for Earth's orbit. (You may need a different scale.)
    (d) Do the typical elliptical orbits shown for planets in this text and other references correspond to the true orbital shapes? Explain your answer.

Table 2 Orbital Eccentricities

Planet	Eccentricity
Mercury	0.206
Venus	0.007
Earth	0.017
Mars	0.093
Jupiter	0.048
Saturn	0.056
Uranus	0.046
Neptune	0.010
Pluto	0.248

52. An astronaut lands on a planet that has $\frac{1}{10}$ the mass of Earth but $\frac{1}{2}$ the diameter. On Earth she weighed 6.1×10^2 N. How much does she weigh on the new planet? Give your answer in newtons.

■ Sir Isaac Newton Contest Question

Electric, Gravitational, and Magnetic Fields

Dr. Marie D'Iorio
Institute for Microstructural Sciences,
National Research Council of Canada

Marie D'Iorio has had many achievements in her physics career. In addition to leading important research at the National Research Council of Canada (NRC), she is an Adjunct Professor at the University of Ottawa where she interacts with graduate students performing research in her lab. Dr. D'Iorio also serves as the president of the Canadian Association of Physicists, an organization dedicated to the development and use of pure and applied sciences in Canada.

After completing an honours bachelor's degree in physics at the University of Ottawa, Dr. D'Iorio's interest directed her toward multidisciplinary research in physics and biology. She chose a graduate program at the University of Toronto that allowed her to explore this new direction.

Dr. D'Iorio's current research focuses on the use of organic materials in electronics and photonics. Organic light emitting diodes (OLEDs) are emerging as an attractive alternative to more known display technologies such as cathode ray tubes, liquid crystal displays, and plasma-based displays. OLED devices offer cheap materials, low power consumption, increased brightness, and wide viewing angles. Dr. D'Iorio is excited to be participating in the development of tomorrow's materials and applications in this rapidly growing field.

▶ Overall Expectations

In this unit, you will be able to

- demonstrate an understanding of the concepts, principles, and laws related to electric, gravitational, and magnetic forces and fields, and explain them in qualitative and quantitative terms

- conduct investigations and analyze and solve problems related to electric, gravitational, and magnetic fields

- explain the roles of evidence and theories in the development of scientific knowledge related to electric, gravitational, and magnetic fields

- evaluate and describe the social and economic impact of technological developments related to the concept of fields

Knowledge and Understanding

1. Copy the diagram of the Bohr–Rutherford model of the atom (**Figure 1**) into
   your notebook.
   (a) For each particle in the atom, list as many characteristics as you can
       remember, for instance, the charge, its mass relative to other types of parti-
       cles, and the magnitude of force acting on it.
   (b) Which particle is responsible for the conduction of electricity in solids?
       Explain your answer.
   (c) Explain the difference between an atom, a positive ion, and a negative ion.

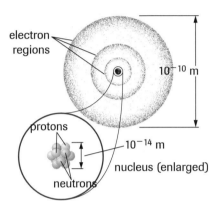

Figure 1
The Bohr–Rutherford
model of the atom

2. There are several principal methods for placing a charge on a neutral object.
   (a) Describe these methods, and draw diagrams for each.
   (b) Summarize these methods of charging by copying **Table 1** into your note-
       book and completing it.

Table 1 Methods of Charging

Method of Charging	Friction	Contact	Induction and Grounding
initial charges on objects	?	?	?
steps	?	?	?
final charges on objects	?	?	?

3. Copy each of the diagrams in **Figure 2** into your notebook, and draw the magnetic field nearby.

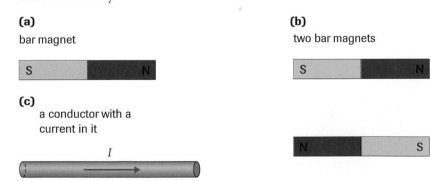

(a)
bar magnet

(b)
two bar magnets

(c)
a conductor with a
current in it

Figure 2

4. Explain how to increase the magnitude of the magnetic field of each of the following:
   (a) a bar magnet
   (b) a straight conductor with an electric current
   (c) an electromagnet

Inquiry and Communication

5. Design an experiment that can be used to demonstrate the laws of electric charges.

6. When a conductor with a current in it is placed in a magnetic field, it can experience a force.
   (a) Under what conditions will the conductor experience a force?
   (b) Design a procedure to determine the effect of each condition from (a) on the force experienced by the conductor.

Making Connections

7. Both the loudspeaker and the motor in **Figure 3** use the principles of electromagnetism in their operation. Explain how each device works.

(a)

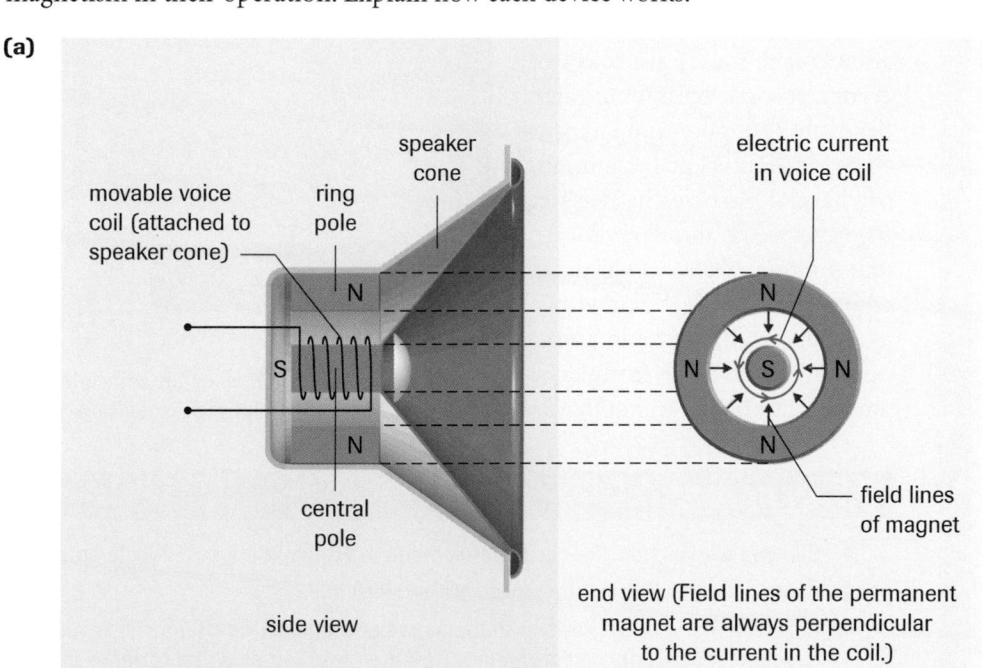

speaker cone

electric current in voice coil

movable voice coil (attached to speaker cone)

ring pole

field lines of magnet

central pole

side view

end view (Field lines of the permanent magnet are always perpendicular to the current in the coil.)

(b)

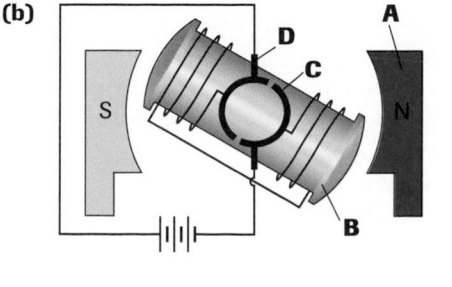

Figure 3
(a) A moving-coil loudspeaker
(b) A DC motor

7

Electric Charges and Electric Fields

In this chapter, you will be able to

- define and describe concepts and units related to electric and gravitational fields

- state Coulomb's law and Newton's law of universal gravitation, and analyze, compare, and apply them in specific contexts

- compare the properties of electric and gravitational fields by describing and illustrating the source and direction of the field in each case

- apply quantitatively the concept of electric potential energy and compare it to gravitational potential energy

- analyze quantitatively, and with diagrams, electric fields and electric forces in a variety of situations

- describe and explain the electric field inside and on the surface of a charged conductor and how the properties of electric fields can be used to control the electric field around a conductor

- perform experiments or simulations involving charged objects

- explain how the concept of a field developed into a general scientific model, and describe how it affected scientific thinking

The study of electric charge and electric fields is fundamental to understanding the world around you. You have felt transfers of electric charge in static shock on a cold winter day and have seen such transfers in the spectacular form of lightning (**Figure 1**). Perhaps you have read of animals that use electric fields to detect prey. You have seen electric principles at work in office equipment such as photocopiers, computer printers, and coaxial cables, and perhaps also in medicine, in heart monitors (**Figure 2**).

In this chapter you will study the concepts of charge, electric force, and electric fields more thoroughly than in your previous school years. You are also likely to encounter some topics for the first time: electric potential energy, electric potential, or the motion of charged particles in electric fields. As we go through various topics of this chapter, we will draw comparisons with the previous two units in this text and apply our new knowledge to diverse areas of nature and technology.

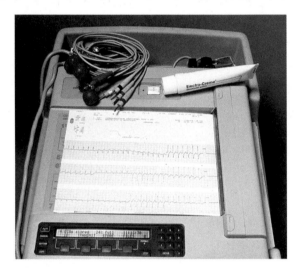

Figure 2
An electrocardiograph applies the principles of this chapter in a way that might someday save your life.

REFLECT on your learning

1. Can you explain how the electrocardiograph in **Figure 2** applies electric principles?

2. Why do you think computer towers are encased in metal?

3. Compare the force of gravity with the force between electric charges in terms of direction, magnitude, and properties. How are these forces different, for example, in the directions of the two forces and in the factors affecting their directions and magnitudes?

4. One mass exerts a force of attraction on another through its gravitational field. How does one charge exert an electric force on another across a distance?

5. As a rocket moves from the surface of Earth, its gravitational potential energy increases. How will the potential energy between (a) two charges of opposite signs and (b) two charges of the same sign change as the charges move farther apart?

6. Describe the motion of a charged particle
   (a) between two oppositely charged parallel plates
   (b) as it is moving directly away from another charge

   Compare these cases to similar gravitational examples.

Charging By Induction

- Place a charge on an ebonite rod by rubbing it with fur. (You may also use acetate or a Plexiglas strip by rubbing it with fur or wool.) Using just these materials, put onto a neutral electroscope a charge opposite to the one you just placed onto your rubbed object.

  (a) Describe your procedure (in terms that make it clear that you did not have to use any additional materials in charging the electroscope).

  (b) Describe some test you could make to confirm that your procedure worked. Would you need additional materials?

Figure 1
Lightning is a spectacular display of the principles in this chapter.

Electric Charge and the Electrical Structure of Matter

Photocopiers, laser printers, and fax machines are all designed to imprint graphic elements, such as lines and letters, onto paper. These machines are so commonplace that most of us probably take them for granted, not considering the technology that makes them work. An understanding of the electrical structure of matter plays a major role in these and future applications, such as electronic ink.

Before looking at the specific principles underlying these technologies, we will review some important concepts.

The following are the fundamental laws of electric charges (**Figure 1**):

> **The Laws of Electric Charges**
> Opposite electric charges attract each other.
> Similar electric charges repel each other.
> Charged objects attract some neutral objects.

Figure 1
Opposite charges attract; similar charges repel.

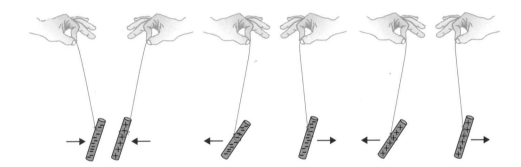

Semiconductors

Semiconductors are another category of electrical material that are intermediate between conductors and insulators in that they have very few conduction electrons for conduction in their pure, or *intrinsic*, state. Semiconductors become very useful in the conduction of electricity when a small amount of a particular impurity is added to them, in a process called "doping." Since semiconductors are solids at room temperature, the field of semiconductor physics is referred to as "solid state." The most commonly used semiconductors are silicon and germanium. Transistors and integrated circuits made from semiconductors have revolutionized electronics.

The Bohr–Rutherford model of the atom explains electrification. Consider, first, electrical effects in solids. Atomic nuclei are not free to move in a solid. Since these fixed nuclei contain all the protons, the total amount of positive charge in a solid is constant and fixed in position. However, it is possible for some of the negative charges within some solids to move because electrons, especially those farthest from the nuclei, have the ability to move from atom to atom.

Electric charges on solid objects result from an excess or deficit of electrons. Thus the charging of an object simply requires a transfer of electrons to or away from the object. If electrons are removed from the object, the object will be charged positively; if electrons are added, the object will be charged negatively. We depict neutral, negatively charged, and positively charged objects with sketches having representative numbers of positive and negative signs, as in **Figure 2**.

In such sketches, the number of + and − signs is not intended to represent the actual number of excess positive or negative charges; it conveys the general idea of balance, excess, or deficit. Notice that in **Figure 2**, the number of + signs is the same in each case, and they are fixed in position in a regular pattern.

An electric conductor is a solid in which electrons are able to move easily from one atom to another. (Most metals, such as silver, gold, copper, and aluminum, are conductors.) Some of the outer electrons in these conductors have been called "conduction electrons" for the way they can move about within the atomic framework of the solid. An insulator is a solid in which the electrons are not free to move about easily from atom to

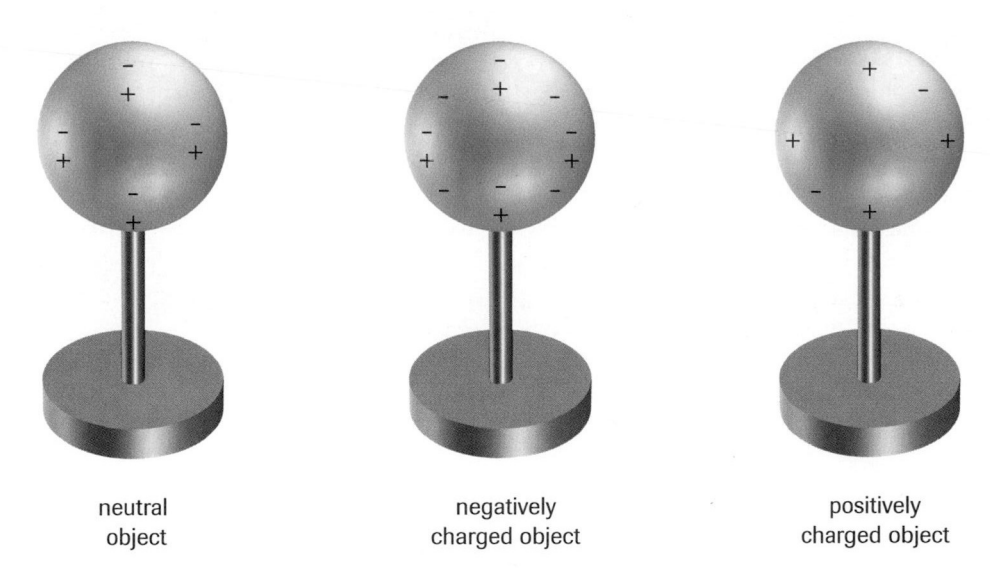

neutral object

negatively charged object

positively charged object

atom (**Figure 3**). Plastic, cork, glass, wood, and rubber are all excellent insulators. Interestingly, the thermal properties of these materials are closely related to their electrical properties.

(a)

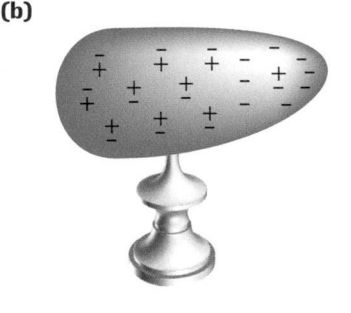

conductor   insulator

(b)

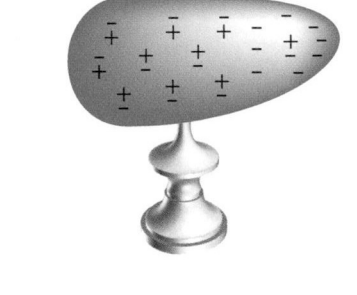

Figure 3
(a) On a spherical conductor charge spreads out evenly. On an insulator the charge remains in the spot where it was introduced.
(b) On conductors that are not spherical the charges tend to repel one another toward the more pointed surfaces.

Certain liquids are also conductors of electricity. The molecules of a liquid are free to move about. In an insulating liquid, these molecules are neutral. Shuffling such molecules around cannot produce a net movement of electric charge through the liquid. If, however, some of the particles in the liquid are charged, whether positively or negatively, the liquid is a conductor. Pure water contains essentially only neutral molecules and is therefore an insulator. However, when a chemical such as table salt (or copper sulphate, potassium nitrate, hydrochloric acid, chlorine, etc.) is added to the water, the solution becomes a conductor. Many substances dissociate, or break apart, into positive and negative ions—charge carriers—when dissolved in water, making it a conducting solution.

A gas can also be a conductor or insulator, depending on the electrical nature of its molecules. A charged object exposed to dry air will remain charged for a long time, which shows that air cannot discharge the object by conduction. On the other hand, if the air were exposed to X rays or nuclear radiation, the object would begin to discharge immediately. Again, the molecules of a gas are normally neutral, but the presence of X rays or other radiation can cause these neutral gas molecules to ionize, and this ionized gas becomes a good conductor. Humid air, containing a large number of water molecules in the form of vapour, is also a good conductor because water molecules are able to partially separate into positive and negative charges. More importantly, humid air usually contains dissolved materials that ionize.

DID YOU KNOW ?

Plasma
A plasma is a fourth state of matter that exists at very high temperatures. It has very different properties than those of the other three states. Essentially, a plasma is a very hot collection of positive and negative ions and electrons. Examples of plasmas are gases used in neon lights, flames, and nuclear fusion reactions.

Electronic Ink

Electronic ink technology (**Figure 4**) illustrates the basic laws of electric charge. Unlike ordinary ink, electronic ink contains clear microcapsules the diameter of a human hair, each filled with dozens of tiny white beads suspended in a dark liquid. The white beads are negatively charged. Millions of these microcapsules are sandwiched between an opaque insulating base and a clear insulating top layer.

(a)

(b)

Figure 4

(a) Microcapsules in electronic ink rest on an opaque base layer, covered by a clear top layer.

(b) Dark pixels are formed when a positive charge is placed on the base layer. White pixels are formed when a negative charge is placed on the base layer.

Computer chips are designed to place charges in specific places on the base layer. Giving the base layer a positive charge in a certain area (a picture element, or "pixel") causes the small, negatively charged beads to sink to the bottom of the microcapsules, making the pixel, as viewed through the transparent top layer, dark. Conversely, a negative charge under the pixel drives the white beads upward in the microcapsule fluid, making the pixel white.

Placing these dark and white pixels in the correct places allows us to form characters and drawings, as on a computer screen. It is possible that in coming years, electronic ink will revolutionize publishing.

Charging By Friction

We know that some substances acquire an electric charge when rubbed with other substances. For example, an ebonite rod becomes negatively charged when rubbed with fur. This phenomenon can be explained with the help of a model of the electrical structure of matter.

An atom holds on to its electrons by the force of electrical attraction to its oppositely charged nucleus. When ebonite and fur are rubbed together, some of the electrons originally in the fur experience a stronger attraction from atomic nuclei in the ebonite than they do from nuclei in the fur. Consquently, after the rubbing, the ebonite has an excess of electrons, and the fur has a deficit (**Figure 5**).

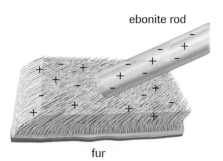

Figure 5

When ebonite and fur are rubbed together, some of the electrons from the fur are captured by more strongly attracting atomic nuclei in the ebonite. After the rubbing, the ebonite has an excess of electrons, and the fur has a deficit.

The same process occurs with many other pairs of substances, such as glass and silk. **Table 1** lists various substances that can be charged by friction. If two substances in the table are rubbed together, the substance that is lower in the table acquires an excess of electrons, the substance higher in the table a deficit.

Table 1 The Electrostatic Series

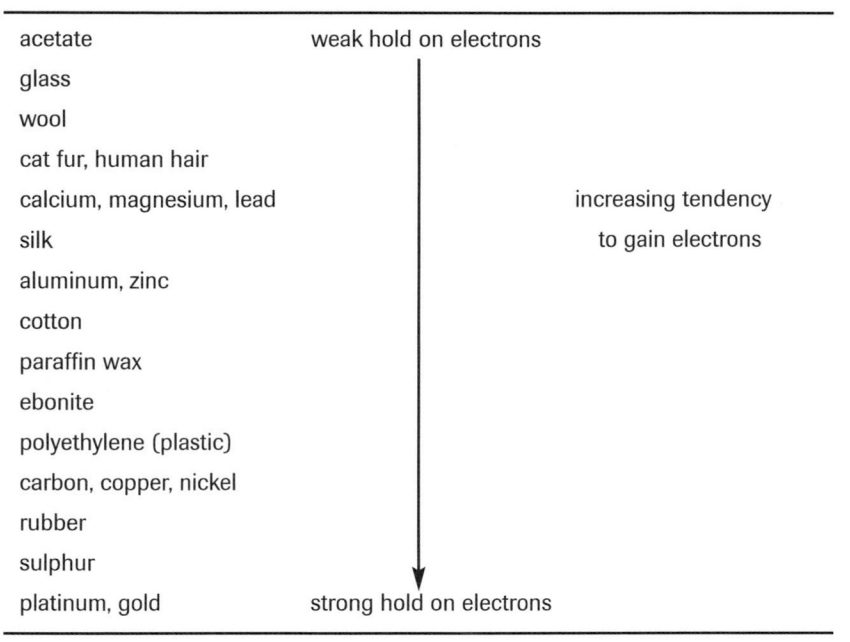

acetate — weak hold on electrons
glass
wool
cat fur, human hair
calcium, magnesium, lead — increasing tendency
silk — to gain electrons
aluminum, zinc
cotton
paraffin wax
ebonite
polyethylene (plastic)
carbon, copper, nickel
rubber
sulphur
platinum, gold — strong hold on electrons

Induced Charge Separation

The positive charges on a solid conductor are fixed, and vibrate around their fixed positions. Some of the negative electrons are quite free to move about from atom to atom. When a negatively charged ebonite rod is brought near a neutral, metallic-coated pith ball or metal-leaf electroscope, some of the many free electrons are repelled by the ebonite rod and move to the far side of the pith ball or metal-leaf electroscope (conductor).

The separation of charge on each of these objects is caused by the presence of the negative distribution of charge on the ebonite rod. This separation is called an **induced charge separation** (**Figure 6**). A charge separation will also result from the presence of a positively charged rod (**Figure 7**).

induced charge separation distribution of charge that results from a change in the distribution of electrons in or on an object

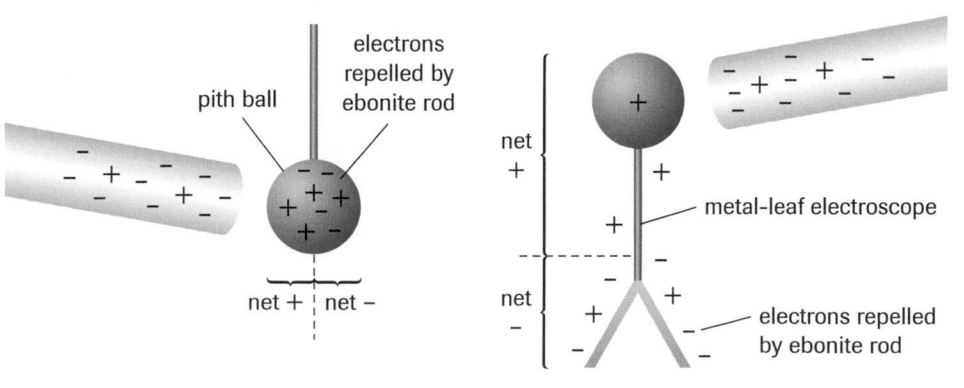

Figure 6
Induced charge separation caused by the approach of a negatively charged ebonite rod

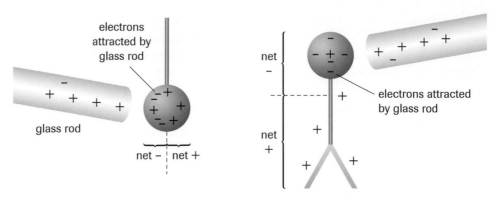

Figure 7
Induced charge separation caused by the approach of a positively charged glass rod

In both examples using the neutral pith ball, the charge induced on the near side of the pith ball is the opposite of the charge on the approaching rod. As a result, the pith ball is attracted to the rod, whether the rod is charged positively or negatively. This is how a charged object can attract some neutral objects (**Figure 8**).

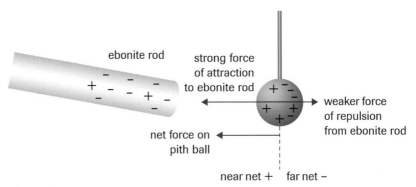

Figure 8
Attraction of a neutral pith ball to a negatively charged ebonite rod

It is true that there is repulsion between the rod and the similar charge on the far side of the ball. However, the strength of the electric forces between similar and opposite charges depends on the distance between the charges. As the distance increases, the magnitude of the force of attraction or repulsion decreases, as you will learn in more detail in the next section. Hence, there is a net attraction of the neutral ball.

Charging By Contact

When a charged ebonite rod makes contact with a neutral pith ball, some of the excess electrons on the ebonite rod, repelled by the proximity of their neighbouring excess electrons, move over to the pith ball. The pith ball and the ebonite rod share the excess of electrons that the charged rod previously had. Both now have some of the excess; hence, both are negatively charged. A similar sharing occurs when a charged ebonite rod makes contact with the knob of a metal-leaf electroscope (**Figure 9**).

When we perform the same operation with a positively charged glass rod, some of the free electrons on the pith ball or metal-leaf electroscope are attracted over to the glass rod to reduce its deficit of electrons (**Figure 10**). The electroscope and the rod share the deficit of electrons that the rod previously had, and both have a positive charge.

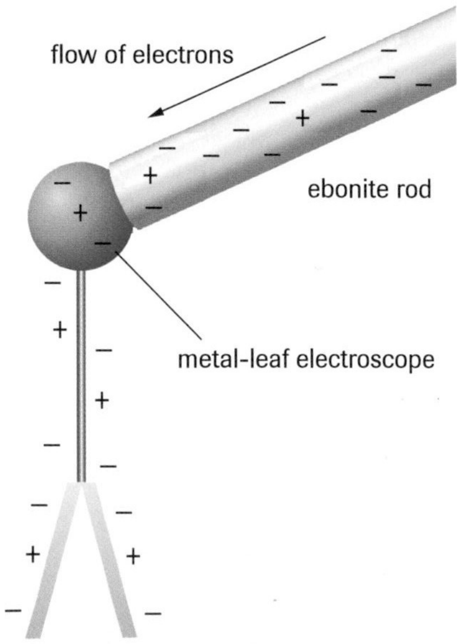

Figure 9
Charging by contact with a negatively charged ebonite rod

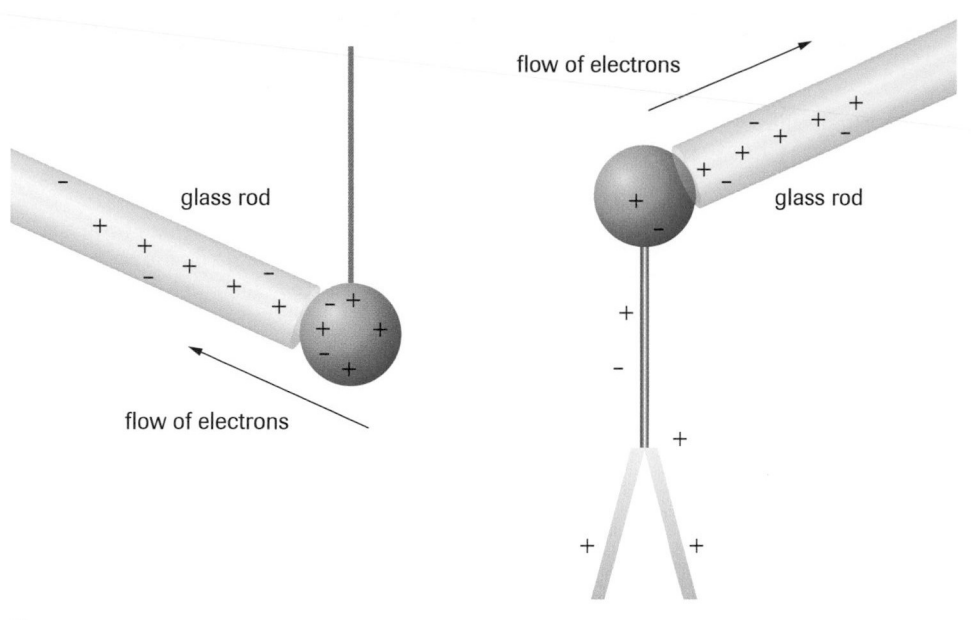

Figure 10
Charging by contact with a positively charged glass rod

Charging By Induction

We learned that a charged rod can induce a charge separation on a neutral conductor. When a charged ebonite rod is brought near the knob of a neutral metal-leaf electroscope, free electrons on the electroscope move as far away as possible from the negative rod. If you touch the electroscope with your finger, keeping the ebonite rod in place, electrons are induced to vacate the electroscope and flow through your finger (**Figure 11(a)**). When your finger is removed, the electroscope is left with a deficit of electrons and, therefore, a positive charge. The leaves will remain apart even when the ebonite rod is removed.

A positively charged rod held near the knob of an electroscope induces electrons to move through your finger onto the electroscope. Now, when the finger is removed, the electroscope is left with an excess of electrons and, therefore, a negative charge (**Figure 11(b)**).

One might ask in all these methods of charging objects how the total charge at the beginning compares to the final total charge. In all the methods of charging, one object gains electrons while the other loses the same amount. As a result, the total charge is always constant. In fact, the total charge in an isolated system is always conserved; this is called the *law of conservation of charge.*

Law of Conservation of Charge

The total charge (the difference between the amounts of positive and negative charge) within an isolated system is conserved.

As we will see in Unit 5, this is true in all cases, not just in charging objects.

(a)

electrons repelled
to ground by
negative rod

grounded electroscope
in the presence of
a negatively charged rod

(b)

electrons attracted
from ground by
positive rod

grounded electroscope
in the presence of
a positively charged rod

Figure 11
Notice that the leaves of the electroscope fall, indicating a neutral condition of the leaves while the finger is in position.

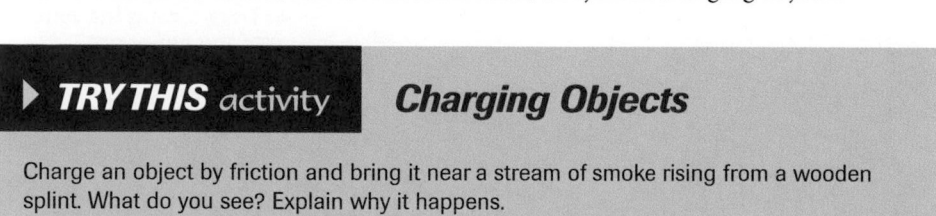

▶ **TRY THIS** activity   *Charging Objects*

Charge an object by friction and bring it near a stream of smoke rising from a wooden splint. What do you see? Explain why it happens.

Electric Charges and Electric Fields   **323**

Understanding Concepts

1. Describe how electronic ink technology illustrates the basic laws of electric charges.

2. As you walk across a rug on a dry winter day, electrons transfer from the rug to your body.
   (a) How does the charge on your body compare to the charge on the rug?
   (b) By what method are you achieving a transfer of charge? Explain your reasoning.
   (c) Why does this method of developing a charge on your body work best when the air is dry?

3. When a negatively charged object comes into contact with the metal knob at the top of a neutral metal-leaf electroscope, the two leaves, which normally hang straight down, move apart.
   (a) Explain why the leaves move apart.
   (b) Explain how the metal-leaf electroscope can be used to indicate the amount of the charge on the object.
   (c) Is it necessary for the charged object to touch the electroscope to cause the leaves to move apart? Explain your reasoning.

4. When physically upgrading the memory in your computer, you are asked to touch the metal casing before handling the chip. Explain why.

The Photocopier

The electrostatic photocopier illustrates the basic properties of electric charges discussed in this section. The central device in the process is an aluminum drum covered with a fine layer, less than 50 μm thick, of the photoconductive metal selenium (**Figure 12(a)**). *Photoconductors* are materials that act as a conductor when exposed to light and as an insulator in the dark. When the copier is being set up to make a copy, an electrode, called a

(a)

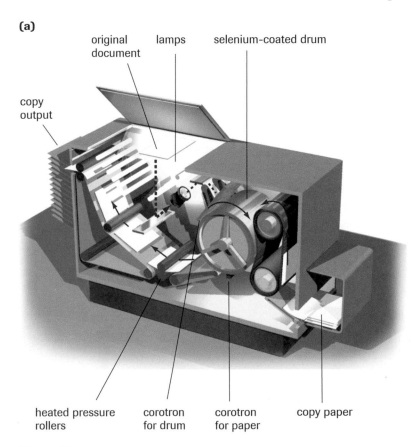

(b)

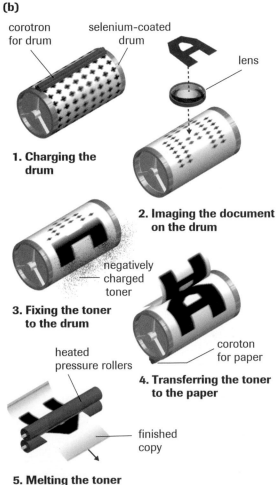

Figure 12
(a) A typical electrostatic photocopier
(b) Steps in making a photocopy

corotron, deposits a positive charge, in darkness, uniformly over the entire surface of the selenium (**Figure 12(b)**, **step 1**). The selenium will retain this charge unless exposed to light, in which case electrons from the underlying aluminum—an excellent conductor— roam through the selenium, neutralizing the positive charge.

When the copier lamp comes on and the actual copying begins, light is reflected from the document through a series of lenses and mirrors onto the selenium (**step 2**). In places where the document is white, light is strongly reflected onto the selenium drum surface, causing it to act as a conductor and lose its charge. Where the document is black, no light is reflected onto the drum, causing the charge to be retained. An electrical image of the document is thus created on the drum—neutral where the original is white, positively charged where the original is black. This image will persist as long as the drum is kept dark.

The electrical image on the drum is developed into a dry copy, using a dry black powder called "toner." Toner particles, made of plastic, are first given a negative charge, and then spread over the rotating drum (**step 3**). The particles are attracted to the charged areas of the drum but not to the neutral areas. Powder that does not adhere to the drum falls into a collecting bin for reuse.

To create a copy of this image, the toner must be transferred to paper. To do this, a second corotron gives a sheet of paper a positive charge greater than the charge on the selenium (**step 4**). As the drum rolls across this paper, toner particles that a moment ago adhered to the drum are attracted to the paper, forming an image on it.

If you were to rub your finger across the paper at this stage, the toner would smudge. To "fix," or immobilize, the image, heat from pressure rollers melts the plastic toner particles, fusing them to the paper (**step 5**).

▶ *Practice*

Understanding Concepts

5. Explain why copies emerging from an electrostatic photocopier are hot, and why they tend to stick together.

6. Which material(s) in the photocopying process have to be replenished from time to time?

7. List the properties of selenium, and explain how they are essential to the operation of an electrostatic photocopier.

Making Connections

8. If you changed the toner on a photocopier and got some toner on your hands, should you use warm water or cold water to remove it? Explain your answer.

SUMMARY *Electric Charge and the Electrical Structure of Matter*

- The laws of electric charges state: opposite electric charges attract each other; similar electric charges repel each other; charged objects attract some neutral objects.

- There are three ways of charging an object: by friction, by contact, and by induction.

Understanding Concepts

1. In the following examples, explain how the charge develops on each rod and where it can be found by discussing the movement of electrons. Compare it to the charge on the material or charging object.
   (a) A glass rod is rubbed with a plastic bag.
   (b) An ebonite rod is rubbed with fur.
   (c) A small metal rod on an insulated stand is touched by a positively charged identical metal rod.
   (d) A small metal rod on an insulated stand is touched by a negatively charged large metal sphere.

2. Explain, with an example, how to charge an object positively using only a negatively charged object.

3. Explain how an electrically neutral object can be attracted to a charged object.

4. (a) The leaves of a charged metal-leaf electroscope will eventually lose their charge and fall back down to vertical. Explain why this occurs.
   (b) Explain why the leaves of the electroscope will lose their charge faster if
   (i) the humidity in the air is higher
   (ii) the electroscope is at a higher altitude

5. (a) Identify each of the following as a conductor or insulator and explain how the properties of this type of substance are essential to photocopying:
   (i) aluminum (iii) selenium (v) rubber rollers
   (ii) paper (iv) toner
   (b) Explain what would go wrong in the photocopying process if the substances above were the opposite of what you identified.

Applying Inquiry Skills

6. Outline, using diagrams and explanations, the design of an electrostatic device suitable for filtering charged particles out of air ducts in a home. Describe any maintenance your device requires.

7. Two oppositely charged pith ball electroscopes are used to determine whether an object has a charge and, if it does, the type of charge. Discuss the observations expected and explain why both electroscopes are needed.

8. Tear a piece of paper into several small pieces. Charge a plastic pen and two other objects by rubbing them on your hair or on some fabric. Bring each charged object near the pieces of paper.
   (a) Describe what you observe, listing the three materials you charged.
   (b) Why are the pieces of paper attracted to the charged object?
   (c) Why do some pieces of paper fall off your charged objects after a short while?
   (d) When using a conducting sphere with a large charge, the paper "jumps" off instead of falling. Explain why this happens.

Making Connections

9. Laser printers work on principles similar to electrostatic photocopiers. Research laser printer technology and answer the following questions:
   (a) What is the role of the laser in making the printouts?
   (b) Why are copies made from laser printers of such high quality?

    www.science.nelson.com

10. Fabric softener sheets claim to reduce static cling between the clothes in a dryer. Research fabric softeners and answer the following questions:
    (a) Why do clothes cling to each other when they are removed from a dryer?
    (b) How does a fabric softener sheet alleviate the problem?

     www.science.nelson.com

11. Long, thin conducting strips are placed near the ends of airplane wings to dissipate the charge that builds up on the plane during flight. Research this technology and answer the following questions:
    (a) Why does an airplane develop a charge in flight?
    (b) What feature of the atmosphere plays a role in removing the charge from the plane?
    (c) Why are the conducting strips long and thin and placed near the end of the wings (**Figure 13**)?

     www.science.nelson.com

Figure 13
Long, thin conducting strips are placed at the end of airplane wings to reduce charge.

Electric Forces: Coulomb's Law **7.2**

All the matter around you contains charged particles, and it is the electric forces between these charged particles that determine the strength of the materials and the properties of the substances. But knowing whether the charges attract or repel is not enough; we must also know the factors that determine the magnitude of the electric force between charges. Investigation 7.2.1 in the Lab Activities section at the end of this chapter explores these factors.

Often scientists use well-established theories, patterns, and laws when investigating new phenomena. For example, when scientists began, in the eighteenth century, to study in a systematic way the electric force between charges, they hypothesized that the force would obey an inverse square law, drawing upon their experience with gravitation. In fact, in 1785, when the French physicist Charles Augustin de Coulomb experimentally established the quantitative nature of the electric force between charged particles, it was already widely expected to be an inverse square law.

Coulomb devised a torsion balance similar to that used by Cavendish in his study of gravitational forces but with small charged spheres in place of Cavendish's masses (**Figure 1**).

Coulomb's apparatus consisted of a silver wire attached to the middle of a light horizontal insulating rod. At one end of the rod was a pith ball covered in gold foil. At the other end, to balance the rod, a paper disk was attached. Coulomb brought an identical stationary ball into contact with the suspended ball. He charged both balls equally by touching one of them with a charged object. The two balls then repelled each other, twisting the wire holding the rod until coming to rest some distance away.

Since Coulomb knew how much force was required to twist his wire through any angle, he was able to show that the magnitude of this electric force, F_E, was inversely proportional to the square of the distance, r, between the centres of his charged spheres (**Figure 2**):

$$F_E \propto \frac{1}{r^2}$$

Coulomb also investigated the relationship between the magnitude of the electric force and the charge on the two spheres. By touching either charged sphere with an identical neutral sphere, he was able to divide its charge in half. By repeatedly touching

⚛ INVESTIGATION 7.2.1

Factors Affecting Electric Force between Charges (p. 372)
How would you show that the force between charged particles obeys an inverse square law? Can you devise two or three different experiments?

(a)

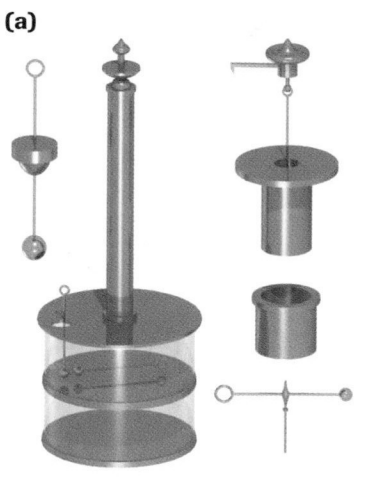

(b)

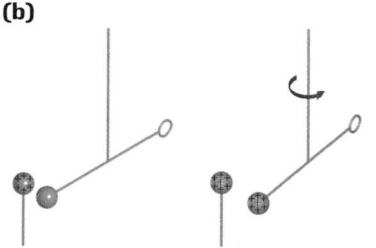

Figure 1
(a) Part of Coulomb's device
(b) The two similarly charged spheres repel each other, twisting the wire until the restoring force from the wire, which resists the twist, balances the electrostatic force.

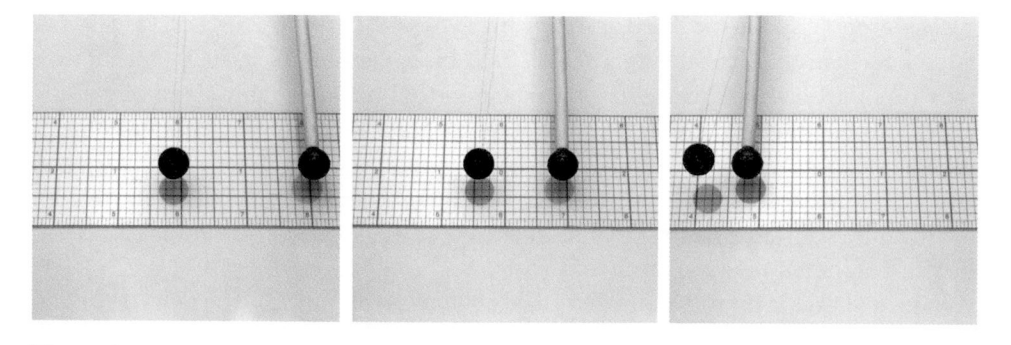

Figure 2
The electrostatic force of repulsion between two identical spheres at different distances

a charged sphere with an identical neutral sphere, he was able to reduce the charge to a quarter, an eighth, a sixteenth, … of its original value. Such manipulations revealed that, for example, halving the charge on one sphere decreased the force of electrostatic repulsion to half its original value, whereas halving both charges reduced the force to a quarter of its initial value. Coulomb concluded that the magnitude of the electric force is directly proportional to the product of the magnitudes of the charges on each sphere:

$$F_E \propto q_1 q_2$$

where q_1 and q_2 are the respective magnitudes of the charges on the two spheres.

Combining these two results, we have what has become known as Coulomb's law of electric forces:

$$F_E \propto \frac{q_1 q_2}{r^2}$$

$$\text{and} \quad F_E = \frac{k q_1 q_2}{r^2}$$

where k is a proportionality constant, known as Coulomb's constant.

Coulomb's law applies when the charges on the two spheres are very small, and the two spheres are small compared to the distance between them. In this case, the charge distribution on the surface of the spheres will be fairly uniform. If the charge on a sphere is uniformly distributed, then the force measured between the two spheres is the same as if all the charge on each sphere is concentrated at the centre. (This is why we measure r from the centre of each sphere.) It can be assumed that Coulomb's law is extremely accurate when using point charges and reasonably accurate when the spheres are small.

The difference in accuracy is due to the presence of the second charged sphere that causes the charge on the surface of each sphere to redistribute so r can no longer be measured from the centre of the spheres. When the spheres are small, the charge distribution stays nearly uniform due to the strong repulsive forces between the charges on each sphere. This is only true if the distance between the spheres is large compared to the size of the spheres.

Now *Coulomb's law* may be defined in words:

Coulomb's Law

The force between two point charges is inversely proportional to the square of the distance between the charges and directly proportional to the product of the charges.

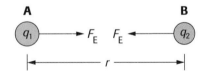

Figure 3
By Newton's third law, the electric force exerted on body A by body B is equal in magnitude and opposite in direction to the force exerted on B by A.

coulomb (C) the SI unit of electric charge

The forces act along the line connecting the two point charges. The charges will repel if the forces are alike and attract if unlike. In all cases, Coulomb's law is consistent with Newton's third law, so when using the equation to find the magnitude of one of the forces, the magnitude of the force on the other sphere is also known to be equal in magnitude but opposite in direction (**Figure 3**). However, to calculate the magnitude of an electric force quantitatively, in newtons, using Coulomb's law, it is necessary to measure the magnitude of each electric charge, q_1 and q_2, as well as establish a numerical value for the Coulomb proportionality constant, k.

Electric charge is measured in units called **coulombs** (SI unit, C). The exact definition of a coulomb of charge depends on the force acting between conductors through which charged particles are moving. This will be explained fully in Chapter 8, when we learn about these forces. How large, in practical terms, is the coulomb? A coulomb is approximately the amount of electric charge that passes through a standard 60-W light bulb (if connected to direct current) in 2 s. In comparison, an electrostatic shock that you might receive from touching a metallic doorknob after walking across a woollen rug, involves the transfer of much less than a microcoulomb. Charging by friction typically builds up around 10 nC (10^{-8} C) for every square centimetre of surface area. The attempt to add more charge typically results in a discharge into the air. Therefore, storing even 1 C of charge is difficult. Because Earth is so large, it actually stores a huge charge, roughly 400 000 C, and releases approximately 1500 C of charge every second in storm-free areas to the atmosphere. The balance of charge is maintained on Earth by other objects dumping excess charge through grounding and when lightning strikes Earth. A bolt may transfer up to 20 C (**Figure 4**).

The value of the proportionality constant k may be determined using a torsional balance similar to that used by Cavendish. By placing charges of known magnitude a given distance apart and measuring the resulting angle of twist in the suspending wire, we can find a value for the electric force causing the twist. Then, using Coulomb's law in the form

$$k = \frac{F_E r^2}{q_1 q_2}$$

a rough value for k can be determined. Over the years, a great deal of effort has gone into the design of intricate equipment for measuring k accurately. To two significant digits, the accepted value for this constant is

$$k = 9.0 \times 10^9 \ \text{N·m}^2/\text{C}^2$$

Figure 4
The charge transfer that occurs between Earth and the clouds maintains the balance of charge.

▶ ***SAMPLE* problem 1**

The magnitude of the electrostatic force between two small, essentially pointlike, charged objects is 5.0×10^{-5} N. Calculate the force for each of the following situations:

(a) The distance between the charges is doubled, while the size of the charges stays the same.

(b) The charge on one object is tripled, while the charge on the other is halved.

(c) Both of the changes in (a) and (b) occur simultaneously.

Solution

$F_1 = 5.0 \times 10^{-5}$ N

$F_2 = ?$

(a) Since $F_E \propto \dfrac{1}{r^2}$,

$$\frac{F_2}{F_1} = \left(\frac{r_1}{r_2}\right)^2$$

$$F_2 = F_1\left(\frac{r_1}{r_2}\right)^2$$

$$= (5.0 \times 10^{-5} \ \text{N})\left(\frac{1}{2}\right)^2$$

$$F_2 = 1.2 \times 10^{-5} \ \text{N}$$

When the distance between the charges is doubled, the magnitude of the force decreases to 1.2×10^{-5} N.

(b) Since $F_E \propto q_A q_B$,

$$\frac{F_2}{F_1} = \frac{q_{A_2} q_{B_2}}{q_{A_1} q_{B_1}}$$

$$F_2 = F_1 \left(\frac{q_{A_2}}{q_{A_1}}\right)\left(\frac{q_{B_2}}{q_{B_1}}\right)$$

$$= (5.0 \times 10^{-5} \text{ N}) \left(\frac{1}{2}\right)\left(\frac{3}{1}\right)$$

$$F_2 = 7.5 \times 10^{-5} \text{ N}$$

When the charge on one object is tripled, and the charge on the other object is halved, the magnitude of the force increases to 7.5×10^{-5} N.

(c) Since $F_E \propto \dfrac{q_A q_B}{r^2}$,

$$\frac{F_2}{F_1} = \left(\frac{q_{A_2} q_{B_2}}{q_{A_1} q_{B_1}}\right)\left(\frac{r_1}{r_2}\right)^2$$

$$F_2 = F_1 \left(\frac{q_{A_2}}{q_{A_1}}\right)\left(\frac{q_{B_2}}{q_{B_1}}\right)\left(\frac{r_1}{r_2}\right)^2$$

$$= (5.0 \times 10^{-5} \text{ N}) \left(\frac{1}{2}\right)\left(\frac{3}{1}\right)\left(\frac{1}{2}\right)^2$$

$$F_2 = 1.9 \times 10^{-5} \text{ N}$$

When the charges and the separation from (a) and (b) change simultaneously, the magnitude of the force decreases to 1.9×10^{-5} N.

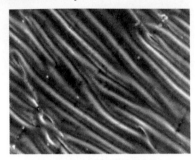
▶ *SAMPLE* problem 2

What is the magnitude of the force of repulsion between two small spheres 1.0 m apart, if each has a charge of 1.0×10^{-12} C?

Solution

$q_1 = q_2 = 1.0 \times 10^{-12}$ C

$r = 1.0$ m

$F_E = ?$

$$F_E = \frac{k q_1 q_2}{r^2}$$

$$= \frac{(9.0 \times 10^9 \text{ N·m}^2/\text{C}^2)(1.0 \times 10^{-12} \text{ C})^2}{(1.0 \text{ m})^2}$$

$$F_E = 9.0 \times 10^{-15} \text{ N}$$

The magnitude of the force of repulsion is 9.0×10^{-15} N, a very small force.

▶ Practice

Understanding Concepts

1. Two charged spheres, 10.0 cm apart, attract each other with a force of magnitude 3.0×10^{-6} N. What force results from each of the following changes, considered separately?
   (a) Both charges are doubled, while the distance remains the same.

Answer

1. (a) 1.2×10^{-5} N

(b) An uncharged, identical sphere is touched to one of the spheres and is then taken far away.

(c) The separation is increased to 30.0 cm.

2. The magnitude of the force of electrostatic repulsion between two small positively charged objects, A and B, is 3.6×10^{-5} N when $r = 0.12$ m. Find the force of repulsion if r is increased to (a) 0.24 m, (b) 0.30 m, and (c) 0.36 m.

3. Calculate the force between charges of 5.0×10^{-8} C and 1.0×10^{-7} C if they are 5.0 cm apart.

4. Calculate the magnitude of the force a 1.5×10^{-6} C charge exerts on a 3.2×10^{-4} C charge located 1.5 m away.

5. Two oppositely charged spheres, with a centre-to-centre separation of 4.0 cm, attract each other with a force of magnitude 1.2×10^{-9} N. The magnitude of the charge on one sphere is twice the magnitude of the charge on the other. Determine the magnitude of the charge on each.

6. Two equal uniform spherical charges, each of magnitude 1.1×10^{-7} C, experience an electrostatic force of magnitude 4.2×10^{-4} N. How far apart are the centres of the two charges?

7. Two identical small spheres of mass 2.0 g are fastened to the ends of an insulating thread of length 0.60 m. The spheres are suspended by a hook in the ceiling from the centre of the thread. The spheres are given identical electric charges and hang in static equilibrium, with an angle of 30.0° between the string halves, as shown in **Figure 5**. Calculate the magnitude of the charge on each sphere.

Answers

1. (b) 1.5×10^{-6} N

(c) 3.3×10^{-7} N

2. (a) 9.0×10^{-6} N

(b) 5.8×10^{-6} N

(c) 4.0×10^{-6} N

3. 1.8×10^{-2} N

4. 1.9 N

5. 1.0×10^{-11} C; 2.0×10^{-11} C

6. 0.51 m

7. 1.2×10^{-7} C

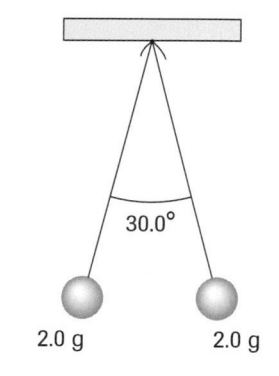

Figure 5
For question 7

Coulomb's Law versus the Law of Universal Gravitation

There are many similarities between Coulomb's law $\left(F_{\mathrm{E}} = \dfrac{kq_1q_2}{r^2} \right)$ and Newton's law of universal gravitation $\left(F_{\mathrm{g}} = \dfrac{Gm_1m_2}{r^2} \right)$:

- Both are inverse square laws that are also proportional to the product of another quantity; for gravity it is the product of two masses, and for the electric force it is the product of the two charges.

- The forces act along the line joining the centres of the masses or charges.

- The magnitude of the force is the same as the force that would be measured if all the mass or charge is concentrated at a point at the centre of the sphere. Therefore, distance in both cases is measured from the centres of the spheres. In both cases we are assuming that r is longer than the radius of the object.

These parallels cannot be viewed as a coincidence. Their existence implies that there may be other parallels between electric and gravitational forces.

However, the two forces also differ in some important ways:

- The electric force can attract or repel, depending on the charges involved, whereas the gravitational force can only attract.

- The universal gravitational constant, $G = 6.67 \times 10^{-11}$ N·m²/kg², is very small, meaning that in many cases the gravitational force can be ignored unless at least one of the masses is very large. In contrast, Coulomb's constant, $k = 9.0 \times 10^9$ N·m²/C², is a very large number (over one hundred billion billion times bigger than G), implying that even small charges can result in noticeable forces.

Just as a mass can be attracted gravitationally by more than one body at once, so a charge can experience electric forces from more than one body at once. Experiments have shown that the force between two charges can be determined using Coulomb's law independently of the other charges present, and that the net force on a single charge is the vector sum of all these independently calculated electric forces acting on it. If all the charges lie on a straight line, we can treat electric forces like scalars, using plus and minus signs to keep track of directions. If the charges do not lie on a straight line, trigonometry and symmetries are used.

▶ SAMPLE problem 3

Charged spheres A and B are fixed in position (**Figure 6**) and have charges $+4.0 \times 10^{-6}$ C and -2.5×10^{-7} C, respectively. Calculate the net force on sphere C, whose charge is $+6.4 \times 10^{-6}$ C.

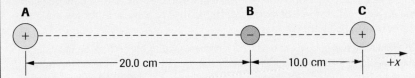

Figure 6

Solution

$q_A = +4.0 \times 10^{-6}$ C $\quad r_{AB} = 20.0$ cm

$q_B = -2.5 \times 10^{-7}$ C $\quad r_{BC} = 10.0$ cm

$q_C = +6.4 \times 10^{-6}$ C $\quad \sum \vec{F}_{net} = ?$

Since all three charges are in a straight line, we can take the vector nature of force into account by assigning forces to the right as positive. Sphere C has forces acting on it from spheres A and B. We first determine the magnitude of the force exerted on C by A:

$$F_{CA} = \frac{kq_A q_C}{r_{CA}^2}$$

$$= \frac{(9.0 \times 10^9 \text{ N·m}^2/\text{C}^2)(4.0 \times 10^{-6} \text{ C})(6.4 \times 10^{-6} \text{ C})}{(0.30 \text{ m})^2}$$

$$F_{CA} = 2.6 \text{ N}$$

Therefore, $\vec{F}_{CA} = 2.6$ N [right].

Next, we determine the magnitude of the force exerted on C by B:

$$F_{CB} = \frac{kq_B q_C}{r_{CB}^2}$$

$$= \frac{(9.0 \times 10^9 \text{ N·m}^2/\text{C}^2)(2.5 \times 10^{-7} \text{ C})(6.4 \times 10^{-6} \text{ C})}{(0.10 \text{ m})^2}$$

$$F_{CB} = 1.4 \text{ N}$$

Our formulation of Coulomb's law gives only the magnitude of the force. But since B and C are dissimilar charges, we know that B attracts C leftward, so the direction of the force exerted on C by B is

$$\vec{F}_{BC} = 1.4 \text{ N [left]}$$

The net force acting on sphere C is the sum of $\vec{F}_{CA}$ and $\vec{F}_{CB}$:

$$\Sigma\vec{F} = \vec{F}_{CA} + \vec{F}_{CB}$$
$$= 2.6 \text{ N [right]} + 1.4 \text{ N [left]}$$
$$\Sigma\vec{F} = 1.2 \text{ N [right]}$$

The net force acting on sphere C is 1.2 N [right].

▶ **SAMPLE** problem **4**

Identical spheres A, B, C, and D, each with a charge of magnitude 5.0×10^{-6} C, are situated at the corners of a square whose sides are 25 cm long. Two diagonally opposite charges are positive, the other two negative, as shown in **Figure 7**. Calculate the net force acting on each of the four spheres.

Solution

$q_A = q_B = q_C = q_D = 5.0 \times 10^{-6}$ C

$s = 25$ cm $= 0.25$ m

$r = 35$ cm $= 0.35$ m

$\Sigma\vec{F} = ?$

Each sphere experiences three electric forces, one from each of the two adjacent charges (acting along the sides of the square) and one from the more distant charge (acting along the diagonal). While some of the 12 forces acting will be attractions and some will be repulsions, each of the 12 forces has one of just two possible magnitudes: one magnitude in the case of equal charges 25 cm apart, the other in the case of equal charges separated by the length of the diagonal, 35.4 cm. We begin by determining these two magnitudes:

$$F_{side} = \frac{kq_1q_2}{s^2}$$

$$= \frac{(9.0 \times 10^9 \text{ N·m}^2/\text{C}^2)(5.0 \times 10^{-6} \text{ C})^2}{(0.25 \text{ m})^2}$$

$$F_{side} = 3.6 \text{ N}$$

$$F_{diag} = \frac{kq_1q_2}{r^2}$$

$$= \frac{(9.0 \times 10^9 \text{ N·m}^2/\text{C}^2)(5.0 \times 10^{-6} \text{ C})^2}{(0.35 \text{ m})^2}$$

$$F_{diag} = 1.8 \text{ N}$$

Then draw a vector diagram showing each of these forces with its vector in the appropriate direction, whether an attraction or repulsion. The required diagram is shown in **Figure 8**. We find that the forces acting on each sphere are similar, comprising in each case an attraction of 3.6 N along two sides of the square and a repulsion of 1.8 N along the diagonal. The net force on each sphere is the vector sum of these three forces. As an example, we find the three-vector sum for sphere A. Using the rules for vector addition, and drawing the vectors tip-to-tail, we obtain the diagram in **Figure 9**.

The desired sum (the dashed vector) has a magnitude equal to the length of the hypotenuse in the vector triangle minus 1.8 N. The magnitude of the hypotenuse is

$$\sqrt{(3.6 \text{ N})^2 + (3.6 \text{ N})^2} = 5.1 \text{ N}$$

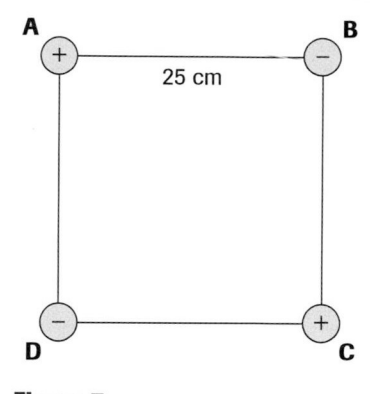

Figure 7
For Sample Problem 4

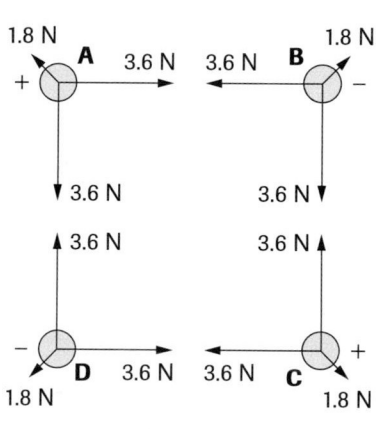

Figure 8
For the solution to Sample Problem 4

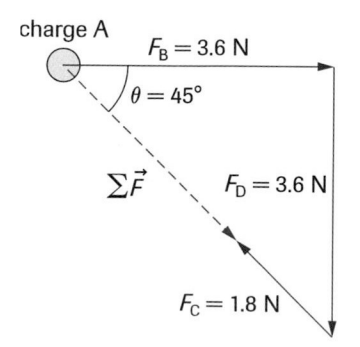

Figure 9
The net force on charge A

Therefore,

$$|\sum \vec{F}| = 5.1 \text{ N} - 1.8 \text{ N}$$
$$|\sum \vec{F}| = 3.3 \text{ N}$$

We can now find the direction of the vector sum from the diagram:

$$\sum \vec{F} = 3.3 \text{ N } [45° \text{ down from right}]$$

The same calculation at each of the other three corners produces the same result: a net force of 3.3 N directed inward along the corresponding diagonal.

The same problem may be readily solved using components of the forces, in the x and y directions, acting on each sphere.

For the force on sphere A:

$$\sum \vec{F} = \vec{F}_B + \vec{F}_C + \vec{F}_D$$

Components in the x direction:

$$F_{Ax} = F_{Bx} + F_{Cx} + F_{Dx} = 3.6 \text{ N} + (-1.8 \text{ N cos } 45°) + 0 = 2.3 \text{ N}$$

Components in the y direction:

$$F_{Ay} = F_{By} + F_{Cy} + F_{Dy} = 0 + (+1.8 \text{ N cos } 45°) + (-3.6 \text{ N}) = -2.3 \text{ N}$$

Therefore,

$$\sum F = \sqrt{(F_{Ax})^2 + (F_{Ay})^2}$$
$$= \sqrt{(2.3 \text{ N}) + (-2.3 \text{ N})^2}$$
$$\sum F = 3.3 \text{ N}$$

$$\theta = \tan^{-1} \frac{|F_{Ay}|}{|F_{Ax}|}$$
$$= \tan^{-1} 1$$
$$\theta = 45°$$

$$\sum \vec{F} = 3.3 \text{ N } [45° \text{ down from right}]$$

The net force acting on each charge is 3.3 N toward the centre of the square.

▶ *Practice*

Understanding Concepts

8. Three objects, carrying charges of -4.0×10^{-6} C, -6.0×10^{-6} C, and $+9.0 \times 10^{-6}$ C, are placed in a line, equally spaced from left to right by a distance of 0.50 m. Calculate the magnitude and direction of the net force acting on each.

9. Three spheres, each with a negative charge of 4.0×10^{-6} C, are fixed at the vertices of an equilateral triangle whose sides are 0.20 m long. Calculate the magnitude and direction of the net electric force on each sphere.

Answers

8. 0.54 N [left]; 2.8 N [right]; 2.3 N [left]

9. 6.2 N [outward, 150° away from each side]

 **SUMMARY** *Electric Forces: Coulomb's Law*

- Coulomb's law states that the force between two point charges is inversely proportional to the square of the distance between the charges and directly proportional to the product of the charges: $F_E = \dfrac{kq_1q_2}{r^2}$, where $k = 9.0 \times 10^9 \ \text{N·m}^2/\text{C}^2$.

- Coulomb's law applies when the charges on the two spheres are very small, and the two spheres are small compared to the distance between them.

- There are similarities and differences between Coulomb's law and Newton's law of universal gravitation: Both are inverse square laws that are also proportional to the product of quantities that characterize the bodies involved; the forces act along the line joining the two centres of the masses or charges; and the magnitude of the force is accurately given by the force that would be measured if all the mass or charge is concentrated at a point at the centre of the sphere. However, the gravitational force can only attract while the electric force can attract or repel. The universal gravitational constant is very small, while Coulomb's constant is very large.

▶ *Section 7.2* **Questions**

Understanding Concepts

1. (a) Describe the electric force between two small charges and compare this force to the gravitational force between two small masses. How are the two forces different?

   (b) State Coulomb's law and Newton's law of universal gravitation. In which respect are these two laws similar? How are they different? Organize your answer by copying and completing **Figure 10**.

   Venn Diagram

   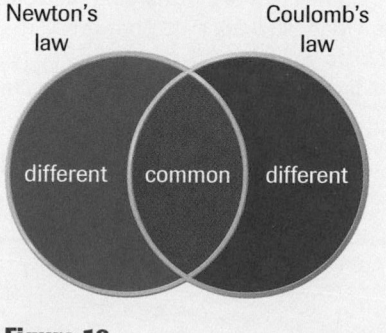

   Figure 10

2. Two identical metal spheres, each with positive charge q, are separated by a centre-to-centre distance r. What effect will each of the following changes have on the magnitude of the electric force F_E exerted on each sphere by the other?

   (a) The distance between the two spheres is tripled.

   (b) The distance between the two spheres is halved.

   (c) Both charges are doubled.

   (d) One of the charges becomes negative.

   (e) One sphere is touched by an identical neutral sphere, which is then taken far away and the distance is decreased to $\dfrac{2}{3}r$.

3. Two small spheres of charge $+5.0 \ \mu C$ and $-4.0 \ \mu C$ are separated by a distance of 2.0 m. Determine the magnitude of the force that each sphere exerts on the other.

4. Two 10.0-kg masses, each with a charge of $+1.0$ C, are separated by a distance of 0.500 km in interstellar space, far from other masses and charges.

   (a) Calculate the force of gravity between the two objects.

   (b) Calculate the electric force between the two objects.

   (c) Draw FBDs showing all the forces acting on the objects.

   (d) Calculate the net force on each object, and use it to find the initial acceleration of each object.

   (e) Repeat (c) ignoring the gravitational force. What have you found?

5. Two identically charged small spheres, of negligible mass, are separated by a centre-to-centre distance of 2.0 m. The force between them is 36 N. Calculate the charge on each sphere.

6. Neutral metal sphere A, of mass 0.10 kg, hangs from an insulating wire 2.0 m long. An identical metal sphere B, with charge $-q$, is brought into contact with sphere A. The spheres repel and settle as shown in **Figure 11**. Calculate the initial charge on B.

Figure 11

7. Three objcts with charges $+5.0\ \mu C$, $-6.0\ \mu C$, and $+7.0\ \mu C$ are placed in a line, as in **Figure 12**. Determine the magnitude and direction of the net electric force on each charge.

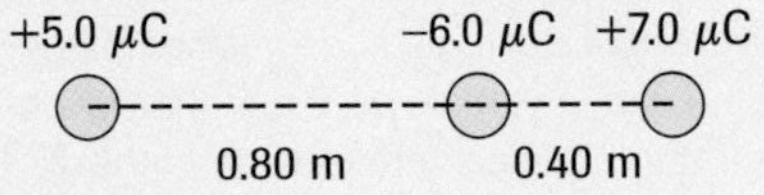

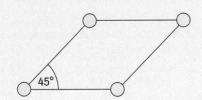

Figure 12

8. Four objects, each with a positive charge of 1.0×10^{-5} C, are placed at the corners of a 45° rhombus with sides of length 1.0 m, as in **Figure 13**. Calculate the magnitude of the net force on each charge.

Figure 13

9. Two small spheres, with charges 1.6×10^{-5} C and 6.4×10^{-5} C, are 2.0 m apart. The charges have the same sign. Where, relative to these two spheres, should a third sphere, of opposite charge 3.0×10^{-6} C, be placed if the third sphere is to experience no net electrical force? Do we really need to know the charge or sign of the third object?

10. Two spheres are attached to two identical springs and separated by 8.0 cm, as in **Figure 14**. When a charge of 2.5×10^{-6} C is placed on each sphere, the distance between the spheres doubles. Calculate the force constant k of the springs.

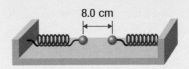

Figure 14

Applying Inquiry Skills

11. A charged sphere is attached to an insulating spring on a horizontal surface. Assume no charge is lost to the surroundings. An identical sphere is attached to an insulating rod. Using only this equipment, design an experiment to verify Coulomb's law. How will the compression of the spring be related to the product of the charges and the distance between the charges?

Making Connections

12. Under normal circumstances, we are not aware of the electric or gravitational forces between two objects.
    (a) Explain why this is so for each force.
    (b) Describe an example for each in which we are aware of the force. Explain why.

13. Assume the electric force, instead of gravity, holds the Moon in its orbit around Earth. Assume the charge on Earth is $-q$ and the charge on the Moon is $+q$.
    (a) Find q, the magnitude of the charge required on each to hold the Moon in orbit. (See Appendix C for data.)
    (b) How stable do you think this orbit would be over long periods of time? (Will the charges stay constant?) Explain what might happen to the Moon.

Most audio equipment and computer towers are encased in metal boxes. Why do you think the metal is necessary? Can you believe that there is some connection between this question and the recent interest in the DNA mapping of the human genome? The common thread is electric force. To learn more about these applications, we must take a closer look at electric force.

The electric force is an "action-at-a-distance" force, since electric charges attract or repel each other even when not in contact. According to Coulomb's law, the magnitude of the force between two point charges is given by

$$F_E = \frac{kq_1q_2}{r^2}$$

As you learned in Section 7.2, this kind of action-at-a-distance force is similar to the gravitational force between two masses. The force of gravity extends through space over vast distances, attracting planets to stars to form solar systems, multitudes of solar systems and stars to each other to form galaxies, and galaxies to each other to form galaxy clusters. How can one piece of matter affect the motion of another across a void, whether gravitationally or electrically? This is a fundamental puzzle in physics. The dominant theory today is the **field theory**.

Field theory was introduced to help scientists visualize the pattern of forces surrounding an object. Eventually, the field itself became the medium transmitting the action-at-a-distance force. We define a *field of force* as follows:

> **Field of Force**
>
> A field of force exists in a region of space when an appropriate object placed at any point in the field experiences a force.

According to this concept, any mass, such as Earth, produces a field of force because any other mass placed within its gravitational field will experience a force of attraction. Similarly, any charged object creates an electric field of force around it because another charged object placed within this field will experience a force of repulsion or attraction. To the founding physicists of electric field theory, the idea of an electric field of force became so fundamental in their explanations of action-at-a-distance forces that the electric field of force changed from representing the pattern of the forces to an actual physical quantity that charges interacted with to experience force. Faraday would explain the electric force by saying that a charged object sends out an electric field into space; another charge detects this field when immersed in it and reacts according to its charge. This is not a new concept for us since both the gravitational and the magnetic forces are commonly represented by fields (**Figure 1**).

Faraday was the first to represent electric fields by drawing lines of force around charges instead of force vectors. Force vectors show the direction and magnitude of the electric force on a small, positive test charge placed at each and every point in the field. For the sake of simplicity, continuous field lines are drawn to show the direction of this force at all points in the field (**Figure 2**).

field theory the theory that explains interactions between bodies or particles in terms of fields

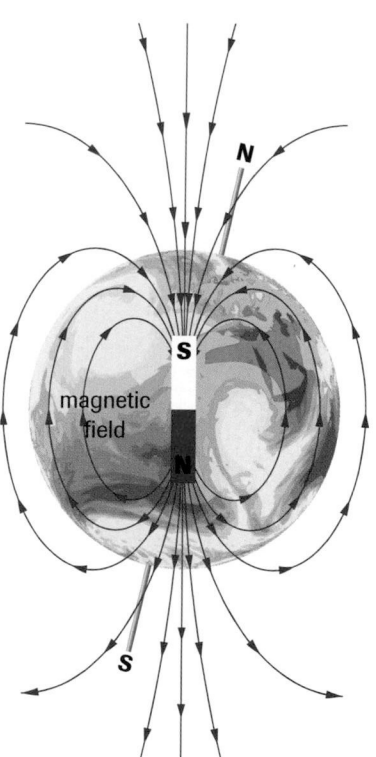

Figure 1
Earth's gravitational field and a magnetic field

Electric Charges and Electric Fields **337**

electric field ($\vec{\varepsilon}$) the region in which a force is exerted on an electric charge; the electric force per unit positive charge

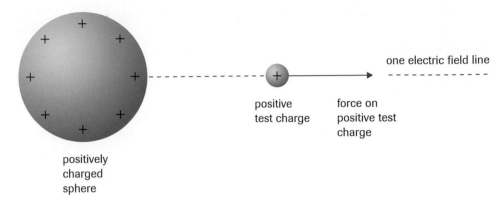

Figure 2
A small positive test charge is used to determine the direction of the electric field lines around a charge.

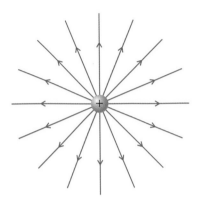

Figure 3
Positively charged sphere

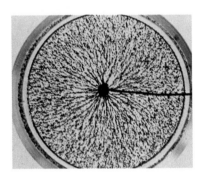

Figure 4
The electric field of a positive charge demonstrated by rayon fibres in oil

Since the electric field is thought of as a quantity that exists independently of whether or not a test charge q is present, then we may define it without referring to the other charge. Therefore, the **electric field** $\vec{\varepsilon}$ at any point is defined as the electric force per unit positive charge and is a vector quantity:

$$\vec{\varepsilon} = \frac{\vec{F}_E}{q}$$

where the units are newtons per coulomb (N/C) in SI.

Consider, for example, the electric field around a sphere whose surface is uniformly covered in positive charge. We consider this the primary charge. The test charge, which is always positive by convention, should be small to minimize its effect on the field we are investigating. Since both charges are positive, the test charge will be repelled no matter where we place it. If we place a test charge some distance to the right of the positively charged sphere, the force on the test charge will be to the right. If the positive test charge is then placed at other similar points around the sphere, and in each case a field line is drawn, the entire electric field will appear as shown in **Figures 3** and **4**.

In an electric field diagram for a single point charge, the relative distance between adjacent field lines indicates the magnitude of the electric field at any point. In a region where the electric field is strong, adjacent field lines are close together. More widely spaced field lines indicate a weaker electric field.

If the positively charged sphere is small enough to be considered a point charge, then the electric field, at any point a distance r from the point, is directed radially outward and has a magnitude of

$$\varepsilon = \frac{F_E}{q}$$
$$= \frac{kq_1q}{r^2q}$$
$$\varepsilon = \frac{kq_1}{r^2}$$

where q_1 is the charge on the sphere.

The electric field of a negatively charged sphere is identical, except that the field lines point in the opposite direction, inward (**Figure 5**).

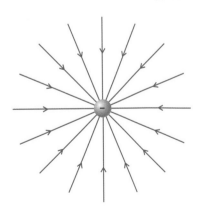

Figure 5
Negatively charged sphere

Electric fields are used in a process called *electrophoresis* to separate molecules. Electrophoresis takes advantage of the fact that many large molecules are charged and will move if placed in an electric field. When placed in a medium under the influence of an electric field, different types of molecules will move at different rates because they have different charges and masses. Eventually, the different types of molecules will separate as they move under the influence of the electric field. The four columns on the left in **Figure 6** result from DNA taken from different family members. Electrophoresis generates the separated bands, which act as a fingerprint unique to each person. You can see in **Figure 6** that each child (C) shares some similar bands with the mother (M) or father (F), as you would expect.

More complex electric fields result when more than one point charge is present or when the object is too large to be considered a point charge. In such cases, the electric field at any point is the vector sum of the electric fields of all the point charges contributing to the net electric force at that point. This idea is called the *superposition principle* in physics. The electric fields of some typical charge distributions are shown in **Figure 7**.

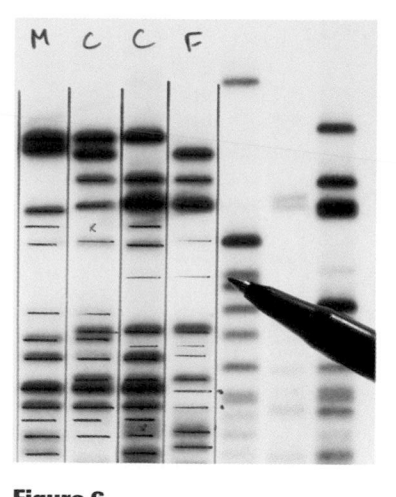

Figure 6
Electrophoresis uses electric fields to separate large charged molecules. The bands of DNA serve as a unique fingerprint for an individual. Related individuals show similarities in their bands.

(a)   **(b)**

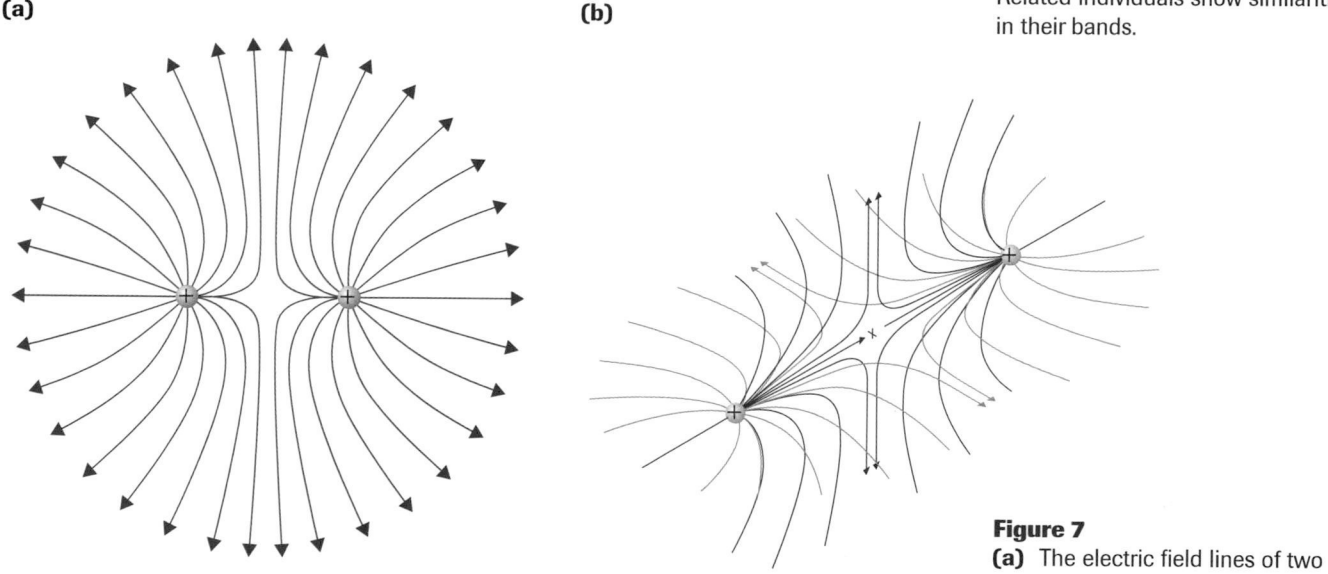

Figure 7
(a) The electric field lines of two equal positive charges viewed along a line of sight perpendicular to the system axis. Notice the electric field is zero at the midpoint of the two charges.
(b) The electric field is actually three-dimensional in nature, but it is often drawn in two dimensions for simplicity. The three-dimensional field can be obtained by rotating diagrams by 180° when symmetry permits (it is often not symmetric).

Drawing Electric Fields

By convention, in electrostatic representations electric field lines start on positive charges and end on negative charges. This means that electric field lines diverge or spread apart from positive point charges and converge onto negative point charges. In many of the diagrams in this text the ends of the field lines are not shown, but when they do end it is always on a negative charge.

When drawing electric fields, keep in mind that *field lines never cross*. You are drawing the net electric field in the region that indicates the direction of the net force on a test charge. If two field lines were to cross, it would mean that the charge has two different net forces with different directions. This is not possible. The test charge will experience a single net force in the direction of the electric field.

The dipole fields in **Figure 8** with two equal and opposite charges are very special cases of an electric field because they revolve around the line connecting the two charges gives a picture of the three-dimensional field. This is not normally the case. When the charges are unequal, the line density is not an accurate representation of the relative field strength.

(a)

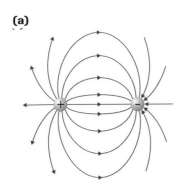

(b)

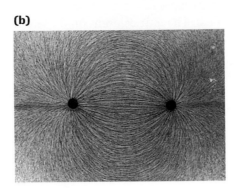

(c)

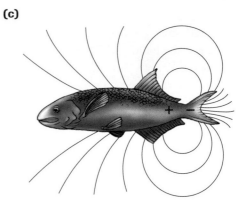

Figure 8
(a) The electric field of two equal but opposite charges (dipole)
(b) The field of a dipole revealed by rayon fibres in oil
(c) Some organisms produce electric fields to detect nearby objects that affect the field.

Consider the case of two charges of different magnitudes, one charge with $\pm 4q$ and the other oppositely charged with $\mp q$. The number of field lines leaving a positive charge or approaching a negative charge is proportional to the magnitude of the charge, so there are many more field lines around the $4q$ charge than the q charge. However, the density of the field lines (the number of lines in a given area) in the area around the charges does not indicate the relative strength of the field in this case. The fact that the electric field is actually strongest on the line between the two charges is not reflected in the field line density. In such a situation, we can use colour as a means of indicating relative strength of field (as in **Figure 9**, where red is chosen for the strongest field and blue for the weakest). Far from both charges, the field resembles the field of a single charge of magnitude $3q$ (**Figure 10**).

Figure 9
The electric field around two charges of different magnitudes. The density of the field lines is arbitrary. In this diagram, colour, not density of field lines, is used to indicate field strength.

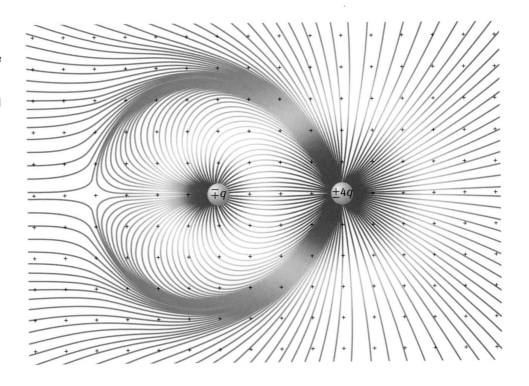

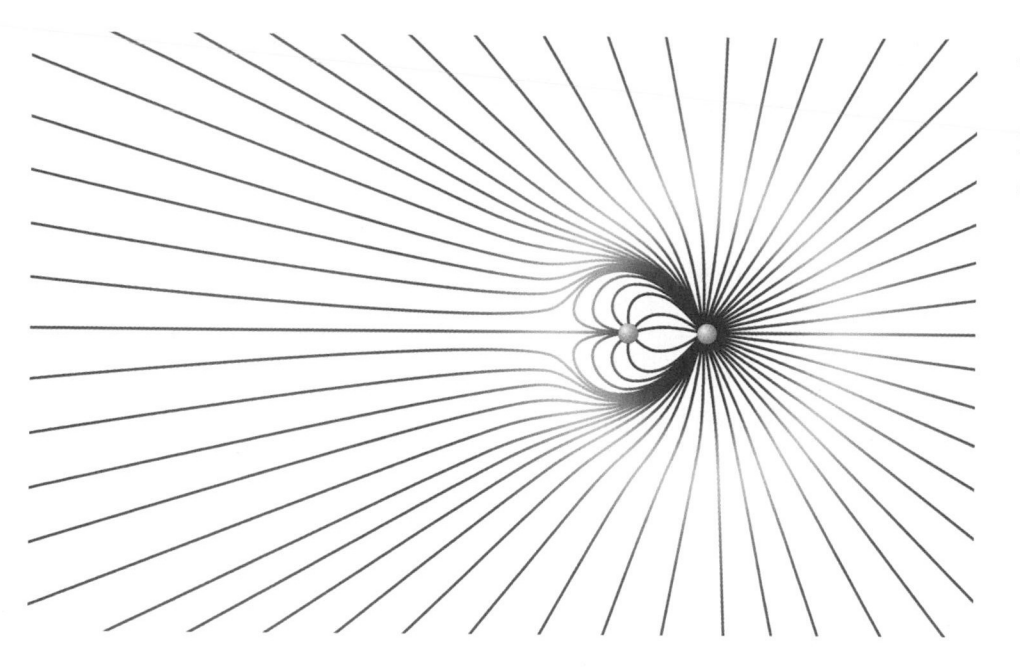

Figure 10
The same charges, showing a more remote portion of the field. At a great distance, the field resembles the field of a single point charge at a distance.

Next, consider the electric field of two large, equally charged, parallel, flat conducting plates close together, the top plate positive and the bottom plate negative (**Figure 11(a)**). The plates are too large, compared to their separation distance, to be considered point charges. The attraction between the charges draws most of the charge to the inner surfaces of the plates. Morever, the charge distributes itself approximately uniformly over the inner surfaces. When a positive test charge is placed anywhere between the two plates, a reasonable distance away from the edges, the charge is repelled by the upper plate and attracted to the lower plate. The net force on the test charge points straight down. This means that the electric field is always straight down and uniform. To indicate this, we draw the electric field lines straight down, parallel to each other, and evenly spaced (**Figure 11(b)**). As long as the spacing between the plates is not too large, the electric field lines will still run straight across from one plate to the other, parallel to each other, so the electric field between the plates does not depend on the separation of the plates. The departures from uniformity are mainly at the edges of the plates, where there are "edge effects" in the electric field. Those effects can be neglected between the plates as long as the plate area is large in comparison with the separation(**Figure 11(c)**. The magnitude of the electric field between the two plates is directly proportional to the charge per unit area on the plates. The parallel plate condenser is used very often when a constant electric field is required.

(a)

(b)

(c)

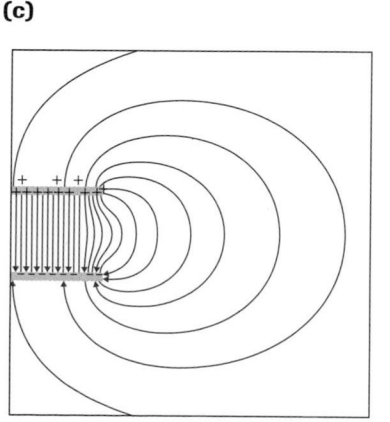

Figure 11
(a) Rayon fibres in oil demonstrate the uniform field between plates.
(b) The electric field between two parallel plates
(c) An "edge effect," negligible in the fundamental theory of parallel plates, produces a weak field, shown here with field lines very far apart at the edge of the plates.

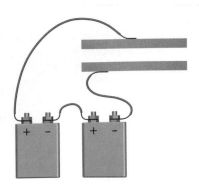

Figure 12
To charge the plates, connect them to opposite terminals of a battery or power supply. Doubling the charge on each plate requires connecting two identical batteries in series or doubling the electric potential difference of the power supply.

Here is a summary of the properties of the electric field produced by parallel plates:

- The electric field in the region outside the parallel plates is zero (except for a slight bulging of the field near the edges of the plates—"edge effects").
- The electric field is constant everywhere in the space between the parallel plates. The electric field lines are straight, equally spaced, and perpendicular to the parallel plates.
- The magnitude of the electric field at any point between the plates (except near the edges) depends only on the magnitude of the charge on each plate.
- $\varepsilon \propto q$, where q is the charge per unit area on each plate (**Figure 12**).

▶ **SAMPLE** problem 1

What is the electric field 0.60 m away from a small sphere with a positive charge of 1.2×10^{-8} C?

Solution

$q = 1.2 \times 10^{-8}$ C

$r = 0.60$ m

$\varepsilon = ?$

$$\varepsilon = \frac{kq}{r^2}$$

$$= \frac{(9.0 \times 10^9 \text{ N·m}^2/\text{C}^2)(1.2 \times 10^{-8} \text{ C})}{(0.60 \text{ m})^2}$$

$\varepsilon = 3.0 \times 10^2$ N/C

$\vec{\varepsilon} = 3.0 \times 10^2$ N/C [radially outward]

The electric field is 3.0×10^2 N/C [radially outward].

▶ **SAMPLE** problem 2

Two charges, one of 3.2×10^{-9} C, the other of -6.4×10^{-9} C, are 42 cm apart. Calculate the net electric field at a point P, 15 cm from the positive charge, on the line connecting the charges.

Solution

$q_1 = 3.2 \times 10^{-9}$ C

$q_2 = -6.4 \times 10^{-9}$ C

$\sum \varepsilon = ?$

$q_1 = 3.2 \times 10^{-9}$ C

P $q_2 = -6.4 \times 10^{-9}$ C

The net field at P is the vector sum of the fields $\vec{\varepsilon}_1$ and $\vec{\varepsilon}_2$ from the two charges. We calculate the fields separately, then take their vector sum:

$r_1 = 15$ cm $= 0.15$ m

$$\varepsilon_1 = \frac{kq_1}{r_1^2}$$

$$= \frac{(9.0 \times 10^9 \text{ N·m}^2/\text{C}^2)(3.2 \times 10^{-9} \text{ C})}{(0.15 \text{ m})^2}$$

$\varepsilon_1 = 1.3 \times 10^3$ N/C

$\vec{\varepsilon}_1 = 1.3 \times 10^3$ N/C [right]

$r_2 = 42 \text{ cm} - 15 \text{ cm} = 27 \text{ cm}$

$$\varepsilon_2 = \frac{kq_2}{r_2{}^2}$$

$$= \frac{(9.0 \times 10^9 \text{ N·m}^2/\text{C}^2)(6.4 \times 10^{-9} \text{ C})}{(0.27 \text{ m})^2}$$

$\varepsilon_2 = 7.9 \times 10^2 \text{ N/C}$

$\vec{\varepsilon}_2 = 7.9 \times 10^2 \text{ N/C [right]}$

$$\Sigma\vec{\varepsilon} = \vec{\varepsilon}_1 + \vec{\varepsilon}_2 = 2.1 \times 10^3 \text{ N/C [right]}$$

The net electric field is 2.1×10^3 N/C [right].

▶ SAMPLE problem 3

The magnitude of the electric field between the plates of a parallel plate capacitor is 3.2×10^2 N/C. How would the field magnitude differ

(a) if the charge on each plate were to double?

(b) if the plate separation were to triple?

Solution

$\varepsilon = 3.2 \times 10^2 \text{ N/C}$

(a) Since $\varepsilon \propto q$, then $\dfrac{\varepsilon_2}{\varepsilon_1} = \dfrac{q_2}{q_1}$

$$\varepsilon_2 = \varepsilon_1\left(\frac{q_2}{q_1}\right)$$

$$= (3.2 \times 10^2 \text{ N/C})\left(\frac{2}{1}\right)$$

$$\varepsilon_2 = 6.4 \times 10^2 \text{ N/C}$$

If the charge on each plate were to double, the magnitude of the electric field would double.

(b) Since $\varepsilon \propto q$ only, changing r has no effect.

Therefore, $\varepsilon_2 = \varepsilon_1 = 3.2 \times 10^2$ N/C.

If the plate separation were to triple, the magnitude of the electric field would not change.

▶ Practice

Understanding Concepts

1. A negative charge of 2.4×10^{-6} C experiences an electric force of magnitude 3.2 N, acting to the left.
   (a) Calculate the magnitude and direction of the electric field at that point.
   (b) Calculate the value of the field at that point if a charge of 4.8×10^{-6} C replaces the charge of 2.4×10^{-6} C.

2. At a certain point P in an electric field, the magnitude of the electric field is 12 N/C. Calculate the magnitude of the electric force that would be exerted on a point charge of 2.5×10^{-7} C, located at P.

3. Calculate the magnitude and direction of the electric field at a point 3.0 m to the right of a positive point charge of 5.4×10^{-4} C.

Answers

1. (a) 1.3×10^6 N/C [right]

   (b) 1.3×10^6 N/C [right]

2. 3.0×10^{-6} N

3. 5.4×10^5 N/C [right]

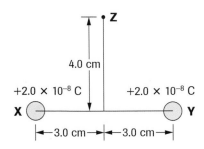

Figure 14
For question 5

4. Calculate the magnitude and direction of the electric field at point Z in **Figure 13**, due to the charged spheres at points X and Y.

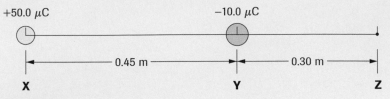

Figure 13

5. Determine the magnitude and direction of the electric field at point Z in **Figure 14**, due to the charges at points X and Y.

6. The electric field strength midway between a pair of oppositely charged parallel plates is 3.0×10^3 N/C. Find the magnitude of the electric field midway between this point and the positively charged plate.

7. In the parallel plate apparatus in question 6, what would the electric field strength become if half of the charge were removed from each plate and the separation of the plates were changed from 12 mm to 8 mm?

Electrostatic Precipitators

Electrostatic precipitators are air pollution control devices that remove tiny particles from the emissions (flue gas) of processing and power plants that burn fossil fuels (**Figure 15**). By relying directly on the properties of electric fields, these devices are capable of removing almost all (about 99%) of the tiny particles of soot, ash, and dust.

Figure 15
Electrostatic precipitators remove particles from the gases in large industrial facilities such as the one shown here.

Dirty flue gas is passed through a series of positively charged plates and negatively charged wires (**Figure 16**). When a very large negative charge is placed on the wires, the electric field near the wire is so strong that the air near it becomes ionized. Electrons freed in the region of ionization move toward the positive plates and attach themselves to the tiny waste particles in the flue gas moving through the plates. These waste product particles will now be negatively charged and are attracted to the plates where they collect on the surface of the plate. The plates are shaken periodically to remove the soot, ash, and dust in a collection hopper. The waste must be disposed of and can be used as a filler in concrete.

(a)

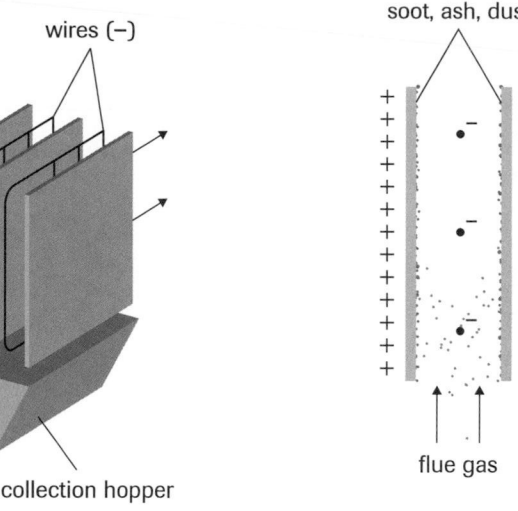

plate (+)

wires (−)

flue gas

collection hopper

(b)

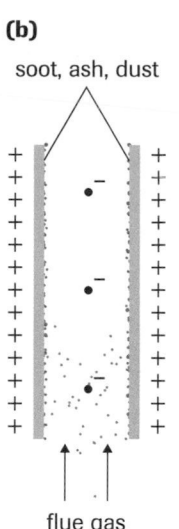

soot, ash, dust

flue gas

Figure 16
Basic operations of an electrostatic precipitator
(a) Flue gases flow between positively charged plates and around negatively charged wires.
(b) Waste collects on the surface of the plates.

Figure 17
The hammerhead shark (as well as other sharks) has cells that respond to weak electric fields produced by moving muscles of its prey.

Electric Fields in Nature

Many animals can detect weak electric fields. Sharks, for example, have cells responsive to the weak electric fields, of magnitudes as low as 10^{-6} N/C, created by the muscles of potential prey. The hammerhead shark swims very close to sandy ocean bottoms, seeking prey that has buried itself beneath the sand or has tunnelled out a shallow home (**Figure 17**). A goby fish will hide from the shark in small holes. Even though the hammerhead cannot see the goby, it can detect electric fields caused by movement and breathing. The electric field produced by the goby will extend about 25 cm above the sand, giving away its presence. Once the hammerhead detects the goby, it will swim in a figure-eight pattern to help centre in on its location.

Case Study Shielding from Electric Fields with Conductors

If we add some electrons to a conductor in an area of space with no net electric field, the excess electrons quickly redistribute themselves over the surface of the conductor until they reach equilibrium and experience no net force. However, since none of the charges experience a net force, the electric field inside the conductor must be zero (otherwise the charges would experience a force). This is referred to as *electrostatic equilibrium*. Faraday demonstrated the effect for enclosed cavities rather dramatically in the early nineteenth century by placing himself and an electroscope inside a tin foil-covered booth (a "Faraday cage"). He had the booth, in effect a solid conductor enclosing a human-sized cavity, charged by means of an electrostatic generator. Even though sparks were flying outside, inside he could detect no electric field (**Figure 18**).

Electric fields do exist outside conductors and even on the surface of conductors. However, the field is always perpendicular to the surface of the conductor; if it were not, it would have a component parallel to the surface causing free electrons inside the conductor to move until the field becomes perpendicular. However, under electrostatic conditions, the charges are in equilibrium; therefore, there can be no component of the electric field parallel to the surface, so the field must be perpendicular at the surface of the conductor (**Figures 19** and **20**).

Figure 18
The Van de Graaff generator, an electrostatic generator, produces a large electric field, as the abundance of sparks suggests. Since the field inside the Faraday cage is zero, the person in the cage is completely safe.

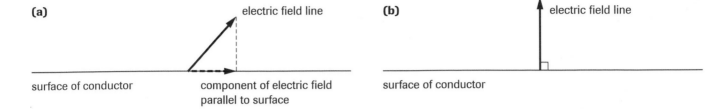

(a) electric field line

surface of conductor

component of electric field parallel to surface

(b) electric field line

surface of conductor

Figure 19
(a) If the electric field at the surface of a conductor had a component parallel to the surface, electrons would move in response to the parallel component.
(b) If the charges are not moving (the charges are in static equilibrium), the parallel component must be zero and the electric field line must be perpendicular to the conductor.

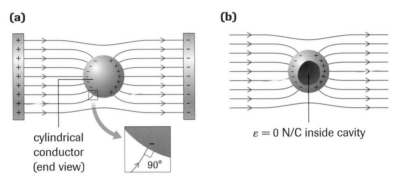

(a)

cylindrical conductor (end view)

90°

(b)

$\varepsilon = 0$ N/C inside cavity

Figure 20
(a) A neutral conductor in the electric field between parallel plates. The field lines are perpendicular to the surface of the conductor.
(b) The electric field is zero inside the conductor.

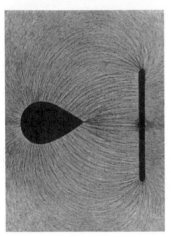

Figure 21
A charged, irregularly shaped conductor near an oppositely charged plate. Notice the concentration of field lines near the pointed end. The field lines are always perpendicular to the surface of the conductor.

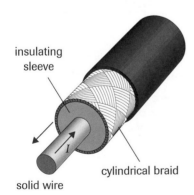

insulating sleeve

solid wire

cylindrical braid

I

Figure 22
Parts of a coaxial cable

This does not mean that the charges must distribute evenly over the surface of the conductor. In fact, on irregularly shaped conductors, the charge tends to accumulate at sharp, pointed areas as shown in **Figure 21**.

Stray electric fields are continually produced in the atmosphere, especially during thunderstorms and by moving water. Many household appliances—such as clocks, blenders, vacuum cleaners, and stereos—produce electric fields; monitors and televisions are the biggest producers. Sensitive electronic circuits, such as those found in computers and in superior tuner-amplifiers, are shielded from stray electric fields by being placed in metal casings. External electric fields are perpendicular to the surface of the metal case, zero inside the metal, and zero inside the case.

Coaxial cables shield electrical signals outside sensitive electric circuits. They are often used for cable TV and between stereo components (speakers and amplifiers). A coaxial cable is a single wire surrounded by an insulating sleeve, in turn covered by a metallic braid and an outer insulating jacket (**Figure 22**). The metallic braid shields the electric current in the central wire from stray electric fields since the external electric fields stop at the surface of the metallic braid. We will look at coaxial cables again in the next chapter, when we investigate magnetic fields.

Keep in mind that we cannot shield against gravitational fields, another difference between these two types of fields. We cannot use a neutral conductor to shield the outside world from a charge either. For example, if we suspend a positive charge inside a spherical neutral conductor, field lines from the positive charge extend out radially toward the neutral conductor (**Figure 23**). These lines must end on an equal amount of negative charge so electrons will quickly redistribute on the interior surface; this causes an induced charge separation, leaving the outer surface with an equal amount of positive charge. The positive charge on the surface of the conductor will cause an external electric field starting from the surface. Notice that the field is still zero inside the conductor.

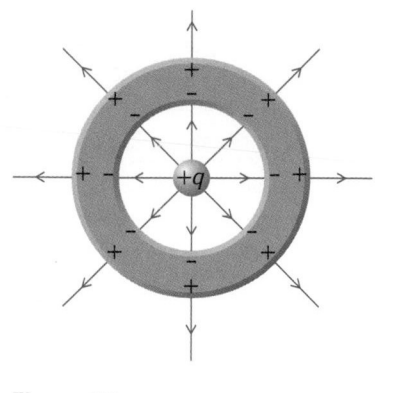

Figure 23
Positive charge inside a neutral conductor. Induced charge is caused on the inner and outer surfaces of the conductor. There is no field inside the conductor but there is a field outside.

> ▶ **Practice**

Understanding Concepts

8. (a) A conductor with an excess of negative charge is in electrostatic equilibrium. Describe the field inside the conductor. Explain your reasoning.
   (b) Explain how a Faraday cage works.
   (c) Why is the electric field perpendicular to a charged conductor in electrostatic equilibrium?

9. (a) Can a neutral hollow spherical conductor be used to shield the outside world from the electric field of a charge placed within the sphere? Explain your answer.
   (b) Is there any way to use the sphere to shield against the electric field of the charge? Explain your answer.

10. Describe the different parts of a coaxial cable, and explain how the wire is shielded from external electric fields.

SUMMARY   *Electric Fields*

- A field of force exists in a region of space when an appropriate object placed at any point in the field experiences a force.
- The electric $\vec{\varepsilon}$ field at any point is defined as the electric force per unit positive charge and is a vector quantity: $\vec{\varepsilon} = \dfrac{\vec{F}_E}{q}$
- Electric field lines are used to describe the electric field around a charged object. For a conductor in static equilibrium, the electric field is zero inside the conductor; the charge is found on the surface; the charge will accumulate where the radius of curvature is smallest on irregularly-shaped objects; the electric field is perpendicular to the surface of the conductor.

> ▶ **Section 7.3** *Questions*

Understanding Concepts

1. A small positive test charge is used to detect electric fields.

   Does the test charge have to be (a) small or (b) positive? Explain your answers.

2. Draw the electric field lines around two negative charges separated by a small distance.

3. Copy **Figure 24** into your notebook to scale.
   (a) Draw the electric field lines in the area surrounding the two charges.
   (b) At what point (A, B, C, or D) is the electric field strongest? Explain your reasoning.
   (c) Draw a circle of radius 3.0 cm around the positive charge. At what point on the circle is the electric field strongest? weakest?

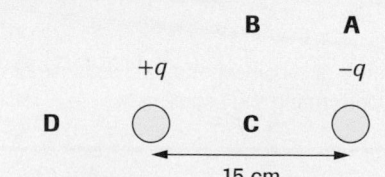

Figure 24

4. Redo question 3, but change the $-q$ in **Figure 24** to $+q$.

5. Explain why electric field lines can never cross.

6. Consider a small positive test charge placed in an electric field. How are the electric field lines related to
   (a) the force on the charge?
   (b) the acceleration of the charge?
   (c) the velocity of the charge?

7. A metallic spherical conductor has a positive charge. A small positive charge q, placed near the conductor, experiences a force of magnitude F. How does the quantity $\dfrac{F}{q}$ compare to the magnitude of the electric field at that position?

8. A negative charge is suspended inside a neutral metallic spherical shell. Draw a diagram of the charge distribution on the metallic shell and all the electric fields in the area. Explain your reasoning.

Applying Inquiry Skills

9. Explain how you would test the properties of the electric fields around and between parallel plates.

10. A spherical metal shell is placed on top of an insulating stand. The outer surface of the shell is connected to an electrometer (a device for measuring charge). The reading on the electrometer is zero. A positively charged hollow sphere is slowly lowered into the shell as shown in **Figure 25** until it touches the bottom. When the sphere is withdrawn, it is neutral.

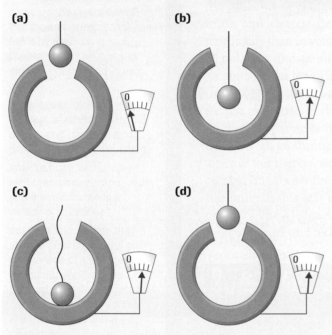

(a)

(b)

(c)

(d)

Figure 25
This is often called Faraday's "ice-pail experiment" because of what he used when first performing the experiment.

(a) Why does the electrometer register a charge in **Figure 25(b)**? Draw the charge distribution on the hollow sphere. (*Hint:* The electrometer can only measure charge on the outer surface.)

(b) What happens to the charge on the sphere in **(c)**? Explain with the help of a diagram.

(c) Why does the electrometer still have the same reading in **(b)** and **(d)**?

(d) Why is the sphere neutral when withdrawn?

(e) The reading on the electrometer did not change during the operations depicted in **(b)**, **(c)**, and **(d)**. What conclusion can you draw regarding the distribution of charge on the hollow conductor?

11. When a small positive test charge is placed near a larger charge, it experiences a force. Explain why this is sufficient evidence to satisfy the conditions for the existence of a field.

12. Explain how the concept of a field can be used to describe the following:
(a) the force of gravity between a star and a planet
(b) the electric force between an electron and a proton in a hydrogen atom

13. The concept of a field is used to describe the force of gravity.
(a) Give three reasons why the same concept of a field is used to describe the electric force.
(b) If a new kind of force were to be encountered, under what conditions would the concept of a field be used to describe it?

Making Connections

14. A friend notices that his computer does not work properly when a nearby stereo is on. What could be the problem, and how could it be solved if he wants to continue using both devices simultaneously?

15. The hammerhead shark is just one of many fish that use electric fields to detect and stun prey. Eels, catfish, and torpedo fish exhibit similar capabilities. Research one of these fish, comparing its abilities with the hammerhead's, and write a short report on your findings.

 www.science.nelson.com

You might be surprised to learn that the way your own body functions and how it senses and reacts to the environment around it have a lot to do with the principles studied in this section. Medical researchers must have a fundamental understanding of the principles of electric potential. Some of these researchers describe the body as a complex biological electric circuit.

Understanding lightning also requires an understanding of these principles. Once considered a mystical force of nature, we now know that the principles behind lightning are firmly tied to the physics of this section (and the entire unit). Lightning can cause property damage, personal injury, and even death; it can also start forest fires. Researchers are currently studying lightning in the hope that the more we understand it, the more we can protect ourselves and our property.

To understand these and other applications, we must first learn more about the interactions between charges. We have often compared interactions between charges to interactions between masses. Keep in mind that any similarities between the two must be carefully considered because the two forces are not identical, as you have learned. The main difference between the two is that gravity is always attractive while the electric force can either attract or repel.

We know that the magnitude of the force of gravity between any two masses is given by

$$F_g = \frac{Gm_1m_2}{r^2}$$

The corresponding gravitational potential energy between two masses is given by

$$E_g = -\frac{Gm_1m_2}{r}$$

provided the zero value of gravitational potential energy is chosen as the value when the two masses are an infinite distance apart. The negative sign associated with this expression for gravitational potential energy reflects the fact that the force between the two masses is attractive, in other words, that potential energy increases (becoming less and less negative) as we force our two gravitating masses farther and farther apart.

Consider now a small test charge q_2, a distance r from a point charge q_1, as in **Figure 1**. From Coulomb's law, the magnitude of the force of attraction or repulsion between these two charges is

$$F_E = \frac{kq_1q_2}{r^2}$$

Therefore, it seems reasonable that an approach similar to that used in Section 6.3 for the gravitational potential energy in a system of two masses would yield a corresponding result for **electric potential energy** stored in the system of two charges q_1 and q_2:

$$E_E = \frac{kq_1q_2}{r}$$

Notice that the sign for electric potential energy, E_E, could be positive or negative depending on the sign of the charges. If q_1 and q_2 are opposite charges, they attract, and our expression performs correctly, giving the electrical potential a negative value, as in the gravitational case. If q_1 and q_2 are similar charges they repel. We now expect the electric potential energy to be positive; that is, energy is stored by moving them closer

DID YOU KNOW ?

Lightning
On average, at any time of the day, there are approximately 2000 thunderstorms, producing 30 to 100 cloud-to-ground lightning strikes each second for a total of about 5 million a day.

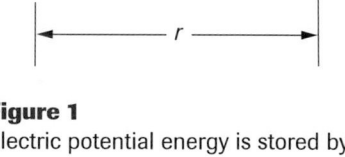

Figure 1
Electric potential energy is stored by two separated charges just as gravitational potential energy is stored by two separated masses.

electric potential energy (E_E) the energy stored in a system of two charges a distance r apart;
$$E_E = \frac{kq_1q_2}{r}$$

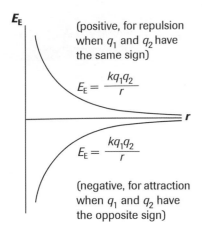

(positive, for repulsion when q_1 and q_2 have the same sign)

$$E_E = \frac{kq_1q_2}{r}$$

$$E_E = \frac{kq_1q_2}{r}$$

(negative, for attraction when q_1 and q_2 have the opposite sign)

Figure 2
A graph of E_E versus r has two curves: one for forces of attraction between opposite charges (negative curve) and one for forces of repulsion between similar charges (positive curve). Also, as in the gravitational analogy, the zero level of electric potential energy in a sytem of two charged spheres is chosen when they are at an infinite separation distance.

electric potential (V) the value, in volts, of potential energy per unit positive charge; 1 V = 1 J/C

together. In either case, substituting the sign of the charge ($+$ or $-$) for q_1 and q_2 will yield the appropriate results for the sign of E_E. Also, in both cases, the zero level of electric potential energy is approached as the separation of the charges q_1 and q_2 approaches infinity (**Figure 2**).

To look at the concept of electric potential energy in a systematic way, we consider the electric potential energy not just of any charge q_2 but of a unit positive test charge when in the field of any other charge q_1. We call this value of potential energy per unit positive charge the **electric potential**, V. It is a property of the electric field of the charge q_1 and represents the amount of work necessary to move a unit positive test charge from rest at infinity to rest at any specific point in the field of q_1.

Thus, at a distance r from a spherical point charge q_1, the electric potential is given by

$$V = \frac{E_E}{q}$$

$$= \frac{\frac{kq_1q}{r}}{q}$$

$$V = \frac{kq_1}{r}$$

The units of electric potential are joules per coulomb, or volts, and

> 1 V is the electric potential at a point in an electric field if 1 J of work is required to move 1 C of charge from infinity to that point; 1 V = 1 J/C.

There are two ways of considering what V represents: the absolute potential considering that $V = 0$ at $r = \infty$, and as a potential difference measured from infinity to r. The electric potential changes with the inverse of the first power of the distance from the charge rather than with the inverse square of the distance, as the electric field does. For a positive charge, the electric potential is large near the charge and decreases, approaching zero, as r increases. For a negative charge, the electric potential is a large negative value near the charge and increases, approaching zero, as r increases (**Figure 3**).

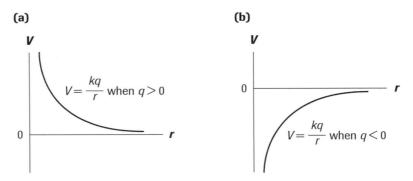

(a)

(b)

Figure 3
The electric potential V of a single point charge q as a function of r
(a) V for a positive charge
(b) V for a negative charge

We must always be very careful to distinguish between E_E, the electric potential energy of a charge at a point, and V, the electric potential at the point. They are related by the equation $E_E = qV$.

This concept of electric potential can be extended to include the electric fields that result from any distribution of electric charge, rather than just a single point charge. The definition of electric potential in these cases is the same: it is the work done per unit positive test charge to move the charge from infinity to any given point. It is more common, however, not to think of the work necessary to move a unit test charge from infinity to a particular point in a field, but rather from one point to another in the field. In this case, we are dealing with the difference in electric potential between these two points, commonly called the **electric potential difference**.

Often Earth is treated as $V = 0$ for convenience, especially when dealing with just electric potential differences rather than individual electric potentials. This method is similar to that used in situations involving gravity where $h = 0$ is set at any convenient height according to what is needed for the problem. Whereas the choice of zero level for potential is arbitrary, differences in potential are physically real. In particular, it is a fundamental physical fact that two conducting objects connected by a conducting wire are at the same potential. If they were not at the same potential, then the electric potential difference would cause a current redistributing the charge until the electric potential difference reached zero. Then the two conductors would be at the same potential as we stated. This process is used in grounding, placing the object at the same electric potential as Earth.

We now examine the change in the electric potential energy of a positive charge q that is moved from point A to point B in an electric field (**Figure 4**).

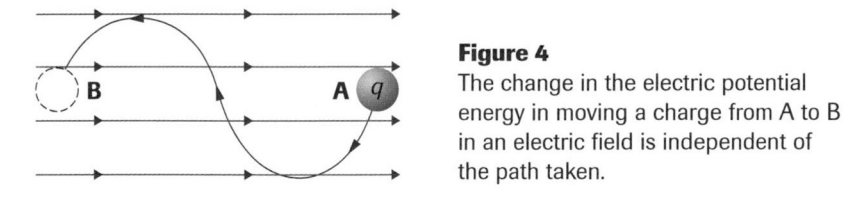

Figure 4
The change in the electric potential energy in moving a charge from A to B in an electric field is independent of the path taken.

electric potential difference the amount of work required per unit charge to move a positive charge from one point to another in the presence of an electric field

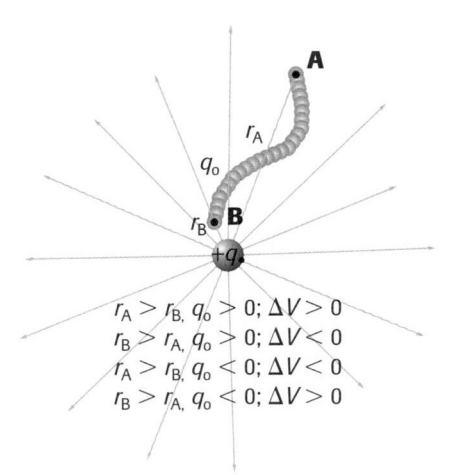

$r_A > r_B, q_0 > 0; \Delta V > 0$
$r_B > r_A, q_0 > 0; \Delta V < 0$
$r_A > r_B, q_0 < 0; \Delta V < 0$
$r_B > r_A, q_0 < 0; \Delta V > 0$

Figure 5
The sign of the electric potential difference depends on the change in the distance and the sign of the charge.

Regardless of the actual path taken by the charge q, in moving from A to B,

$$\left\{ \begin{array}{l} \text{the difference between} \\ \text{the electric potential} \\ \text{at B and the electric} \\ \text{potential at A} \end{array} \right\} = \left\{ \begin{array}{l} \text{the work-per-unit-charge that} \\ \text{we would perform in moving our} \\ \text{hypothetical positive test charge} \\ \text{from A to B in the electric field} \end{array} \right\}$$

$$\Delta E_E = qV_B - qV_A$$
$$= q(V_B - V_A)$$
$$\Delta E_E = q\Delta V$$

ΔV, often written V_{BA}, is the potential difference between points B and A in the field. The potential decreases in the direction of the electric field (and therefore increases in the opposite direction).

For a point charge q, the electric potential difference between two points A and B can be found by subtracting the electric potentials due to the charge at each position:

$$\Delta V = V_B - V_A = \frac{kq}{r_B} - \frac{kq}{r_A} = kq\left(\frac{1}{r_B} - \frac{1}{r_A} \right)$$

Multiplying by the charge that is moved from A to B gives the change in electric potential energy, ΔE. The sign on the electric potential difference depends on both the magnitudes of the distances from the charge and the sign of the charge itself, as summarized in **Figure 5**.

For a second example of a potential difference calculation, consider the electric field between two large, oppositely charged parallel plates whose area is large in comparison with their separation r (**Figure 6**).

Recall that the electric field is, in the case of parallel plates, constant in magnitude and direction at essentially all points and is defined as the force per unit positive charge:

$$\vec{\varepsilon} = \frac{\vec{F}_E}{q}$$

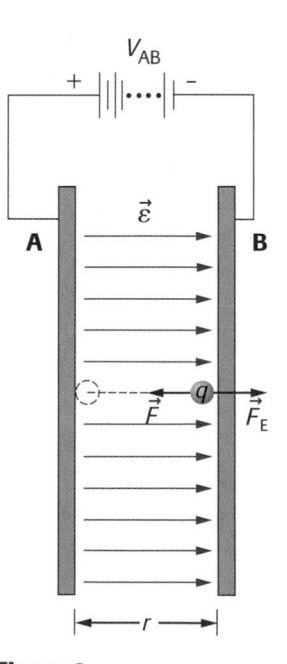

Figure 6
Since the electric field between the two parallel plates is uniform, the force on the charge is constant.

Electric Charges and Electric Fields **351**

The increase in electric potential energy of the charge q, in moving from plate B to plate A, is equal to the work done in moving it from B to A. To do so, a force $\vec{F}$, equal in magnitude but opposite in direction to $\vec{F}_E$, must be applied over a distance r. The magnitude of the work done is given by

$$W = Fr \quad \text{since } F \text{ and } r \text{ are in the same direction}$$
$$W = q\varepsilon r \quad \text{since } F = F_E = q\varepsilon$$

Therefore, since $W = \Delta E_E = q\Delta V$

$$q\Delta V = q\varepsilon r$$

$$\text{or} \quad \varepsilon = \frac{\Delta V}{r}$$

This is an expression for the magnitude of the electric field at any point in the space between two large parallel plates, a distance r apart, with a potential difference $\Delta V = V_{BA}$. Remember: the electric field direction is from the $+$ plate to the $-$ plate, in the direction of decreasing potential.

For a constant electric field, between parallel plates for example, the electric potential difference is directly proportional to the distance r:

$$\Delta V = \varepsilon r$$

Therefore, $\Delta V \propto r$ since ε is constant.

This means that if the electric potential difference between two plates is ΔV and a charge moves one-third of the distance between the plates, the charge will experience a potential difference of $\dfrac{\Delta V}{3}$.

> ### ▶ SAMPLE problem 1
>
> Calculate the electric potential a distance of 0.40 m from a spherical point charge of $+6.4 \times 10^{-6}$ C. (Take $V = 0$ at infinity.)
>
> #### Solution
>
> $r = 0.40$ m
> $q = +6.4 \times 10^{-6}$ C
> $V = ?$
>
> $$V = \frac{kq}{r}$$
>
> $$= \frac{(9.0 \times 10^9 \text{ N·m}^2/\text{C}^2)(6.4 \times 10^{-6} \text{ C})}{0.40 \text{ m}}$$
>
> $$V = 1.5 \times 10^5 \text{ V}$$
>
> The electric potential is 1.5×10^5 V.

Note that the value for the potential created by a positive charge has a positive value, characteristic of a system where the force acting on the test charge is repulsion. If the spherical point charge in the above example had been a negative charge, then substituting a negative value for q would have yielded a negative value for V, which is consistent with a system in which the force acting is attractive.

> ▶ **SAMPLE** problem 2

How much work must be done to increase the potential of a charge of 3.0×10^{-7} C by 120 V?

Solution

$q = 3.0 \times 10^{-7}$ C

$\Delta V = 120$ V

$W = ?$

$$W = \Delta E_E$$
$$= q\Delta V$$
$$= (3.0 \times 10^{-7} \text{ C})(120 \text{ V})$$
$$W = 3.6 \times 10^{-5} \text{ J}$$

The amount of work that must be done is 3.6×10^{-5} J.

> ▶ **SAMPLE** problem 3

In a uniform electric field, the potential difference between two points 12.0 cm apart is 1.50×10^2 V. Calculate the magnitude of the electric field strength.

Solution

$r = 12.0$ cm

$\Delta V = 1.50 \times 10^2$ V

$\varepsilon = ?$

$$\varepsilon = \frac{\Delta V}{r}$$
$$= \frac{1.50 \times 10^2 \text{ V}}{1.20 \times 10^{-1} \text{ m}}$$
$$\varepsilon = 1.25 \times 10^3 \text{ N/C}$$

The magnitude of the electric field strength is 1.25×10^3 N/C.

> ▶ **SAMPLE** problem 4

The magnitude of the electric field strength between two parallel plates is 450 N/C. The plates are connected to a battery with an electric potential difference of 95 V. What is the plate separation?

Solution

$\varepsilon = 450$ N/C

$\Delta V = 95$ V

$r = ?$

For parallel plates, $\varepsilon = \dfrac{\Delta V}{r}$. Thus,

$$r = \frac{\Delta V}{\varepsilon}$$
$$= \frac{95 \text{ V}}{450 \text{ N/C}}$$
$$r = 0.21 \text{ m}$$

The separation of the plates is 0.21 m.

Understanding Concepts

1. The electric potential at a distance of 25 cm from a point charge is -6.4×10^4 V. Determine the sign and magnitude of the point charge.

2. It takes 4.2×10^{-3} J of work to move 1.2×10^{-6} C of charge from point X to point Y in an electric field. Calculate the potential difference between X and Y.

3. Calculate the magnitude of the electric field strength in a parallel plate apparatus whose plates are 5.0 mm apart and have a potential difference of 3.0×10^2 V between them.

4. What potential difference would have to be maintained across the plates of a parallel plate appratus if the plates were 1.2 cm apart, to create an electric field strength of 1.5×10^4 N/C?

Lightning and Lightning Rods

We have all experienced small electric shocks when touching a metal doorknob after walking across a woollen rug on a dry winter day. Lightning discharges are similar but operate on a grand scale, with potential differences between the ground and the air of approximately 10^8 V. A cloud will typically develop a large charge separation before a lightning strike, with about −40 C centred at a region such as N in **Figure 7** and +40 C centred at P. Each lightning flash has a maximum current of 30 000 A, or 30 000 C/s, lasts 30 μs, and delivers about a coulomb of charge.

According to one current theory (research is ongoing), the separation of charge in a cloud results from the presence of the mixed phases of water typical of large clouds—liquid water, ice crystals, and soft hail. Air resistance and turbulent air flows within the cloud jointly cause the soft hail to fall faster than the smaller ice crystals. As the soft hail collides with the ice crystals, both are charged by friction, the hail negatively and the ice crystals positively. Charge separation occurs because the hail moves down relative to the ice crystals.

Now that the bottom of the cloud is negatively charged, it induces a positive charge on the surface of Earth. The two relatively flat surfaces—the positively charged ground and the negatively charged bottom of the cloud—resemble oppositely charged parallel plates separated by the insulating air. The air stops acting as an insulator and serves as a conductor for the lightning when the charge at the bottom of the cloud becomes large enough to increase the electric field strength to about 3.0×10^6 N/C. When the magnitude of the electric field reaches this critical value, the air ionizes and changes from insulator to conductor.

The lightning strike itself is a sequence of three events. First, the step leader, a package of charge moving erratically along the path of least resistance, moves from the bottom of the cloud toward the ground. On its way down, it often halts temporarily and

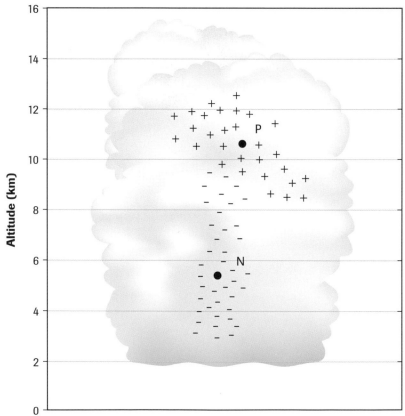

Figure 7
A side view of the separation of charge in a typical thundercloud. The black dots indicate the charge centres for both the positive and negative charge distributions.

Figure 8
Notice the different branches of the lightning caused by the step leader. The ground and bottom of the cloud are modelled after parallel plates.

breaks up into different branches. But whatever its path, it leaves a path of weakly ionized air in its wake. Second, the step leader, now near the ground, induces a strong positive charge, and when it makes contact, a continuous ionized path is opened. Finally, this causes a return stroke from the ground to the cloud producing visible light and increasing the ionization. If the charge on the cloud is large enough, the process continues with a dart leader descending from the cloud, causing another return stroke. Typically, there are three or four return strokes, each lasting 40 to 80 ms (**Figure 8**).

We know what lightning rods are used for, but the physics behind how they protect buildings and people is less well known. Lightning rods are long, thin, pointed metal stakes, usually placed at the highest point on a building and connected to the ground with a conductor (**Figure 9**). The key to influencing the course of a lightning bolt is the ionized path. The step leader, we have seen, follows the path of least resistance through air, which is normally an insulator. How does the lightning rod help?

To answer, we first consider two conducting spheres of different radii connected by a long conducting wire (**Figure 10**). Since a conductor connects the two spheres, they must be at the same electric potential.

Therefore,

$$V_{small} = V_{large}$$

$$\frac{kq}{r} = \frac{kQ}{R}$$

$$\frac{q}{r} = \frac{Q}{R}$$

$$\frac{q}{Q} = \frac{r}{R}$$

The magnitude of the electric field near each sphere is given by the equations

$$\varepsilon_{small} = \frac{kq}{r^2} \quad \text{and} \quad \varepsilon_{large} = \frac{kQ}{R^2}$$

We use these equations to find the ratio of the magnitudes of the electric fields:

$$\frac{\varepsilon_{small}}{\varepsilon_{large}} = \frac{\left(\dfrac{kq}{r^2}\right)}{\left(\dfrac{kQ}{R^2}\right)} = \frac{q}{Q}\left(\frac{R^2}{r^2}\right) = \frac{r}{R}\left(\frac{R^2}{r^2}\right)$$

$$\frac{\varepsilon_{small}}{\varepsilon_{large}} = \frac{R}{r}$$

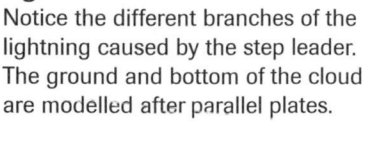

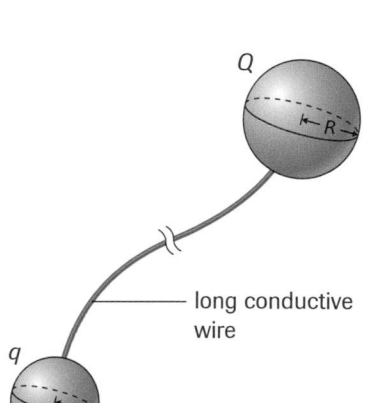

Figure 9
A long, thin conductor, pointed at the top, makes an effective lightning rod.

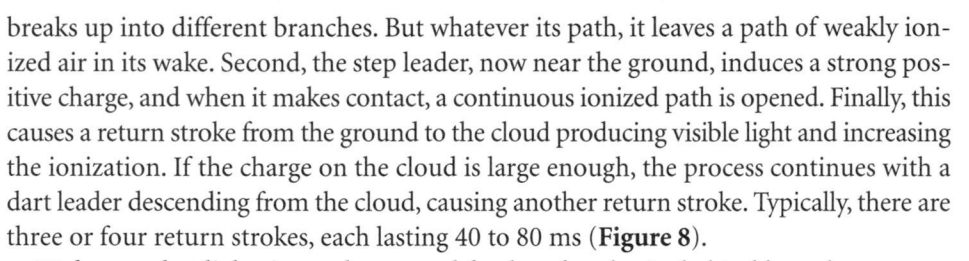

Figure 10
A long, thin conducting wire connecting two conducting spheres of different radii

Electric Charges and Electric Fields **355**

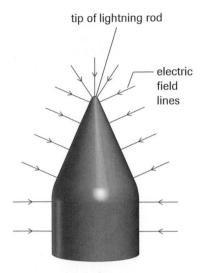

tip of lightning rod

electric field lines

Figure 11
The tip of a lightning rod is small, creating a large electric field near its surface; this ionizes the surrounding air.

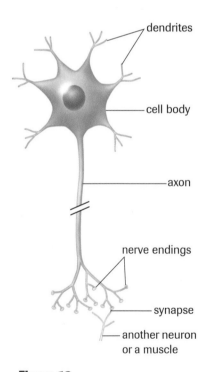

dendrites

cell body

axon

nerve endings

synapse

another neuron or a muscle

Figure 12
Typical structure of a neuron

Since R is the radius of the larger sphere, the ratio is greater than 1, so $\varepsilon_{small} > \varepsilon_{large}$. We can increase the electric field near the smaller sphere by decreasing its size relative to the larger. The tip of a lightning rod has a very small radius of curvature in comparison with the adjoining rooftop surfaces (**Figure 11**). The electric field near the tip is correspondingly large, indeed large enough to ionize the surrounding air, changing the air from insulator to conductor and influencing the path of any nearby lightning. Lightning is thus induced to hit the rod and to pass safely along the grounding wire, without striking the adjoining rooftop.

Medical Applications of Electric Potential

The concept of electric potential is necessary for an understanding of the human nervous system and how it can transmit information in the form of electric signals throughout the body.

A nerve cell, or neuron, consists of a cell body with short extensions, or dendrites, and also a long stem, or axon, branching out into numerous nerve endings (**Figure 12**). The dendrites convert external stimuli into electrical signals that travel through the neuron most of the way through the long axon toward the nerve endings. These electrical signals must then cross a synapse (or gap) between the nerve endings and the next cell, whether neuron or muscle cell, in the transmission chain. A nerve consists of a bundle of axons.

The fluid within the nerve cell (the intracellular fluid) contains high concentrations of negatively charged proteins. The extracellular fluid, on the other hand, contains high concentrations of positive sodium ions (Na^+). The difference in concentrations is due to the selectively permeable membrane that surrounds the cell, causing a buildup of equal amounts of negative charge inside and positive charge outside the cell membrane (**Figure 13**). This charge separation gives rise to an electric potential difference across the membrane. A normal "resting" membrane electric potential difference (present when the cell is not sending a signal), between inside and outside, is typically –70 mV, negative because the inside of the cell is negative with respect to the outside.

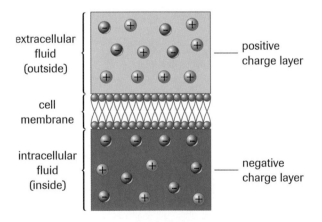

extracellular fluid (outside)

positive charge layer

cell membrane

intracellular fluid (inside)

negative charge layer

Figure 13
The buildup of equal but opposite charges on either side of the cell membrane causes an electric potential difference.

When exposed to a sufficiently strong stimulus at the right point on the neuron, "gates" open in the cell membrane, allowing the positively charged sodium ions to rush into the cell (**Figure 14**). The sodium ions enter the cell by diffusion, driven by the electrical attraction between positive and negative charges. Upon entry of the sodium ions,

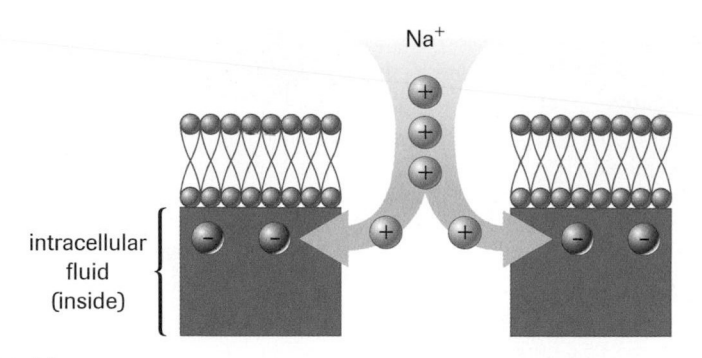

Figure 14
A strong enough stimulus can open "gates," allowing positively charged sodium ions to rush into the cell. The inrush causes the interior surface of the membrane to attain, momentarily, a higher potential than the exterior.

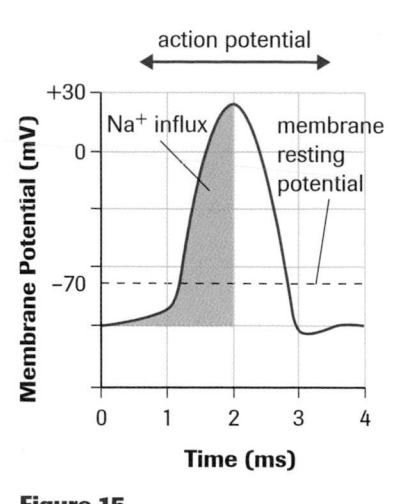

Figure 15
As the sodium ions rush in, the action potential starts. The electric potential difference across the membrane changes from −70 mV to +30 mV, then back to −70 mV.

the interior of the cell is momentarily positive, with the electric potential difference changing very rapidly from −70 mV to +30 mV. The gates then close and the electric potential difference quickly returns to normal. This cycle of potential changes, called the action potential, lasts only a few milliseconds. The cycle creates an electrical signal that travels down through the axon at about 50 m/s to the next neuron or muscle cell (**Figure 15**).

These changes in electric potential in neurons produce electric fields that have an effect on the electric potential differences measured at different points on the surface of the body ranging from 30 to 500 μV. The activity of the heart muscle causes such electric potential differences; measuring these changes is called electrocardiography. If the heart is healthy, its regular beating pattern will produce a predictable change in the electric potential difference between different points on the skin that doctors can use as a diagnostic tool. A graph of electric potential difference versus time between two points on the skin of a patient is called an electrocardiogram (EKG); the shape of the graph depends on how healthy the heart is and the placement of the two measuring points on a patient (**Figure 16**).

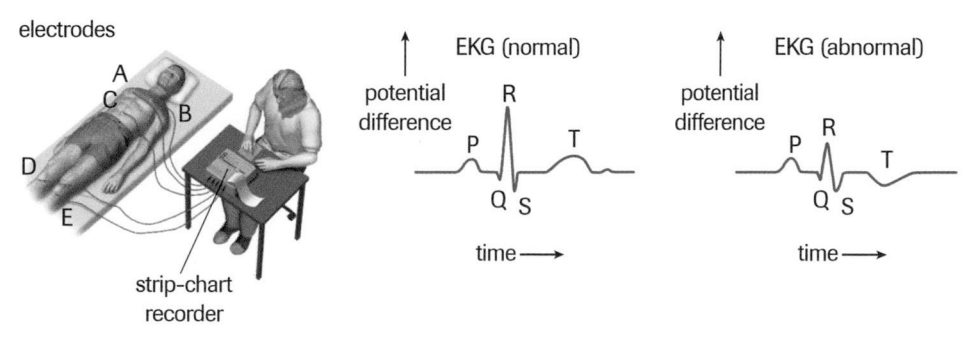

Figure 16
Electrocardiography measures the electric potential difference between any of the two points shown on the patient. The graphs represent normal and abnormal EKGs, with specific parts of a single beating cycle labelled.

The main features of a normal electrocardiogram are labelled P, Q, R, S, and T in **Figure 16**. The first peak (P) indicates the activity of the atria in the upper portion of the heart. QRS shows the activity of the larger, lower ventricles. T indicates that the ventricles are preparing for the next cycle. **Figure 17** is a map of the potentials on the skin.

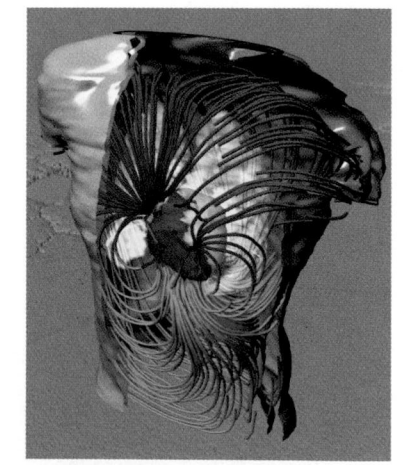

Figure 17
A map of potential differences over the skin caused by heart-muscle activity.

Electric Charges and Electric Fields **357**

▶ **Practice**

Understanding Concepts

5. Thunderclouds develop a charge separation as they move through the atmosphere.
   (a) What causes the attraction between the electrons in the cloud and the ground?
   (b) What kind of charge will be on a lightning rod as a negatively charged cloud passes overhead? Explain your answer.
   (c) Explain why lightning is more likely to strike a lightning rod than other places nearby.

6. The electric potential difference between the inside and outside of a neuron cell membrane of thickness 5.0 nm is typically 0.070 V.
   (a) Explain why the inner and outer surfaces of the membrane can be thought of as oppositely charged parallel plates.
   (b) Calculate the magnitude of the electric field in the membrane.
   (c) Calculate the work you would have to do on a single sodium ion, of charge $+1.6 \times 10^{-19}$ C, to move it through the membrane from the region of lower potential into the region of higher potential.

SUMMARY *Electric Potential*

- The electric potential energy stored in the system of two charges q_1 and q_2 is
  $$E_E = \frac{kq_1q_2}{r}.$$
- The electric potential a distance r from a charge q is given by $V = \dfrac{kq}{r}$.

- The potential difference between two points in an electric field is given by the change in the electric potential energy of a positive charge as it moves from one point to another: $\Delta V = \dfrac{\Delta E_E}{q}$

- The magnitude of the electric field is the change in potential difference per unit radius: $\varepsilon = \dfrac{\Delta V}{r}$

▶ **Section 7.4** *Questions*

Understanding Concepts

1. The electric potential 0.35 m from a point charge is +110 V. Find the magnitude and sign of the electric charge.

2. Charge q_1 is 0.16 m from point A. Charge q_2 is 0.40 m from point A. The electric potential at A is zero. Calculate the ratio $\dfrac{q_1}{q_2}$ of the two charges.

3. Draw two equal positive point charges and connect them with a line.
   (a) Is there a point on the line at which the electric field is zero?
   (b) Is there a point on the line at which the electric potential is zero?
   (c) Explain the difference between the two answers.

4. Explain the difference between each of the following:
   (a) electric potential and electric field
   (b) electric potential and electric potential energy

5. The electric potential at a point is zero. Is it possible for the electric field at that point to be nonzero? If "yes," give an example. If "no," explain why not.

6. A particle moves from a region of low electric potential to a region of high electric potential. Is it possible for its electric potential energy to decrease? Explain your answer.

7. Two parallel plates are connected to a 120-V DC power supply and separated by an air gap. The largest electric field in air is 3.0×10^6 N/C. (When this "breakdown value" is exceeded, charge is transferred between the plates, reducing the separated charge and the field through sparks or arcing.) Calculate the smallest possible gap between the plates.

8. Three charges are placed at the corners of an equilateral triangle with sides of length 2.0 m, as shown in **Figure 18**.
   (a) Calculate the total electric potential energy of the group of charges.
   (b) Determine the electric potential at the midpoint of each side of the triangle.

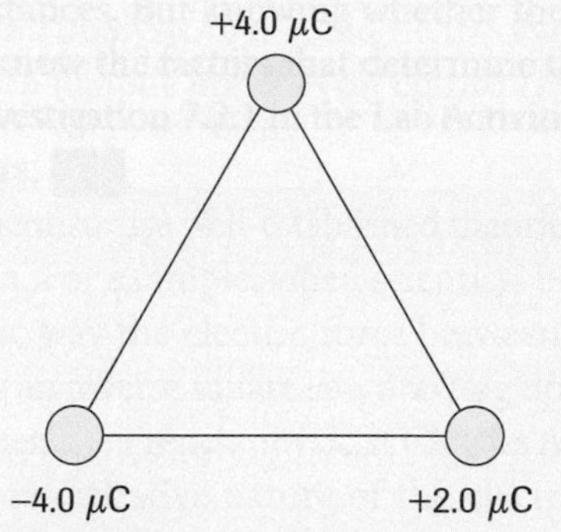

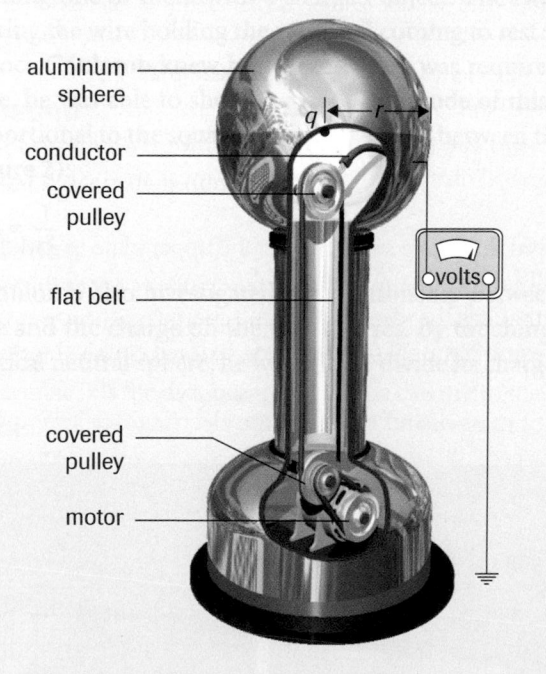

−4.0 μC   +2.0 μC

Figure 18

9. **Figure 19** shows a typical Van de Graaff generator with an aluminum sphere of radius 12 cm, producing an electric potential of 85 kV near its surface. The sphere is uniformly charged so we can assume that all the charge is concentrated at the centre. Notice that the voltmeter is connected to the ground, meaning Earth's electric potential is being set as zero.

aluminum sphere
conductor
covered pulley
flat belt
covered pulley
motor

Figure 19
Measuring the electric potential difference near a Van de Graaff generator

(a) Calculate the charge on the sphere.
(b) Calculate the magnitude of the electric field near the surface of the sphere.
(c) Is there likely to be a discharge (a spark or arc) from the surface due to ionization of the air? Explain your answer.

Applying Inquiry Skills

10. Design an experiment to show that two conducting spheres connected by a long wire are at the same electric potential.

11. Researchers place two oppositely charged plates, a negatively charged sphere, and a positively charged sphere near three different lightning rods. They wait for a thunderstorm to pass overhead and monitor the situations by computer in a lab. Discuss what the scientists might observe about the charges and explain why it would happen.

Making Connections

12. Explain how a spark plug operates by examining **Figure 20** and discussing the following factors:
   (a) the small gap (0.75 mm) between the two metal conductors
   (b) the breakdown value (1.6×10^4 N/C) between the conductors
   (c) the changes in the electric potential across the two conductors while the spark plug is operating

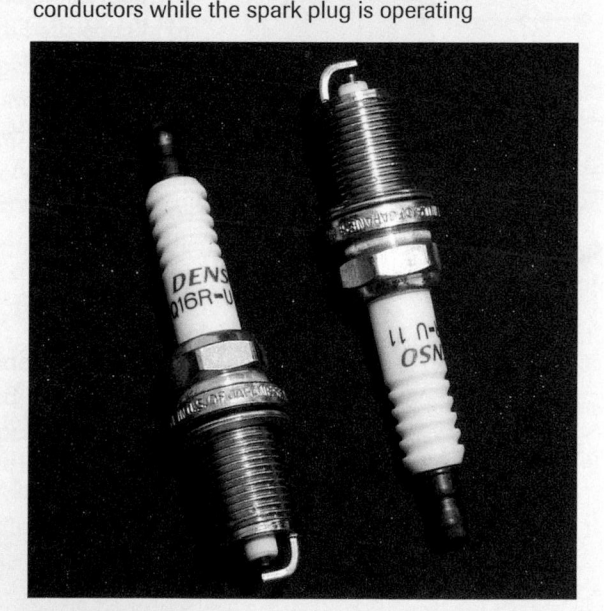

Figure 20
Typical spark plugs

13. Some researchers believe that lightning rods can actually prevent lightning from forming at all. Discuss how the ions formed near the tip of lightning rods might play a role in lightning prevention.

7.5 The Millikan Experiment: Determining the Elementary Charge

One of the main characteristics of fundamental particles is their electric charge. In this section, you will learn about a brilliant experiment investigating nature's elementary charge, namely, the charge of the electron.

At the turn of the twentieth century, when our understanding of electric forces was beginning to increase, two fundamental questions arose regarding the nature of electric charge:

1. Does there exist, in nature, a smallest unit of electric charge of which other units are simple multiples?

2. If so, what is this elementary charge, and what is its magnitude, in coulombs?

Lab Exercise 7.5.1, in the Lab Activities section at the end of this chapter, allows you to calculate the elementary charge.

To answer these questions, the American Nobel laureate Robert Andrews Millikan (**Figure 1**) devised and performed a series of creative experiments. He reasoned that the elementary charge would be the charge on an individual electron. He assumed, further, that when tiny oil drops are sprayed in a fine mist from an atomizer, they become electrically charged by friction, some acquiring an excess of a few electrons, others acquiring a deficit. Although there was no way of knowing how many extra electrons there were on any given oil drop or how many were missing, Millikan hypothesized that if he were able to measure the total charge on any oil drop, it would have to be some small integral multiple of the elementary charge.

To measure this charge, Millikan made use of the uniform electric field in the region between two oppositely charged parallel plates. He charged the plates by connecting each to opposite terminals of a large bank of storage batteries whose potential difference could be varied. Millikan was able to use this apparatus, called an *electrical microbalance*, to isolate and suspend charged oil drops, and ultimately to measure the total charge on each.

Once a mist of oil drops is sprayed through a small hole in the upper plate in a Millikan apparatus, it is possible, by carefully adjusting the potential difference between the plates, to "balance" a particular droplet that has the same sign as the charge on the lower plate. When the droplet is balanced, the gravitational force pulling it down equals the electric force pulling it up (**Figure 2**).

For a positively charged drop of mass m and charge q, the electric force acts upward if the lower plate is positively charged:

$$\vec{F}_E = q\vec{\varepsilon}$$

where $\vec{\varepsilon}$ is the electric field between the plates.

When the droplet is in balance,

$$F_E = F_g$$
$$q\varepsilon = mg$$

But in Section 7.4, we learned that the electric field in the region between two parallel plates is constant and has a magnitude given by

$$\varepsilon = \frac{\Delta V}{r}$$

where ΔV is the electric potential difference between the plates, and r is the separation between the plates.

LAB EXERCISE 7.5.1

The Elementary Charge (p. 374)
Can you think of a method that could be used to suggest that an elementary charge exists?

Figure 1
Robert Millikan (1868–1953)

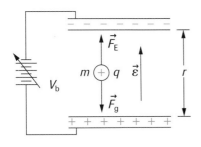

Figure 2
When the total force on the oil droplet is zero, the electric force up is equal in magnitude to the gravitational force down.

Consequently, for an oil drop of mass m and charge q, balanced by a potential difference $\Delta V = \Delta V_b$,

$$q = \frac{mg}{\varepsilon}$$

$$q = \frac{mgr}{\Delta V_b}$$

where ΔV_b is the balancing value of electric potential difference between the plates.

Thus, it is possible to determine the total charge on an oil drop if its mass is known. The mass of any individual drop may be determined by measuring the terminal speed with which it falls when the electric balancing force is removed (when the batteries are disconnected) and only gravity and friction are acting on it.

By measuring the terminal speed of an oil droplet as it falls under the force of gravity, Millikan was able to calculate its mass. Then, by measuring the value of potential difference between the plates necessary to balance the droplet, he was able to calculate the total electric charge on the droplet.

Millikan repeated the experiment over and over, meticulously balancing a charged oil droplet, measuring its balancing voltage, and then allowing the droplet to fall under gravity and measuring its terminal speed. The list of values he determined for the total electric charge on each of the drops studied contained a significant pattern: all the values were simple multiples of some smallest value. Many of the droplets had this smallest value of charge on them, but none had less. Millikan concluded that this smallest value represented the smallest quantity of electric charge possible, the charge on an electron, or the elementary charge. Accurate measurements of the elementary charge have yielded values close to Millikan's. The currently accepted value for the elementary charge, commonly called e, is, to four significant digits,

$$e = 1.602 \times 10^{-19} \text{ C}$$

Knowing the value of the elementary charge enables us to understand the nature of electric charge on a fundamental level. In Section 7.1, we noted that all electric charges in solids are due to an excess or deficit of electrons. If we now know a value for the charge on an individual electron, we can calculate the number of excess or deficit electrons that constitute any observed electric charge.

An object with an excess (or deficit) of N electrons has a charge q that is given by

$$q = Ne$$

> **SAMPLE** problem **1**

Calculate the charge on a small sphere with an excess of 5.0×10^{14} electrons.

Solution

$N = 5.0 \times 10^{14}$

$q = ?$

$$q = Ne$$
$$= (5.0 \times 10^{14})(1.6 \times 10^{-19} \text{ C})$$
$$q = 8.0 \times 10^{-5} \text{ C}$$

The charge on the sphere is -8.0×10^{-5} C (negative because of the excess of electrons).

SAMPLE problem 2

In a Millikan-type experiment, two horizontal plates are 2.5 cm apart. A latex sphere, of mass 1.5×10^{-15} kg, remains stationary when the potential difference between the plates is 460 V with the upper plate positive.

(a) Is the sphere charged negatively or positively?

(b) Calculate the magnitude of the charge on the latex sphere.

(c) How many excess or deficit electrons does the sphere have?

Solution

$r = 2.5$ cm $q = ?$

$m = 1.5 \times 10^{-15}$ kg $N = ?$

$\Delta V = 460$ V

(a) The electric force must be up, to balance the downward force of gravity. Since the upper plate is positive, the latex sphere must be charged negatively to be attracted to the upper plate and repelled by the lower plate. The electric field is downward, giving an upward force on a negative charge.

(b) When the sphere is balanced,

$$F_E = F_g$$
$$q\varepsilon = mg$$

But $\varepsilon = \dfrac{\Delta V}{r}$. Therefore,

$$\frac{q\Delta V}{r} = mg$$

$$q = \frac{mgr}{\Delta V}$$

$$= \frac{(1.5 \times 10^{-15}\ \text{kg})(9.8\ \text{m/s}^2)(2.5 \times 10^{-2}\ \text{m})}{460\ \text{V}}$$

$$q = 8.0 \times 10^{-19}\ \text{C}$$

The magnitude of the charge is 8.0×10^{-19} C.

(c)
$$N = \frac{q}{e}$$

$$= \frac{8.0 \times 10^{-19}\ \text{C}}{1.6 \times 10^{-19}\ \text{C}}$$

$$N = 5$$

The sphere has 5 excess electrons (since the charge is negative).

▶ Practice

Understanding Concepts

Answers

1. 5.0×10^{11} electrons

2. 2.3×10^{-12} N

3. 29 N/C; -14.0 V

1. Calculate the number of electrons that must be removed from a neutral, isolated conducting sphere to give it a positive charge of 8.0×10^{-8} C.

2. Calculate the force of electric repulsion between two small spheres placed 1.0 m apart if each has a deficit of 1.0×10^{8} electrons.

3. A small object has an excess of 5.00×10^{9} electrons. Calculate the magnitude of the electric field intensity and the electric potential at a distance of 0.500 m from the object.

4. Two large, horizontal metal plates are separated by 0.050 m. A small plastic sphere is suspended halfway between them. The sphere experiences an upward electric force of 4.5×10^{-15} N, just sufficient to balance its weight.
   (a) If the charge on the sphere is 6.4×10^{-19} C, what is the potential difference between the plates?
   (b) Calculate the mass of the sphere.

5. An oil drop of mass 4.95×10^{-15} kg is balanced between two large, horizontal parallel plates 1.0 cm apart, maintained at a potential difference of 510 V. The upper plate is positive. Calculate the charge on the drop, both in coulombs and as a multiple of the elementary charge, and state whether there is an excess or deficit of electrons.

6. Delicate measurements reveal Earth to be surrounded by an electric field similar to the field around a negatively charged sphere. At Earth's surface, this field has a magnitude of approximately 1.0×10^2 N/C. What charge would an oil drop of mass 2.0×10^{-15} kg need in order to remain suspended by Earth's electric field? Give your answer both in coulombs and as a multiple of the elementary charge.

Answers

4. (a) 3.5×10^2 V
   (b) 4.6×10^{-16} kg
5. 9.6×10^{-19} C; $6e$; excess
6. -2.0×10^{-16} C; $-1.2 \times 10^3 e$

Charge of the Proton

The proton and the electron are believed to have charges equal in magnitude but opposite in sign. Modern experiments have revealed that the ratio of the magnitudes of the two charges is essentially 1, since the difference in coulombs does not differ by more than 10^{-20}, an extremely small number to say the least. But this is not obvious for particle physicists. One reason for the curiosity is that, other than the similarity in the charge of the two particles they are quite different. Unlike the electron, the proton does have a complex structure. And like most other heavy subatomic particles, it is comprised of other fundamental entities called quarks. Quarks themselves have charges of $\pm\frac{1}{3}e$ and $\pm\frac{2}{3}e$. However, this does not change our view of what the fundamental charge should be since quarks have not been found to exist in a free state under ordinary conditions. All known fundamental particles do have charges that are integral multiples of e. (Quarks will be studied further in Chapter 13.)

At first, one might think that Millikan just discovered the magnitude of the charge on the electron that happens to be the same as the charge on the proton. However, his discovery has greater implications. In fact, every subatomic particle that has been observed to date (only a small number exist) has a charge that is a whole number multiple of this truly "fundamental" charge. It appears that charge is quantized, meaning it appears in specific amounts, whether positive or negative. This might not seem so surprising when we remember that matter also comes in specific packages (particles), so why not the charge associated with those particles? However, unlike mass, which can be changed into energy (which is really another form of mass) or vice versa in chemical and nuclear reactions, charge is always conserved and cannot be changed into another quantity.

The Millikan Experiment: Determining the Elementary Charge

- There exists a smallest unit of electric charge, called the elementary charge, e, of which other units are simple multiples; $e = 1.602 \times 10^{-19}$ C.

Understanding Concepts

1. Sphere A with charge $-3q$ is 1.5 m from another identical sphere B with charge $+5q$. The two spheres are brought into contact and then separated by a distance of 1.5 m; the magnitude of the force between the spheres is 8.1×10^{-2} N.
   (a) Find the number of electrons transferred from one sphere to the other. Explain which way they moved.
   (b) Find the magnitude of the electric field and the electric potential midway between the two spheres.
   (c) Determine the magnitude of the initial electric force between the spheres.

2. A small drop of water, of mass 4.3×10^{-9} kg, is suspended motionless by a uniform electric field of 9.2×10^2 N/C [up].
   (a) Is the charge on the drop positive or negative? Explain.
   (b) Find the number of extra electrons or protons on the drop.

3. An oil drop, of mass 4.7×10^{-15} kg, is suspended between two parallel plates, as in **Figure 3**.
   (a) Calculate the charge on the oil drop.
   (b) Calculate the number of elementary charges required to make up this charge.
   (c) Does the oil drop have a deficit or excess of electrons? Explain your answer.

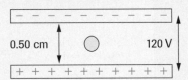

0.50 cm   120 V

Figure 3

4. Two small, equally charged objects have the same mass of 2.0×10^{-5} kg. Find the possible charges on each object if the electric force cancels the gravitational force between each object.

5. Sphere A of mass 5.0×10^{-2} kg has an excess of 1.0×10^{12} electrons. Sphere B has a deficit of 4.5×10^{12} electrons. The two spheres are separated by 0.12 m, as in **Figure 4**.
   (a) Find the angle between the thread and the vertical.
   (b) Find the tension in the thread.

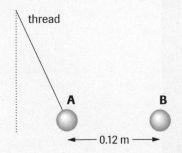

thread

A   B

◄— 0.12 m —►   **Figure 4**

Applying Inquiry Skills

6. When Millikan began his investigation, he used water droplets rather than oil. He later switched to oil droplets because he experienced problems when examining the water. (He found it difficult to suspend the water droplets for any length of time.)
   (a) Why might it be more difficult to keep water droplets suspended than oil droplets? (*Hint:* Consider changes of state.)
   (b) Describe what would be observed when doing an experiment of this nature with water.
   (c) Another scientist might have assumed that other problems were causing the observed results using water. Explain one of these false assumptions.

7. An investigator determines the charges on several different oil droplets with apparatus similar to Millikan's and claims that the data in **Table 1** are accurate to the number of digits shown.

Table 1

Oil Drop	Charge (C)
1	6.40×10^{-19}
2	1.80×10^{-18}
3	1.08×10^{-18}
4	1.44×10^{-18}
5	2.16×10^{-18}

(a) Without using any prior knowledge about the fundamental charge, describe a procedure that could be used to find the value of a fundamental charge, assuming that all charges in nature are integral multiples of this charge.
(b) Use the procedure to determine the fundamental charge.
(c) Can the scientist be certain that this value is the fundamental charge? Explain your answer.
(d) We know the value of the fundamental charge. Discuss the experimental results and explain any problems.

Making Connections

8. Earth actually has an electric field of 1.0×10^2 N/C at its surface pointing toward the centre.
   (a) A uniformly charged sphere produces an electric field outside the object exactly the same as the field that would be produced if the charge is concentrated at the centre of the field. Assume Earth is uniformly charged. What is the type and magnitude of the charge on Earth?
   (b) Compare Earth's electric field and gravitational field in terms of (i) direction and shape, (ii) effect on objects, and (iii) how it changes as height increases.
   (c) What is the largest mass that can be suspended by the electric field of Earth if the particle has the elementary charge on it?
   (d) Could the electric field of Earth be used to suspend (i) a proton and (ii) an electron? Explain your reasoning.

9. In still air under direct sunlight, tiny dust particles can often be observed to float. Explain how this happens. How could you test your answer?

In the Millikan experiment, when charged oil drops were sprayed between two charged parallel plates, the electric field they experienced caused some of them to move slowly in one direction and others to move more slowly or more quickly in the other direction. By adjusting the magnitude of the electric field between the plates, it was possible to get some drops to remain stationary, balanced by the downward force of gravity and the upward force of the electric field.

The Millikan apparatus does not, however, give a true picture of the motion of charged particles in an electric field because of the presence of air and its resistant effect on the motion of such tiny particles, resulting in a constant terminal velocity. Consider a small positive charge q_1, with a very small mass m, in a vacuum a distance r from a fixed positive charge q_2. We will assume that the mass m is so small that gravitational effects are negligible.

In **Figure 1**, the charge q_1 experiences a Coulomb force, to the right in this case, whose magnitude is given by

$$F_E = \frac{kq_1q_2}{r^2}$$

If the charged mass is free to move from its original position, it will accelerate in the direction of this electric force (Newton's second law) with an instantaneous acceleration whose magnitude is given by

$$a = \frac{F_E}{m}$$

Describing the subsequent motion of the charged mass becomes difficult because as it begins to move, r increases, causing F_E to decrease, so that a decreases as well. (You can see that a decrease is inevitable, since the acceleration, like the magnitude of the electrical force, is inversely proportional to the square of the distance from the repelling charge.) Motion with a decreasing acceleration poses a difficult analytical problem if we apply Newton's laws directly.

If we use considerations of energy to analyze its motion, it becomes much simpler. As the separation distance between q_1 and q_2 increases, the electric potential energy decreases, and the charged mass q_1 begins to acquire kinetic energy. The law of conservation of energy requires that the total energy remain constant as q_1 moves away from q_2. Activity 7.6.1 in the Lab Activities section at the end of this chapter provides the opportunity for you to simulate the motion of charged particles in electric fields.

This aspect of the system is illustrated in **Figure 2**. When q_1 is at r_1, q_1 is at rest, and so the total energy of the charged mass equals its potential energy:

$$E = E'$$

$$E_E + E_K = E_E' + E_K'$$

$$\frac{kq_1q_2}{r} + \frac{1}{2}mv^2 = \frac{kq_1q_2}{r'} + \frac{1}{2}m(v')^2$$

$$\frac{kq_1q_2}{r} - \frac{kq_1q_2}{r'} = \frac{1}{2}m(v')^2 - \frac{1}{2}mv^2$$

$$-\left(\frac{kq_1q_2}{r'} - \frac{kq_1q_2}{r}\right) = \frac{1}{2}mm(v')^2 - 0$$

$$-\Delta E_K = \Delta E_K$$

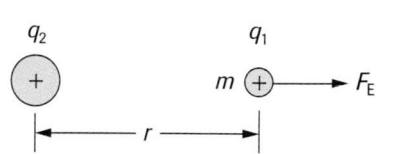

Figure 1
Charge will accelerate in the direction of the electric force according to Newton's second law.

⊙ ACTIVITY 7.6.1

The Motion of Charged Particles in Electric Fields (p. 375)
How many ways can you think of to show that the law of conservation of energy governs the motion of charged particles? How do the force, acceleration, and velocity of the charged particles change?

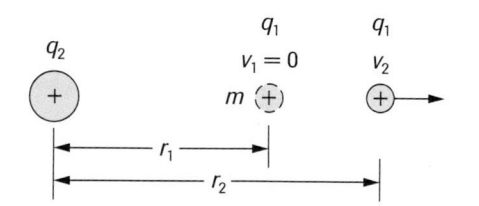

Figure 2
The total energy of the charges remains constant even though the distance between them changes.

The charged particle q_1 thus moves in the electric field of q_2 in such a way that the electric potential energy it loses $(-\Delta E_E)$ is equal to the kinetic energy it gains (ΔE_K). A sample problem will illustrate this.

▶ SAMPLE problem 1

Figure 3 shows two small conducting spheres placed on top of insulating pucks. One puck is anchored to the surface, while the other is allowed to move freely on an air table. The mass of the sphere and puck together is 0.15 kg, and the charge on each sphere is $+3.0 \times 10^{-6}$ C and $+5.0 \times 10^{-9}$ C. The two spheres are initially 0.25 m apart. How fast will the sphere be moving when they are 0.65 m apart?

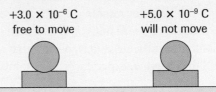

$+3.0 \times 10^{-6}$ C
free to move

$+5.0 \times 10^{-9}$ C
will not move

Figure 3

Solution

$m = 0.15$ kg $\qquad\qquad r = 0.25$ m

$q_1 = +3.0 \times 10^{-6}$ C $\qquad r' = 0.65$ m

$q_2 = +5.0 \times 10^{-9}$ C $\qquad v' = ?$

To find the speed, the kinetic energy at $r' = 0.65$ m is required. Since the initial kinetic energy is 0, the final kinetic energy is equal to the change in kinetic energy. To determine the change in kinetic energy, we first find the change in electric potential energy:

$$E_K' = \Delta E_K$$
$$= -\Delta E_E$$
$$= -\left(\frac{kq_1q_2}{r'} - \frac{kq_1q_2}{r}\right)$$
$$= -\frac{(9.0 \times 10^9 \text{ N·m}^2/\text{C}^2)(3.0 \times 10^{-6} \text{ C})(5.0 \times 10^{-9} \text{ C})}{0.65 \text{ m}} + \frac{(9.0 \times 10^9 \text{ N·m}^2/\text{C}^2)(3.0 \times 10^{-6} \text{ C})(5.0 \times 10^{-9} \text{ C})}{0.25 \text{ m}}$$
$$E_K' = 3.3 \times 10^{-4} \text{ J}$$

We can now find the speed:

$$v' = \sqrt{\frac{2E_K'}{m}}$$
$$= \sqrt{\frac{2(0.33 \text{ J})}{0.15 \text{ kg}}}$$
$$v' = 0.07 \text{ m/s}$$

The sphere will be moving with a speed of 0.07 m/s.

When the electric field in which the charged particle is moving is uniform, its motion is much simpler. In a uniform electric field

$$\vec{F}_E = q\vec{\varepsilon} = \text{constant}$$

Therefore,

$$\vec{a} = \frac{\vec{F}_E}{m} = \text{constant}$$

Thus, the charged particle moves with uniform acceleration. This will be the case for small charged particles (such as ions, electrons, and protons) where gravitational effects are negligible and they are moving between two parallel plates in a vacuum.

The work done by a constant force in the same direction as the displacement is the scalar product of the force and the displacement. In a parallel-plate apparatus with plate separation r, the work done by the electric force in moving a charge q from one plate to the other is

$$
\begin{aligned}
W &= \vec{F}_E \cdot \vec{r} \\
&= \varepsilon qr \qquad \text{(since } \vec{\varepsilon} \text{ and } \vec{r} \text{ are in the same direction)} \\
&= \frac{\Delta V}{d} qr \\
W &= \Delta Vq
\end{aligned}
$$

This amount of work is equal in magnitude to the change in electric potential energy and the change in kinetic energy of the particle as it moves from one plate to the other. A sample problem will illustrate many of these relationships.

▶ SAMPLE problem 2

The cathode in a typical cathode-ray tube (**Figure 4**), found in a computer terminal or an oscilloscope, is heated, which makes electrons leave the cathode. They are then attracted toward the positively charged anode. The first anode has only a small potential rise while the second is at a large potential with respect to the cathode. If the potential difference between the cathode and the second anode is 2.0×10^4 V, find the final speed of the electron.

Solution

The mass and charge of an electron can be found in Appendix C.

$\Delta V = 2.0 \times 10^4$ V $\qquad q = 1.6 \times 10^{-19}$ C

$m = 9.1 \times 10^{-31}$ kg $\qquad v = ?$

For the free electron,

$$
\begin{aligned}
-\Delta E_E &= \Delta E_K \\
q\Delta V &= \frac{1}{2} mv^2 \\
v &= \sqrt{\frac{2q\Delta V}{m}} \\
&= \sqrt{\frac{2(1.6 \times 10^{-19} \text{ C})(2.0 \times 10^4 \text{ V})}{9.1 \times 10^{-31} \text{ kg}}} \\
v &= 8.4 \times 10^7 \text{ m/s}
\end{aligned}
$$

The final speed of the electron is 8.4×10^7 m/s.

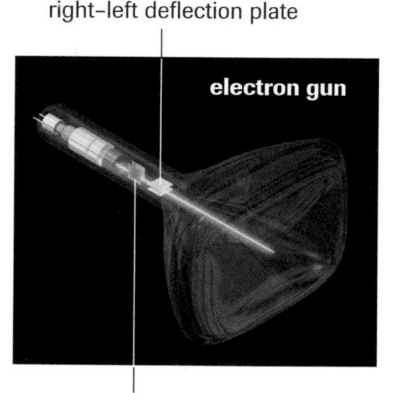

right–left deflection plate

electron gun

up–down deflection plate

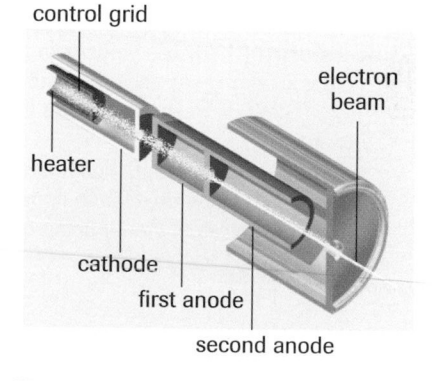

electron gun

control grid

electron beam

heater

cathode

first anode

second anode

Figure 4
A typical cathode ray tube

Note that this speed is not negligible compared to the speed of light (about 28%). The high velocity is due to the high electric potential difference and very low mass of the electron. This analysis becomes unsatisfactory for electrons accelerated by potentials of more than a few thousand volts because they begin to show relativistic effects (see Chapter 11).

> ▶ **Practice**

Understanding Concepts

1. The potential difference between two parallel plates is 1.5×10^2 V. You would have to do 0.24 J of work if you were to move a small charge, in opposition to the electric force, from one plate to the other. Calculate the magnitude of the charge.

2. An α particle has a positive charge of $2e$ and a mass of 6.6×10^{-27} kg. With what velocity would an α particle reach the negative plate of a parallel-plate apparatus with a potential difference of 2.0×10^3 V
   (a) if it started from rest at the positive plate
   (b) if it started from rest at a point halfway between the plates

3. A pith ball of mass 1.0×10^{-5} kg with a positive charge of 4.0×10^{-7} C is slowly pulled at a constant speed by a string a distance of 50.0 cm through a potential difference of 8.0×10^2 V. It is then released from rest and "falls" back to its original position.
   (a) Calculate the work done by the string in moving the pith ball.
   (b) Calculate the magnitude of the average force required to do this work.
   (c) Calculate the kinetic energy of the pith ball when it arrives back at its original position.
   (d) Calculate the speed of the pith ball just as it reaches its final position.

4. Two electrons are held, at rest, 1.0×10^{-12} m apart, then released. With what kinetic energy and speed is each moving when they are a "large" distance apart?

5. What is the potential difference required to accelerate a deuteron of mass 3.3×10^{-27} kg and charge 1.6×10^{-19} C from rest to a speed of 5.0×10^6 m/s?

Inkjet Printers

An inkjet printer uses charged parallel plates to deflect droplets of ink headed toward the paper. One type of inkjet print head ejects a thin stream of small ink droplets while it is moving back and forth across the paper (**Figure 5**). Typically, a small nozzle breaks up the stream of ink into droplets 1×10^{-4} m in diameter at a rate of 150 000 droplets per second and moving at 18 m/s. When the print head passes over an area of the paper that should have no ink on it, the charging electrode is turned on, creating an electric field between the print head and the electrode. The ink droplets acquire an electric charge by induction (the print head itself is grounded), and the deflection plates prevent the charged droplets from reaching the paper by diverting them into a gutter. When the print head passes over an area where ink is to be placed, the electrode is turned off and the uncharged ink droplets pass through the deflection plates in a straight line, landing on the paper. The movement of the print head across the paper determines the form of what appears on the paper.

Another type of inkjet printer places a charge on all the ink droplets. Two parallel plates are charged proportionately to a control signal from a computer, steering the droplets vertically as the paper moves horizontally (**Figure 6**). In the areas where no ink is to be placed, the droplets are deflected into a gutter as in the previous design.

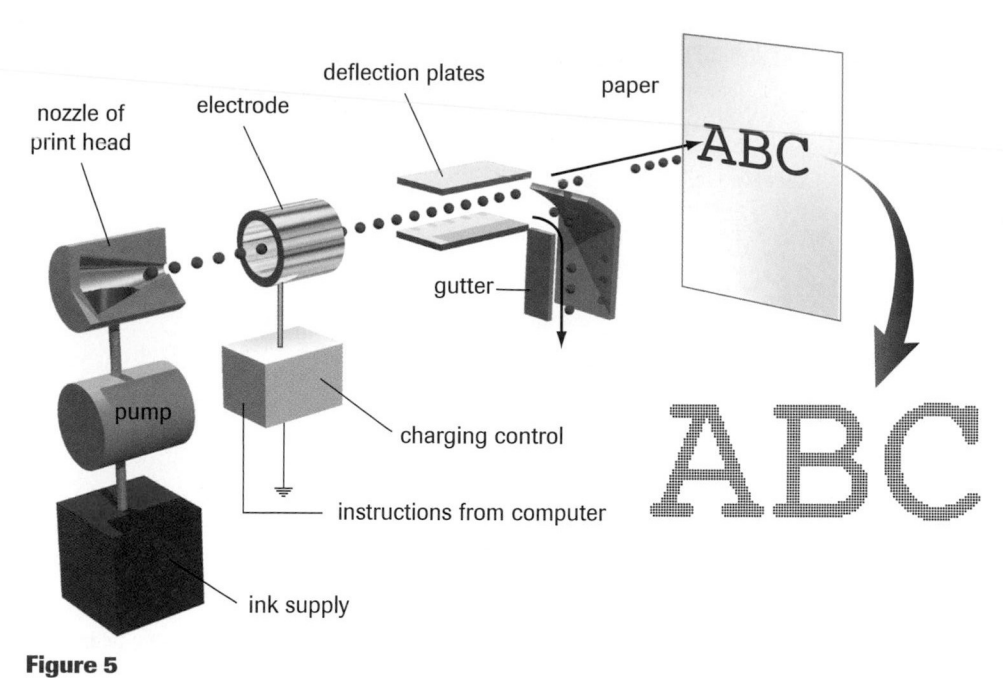

Figure 5
The print head emits a steady flow of ink droplets. Uncharged ink droplets pass straight through the deflection plates to form letters. Charged droplets are deflected into the gutter when the paper is to be blank. Notice that the evidence of the ink drops can be seen when the letters are enlarged.

▶ **SAMPLE** problem **3**

An electron is fired horizontally at 2.5×10^6 m/s between two horizontal parallel plates 7.5 cm long, as shown in **Figure 7**. The magnitude of the electric field is 130 N/C. The plate separation is great enough to allow the electron to escape. Edge effects and gravitation are negligible. Find the velocity of the electron as it escapes from between the plates.

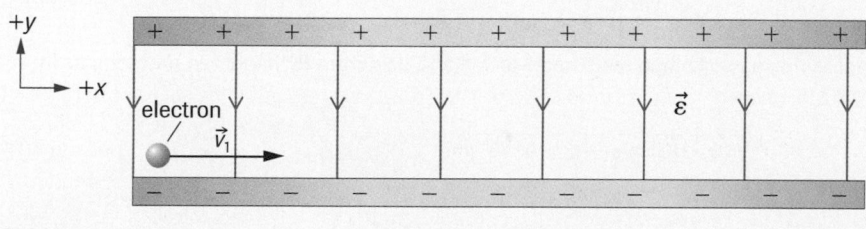

Figure 7

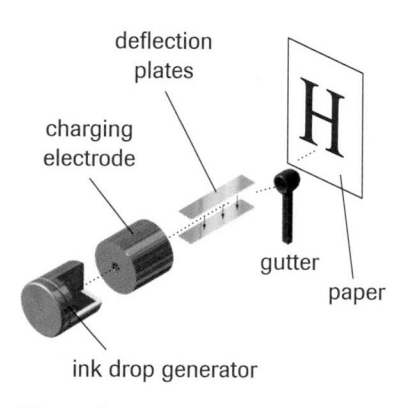

Figure 6
Charged droplets are deflected vertically to form the letters.

Solution

$q = 1.6 \times 10^{-19}$ C $\varepsilon = 130$ N/C

$\vec{v}_1 = 2.5 \times 10^6$ m/s [horizontally] $\vec{v}_2 = ?$

$l = 7.5$ cm

Note that $\vec{v}_2$ has two components, v_{2x} and v_{2y}.

The magnitude of the electric field is constant, and the field is always straight down; therefore, the electric force on the electron is constant, meaning its acceleration is constant and vertical. We can break the problem up into a horizontal part, which involves just uniform motion, and a vertical part, which involves constant acceleration. There is no need to use energy here (although you could). We will use forces and kinematics instead.

The magnitude of the net force on the electron is

$$F_{net} = F_E$$
$$= q\varepsilon$$
$$F_{net} = e\varepsilon$$

Therefore, the magnitude of the acceleration of the electron is given by

$$a_y = \frac{e\varepsilon}{m_e}$$
$$= \frac{(-1.6 \times 10^{-19}\ \text{C})(-130\ \text{N/C})}{9.1 \times 10^{-31}\ \text{kg}}$$
$$a_y = 2.3 \times 10^{13}\ \text{m/s}^2$$
$$\vec{a} = 2.3 \times 10^{13}\ \text{m/s}^2\ [\text{up}]$$

This acceleration is upward because the electron is repelled by the lower plate and attracted to the upper plate, as indicated by the direction of the electric field.

The initial velocity in the vertical direction is zero. To find the final vertical velocity, it suffices to find the time spent on the vertical movement, which equals the time spent passing through the plates. That time, in turn, is given to us by the horizontal velocity and the width of the plates. (Remember that the electron moves with uniform motion in the horizontal direction.)

$$\Delta t = \frac{\Delta l}{v_x}$$
$$= \frac{7.5 \times 10^{-2}\ \text{m}}{2.5 \times 10^6\ \text{m/s}}$$
$$\Delta t = 3.0 \times 10^{-8}\ \text{s}$$

The final vertical component of the velocity is

$$v_{2y} = v_{1y} + a_y\Delta t$$
$$= 0 + (2.3 \times 10^{13}\ \text{m/s}^2)(3.0 \times 10^{-8}\ \text{s})$$
$$v_{2y} = 6.9 \times 10^5\ \text{m/s}\ [\text{up}]$$

Adding these two components head-to-tail and using the Pythagorean theorem, as in **Figure 8**, gives

$$v_2 = \sqrt{(6.9 \times 10^5\ \text{m/s}) + (2.5 \times 10^6\ \text{m/s})}$$
$$v_2 = 2.6 \times 10^6\ \text{m/s}$$

We determine the angle upward from the horizontal:

$$\theta = \tan^{-1}\left(\frac{6.9 \times 10^5\ \text{m/s}}{2.5 \times 10^6\ \text{m/s}}\right)$$
$$\theta = 15°$$

The final velocity is 2.6×10^6 m/s [right 15° up from the horizontal].

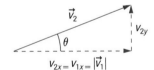

Figure 8

SUMMARY   **The Motion of Charged Particles in Electric Fields**

- A charged particle in a uniform electric field moves with uniform acceleration.
- From conservation principles, any changes to a particle's kinetic energy result from corresponding changes to its electric potential energy (when moving in any electric field and ignoring any gravitational effects).

Understanding Concepts

1. **Figure 9** shows a common technique used to accelerate electrons, usually released from a hot filament from rest. The small hole in the positive plate allows some electrons to escape providing a source of fast-moving electrons for experimentation. The magnitude of the potential difference between the two plates is 1.2×10^3 V. The distance between the plates is 0.12 m.
   (a) At what speed will an electron pass through the hole in the positive plate?
   (b) Is the electron pulled back to the positive plate once it passes through the hole? Explain your answer.
   (c) How could the apparatus be modified to accelerate protons?
   (d) Find the speed of the emerging protons in an appropriate apparatus.

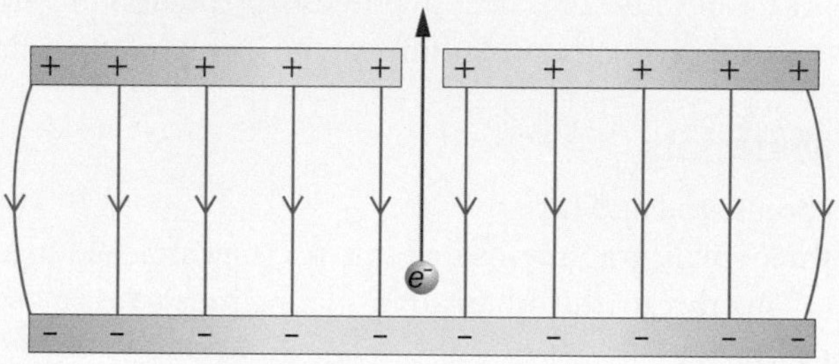

Figure 9

2. An electron is accelerated through a uniform electric field of magnitude 2.5×10^2 N/C with an initial speed of 1.2×10^6 m/s parallel to the electric field, as shown in **Figure 10**.
   (a) Calculate the work done on the electron by the field when the electron has travelled 2.5 cm in the field.
   (b) Calculate the speed of the electron after it has travelled 2.5 cm in the field.
   (c) If the direction of the electric field is reversed, how far will the electron move into the field before coming to rest?

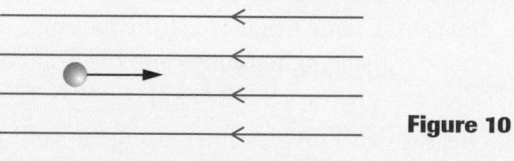

Figure 10

3. Two electrons are fired at 3.5×10^6 m/s directly at each other.
   (a) Calculate the smallest possible distance between the two electrons.
   (b) Is it likely that two electrons in this situation will actually get this close to each other if the experiment is performed? Explain your answer.

4. Ernest Rutherford in his lab at McGill University, Montreal, fired α particles of mass 6.64×10^{-27} kg at gold foil to investigate the nature of the atom. What initial energy must an α particle (charge $+2e$) have to come within 4.7×10^{-15} m of a gold nucleus (charge $+79e$) before coming to rest? This distance is approximately the radius of the gold nucleus.

5. An electron with a velocity of 3.00×10^6 m/s [horizontally] passes through two horizontal parallel plates, as in **Figure 11**. The magnitude of the electric field between the plates is 120 N/C. The plates are 4.0 cm across. Edge effects in the field are negligible.
   (a) Calculate the vertical deflection of the electron.
   (b) Calculate the vertical component of the final velocity.
   (c) Calculate the angle at which the electron emerges.

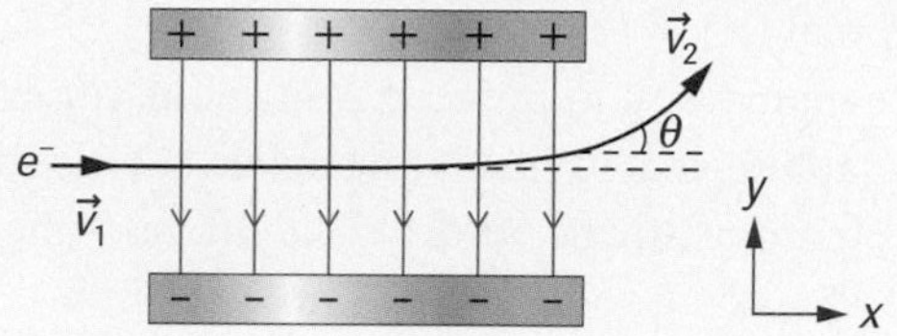

Figure 11

Making Connections

6. An oscilloscope is a device that deflects a beam of electrons vertically and horizontally across a screen. Its many applications (e.g., electrocardiography) rely on its high sensitivity to electric potential differences.
   (a) How can we deflect the beam of electrons in the oscilloscope vertically, whether upward or downward, by various amounts?
   (b) How can we deflect the beam horizontally from left to right, and then horizontally again, more quickly, from right to left?
   (c) If an oscilloscope is to be used to monitor the heartbeat of a patient, what will determine the amount of vertical and horizontal deflection of the electrons?
   (d) Design an oscilloscope that can deflect the electrons 5° vertically up and down and 10° horizontally left and right. Discuss the changes in potential that will be required in its operation if heartbeats are to be measured.

7. Two oppositely charged objects, of some nonneglible mass m_1, are placed in deep interstellar space, in a region essentially free of gravitational forces from other objects.
   (a) Discuss the resulting motion of the two objects and the energy transformations.
   (b) Compare the motion of these two charged objects with the motion of two neutral objects, of some nonneglible mass m_2, under similar circumstances.

INVESTIGATION 7.2.1

Factors Affecting Electric Force between Charges

Inquiry Skills

○ Questioning   ○ Planning   ● Analyzing
● Hypothesizing   ● Conducting   ● Evaluating
● Predicting   ● Recording   ● Communicating

The purpose of this investigation is to determine the relationship between the electric force and the distance between charges, and between the electric force and the magnitudes of charges. We start by investigating each relationship separately. Later in the investigation, we combine the relationships to yield a general equation for the electric force between small spherical charged objects. Your teacher may require you to perform this investigation with lab equipment other than what is suggested here or with a simulation program in place of lab equipment.

There are many ways to proceed. You could, for example, try small, graphite-coated insulating spheres. One sphere is suspended from a thread, and two identical spheres are attached to insulating rods. Usually, no equipment is available for determining the magnitude of the charge on each sphere. However, once you have placed a charge on a sphere, you can reduce it in half by touching the charged sphere with an identical neutral sphere. You can measure electrostatic forces, at least to low precision, with the setup suggested in **Figure 1**.

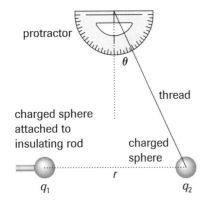

Figure 1
Setup for Investigation 7.2.1

protractor

θ

thread

charged sphere attached to insulating rod

charged sphere

r

q_1 q_2

Questions

(i) How does the electric force between small, spherical charged objects depend on the charges of the objects and the distance between them?

(ii) How can this relationship be expressed in a single equation?

LEARNING TIP

Hints: Keep the two spheres at the same height. Measure distances and angles carefully. Redo the experiment if necessary. Perform the experiment as quickly as you can without sacrificing accuracy, since your charged spheres will be leaking charge to the atmosphere as time passes.

Hypothesis/Prediction

(a) Communicate your hypothesis/prediction in words, mathematical notation, or with a graph.

Materials

ebonite rod and fur
three small, graphite-coated spheres (one attached to a long thread, the others to insulating rods)
protractor
ruler
balance

Procedure
Part A: Electric Force and Distance

1. Measure and record the mass of the sphere on the thread.

2. Set up your equipment carefully and check that it will function properly.

3. Charge the sphere on the thread and one sphere on the rod. Bring the rod's sphere close to the hanging one at the same height. Measure the angle of deflection for the hanging sphere and the distance between the two spheres.

4. Repeat step 3 several times, using the same charges at different distances.

⚛ INVESTIGATION 7.2.1 *continued*

Part B: Electric Force and the Charges

5. Charge two spheres and bring them together, ensuring they are at the same height. Measure the distance and angle carefully.

6. Ensure that the third sphere on the insulating rod is neutral. Touch it to one of the charged spheres. Repeat step 3, keeping the two spheres the same distance apart. (You will have to change the height slightly.)

7. Ensure that the third sphere is neutral again. Touch it to the other charged sphere. Repeat step 3, keeping the two spheres the same distance apart.

8. Continue with this process using the neutral sphere until you have enough data or the angle is too small to measure accurately. If your final data set is too small, try repeating the procedure by placing larger charges on the spheres.

Analysis

(b) Draw a free-body diagram for the charged sphere on the thread. Find the electric force on the sphere in terms of the force of gravity and the angle θ between the thread and the vertical.

(c) Copy and complete **Table 1**. Plot the electric force versus the distance between the charges.

Table 1 Constant Charges, Changing Distance

r	θ	F_E
?	?	?

(d) Find a relationship between the magnitude of the electric force and the distance between the charges. Graph the relationship to ensure you are correct.

(e) Copy and complete **Table 2**.

Table 2 Constant Distance, Changing Charge

Fraction of q_1 $\left(1, \frac{1}{2}, \frac{1}{4}, \text{etc.}\right)$	Fraction of q_2 $\left(1, \frac{1}{2}, \frac{1}{4}, \text{etc.}\right)$	θ	F_E
?	?	?	?

(f) Find a relationship and a proportionality statement between the magnitude of the electric force and the two charges. Graph the relationship to ensure you are correct.

(g) Combine the two relationships into one proportionality statement.

Evaluation

(h) Comment on the accuracy of your prediction.

(i) List the most likely sources of random and systematic error in this experiment. Discuss ways to minimize these errors.

(j) Discuss any discrepancies between what you have found and Coulomb's law. Suggest explanations of these discrepancies where possible.

Synthesis

(k) If you have used a simulation, is Coulomb's law consistent with Newton's third law? Explain and discuss how it can be verified. Perform the experiment if you have time.

Inquiry Skills

○ Questioning   ● Planning   ● Analyzing
○ Hypothesizing   ● Conducting   ● Evaluating
● Predicting   ● Recording   ● Communicating

The Elementary Charge

In this lab exercise, you will start with an activity similar to Millikan's. You will then find the actual elementary charge with data from an oil drop experiment.

Part 1: An Activity Similar to Millikan's

Materials

several bags containing different numbers of identical objects such as marbles, paper clips, or other small objects

Procedure

1. Measure the mass of each bag without looking inside or trying to count the number of objects. (You may find the mass of an empty bag if your teacher recommends it.)

2. Design a procedure (method) for predicting the mass of an individual object contained inside the bag.

3. Use your method to predict the mass of an individual object.

Part 2: Lab Exercise Using Millikan's Experimental Data

Evidence

separation of the plates: $r = 0.50$ cm
mass of oil drops and electric potential differences in **Table 1**

Analysis

(a) Using the data in **Table 1**, calculate the value of the elementary charge.

(b) Describe the method you used to determine the elementary charge. Was this method similar to the method you used to find the mass of an individual object in Part 1 once the charge is determined?

(c) What must be true about individual elementary charges for your method for determining their values to be valid?

Table 1 Millikan's Experimental Data

Mass of Oil Drop (kg)	Electric Potential Difference (V)	Charge on Oil Drop (C)
3.2×10^{-15}	140.0	?
2.4×10^{-15}	147.0	?
1.9×10^{-15}	290.9	?
4.2×10^{-15}	214.4	?
2.8×10^{-15}	428.8	?
2.3×10^{-15}	176.1	?
3.5×10^{-15}	214.4	?
3.7×10^{-15}	566.6	?
2.1×10^{-15}	160.8	?
3.9×10^{-15}	597.2	?
4.3×10^{-15}	263.4	?
2.5×10^{-15}	382.8	?
3.1×10^{-15}	237.3	?
3.4×10^{-15}	173.5	?
2.2×10^{-15}	673.8	?

(d) Why must a large number of values be used to get a reliable answer? What error might result if only a few oil drops were used, all containing an even number of charges?

Evaluation

(e) List some possible sources of random and systematic error in an experiment of this nature. What can be done to minimize the errors? (Millikan's experiment is an unusually good one for thinking about sources of error. Try to be creative.)

◎ ACTIVITY 7.6.1

The Motion of Charged Particles in Electric Fields

In this activity, you will simulate the motion of charged particles in electric fields and determine the effect of energy and electric force of the charge.

Questions

(i) How do electric potential energy and kinetic energy change as two similarly charged particles start from rest and move away from each other?

(ii) How are the electric potential energy and the kinetic energies of the charged particles related?

(iii) How do the force, acceleration, and velocity of the charged particles change?

Materials
computer with an appropriate simulation program

Procedure

1. Run the simulation with two charged particles of the same mass and equal charge. Make sure that the only force between the two particles is the electrostatic force. (Turn off gravity if it is on your simulation.)

2. Choose appropriate values for the mass of the particles, the separation between them, and the charge on each. Remember that 1 C is a very large charge and that choosing a very large charge makes it inappropriate to choose very small masses. Try a few runs until you get output that suggests you have made a physically reasonable compromise between mass and magnitude of charge. Your simulation should look something like **Figure 1**.

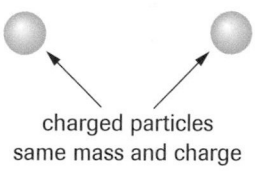

charged particles
same mass and charge

Figure 1
Two identical objects with charges on them

3. Find the initial distance between the particles and record the charges and the masses.

4. Use the simulation to measure all the quantities to be investigated.

5. Run the simulation until the particles have moved far apart. If your program has a tracking feature, turn it on.

6. Record data from the simulation. Use the step function if available.

Analysis

(a) Describe how the following quantities change as the simulation is running:

    (i) electric potential energy

    (ii) kinetic energy

    (iii) electric force

    (iv) acceleration

    (v) velocity

    Graph each quantity as a function of time.

(b) How are the different types of energy related? What happens to these energies as the distance becomes very large?

(c) Why are energy considerations, rather than direct calculations with kinematics equations and Newton's laws, used to solve these kinds of problems?

Synthesis

(d) Are your observations consistent with all of Newton's laws and the law of conservation of momentum? Explain your answers.

Key Expectations

- state Coulomb's law and Newton's law of universal gravitation, and analyze and compare them in qualitative terms (7.2)
- apply Coulomb's law and Newton's law of universal gravitation quantitatively in specific contexts (7.2)
- define and describe the concepts and units related to electric and gravitational fields (e.g., electric and gravitational potential energy, electric field, gravitational field strength) (7.2, 7.3, 7.4, 7.5, 7.6)
- determine the net force on, and the resulting motion of, objects and charged particles by collecting, analyzing, and interpreting quantitative data from experiments or computer simulations involving electric and gravitational fields (e.g., calculate the charge on an electron, using experimentally collected data; conduct an experiment to verify Coulomb's law and analyze discrepancies between theoretical and empirical values) (7.2, 7.5, 7.6)
- describe and explain, in qualitative terms, the electric field that exists inside and on the surface of a charged conductor (e.g., inside and around a coaxial cable) (7.3)
- explain how the concept of a field developed into a general scientific model, and describe how it affected scientific thinking (e.g., explain how field theory helped scientists understand, on a macro scale, the motion of celestial bodies and, on a micro scale, the motion of particles in electric fields) (7.3)
- analyze and explain the properties of electric fields and demonstrate how an understanding of these properties can be applied to control or alter the electric field around a conductor (e.g., demonstrate how shielding on electronic equipment or on connecting conductors [coaxial cables] affects electric fields) (7.3)
- analyze in quantitative terms, and illustrate using field and vector diagrams, the electric field and the electric forces produced by a single point charge, two point charges, and two oppositely charged parallel plates (e.g., analyze, using vector diagrams, the electric force required to balance the gravitational force on an oil drop or on latex spheres between parallel plates) (7.3, 7.5)
- compare the properties of electric and gravitational fields by describing and illustrating the source and direction of the field in each case (7.3, 7.6)
- apply quantitatively the concept of electric potential energy in a variety of contexts, and compare the characteristics of electric potential energy with those of gravitational potential energy (7.4, 7.6)

Key Terms

induced charge separation

law of conservation of charge

Coulomb's law

coulomb

field theory

field of force

electric field

electric potential

electric potential difference

electric potential energy

Key Equations

- $F_E = \dfrac{kq_1q_2}{r^2}$ (7.2)
- $k = 9.0 \times 10^9 \ N\cdot m^2/C^2$ Coulomb's law   (7.2)
- $\varepsilon = \dfrac{kq_1}{r^2}$ (7.3)
- $E_E = \dfrac{kq_1q_2}{r}$ (7.4)
- $V = \dfrac{kq_1}{r}$ (7.4)
- $\Delta E = q\Delta V$ for charged plates $\varepsilon = \dfrac{\Delta V}{r}$ (7.4)
- $e = 1.602 \times 10^{-19} \ C$ elementary charge   (7.5)
- $q = Ne$ (7.5)

▶ **MAKE** a summary

There are many different concepts and equations in this chapter that are closely related to each other. List all the equations in this chapter and show how they are related. Identify which quantities in your equations are vectors, which of your equations apply to point charges, and which equations apply to parallel plates. Give an application for each equation, and discuss any principles or laws from other chapters that are related to them.

Write numbers 1 to 6 in your notebook. Indicate beside each number whether the corresponding statement is true (T) or false (F). If it is false, write a corrected version.

1. If a charge q exerts a force of attraction of magnitude F on a charge $-2q$, then the charge $-2q$ exerts a force of attraction of magnitude $2F$ on the charge q.

2. The only difference between electric and gravitational forces is that the electric force is larger.

3. The electric field at the surface of a conductor in static equilibrium is perpendicular to the surface of the conductor.

4. Electric field lines indicate the path that charged particles will follow near another charged object.

5. It is safe to stay in your car during a lightning storm because the tires act as insulators.

6. The acceleration experienced by two small charges as they start from rest and move apart is inversely proportional to the square of the distance between them.

Write numbers 7 to 13 in your notebook. Beside each number, write the letter corresponding to the best choice.

7. When comparing the force of attraction between an electron and a proton due to the electric force and gravity, it can be concluded that
   (a) the gravitational force is a lot stronger
   (b) the electric force is a lot stronger
   (c) the two types of forces are the same
   (d) they cannot be compared
   (e) the electric force is slightly stronger

8. The electric force on each of two small charged spheres due to the other sphere has a magnitude of F. The charge on one sphere is doubled, and the distance between the centres of the spheres is tripled. The magnitude of the force on each small charged sphere is
   (a) $2F$ (c) $\dfrac{2F}{3}$ (e) $\dfrac{2F}{9}$
   (b) $\dfrac{F}{3}$ (d) $\dfrac{F}{9}$

9. The magnitude of the electric field due to a small charged object is 12 N/C at a distance of 3.0 m from the charge. The field 6.0 m away from the charge is
   (a) 36 N/C   (c) 6.0 N/C   (e) 3.0 N/C
   (b) 12 N/C   (d) 4.0 N/C

10. Which diagram in **Figure 1** represents the net electric field between two charged parallel plates if a neutral conducting sphere is placed between the plates?
    (a)   (b)   (c)   (d)   (e) none of these

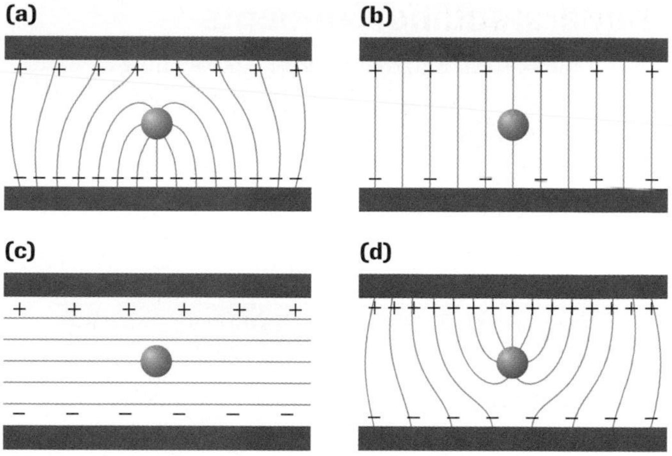

Figure 1

11. A neutral charged conductor is placed near a positively charged object. The electric field inside the neutral conductor is
    (a) perpendicular to the surface
    (b) zero
    (c) directed toward the negative charge
    (d) stronger than the electric field at the surface of the conductor
    (e) none of these

12. A mass has a charge on it. Another small mass with a positive charge is moved away from the first mass, which remains at rest. As the distance increases, what happens to the gravitational potential energy E_g and the electric potential energy E_E?
    (a) E_g decreases and E_E decreases
    (b) E_E either decreases or increases, depending on the unknown sign of charge, and E_g decreases
    (c) E_g decreases and E_E increases
    (d) E_E decreases or increases, depending on the unknown sign of charge, and E_g increases
    (e) E_g increases and E_E decreases

13. Two isolated electrons starting from rest move apart. Which of the following statements is true as the distance between the electrons increases?
    (a) The velocity increases and the acceleration is constant.
    (b) The velocity increases and the acceleration decreases.
    (c) The velocity decreases and the acceleration is constant.
    (d) The velocity increases and the acceleration increases.
    (e) The velocity is constant and the acceleration is constant.

Understanding Concepts

1. One of the children in **Figure 1** is touching an electrostatic generator.
   (a) Why does the hair of the child touching the electrostatic generator stand on end?
   (b) Why does the hair of the other child likewise stand on end?
   (c) Are the children grounded? Explain your answer.

Figure 1
Two children holding hands; one is touching an electrostatic generator.

2. In a chart, compare similarities and differences between Newton's law of universal gravitation and Coulomb's law.

3. Coulomb's law may be used to calculate the force between charges only under certain conditions. State the conditions, and explain why they are imposed.

4. Two small, oppositely charged conducting spheres experience a mutual electric force of attraction of magnitude 1.6×10^{-2} N. What does this magnitude become if each sphere is touched with its identical, neutral mate, the initially neutral spheres are taken far away, and the separation of the two initially charged spheres is doubled?

5. What is the distance between two protons experiencing a mutually repelling force of magnitude 4.0×10^{-11} N?

6. One model of the structure of the hydrogen atom consists of a stationary proton with an electron moving in a circular path around it. The orbital path has a radius of 5.3×10^{-11} m. The masses of a proton and an electron are 1.67×10^{-27} kg and 9.1×10^{-31} kg, respectively.
   (a) Calculate the electrostatic force between the electron and the proton.
   (b) Calculate the gravitational force between them.
   (c) Which force is mainly responsible for the electron's circular motion?
   (d) Calculate the speed and period of the electron in its orbit around the proton.

7. Two point charges, $+4.0 \times 10^{-5}$ C and -1.8×10^{-5} C, are placed 24 cm apart. What is the force on a third small charge, of magnitude -2.5×10^{-6} C, if it is placed on the line joining the other two,
   (a) 12 cm outside the originally given pair of charges, on the side of the negative charge?
   (b) 12 cm outside the originally given pair of charges, on the side of the positive charge?
   (c) midway between the originally given pair of charges?

8. Explain why we use a "small" test charge to detect and measure an electric field.

9. If a stationary charged test particle is free to move in an electric field, in what direction will it begin to travel?

10. Why is it safer to stay inside an automobile during a lightning storm? (*Hint:* It is not due to the insulating rubber tires.)

11. Three small, negatively charged spheres are located at the vertices of an equilateral triangle. The magnitudes of the charges are equal. Sketch the electric field in the region around this charge distribution, including the space inside the triangle.

12. A small test charge of $+1.0$ μC experiences an electric force of 6.0×10^{-6} N to the right.
   (a) What is the electric field strength at that point?
   (b) What force would be exerted on a charge of -7.2×10^{-4} C located at the same point, in place of the test charge?

13. What are the magnitude and direction of the electric field strength 1.5 m to the right of a positive point charge of magnitude 8.0×10^{-3} C?

14. What are the magnitude and direction of the electric field strength at point Z in **Figure 2**?

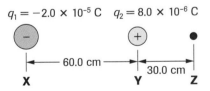

$q_1 = -2.0 \times 10^{-5}$ C $q_2 = 8.0 \times 10^{-6}$ C

$\longleftarrow$ 60.0 cm $\longrightarrow$ | 30.0 cm |

X   Y   Z

Figure 2

15. A ping-pong ball of mass 3.0×10^{-4} kg hangs from a light thread 1.0 m long, between two vertical parallel plates 10.0 cm apart (**Figure 3**). When the potential difference across the plates is 420 V, the ball comes to equilibrium 1.0 cm to one side of its original position.

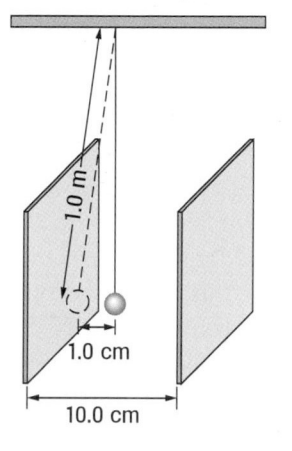

1.0 m

1.0 cm

10.0 cm

Figure 3

    (a) Calculate the electric field strength between the plates.
    (b) Calculate the tension in the thread.
    (c) Calculate the magnitude of the electric force deflecting the ball.
    (d) Calculate the charge on the ball.

16. If two points have the same electric potential, is it true that no work is required to move a test charge from one point to the other? Does that mean that no force is required, as well?

17. How much work is required to move a charged particle through an electric field if it moves along a path that is always perpendicular to an electric field line? How would the potential change along such a path?

18. A charge of 1.2×10^{-3} C is fixed at each corner of a rectangle 30.0 cm wide and 40.0 cm long. What are the magnitude and direction of the electric force on each charge? What are the electric field and the electric potential at the centre?

19. Calculate the electric potential 0.50 m from a 4.5×10^{-4} C point charge.

20. A 1.0×10^{-6} C test charge is 40.0 cm from a 3.2×10^{-3} C charged sphere. How much work was required to move it there from a point 1.0×10^2 cm away from the sphere?

21. How much kinetic energy is gained by an electron that is allowed to move freely through a potential difference of 2.5×10^4 V?

22. How much work must be done to bring two protons, an infinite distance apart, to within 1.0×10^{-15} m of each other, a distance comparable to the width of an atomic nucleus? (The work required, while small, is enormous in relation to the typical kinetic energies of particles in a school lab. This shows why particle accelerators are needed.)

23. What is the magnitude of the electric field between two large parallel plates 2.0 cm apart if a potential difference of 450 V is maintained between them?

24. What potential difference between two parallel plates, at a separation of 8.0 cm, will produce an electric field strength of magnitude 2.5×10^3 N/C?

25. Most experiments in atomic physics are performed in a vacuum. Discuss the appropriateness of performing the Millikan oil drop experiment in a vacuum.

26. Assume that a single, isolated electron is fixed at ground level. How far above it, vertically, would another electron have to be so that its mass would be supported against gravitation by the force of electrostatic repulsion between them?

27. An oil droplet of mass 2.6×10^{-15} kg, suspended between two parallel plates 0.50 cm apart, remains stationary when the potential difference between the plates is 270 V. What is the charge on the oil droplet? How many excess or deficit electrons does it have?

28. A metallic table tennis ball of mass 0.10 g has a charge of 5.0×10^{-6} C. What potential difference, across a large parallel plate apparatus of separation 25 cm, would be required to keep the ball stationary?

29. Calculate the electric potential and the magnitude of the electric field at a point 0.40 m from a small sphere with an excess of 1.0×10^{12} electrons.

30. An electron is released from rest at the negative plate in a parallel plate apparatus kept under vacuum and maintained at a potential difference of 5.0×10^2 V. With what speed does the electron collide with the positive plate?

31. What potential difference would accelerate a helium nucleus from rest to a kinetic energy of 1.9×10^{-15} J? (For a helium nucleus, $q = +2e$.)

32. An electron with a speed of 5.0×10^6 m/s is injected into a parallel plate apparatus, in a vacuum, through a hole in the positive plate. The electron collides with the negative plate at 1.0×10^6 m/s. What is the potential difference between the plates?

33. Four parallel plates are connected in a vacuum as in **Figure 4**. An electron, essentially at rest, drifts into the hole in plate X and is accelerated to the right. The vertical motion of the electron continues to be negligible. The electron passes through holes W and Y, then continues moving toward plate Z. Using the information given in the diagram, calculate
    (a) the speed of the electron at hole W
    (b) the distance from plate Z to the point at which the electron changes direction
    (c) the speed of the electron when it arrives back at plate X

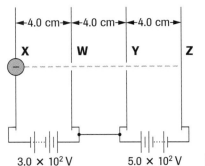

3.0 × 10² V   5.0 × 10² V   **Figure 4**

34. Two α particles, separated by an enormous distance, approach each other. Each has an initial speed of 3.0×10^6 m/s. Calculate their minimum separation, assuming no deflection from their original path.

35. An electron enters a parallel plate apparatus 10.0 cm long and 2.0 cm wide, moving horizontally at 8.0×10^7 m/s, as in **Figure 5**. The potential difference between the plates is 6.0×10^2 V. Calculate
    (a) the vertical deflection of the electron from its original path
    (b) the velocity with which the electron leaves the parallel plate apparatus

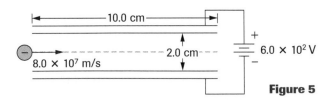

Figure 5

Applying Inquiry Skills

36. A versorium is a device that detects the presence of an electric charge on an object. The device consists of any convenient material (e.g., a straw or a long strip of folded paper) balanced on a needle or tack with some sort of base, such as modelling clay. The straw will rotate if a charged object is brought close to one end.

Build your own versorium. Charge several objects and try your device. Also try it on an operating television screen. Examine the effect of turning the television off and on while keeping your versorium near the screen. Write a short report on your findings.

37. Design an experiment that can be used to test the properties of conductors in electric fields. You may use either or both of the following as is convenient: a probe that can detect electric fields; a charged neutral object attached to an insulating rod.

38. The electric field of Earth always points toward Earth. The magnitude of the field strength varies locally from as low as 100 N/C in fair weather to 20 000 N/C in a thunderstorm. A field mill measures the local electric field strength. In this device, the lower plate, parallel to the ground, is connected to Earth through an ammeter. The upper plate can be moved horizontally, and it, too, is connected to Earth.
    (a) When the mill is arranged as in **Figure 6(a)**, what kind of charge is on the surface of Earth and on each plate? (*Hint:* Examine the field lines.)
    (b) What will the ammeter show when you move the upper plate rapidly over the lower plate, as in **Figure 6(b)**? Explain your answer.
    (c) What will the ammeter show when the upper plate is quickly pushed away from the lower plate? Explain your answer.
    (d) What will the ammeter show if the upper plate is attached to a motor and is rotated in a circle, passing periodically over the lower plate?
    (e) How is the ammeter reading related to the magnitude of the electric field of Earth?

(a)   **(b)**

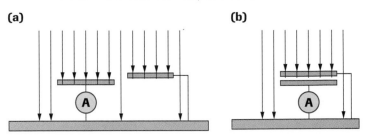

Figure 6
A field mill is used to detect the magnitude of Earth's electric field.

39. You place a circular conductor near a charged plate in oil with suspended rayon fibres, as in **Figure 7**. The configuration assumed by the fibres indicates the geometry of the electric field. Explain what conclusions this demonstration suggests regarding the nature of electric fields (a) near the surfaces of conductors and (b) inside conductors.

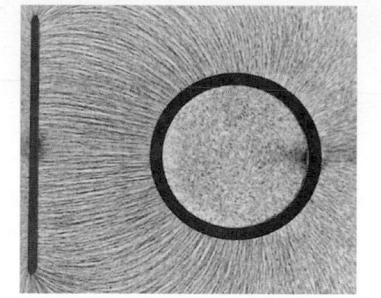

Figure 7

40. Using different materials—wool, fur, plastic, and paper—charge a small fluorescent tube in a dark room. A 45-cm tube, rated at 15 W, works well. The brightness of the tube depends on the potential difference achieved. Charge a plastic rod or a length of PVC pipe and move it close to the fluorescent tube. (**Figure 8** depicts this phenomenon using large fluorescent bulbs.) Write a short report on your observations.

Figure 8
Power lines in rural areas are operated at a potential difference of several hundred thousand volts relative to Earth. This voltage drop is high enough to create a significant potential difference across these fluorescent bulbs, causing them to glow.

Making Connections

41. When laboratories process photographs, the film often becomes positively charged, attracting dust and even causing sparks. One variety of static eliminator uses a radioactive source, polonium-210, that emits positively charged particles (α particles). Explain how this can help to reduce dust on the film.

42. Research the principles of piezoelectric crystals and the use of these crystals in wrist watches. Write a one-page report.

 www.science.nelson.com

43. **Figure 9** shows the climbing arc, or "Jacob's ladder." It operates by applying a potential difference to the plates. If the potential difference is large enough, an arc will jump between the gap between the two plates, where they are closest. The arc will then slowly climb up the ever-widening gap between the two plates. Discuss how the device operates by explaining the conditions necessary to start the arc, why it starts where the plates are closest, and why it then "climbs" up the space between the plates.

Figure 9
Climbing arc (or Jacob's ladder)

Extension

44. Gauss's law is considered even more general than Coulomb's law and is useful in relating the electric field to the total charge. Research Gauss's law and its applications and make a display showing what you have found.

45. An electron with an initial velocity of 2.4×10^6 m/s [45° up from the horizontal] passes into two parallel plates separated by 2.5 mm, as in **Figure 10**. The potential difference between the plates is 1.0×10^2 V.
    (a) How close does the electron come to the top plate?
    (b) Determine where it strikes the bottom plate.

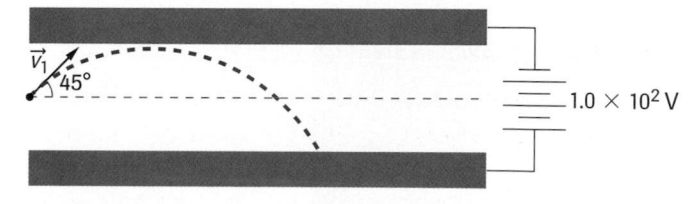

Figure 10

Magnetic Fields and Electromagnetism

Force acting-at-a-distance is the prevailing theme in this unit, and magnetism is another familiar force that behaves in this manner. A magnet can easily cause a compass needle to turn without making any contact with the needle or cause iron filings to "leap" off a desk without touching them. In this chapter we will draw on what we know about gravity and the electric force to expand our understanding of magnetism.

As in the last chapter the goal is to provide a more complete picture of magnetism through a rigorous, quantitative study. We will also look at many different applications of magnetism in areas such as nature (**Figure 1**), transportation, communication, and safety.

REFLECT on your learning

1. When a charge passes through a conductor, it produces a magnetic field.
   (a) How is the magnetic field oriented around a straight conductor?
   (b) How does the magnetic field strength vary with distance from the conductor?
   (c) What factors other than distance affect the magnitude of the magnetic field?
   (d) What factors affect the magnitude of the magnetic field produced by a coiled conductor?

2. (a) If a wire with a current in it can experience a force in a magnetic field, can a single charge moving in a magnetic field experience a force? If so, under what circumstances can this occur?
   (b) What factors affect the magnitude and direction of the force on the charge in the magnetic field?
   (c) What happens to the velocity of a particle fired into a uniform magnetic field, perpendicular to the field?
   (d) Will the resulting motion of a charged particle fired into a magnetic field resemble projectile motion for a mass in a gravitational field in the same way as a charged particle in a uniform electric field?

3. We have seen that the central conductor in a coaxial cable is shielded from electric fields. Does the conductor also shield magnetic fields? Why or why not?

4. List four devices that use the principles of magnetism. Explain how they work.

> ▶ **TRY THIS** activity ⠀⠀⠀ *Magnetic Fields*
>
> For this activity you will need an old cathode-ray tube and a bar magnet.
>
> **Have your teacher check all power arrangements. Cathode-ray tube potentials can be hazardous.**
>
> - Set up the cathode-ray tube so that a beam of electrons is clearly visible.
> - Bring the north-seeking pole of a bar magnet close to the tube from several different directions. Repeat with the south-seeking pole of the magnet.
>
> (a) What happens to the beam when you bring the north-seeking pole near?
>
> (b) How does this compare to what happens when the south-seeking pole is brought near?
>
> (c) What causes the change in trajectory of the beam? Do rays of light and streams of water behave in the same way in the presence of magnetic poles? Test your hypothesis and try to explain the results.

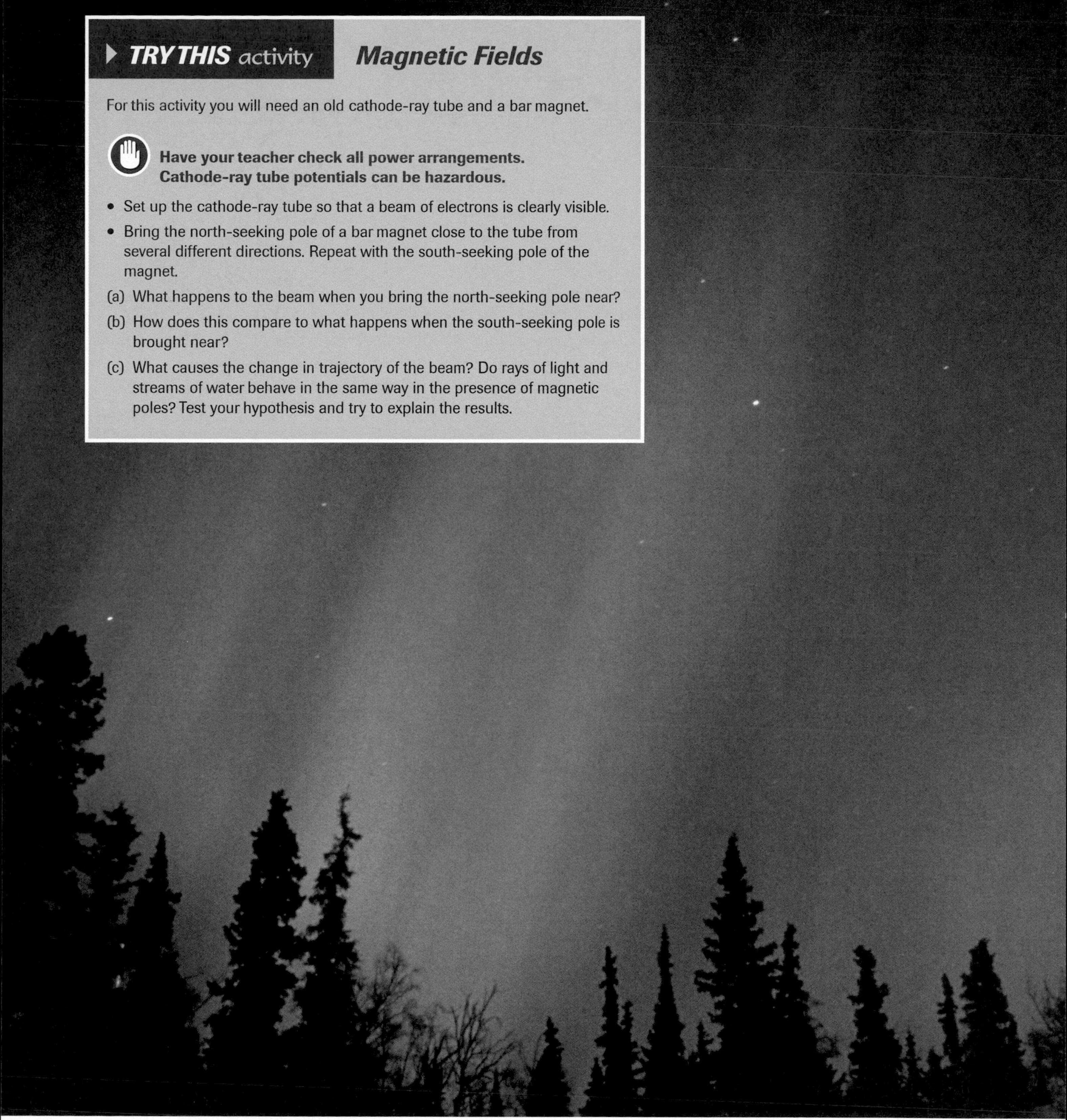

Figure 1
The aurora borealis is a result of ionized particles interacting with Earth's magnetic field.

poles the regions at the end of a magnetized body at which magnetic attraction is strongest

A systematic study of magnetism has been going on for the past two hundred years, yet physicists are still not able to fully explain the magnetic characteristics of the neutron and proton, and they are still puzzled about the origin of Earth's magnetic field. And while there are currently many applications of the principles of magnetism and electromagnetism in nature and society, scientists are continuously discovering new ways to use them.

Magnets

When a bar magnet is dipped into iron filings, the filings are attracted to it, accumulating most noticeably around regions at each end of the magnet—the **poles**. When the bar magnet is allowed to rotate freely the pole that tends to seek the northerly direction is called the north-seeking pole, or simply, the N-pole. The other is called the south-seeking pole, or S-pole.

By placing two bar magnets first with similar poles together, then with opposite poles together, you can demonstrate the *law of magnetic poles* (**Figure 1**):

Law of Magnetic Poles

Opposite magnetic poles attract. Similar magnetic poles repel.

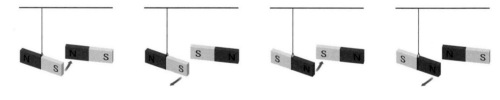

Figure 1
The law of magnetic poles

Magnetic Fields

magnetic force field the area around a magnet in which magnetic forces are exerted

Since an iron filing experiences a force when placed near a magnet, then, by definition, a magnet is surrounded by a **magnetic force field**. This field is often detected by its effect on a small test compass (magnetized needle). It is visually depicted by drawing magnetic field lines that show the direction in which the N-pole of the test compass points at all locations in the field. Experimentally, the lines in a magnetic field can easily be traced by sprinkling iron filings on a sheet of paper placed in the field. The filings behave like many tiny compasses and line up in the direction of the field at all points. They produce a "picture" of the magnetic field, as shown in **Figure 2**.

Figure 2
(a) The magnetic field of a single bar magnet is revealed by a number of compasses.
(b) Iron filings show the field clearly but do not reveal the pole orientation.
(c) The field in one plane is represented by a series of directed lines that by convention emerge from the N-pole and curve toward the S-pole.

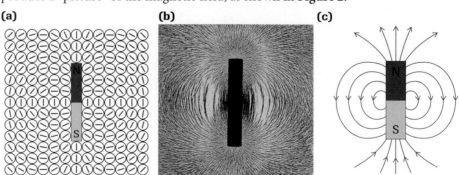

Since iron filings have no marked north or S-poles, they reveal only the pattern of the magnetic field lines, not their direction (**Figure 3**). The relative strength of the magnetic field is indicated by the spacing of adjacent field lines: where lines are close together, the magnetic field is strong.

(a)

(b)

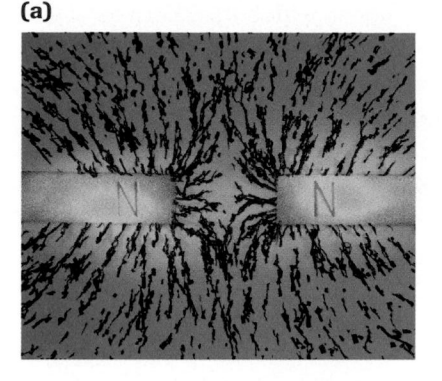

Figure 3
(a) Similar poles face each other.
(b) Opposite poles face each other.

The magnetic field at any point is a vector quantity, represented by the symbol $\vec{B}$. The magnitude B is given by the magnitude of the torque (or turning action) on a small test compass not aligned with the direction of the field. We will make a more precise definition of B later in this chapter, when we examine electromagnetism.

Earth's Magnetic Field

A pivoted magnet will rotate and point north–south because of its interaction with the magnetic field of Earth. As early as the 16th century, Sir William Gilbert, the distinguished English physicist, had devised a model to describe Earth's magnetism. He determined that Earth's magnetic field resembled the field of a large bar magnet, inclined at a slight angle to Earth's axis, with its S-pole in the northern hemisphere. **Figure 4(a)** shows this field and the bar magnet that was thought, in Gilbert's time, to be responsible for it.

(a)

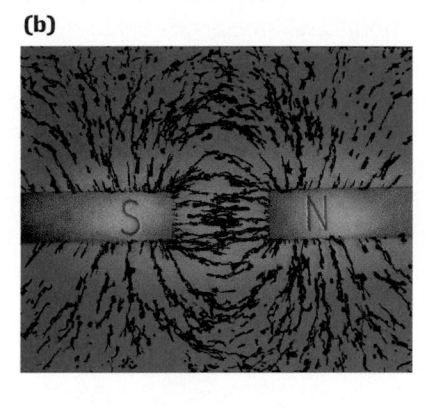

(b)

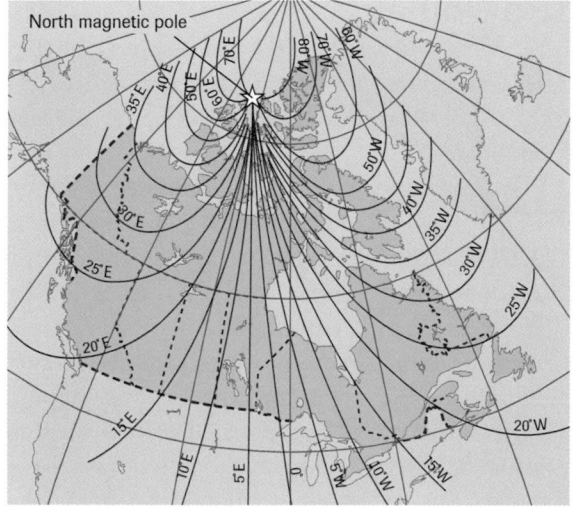

Figure 4
(a) The magnetic field of Earth closely resembles the field of a large bar magnet.
(b) Lines of magnetic declination in Canada

Figure 5
A dipping needle is a compass pivoted at its centre of gravity and free to rotate in a vertical plane. When aligned with a horizontal compass pointing north, it points in the direction of Earth's magnetic field. The angle of inclination is then read directly from the attached protractor.

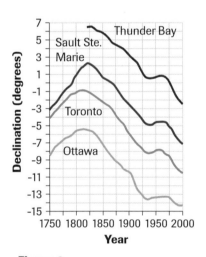

Figure 6
This chart shows how the magnetic declination in Ontario has changed since 1750 at Thunder Bay, Sault Ste Marie, Ottawa, and Toronto. The negative signs indicate a westerly declination.

Source: Natural Resources Canada

domain theory of magnetism
theory that describes, in terms of tiny magnetically homogeneous regions ("domains"), how a material can become magnetized: each domain acts like a bar magnet

A compass points toward Earth's magnetic N-pole, rather than toward its geographic north pole (the north end of Earth's axis of rotation). The angle, or *magnetic declination,* between magnetic north and geographic north varies from position to position on the surface of Earth (**Figure 4(b)**). In navigating by compass, the angle of declination for a particular location must be known so that true north can be determined.

In addition, Earth's magnetic field is three-dimensional, with both a horizontal and a vertical component. A magnetic compass on a horizontal surface reveals only the horizontal component. The angle between Earth's magnetic field, at any point, and the horizontal is called the *magnetic inclination,* or "dip," and is measured with a magnetic dipping needle (**Figure 5**).

Inclination and declination charts must be revised from time to time because Earth's magnetic field is slowly changing. It is believed that these changes result from the rotation of the magnetic field about Earth's axis; one complete rotation takes about 1000 years (**Figure 6**).

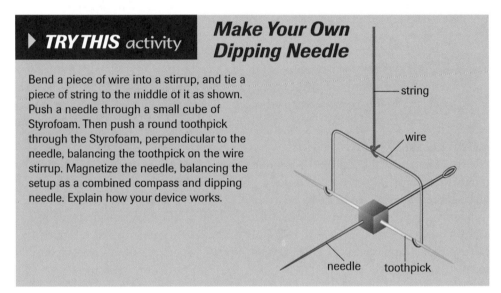

▶ **TRY THIS** activity

Make Your Own Dipping Needle

Bend a piece of wire into a stirrup, and tie a piece of string to the middle of it as shown. Push a needle through a small cube of Styrofoam. Then push a round toothpick through the Styrofoam, perpendicular to the needle, balancing the toothpick on the wire stirrup. Magnetize the needle, balancing the setup as a combined compass and dipping needle. Explain how your device works.

The Domain Theory of Magnetism

Although not normally magnetized, some *ferromagnetic* materials, such as iron, nickel, cobalt, and gadolinium, may become magnetized under certain circumstances. How they are able to acquire magnetic properties may be explained by the **domain theory of magnetism**.

Ferromagnetic substances are composed of a large number of tiny regions called *magnetic domains.* Each domain behaves like a tiny bar magnet, with its own N- and S-poles. When a specimen of the material is unmagnetized, these millions of domains are oriented at random, with their magnetic effects cancelling each other out, as in **Figure 7**.

However, if a piece of ferromagnetic material is placed in a sufficiently strong magnetic field, some domains rotate to align with the external field, while others, already aligned, tend to increase in size at the expense of neighbouring nonaligned domains (**Figure 8**). The net result is a preferred orientation of the domains (in the same direction as the external field), causing the material to behave like a magnet. When the external field is removed, this orientation will either remain for a long time or disappear almost immediately, depending on the material. When magnets are made in this way, they are known as *induced* magnets.

The domain model provides a simple explanation for many properties of induced magnets:

1. A needle is magnetized by rubbing it in one direction with a strong permanent magnet. This aligns the domains with the field of the permanent magnet.

2. When a bar magnet is broken in two, two smaller magnets result, each with its own N- and S-poles. It is impossible to produce an isolated N- or S-pole by breaking a bar magnet.

3. Induced magnets made of "soft" iron demagnetize as soon as the external field is removed. Examples include temporary magnets such as lifting electromagnets. In contrast, hard steel or alloys remain magnetized indefinitely. These include permanent magnets such as magnetic door catches. Impurities in the alloys seem to "lock" the aligned domains in place and prevent them from relaxing to their random orientation.

4. Heating or dropping a magnet can cause it to lose its magnetization, jostling the domains sufficiently to allow them to move and resume their random orientation. Each ferromagnetic material has a critical temperature above which it becomes demagnetized and remains demagnetized even upon cooling.

5. A strong external magnetic field can reverse the magnetism in a bar magnet, causing the former south-seeking pole to become north-seeking. This occurs when the domains reverse their direction of orientation by 180° due to the influence of the strong external field in the opposite direction.

6. Ships' hulls, columns and beams in buildings, and many other steel structures are often found to be magnetized by the combined effects of Earth's magnetic field and the vibrations imposed during construction. The effect is similar to stroking a needle with a strong magnet, in that the domains within the metals are caused to line up with Earth's magnetic field. Vibrations during construction aid in the realignment of the domains.

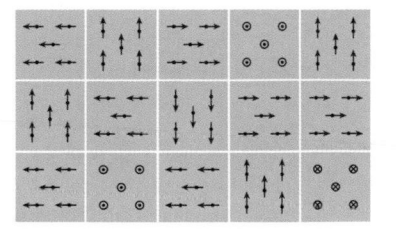

Figure 7
The atomic dipoles are lined up in each domain. The domains point in random directions. The magnetic material is unmagnetized.

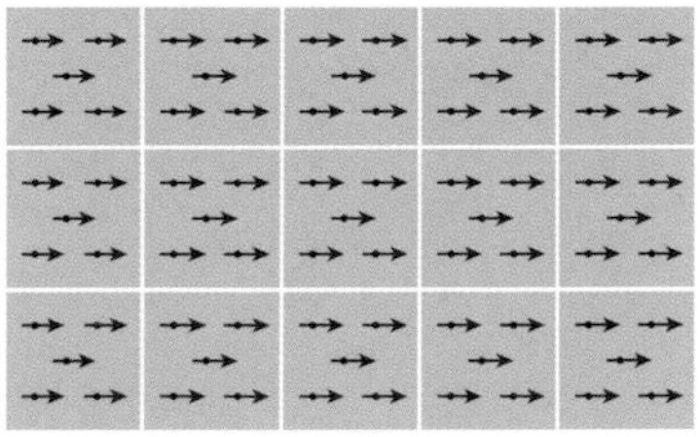

Figure 8
The atomic dipoles (not the domains) turn so that all domains point in the direction of the magnetizing field. The magnetic material is fully magnetized.

Prior to the nineteenth century, electricity and magnetism, although similar in many respects, were generally considered separate phenomena. It was left to an accidental discovery by the Danish physicist Hans Christian Oersted (1777–1851), while teaching at the University of Copenhagen, to reveal a relationship between the two. Observing that a magnetic compass needle was deflected by an electric current flowing through a nearby wire, Oersted formulated the basic *principle of electromagnetism:*

Principle of Electromagnetism
Moving electric charges produce a magnetic field.

Magnetic Field of a Straight Conductor

When an electric current flows through a long, straight conductor, the resulting magnetic field consists of field lines that are concentric circles, centred on the conductor (**Figure 9**).

You can remember the direction of these field lines (as indicated by the N-pole of a small test compass) if you use the *right-hand rule for a straight conductor:*

Right-Hand Rule for a Straight Conductor
If a conductor is grasped in the right hand, with the thumb pointing in the direction of the current, the curled fingers point in the direction of the magnetic field lines.

LEARNING *TIP*

Current Direction
Conventional current direction is being used, not electron flow direction.

Figure 9
(a) Iron filings reveal the circular pattern of the magnetic field around a conductor with a current.
(b) If the right thumb points in the direction of the current, then the fingers curl around the wire in the direction of the magnetic field lines.

(a)

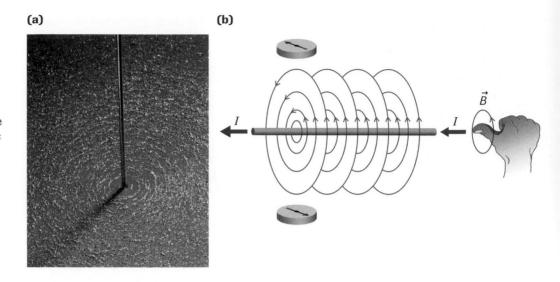

(b)

Magnetic Field of a Current Loop

When a straight wire is formed into a circular loop, its magnetic field will appear as shown in **Figure 10**. Note that the field lines inside the loop are closer together, indicating a stronger magnetic field than on the outside of the loop.

Figure 10
(a) Each individual segment produces its own magnetic field, in the manner of a straight conductor.
(b) The individual fields combine to form a net field similar to the three-dimensional field of a bar magnet.
(c) The right-hand rule for straight conductors gives the direction of the magnetic field of a single loop.
(d) Iron filings reveal the magnetic field pattern.

(a)

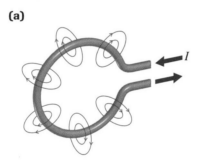

(b)

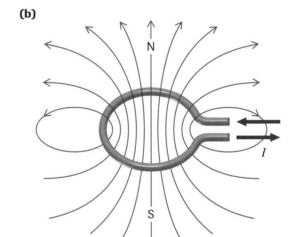

(c)

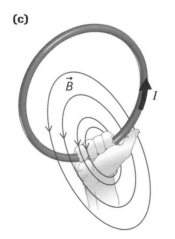

(d)

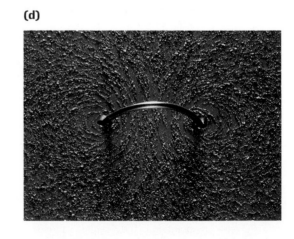

Magnetic Field of a Coil or Solenoid

A **solenoid** is a long conductor wound into a coil of many loops. The magnetic field of a solenoid (**Figure 11**) is the sum of the magnetic fields of all of its loops. The field inside the coil can consequently be very strong. If the coil is tightly wound, the field lines are nearly straight and very close together (**Figure 12**).

solenoid a coiled conductor used to produce a magnetic field; when a current is passed through the wire, a magnetic field is produced inside the coil

(a)

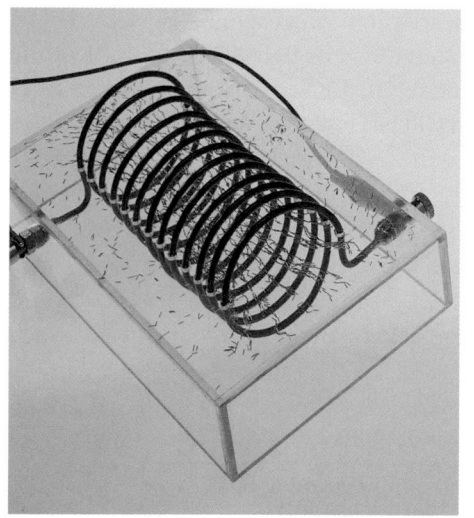

(b)

Figure 11
(a) A solenoid
(b) Iron filings reveal the field lines in and around a solenoid.

(a)

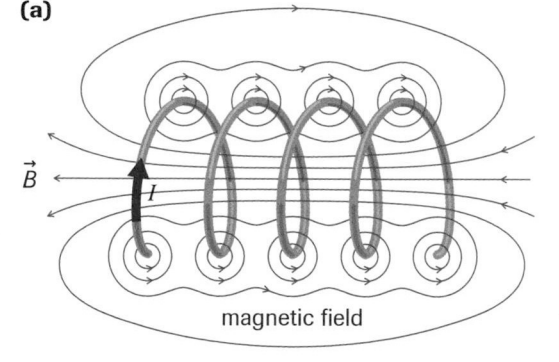

magnetic field

(b)

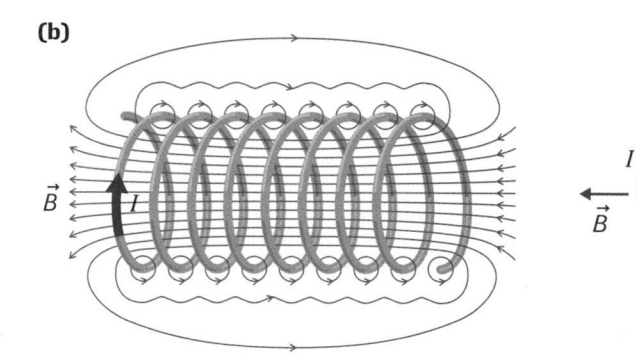

Figure 12
(a) When the solenoid is loosely wound, field lines within the coil are curved.
(b) The field becomes stronger and straighter inside the coil when the coil is wound tighter. The right-hand rule for solenoids (a corollary of the right-hand rule for a straight conductor) gives the direction of the field inside the coil.

A solenoid has a magnetic field very similar to the field of a bar magnet, with the convenient additional feature that the field can be switched off and on. To remember the direction of the magnetic field of a solenoid, we apply a special right-hand rule for a solenoid:

Right-Hand Rule for a Solenoid

If a solenoid is grasped in the right hand, with the fingers curled in the direction of the electric current, the thumb points in the direction of the magnetic field lines in its core.

Note that the right-hand rule for a solenoid is consistent with the right-hand rule for a straight conductor if we point our thumb along, or tangent to, the curved wire of the coil.

DID YOU KNOW ?

Strength Outside the Coil
The field lines outside the coil have an enormous volume of space to fill; therefore, they spread out so much that the field strength is negligible.

Using Electromagnets and Solenoids

If a piece of a ferromagnetic material, such as iron, is placed in the core of a solenoid, the magnetic field can become stronger, even by a factor of several thousand. The domains in the iron are aligned by the magnetic field of the coil, with the total magnetic field now the sum of the field due to the coil and the field due to the magnetized core material. The ratio of magnetic field strength for a particular core material to magnetic field strength in the absence of the material is called the *relative permeability* of the material. In other words, permeability is a measure of the extent to which a material is affected by a magnetic field. A high permeability of a material means that the magnitude of the magnetic field will be high when using that material; a low permeability (close to 1) means that the magnitude of the magnetic field will be close to that of a vacuum. **Table 1** lists relative magnetic permeabilities of some common materials. It shows that the magnetic field with a nickel core will be 1000 times stronger than a vacuum core.

Typical engineering applications demand that the iron in a solenoid core be "magnetically soft," or free of impurities that tend to lock domains into place after the external field disappears. Iron-core solenoids that lose their magnetism the instant the current is disconnected are useful not only in lifting electromagnets, but in many other devices, such as bells, relays, and magnetic speakers.

Table 1 Relative Magnetic Permeabilities of Common Materials

Material	Relative Magnetic Permeability
copper	0.999 99
water	0.999 999
vacuum	1.000 000
oxygen	1.000 002
aluminum	1.000 02
cobalt	170
nickel	1 000
steel	2 000
iron	6 100
permalloy	100 000

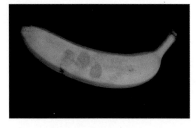
SUMMARY Natural Magnetism and Electromagnetism

- The law of magnetic poles states that opposite magnetic poles attract and similar magnetic poles repel.
- A magnet is surrounded by a magnetic force field.
- The domain theory states that ferromagnetic substances are composed of a large number of tiny regions called magnetic domains, with each domain acting like a tiny bar magnet. These domains can be aligned by an external magnetic field.
- The principle of electromagnetism states that moving electric charges produce a magnetic field.

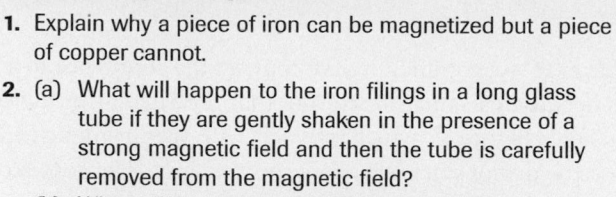

▶ *Section 8.1* *Questions*

Understanding Concepts

1. Explain why a piece of iron can be magnetized but a piece of copper cannot.

2. (a) What will happen to the iron filings in a long glass tube if they are gently shaken in the presence of a strong magnetic field and then the tube is carefully removed from the magnetic field?
   (b) What will happen if the glass tube is shaken again?
   (c) How is this process related to a solid bar of iron as described by the domain theory?

3. In the section discussing "The Domain Theory of Magnetism," a list of explanations for many properties of magnets is provided. Draw diagrams to illustrate "before" and "after" scenarios for each of the cases listed.

4. Compare the magnetic, electric, and gravitational fields of Earth in a table of similarities and differences.

5. Consider the magnetic field around a long, straight conductor with a steady current.
   (a) How is this field related to the field around a loop of wire?
   (b) How is the field around a loop of wire related to the field around a long coil of wire?

Applying Inquiry Skills

6. The equipment shown in **Figure 13** was used by James Clerk Maxwell to confirm the nature of the magnetic field around a long, straight conductor. He found that no matter how large the current through the wire, the disk did not rotate at all.
   (a) Explain how this device can be used to determine the nature of the magnetic field around a conductor with a steady current.
   (b) Outline the steps you would use in an experiment of this nature.

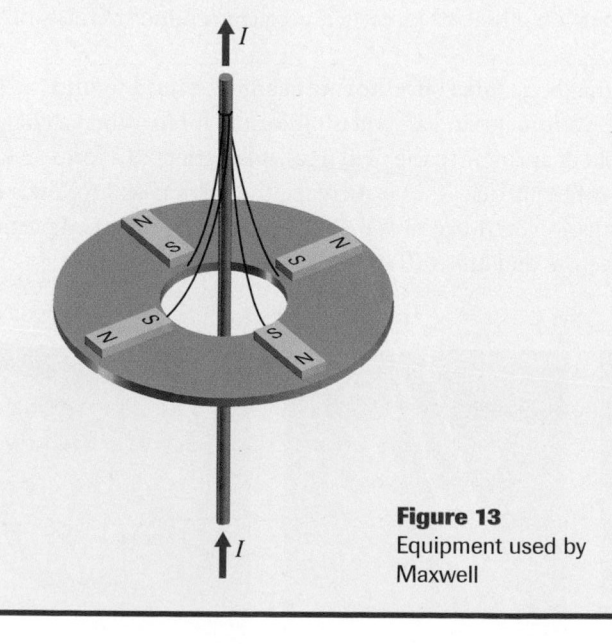

Figure 13
Equipment used by Maxwell

7. Examine the diagram of the electric doorbell in **Figure 14** and explain how it works.

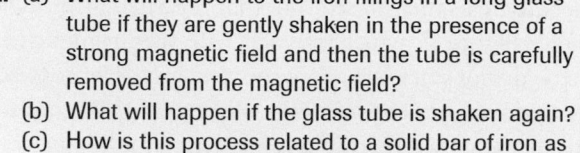

Figure 14

Making Connections

8. **Figure 15** is a micrograph of a magnetotactic bacterium. Prominent in this image is a row of dark, circular dots, in reality a chain of magnetite crystals. What purpose do you think the crystals serve? How could you test your hypothesis? Research the bacterium to check your answer.

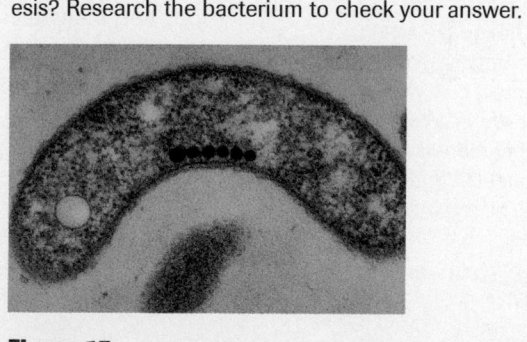

Figure 15
A magnetotactic bacterium

If you place a compass needle next to a conductor, then connect the conductor to a DC power supply, the compass needle turns, demonstrating that the current in the conductor produces a magnetic field (**Figure 1**), which interacts with the magnetic field of the compass needle. Therefore, a current can exert a force on a magnet. Hence two conductors with currents can experience a force between each other: place two conductors (wires) side by side, both with a current passing through them, and they will attract or repel each other. This means that a magnetic field can exert a force on a current, or moving charges. One can argue that this follows from Newton's third law: if a current produces a force on a magnet, then the magnet must produce an equal but opposite force on the current.

Figure 1
(a) The compass needle points north when there is no current in the wire.
(b) The magnetic compass needle turns when there is a current in the wire. If Earth's magnetic field were not present, the compass needle would be exactly perpendicular to the wire.

(a)

(b)

⚛ INVESTIGATION 8.2.1

Magnetic Force on a Moving Charge (p. 421)
How is the motion of a charged particle influenced by a magnetic field? How could you test your predictions with an experiment or simulation? Investigation 8.2.1 at the end of the chapter will allow you to check your answers.

This principle explains some natural phenomena such as the spectacular light displays of the aurora borealis and aurora australis and the methods bees use for navigation. This principle also has many technological applications, including television tubes and the technology used by particle physicists in particle accelerators and chemists in laboratory mass spectrographs.

To better understand the magnetic force on a moving charge, we need to find the factors that affect the force and eventually find an equation for the force. When a charged particle enters a magnetic field at an angle to the field lines, it experiences a force and the path of the particle curves. If the particle does not escape the field, it will follow a circular path (**Figure 2**). Investigation 8.2.1 explores the path followed by charged particles in magnetic fields and the factors that affect the path. ⚛

Figure 2
(a) A traditional cathode-ray tube showing a beam of electrons
(b) The beam curves in a magnetic field.
(c) A beam of electrons is bent into a circular path by the uniform magnetic field from a pair of Helmholtz coils. The pale purple glow is caused by ionized gas, created when electrons collide with atoms in the imperfect vacuum of the tube.

(a)

(b)

(c)
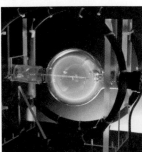

Measuring Magnetic Fields

The magnitude of the magnetic force $\vec{F}_M$ on a charged particle

- is directly proportional to the magnitude of the magnetic field $\vec{B}$, the velocity $\vec{v}$, and the charge q of the particle.
- depends on the angle θ between the magnetic field $\vec{B}$ and the velocity $\vec{v}$. When $\theta = 90°$ (particle is moving perpendicular to the field lines), the force is at a maximum, and when $\theta = 0°$ or $180°$ (particle is moving parallel to the field lines), the force vanishes. This is consistent with the fact that the magnitude of the magnetic force experienced by the charged particle is also proportional to $\sin \theta$.

Combining these factors gives

$$F_M = qvB \sin \theta$$

where F_M is the magnitude of the force on the moving charged particle, in newtons; q is the amount of charge on the moving particle, in coulombs; v is the magnitude of the velocity of the moving particle, in metres per second; B is the magnitude of the magnetic field strength, in teslas (SI unit, T; $1 \text{ T} = 1 \text{ kg/C·s}$); and θ is the angle between $\vec{v}$ and $\vec{B}$.

This equation specifies the magnitude of the force but not its direction. Consider a plane parallel to both the magnetic field $\vec{B}$ and the velocity $\vec{v}$ of a charged particle; the force is perpendicular to this plane. A simple right-hand rule can be used to determine the direction of the force as follows: if the right thumb points in the direction of motion of a positive charge, and the extended fingers point in the direction of the magnetic field, the force is in the direction in which the right palm would push (**Figure 3**).

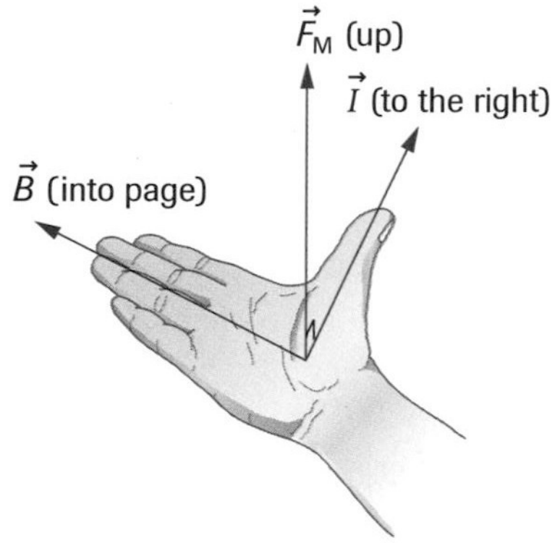

If the charge is negative, reverse the direction of your thumb when using the rule. (In other words, point your thumb in the opposite direction of the velocity of the charge.) This works because a negative charge flowing in one direction is equivalent to a positive charge flowing in the opposite direction.

The *Yamato 1* (**Figure 4**) is the first ship to apply this principle in propulsion. Instead of using propellers, it uses magnetohydrodynamic (MHD) propulsion; that is, it exerts

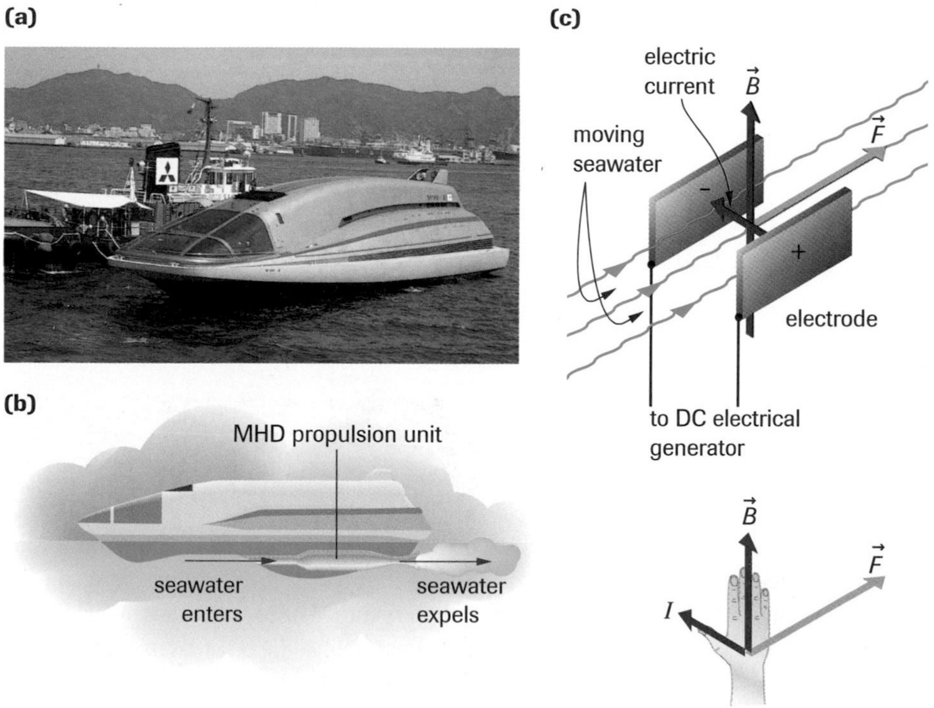

$\vec{F}_M$ (up)

$\vec{I}$ (to the right)

$\vec{B}$ (into page)

Figure 3
The right-hand rule specifies the direction of the magnetic force.

(a)

(b)

MHD propulsion unit

seawater enters

seawater expels

(c)

electric current $\vec{B}$

moving seawater

$\vec{F}$

electrode

to DC electrical generator

$\vec{B}$

$\vec{F}$

I

Figure 4
(a) The *Yamato 1*
(b) The MHD propulsion unit pushes seawater backward, moving the ship forward.
(c) Use the right-hand rule to determine the direction of the force on the seawater.

The Vector or Cross Product

The equation for the force on a moving charge in a magnetic field stems from the vector or cross product of two vectors defined by the equation $\vec{C} = \vec{A} \times \vec{B}$. The magnitude and direction of this vector can be found in Appendix A. Let $\vec{A}$ represent the charge multiplied by the velocity and $\vec{B}$ represent the magnetic field.

(a) Show that the cross product can be used to derive the magnitude of the magnetic force on a charged particle moving in an external magnetic field.

(b) Verify that the direction of the force found by applying the right-hand rule for the cross product is the same as the direction obtained using the right-hand rule described earlier.

a magnetic force on a current. A typical MHD propulsion unit uses a large superconducting magnet to create a strong magnetic field. Large metal parallel plates connected to either side of the unit have a large potential difference across them caused by a DC electric generator. This creates an electric current in the seawater (due to the presence of ions) perpendicular to the magnetic field. Using the right-hand rule with your thumb in the direction of the positive charge and fingers in the direction of the magnetic field, your palm will push in the direction of the force on the charges (ions) causing the seawater to be pushed out the back of the unit. According to Newton's third law, if the unit pushes the water out the back of the ship, the water will exert an equal and opposite force on the unit (ship), causing it to move forward.

MHD propulsion is promising because it offers the prospect of an inexpensive alternative to bulky, expensive, fuel-burning marine engines. Since there are no propellers, drive shafts, gears, or engine pistons, noise levels are minimized, and maintenance costs could also prove low.

Let us now take a closer look at the trajectory of a charged particle in a magnetic field. Since $\vec{F}_M$ is always perpendicular to $\vec{v}$, it is a purely deflecting force, meaning it changes the direction of $\vec{v}$ but has no effect on the magnitude of the velocity or speed. This is true because no component of the force acts in the direction of motion of the charged particle. As a result, the magnetic field does not change the energy of the particle and does no work on the particle.

Figure 5 shows a positively charged particle in a magnetic field perpendicular to its velocity. (If the particle were negative, its trajectory would curve the other way, in a clockwise circle.) If the magnetic force is the sole force acting on the particle, it is equal to the net force on the particle and is always perpendicular to its velocity. This is the condition for uniform circular motion; in fact, if the field is strong enough and the particle doesn't lose any energy, it will move in a complete circle as shown.

Figure 5
(a) A positive charge moving at constant speed through a uniform magnetic field follows a curved path.
(b) Ideally, a charged particle will move in a circle because the magnetic force is perpendicular to the velocity at all times.

(a)

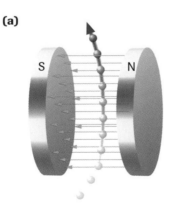

(b)

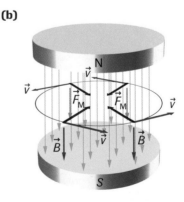

We represent these magnetic fields in two-dimensional diagrams by drawing Xs for field lines directed into and perpendicular to the page and dots for field lines pointing out of and perpendicular to the page. If the velocity is perpendicular to the magnetic field lines, then both the velocity and the magnetic force are parallel to the page, as in **Figure 6.**

▶ **SAMPLE** problem **1**

An electron accelerates from rest in a horizontally directed electric field through a potential difference of 46 V. The electron then leaves the electric field, entering a magnetic field of magnitude 0.20 T directed into the page (**Figure 7**).

(a) Calculate the initial speed of the electron upon entering the magnetic field.

(b) Calculate the magnitude and direction of the magnetic force on the electron.

(c) Calculate the radius of the electron's circular path.

Solution

$\Delta V = 46$ V

$B = 0.20$ T $= 0.20$ kg/C·s

$m_e = 9.11 \times 10^{-31}$ kg (from Appendix C)

$q = 1.6 \times 10^{-19}$ C

$v = ?$

$F_M = ?$

$r = ?$

(a) The electric potential energy lost by the electron in moving through the electric potential difference equals its gain in kinetic energy:

$$-\Delta E_E = \Delta E_K$$

$$q\Delta V = \frac{1}{2}mv^2$$

$$v = \sqrt{\frac{2q\Delta V}{m}}$$

$$= \sqrt{\frac{2(1.6 \times 10^{-19}\ \text{C})(46\ \text{V})}{9.11 \times 10^{-31}\ \text{kg}}}$$

$$v = 4.0 \times 10^6\ \text{m/s}$$

The initial speed of the electron upon entering the magnetic field is 4.0×10^6 m/s.

(b)

$$F_M = qvB \sin \theta$$

$$= (1.6 \times 10^{-19}\ \text{C})(4.0 \times 10^6\ \text{m/s})(0.20\ \text{kg/C·s}) \sin 90°$$

$$F_M = 1.3 \times 10^{-13}\ \text{N}$$

The magnitude of the force is 1.3×10^{-13} N.

To apply the right-hand rule, point your right thumb in the direction opposite to the velocity, as required for a negative charge. Point your fingers into the page and perpendicular to it. Your palm now pushes toward the bottom of the page. Therefore, $\vec{F}_M = 1.3 \times 10^{-13}$ N [down].

(c) Since the magnetic force is the only force acting on the electron and it is always perpendicular to the velocity, the electron undergoes uniform circular motion. The magnetic force is the net (centripetal) force:

$$F_M = F_c$$

$$qvB = \frac{mv^2}{r} \quad \text{(since } \sin 90° = 1\text{)}$$

or $\quad r = \dfrac{mv}{Bq}$

$$= \frac{(9.11 \times 10^{-31}\ \text{kg})(4.0 \times 10^6\ \text{m/s})}{(0.20\ \text{T})(1.6 \times 10^{-19}\ \text{C})}$$

$$r = 1.1 \times 10^{-4}\ \text{m}$$

The radius of the circular path is 1.1×10^{-4} m.

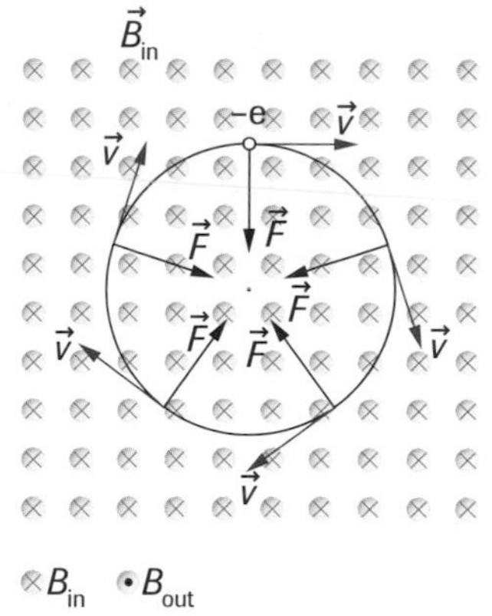

Figure 6
In this case, the particle is negatively charged, with the magnetic field directed into the page, perpendicular to the velocity. To determine the direction of the magnetic force, point your thumb in the opposite direction of the velocity because the charge is negative.

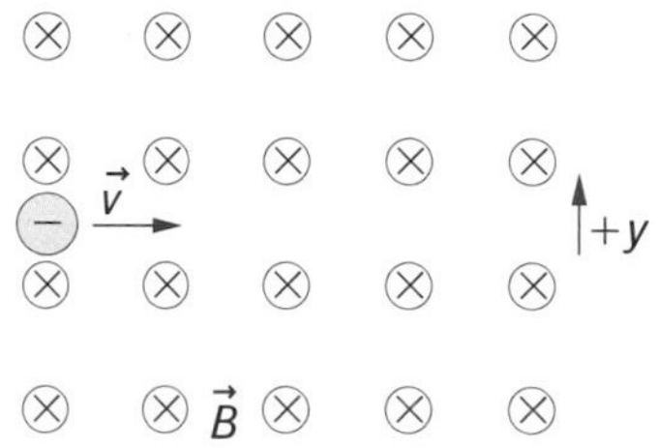

Figure 7
For Sample Problem 1

LEARNING TIP

In problems involving charged particles moving in an external magnetic field, the absolute value of the elementary charge $\left(|q| = 1.16 \times 10^{-19}\ \text{C}\right)$ will be used.

Answers

2. 1.7×10^{-14} N [E]

3. 0.16 T [horizontal, toward observer]

4. 0.13 m

5. 1.1×10^7 m/s; 6.9×10^5 V

6. 1.0 N

Cathode Rays

The beam of electrons was called a cathode ray because the electron had not yet been discovered. The old terminology survives in electronic engineering, where a cathode-ray tube is any tube constructed along Thomson's lines—whether in a computer monitor, a television, or an oscilloscope.

Figure 8

Thomson's cathode-ray tube. The path of the electron is curved only in the magnetic field of the coils (along a circular arc) or the electric field of the plates (along a parabola). After leaving these fields, the electrons move, in a straight line, to points X or Y.

▶ **Practice**

Understanding Concepts

1. Explain how the MHD propulsion system of the *Yamato 1* works.

2. Determine the magnitude and direction of the magnetic force on a proton moving horizontally northward at 8.6×10^4 m/s, as it enters a magnetic field of 1.2 T directed vertically upward. (The mass of a proton is 1.67×10^{-27} kg.)

3. An electron moving through a uniform magnetic field with a velocity of 2.0×10^6 m/s [up] experiences a maximum magnetic force of 5.1×10^{-14} N [left]. Calculate the magnitude and direction of the magnetic field.

4. Calculate the radius of the path taken by an α particle (He^{2+} ion, of charge 3.2×10^{-19} C and mass 6.7×10^{-27} kg) injected at a speed of 1.5×10^7 m/s into a uniform magnetic field of 2.4 T, at right angles to the field.

5. Calculate the speed of a proton, moving in a circular path of radius 8.0 cm, in a plane perpendicular to a uniform 1.5-T magnetic field. What voltage would be required to accelerate the proton from rest, in a vacuum, to this speed? ($m_{proton} = 1.67 \times 10^{-27}$ kg)

6. An airplane flying through Earth's magnetic field at a speed of 2.0×10^2 m/s acquires a charge of 1.0×10^2 C. Calculate the maximum magnitude of the magnetic force on it in a region where the magnitude of Earth's magnetic field is 5.0×10^{-5} T.

Charge-to-Mass Ratios

The British scientist J.J. Thomson (1856–1940) used the apparatus in **Figure 8** to accelerate a thin beam of electrons between the parallel plates and the coils. Applying either an electric field or a magnetic field across the tube caused the beam to be deflected up, down, left, or right relative to its original path, depending on the direction of the applied field. In all cases, the direction of deflection was consistent with a stream of negatively charged particles. Thomson concluded that cathode rays consist of negatively charged particles moving at high speed from the cathode to the anode. He called these particles electrons.

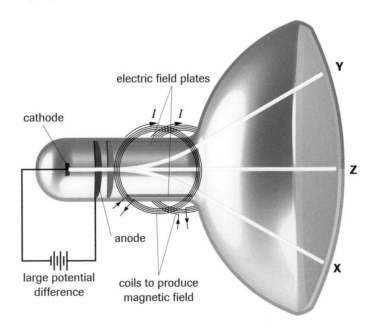

When there is a current in the coils, it creates a magnetic field of magnitude B, which deflects the electrons along a circular arc of radius r so that they hit the end of the tube at point X. From our previous work on magnetic deflection, we know that

$$F_M = F_c$$

$$evB = \frac{mv^2}{r} \quad (\text{since } \sin 90° = 1)$$

or $\quad \dfrac{e}{m} = \dfrac{v}{Br}$

We can calculate B if we know the physical dimensions of the coils and the amount of current flowing through them. We can measure r directly.

To determine the electron's speed v, Thomson used a set of parallel plates. When a potential difference is applied to the plates (with the lower plate negative) and there is no current in the coils, an electron is deflected upward, reaching the end of the tube at point Y. (For an electron moving at a typical laboratory speed, the effect of gravitation is negligible.) With current in the coils and a magnetic field again acting on the electrons, the potential difference across the plates can be adjusted until the two deflections (electric and magnetic) cancel, causing the electron beam to reach the end of the tube at point Z. When this has been done,

$$F_M = F_E$$

$$evB = e\varepsilon$$

or $\quad v = \dfrac{\varepsilon}{B}$

where ε is the magnitude of the electric field between the parallel plates $\left(\varepsilon = \dfrac{V}{d}\right)$.

Conversely, this setup can be used as a "velocity selector," allowing only those particles with velocity equal to the ratio of the electric field over the magnetic field to pass through undeflected.

Thomson could now express the ratio of charge to mass for electrons (**Figure 9**) in terms of the measurable quantities of electric field strength, magnetic field strength, and radius of curvature:

$$\frac{e}{m} = \frac{v}{Br}$$

$$\frac{e}{m} = \frac{\varepsilon}{B^2 r}$$

The accepted value of the ratio of charge to mass for an electron is, to three significant figures,

$$\frac{e}{m} = 1.76 \times 10^{11} \text{ C/kg}$$

Figure 9
(a) The apparatus used to determine the *e/m* ratio
(b) The electrons in the beam move in a straight line vertically.
(c) The electrons move in a circular path in the magnetic field of the coils.
(d) Increasing the magnetic field strength decreases the radius of the path.

(a)

(b)

(c)

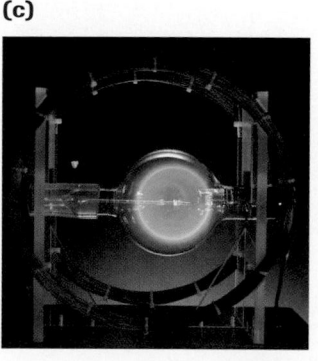

(d)

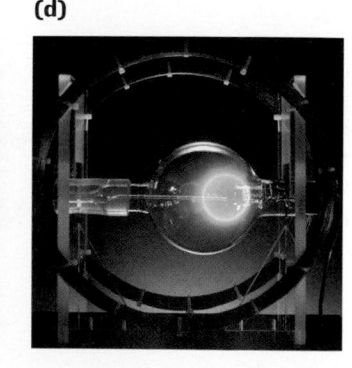

A few years later, Millikan (as we saw in Section 7.5) determined the charge on an electron to be 1.60×10^{-19} C. Combining these two results, we find the electron mass to be 9.11×10^{-31} kg.

Thomson's technique may be used to determine the charge-to-mass ratio for any charged particle moving through known electric and magnetic fields under negligible gravitation. Upon measuring the radius of curvature of the particle trajectory in the magnetic field only, and then adjusting the electric field to produce no net deflection, the charge-to-mass ratio is found to be

$$\frac{q}{m} = \frac{\varepsilon}{B^2 r}$$

Thomson's research led to the development of the mass spectrometer, an instrument used for separating particles, notably ions, by mass. The particles are first accelerated by high voltages, then directed into a magnetic field perpendicular to their velocity. The particles follow different curved paths depending on their mass and charge.

> ### ▶ SAMPLE problem 2
>
> Calculate the mass of chlorine-35 ions, of charge 1.60×10^{-19} C, accelerated into a mass spectrometer through a potential difference of 2.50×10^2 V into a uniform 1.00-T magnetic field. The radius of the curved path is 1.35 cm.
>
> #### Solution
>
> $q = 1.60 \times 10^{-19}$ C $\qquad\qquad\qquad$ $r = 1.35$ cm $= 1.35 \times 10^{-2}$ m
>
> $\Delta V = 2.50 \times 10^2$ V $\qquad\qquad\qquad$ $m = ?$
>
> $B = 1.00$ T $= 1.00$ kg/C·s
>
> From $\Delta E_c = \Delta E_K$ and $F_M = F_c$, we have the following two equations:
>
> $$qvB = \frac{mv^2}{r} \quad \text{and} \quad \frac{1}{2}mv^2 = q\Delta V$$
>
> Isolating v in both
>
> $$v = \frac{qBr}{m} \quad \text{and} \quad v = \sqrt{\frac{2qV}{m}}$$
>
> Equating the two expressions for the speed:
>
> $$\frac{qBr}{m} = \sqrt{\frac{2q\Delta V}{m}}$$
>
> Squaring both sides:
>
> $$\frac{q^2 B^2 r^2}{m^2} = \frac{2q\Delta V}{m}$$
>
> $$m = \frac{qB^2 r^2}{2\Delta V}$$
>
> $$= \frac{(1.60 \times 10^{-19} \text{ C})(1.00 \text{ kg/C·s})^2 (1.35 \times 10^{-2} \text{ m})^2}{2(2.50 \times 10^2 \text{ V})}$$
>
> $$m = 5.83 \times 10^{-26} \text{ kg}$$
>
> The mass of the chlorine-35 ions is 5.83×10^{-26} kg.

Effects of Magnetic Fields

When electrons are not moving perpendicular to the magnetic field lines, the component of the velocity parallel to the lines is unaffected, and the component perpendicular to the field lines rotates as we saw before. Together, these two components combine to produce the spiralling motion of the particle. If the magnetic field is not uniform but increases in magnitude in the direction of motion, the force on the electron due to the magnetic field will slow the charges by reducing the component of the velocity parallel to the field and may even cause the spiralling electron to reverse direction, forming a magnetic mirror (**Figure 10**).

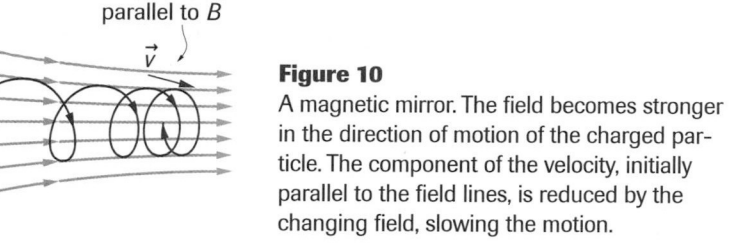
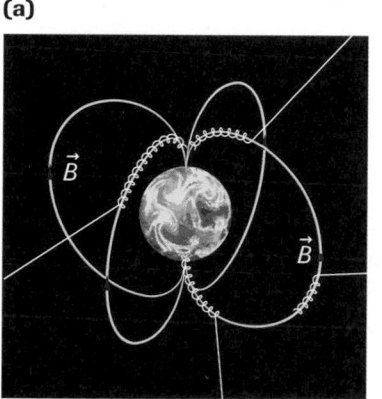

Figure 10
A magnetic mirror. The field becomes stronger in the direction of motion of the charged particle. The component of the velocity, initially parallel to the field lines, is reduced by the changing field, slowing the motion.

DID YOU KNOW ?

Van Allen Belts
In the late 1950s, scientists believed that particles could be trapped by Earth's magnetic field but lacked proof. In 1958, James Van Allen, of the University of Iowa, built the small satellite *Explorer 1*, which carried one instrument: a Geiger counter. The experiment worked well at low altitudes. At the top of the orbit, however, no particles were counted. Two months later, a counter on *Explorer 3* revealed a very high level of radiation where *Explorer 1* had found none. It turns out that the first counter had detected so much radiation it was overwhelmed and gave a zero reading.

(a)   **(b)**

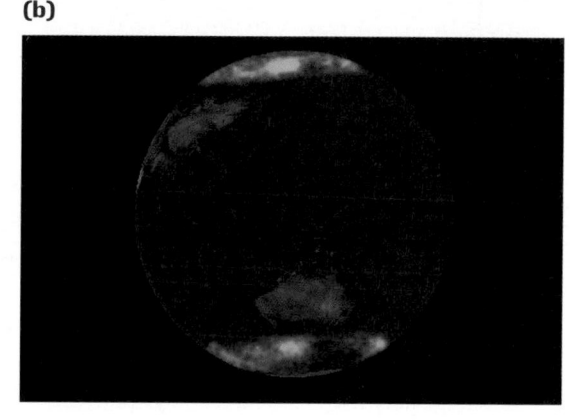

Figure 11
(a) Cosmic rays from the Sun and deep space consist of energetic electrons and protons. These particles often spiral around Earth's magnetic field lines toward the poles.
(b) The first spacecraft image to show auroras occurring simultaneously at both magnetic poles

Charged particles from the Sun (cosmic rays) enter Earth's atmosphere by spiralling around the magnetic field lines connecting Earth's two magnetic poles. As a result, the concentration of incoming particles is higher in polar regions than at the equator, where the charged particles must cross the magnetic field lines. These charged particles headed for the poles get trapped in spiral orbits about the lines instead of crossing them. Since the field strength increases near the poles the aurora borealis can occur in the Northern Hemisphere and the aurora australis in the Southern Hemisphere. Collisions between the charged particles and atmospheric atoms and molecules cause the spectacular glow of an aurora (**Figure 11**).

Earth has two major radiation belts, areas composed of charged particles trapped by the magnetic field of Earth (**Figure 12**). The radiation in these belts is so intense that it can damage sensitive electronic equipment in satellites; all types of spacecraft avoid them. The ring current, or outer belt, is approximately 25 500 km above the surface of Earth, and the inner belt—often called the Van Allen belt after its discoverer—is approximately 12 500 km above the surface of Earth. (The inner belt is now thought to consist of two belts.) The charged particles in these belts spiral around magnetic field lines and are often reflected away from the stronger fields near the poles.

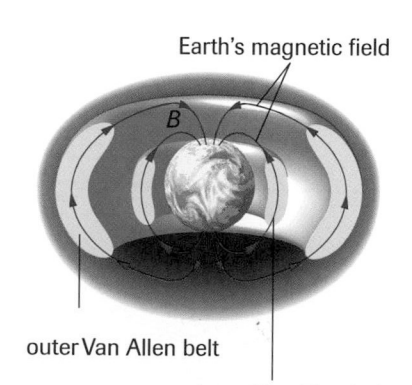

Earth's magnetic field

outer Van Allen belt

inner Van Allen belt

Figure 12
The radiation belts are formed by charged particles in cosmic rays trapped in Earth's magnetic field.

(a)

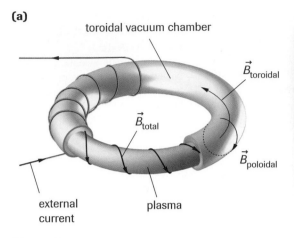

toroidal vacuum chamber

$\vec{B}_{\text{toroidal}}$

$\vec{B}_{\text{total}}$

$\vec{B}_{\text{poloidal}}$

external
current

plasma

Figure 13

(a) Schematic of the toroidal plasma-containment chamber of a tokamak fusion reactor

(b) The inside of a tokamak

(b)

Magnetic field principles are applied in toroidal (i.e., doughnut-shaped) tokamak prototypes for nuclear-fusion reactors (**Figure 13**). This reactor design uses magnetic fields to contain the hot, highly ionized gases (plasmas) needed for a controlled thermonuclear reaction. It is hoped that controlled thermonuclear fusion will, some decades from now, provide abundant energy without the radioactive wastes characteristic of fission reactors.

Field Theory

It is easy to be satisfied with the concept of a force being transmitted from one object to another through direct contact: when your hand pushes on a book, the book moves, because both your hand and the book touch. But we have learned that all objects are composed of spatially separated atoms that interact but do not actually touch one another, so the concept of contact becomes meaningless. When your hand pushes on the book, it really involves electromagnetic forces between the electrons in each object.

To understand gravitational, electric, and magnetic forces we need the concept of a field. At first, fields were just a convenient way of describing the force in a region of space, but with the undeniable success of fields in describing different types of forces, field theory has developed into a general scientific model and is now viewed as a physical reality that links together different kinds of forces that might otherwise be seen as completely separate phenomena. Now we can say that if an object experiences a particular kind of force over a continuous range of positions, then a force field exists in that region. The concept of a field is of vast importance with wide-ranging applications, from describing the motion of the planets, to the interactions of charged particles in the atom.

Even though these three types of forces can be explained using fields, there are some obvious differences between the forces and the fields themselves as well as some striking similarities. The gravitational force—although considered the weakest of the three—controls the motion of celestial bodies reaching across the vast distances of space (**Figure 14**). The electric and magnetic forces are much stronger and have greater influence on the motion of charged particles such as electrons and protons.

The direction of the gravitational and electric forces is determined by the centre of mass of the objects in question or the centre of the charge distribution on the charges in question. However, the magnetic force is determined by the direction of motion of the charge with respect to the magnetic field, and the force is zero if the relative motion between the

Figure 14
The gravitational forces from the larger galaxy are causing the two galaxies to merge, a process that will take billions of years.

field and charge is zero. For the other two, the motion of the particle does not influence the direction of the force.

The two fields that are most closely related are the electric and magnetic fields. For both fields the appropriate particle is charged. The fields have also been linked through Maxwell's equations, which will be studied in more advanced courses, and they are used together to describe the properties of light and to discover the nature of matter and new particles in particle accelerators. In particle accelerators, electric fields are used to accelerate particles such as electrons and protons, and magnetic fields are used to steer them in huge circular paths (**Figure 15**). Particle accelerators will be revisited in Chapter 13.

(a)

(b)

(c)

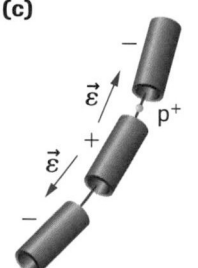

Figure 15
(a) A synchrotron consists of a ring of magnets and accelerating cylinders arranged in a circular tunnel.
(b) A particle passes through the gap between two charged cylinders.
(c) The charges on the cylinders are adjusted to keep the particle accelerating.

▶ *EXPLORE* an issue

Government Spending on Developing New Technologies

Decision-Making Skills

- Define the Issue
- Analyze the Issue
- Research
- Defend the Position
- ○ Identify Alternatives
- Evaluate

A portion of the federal budget goes toward scientific research involving expensive new technologies (e.g., through the National Science and Engineering Research Council, NSERC). This support includes funding technologies that use gravitational, electric, and magnetic fields, for example, satellites. Many people think this money is well spent; others think it is not justified since it comes from public funds.

Take a Stand
Should public funds be spent on scientific research involving gravitational, electric, and magnetic fields to develop new technologies?

Forming an Opinion
In a group, choose a new technology that uses gravitational, electric, or magnetic fields, and discuss the social and economic impact on our society. Discuss the benefits and drawbacks both of this new technology and the spending of public funds on research. Research the Internet and/or other sources.

GO www.science.nelson.com

Develop a set of criteria that you will use to evaluate the social and economic impact of your chosen technology. Write a position paper in which you state your opinion, the criteria you used to evaluate social and economic impacts in forming your opinion, and any evidence or arguments that support your opinion. Your "paper" can be a Web page, a video, a scientific report, or some other creative way of communicating.

SUMMARY Magnetic Force on Moving Charges

- A current can exert a force on a magnet, and a magnet can exert a force on a current.
- $F_M = qvB \sin \theta$
- The direction of the magnetic force is given by the right-hand rule.
- The speed of an electron in a cathode-ray tube can be determined with the help of magnetic deflecting coils and electric deflecting plates. The same apparatus then gives the charge-to-mass ratio of the electron. Combining this determination with the charge of an electron from the Millikan oil-drop experiment yields the mass of the electron.

Section 8.2 Questions

Understanding Concepts

1. Determine the direction of the missing quantity for each of the diagrams in **Figure 16**.

(a)

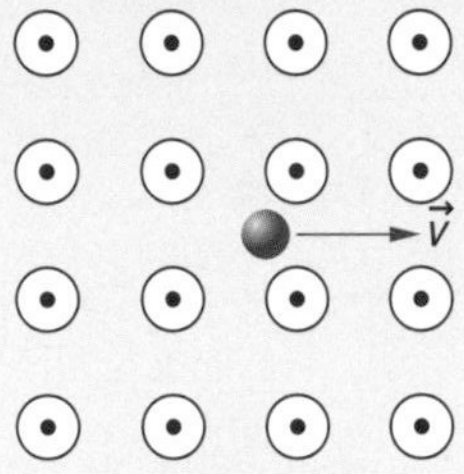

positive charge in a magnetic field

(b)

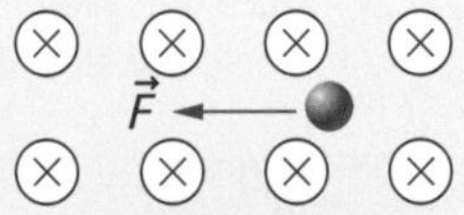

positive charge in a magnetic field

Figure 16

2. A student charges an ebonite rod with a charge of magnitude 25 nC. The magnetic field in the lab due to Earth is 5.0×10^{-5} T [N]. The student throws the ebonite at 12 m/s [W]. Determine the resulting magnetic force.
3. If a magnet is brought close to the screen of a colour television, the tube can be permanently damaged (so don't do this). The magnetic field will deflect electrons, deforming the picture and also permanently magnetizing the TV (**Figure 17**). Calculate the radius of the circular path followed by an electron which, having been accelerated through an electric potential difference of 10.0 kV in the neck of the tube, enters a magnetic field of magnitude 0.40 T due to a strong magnet placed near the screen.

(a)

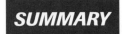

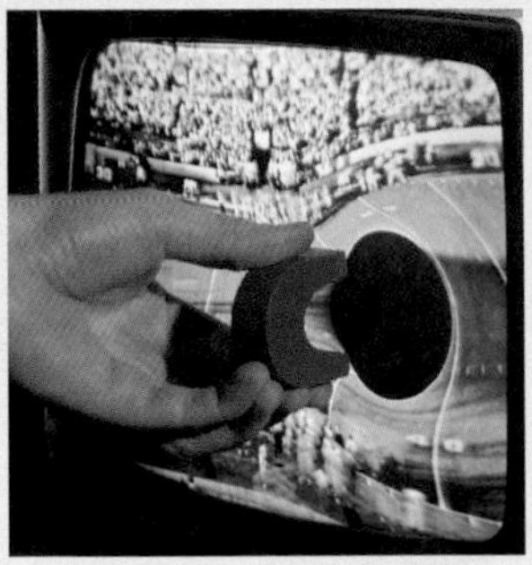

(b)

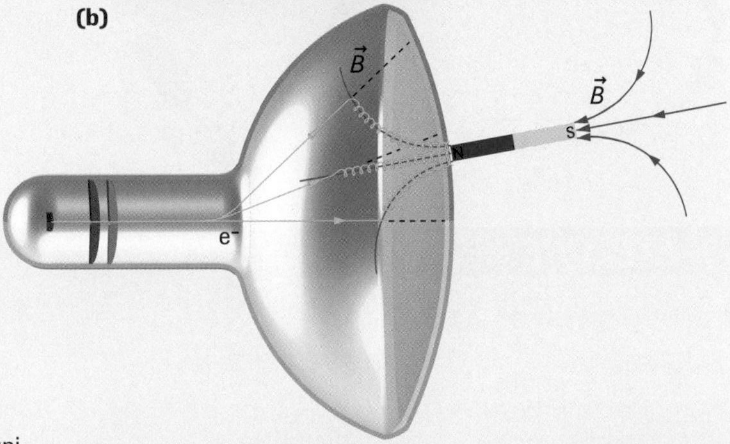

Figure 17
(a) A magnet can permanently damage a computer monitor or colour-television tube.
(b) Electrons spiral toward the screen in the field of the bar magnet.

4. An electron is at rest. Can this electron be set into motion by applying
   (a) a magnetic field?
   (b) an electric field?
   Explain your answers.

5. A charged particle is moving in a circle in a uniform magnetic field. A uniform electric field is suddenly created, running in the same direction as the magnetic field. Describe the motion of the particle.

6. Describe the left-hand rule for negatively charged particles in a magnetic field, and explain why it is equivalent to the right-hand rule for positively charged particles.

7. A charged particle moves with a constant velocity in a certain region of space. Could a magnetic field be present? Explain your answer.

8. A negatively charged particle enters a region with a uniform magnetic field perpendicular to the velocity of the particle. Explain what will happen to the kinetic energy of the particle.

9. Explain why magnetic field lines never cross.

10. How can you tell if moving electrons are being deflected by a magnetic field, an electric field, or both?

11. From space, a proton approaches Earth, toward the centre in the plane of the equator.
    (a) Which way will the proton be deflected? Explain your answer.
    (b) Which way would an electron be deflected under similar circumstances? Explain your answer.
    (c) Which way would a neutron be deflected under similar circumstances? Explain your answer.

12. (a) Define a field of force.
    (b) Compare the properties of gravitational, electric, and magnetic fields by completing **Table 1**.
    (c) Explain why field theory is considered a general scientific model.

Applying Inquiry Skills

13. Explain the procedure you would use to show that charged particles spiral around magnetic field lines and even form a magnetic mirror when they are not moving perpendicular to the field. You may assume a strong magnet and a TV tube are available. (The tube will be permanently damaged in the experiment.)

Making Connections

14. Compare and contrast the energy source of the MHD marine propulsion unit with a typical jet engine.

15. A strong magnet is placed on the screen of a television set (permanently damaging the tube). Explain the following observations:
    (a) The picture becomes distorted.
    (b) The screen is completely dark where the field is strongest.

16. Naturally occurring charged particles in background radiation can damage human cells. How can magnetic fields be used to shield against them?

17. Thomson and Millikan deepened our understanding of the electrical nature of matter.
    (a) What principles of gravity, electricity, and magnetism did they apply in designing their experiments?
    (b) What technology was involved in these discoveries?
    (c) How did the use of this technology change our view of charge and the nature of matter?

18. Launching a satellite into orbit requires an understanding of gravitational, electric, and magnetic fields. Research how these three fields are important in designing a launch. Report on three different ways in which the development of launch technology has changed scientific theories (e.g., in weather patterns) or has affected society and the environment (e.g., with telecommunications or wildlife preservation).

Table 1

	Gravitational	Electric	Magnetic
appropriate particle	?	?	?
factors affecting magnitude of the force	?	?	?
relative strength	?	?	?

A beam of charged particles moving through a magnetic field in a vacuum experiences a magnetic force. This also occurs if the charged particles are inside a conductor. Under normal circumstances, the charged particles cannot leave the conductor, so the force they experience is transferred to the conductor as the deflected electrons collide with the ions comprising the conducting material.

This principle is applied in electric motors and audio speakers. Some countries are even experimenting with *maglev*, or magnetic levitation, trains that use this force to suspend an entire train, moving without wheel-on-rail friction, at speeds over 500 km/h.

The factors that affect the magnitude of the magnetic force on a conductor are similar to those affecting the force on a single charged particle (**Figure 1**). Investigation 8.3.1 in the Lab Activities section at the end of this chapter investigates two of these factors.

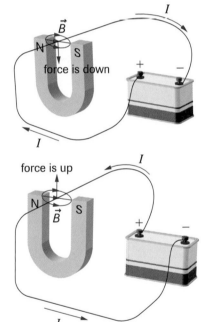

INVESTIGATION 8.3.1

Force on a Conductor in a Magnetic Field (p. 422)
What factors affect the magnitude of the force on a conductor in a magnetic field? Performing this investigation will allow you to check your answer.

force is down

force is up

Figure 1
Changing the direction of the current in the conductor changes the direction of the force.

Consider a conductor with a current I, placed in a magnetic field of magnitude B. Careful measurements reveal that the force on the conductor is directly proportional to the magnitude of the magnetic field, to the current in the conductor, and to the length of the conductor. In addition, if the angle between the conductor (or current) and the magnetic field lines is θ, then the magnetic force is at a maximum when $\theta = 90°$ and zero when $\theta = 0°$ or $180°$. Hence the magnitude of the magnetic force is directly proportional to $\sin \theta$. Combining these relationships produces an expression for the force acting on the conductor that is very similar to the magnetic force on a single point charge:

$$F \propto IlB \sin \theta \qquad \text{or} \qquad F = kIlB \sin \theta$$

In SI, units have already been chosen for length, current, and force, but if we use this equation as the defining equation for the units of magnetic field strength B, then

$$B = \frac{F}{k\,Il\,\sin \theta}$$

The SI unit of magnetic field strength is the tesla (T), defined so that

> 1 T is the magnetic field strength present when a conductor with a current of 1 A and a length of 1 m at an angle of 90° to the magnetic field experiences a force of 1 N; 1 T = 1 N/A·m.

Then in the defining equation for B we have

$$B = \frac{1\,\text{N}}{k(1\,\text{A})(1\,\text{m})(1)}$$

$$1\,\text{T} = \frac{1\,\text{N/(A·m)}}{k}$$

As a result, the value of k will always be 1 (when appropriate units are used for B, I, F, and l), so the expression for the magnitude of the force on a conductor with a current in it in a magnetic field becomes

$$F = IlB \sin \theta$$

where F is the force on the conductor, in newtons; B is the magnitude of the magnetic field strength, in teslas; I is the current in the conductor, in amperes; l is the length of the conductor in the magnetic field, in metres; and θ is the angle between I and B.

There are other important observations to be made from the use of a conductor in a magnetic field:

- The force on the conductor $\vec{F}$ is in a direction perpendicular to both the magnetic field $\vec{B}$ and the direction of the current I.
- Reversing either the current direction or the magnetic field reverses the direction of the force.

Another simple right-hand rule, equivalent to the one for charges moving in a magnetic field, can be used to determine the relative directions of $\vec{F}$, I, and $\vec{B}$ (**Figure 2**):

> **Right-Hand Rule for the Motor Principle**
>
> If the right thumb points in the direction of the current (flow of positive charge), and the extended fingers point in the direction of the magnetic field, the force is in the direction in which the right palm pushes.

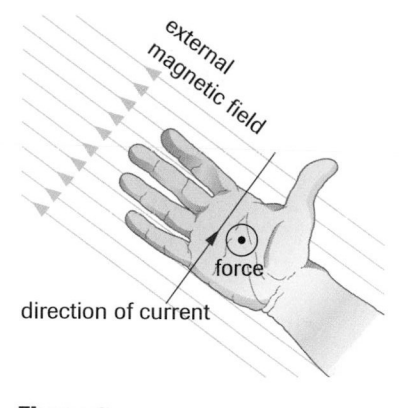

Figure 2
The right-hand rule for determining the direction of the magnetic force

---

▶ SAMPLE problem

A straight conductor 10.0 cm long with a current of 15 A moves through a uniform 0.60-T magnetic field. Calculate the magnitude of the force on the conductor when the angle between the current and the magnetic field is (a) 90°, (b) 45°, and (c) 0°.

Solution

$I = 15$ A $B = 0.60$ T

$l = 10.0$ cm $F = ?$

In the general case, the magnitude of the force is given by

$$F = IlB \sin \theta$$
$$= (15 \text{ A})(0.60 \text{ T})(0.10 \text{ m}) \sin \theta$$
$$F = (0.90 \text{ N}) \sin \theta$$

(a) when $\theta = 90°$, $\sin \theta = 1$ and $F = 0.90$ N

(b) when $\theta = 45°$, $\sin \theta = 0.707$ and $F = (0.90 \text{ N})(0.707) = 0.64$ N

(c) when $\theta = 0°$, $\sin \theta = 0$ and $F = 0$ N

The magnitude of the force is 0.90 N at $\theta = 90°$, 0.64 N at $\theta = 45°$, and 0 N at $\theta = 0°$. In each case, the direction of the force is given by the right-hand rule for the motor principle.

▶ Practice

Understanding Concepts

1. A wire in the armature of an electric motor is 25 cm long and remains in, and perpendicular to, a uniform magnetic field of 0.20 T. Calculate the force exerted on the wire when it has a current of 15 A.

2. What length of conductor, running at right angles to a 0.033-T magnetic field and with a current of 20.0 A, experiences a force of 0.10 N?

3. A straight 1.0-m wire connects the terminals of a motorcycle battery to a taillight. The motorcycle is parked so that the wire is perpendicular to Earth's magnetic field. The wire experiences a force of magnitude 6.0×10^{-5} N when there is a current of 1.5 A. Calculate the magnitude of Earth's magnetic field at that location.

4. Two electrical line poles are situated 50.0 m apart, one directly north of the other. A horizontal wire running between them carries a DC current of 2.0×10^2 A. If Earth's magnetic field in the vicinity has a magnitude of 5.0×10^{-5} T and the magnetic inclination is 45°, calculate the magnitude of the magnetic force on the wire.

Answers

1. 0.75 N

2. 0.15 m

3. 4.0×10^{-5} T

4. 0.35 N

Deriving the Equation for the Magnetic Force

The connection between the two equations for the magnetic force on a moving point charge and a conductor with a current can be made algebraically as follows. The force on a single point charge is

$$F_M = qvB \sin \theta$$

If there are n such charges in a conductor with length l in the magnetic field and current I, then the net magnetic force on the conductor due to all the charges is

$$F_M = n(qvB \sin \theta) \qquad \text{Equation (1)}$$

We could use this equation to specify the magnetic force on a conductor with a current, but it would not be very useful, since some of the quantities in the equation are difficult to measure directly. However, we can measure the current easily. If n charged particles pass a point in a conductor in time Δt, then the electric current is given by

$$I = \frac{nq}{\Delta t}$$

$$q = \frac{I\Delta t}{n} \qquad\qquad \text{Equation (2)}$$

The speed of the charges in the conductor can be found by dividing the distance they travel through the magnetic field, or l, the length of the conductor, by the time Δt:

$$v = \frac{l}{\Delta t} \qquad\qquad \text{Equation (3)}$$

Substituting Equations (2) and (3) into Equation (1), and simplifying:

$$F_M = n(qvB \sin \theta)$$

$$= n\left(\frac{I\Delta t}{n}\right)\left(\frac{l}{\Delta t}\right)B \sin \theta$$

$$F_M = IlB \sin \theta$$

This yields the same equation as that determined experimentally.

Maglev Trains

Maglev trains eliminate wheels-on-rails friction by using electromagnetic force to levitate the cars. Other electromagnets, mounted on the train itself and on a track guideway (**Figure 3**), then move the train forward through attraction between dissimilar poles and repulsion between similar poles. In reality, the train is flying, encountering only fluid friction from the air. Consequently, these trains can reach top speeds that are much higher than is possible with conventional rail. When the time comes to slow the train down, the currents are reversed, so that the magnetic attraction and repulsion are opposite to the direction of motion.

Figure 3
(a) A maglev train
(b) Electromagnets support the maglev train.
(c) Another set of magnets is used to drive the train forward and to slow it down.

(a)

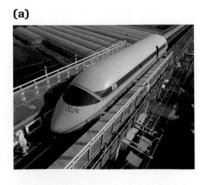

(b)

(c)

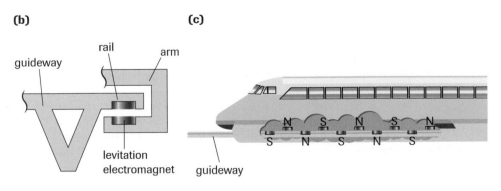

Magnetic Force on a Conductor

- The magnitude of the force on the conductor F is in a direction perpendicular to both the magnitude of the magnetic field B and the direction of the current I: in SI units, $F = IlB\sin\theta$.
- Reversing either the current direction or the magnetic field reverses the direction of the force.

▶ Section 8.3 Questions

Understanding Concepts

1. A 1.8-m long, straight wire experiences a maximum force of magnitude 1.8 N as it rotates in a uniform magnetic field of magnitude 1.5 T.
   (a) Calculate the angle between the magnetic field and the current in the wire when the force is a maximum.
   (b) Calculate the current in the wire.
   (c) What is the magnitude of the minimum force on the conductor in this magnetic field with the current found in (b)? Explain your answer.

2. A straight horizontal wire 2.0 m long has a current of 2.5 A toward the east. The local magnetic field of Earth is 5.0×10^{-5} T [N, horizontal]. Calculate the magnitude and direction of the force on the conductor.

3. What is the magnitude of the force on a straight 1.2-m wire with a current of 3.0 A and inclined at an angle of 45° to a 0.40-T uniform magnetic field?

4. Examine the experimental setup shown in **Figure 4**.
   (a) Describe what will happen when the circuit is complete.
   (b) How will the following changes, considered one at a time, affect what is observed? (i) The current is increased. (ii) The magnet is inverted. (iii) A stronger magnet is used.
   (c) A student claims that the force on the conductor will decrease if the bar is not horizontal. Discuss the validity of this statement.

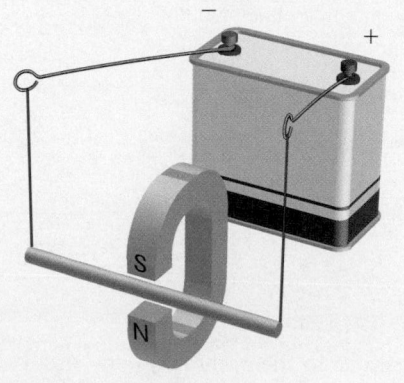

Figure 4

5. Explain how a maglev train uses electromagnets (a) to move forward and (b) to slow down.

Applying Inquiry Skills

6. Some students design an experiment to investigate the properties of Earth's magnetic field in their area using a long, straight wire suspended from string. The teacher tells the class that the accepted value of the magnetic field of Earth is 5.0×10^{-5} T [N, horizontal] in their area. Using a string, the students hang a wire in a north–south direction, connect the wire to a power supply, and begin investigating by varying the amount of current. They intend to measure the angle between the string and the horizontal to determine the force.
   (a) What is wrong with the design of this experiment?
   (b) Can the experimental method be adjusted so that it will work? Explain your answer.
   (c) Try to think of a better design using similar principles.

Making Connections

7. Faraday devised a primitive motor (a "rotator") by immersing wires and bar magnets in mercury (**Figure 5**). There were two versions of this motor, one in which the wire was fixed and a bar magnet rotated around it (left) and another where the magnet was fixed and the wire rotated around it (right). Explain how this motor works.
   (a) Trace the path of the current.
   (b) Explain how this motor works.

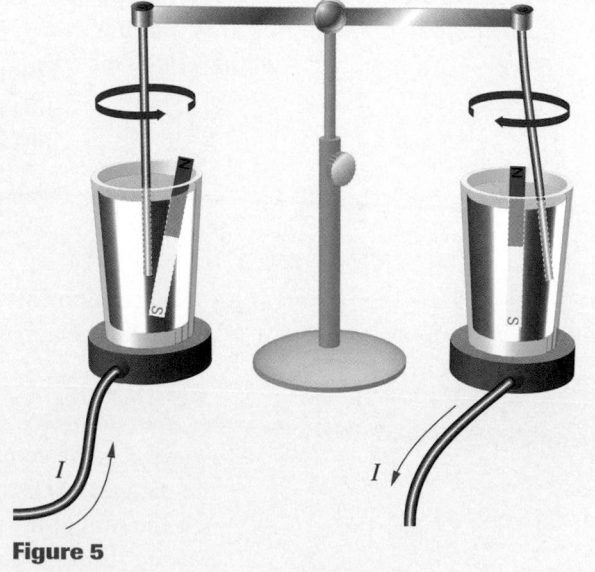

Figure 5

The magnetic fields that we have been considering, when discussing the force on a conductor with a current or on a moving charged particle, have been uniform magnetic fields, that is, magnetic fields constant in both direction and magnitude. The magnetic field between the poles of a horseshoe magnet and the magnetic field in the core of a solenoid are very nearly uniform. However, magnetic fields vary in magnitude and direction as you move from position to position in the field, as is the case for the magnetic field of Earth, the field surrounding a bar magnet, the field outside the core of a solenoid, and the field outside a long, straight, isolated conductor. How can we determine the strength of such a field at any given point?

Let us start with the long, straight conductor, originally investigated by Oersted and studied in Section 8.3. Activity 8.4.1 in the Lab Activities section at the end of this chapter investigates the nature of the magnetic fields around a long wire and a solenoid.

Recall from Section 8.1 that the magnetic field around a straight conductor consists of field lines that are concentric circles, centred on the conductor. The circles become more widely spaced as the distance from the conductor increases. Measurements of the magnitude of the magnetic field strength B show that $B \propto I$ and $B \propto \dfrac{1}{r}$, where I is the current in the conductor and r is the distance from the point of observation to the conductor.

Therefore, the magnitude of the magnetic field strength can be written as

$$B = k \frac{I}{r}$$

where k is a proportionality constant. The direction of B is given by the right-hand rule discussed earlier.

This mathematical relationship became apparent to Oersted soon after he discovered electromagnetism. It inspired the noted French scientist André Marie Ampère (1775–1836) to begin working on a general relationship between the current in any conductor (not just a straight one) and the strength of the magnetic field it produces. Ampère soon found that there was such a relationship and proposed the following statement to express it:

Ampère's Law

Along any closed path through a magnetic field, the sum of the products of the scalar component of $\vec{B}$, parallel to the path segment with the length of the segment, is directly proportional to the net electric current passing through the area enclosed by the path.

This relationship, called *Ampère's law*, can be written in mathematical terms: Along any closed path in a magnetic field,

$$\sum B_{\parallel} \Delta l = \mu_0 I$$

where $B_{\parallel}$ is the component of B that is parallel to the path along any small segment of the path Δl; Δl is one of the small segments into which the path can be subdivided; Σ is the sum of the products $B_{\parallel}\Delta l$ for every segment along the path; I is the net current flowing through the area enclosed by the path; and μ_0 is a proportionality constant, called the *permeability of free space*, whose value is $4\pi \times 10^{-7}$ T·m/A.

To fully appreciate this law, let us apply it to the simple magnetic field whose characteristics Ampère already knew—that of a long, straight conductor carrying a current I.

To calculate the magnitude of the magnetic field strength at a point X, a distance r from the wire, we apply Ampère's law as follows. Since the law applies for *any* closed path, let us choose a circle for a path, passing through X in a plane perpendicular to the wire, with the wire as its centre and with radius r (**Figure 1**). This is a good choice of path because, from previous work, we observed that the magnetic field at all points along this path is constant in magnitude and points in a direction tangent to the circular path.

Since a circular path centred around the current is used, we can make the simplification that $B_{\parallel} = B =$ constant, since the magnitude of the magnetic field around a current-carrying wire is constant in magnitude at a constant distance from the wire because it is circular. Also $\vec{B}$ is parallel to Δl, since Δl is tangent to the circle (i.e., $\vec{B}$ has only one component, $B_{\parallel}$). Therefore,

$$\sum B_{\parallel} \Delta l = \sum B \Delta l = B \sum \Delta l = B(2\pi r)$$

because $\sum \Delta l$ represents the length of the path around a circle of radius r. Therefore,

$$B(2\pi r) = \mu_0 I$$

or

$$B = \mu_0 \left(\frac{I}{2\pi r} \right)$$

where B is the magnitude, in teslas, of the magnetic field a distance r, in metres, from a long, straight conductor with a current I, in amperes.

Note that this is the same relationship that Oersted found experimentally but with the proportionality constant expressed differently.

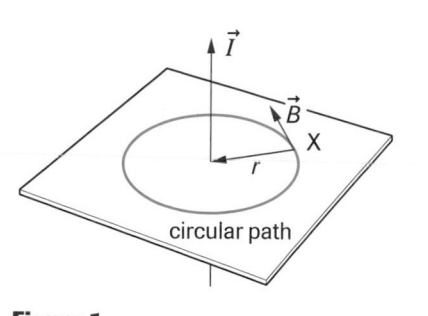

Figure 1
Since Ampère's law works for any closed path, we select a circular path, simplifying the calculation.

▶ SAMPLE problem 1

What is the magnitude of the magnetic field 2.0 cm from a long, straight conductor with a current of 2.5 A?

Solution

$r = 2.0$ cm $= 0.020$ m

$I = 2.5$ A

$B = ?$

$$B = \mu_0 \left(\frac{I}{2\pi r} \right)$$

$$= \frac{(4\pi \times 10^{-7} \text{ T·m/A})(2.5 \text{ A})}{2\pi (0.020 \text{ m})}$$

$B = 2.5 \times 10^{-5}$ T

▶ Practice

Understanding Concepts

1. Calculate the magnetic field strength 3.5 cm from a long, straight conductor with a current of 1.8 A.

2. The magnetic field strength 10.0 cm from a long, straight wire is 2.4×10^{-5} T. Calculate the current.

3. At what distance from a straight conductor, with a current of 2.4 A, is the magnitude of the magnetic field 8.0×10^{-5} T?

Answers

1. 1.0×10^{-5} T

2. 12 A

3. 6.0×10^{-3} m

4. Calculate the magnitude of the magnetic field at a point midway between two long, parallel wires that are 1.0 m apart and have currents of 10.0 A and 20.0 A, respectively, if the currents are (a) in opposite directions and (b) in the same direction.

5. A long, solid, copper rod has a circular cross-section of diameter 10.0 cm. The rod has a current of 5.0 A, uniformly distributed across its cross-section. Calculate the magnetic field strength
   (a) at the centre of the rod
   (b) 2.5 cm from the centre
   (c) 5.0 cm from the centre
   (d) 7.5 cm from the centre

   (*Hint:* As always, the net current in Ampère's law is the current through the area enclosed by the chosen path. Current outside the chosen path does not contribute to the net current.)

Coaxial Cables and Magnetic Fields

We can apply Ampère's law to a coaxial cable to determine the nature of the nearby magnetic field. If we imagine a circular path around the inner solid wire in the space between the conductors shown in **Figure 2**, then the magnitude of the magnetic field is given by

$$B = \mu_0 \left(\frac{I}{2\pi r} \right)$$

Remember Ampère's law uses only current enclosed by the path, so the current in the outer cylindrical braid has no effect on the result.

If we imagine, instead, a circular path outside the cable, then two equal currents in opposite directions are enclosed within the path, making the net current zero. According to Ampère's law, the magnetic field outside the cable must also be zero. Not only do coaxial cables shield against external electric fields, they also succeed in shielding their own magnetic fields.

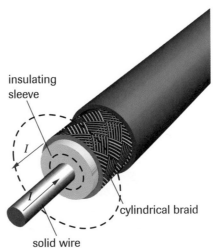

insulating sleeve

cylindrical braid

solid wire

Figure 2
Coaxial cable

Ampère's law also allows us to calculate the magnetic field strength in the core of a solenoid, using the same elegant technique. We have seen that the magnetic field of a solenoid consists of straight, equally spaced field lines in the core, bulging out slightly at the ends. There is virtually no magnetic field in the region outside the coil. **Figure 3** shows a cross-section of a long solenoid, of length L, with N loops, and a current I.

This time, as a closed path around which to apply Ampère's law, we choose the rectangle WXYZ shown in **Figure 3**. We can consider this path as four distinct line segments: WX, XY, YZ, and ZW. However, the magnitude of the magnetic field is perpendicular to the paths WX and YZ and zero along ZW. Along XY the magnetic field is straight, parallel to XY, and constant with magnitude B. The length of XY is equal to the length of the solenoid L; therefore,

$$\sum B_{\parallel}\,\Delta l \;=\; BL$$

Note that the total current flowing through the area bounded by the path WXYZ is NI, since the current I flows down through each of the N conductors within the area:

$$\sum B_{\parallel}\,\Delta l \;=\; BL \;=\; \mu_0 NI$$

Solving for the magnitude of the magnetic field, we can write:

$$B \;=\; \mu_0\!\left(\frac{NI}{L}\right)$$

where B is the magnitude of the magnetic field strength in the core of the solenoid, in teslas; I is the current flowing through the coil, in amperes; L is the length of the solenoid, in metres; and N is the number of turns on the coil.

Again, the direction of the magnetic field is given by the right-hand rule.

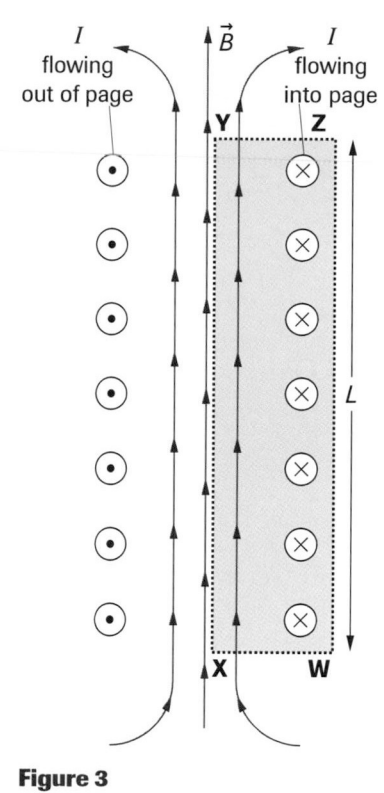

Figure 3
Cross-section of a solenoid

▶ **SAMPLE** problem **2**

What is the magnitude of the magnetic field in the core of a solenoid 5.0 cm long, with 300 turns and a current of 8.0 A?

Solution

$L = 5.0 \text{ cm} = 5.0 \times 10^{-2}\text{ m}$

$N = 300$

$I = 8.0\text{ A}$

$B = ?$

$$B = \mu_0\!\left(\frac{NI}{L}\right)$$

$$= \frac{(4\pi \times 10^{-7}\,\text{T·m/A})(300)(8.0\text{ A})}{5.0 \times 10^{-2}\text{ m}}$$

$$B = 6.0 \times 10^{-2}\text{ T}$$

The magnitude of the magnetic field is 6.0×10^{-2} T.

▶ **Practice**

Understanding Concepts

6. A 14-gauge copper wire has a current of 12 A. How many turns would have to be wound on a coil 15 cm long to produce a magnetic field of strength 5.0×10^{-2} T?

7. Calculate the magnitude of the magnetic field strength in the core of a coil 10.0 cm long, with 420 turns and a current of 6.0 A.

8. A coil 8.0 cm long, with 400 turns, produces a magnetic field of magnitude 1.4×10^{-2} T in its core. Calculate the current in the coil.

Answers

6. 5.0×10^2

7. 3.2×10^{-2} T

8. 2.2 A

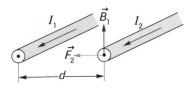

Figure 4
Two long, straight conductors, each with a current

The Ampere As a Unit of Electric Current

In previous studies, you learned that an ampere was defined as the electric current that transports 1 C of charge past a given point in a conductor in 1 s. This statement, while true, is just a temporary and nonoperational description of the ampere, since it is difficult to actually measure how many coulombs of charge pass by a given point. The accepted SI definition of the ampere is a magnetic one and depends on an understanding of the force between two parallel conductors with a current in each.

Consider two long, straight, parallel conductors, a distance d apart in a vacuum, with currents I_1 and I_2, respectively, as in **Figure 4**.

Each wire creates a magnetic field, and the other wire has a current through, and perpendicular to, that field. The magnitude of the magnetic field created by wire 1 and experienced by wire 2, a distance d away, is given by

$$B_1 = \mu_0\left(\frac{I_1}{2\pi d}\right)$$

Then the magnitude of the force acting on wire 2, perpendicular to this field, is given by

$$F_2 = I_2 \, l \, B_1 \sin \theta$$
$$F_2 = I_2 \, l \, B_1 \qquad \text{(since } \sin \theta = 1\text{)}$$

If we express this as the force per unit length and substitute the value for B_1 obtained previously, we can write

$$\frac{F_2}{l} = \frac{\mu_0 I_1 I_2}{2\pi d}$$

as the expression for the force acting on wire 2 due to the current in wire 1. However, according to Newton's third law, an oppositely directed force of the same magnitude acts on wire 1 because of the current in wire 2. By applying the right-hand rule, we can see that these mutual forces will cause an attraction if I_1 and I_2 are in the same direction, or a repulsion if I_1 and I_2 are in opposite directions.

Then, using this equation to define the **ampere**, we simply choose $d = 1$ m and define $I_1 = I_2 = 1$ A, so that

ampere (A) SI unit of electric current; $\dfrac{F}{l} = 2 \times 10^{-7}$ N/m

$$\frac{F}{l} = \frac{(4\pi \times 10^{-7} \text{ T·m/A})(1 \text{ A})(1 \text{ A})}{2\pi(1 \text{ m})}$$

$$\frac{F}{l} = 2 \times 10^{-7} \text{ N/m}$$

That is,

> 1 A is the current in each of two long, straight, parallel conductors 1 m apart in a vacuum, when the magnetic force between them is 2×10^{-7} N per metre of length.

coulomb (C) SI unit of electric charge; $1 \text{ C} = 1 \text{ A·s}$

Then the **coulomb** is defined, using this relationship for the ampere, as

> 1 C is the charge transported by a current of 1 A in a time of 1 s; $1 \text{ C} = 1 \text{ A·s}$.

▶ **SAMPLE** problem 2

What is the magnitude of the force between two parallel conductors 2.0 m long, with currents of 4.0 A and 10.0 A, 25 cm apart in a vacuum?

Solution

$l = 2.0$ m

$I_1 = 4.0$ A

$I_2 = 10.0$ A

$d = 25$ cm $= 0.25$ m

$F = ?$

$$\frac{F_2}{l} = \frac{\mu_0 I_1 I_2}{2\pi d}$$

or $\quad F_2 = \dfrac{\mu_0 I_1 I_2 l}{2\pi d}$

$$= \frac{(4\pi \times 10^{-7}\,\text{T·m/A})(4.0\,\text{A})(10.0\,\text{A})(2.0\,\text{m})}{2\pi(0.25\,\text{m})}$$

$F_2 = 6.4 \times 10^{-5}$ N

The magnitude of the force between the two parallel conductors is 6.4×10^{-5} N.

▶ **Practice**

Understanding Concepts

9. Calculate the magnitude of the force per unit length between two parallel, straight conductors 1.0 cm apart, each with a current of 8.0 A.

10. Two parallel straight conductors 5.0 m long and 12 cm apart are to have equal currents. The force each conductor experiences from the other is not to exceed 2.0×10^{-2} N. What is the maximum possible current in each conductor?

11. How far from a straight wire with a current of 5.0 A is a second, parallel wire with a current of 10.0 A, if the magnitude of the force per metre between them is 3.6×10^{-4} N/m?

12. Calculate the magnitude of the force per metre pushing two straight wires in an extension cord apart when 1.0 A of DC current lights a 100-W study lamp. The separation of the wires is 2.0 mm, and the insulation behaves like a vacuum.

Answers

9. 1.3×10^{-3} N/m

10. 49 A

11. 2.8×10^{-2} m

12. 1.0×10^{-4} N/m

SUMMARY   *Ampère's Law*

- Ampère's law states: $\sum B_\parallel \, \Delta l = \mu_0 \, I$.
- SI defines an ampere as the current in each of two long, straight, parallel conductors 1 m apart in a vacuum, when the magnetic force between them is 2×10^{-7} N per metre of length.
- SI defines the coulomb as the charge transported by a current of 1 A in a time of 1 s.

Understanding Concepts

1. Calculate the magnitude of the magnetic field 0.50 m from a long, straight wire with a current of 8.0 A.

2. A typical return stroke from a lightning bolt has a current of 2.0×10^4 A upward from the ground. Calculate the magnitude of the magnetic field 2.5 m from a straight bolt.

3. A solenoid, 25 cm long, consists of 250 turns. What is the magnitude of the magnetic field at its centre when the current in the coil is 1.2 A?

4. Two parallel, straight conductors, each 3.0 m long, are 5.0 mm apart with currents in opposite directions. The current in each conductor is 2.2 A. Calculate the magnitude of the magnetic force acting on each conductor.

5. A flexible, electrically conducting coil is suspended above a mercury bath as shown in **Figure 5**. What will happen if a large current is sent through the coil? What effect will suspending an iron rod in the middle of the coil have?

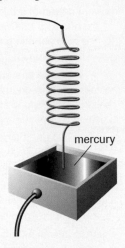

Figure 5

6. In a typical application of coaxial cables, the inner wire and the outer cylindrical braid have currents equal in magnitude but opposite in direction. An insulator separates the two conductors. Describe the magnetic field (a) between the two conductors and (b) outside the cable. Explain your reasoning.

7. Explain how SI defines the ampere and coulomb.

Applying Inquiry Skills

8. A single loop of wire does not have a uniform magnetic field in its core but a long solenoid made from many loops will. Design an experiment to determine how long a coil of radius r has to be before the field in the core is uniform.

9. Light threads 0.80 m long suspend two long, straight, parallel wires of length 1.0 m and mass 6.0×10^{-2} kg (**Figure 6**). The currents in the two wires are in opposite directions and the angle between the strings is 12°.
   (a) Calculate the current in each wire.
   (b) Outline a procedure, with similar equipment, that could be used to determine the factors affecting the magnitude of the magnetic force per unit length between parallel conductors.

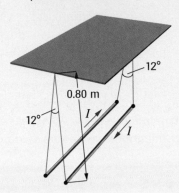

Figure 6

Making Connections

10. **Figure 7** shows the equipment used to record sound on a magnetic tape in a tape recorder. Explain how it works.

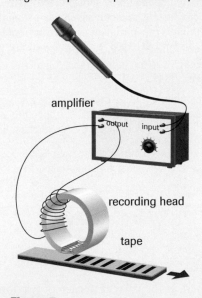

Figure 7

Electromagnetic Induction **8.5**

The principle of electromagnetic induction has a wide variety of applications: it is used in the continent-wide infrastructure that distributes our electric power, in automobiles, at some traffic lights, in security systems, in computer hard drives, and even in amusement-park rides.

As we have seen, a steady electric current (a steady stream of electric charges) produces a steady magnetic field. If a stream of electric charges can cause a magnetic field, then can a magnetic field cause such a stream? It was first thought that a steady magnetic field would produce a steady electric current, but experiments quickly established this to be false. Faraday investigated this very problem and discovered that the way in which a magnetic field can produce a current is more subtle.

Faraday first used a solenoid around a wooden core, connected in series with a switch and a powerful battery to form a so-called "primary" circuit. He added a "secondary" circuit, consisting of a second solenoid around the same wooden core, wired in series with a galvanometer configured as an *ammeter,* or current meter (**Figure 1**). Closing the switch

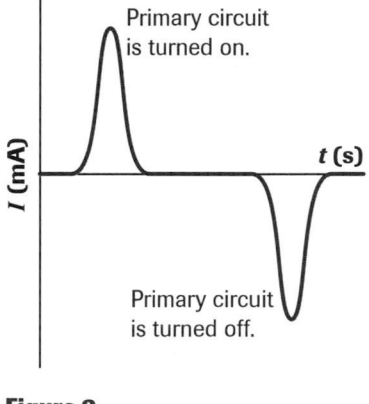

Current in Secondary circuit

Figure 2
Only when the primary circuit is turned on and off is a current induced in the secondary circuit. There is no current in the secondary circuit when the current in the primary circuit is constant. The plot shows the two currents to be in opposite directions.

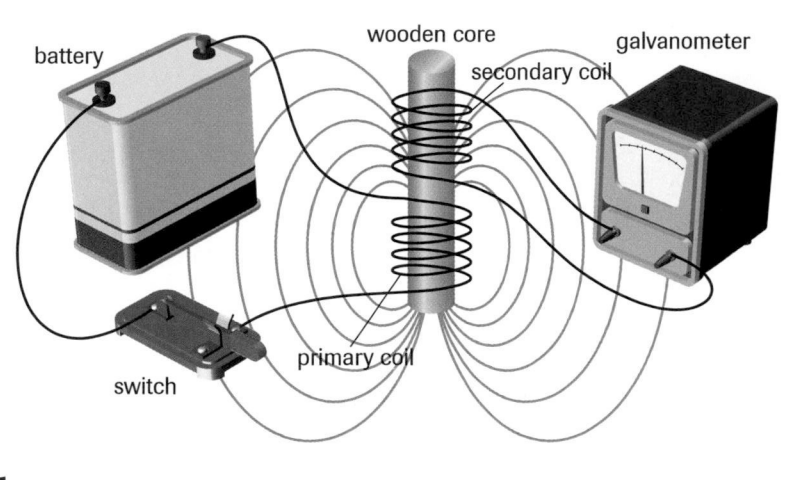

Figure 1
Faraday's first induction apparatus. There are two separate circuits.
Charges do not pass from the primary circuit into the secondary circuit.

induced a weak, short-lived current in the secondary circuit, as the galvanometer needle showed, but only for a very short time. Once the current dropped back to zero in the secondary circuit, no other current was produced, in spite of the constant current in the primary circuit. When the primary current was switched off, a small current was induced in the opposite direction in the secondary circuit, again only for a short time (**Figure 2**).

To improve his results, Faraday built a new device (now called "Faraday's ring"), which utilized an iron ring to increase the magnetic field inside the solenoids (**Figure 3**). The currents were large enough to be easily apparent but still found to occur only when the current was being switched on or off. How were the currents to be explained?

When the current is steady in the primary circuit, the magnetic field in the solenoid is constant over time. In particular, the magnetic field at each point around and in the secondary coil is constant. No current is induced in the secondary circuit. When the primary circuit is turned on, the magnetic field in the secondary solenoid changes very quickly from zero to some maximum value, causing a current. When the primary circuit is turned off, the magnetic field in the secondary solenoid changes from the maximum

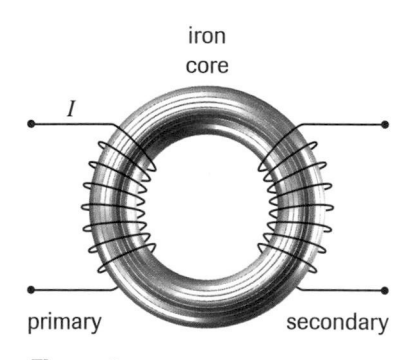

Figure 3
Faraday's iron ring. Even though the magnetic fields are stronger than in Faraday's first apparatus, an induced current is produced in the secondary circuit only when the primary circuit is turned on or off, changing the magnetic field.

Magnetic Fields and Electromagnetism

value to zero, causing a current in the opposite direction. The key is this: in each case the magnetic field is changing when the current is induced in the secondary circuit. A constant magnetic field, even a large one, induces no current at all.

Faraday combined all his observations into the *law of electromagnetic induction*.

Figure 4

(a) When the S-pole is pushed into the coil, a current (registered here indirectly, by a potential difference across oscilloscope terminals) is produced in the coil.

(b) When the magnet stops, the current drops to zero.

(c) Removing the magnet causes a current in the opposite direction.

(d) When the magnet stops moving, the current again drops to zero.

> **Law of Electromagnetic Induction**
>
> An electric current is induced in a conductor whenever the magnetic field in the region of the conductor changes with time.

You can demonstrate Faraday's law of electromagnetic induction by plunging a bar magnet into a solenoid connected to a galvanometer (configured as an ammeter) or to an oscilloscope, as shown in **Figure 4**. (The oscilloscope does not directly indicate a current. It does, however, indicate a potential difference in the secondary coil, caused by the changing magnetic field and driving the flow of charges.) As the S-pole enters the solenoid, the magnetic field in the region of the conductor changes and a current is induced in the circuit. When the magnet comes to rest, no current is present. When the magnet is withdrawn, a current is induced in the opposite direction, falling to zero as the magnet comes to rest.

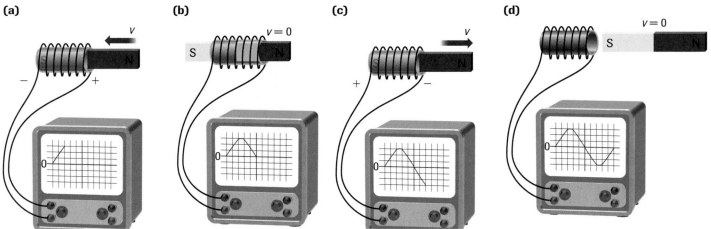

The maximum current measured in such a demonstration is larger if the magnet is moved faster, if a stronger magnet is used, or if the coil has more turns. A current is produced even if the magnet is held stationary and the coil moved around it. We conclude, as Faraday did, that the current is produced by a *changing* magnetic field and the greater the change, the larger the induced current.

Faraday's law is applied in some automobile cruise-control devices, which maintain the speed of a vehicle (**Figure 5**). Two magnets are attached to opposite sides of the drive

Figure 5

Rotating magnets induce brief pulses of current in a loop connected to a microprocessor in a cruise-control device. Similar measurement devices are used for ABS (the automatic/anti-lock braking system) and traction control on individual halves of the axle, or on wheels.

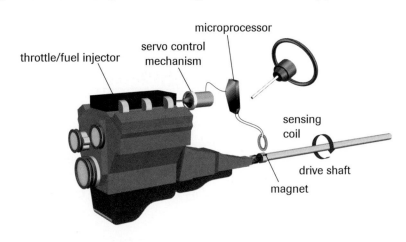

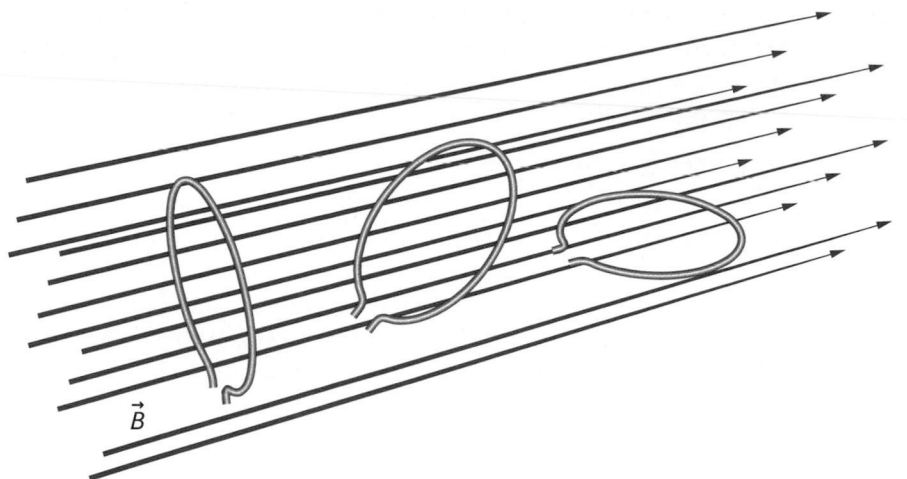

Figure 6
A current is produced in a coil rotating in a uniform magnetic field.

shaft. A small coil near the drive shaft is connected to a microprocessor, which detects small variations in electric current. As both magnets rotate past the coil, they induce a small, brief pulse of electric current, registered by the microprocessor. The frequency of the pulses indicates the speed of rotation of the shaft and, therefore, the speed of the vehicle. If the driver sets the cruise control at a certain speed, the microprocessor can maintain that speed by sending a signal to a control mechanism which injects more fuel into the engine if the frequency decreases, less if the frequency increases.

Currents can be produced in a loop of wire rotated in a uniform magnetic field and connected to a galvanometer in its ammeter configuration (**Figure 6**). The magnetic field through the loop is changing most when the loop is perpendicular to the field (raising the current to its maximum) and is not changing when it is parallel (the current drops to zero for an instant). This principle is fundamental to the construction of generators.

What determines the direction of the induced current? In 1834, Heinrich Lenz, using the law of conservation of energy, discovered the answer. Lenz reasoned that when the field from a moving bar magnet induces a current in a solenoid, this current gives rise to another magnetic field (the "induced" field). There are only two possible directions for the flow of charge through the coil. Let us assume that the current spirals toward the magnet when a N-pole is pushed into the coil, as in **Figure 7**. The right-hand rule for coils then tells us that the right end of the coil becomes a S-pole, attracting the magnet.

Lenz reasoned that this situation is not possible because the attractive force will speed up the magnet, increasing its kinetic energy, inducing a larger current (more energy) and increasing the induced magnetic field (with the magnet speeded up still further, making its kinetic energy even higher). Since the total energy of the system cannot increase, our assumption must be false, and the current in the solenoid must spiral away from the incoming N-pole, as in **Figure 8**.

Therefore, the near end of the coil is a N-pole. The moving bar magnet induces a current in the coil which produces a magnetic field in opposition to the inward motion of the bar magnet. The work done in pushing the magnet into the coil against the opposing induced field is transformed into electrical energy in the coil. Lenz summarized this reasoning in *Lenz's law*.

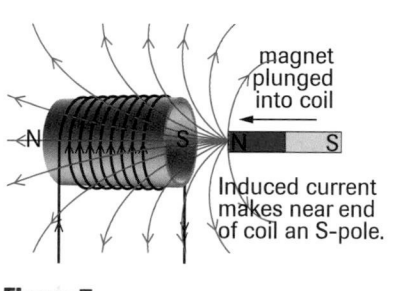

Figure 7
Violating the law of conservation of energy

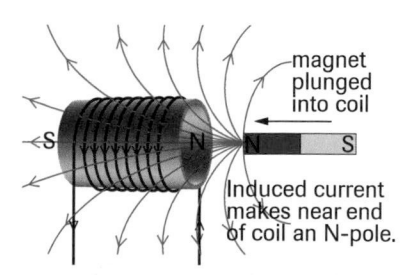

Figure 8
Obeying the law of conservation of energy

> **Lenz's Law**
>
> When a current is induced in a coil by a changing magnetic field, the electric current is in such a direction that its own magnetic field opposes the change that produced it.

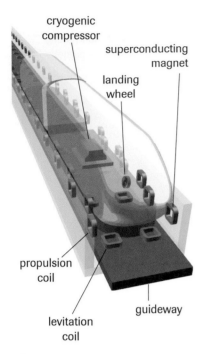

cryogenic
compressor

superconducting
magnet

landing
wheel

propulsion
coil

levitation
coil

guideway

Figure 9
Superconducting electromagnets induce currents in coils beneath the maglev train. By Lenz's law, these currents set up magnetic fields opposing the downward motion of the train, thus lifting it above the rails.

Figure 10
The surface of an induction stove is always cool to the touch. Water in a metal pot will boil; water in a glass pot will not heat up at all. Why would it be unsafe to touch the top of an induction stove if you are wearing a metal ring?

Figure 11
For question 3

Keep in mind that Lenz's law is consistent with the conservation of energy because the energy lost by the magnet due to the induced field is equal to the energy gained by the current due to the inducing field. The total energy remains constant.

Applying Lenz's Law

We have already introduced the idea of a maglev train. But having studied the ideas of Lenz, we can examine another form of maglev train that uses Lenz's law to levitate the train above the rails. Powerful superconducting electromagnets at the bottom of the train pass above two rows of coils on the guideway. A current is induced in these coils. By Lenz's law, the current acts to oppose the downward motion of the electromagnets, keeping the train hovering safely above the guideway (**Figure 9**).

Coils are not necessary for demonstrating Lenz's law. If a magnetic field changes near a conducting plate, currents are induced within the plate, forming closed circular paths. These so-called *eddy currents* produce magnetic fields in opposition to the inducing action. This principle is used in induction stoves. The surface of an induction stove is always cool to the touch. If two pots—one glass, the other metal—are filled with water and placed on such a stove, the water in the metal pot will boil, while the water in the glass pot will not heat up at all (**Figure 10**).

Below the surface of the stove are electromagnets operating on an AC current. Because the current is alternating, the magnetic field produced is not constant, inducing eddy currents in the metal pot because metal acts as a conductor. No eddy currents are produced in the glass pot because glass acts as an insulator. The metal pot has some internal resistance, causing it to heat up. This heat is transferred to the water, causing it to boil.

metal pot

glass pot

▶ *Practice*

Understanding Concepts

1. Explain how Faraday's law of electromagnetic induction is applied in the operation of a cruise-control device.

2. Explain how Lenz used the law of conservation of energy to determine the direction of the induced current produced by a moving magnet near a coil.

3. Two magnets are dropped through thin metal rings (**Figure 11**). One of the rings has a small gap.
   (a) Will both magnets experience a retarding force? Explain your reasoning, sketching the magnetic fields of the falling magnets and any induced currents or current-created magnetic fields.
   (b) Will your answers change if the rings are replaced with long cylinders, one with a long thin gap down one side?

Electromagnetic Induction

- The law of electromagnetic induction states that an electric current is induced in a conductor whenever the magnetic field in the region of the conductor changes.

- The greater the change in the magnetic field per unit time, the larger the induced current.

- Lenz's law states that when a changing magnetic field induces a current in a conductor, the electric current is in such a direction that its own magnetic field opposes the change that produced it.

▶ **Section 8.5** *Questions*

Understanding Concepts

1. Examine the circuit shown in **Figure 12**. When the switch is closed, assume the magnetic field produced by the solenoid is very strong.
   (a) Explain what will happen to the copper ring (which is free to move) when the switch is closed.
   (b) Explain what will happen to the copper ring when there is a steady current in the circuit.
   (c) Explain what will happen to the copper ring when the switch is opened.
   (d) How would your answers change if the terminals on the power supply are reversed? Explain your answer.

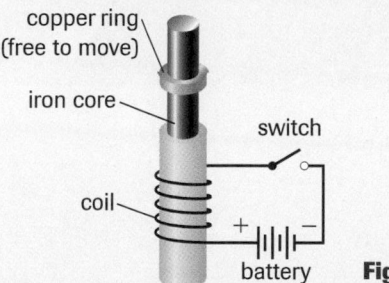

copper ring (free to move)

iron core

switch

coil

+ ||||| −

battery **Figure 12**

2. **Figure 13** shows a light bulb connected to a coil around a metal core. What causes the light bulb to glow?

3. A bolt of lightning can cause a current in an electric appliance even when the lightning does not strike the device. Explain how this could occur.

4. You place a copper ring onto an insulating stand inside a solenoid connected to an AC current. Explain what will happen to the ring.

Applying Inquiry Skills

5. A coil of wire connected to a galvanometer is placed with its axis perpendicular to a uniform magnetic field. When the coil is compressed, the galvanometer registers a current. Design an experiment to determine the factors that affect the magnitude of the induced current in the coil.

6. Explain how you would construct a device for investigating the magnitude of the induced current produced by a moving bar magnet. Assume you have access to a bar magnet, a compass, a coil, and wire. You may not use a galvanometer. Draw a diagram of your device and explain how it works.

Figure 13
For question 4

Making Connections

7. Explain how Lenz's law is applied in levitating one type of maglev train.

8. Explain how an induction stove works.

9. **Figure 14** shows a *ground-fault interrupter*, inserted for safety between the power outlet and an appliance such as a clothes dryer. The ground-fault interrupter consists of an iron ring, a sensing coil, and a circuit breaker. The circuit breaker interrupts the circuit only if a current appears in the sensing coil.
   (a) The circuit breaker will not interrupt the circuit if the dryer is operating normally. Explain why.
   (b) If a wire inside the dryer touches the metal case, charge will pass through a person touching the dryer instead of going back through the ground-fault interrupter. How does the interrupter protect the person?
   (c) Should all electrical devices be plugged into ground-fault interrupters? If so, why? If not, why not?

Magnetic Fields and Electromagnetism   **419**

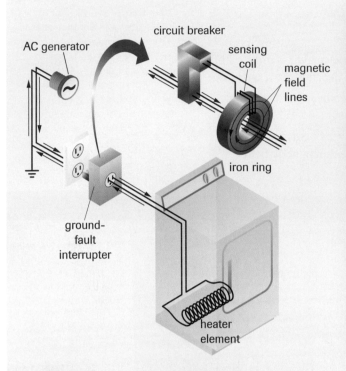

Figure 14
Schematic of a ground-fault interrupter (for question 9)

10. You are a civil engineer, seeking to reduce the number of traffic jams along a very busy road during rush hour. You notice that the side streets off the busy road often have green lights, causing the lights on the main road to be red, even in the absence of side-street traffic. You decide to solve this problem by installing large coils of wire just beneath the surface of the road, near the intersections on the side streets. You connect the coils to small micro-processors in the traffic lights. Explain how your device works and how it will help prevent traffic jams.

11. An amusement-park ride like the one in **Figure 15** elevates riders on a lift, then drops them. The lift and the riders accelerate downward under the force of gravity. Research the method used to slow them down safely, and write a short report explaining the physics involved. Design another ride that uses the same principles.

 www.science.nelson.com

12. **Figure 16** is a schematic of an electric-guitar pickup, a device that changes the vibrational energy of a guitar string into sound.
   (a) Describe how the pickup works, explaining the need for the string to vibrate and the purpose of the coil and permanent magnet.
   (b) The string of the guitar vibrates in a standing-wave pattern, with a series of nodes and antinodes. Where should a pickup be placed to send the largest possible current to the amplifier?

Figure 15
For question 11

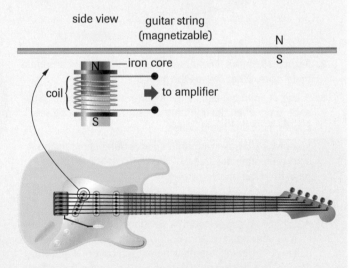

Figure 16
The schematic of a pickup on an electric guitar (for question 12)

⚛ INVESTIGATION 8.2.1

Magnetic Force on a Moving Charge

Inquiry Skills

○ Questioning	○ Planning	● Analyzing
● Hypothesizing	● Conducting	● Evaluating
● Predicting	● Recording	● Communicating

This investigation explores the factors affecting the magnitude and direction of the magnetic force on a moving charged particle in a magnetic field. Completion of all the parts of this investigation may require use of simulation software, in which you can send charged particles through magnetic fields. If a program is not available in class, search for a program available through the Internet. If you cannot complete all parts of the investigation, do as much as possible with the resources available. Be quantitative wherever equipment, software, and time permit. Where quantitative work is not possible, determine a trend.

Decide with your group how you will approach the investigation and what equipment (or, where necessary, what software) you will use for each part. Include diagrams of the paths of your particles, clearly showing the effect of each factor on the magnetic force they experience. Summarize any quantitative data in appropriate tables and graphs.

Question

What factors affect the magnitude and direction of the magnetic force on moving charges?

Hypothesis/Prediction

(a) Predict how the following factors affect the magnitude and direction of the magnetic force on a moving charged particle:

 (i)   the strength of the magnetic field

 (ii)   the speed of the moving charge

 (iii)   the angle between the velocity and the magnetic field

 (iv)   the amount of charge on the particle

 (v)   the sign of the charge on the particle

Materials

cathode-ray tube (0–12 V)
variable DC power supply
permanent magnets of various strengths
Helmholtz coils
computer with simulation software

Procedure

Part A: The Magnetic Field Strength

1. Power the cathode-ray tube and observe the beam. Sketch the path of the charged particles in the absence of a magnetic field.

   Have your teacher check all power arrangements. Cathode-ray tube potentials can be hazardous. A moving charge through a cathode-ray tube will emit harmful X rays. Only power the cathode-ray tube for a period sufficient to make your observations and ensure that you stay a safe distance from the cathode-ray tube. Carefully follow your teacher's instructions.

2. Establish a weak magnetic field near the path of the particles and perpendicular to the path. Sketch the new path of the particles. Calculate the force on an individual particle if using a simulation.

3. Repeat step 2 using stronger magnetic fields. Record any differences.

Part B: Speed of the Charges

4. If possible, increase the speed of the charged particles before they enter the magnetic field in your simulation. Note the effect on the magnetic force by sketching several paths of the charged particles at different velocities. (If you have a good cathode-ray tube, you can increase the accelerating potential. Only power the cathode-ray tube for a period sufficient to make your observations and ensure that you stay a safe distance from the cathode-ray tube. If you are using simulation software, you can adjust the initial speed.) Be as quantitative as possible in recording the effect of the force on the charges.

Part C: The Angle Between the Velocity and Magnetic Field

5. Rotate the magnetic field (if your equipment mountings allow you to do so) around the direction of motion of the charges. Record the effect on the path of the charges. At what angle(s) to the undeflected beam is the deflection greatest? least?

Part D: The Amount of Charge on the Particles

6. Use your software simulation to represent charges being fired into a magnetic field, perpendicular to the field lines. Change the amount of charge on the particles, recording the effect of the force on the charge.

Part E: The Sign of the Charge on the Particle

7. Repeat step 6, using charges of opposite sign. Record any changes in the path of the particles.

Analysis

(b) Which of your observations regarding the paths of charged particles indicate a larger magnetic force on the charged particles? Explain your answer.

(c) How is the magnetic field strength related to the magnetic force on the charges? Discuss any observational evidence you may have to support your position.

(d) How is the speed of the charges related to the magnetic force on the charges? (In particular, what happens to the speed of a charge when it suddenly moves into a strong uniform magnetic field from a region lacking strong fields?) Discuss the evidence that supports your position.

(e) How is the angle between the velocity and the magnetic field related to the magnetic force on the charges? Discuss the evidence that supports your position.

(f) How is the amount of charge on the particles related to the magnetic force they experience? Discuss the evidence that supports your position.

(g) What happens to the path of the particles if the sign of the charge is changed? Discuss the evidence that supports your position.

Evaluation

(h) What additional equipment would improve the results of your experiment?

Synthesis

(i) Describe the motion of charged particles in a uniform magnetic field. Where have you seen this kind of motion before? What happens to the speed of a charged particle in a uniform magnetic field?

INVESTIGATION 8.3.1

Force on a Conductor in a Magnetic Field

Inquiry Skills

○ Questioning   ○ Planning   ● Analyzing
● Hypothesizing   ● Conducting   ○ Evaluating
● Predicting   ● Recording   ● Communicating

This investigation explores factors affecting the magnitude of the force on a conductor in a magnetic field.

Question

What factors affect the magnitude of the force on a conductor in a magnetic field?

Hypothesis/Prediction

(a) Predict how the following factors will affect the magnitude and direction of the magnetic force on a conductor with a current in a magnetic field:
   (i)   the strength of the magnetic field
   (ii) the current in the conductor

Materials

current balance and solenoid apparatus
2 DC ammeters
2 variable-voltage DC power supplies (0–12 V)
string and scissors
electronic balance

Procedure

1. Set up the apparatus as shown in **Figure 1**.

2. By rotating the support points slightly, balance the conducting strip so that when both power supplies are off, the strip remains horizontal and motionless.

INVESTIGATION 8.3.1 *continued*

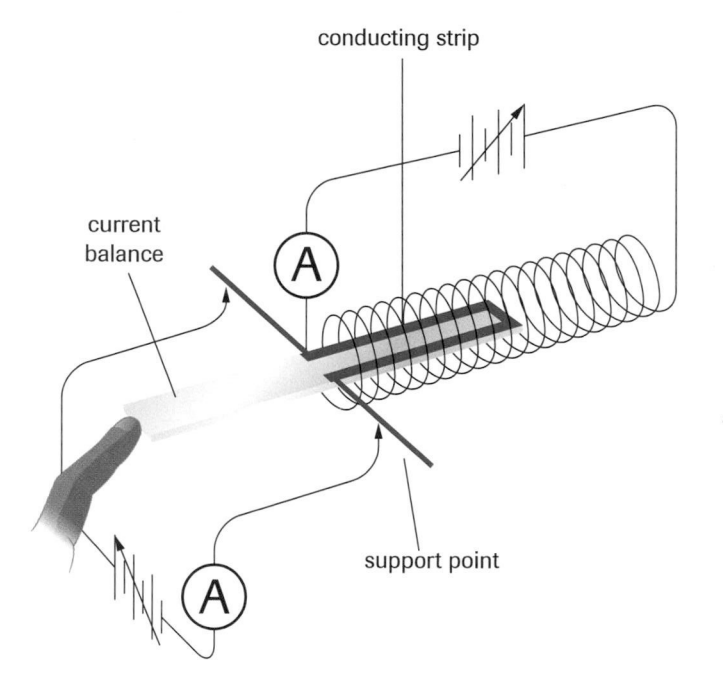
conducting strip
current balance
A
A
support point

Figure 1
Setup for Investigation 8.3.1

3. Turn on the current in both the coil and the conducting strip. Arrange the polarity of the connections to both power supplies so that the end of the strip inside the coil is forced downward if you increase the current in the conducting strip. Set the current in the coil to approximately the midpoint of its range.

4. Increase the current in the conducting strip to its maximum value (thereby forcing the end inside the coil down). Loop a length of string over the other end of the conducting strip, making your loop long enough to overbalance the strip and force the end inside the coil up above the balance point. Cut off small segments of the string very carefully, with scissors, until the conducting strip just balances horizontally. Turn off both currents. Determine the mass of the piece of string that was looped over the conducting strip. Record the string's mass and the current in the conducting strip in a table.

5. Repeat this procedure at least four more times, passing successively smaller currents through the strip. Again, record in your table the value of this current and the mass of string required to balance the strip.

6. Set the current through the conducting strip at a constant value near the middle of its range of values. Repeat the experiment five times, this time varying the current through the coil from its minimum to its maximum value. For each trial, record the current through the coil and the mass of string required to achieve balance.

7. Make careful measurements of the following quantities:
   (i)   the distance from the pivot point of the conducting strip to each of its ends
   (ii) the diameter of the coil
   (iii) the length of the coil
   (iv) the number of turns on the coil

Analysis

(b) Using the physical dimensions of the coil and the equation $B = \mu_0 \left(\dfrac{NI}{L} \right)$, (where B is the magnetic field strength in the core of the solenoid, in teslas; I is the current flowing through the coil, in amperes; L is the length of the solenoid, in metres; N is the number of turns on the coil; and $\mu_0 = 4\pi \times 10^{-7}$ T·m/A), calculate the magnitude B of the magnetic field in the core of the coil for each value of current in it. Include these values in your table.

(c) Using the mass of each piece of string and the lever principle (the force of gravity on the string multiplied by the distance from the support point equals the force on the conducting strip multiplied by its distance to the support point), determine the magnitude of the magnetic force acting downward on the conducting strip in each trial. Include these values in your table.

(d) Draw a graph of the magnitude of the force F on the conducting strip versus the current I in the conducting strip for a constant value of the magnetic field strength of magnitude B. What relationship between I and F does your graph suggest?

(e) Draw a separate graph of the magnitude of the force F on the conducting strip versus the magnitude of the magnetic field strength B, for a constant value of the current I in the conducting strip. What relationship between F and B does your graph suggest?

(f) Using the results from these two graphs, write a proportionality statement that shows how F varies jointly with B and I. On what additional factor or factors, not investigated in this experiment, might F depend?

Magnetic Fields near Conductors and Coils

In this activity, you will explore the magnitude and shape of the magnetic field near a long, straight conductor and a solenoid.

Question

What are the characteristics of the magnetic fields around a long, straight conductor and a solenoid?

Experimental Design

(a) Decide on a procedure to determine the nature of the magnetic field around a conductor with a current and a solenoid. Try to be as quantitative as possible in your observations. Record your observations in appropriate tables and diagrams.

Long straight conductor

Try to determine how the following factors affect the magnetic field:

(i)   the current

(ii) the distance from the wire

Solenoid

Try to determine how the following factors affect the magnetic field:

(i)   the current

(ii) the number of turns per unit length

 It is possible to pass too much current through a wire of low resistance. Have your teacher check that your currents are within reasonable bounds.

Even a wire of sufficiently high resistance with a low current can heat up, so take care not to keep currents flowing any longer than necessary while taking accurate measurements.

Materials

long, straight wire
variable DC power supply
solenoids with different numbers of turns
magnetic probes

Analysis

(b) How is the magnitude of the magnetic field around a straight conductor related to the perpendicular distance from the observation point to the conductor?

(c) How is the magnitude of the magnetic field around a straight conductor related to the current in it?

(d) How is the magnitude of the magnetic field inside a solenoid related to the current it is carrying and the number of turns per unit length?

(e) Describe in words and with a diagram the magnetic field

(i)   around a long, straight conductor

(ii) inside and outside a solenoid

Evaluation

(f) Evaluate your experimental design.

There are many different types of careers that involve the study of electrical, gravitational, and magnetic fields. Find out more about the careers described below or about some other interesting career in electric, gravitational, or magnetic fields.

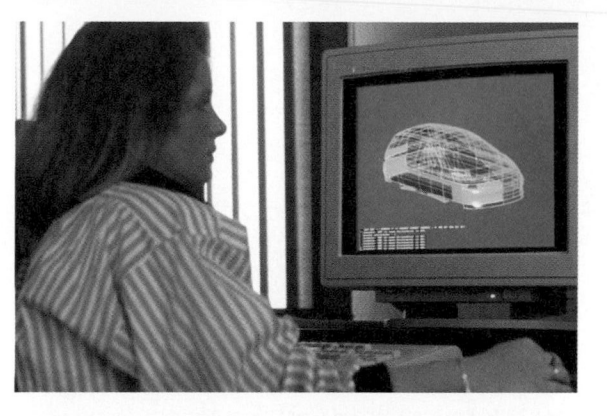

Automobile Engineering Designer

Automobile engineering designers must complete at least a four-year degree in mechanical engineering, having taken science and mathematics in high school. They typically work either for the large auto manufacturers (such as General Motors, Ford, or Honda) or in university research facilities. These engineers use computers, prototype machines, welding machines, injection moulding machines, and robotics to design and manufacture automobiles.

Industrial Electrician

Industrial electricians must complete a five-year apprenticeship program and pass a written examination. To become accepted as an apprentice, you need a high-school diploma, including Grade 12 mathematics and physics. Industrial electricians work in factories and plants to set up and maintain motors, distribution systems, and electronic equipment. These trades people use a variety of hand tools, including soldering and pipe-threading gear, hammers, spanners, pliers, cutters, and strippers. Proficiency in reading blueprints and reference diagrams is essential.

Electronic Engineering Technicians

Electronic engineering technicians must complete a 12-month community-college diploma, having taken English, mathematics, and physics in high school. These technicians build, repair, and maintain high-technology equipment such as CAT scanners, lasers, and assembly-line robots. Proficiency in the use of electronics testing equipment, especially multimeters and oscilloscopes, is essential. Electronic engineering technicians work in hospitals, factories, and boards of education, and in the high-tech industries.

▶ Practice

Making Connections

1. Identify several careers that require knowledge of electric, gravitational, or magnetic fields. Select a career you are interested in from the list you made or from the careers described above. Imagine that you have been employed in your chosen career for five years and that you are applying to work on a new project of interest.

   (a) Describe the project. It should be related to some of the new things you learned in this unit. Explain how the concepts from this unit are applied in the project.

   (b) Create a résumé listing your credentials and explaining why you are qualified to work on the project. Include in your résumé
   - your educational background: what university degree or diploma program you graduated with, which educational institute you attended, post-graduate training (if any)
   - your skills
   - your duties in previous positions
   - your salary expectations

   GO ▶ www.science.nelson.com

Key Expectations

- define and describe the concepts and units related to magnetic fields (e.g., magnetic field, electromagnetic induction) (8.1, 8.2, 8.3, 8.4, 8.5)
- compare the properties of electric, gravitational, and magnetic fields by describing and illustrating the source and direction of the field in each case (8.1)
- predict the forces acting on a moving charge and on a current-carrying conductor (8.2, 8.3, 8.4)
- determine the net force on, and resulting motion of, objects and charged particles by collecting, analyzing, and interpreting quantitative data from experiments or computer simulations (8.2, 8.3)
- analyze and explain the properties of electric fields, and demonstrate how an understanding of these properties can be applied to control or alter the electric field around a conductor (e.g., demonstrate how shielding on electronic equipment or on connecting conductors [coaxial cables] affects magnetic fields)(8.4, 8.5)
- describe instances where developments in technology resulted in the advancement or revision of scientific theories, and analyze the principles involved in these discoveries and theories (8.2, 8.4)
- evaluate, using your own criteria, the social and economic impact of new technologies based on a scientific understanding of electric and magnetic fields (8.2)

Key Terms

poles

law of magnetic poles

magnetic force field

domain theory of magnetism

principle of electromagnetism

solenoid

Ampère's law

ampere

coulomb

law of electromagnetic induction

Lenz's law

Key Equations

- $F_M = qvB \sin \theta$ (8.2)

- $\dfrac{e}{m} = 1.76 \times 10^{11}$ C/kg   (8.2)

- $\dfrac{q}{m} = \dfrac{\varepsilon}{B^2 r}$ (8.2)

- $B = \dfrac{F}{kIl \sin \theta}$ (8.3)

- $F = IlB \sin \theta$ (8.3)

- $\sum B_\parallel \, \Delta l = \mu_0 I$ (8.4)

- $B = \mu_0 \left(\dfrac{I}{2\pi r} \right)$ (8.4)

- $B = \mu_0 \left(\dfrac{NI}{L} \right)$ (8.4)

▶ MAKE a summary

In a table, summarize the similarities and differences between the two major topics in this chapter: the motion of charged particles in magnetic fields and how that motion describes the force on a conductor in a magnetic field (**Figure 1**). Your table should compare and contrast the right-hand rules, the resulting motions of the wire and/or charges, the effect of changing current direction or sign of charge, the effect of varying the angle between the charge velocity and the magnetic field, and any other way of changing the magnitude or direction of the magnetic force.

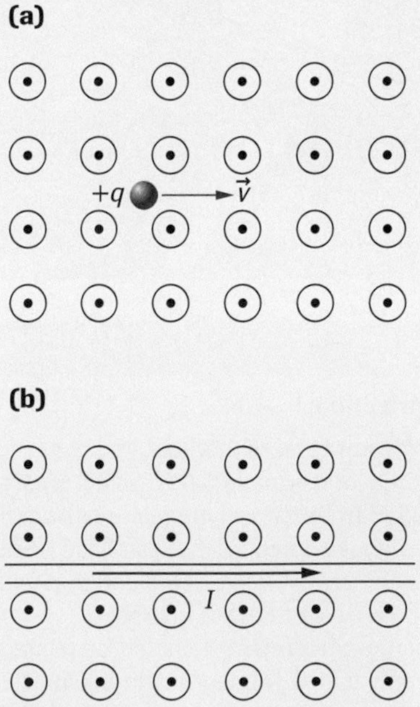

(a)

(b)

Figure 1

Write numbers 1 to 7 in your notebook. Indicate beside each number whether the corresponding statement is true (T) or false (F). If it is false, write a corrected version.

1. A charge moving in a direction perpendicular to a uniform magnetic field experiences a force, but its velocity does not change.

2. When a charged particle is fired into and perpendicular to a uniform magnetic field, it moves along a circular path until it escapes the field.

3. The force on a conductor in a uniform magnetic field is perpendicular to both the current in the conductor and the magnetic field.

4. Reversing the direction of the current in a conductor in a uniform magnetic field reverses the direction of the force on the conductor.

5. The magnetic field on the outside of a coaxial cable is proportional to the current in the cable.

6. The magnetic field inside a long, straight coil with many closely packed turns is essentially uniform.

7. It is possible to shield against gravitational, electric, and magnetic fields.

Write numbers 8 to 13 in your notebook. Beside each number, write the letter corresponding to the best choice.

8. A charged particle is placed into a uniform magnetic field with an initial velocity of zero. If no electric or gravitational forces act on the particle, then it
   (a) accelerates straight forward
   (b) does not move
   (c) moves in a circle
   (d) moves at constant speed
   (e) none of these

9. If particles with the same initial velocity and charge pass into and perpendicular to a uniform magnetic field, then
   (a) the radius of curvature is the same for each particle
   (b) the radius of curvature is greater for the more massive particles
   (c) the radius of curvature is greater for the less massive particles
   (d) all the particles spiral with decreasing radius under all circumstances
   (e) none of the these

10. If two wires, with currents as in **Figure 1**, cross each other at right angles, one slightly above the other, forming four regions, which region has the strongest magnetic field pointing out of the page?
    (a) I   (c) III   (e) The fields are the same
    (b) II   (d) IV   in each region.

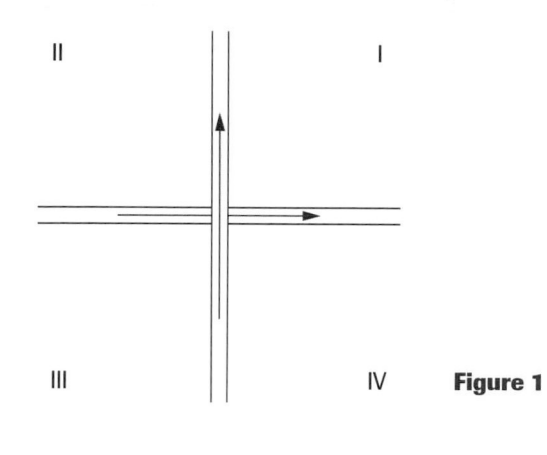

Figure 1

11. Particles A, B, C, and D with the same charge and speed are placed into a uniform magnetic field (**Figure 2**). Which one experiences the smallest force?
    (a) A   (c) C   (e) They all experience
    (b) B   (d) D   the same force.

12. Four particles with the same charge and speed are placed into a uniform magnetic field (**Figure 2**). Which particle experiences a force directed into the page?
    (a) A   (c) C   (e) They all experience a
    (b) B   (d) D   force out of the page.

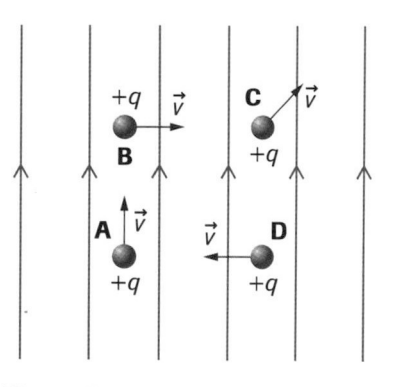

Figure 2
For questions 11 and 12

13. The magnitude of the magnetic field a distance r from a long, straight conductor with current I is B. The same magnetic field will have magnitude $2B$ if the current is tripled at a distance of
    (a) $\frac{2r}{3}$ (b) $2r$ (c) $3r$ (d) $\frac{3r}{2}$ (e) none of these

NEL   An interactive version of the quiz is available online.
GO www.science.nelson.com

Magnetic Fields and Electromagnetism **427**

Understanding Concepts

1. Describe the effect of Earth's magnetic field on the motion of a charged particle approaching from space. Are there any directions along which the particle can reach Earth without deflection?

2. Explain why the magnetic field created by the electric currents in the wires in your home is unlikely to have any effect on a nearby compass.

3. A horizontal east–west wire carries a westward current. A beam of positively charged particles is shot directly down at the wire from above. In what direction will the particles be deflected?

4. A charged particle is moving in a circular path under the influence of a uniform magnetic field. Describe how the path would change in response to each of the following factors, considered separately:
   (a) The strength of the magnetic field is increased.
   (b) An electric field is added, in the same direction as the magnetic field.
   (c) The magnetic field is removed.

5. Two atoms of the same substance, one singly ionized and the other doubly ionized, are each accelerated from rest by the same potential difference. The ions enter the same uniform magnetic field at 90°. Compare
   (a) their velocities upon entering the field
   (b) their radii of curvature in the field

6. A straight wire 15 cm long, with a current of 12 A, lying at right angles to a uniform magnetic field, experiences a magnetic force of magnitude 0.40 N. What is the magnitude of the magnetic field?

7. A conductor 45 cm long, with a mass of 15 g, lies in a horizontal position at a 90° angle to a uniform horizontal magnetic field of magnitude 0.20 T. What must the current in the conductor be if the magnetic force is to support the weight of the conductor?

8. Calculate the magnitude and direction of the force on an electron moving horizontally westward at 3.2×10^6 m/s through a uniform magnetic field of 1.2 T directed horizontally southward.

9. An α particle of charge $+3.2 \times 10^{-19}$ C and mass 6.7×10^{-27} kg first accelerates through a potential difference of 1.2×10^3 V, then enters a uniform magnetic field of magnitude 0.25 T at 90°. Calculate the magnetic force.

10. Calculate the magnitude and direction of the magnetic field 25 cm to the east of a straight vertical wire with a current of 12 A downward through air.

11. A straight wire has a current of 15 A vertically upward, in a vacuum. An electron, presently 0.10 m from the wire, moves at a speed of 5.0×10^6 m/s. Its instantaneous velocity is parallel to the wire but downward. Calculate the magnitude and direction of the force on the electron. Will this force remain constant?

12. What is the magnetic field strength in the air core of a solenoid, 0.10 m long, consisting of 1200 loops of wire and with a current of 1.0 A?

13. A coil 15 cm long, with 100 turns and a current of 20.0 A, lies in a horizontal plane. A light frame supports rectangular conducting wire WXYZ, balanced horizontally at its midpoint in the core of the coil, as in **Figure 1**. Sides WX and YZ are 5.0 cm long and parallel to the axis of the coil. Side XY is 1.5 cm long and perpendicular to the axis of the coil. A mass of 1.8×10^{-2} g hangs from the outside end of the light frame. What current must flow through the rectangular conductor to keep it in horizontal balance?

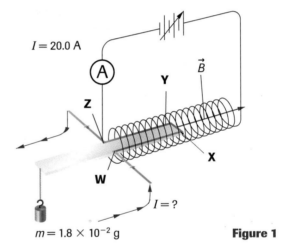

$I = 20.0$ A

$m = 1.8 \times 10^{-2}$ g

Figure 1

14. Calculate the magnetic force between two parallel wires, 45 m long and 0.10 m apart, carrying currents of 1.0×10^2 A in the same direction.

15. A straight wire of linear mass density 150 g/m has a current of 40.0 A (supplied by a flexible connection of negligible mass). This wire lies parallel to, and on top of, another straight horizontal wire on a table. What current must the bottom wire have in order to repel and support the top wire at a separation of 4.0 cm? (Frictionless guide plates keep the top wire parallel to the bottom wire as it rises.)

16. What is the charge-to-mass ratio of a particle accelerated to 6.0×10^6 m/s, moving in a circular path of radius 1.8 cm perpendicular to a uniform magnetic field of magnitude 3.2×10^{-2} T?

17. A proton, of mass 1.67×10^{-27} kg, moves in a circle in the plane perpendicular to a uniform magnetic field of magnitude 1.8 T. The radius of curvature is 3.0 cm. What is the speed of the proton?

18. A singly ionized atom ($q = +e$) moves at 1.9×10^4 m/s perpendicular to a uniform magnetic field of magnitude 1.0×10^{-3} T. The radius of curvature is 0.40 m. What is the mass of the ion?

19. A singly ionized $^{235}_{92}$U atom of mass 3.9×10^{-25} kg is accelerated through a potential difference of 1.0×10^5 V.
    (a) Calculate its maximum speed.
    (b) What is the radius of the path it would take if injected at this speed and at 90° into a uniform magnetic field of magnitude 0.10 T?

20. A loop of wire tied to a string is allowed to fall from the horizontal into a uniform magnetic field, as in **Figure 2**. The loop remains perpendicular to the plane of the page at all times, with the segment XYZ behind the plane of the page.
    (a) Indicate the direction of the current, using these letters, as the loop swings from left to right through positions I and II, with the loop still rising at II.
    (b) Indicate the direction of the current, using these letters, as the loop swings from right to left through positions I and II, with the loop already descending at II.
    (c) Describe the motion of the loop. Explain your reasoning.

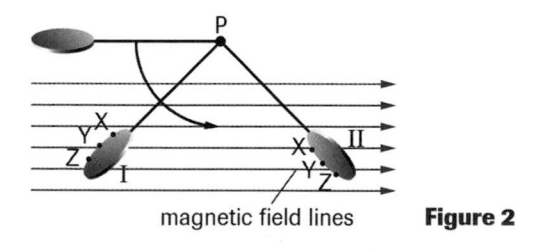

magnetic field lines   **Figure 2**

Applying Inquiry Skills

21. Design an experiment to determine the factors affecting the force on a long, straight conductor suspended from two conducting springs in a uniform magnetic field.

22. (a) Design an experiment to investigate the magnetic field around two long parallel conductors with equal currents in opposite directions. Assume the wires are very close together and the measurements are taken from at least 5.0 cm away.

(b) What results do you expect from this experiment?
(c) How would your observations differ if the currents were in the same direction?

Making Connections

23. A typical speaker has a coil fixed to the back of a cone. The cone has a flexible edge, allowing it to move back and forth (**Figure 3**). The coil is wrapped around a core that is a magnetic N-pole and is surrounded by a circular S-pole. Explain how such a speaker works.

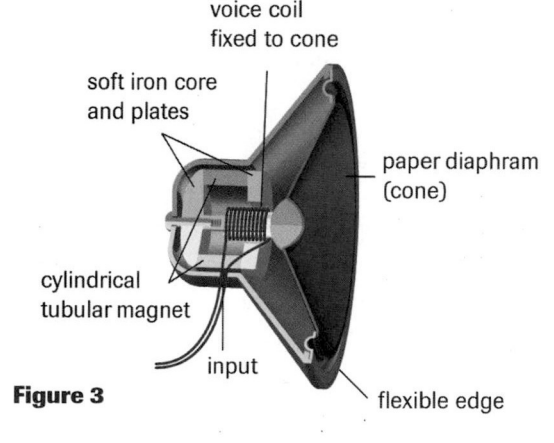

Figure 3

24. **Figure 4** is a schematic of a variable-reluctance microphone. A light flexible rod is attached to a permanent magnet at one end, to a diaphragm at the other. The C-shaped structure around the magnet is also made of magnetic material. Explain how such a microphone works, paying special attention to the purpose of the windings in each coil.

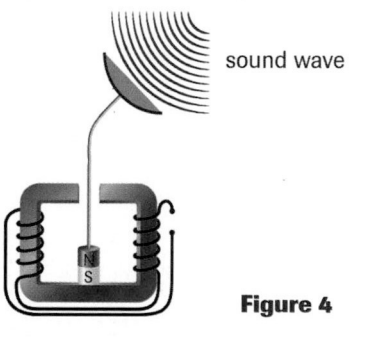

Figure 4

Extension

25. A source emits a variety of charged particles, with different masses and charges, at different speeds. Some of the particles have the same charge-to-mass ratio. Design a device, or set of devices, that could be used to find all the different particles emitted from the source, and describe how the masses, charges, and speeds of these particles could be determined.

PERFORMANCE TASK

Process

- Choose appropriate research tools, such as books, magazines, the Internet, and experts in the field of your chosen technology.

- Research a technology that applies field theory and summarize your findings appropriately.

- Analyze the physics principles of fields involved in the technology.

- Develop criteria to evaluate the social and economic impacts of the chosen technology, and perform the corresponding evaluation.

Product

- Demonstrate an understanding of the related physics concepts, principles, laws, and theories.

- Prepare a suitable research portfolio in print and/or audiovisual format.

- Use terms, symbols, equations, and SI metric units correctly.

- Produce a final communication such as an audiovisual presentation, simulation, or demonstration model to summarize the analysis.

Field Theory and Technology

The principles of field theory are applied in many areas: technology, communications, transportation, entertainment, and scientific research, to name just a few (**Figure 1**). Building and launching a sophisticated satellite requires in-depth understanding of gravitational, electric, and magnetic fields. Designing a television picture tube, on the other hand, requires an in-depth understanding of only electric and magnetic fields.

Figure 1
An understanding of gravitational, electrical, and magnetic fields is involved in the different technologies shown in these photographs.

In this performance task, you are expected to display an understanding of the concepts related to gravitational, electric, and magnetic fields presented in Chapters 7 and 8 as you analyze the impacts of a technology. Your skill in creating your own criteria to evaluate the impact is more important here than in the other unit performance tasks in this text because you are given more freedom to design this particular task.

Task

Your task is to investigate an emerging technology or an advance in an established technology, and explain how the concepts of gravitational, electric, and magnetic fields are involved in your choice. Ensure that your chosen technology uses at least two of the three types of fields. Once you have chosen a technology to research, create your own criteria for evaluating the social and economic impacts of that technology. If you have selected an emerging technology, discuss the impacts it will have. If you have chosen an advance in an established technology, discuss the impacts your technology has already had and what new effects may be predicted in the future.

Present a polished technical communication in some format agreed upon by you and your teacher (e.g., a printed report, a poster presentation, a science fair booth with a working model, an audiovisual presentation, a video clip, a computer simulation, or a Web site). Your teacher may also ask you to present your raw research notes.

Analysis

The following criteria should be considered in your analysis:

(a) What physics principles are applied to the design and use of your chosen technology?

(b) What are the advantages and disadvantages of your chosen technology?

(c) How is the design of your chosen technology affected by its function?

(d) What social, economic, and environmental impacts has your chosen technology had on individual users and society in general? (Use your own criteria to evaluate those impacts.)

(e) What careers are related to the use of your chosen technology?

(f) What research is being carried out to improve the design and use of your chosen technology?

(g) Create your own analysis questions and answer them.

Evaluation

(h) Evaluate the resources you used during your research for this task.

(i) If you were to embark on a similar task with a different goal, what changes to the process would you make to ensure that you were successful in your research and in communicating that research?

Write numbers 1 through 14 in your notebook. Indicate beside each number whether the corresponding statement is true (T) or false (F). If it is false, write a corrected version.

1. The electric force between two point charges is directly proportional to the product of the charges and inversely proportional to the square of the distance between them.

2. If the sum of all the electric forces on a charge is zero, the charge must be at rest.

3. Electric charges always move along a path given by electric field lines.

4. If the electric field in a region of space is zero, the electric force on any single charge placed in that region is also zero.

5. When a small positive test charge is moved toward another positive charge, the test charge experiences an increasing electric force, an increasing electric field, and an increase in electric potential energy. Further, the charge finds itself moving into a region of higher electric potential.

6. Negative charges move from regions of high electric potential to regions of lower electric potential.

7. An oil droplet in a Millikan apparatus with uncharged plates falls at a constant speed because it has a charge.

8. The laws of conservation of momentum and conservation of mechanical energy determine the motion of interacting charged particles.

9. A negatively charged object that is fired directly away from a positively charged object will cause the kinetic energy to increase and the potential energy to decrease.

10. Magnetic field lines never cross.

11. Uniform electric, gravitational, and magnetic fields can change the speeds of particles that are initially moving perpendicular to the fields.

12. A charged particle moving parallel to an electric, gravitational, or magnetic field experiences a force.

13. Charges moving perpendicular to a uniform magnetic field experience circular motion because the magnetic force is always perpendicular to the velocity of the charge.

14. Two long, parallel, straight wires repel each other if their currents are in the same direction.

Write numbers 15 to 26 in your notebook. Beside each number, write the letter corresponding to the best choice.

15. The force on a small, uniform conducting sphere of charge q_1 a distance d from another sphere of charge q_2 is $+F$. If the sphere of charge q_1 is touched with an identical neutral conducting sphere, which is moved far away and then placed a distance $\frac{d}{2}$ from q_2, the force on the sphere is
    (a) $+F$ (c) $+\dfrac{F}{2}$ (e) none of these
    (b) $+2F$ (d) $-F$

16. Three identical charges are placed on a line from left to right, with adjacent charges separated by a distance d. The magnitude of the force on a charge from its nearest neighbour is F. The net force on each charge, from left to right, is
    (a) $+2F, +2F, +2F$ (d) $F, 0, F$
    (b) $-\dfrac{5F}{4}, 0, +\dfrac{5F}{4}$ (e) none of these
    (c) $+2F, 0, +2F$

17. An electron experiences a force of 1.6×10^{-16} N [left] from an electric field. The electric field is
    (a) 1.6×10^3 N/C   (d) 1.0 N [right]
    (b) 1.0×10^3 N/C [left]   (e) none of these
    (c) 1.0×10^3 N/C [right]

18. As the distance between two charges increases, the electric potential energy of the two-charge system
    (a) always increases
    (b) always decreases
    (c) increases if the charges have the same sign, decreases if they have opposite signs
    (d) increases if the charges have opposite signs, decreases if they have the same sign
    (e) is always negative

19. Two oppositely charged parallel plates are separated by 12 mm. The uniform electric field between the plates has a magnitude of 3.0×10^3 N/C. An electron is ejected from the negative plate, with an initial velocity of zero. The kinetic energy of the electron when it has moved halfway to the positive plate is
    (a) 2.9×10^{-18} J   (d) 0 J
    (b) 5.8×10^{-18} J   (e) none of these
    (c) 1.4×10^{-18} J

20. A positive charge of mass $2m$ is initially at rest, directly to the left of a negative charge of mass m, moving rightward with speed v. When the negative charge has velocity $\frac{v}{2}$ [right], the velocity of the positive charge is
    (a) 0
    (b) $\frac{v}{4}$ [right]
    (c) $\frac{v}{4}$ [left]
    (d) $\frac{v}{2}$ [right]
    (e) $\frac{v}{2}$ [left]

21. Which of the following statements is true about any type of field line:
    (a) They never cross.
    (b) They are always perpendicular to the surface of the object producing the field.
    (c) They point in the direction of motion.
    (d) They signify a force, experienced by a test particle of positive charge q, whose magnitude equals the product of q and the field magnitude.
    (e) They never form closed loops.

22. Through a narrow hole you view an apparatus in which a small charged sphere, attached to a thin thread, hangs at rest at an angle of 10° to the right of the vertical when there is no wind. From your observation, you can infer that
    (a) the electric field points right
    (b) the electric field points left
    (c) the electric field is zero
    (d) the net force on the sphere is zero
    (e) the tension in the thread is smaller than the gravitational force on the sphere

23. An electron moves within a uniform magnetic field of 0.20 T, at a speed of 5.0×10^5 m/s. The magnetic force on the electron
    (a) is 1.6×10^{-14} N
    (b) is 1.6×10^{-14} N [perpendicular to velocity]
    (c) is 1.6×10^{-14} N [perpendicular to magnetic field]
    (d) is zero
    (e) cannot be determined from the information

24. If a straight length of wire with a current is immersed in a uniform magnetic field, then the wire
    (a) experiences no force if it is perpendicular to the field
    (b) experiences some magnetic force, no matter what its orientation in the field
    (c) experiences no force if it is parallel to the field
    (d) experiences no force if the current is alternating
    (e) does not satisfy any of the above descriptions

25. An electron passes into a magnetic field at 90°. Its consequent circular path has radius r. If the speed of the electron were twice as great and the magnetic field were twice as strong, the radius would be
    (a) r (b) $2r$ (c) $4r$ (d) $\frac{r}{2}$ (e) $\frac{r}{4}$

26. Particles in a mass spectrograph emerge from a velocity selector into a uniform magnetic field at 90°. If the radius of the circular path of particle 1 is larger than the radius for particle 2, then
    (a) particle 1 is of greater mass than particle 2
    (b) particle 1 has a smaller charge than particle 2
    (c) the charge-to-mass ratio of particle 1 is smaller than the charge-to-mass ratio of particle 2
    (d) the charge-to-mass ratio of particle 1 is larger than the charge-to-mass ratio of particle 2
    (e) particle 1 is moving faster than particle 2

Write numbers 27 to 30 in your notebook. Beside each number place the word, phrase, or equation that completes the sentence.

27. (a) A(n) __?__ exists in a region of space when an appropriate object experiences a force in that region.
    (b) The gravitational and electric forces are governed by a(n) __?__ law with respect to the distance between the objects.
    (c) If a charged particle passes into a(n) __?__ field perpendicular to the field lines, the speed does not change.

28. (a) Electric field lines are always __?__ to a conductor in static equilibrium.
    (b) A(n) __?__ cable is shielded from both electric and magnetic fields.
    (c) The area under the curve on an electric force-displacement graph represents the change in __?__.
    (d) To analyze the motion of an elastic collision between two charged particles we use conservation of __?__ and __?__.

29. When a charged particle of mass m passes into either a uniform gravitational field or an electric field perpendicular to the field lines, it follows a(n) __?__ path; however if it passes into a magnetic field it follows a(n) __?__ path.

30. When separating two charges of mass m the gravitational and electric force __?__, the gravitational potential energy __?__, and the electric potential energy __?__.

NEL   An interactive version of the quiz is available online.
GO www.science.nelson.com

Electric, Gravitational, and Magnetic Fields **433**

Understanding Concepts

1. When using oxygen in the operating room, should the doctors and nurses wear conducting shoes or insulating rubber shoes? Explain your answer.

2. Two small charges, $+6.0 \times 10^{-5}$ C and -2.0×10^{-5} C, are placed 36 cm apart. Calculate the following:
   (a) the force on a third small charge, $+5.0 \times 10^{-5}$ C, placed midway between the two charges
   (b) the force on a third small charge, $+5.0 \times 10^{-5}$ C, placed 18 cm outside them on the line joining the two charges, closer to the negative charge
   (c) the magnitude and direction of the electric field 18 cm outside the charges on the line joining them, closer to the positive charge
   (d) the magnitude of the electric field at a point 18 cm above the midpoint of the line joining the two charges, on the perpendicular to that line (and thus equidistant from the charges)
   (e) the point at which the magnitude of the electric field is zero

3. Three charges are arranged as in **Figure 1**. Calculate the magnitude and direction of the net electric force on each charge.

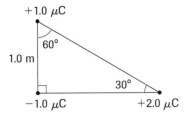

$+1.0\ \mu C$

$60°$

1.0 m

$30°$

$-1.0\ \mu C$ $+2.0\ \mu C$

Figure 1

4. **Figure 2** represents a neutral helium atom with two electrons on either side of the nucleus, in a well-defined circular orbit of radius 2.64×10^{-11} m. Calculate the magnitude and direction of the electric force on either electron.

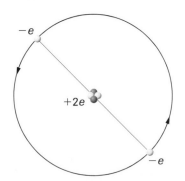

$-e$

$+2e$

$-e$

Figure 2

5. **Figure 3** shows the electric field near an object.
   (a) Could the object be a conductor in electrostatic equilibrium? Explain.
   (b) Could the object be an insulator? Explain.

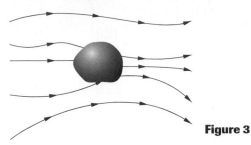

Figure 3

6. The conductors in **Figure 4** are introduced, one at a time, into a uniform electric field directed to the right, changing the field. Sketch the field near the conductors.

Figure 4

7. A charged insulating ball of mass 7.0 g with a uniform charge of 1.5 μC, hangs from a light thread inclined at an angle of 8.0° to the vertical (**Figure 5**). Calculate the magnitude of the electric field.

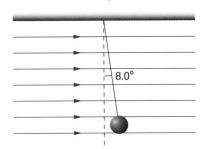

$8.0°$

Figure 5

8. **Figure 6** shows two oppositely charged uniform spheres and the electric field between them.
   (a) What are the signs of q_1 and q_2?
   (b) What is the value of the ratio $\dfrac{q_1}{q_2}$? Explain.

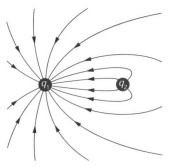

q_1 q_2

Figure 6

9. Two electrons separated by a large distance are fired directly at each other. The closest approach in this head-on collision is 4.0×10^{-14} m. One electron starts with twice the speed of the other. Assuming there is no deflection from the original path, determine the initial speed of each electron.

10. A charged particle moves at a constant velocity in a straight line through a region of space.
    (a) Is the electric field zero in the region? Explain your answer.
    (b) Is the magnetic field zero in the region? Explain your answer.

11. An electron, having been accelerated from rest through 2.4×10^3 V, encounters a uniform magnetic field of magnitude 0.60 T at 90°.
    (a) Calculate the magnitude of the magnetic force on the electron.
    (b) Describe the resulting motion of the electron.
    (c) Will the electron be trapped in the magnetic field? Explain your answer.

12. A wire 25 cm long, placed at right angles to a 0.18-T uniform magnetic field, experiences a magnetic force of magnitude 0.14 N. Calculate the current in the wire.

13. Each of two parallel horizontal wires, running east–west and separated by 3.0 m, has a current of 1.2 A (**Figure 7**). Calculate the magnitude and direction of the magnetic field midway between the two wires if
    (a) the current is directed east in wire 1, west in wire 2
    (b) the currents in both wires are directed east

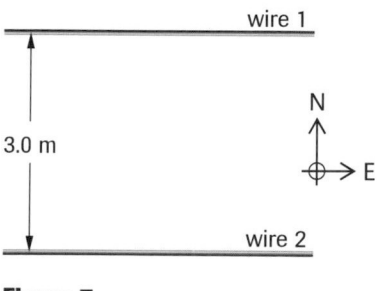

Figure 7

14. A coil 12 cm long, with 500 turns, produces a magnetic field strength of magnitude 1.6×10^{-2} T in its core. Calculate the current in the coil.

15. The magnitude of the magnetic force between two conductors 4.00 m long, separated by 8.00 cm, is 2.80×10^{-5} N. The current in one conductor is twice the current in the other. Calculate both currents.

16. **Figure 8** is a schematic of a velocity selector and a mass spectrometer. The electric field is perpendicular to the magnetic field in the velocity selector. The electric field between the plates is 1.2×10^4 V/m, and the magnitude of the magnetic field is 0.20 T. A singly charged ion, of mass 2.2×10^{-26} kg, is fired into the velocity selector at right angles to both the electric and the magnetic fields. The particle passes through the selector undeflected.
    (a) Calculate the speed of the particle.
    (b) Calculate the radius of the path of the particle as it emerges from the velocity selector.

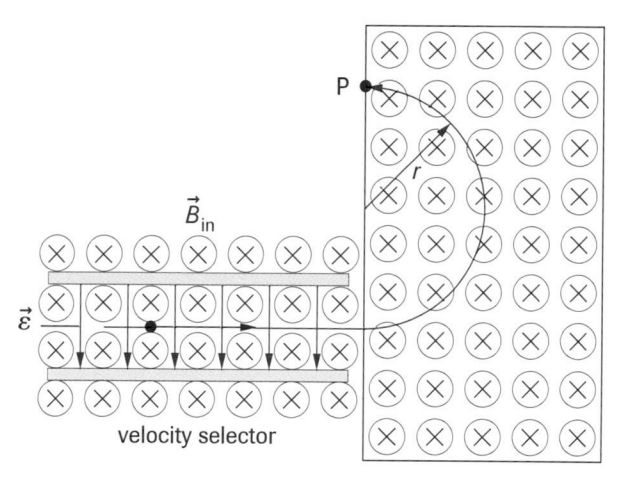

Figure 8

17. **Figure 9** is a cross-sectional view of a coaxial cable. The current in the inner conductor is 1.0 A, directed into the page, while the current in the outer conductor is 1.5 A, directed out of the page. Determine the magnitude and the direction of the magnetic field at A and B.

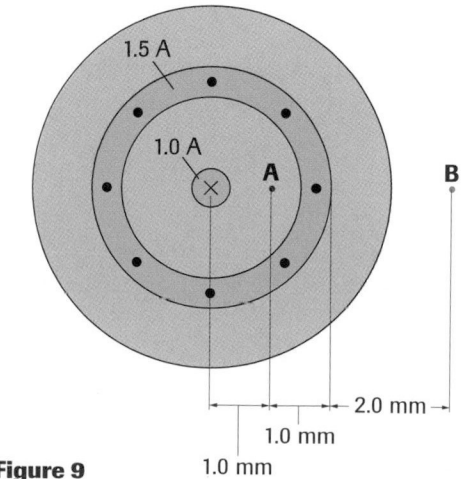

Figure 9

Applying Inquiry Skills

18. A typical problem when investigating the forces between charges or the properties of a single charge is that the charge on the object being investigated often decreases over time. Design an experiment that could be used to investigate the factors that cause objects to lose their charge.

19. Two parallel, straight wires 35 cm long, each with a mass of 12 g, are supported by threads 7.0 cm long (**Figure 10**). When the current in each wire is I, the angle between the threads is 14°.
    (a) Determine the magnitude and the direction of the current in each wire.
    (b) Design an experiment to investigate the relationship between the force on each conductor and the current in each wire.

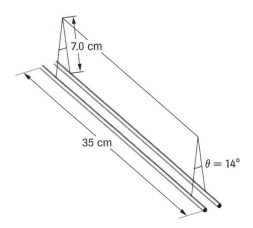

Figure 10

20. A charge moving through a magnetic field can experience a force. Design an experiment in which you use a small conducting ball to determine the factors affecting this force.

21. Under the right conditions, a current can experience a magnetic force due to an external magnetic field. This principle is used in electromagnetic pumps in nuclear reactors as a way to transfer heat. In these pumps liquid mercury or sodium is placed in a pipe, and a current is created in the conducting liquid in the presence of an external magnetic field. Design an electromagnetic pump, explaining how it works and how it can be used to transfer heat. (Note: mercury and sodium are very dangerous substances that require special care to prevent leaks and should not be handled by students.)

Making Connections

22. **Figure 11** shows a large open loop constructed below a high-voltage (AC) power line.
    (a) Can this loop be used to draw power from the lines? Where would the energy come from and how would it work?
    (b) If no one actually saw the loop, would the power company be able to detect the crime?
    (c) Could a similar approach be used to bug a telephone line? Explain your answer.

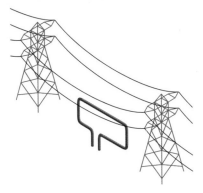

Figure 11

23. Explain why the surface of a television screen, even if recently cleaned, is often covered in a light layer of dust.

24. **Figure 12** is a simplified diagram of a neutral water molecule. The molecule has a permanent charge separation because the electrons spend more time near the oxygen than the hydrogen. For this reason, water is said to have *polar molecules*.

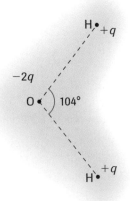

Figure 12

(a) Why is water attracted to both positive and negative charges?

(b) What effect does humidity have on removing excess charges from objects? Explain your answer.

(c) Ions in the air can often form *nucleation centres* (the starting points for the collecting of water-vapour molecules into liquid water). Explain why this happens.

25. Another name for parallel plates is a capacitor. Capacitors have different applications in many devices, such as in camera flash attachments, defibrillators used to return a person's heart to a normal beating pattern, and underneath the keys of some computer keyboards. Using the Internet and other sources, research capacitors. Pick one application and write a short report on your findings.

www.science.nelson.com

26. **Figure 13** shows a piece of magnetic tape passing near a playback head in a tape recorder. The playback head consists of a coil wrapped around a C-shaped ferromagnetic core. Describe how this playback head works.

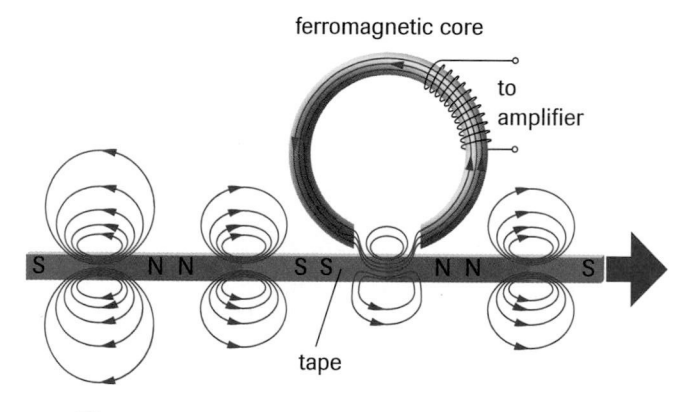

Figure 13

27. A degausser is a device that is used to demagnetize permanently magnetized materials. Using the Internet and other sources, investigate how these devices work. Prepare a short oral presentation on your findings.

www.science.nelson.com

28. Birds use the magnetic field of Earth to navigate over long distances. Using the Internet and other sources, investigate this application or any other way that animals use magnetism, and write a short report on the current research.

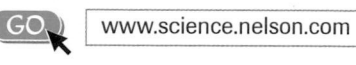
www.science.nelson.com

Extension

29. A small particle of charge q_1 and initial velocity $\vec{v}_1$ approaches a stationary charge q_2 (**Figure 14**). Create graphs of the kinetic energy of the moving charge, the electric potential energy of each charge, and the total energy of each charge, for different values of y (ranging from zero, through large compared to the radius of the charge, to very large). How does the value of y affect each quantity? You may use simulations or any other method to investigate.

Figure 14

30. Research how principles of gravitational, electric, and magnetic fields are used to investigate astronomical objects such as stars, quasars, and black holes. Make a poster showing how these concepts are involved in researching these objects and what scientists have learned about them.

31. A point charge of $+q$ is placed 3 cm to the left of a point charge of $-4q$, as in **Figure 15**. Determine the location where a third point charge will experience no force.

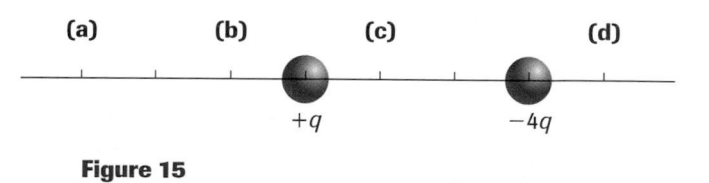

Figure 15

 Sir Isaac Newton Contest Question

The Wave Nature of Light

Mike Lazaridis
Co-founder of RIM

Wireless communication is an integral part of our lives. Billions of people use radio, television, satellites, cell phones, and mobile communications devices each day. A leader in this world of wireless communication is Research In Motion (RIM), based in Waterloo, Ontario. The current president and co-chief executive officer of RIM, electrical engineer Mike Lazaridis, was also one of its founders. Thanks to the efforts of Lazaridis and his colleagues, RIM holds many of the key patents for radio technologies and is a world leader in the mobile communications market.

Lazaridis knows the connection between theory and application. "Just about everything that we value in our great industrial growth today has come about because of theoretical physical studies," he says. The discoveries of scientists in the last 200 years, including Young, Maxwell, Hertz, and Marconi, form the basis of our knowledge today. "That's the basis of radio," he says. "Without their work we wouldn't have a wireless society." Lazaridis believes we must invest more in fundamental research, a conviction he has backed with a donation of $100 million to found the Perimeter Institute for Theoretical Physics, not far from the University of Waterloo. At any one time, this institute, with a mandate of fundamental research, houses up to 40 internationally renowned scientists.

▶ Overall Expectations

In this unit, you will be able to

- demonstrate an understanding of the wave model of electromagnetic radiation and describe how it explains diffraction patterns, interference, and polarization

- perform experiments relating the wave model of light and technical applications of electromagnetic radiation to the phenomena of refraction, diffraction, interference, and polarization

- analyze phenomena involving light and colour, explain them in terms of the wave model of light, and explain how this model provides a basis for developing technological devices

ARE YOU READY?

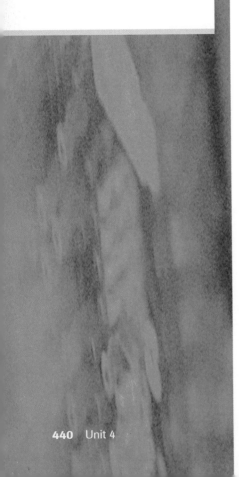

▸ **Prerequisites**

Concepts

- properties of electromagnetic radiation, including diffraction, interference, and polarization
- wave and particle theories of light
- real-world applications of electromagnetic radiation

Skills

- describe schematically
- describe mathematically
- calculate
- define
- solve for an unknown
- apply trigonometric functions
- use SI units

Knowledge and Understanding

1. Parallel rays of light are incident on a plane mirror, as in **Figure 1**. Copy the diagram into your notes and draw in the reflected rays.

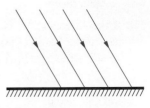

Figure 1
For question 1

2. Choose the correct alternatives in the following statements: "Rays of light travelling from air into glass at an oblique angle *speed up/slow down* when they reach the glass. The change in speed causes them to bend *away from/toward* the normal."

3. **Figure 2** shows light passing from water into glass and then into air. Copy the diagram into your notebook and sketch the refracted ray in both glass and air.

4. Light travels from air into diamond with an angle of incidence of 60.0°. The angle of refraction is 21.0°.
   (a) What is the index of refraction of the diamond?
   (b) If the speed of light in air is 3.00×10^8 m/s, calculate the speed of light in diamond.
   (c) What would happen if the light were to travel from the interior of the diamond to air at an angle of incidence of 60.0°? Justify your answer with a calculation.

5. Light is travelling from glass to air. Sketch what you will see if the angle of incidence in glass is (a) less than the critical angle and (b) greater than the critical angle.

6. Sketch the dispersion of white light into the colours of the spectrum using a prism.

7. Distinguish between longitudinal and transverse waves.

8. **Figure 3** shows a cross section of a transverse wave. Copy the diagram into your notebook.
   (a) Name the parts or properties of the wave indicated by the labels A, B, C, and D.
   (b) Label a point F that is in phase with the labelled point E.
   (c) If the wave is moving to the left, draw a vector to represent the instantaneous velocity of a particle in the medium at point E.
   (d) Calculate the period of the wave if it makes 10 vibrations in 2.0 s.

9. A certain wave source has a frequency of 3.0 Hz. The waves have a speed of 5.0 m/s. What is the distance between adjacent troughs?

10. A pulse is sent along a thin rope attached to a thick rope. The thick rope, in turn, is fixed firmly to a wall, as in **Figure 4**. Copy the diagram into your notebook.

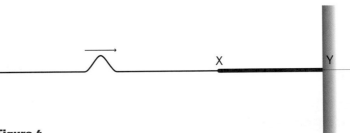

X   Y

Figure 4

   (a) Sketch what you would see after the pulse has passed completely through point X.
   (b) Sketch what you would see after the pulse is reflected at point Y.
   (c) Sketch what you would see after the reflected pulse passes through point X.

11. List the three conditions necessary for two pulses to completely interfere destructively.

12. In an experiment to find the speed of waves in a rope, a standing wave pattern is established as in **Figure 5**. The vibrating end makes 90 complete vibrations in one minute. Calculate (a) the wavelength of the waves and (b) the speed of the waves.

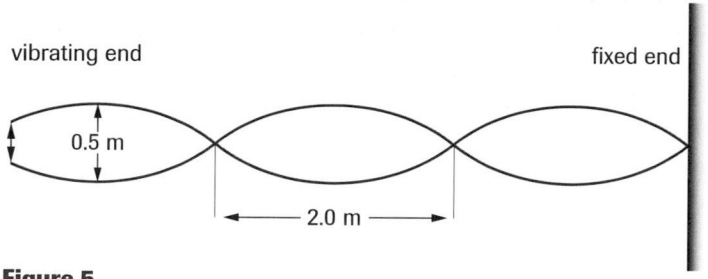

Figure 5

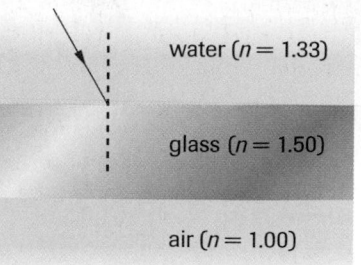
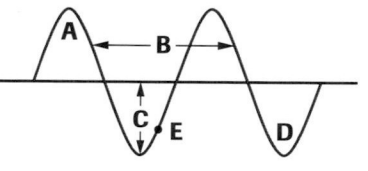

Figure 2
For question 3

Inquiry and Communication

13. **Figure 6** presents observations of diffraction in a ripple tank. What conclusions about diffraction do these observations suggest?

(a)   (b)   (c)

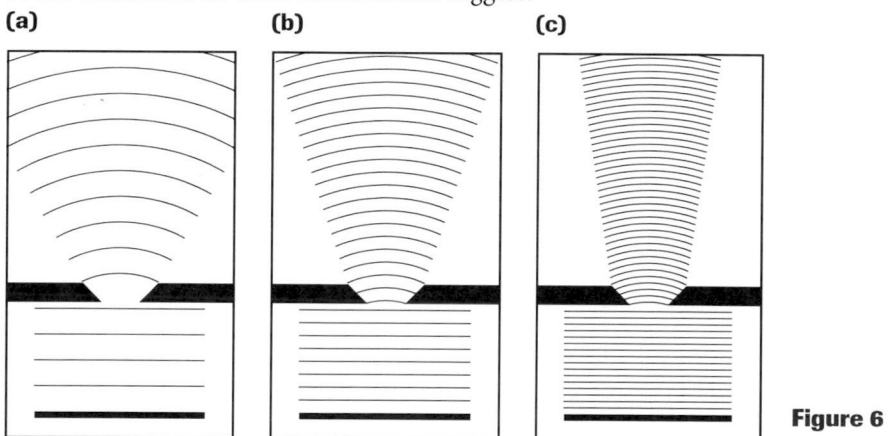

Figure 6

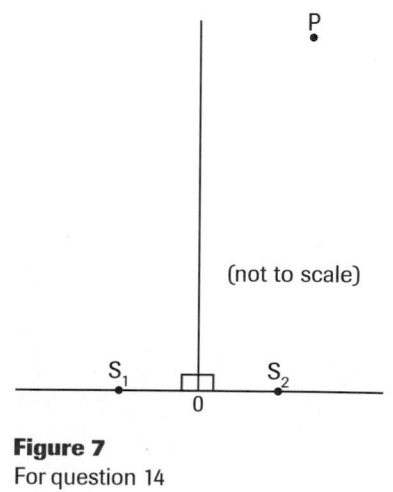

Figure 3
For question 8

14. In **Figure 7**, S_1 and S_2 are two point sources situated 6.0 cm apart, vibrating in phase, and producing wavelengths of 1.2 cm. P is a point on a nodal line (a line of destructive interference). What are possible path differences ($PS_1 - PS_2$), expressed in wavelengths? Explain how you reached your answers.

Math Skills

15. Rearrange the following equation to yield an expression for λ:
$$x_n = \left(n - \frac{1}{2}\right) L \left(\frac{\lambda}{d}\right)$$

16. Given the following equation and the values $n = 3$, $\lambda = 632$ nm, and $d = 10.0\ \mu m$, use a calculator to find θ to the correct number of significant figures:
$$\sin \theta_n = \left(n - \frac{1}{2}\right) \frac{\lambda}{d}$$

Figure 7
For question 14

Technical Skills and Safety

17. What precautions are necessary when working with bright sources of light, such as the Sun, a welding torch, or a laser? Explain.

Waves and Light

▶ **In this chapter, you will be able to**

- analyze and interpret the properties of two-dimensional mechanical waves in a ripple tank and relate them to light

- derive and apply equations involving the speed, wavelength, frequency, and refractive index of waves and apply them to the behaviour light

- analyze two-point-source interference patterns in a ripple tank and in the interference of light (Young's experiment) using diagrams

- derive and apply equations relating the properties of wave interference and wavelength

- outline the historical development of the particle and wave theories of light, including the development of new technologies and discoveries, and summarize the successes and failures of each theory

- apply the wave theory to the property of dispersion and determine the wavelengths of the colours of the visible spectrum

Light is not only energy but it is also a messenger: it carries information from distant stars and other celestial objects (**Figure 1**). This information arrives, not just as visible light, but as a host of other electromagnetic radiations, such as radio waves, X rays, and cosmic rays.

Everyday we hear about fibre optics, lasers, and light-emitting diodes used in communication; all these technologies use light for their operation. But how? How is the light energy transmitted from its source?

This was a difficult question for scientists to answer. There were two opposing camps: some believed that light travels as a wave; others believed it travels as a particle. The evidence seemed to favour one side and then the other until 1830, when most physicists accepted the wave theory. By the end of the nineteenth century, visible light was considered to be only one type of electromagnetic wave. But at the beginning of the twentieth century it was shown that light had a particle and a wave nature.

In this chapter, we will investigate the evidence for both theories. We will also use the wave theory to reveal some properties of light not commonly observed. Our investigations will help prepare the way for Chapter 10, in which we examine modern technological applications of the wave aspect of light, such as CDs, DVDs, and holography.

💡 REFLECT on your learning ▼

1. What conditions do you think produce the phenomenon shown in **Figure 2**?

2. What do you think determines the particular colours we see?

3. Recall that sound waves from speakers vibrating in phase interfere and that areas of lower intensity, which lie along a nodal line, and areas of higher intensity were heard in front of the speakers. What would the nodal lines look like if the speakers were replaced with light sources oscillating in phase?

4. What do you think the dark vertical lines on the photograph in **Figure 2** represent?

Figure 2
The wave theory of light explains this dramatic effect in a simple way.

Figure 1
This Hubble Space Telescope image shows spiral galaxy NGC 4603. The HST gathers light of various wavelengths, enabling scientists to measure precise distances to far-flung galaxies.

▶ TRY THIS activity

Diffraction and Interference of Light

For this activity you will need a prepared slit plate, a showcase lamp, and red and green filters.

1. Examine the slit plate and select a pair of double slits.
2. Holding the double slits vertically in front of one eye, look at a showcase lamp covered with a red filter. Describe what you see.
3. Repeat step 2, using the green filter. Describe what you see.
4. Repeat step 3 with a different slit pair. Describe what you see.

(a) Which slit-pair width produced the wider pattern for a single choice of colour?

(b) Which colour produced the wider pattern for a single choice of slit-pair width?

(c) How do you know that diffraction and interference of light have occurred?

You have just recreated a key experiment in the development of the wave theory of light. You will understand the experiment thoroughly by the end of this chapter.

⚛ **INVESTIGATION 9.1.1**

Transmission, Reflection, and Refraction of Water Waves in a Ripple Tank
How can we view waves to study them? How are waves transmitted, reflected, and refracted in a ripple tank?

It is difficult to study the properties of waves for sound, light, and radio because we cannot view the waves directly. However, if we use a ripple tank, not only can we view the waves directly, but we can create most conditions needed to demonstrate the properties of **transverse waves** in this two-dimension space. Investigation 9.1.1, in the Lab Activities section at the end of this chapter, provides you with an opportunity to study the properties of waves in a ripple tank in order to better understand and predict similar behaviours and relationships for other waves. ⚛ ■

Transmission

A wave originating from a point source is circular, whereas a wave originating from a linear source is straight. We confine ourselves for the moment to waves from sources with a constant frequency. As a wave moves away from its constant-frequency source, the spacing between successive crests or successive troughs—the wavelength—remains the same provided the speed of the wave does not change. A continuous crest or trough is referred to as a **wave front**. To show the direction of travel, or transmission, of a wave front, an arrow is drawn at right angles to the wave front (**Figure 1**). This line is called a **wave ray**. Sometimes we refer to wave rays instead of wave fronts when describing the behaviour of a wave.

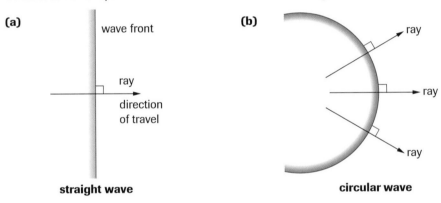

(a) wave front / ray / direction of travel / **straight wave**

(b) ray / ray / ray / **circular wave**

Figure 1
In both cases the wave ray is at 90° to the wave front.

transverse wave periodic disturbance where particles in the medium oscillate at right angles to the direction in which the wave travels

wave front the leading edge of a continuous crest or trough

wave ray a straight line, drawn perpendicular to a wave front, indicating the direction of transmission

When the speed decreases, as it does in shallow water, the wavelength decreases (**Figure 2**), since wavelength is directly proportional to speed ($\lambda \propto v$). When the frequency of a source is increased, the distance between successive crests becomes smaller, since wavelength is inversely proportional to frequency $\left(\lambda \propto \dfrac{1}{f}\right)$. Both proportionalities are consequences of the universal wave equation, $v = f\lambda$. This equation holds for all types of waves—one-dimensional, two-dimensional, and three-dimensional.

The wave travelling in deep water has a speed $v_1 = f_1\lambda_1$. Similarly, $v_2 = f_2\lambda_2$ for the wave travelling in shallow water. In a ripple tank, the frequency of a water wave is determined by the wave generator and does not change when the speed changes. Thus $f_1 = f_2$.

If we divide the first equation by the second equation, we get

$$\frac{v_1}{v_2} = \frac{f_1\lambda_1}{f_2\lambda_2}$$

However, $f_1 = f_2$. Therefore,

$$\frac{v_1}{v_2} = \frac{\lambda_1}{\lambda_2}$$

(a)

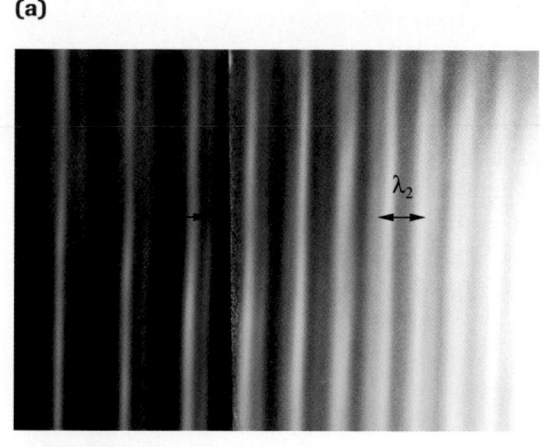

(b)

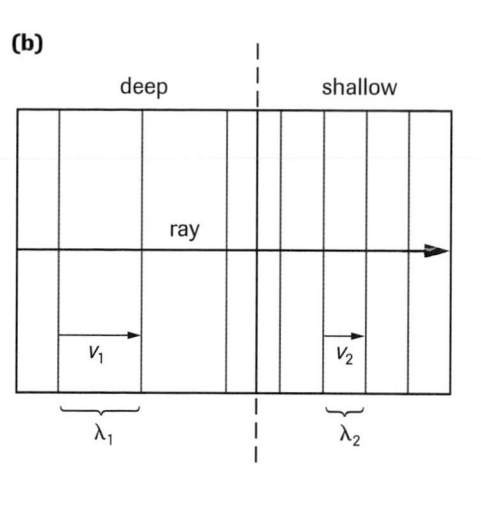

Figure 2
Periodic straight waves travelling from deep water to shallow water (left to right)

▶ *SAMPLE* problem *1*

A water wave has a wavelength of 2.0 cm in the deep section of a tank and 1.5 cm in the shallow section. If the speed of the wave in the shallow water is 12 cm/s, what is its speed in the deep water?

Solution

$\lambda_1 = 2.0$ cm

$\lambda_2 = 1.5$ cm

$v_2 = 12$ cm/s

$v_1 = ?$

$$\frac{v_1}{v_2} = \frac{\lambda_1}{\lambda_2}$$

$$v_1 = \left(\frac{\lambda_1}{\lambda_2}\right)v_2$$

$$= \left(\frac{2.0 \text{ cm}}{1.5 \text{ cm}}\right)12 \text{ cm/s}$$

$$v_1 = 16 \text{ cm/s}$$

The speed of the wave in deep water is 16 cm/s.

▶ Practice

Understanding Concepts

1. The speed and the wavelength of a water wave in deep water are 18.0 cm/s and 2.0 cm, respectively. The speed in shallow water is 10.0 cm/s. Find the corresponding wavelength.

2. A wave travels 0.75 times as fast in shallow water as it does in deep water. Find the wavelength of the wave in deep water if its wavelength is 2.7 cm in shallow water.

3. In question 1, what are the respective frequencies in deep and shallow water?

Answers

1. 1.1 cm

2. 3.6 cm

3. 9.0 Hz; 9.0 Hz

Reflection from a Straight Barrier

A straight wave front travels in the "wave ray" direction perpendicular to the wave front, but how will it behave when encountering obstacles? When a straight wave front runs into a straight reflective barrier, head on, it is reflected back along its original path (**Figure 3**). If a wave encounters a straight barrier obliquely (i.e., at an angle other than 90°), the wave front is likewise reflected obliquely. The angle formed by the incident wave front and the normal is equal to the angle formed by the reflected wave front and the normal. These angles are called the **angle of incidence** (θ_i) and the **angle of reflection** (θ_r), respectively (**Figure 4**). Reflection leaves wavelength, speed, and frequency unchanged.

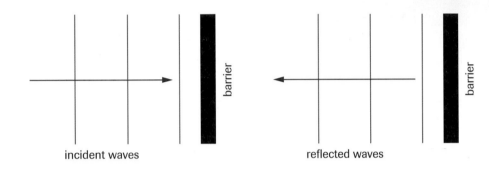

incident waves   reflected waves

Figure 3
A straight wave front meeting a straight barrier head on is reflected
back along its original path.

(a)

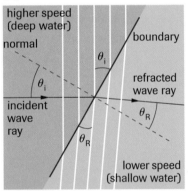

(b)

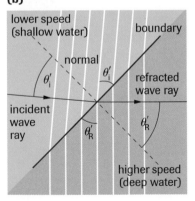

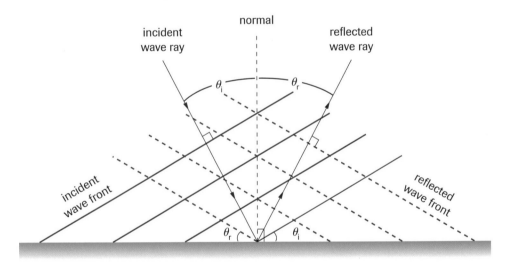

Figure 4
When a wave encounters a straight barrier obliquely, rather than
head on, the angle of incidence equals the angle of reflection.

Figure 5
(a) When water waves travel
obliquely into a slower medium,
the wave ray bends toward the
normal.
(b) If the new medium is a faster
one, the wave ray bends away
from the normal.

Refraction

When a wave travels from deep water to shallow water in such a way that it meets the boundary between the two depths straight on, no change in direction occurs. On the other hand, if a wave meets the boundary at an angle, the direction of travel does change. This phenomenon is called **refraction** (**Figure 5**).

We usually use wave rays to describe refraction. The **normal** is a line drawn at right angles to a boundary at the point where an incident wave ray strikes the boundary. The angle formed by an incident wave ray and the normal is called the angle of incidence, θ_i. The angle formed by the normal and the refracted wave ray is called the **angle of refraction**, θ_R.

When a wave travels at an angle into a medium in which its speed decreases, the refracted wave ray is bent (refracted) toward the normal, as in **Figure 5(a)**. If the wave travels at an angle into a medium in which its speed increases, the refracted wave ray is bent away from the normal, as in **Figure 5(b)**.

Figure 6 shows geometrically that θ_i is equal to the angle between the incident wave front and the normal and that θ_R is equal to the angle between the refracted wave front and the normal. In the ripple tank, it is easier to measure the angles between the wave rays and the boundary, that is, θ_i' and θ_R'.

To analyze wave fronts refracted at a boundary, the angles of incidence and refraction can be determined using the equations $\sin \theta_i = \dfrac{\lambda_1}{xy}$ and $\sin \theta_R = \dfrac{\lambda_2}{xy}$, respectively (**Figure 7**).

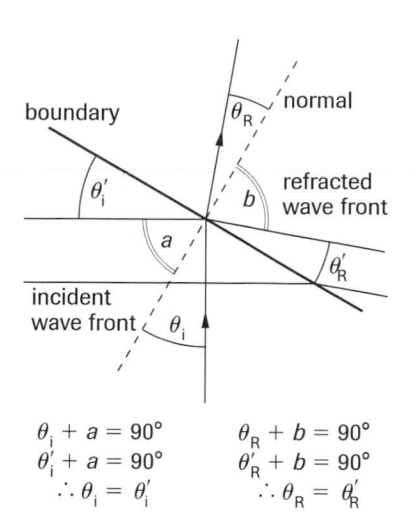

$$\theta_i + a = 90° \qquad \theta_R + b = 90°$$
$$\theta_i' + a = 90° \qquad \theta_R' + b = 90°$$
$$\therefore \theta_i = \theta_i' \qquad \therefore \theta_R = \theta_R'$$

Figure 6

normal a straight line drawn perpendicular to a barrier struck by a wave

angle of refraction (θ_R) the angle between the normal and the refracted ray, or between the refracted wave front and the boundary

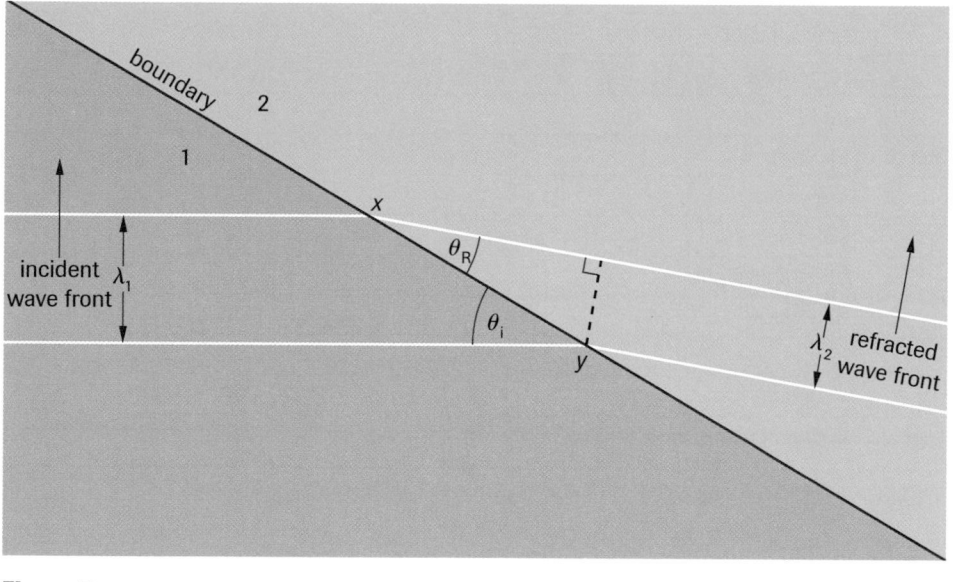

Figure 7

The ratio of the sines gives

$$\frac{\sin \theta_i}{\sin \theta_R} = \frac{\left(\dfrac{\lambda_1}{xy}\right)}{\left(\dfrac{\lambda_2}{xy}\right)}$$

which reduces to

$$\frac{\sin \theta_i}{\sin \theta_R} = \frac{\lambda_1}{\lambda_2}$$

For a specific change in medium, the ratio $\dfrac{\lambda_1}{\lambda_2}$ has a constant value. Recall Snell's law from optics, $\sin \theta_i \propto \sin \theta_R$. This equation can be converted to $\sin \theta_i = n \sin \theta_R$. The constant of proportionality (n) and the index of refraction (n) are one and the same thing.

Consequently, we can write

$$\frac{\sin \theta_i}{\sin \theta_R} = n$$

This relationship holds for waves of all types, including light, which we will see shortly. When light passes from a vacuum into a substance, n is called the **absolute index of refraction**. (See **Table 1** for a list of absolute indexes of refraction.) The value for the absolute index of refraction is so close to the value from air to a substance that we rarely distinguish between them. In this text, when we refer to the index of refraction, we will be referring to the absolute index of refraction.

Table 1 Approximate Absolute Indexes of Refraction for Various Substances*

Substance	Absolute Refractive Index
vacuum	1.000 000
air	1.000 29
ice	1.31
water	1.333
ethyl alcohol	1.36
turpentine	1.472
glass	1.50
Plexiglas	1.51
crown glass	1.52
polystyrene	1.59
carbon disulphide	1.628
flint glass	1.66
zircon	1.923
diamond	2.417
gallium phosphide	3.50

*Measured with a wavelength of 589 nm. Values may vary with physical conditions.

You will also recall that we derived a general equation for Snell's law that applies to any two substances:

$$n_1 \sin \theta_1 = n_2 \sin \theta_2$$

where n_1 is the index of refraction in the first medium, n_2 is the index of refraction in the second medium, and θ_1 and θ_2 are angles in each respective medium.

For waves we found that $\dfrac{\sin \theta_i}{\sin \theta_R} = \dfrac{\lambda_1}{\lambda_2}$, which we can generalize to $\dfrac{\sin \theta_1}{\sin \theta_2} = \dfrac{\lambda_1}{\lambda_2}$. But from the universal wave equation, $v = f\lambda$, we can show that $\dfrac{v_1}{v_2} = \dfrac{\lambda_1}{\lambda_2}$ since f is constant. Therefore, we can write

$$\frac{\sin \theta_1}{\sin \theta_2} = \frac{v_1}{v_2} = \frac{\lambda_1}{\lambda_2} = \frac{n_2}{n_1}$$

The following sample problems will illustrate the application of these relationships in both in the ripple tank and for light.

▶ **SAMPLE** problem **2**

A 5.0 Hz water wave, travelling at 31 cm/s in deep water, enters shallow water. The angle between the incident wave front in the deep water and the boundary between the deep and shallow regions is 50°. The speed of the wave in the shallow water is 27 cm/s. Find

(a) the angle of refraction in the shallow water

(b) the wavelength in shallow water

Solution

(a) $f = 5.0$ Hz $\qquad \theta_1 = 50.0°$

$\quad v_1 = 31$ cm/s $\qquad \theta_2 = ?$

$\quad v_2 = 27$ cm/s

$$\frac{\sin \theta_1}{\sin \theta_2} = \frac{v_1}{v_2}$$

$$\sin \theta_2 = \left(\frac{v_2}{v_1}\right) \sin \theta_1$$

$$\sin \theta_2 = \left(\frac{27 \text{ cm/s}}{31 \text{ cm/s}}\right) \sin 50.0°$$

$$\theta_2 = 41.9, \text{ or } 42°$$

The angle of refraction is 42°.

(b) $\qquad \lambda_2 = \dfrac{v_2}{f_2} \quad$ but $f_2 = f_1 = 5.0$ Hz

$$\qquad\quad = \frac{27 \text{ cm/s}}{5.0 \text{ Hz}}$$

$$\lambda_2 = 5.4 \text{ cm}$$

The wavelength in shallow water is 5.4 cm.

▶ **SAMPLE** problem **3**

For a light ray travelling from glass into water, find

(a) the angle of refraction in water, if the angle of incidence in glass is 30.0°

(b) the speed of light in water

Solution

From **Table 1**,

$n_g = n_1 = 1.50 \qquad \theta_g = \theta_1 = 30.0°$

$n_w = n_2 = 1.333 \qquad \theta_w = \theta_2 = ?$

(a) $\qquad \dfrac{\sin \theta_1}{\sin \theta_2} = \dfrac{n_2}{n_1}$

$$\frac{\sin \theta_g}{\sin \theta_w} = \frac{n_w}{n_g}$$

$$\frac{\sin 30.0°}{\sin \theta_w} = \frac{1.333}{1.50}$$

$$\sin \theta_w = \frac{1.50 \sin 30.0°}{1.333}$$

$$\theta_w = 34.3°$$

The angle of refraction in water is 34.3°.

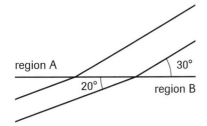

region A

30°

20°

region B

Figure 8
For question 7

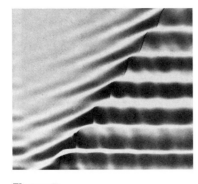

Figure 9
At higher angles of incidence, there is reflection as well as refraction. You can see such partial reflection-partial refraction on the right.

total internal reflection the reflection of light in an optically denser medium; it occurs when the angle of incidence in the denser medium is greater than a certain critical angle

(b) $n_a = n_1 = 1.00$

$n_w = n_2 = 1.333$

$v_1 = c = 3.00 \times 10^8$ m/s

$v_2 = ?$

$$\frac{v_1}{v_2} = \frac{n_2}{n_1}$$

$$v_2 = \frac{n_1 v_1}{n_2}$$

$$= \frac{(1.00)(3.00 \times 10^8 \text{ m/s})}{1.333}$$

$$v_2 = 2.26 \times 10^8 \text{ m/s}$$

The speed of light in water is 2.26×10^8 m/s.

▶ Practice

Understanding Concepts

4. A wave in a ripple tank passes from a deep to a shallow region with $\theta_1 = 60°$ and $\theta_2 = 45°$. Calculate the ratios in the two media of (a) the wavelengths, (b) the speeds, and (c) the frequencies.

5. Water waves travelling at a speed of 28 cm/s enter deeper water at $\theta_1 = 40°$. Determine the speed in the deeper water if $\theta_2 = 46°$.

6. A 10.0-Hz water wave travels from deep water, where its speed is 38.0 cm/s, to shallow water, where its speed is 28.0 cm/s and $\theta_1 = 30°$. Find (a) the index of refraction, (b) the wavelengths in the two media, and (c) the angle of refraction in the shallow water.

7. A plane wave generator with a frequency of 6.0 Hz creates a water wave of wavelength 2.0 cm in region A of a ripple tank (**Figure 8**). The angle between the wave crests and the straight boundary between regions A and B is 30°. In region B the angle is 20°.
   (a) Use Snell's law to determine the refractive index of the two regions.
   (b) Find the speed in each region.

8. Light travels from crown glass into air. (Refer to **Table 1** for the indexes of refraction.) The angle of refraction in air is 60.0°. Calculate the angle of incidence in the crown glass.

9. If the index of refraction for diamond is 2.42, what will the angle of refraction be in diamond for an angle of incidence of 60.0° in water?

Partial Reflection–Partial Refraction

When refraction occurs, some of the energy usually reflects as well as refracts. This phenomenon was referred to in optics as partial reflection–partial refraction, a description that can also be used when referring to this behaviour in waves. We can demonstrate the same behaviour in a ripple tank, with waves travelling from deep to shallow water, provided we make the angle of incidence large, as in **Figure 9**.

The amount of reflection is more noticeable when a wave travels from shallow to deep water, where the speed increases and again becomes more pronounced as the angle of incidence increases. **Figure 10** shows that an incident angle is reached where the wave is refracted at an angle approaching 90°. For still larger incident angles there is no refraction at all, with all the wave energy being reflected; this behaviour of light is referred to as **total internal reflection**. This phenomenon is analogous to the total internal reflection of light.

(a)

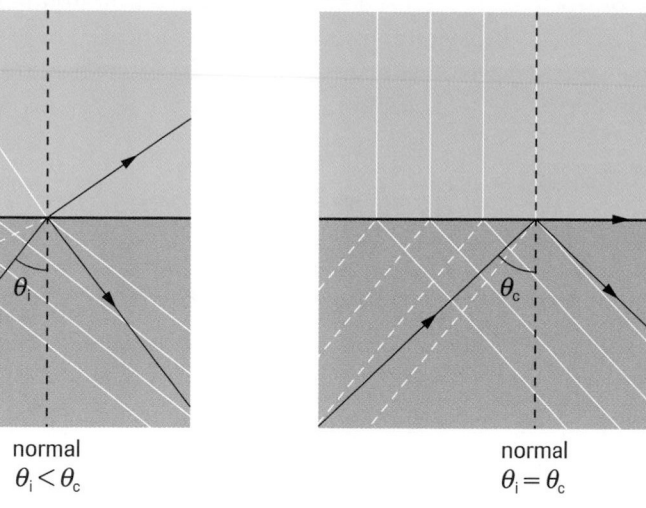

normal
$\theta_i < \theta_c$

(b)

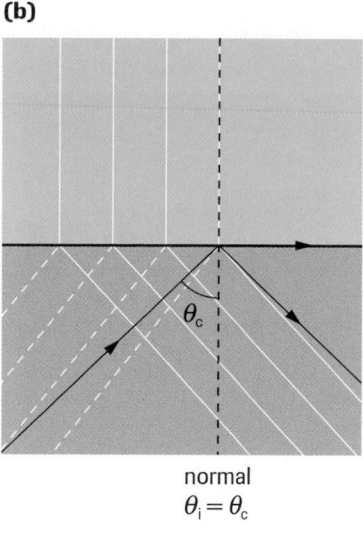

normal
$\theta_i = \theta_c$

(c)

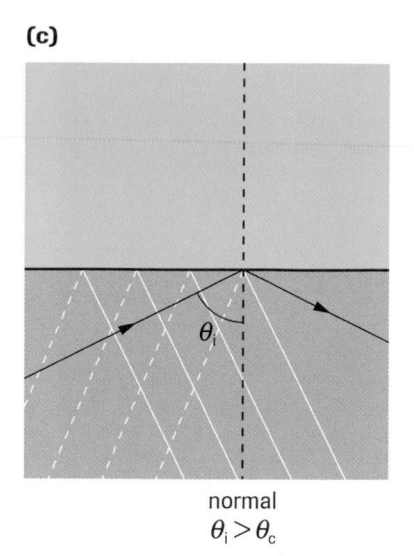

normal
$\theta_i > \theta_c$

Figure 10
(a) Partial refraction–partial reflection
(b) At the critical angle
(c) Total internal reflection

We have remarked that the frequency of a wave does not in general change when its speed changes. Since $\dfrac{v_1}{v_2} = \dfrac{\lambda_1}{\lambda_2}$, you might expect that the index of refraction and the amount of bending would not change for waves of different frequencies, provided the medium remains the same (e.g., water of the same depth in both cases).

Figure 11, however, shows that indexes of refraction do, in general, depend on wavelength. In **Figure 11(a)**, the low-frequency (long-wavelength) waves are refracted, as indicated by a rod placed on the screen below the transparent ripple tank. The rod is exactly parallel to the refracted wave fronts. In **Figure 11(b)**, the frequency has been increased (the wavelength decreased), with the rod left in the same position. The rod is no longer parallel to the refracted wave fronts. It appears that the amount of bending, and hence the index of refraction, is affected slightly by the frequency of a wave. We can conclude that, since the index of refraction represents a ratio of speeds in two media, the speed of the waves in at least one of those media must depend on their frequency. Such a medium, in which the speed of the waves depends on the frequency, is called a *dispersive medium*.

Figure 11
(a) The refraction of straight waves, with a rod marker placed parallel to the refracted wave fronts.
(b) The refracted wave fronts of the higher frequency waves are no longer parallel to the marker.

(a)

(b)

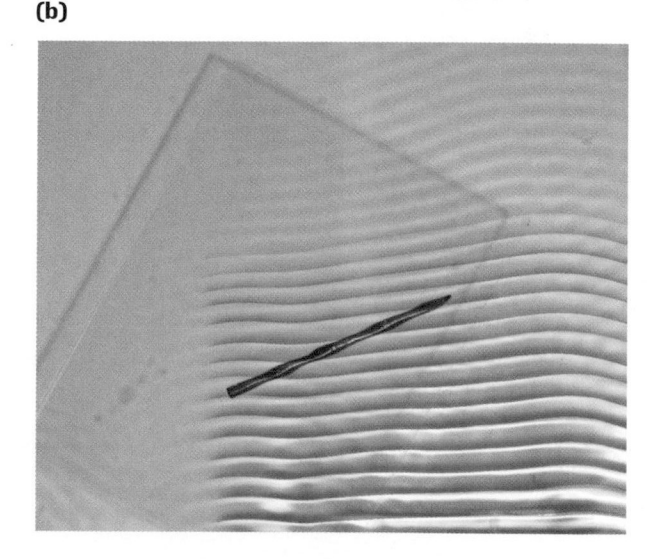

We stated previously that the speed of waves depends only on the medium. This statement now proves to be an idealization. Nevertheless, the idealization is a good approximation of the actual behaviour of waves, since the dispersion of a wave is the result of minute changes in its speed. For many applications, it is acceptable to make the assumption that frequency does not affect the speed of waves.

<table>
<tr><td>**SUMMARY**</td><td>**Waves in Two Dimensions**</td></tr>
</table>

- The wavelength of a periodic wave is directly proportional to its speed.
- The frequency of a periodic wave is determined by the source and does not change as the wave moves through different media or encounters reflective barriers.
- All periodic waves obey the universal wave equation, $v = f\lambda$.
- The index of refraction for a pair of media is the ratio of the speeds or the ratio of the wavelengths in the two media $\left(\dfrac{v_1}{v_2} = \dfrac{\lambda_1}{\lambda_2}\right)$.
- Snell's law $\left(n = \dfrac{\sin \theta_i}{\sin \theta_R}\right)$ holds for waves and for light.
- When a wave passes from one medium to another, the wavelength changes and partial reflection–partial refraction can occur.

▶ Section 9.1 Questions

Understanding Concepts

1. Straight wave fronts in the deep region of a ripple tank have a speed of 24 cm/s and a frequency of 4.0 Hz. The angle between the wave fronts and the straight boundary of the deep region is 40°. The wave speed in the shallow region beyond the boundary is 15 cm/s. Calculate
   (a) the angle the refracted wave front makes with the boundary
   (b) the wavelength in the shallow water

2. The following observations are made when a straight periodic wave crosses a boundary between deep and shallow water: 10 wave fronts cross the boundary every 5.0 s, and the distance across 3 wave fronts is 24.0 cm in deep water and 18.0 cm in shallow water.
   (a) Calculate the speed of the wave in deep water and in shallow water.
   (b) Calculate the refractive index.

3. Straight wave fronts with a frequency of 5.0 Hz, travelling at 30 cm/s in deep water, move into shallow water. The angle between the incident wave front in the deep water and the straight boundary between deep and shallow water is 50°. The speed of the wave in the shallow water is 27 cm/s.
   (a) Calculate the angle of refraction in the shallow water.
   (b) Calculate the index of refraction.
   (c) Calculate the wavelength in the shallow water.

4. Straight wave fronts in the deep end of a ripple tank have a wavelength of 2.0 cm and a frequency of 11 Hz. The wave fronts strike the boundary of the shallow section of the tank at an angle of 60° and are refracted at an angle of 30° to the boundary. Calculate the speed of the wave in the deep water and in the shallow water.

5. The speed of a sound wave in cold air (−20°C) is 320 m/s; in warm air (37°C), the speed is 354 m/s. If the wave front in cold air is nearly linear, find θ_R in the warm air if θ_i is 30°.

6. A straight boundary separates two bodies of rock. Longitudinal earthquake waves, travelling through the first body at 7.75 km/s, meet the boundary at an angle of incidence of 20.0°. The wave speed in the second body is 7.72 km/s. Calculate the angle of refraction.

7. Under what conditions do wave rays in water and light rays exhibit total internal reflection?

8. Light travels from air into a certain transparent material of refractive index 1.30. The angle of refraction is 45°. What is the angle of incidence?

9. A ray of light passes from water, with index of refraction 1.33, into carbon disulphide, with index of refraction 1.63. The angle of incidence is 30.0°. Calculate the angle of refraction.

Periodic straight wave fronts in a ripple tank travel in a straight line as long as the depth of the water is constant and the water is free of obstacles. If the waves pass by a sharp edge of an obstacle or through a small opening or aperture in an obstacle, the waves spread out, as illustrated in **Figure 1(a)**. This bending is called **diffraction**. One of the easiest ways to observe the properties of the diffraction of waves is with a ripple tank. Investigation 9.2.1, in the Lab Activities section at the end of this chapter, provides an opportunity for you to observe and interpret the phenomenon of diffraction.

How much the waves are diffracted at an opening in a barrier depends on both their wavelength and the size of the opening. **Figures 1(b)** and **(c)** show that shorter wavelengths are diffracted slightly, while longer wavelengths are diffracted to a greater extent by the same edge or opening.

diffraction the bending effect on a wave's direction as it passes through an opening or by an obstacle

INVESTIGATION 9.2.1

Diffraction of Water Waves (p. 482)
What factors determine how much a wave will diffract? How do these factors relate to one another?

(a)   **(b)** short wavelengths   **(c)** long wavelengths

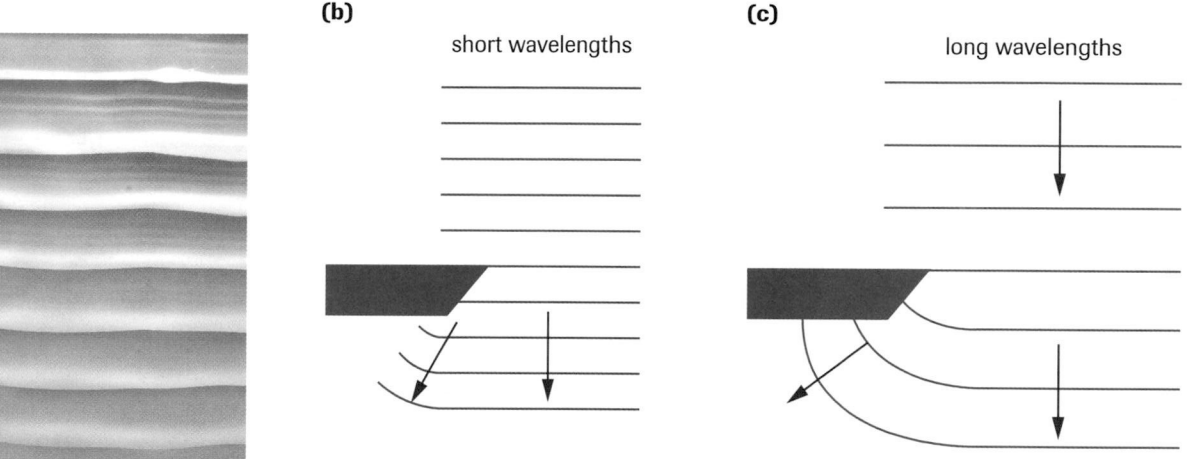

Figure 1
When waves travel by an edge, longer wavelengths are diffracted more than shorter wavelengths.

You can predict how diffraction will vary if you keep the width of the aperture constant and try waves of different wavelengths. In each of the situations in **Figure 2**, the width *w* of the aperture is the same. In **Figure 2(a)**, the wavelength λ is approximately a third of *w*. Only part of the straight wave fronts pass through, to be converted to small sectors of a series of circular wave fronts. In **(b)**, λ is approximately half of *w* and there is considerably more diffraction. There are still shadow areas to the left and right, where none of the waves are diffracted. In **(c)**, λ is approximately three-quarters of *w*. Here, the small sections of the straight wave that get through the opening are almost entirely converted

(a) 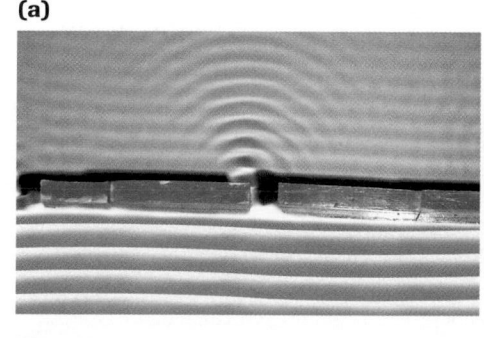   **(b)** 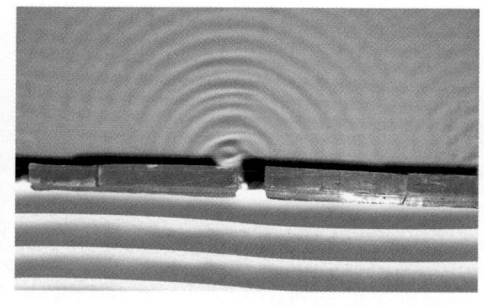   **(c)**

Figure 2
As the wavelength increases, the amount of diffraction increases.

into circular wave fronts. The wave has bent around the side of the opening, filling almost the entire region beyond the barrier.

When we keep λ fixed and change w, we find that the amount of diffraction increases as the size of the aperture decreases. In both instances, if waves are to be strongly diffracted they must pass through an opening of width comparable to their wavelength or smaller $\left(w \le \lambda; \text{ equivalently } \frac{\lambda}{w} \ge 1\right)$. This means that if the wavelength is very small, a very narrow aperture is required to produce significant diffraction (**Figure 3**).

(a)

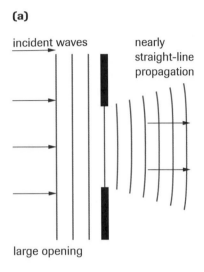

large opening

(b)

(c)

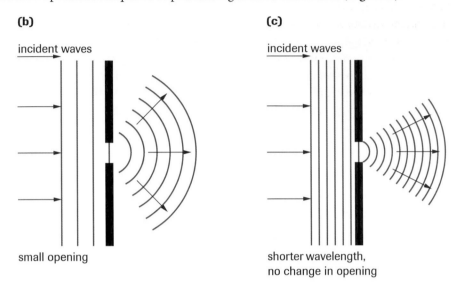

Figure 3
In **(a)** and **(b)**, similar wavelengths are diffracted more through a smaller opening; in **(b)** and **(c)**, the openings are the same size but the wavelengths are shorter in **(c)**, and there is less diffraction.

Perhaps the most obvious example of the diffraction of waves occurs with sound. The sounds of a classroom can be heard through an open door, even though the students are out of sight and behind a wall. Sound waves are diffracted around the corner of the doorway primarily because they have long wavelengths, relative to the width of the opening. If a sound system is operating in the room, its low frequencies (the long wavelengths) are diffracted around the corner more than are its higher frequencies (the shorter wavelengths).

SUMMARY *Diffraction of Water Waves*

- Waves diffract when they pass by an obstacle or through a small opening.
- Waves of longer wavelength experience more diffraction than waves with a smaller wavelength.
- For a given opening or aperature, the amount of diffraction depends on the ratio $\frac{\lambda}{w}$. For observable diffraction, $\frac{\lambda}{w} \ge 1$.

▶ *Section 9.2 Questions*

Understanding Concepts

1. State the condition required to maximize the diffraction of waves through an aperature.

2. If waves with a wavelength of 2.0 m pass through an opening of 4.0 m in a breakwater barrier, will diffraction be noticeable?

3. Electromagnetic radiation with a wavelength of 6.3×10^{-4} m passes through a slit. Find the maximum slit width that will produce noticeable diffraction.

4. Will the electromagnetic radiation of question 3 be diffracted by slits wider than the width you calculated? Explain your answer.

Constructive and **destructive interference** may occur in two dimensions, sometimes producing fixed patterns of interference. To produce a fixed pattern, the interfering waves must have the same frequency (and thus the same wavelength) and also similar amplitudes. Standing waves in a string or rope, fixed at one end, illustrate interference in one dimension. Patterns of interference also occur between two identical waves when they interfere in a two-dimensional medium such as the water in a ripple tank.

Figure 1 shows two point sources vibrating with identical frequencies and amplitudes and in phase. As successive crests and troughs travel out from the two sources, they interfere with each other, sometimes crest on crest, sometimes trough on trough, and sometimes crest on trough, producing areas of constructive and destructive interference.

constructive interference occurs when waves build each other up, producing a resultant wave of greater amplitude than the given waves

destructive interference occurs when waves diminish one another, producing a resultant wave of lower amplitude than the given waves

nodal line a line of destructive interference

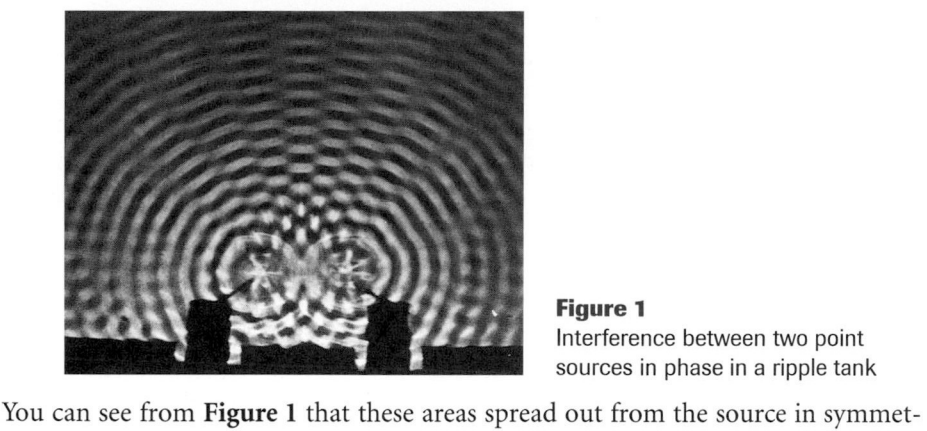

Figure 1
Interference between two point sources in phase in a ripple tank

You can see from **Figure 1** that these areas spread out from the source in symmetrical patterns, producing **nodal lines** and areas of constructive interference. When illuminated from above, the nodal lines appear on the surface below the water in the ripple tank as stationary grey areas. Between the nodal lines are areas of constructive interference that appear as alternating bright (double-crest) and dark (double-trough) lines of constructive interference. You can see these alternating areas of constructive and destructive interference in **Figure 2**. Although the nodal lines appear to be straight, their paths from the sources are actually hyperbolas.

Figure 2
The interference pattern between two identical sources (S₁ and S₂), vibrating in phase, is a symmetric pattern of hyperbolic lines of destructive interference (nodal lines) and areas of constructive interference.

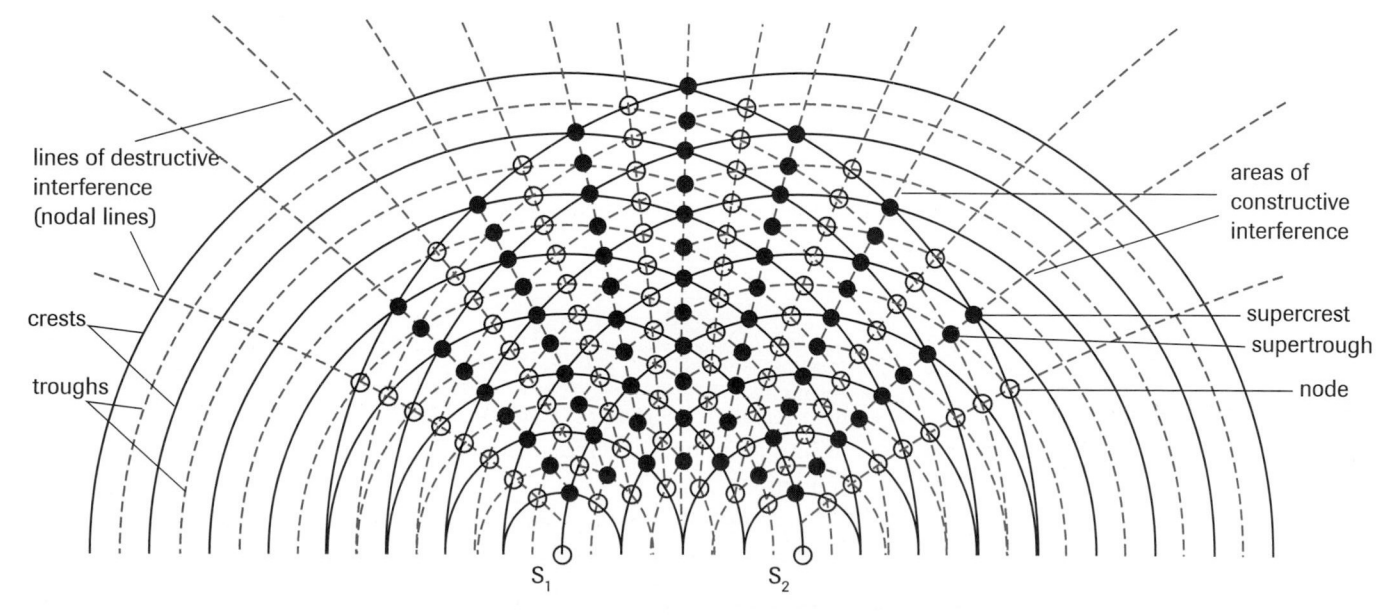

lines of destructive interference (nodal lines)

crests

troughs

areas of constructive interference

supercrest

supertrough

node

S₁   S₂

(a)

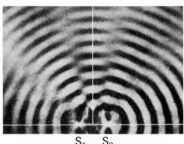

S_1 S_2

(b)

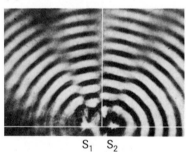

S_1 S_2

Figure 3
The effect of a phase delay on the interference pattern for two point sources. In **(a)** the sources are in phase; in **(b)** the phase delay is 180°.

difference in path length in an interference pattern, the absolute value of the difference between the distance of any point P from one source and the distance of the same point P from the other source: $|P_1S_1 - P_1S_2|$

This symmetrical pattern remains stationary, provided three factors do not change: the frequency of the two sources, the distance between the sources, and the relative phase of the sources. When the frequency of the sources is increased, the wavelength decreases, bringing the nodal lines closer together and increasing their number. If the distance between the two sources is increased, the number of nodal lines also increases. As you would expect, neither of these factors changes the symmetry of the pattern: provided the two sources continue to be in phase, an area of constructive interference runs along the right bisector, and equal numbers of nodal lines appear on the two sides of the right bisector. If other factors are kept constant, but the relative phase of the two sources changes, the pattern shifts (as in **Figure 3**), with the number of nodal lines remaining the same. For example, if S_1 is delayed, the pattern shifts to the left of the right bisector.

Mathematical Analysis of the Two-Point-Source Interference Pattern

The two-point-source interference pattern is useful because it allows direct measurement of the wavelength (since it is easy to keep the interference pattern relatively stationary). By taking a closer look at the two-point-source interference pattern, we can develop some mathematical relationships that will be useful in Section 9.5 and the next chapter for analyzing the interference of other kinds of waves.

Consider the ripple-tank interference pattern produced by a pair of identical point sources S_1 and S_2, vibrating in phase and separated by three wavelengths. In this pattern, there are an equal number of nodal lines on either side of the right bisector. These lines are numbered 1 and 2 on both sides of the right bisector (**Figure 4**). (So, for example, there are two nodal lines labelled $n = 1$: the first line on either side of the right bisector.) If we take a point P_1 on one of the first nodal lines and connect it to each of the two sources by the lines P_1S_1 and P_1S_2 as in **Figure 4**, we might find that $P_1S_1 = 4\lambda$ and $P_1S_2 = \frac{7}{2}\lambda$. The difference between these two distances, called the **difference in path length**, is

$$|P_1S_1 - P_1S_2| = \frac{1}{2}\lambda$$

This relationship holds for any point on the first nodal line on either side of the right bisector. (We take absolute values when expressing the difference in path length because our only interest is in the size of the discrepancy in lengths. We do not care which length is the greater of the two.) When we measure in the same way the difference in path length for any point P_2 on a nodal line second from the centre, we find that

$$|P_2S_1 - P_2S_2| = \frac{3}{2}\lambda$$

Continuing this procedure, we can arrive at a general relationship for any point P on the nth nodal line:

$$|P_nS_1 - P_nS_2| = \left(n - \frac{1}{2}\right)\lambda \qquad \text{Equation (1)}$$

You can use this relationship to find the wavelength of interfering waves in the ripple tank by locating a point on a specific nodal line, measuring the path lengths, and substituting in Equation (1).

If the wavelengths are too small or the point P is too far away from the two sources, the difference in path length is too small to be measured accurately. To handle these two cases (which could occur either individually or together), we need another technique.

For any point P$_n$, the difference in path length is the distance AS$_1$ in **Figure 5(a)**:

$$|P_nS_1 - P_nS_2| = AS_1$$

Figure 5(b) shows that when P$_n$ is very far away compared to the separation d of the two sources, the lines P$_n$S$_1$ and P$_n$S$_2$ are very nearly parallel; that is, as P$_n \to \infty$, P$_n$S$_1$ and P$_n$S$_2$ become nearly parallel. In this case, the line AS$_2$ forms a right angle with both of these lines, as illustrated, making the triangle S$_1$S$_2$A a right-angled triangle (**Figure 5(b)**). Therefore, the difference in path length can be expressed in terms of the sine of the angle θ_n:

$$\sin \theta_n = \frac{AS_1}{d}$$
$$AS_1 = d \sin \theta_n \qquad \text{Equation (2)}$$

But AS$_1$ = P$_n$S$_1$ − P$_n$S$_2$. Therefore, by combining Equations (1) and (2) we get

$$d \sin \theta_n = \left(n - \frac{1}{2}\right)\lambda$$

$$\boxed{\sin \theta_n = \left(n - \frac{1}{2}\right)\frac{\lambda}{d}}$$

where θ_n is the angle for the nth nodal line, λ is the wavelength, and d is the distance between the sources.

This equation allows us to make a quick approximation of the wavelength for a specific interference pattern. Since $\sin \theta_n$ cannot be greater than 1, $\left(n - \frac{1}{2}\right)\frac{\lambda}{d}$ cannot be greater than 1. The largest value of n that satisfies this condition is the number of nodal lines on either side of the right bisector. Measuring d and counting the number of nodal lines gives an approximation for the wavelength. For example, if d is 2.0 m and the number of nodal lines is 4, the wavelength can be approximated as follows:

$$\sin \theta_n = \left(n - \frac{1}{2}\right)\frac{\lambda}{d}$$

Or, since the maximum possible value of $\sin \theta_n$ is 1,

$$\left(n - \frac{1}{2}\right)\frac{\lambda}{d} \approx 1$$
$$\left(4 - \frac{1}{2}\right)\frac{\lambda}{2.0\,\text{m}} \approx 1$$
$$\lambda \approx 0.57\,\text{cm}$$

In the ripple tank, it is relatively easy to measure the angle θ_n. The measurement is not, however, easy for light waves (Section 9.5), where both the wavelength and the distance between the sources are very small and the nodal lines are close together. We therefore seek a technique for measuring $\sin \theta_n$ without measuring θ_n itself.

We noted earlier that a nodal line is a hyperbola. But at positions on nodal lines relatively far away from the two sources, the nodal lines are nearly straight, appearing to originate from the midpoint of a line joining the two sources.

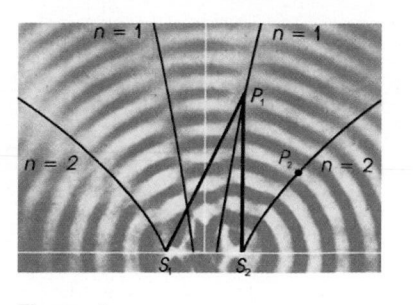

Figure 4
For any point P$_1$ on the first nodal line, the difference in path length from P$_1$ to S$_1$ and from P$_1$ to S$_2$ is $\frac{1}{2}\lambda$. For any point P$_2$ on the second nodal line, the difference in path length is $\frac{3}{2}\lambda$.

(a)

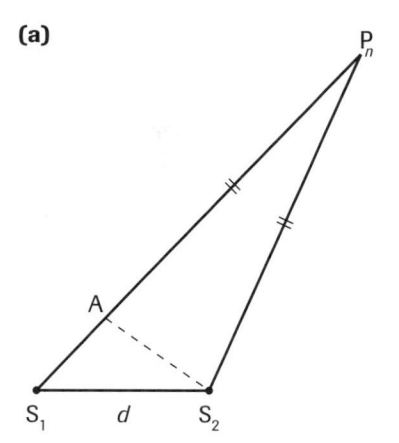

(b)

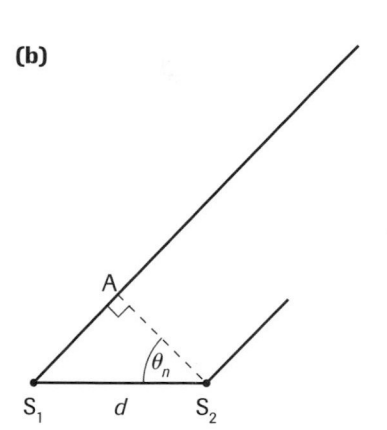

Figure 5
(a) Point P$_n$ is near.
(b) Point P$_n$ is far enough away that P$_n$S$_1$ and P$_n$S$_2$ are considered parallel.

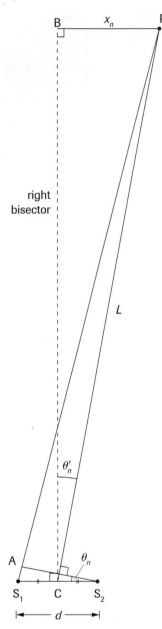

Figure 6

For a point P_n located on a nodal line, far away from the two sources, the line from P_n to the midpoint between the two sources, P_nC, is essentially parallel to P_nS_1 (**Figure 6**). This line is also perpendicular to AS_2. Since the right bisector (CB) is perpendicular to S_1S_2, we can easily show that $\theta'_n = \theta_n$ (**Figure 7**).

In **Figure 6**, $\sin \theta'_n$ can be determined from the triangle P_nBC as follows:

$$\sin \theta'_n = \frac{x_n}{L}$$

Since $\sin \theta_n = \left(n - \frac{1}{2}\right)\frac{\lambda}{d}$

and $\sin \theta'_n = \sin \theta_n$,

$$\frac{x_n}{L} = \left(n - \frac{1}{2}\right)\frac{\lambda}{d}$$

In this derivation, d is the distance between the sources, x_n is the perpendicular distance from the right bisector to the point on the nodal line, L is the distance from the point P_n to the midpoint between the two sources, and n is the number of the nodal line.

Note that our derivation assumes a pair of point sources, vibrating in phase.

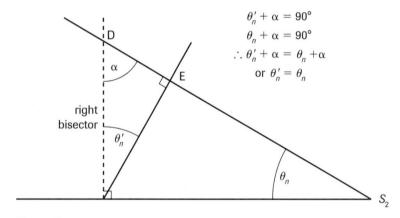

Figure 7

> **SAMPLE** problem **1**

The distance from the right bisector to the second nodal line in a two-point interference pattern is 8.0 cm. The distance from the midpoint between the two sources to point P is 28 cm. What is angle θ_2 for the second nodal line?

Solution

$x_2 = 8.0$ cm

$L = 28$ cm

$\theta_2 = ?$

$$\sin \theta_2 = \frac{x_2}{L}$$

$$= \frac{8.0 \text{ cm}}{28 \text{ cm}}$$

$$\theta_2 = 16.6°, \text{ or } 17°$$

The angle θ_2 for the second nodal line is 17°.

▶ **SAMPLE** problem 2

Two identical point sources 5.0 cm apart, operating in phase at a frequency of 8.0 Hz, generate an interference pattern in a ripple tank. A certain point on the first nodal line is located 10.0 cm from one source and 11.0 cm from the other. What is (a) the wavelength of the waves and (b) the speed of the waves?

Solution

$d = 5.0$ cm $PS_2 = 10.0$ cm $\lambda = ?$

$f = 8.0$ Hz $PS_1 = 11.0$ cm $v = ?$

(a) $\left| PS_1 - PS_2 \right| = \left(n - \dfrac{1}{2} \right)\lambda$

$\left| 11.0 \text{ cm} - 10.0 \text{ cm} \right| = \left(1 - \dfrac{1}{2} \right)\lambda$

$\lambda = 2.0$ cm

The wavelength of the waves is 2.0 cm.

(b) $v = f\lambda$

$= (8.0 \text{ Hz})(2.0 \text{ cm})$

$v = 16$ cm/s

The speed of the waves is 16 cm/s.

▶ **Practice**

Understanding Concepts

1. Two point sources, S_1 and S_2, oscillating in phase send waves into the air at the same wavelength, 1.98 m. Given that there is a nodal point where the two waves overlap, find the smallest corresponding path length difference.

2. In a ripple tank, a point on the third nodal line from the centre is 35.0 cm from one source and 42.0 cm from another. The sources are 11.2 cm apart and vibrate in phase at 10.5 Hz. Calculate the wavelength and the speed of the waves.

3. An interference pattern is set up by two point sources of the same frequency, vibrating in phase. A point on the second nodal line is 25.0 cm from one source, 29.5 cm from the other. The speed of the waves is 7.5 cm/s. Calculate the wavelength and the frequency of the sources.

Answers

1. 0.99 m

2. 2.80 cm; 29.4 cm/s

3. 3.0 cm; 2.5 Hz

Up to this point, we have discussed two-point-source wave interference in the abstract, with formulas and geometrical diagrams, and have inspected some photographs. However, we have not studied this phenomenon first hand. Investigation 9.3.1 in the Lab Activities section at the end of this chapter provides you with the opportunity to confirm the analysis of two-point-source interference in the lab. ◈▮

⊚ **INVESTIGATION 9.3.1**

Interference of Waves in Two Dimensions (p. 482)
How can you test our analysis of two-point wave interference? What equipment will you need?

SUMMARY   **Interference of Waves in Two Dimensions**

- A pair of identical point sources operating in phase produces a symmetrical pattern of constructive interference areas and nodal lines. The nodal lines are hyperbolas radiating from between the two sources.

- Increasing the frequency (lowering the wavelength) of the sources increases the number of nodal lines.

- Increasing the separation of the sources increases the number of nodal lines.
- Changing the relative phase of the sources changes the position of the nodal lines but not their number.
- The relationship $\sin \theta_n = \left(n - \dfrac{1}{2}\right)\dfrac{\lambda}{d}$, or $\dfrac{x_n}{L} = \left(n - \dfrac{1}{2}\right)\dfrac{\lambda}{d}$, can be used to solve for an unknown in a two-point-source interference pattern.

Section 9.3 Questions

Understanding Concepts

1. List three conditions necessary for a two-point-source interference pattern to remain stable.

2. By how much must path lengths differ if two waves from identical sources are to interfere destructively?

3. What ratio of $\dfrac{\lambda}{d}$ would produce no nodal line?

4. Explain why the interference pattern between two point sources is difficult to see
   (a) if the distance between the sources is large
   (b) if the relative phase of the two sources is constantly changing

5. Two point sources, 5.0 cm apart, are operating in phase, with a common frequency of 6.0 Hz, in a ripple tank. A metre stick is placed above the water, parallel to the line joining the sources. The first nodal lines (the ones adjacent to the central axis) cross the metre stick at the 35.0-cm and 55.0-cm marks. Each of the crossing points is 50.0 cm from the midpoint of the line joining the two sources. Draw a diagram of the tank, and then calculate the wavelength and speed of the waves.

6. Two sources of waves are in phase and produce identical waves. These sources are mounted at the corners of a square. At the centre of the square, waves from the sources produce constructive interference, no matter which two corners of the square are occupied by the sources. Explain why, using a diagram.

7. In a large water tank experiment, water waves are generated with straight, parallel wave fronts, 3.00 m apart. The wave fronts pass through two openings 5.00 m apart in a long board. The end of the tank is 3.00 m beyond the board. Where would you stand, relative to the perpendicular bisector of the line between the openings, if you want to receive little or no wave action?

8. A page in a student's notebook lists the following information, obtained from a ripple tank experiment with two point sources operating in phase: $n = 3$, $x_3 = 35$ cm, $L = 77$ cm, $d = 6.0$ cm, $\theta_3 = 25°$, and 5 crests = 4.2 cm. Calculate the wavelength of the waves using three methods.

9. Two very small, identical speakers, each radiating sound uniformly in all directions, are placed at points S_1 and S_2 as in **Figure 8**. The speakers are connected to an audio source in such a way that they radiate in phase, at the common wavelength of 2.00 m. Sound propagates in air at 338 m/s.
   (a) Calculate the frequency of the sound.

(b) Point M, a nodal point, is 7.0 m from S_1 and more than 7.0 m from S_2. Find three possible distances M could be from S_2.

(c) Point N, also a nodal point, is 12.0 m from S_1 and 5.0 m from S_2. On which nodal line is N located?

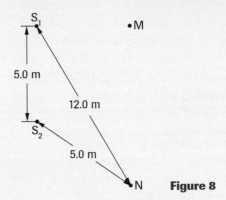

Figure 8

Applying Inquiry Skills

10. We have said that waves in a ripple tank are a "reasonable approximation" to true transverse waves.
    (a) Research the Internet or other sources and report on how the behaviour of a particle in a water wave does not exhibit strict transverse wave characteristics.

 www.science.nelson.com

(b) When water waves enter very shallow water, for example as they approach a beach, they not only slow down but also curl and "break." Explain this behaviour using the information you obtained in (a).

(c) If water waves are not true transverse waves, how can we justify using them to discover the properties of transverse waves?

Making Connections

11. Two towers of a radio station are 4.00×10^2 m apart along an east–west line. The towers act essentially as point sources, radiating in phase at a frequency of 1.00×10^6 Hz. Radio waves travel at 3.00×10^8 m/s.
    (a) In which directions is the intensity of the radio signal at a maximum for listeners 20.0 km north of the transmitter (but not necessarily directly north of it)?
    (b) In which directions would you find the intensity at a minimum, north of the transmitter, if the towers were to start transmitting in opposite phase?

The Nature of Light

Energy can move from one place to another as the energy of moving objects or as the energy of waves. A moving object, whether as small as a subatomic particle such as an electron, or as large as a baseball or a rocket, possesses kinetic energy. In classical Newtonian mechanics, the object has to have both mass and velocity if it is to transfer energy. Energy is conveyed over long distances in waves, even though individual particles do not travel these distances. How, then, does light travel? How does light from a distant source, such as the Sun, bring us energy?

The earliest recorded views on the nature of light come to us from the Greeks. Plato thought that light consisted of "streamers," or filaments, emitted by the eye. Sight was achieved when these streamers came into contact with an object. Euclid agreed with him, arguing, "How else can we explain that we do not see a needle on the floor until our eyes fall on it?" Not all Greeks held this view, however. The Pythagoreans believed that light travelled as a stream of fast-moving particles, while Empedocles taught that light travelled as a wave-like disturbance.

By the seventeenth century, these apparently contradictory views of the nature of light placed scientists into two opposing camps. Isaac Newton was the principal advocate of the particle, or corpuscular, theory. The French mathematician, physicist, and astronomer Pierre Simon de Laplace supported him. One of the principal advocates of the competing wave theory was Christiaan Huygens of Holland, also a mathematician, physicist, and astronomer. Robert Hooke, president of the Royal Society in London, and a vigorous personal opponent of Newton, in turn supported Huygens. The debate continued for more than a hundred years. By the late nineteenth century, there appeared to be overwhelming evidence that the nature of light could be better explained using the wave model. In this section, we will see how appropriate the two theories are for explaining the observed properties of light.

Before beginning this discussion, it is important to recall the two chief functions of a scientific model or theory (the terms can be used interchangeably):

- to explain the known properties of a phenomenon
- to predict new behaviour, or new properties, of a phenomenon

Newton and his supporters used the corpuscular theory to explain known features of light. Newton's arguments are significant historically; moreover they serve as illustrations of the scientific method.

Newton's Particle Theory

Building on an earlier theory by French philosopher and mathematician René Descartes, Newton imagined that light consisted of streams of tiny particles, which he called "corpuscles," shooting out like bullets from a light source.

Rectilinear Propagation

Sharp shadows and "rays" from the Sun streaming through clouds show that light travels in straight lines. This is sometimes referred to as the **rectilinear propagation of light**. A ball thrown through space follows a curved path under the influence of gravity. The path of a bullet shot from a gun, on the other hand, curves less because the speed is greater.

Robert Hooke
Robert Hooke (1635–1703), an English scientist, invented the air pump, the balance spring for watches, the first efficient compound microscope, the hygrometer, a wind gauge, a spiral gear, the iris diaphragm, and the refractometer. He also made the first microscopic study of insect anatomy, was the first to use the word "cell" in biology, proposed zero as the freezing point of water, was the first to study crystal structure, explained the nature of colour in thin films, formulated the law of elasticity, surveyed London after the Great Fire, and discovered (but was unable to prove) the inverse square law for gravitation.

rectilinear propagation of light
the term used to describe light travelling in straight lines

As with the ball, particles travelling at normal speeds are observed to follow a curved path, due to the effect of gravity. However, faster particles curve less over the same distance. Newton argued that since the path of light has no noticeable curve, light consists of particles whose speed is extremely high. Further, since he was not aware that light exerted any noticeable pressure, he argued that the mass of its particles must be extremely low.

DID YOU KNOW?

Light Bends
In 1905, as part of his general theory of relativity, Einstein proposed that light bends slightly when it passes through a strong gravitational field such as that near a star or a galaxy. Experimental observation during a solar eclipse verified this in 1919. This bending is so slight that one can say that, for most applications of light, it travels in straight lines.

Diffraction

Newton further argued that light does not travel "around a corner," as do waves. In this case he discounted the work of Francesco Grimaldi (an Italian Jesuit mathematician) who had shown that a beam of light passing through two successive narrow slits produced a band of light slightly larger than the width of the slits. Grimaldi believed that the beam had been bent slightly outward at the edges of the second aperature, a phenomenon he named diffraction. Newton maintained that Grimaldi's effect resulted from collisions between the light particles at the edges of the slit rather than from the outward spreading of waves.

Reflection

We know that light falling on a mirror obeys the laws of reflection. How do particles behave under similar conditions? **Figure 1(a)** shows light rays reflected by a mirror (bouncing, Newton would say), and **(b)** shows a series of images of a bouncing steel ball.

(a) **(b)**

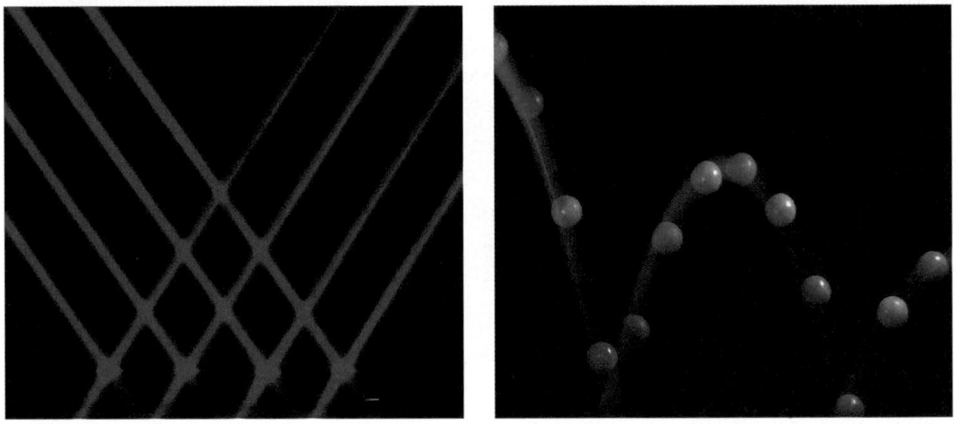

Figure 1
(a) Reflected parallel rays of light
(b) Steel ball bouncing off a hard surface

Newton demonstrated that, under the assumption of perfectly elastic collisions, the laws of reflection follow from the laws of motion. Consider a hard, spherical particle approaching a frictionless, horizontal surface with a velocity whose horizontal and vertical components are v_x and v_y respectively. When the particle is reflected, there is no change in v_x. The vertical velocity component v_y is reversed in direction because of the reactive force of the horizontal surface on the sphere, leaving its magnitude unchanged (**Figure 2**). (Since the collision is perfectly elastic, $\Delta E_K = 0$.) The incident velocity is thus equal in magnitude to the reflected velocity, and $\theta_i = \theta_r$.

Figure 2
Vector analysis of the bouncing steel ball in a collision assumed to be perfectly elastic. The ball obeys the same law of reflection as a ray of light.

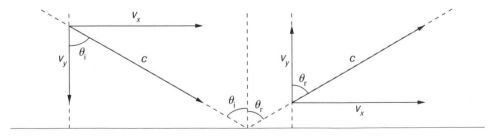

Refraction

Newton was also able to demonstrate the nature of refraction with the particle model: when light passes from air to water, it bends toward the normal (**Figure 3**). Particles, too, will bend toward the normal if their speed increases. For example, if a ball is rolled at a transverse angle down a ramp from a raised horizontal surface to a lower horizontal surface, it will bend, or refract, toward the normal.

(a)   **(b)**

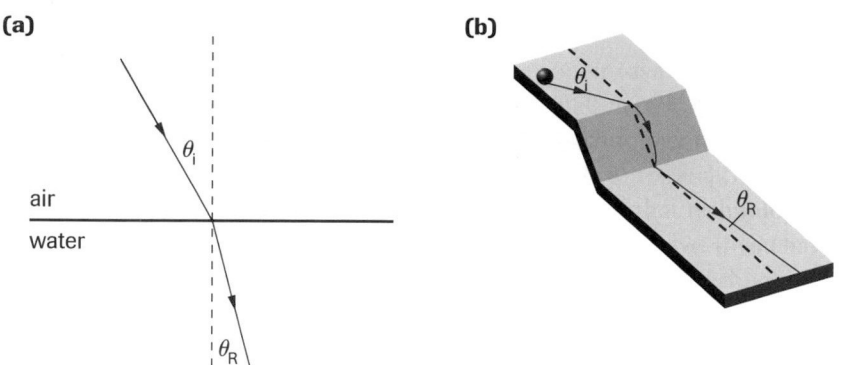

Figure 3
(a) Light travelling obliquely from air into water bends toward the normal.
(b) When the speed of a moving particle increases, it bends toward the normal.

Newton believed that water attracted approaching particles of light in much the same way as gravity attracts a rolling ball on an incline. On the strength of the rolling ball analogy, he conjectured that particles of light accelerate, specifically at the boundary, as they pass from air into a medium with a higher index of refraction, such as glass or water. He therefore predicted that the speed of light in water would be greater than the speed of light in air. At the time, the speed of light in water was not known. It was not until 1850, 123 years after Newton's death, that the French physicist Jean Foucault demonstrated experimentally that the speed of light in water is, in fact, *less* than the speed of light in air—the opposite of what Newton's particle theory predicted.

Partial Reflection–Partial Refraction

When light refracts, some of the light is reflected. Newton had difficulty explaining this phenomenon in his corpuscular framework. He did, however, propose a so-called "theory of fits": particles of light arrive at the surface sometimes in a "fit" of easy reflection, sometimes in a "fit" of easy refraction. However, Newton recognized that this explanation was weak.

Dispersion

When white light passes through a glass prism, different wavelengths are refracted through different angles, generating a display of spectral colours (**Figure 4**). This phenomenon, called *dispersion*, has been known since at least the time of the ancient Egyptians. In 1666, however, Newton became the first physicist to investigate the phenomenon systematically.

To explain dispersion in his corpuscular theory, Newton hypothesized that each particle in the spectrum had a different mass. Since the violet-light particles are refracted more than the blue, Newton argued that the violet-light particles must have a lower mass than blue-light particles. (The lower masses, having less momentum, would be diverted more easily.) Similarly, the blue-light particles must be lower in mass than the still less deflection-prone green-light particles. Red-light particles must have the highest masses of all the species of light in the visible spectrum.

Newton's corpuscular theory provided, at the time, a satisfactory explanation for four properties of light: straight-line transmission, reflection, refraction, and dispersion. It was

Figure 4
Dispersion occurs when white light is refracted in a prism, producing the spectrum.

weak in its explanation of diffraction and partial reflection–partial refraction. Considering the evidence available to Newton, his hypothesis was valid. It was, in its day, superior to the competing wave theory of light because it used the laws of mechanics, which had been proven to be valid in other areas of physics. When new evidence became available that could not be explained using Newton's corpuscular theory, this was bound to give stronger support to the wave theory. However, Newton's stature and authority were so compelling that the corpuscular theory of light dominated for more than a century. In fact, his successors adhered to the corpuscular view of light more strongly than Newton ever did himself.

Newton recognized that the experimental evidence was not exclusively strong enough for either particles or waves. Although he preferred the particle theory, he was not dogmatic about it. He considered both theories to be hypotheses, theories that required further testing.

The lesson to be learned from Newton's example is that the theories—in fact, any pronouncements—of esteemed, famous people should be evaluated on the basis of supporting evidence. A theory should not be accepted simply because it is put forward by an eminent person.

Huygens' Wave Model

Robert Hooke proposed the wave theory of light in 1665. Twenty years later, Huygens developed the theory further, introducing *Huygens' principle* (still used today as a diagram-drawing aid) for predicting the position of a wave front:

> **Huygens' Principle**
>
> Every point on a wave front can be considered as a point source of tiny secondary wavelets that spread out in front of the wave at the same speed as the wave itself. The surface envelope, tangent to all the wavelets, constitutes the new wave front.

As an illustration of the use of Huygens' principle, consider **Figure 5**, in which the wave front AB is travelling away from the source at some instant. The points on the wave

Figure 5
Every point on a wave front can be considered as a point source of tiny secondary wavelets that spread out in front of the wave at the same speed as the wave itself. The surface envelope, tangent to all the wavelets, constitutes the new wave front.

circular wave front

straight wave front

front represent the centres of the new wavelets, drawn as a series of small arcs of circles. The common tangent to all these wavelets, A'B', is the new position of the wave front a short time later.

Huygens and his supporters were able to use the wave theory to explain some of the properties of light, including reflection, refraction, partial reflection–partial refraction, dispersion, and diffraction. However, they encountered difficulties when trying to explain rectilinear propagation, since waves as encountered in a ripple tank tend to spread out from a source. (This was the primary reason for Newton's rejection of the wave theory.)

Reflection

As **Figure 6** shows, waves obey the laws of reflection from optics. In each case, the angle of incidence equals the angle of reflection for both straight and curved reflectors.

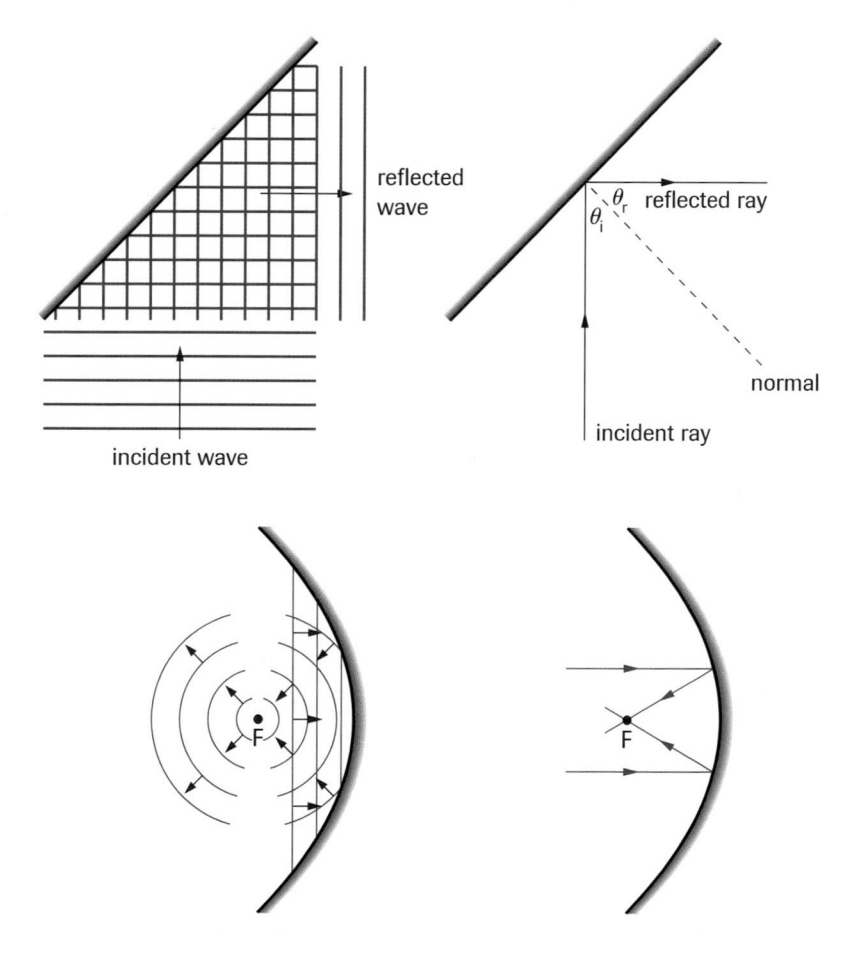

Figure 6
Waves, like light, obey the laws of reflection when reflected by a plane or curved surface.

Refraction

Huygens, using his wavelet model, predicted that light would bend toward the normal as it passes into an optically denser medium such as glass because its speed is slower in the second medium ($v_2 < v_1$). In a given interval Δt, the wavelet whose source is point A in **Figure 7** travels a shorter distance ($v_2\Delta t$) than does the wavelet whose source is B ($v_1\Delta t$). The new wave front, tangent to these wavelets, is CD (consistent with Snell's law). We have seen that Newton's corpuscular theory predicted the reverse, that is, $v_2 > v_1$. By 1850, when a technique was available for measuring the speed of light in a material other than a vacuum, the wave theory had already prevailed, for reasons which we shall examine shortly.

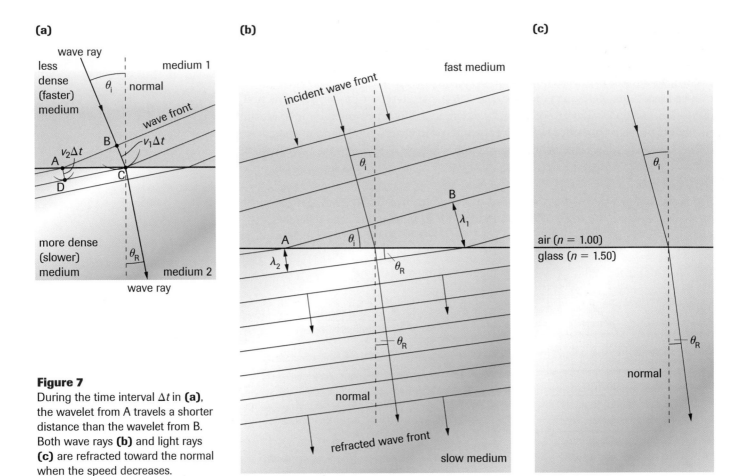

(a)

wave ray

less dense (faster) medium

medium 1

θ_i normal

wave front

$v_2\Delta t$ $v_1\Delta t$

B

A

C

D

more dense (slower) medium

θ_R

medium 2

wave ray

Figure 7
During the time interval Δt in **(a)**, the wavelet from A travels a shorter distance than the wavelet from B. Both wave rays **(b)** and light rays **(c)** are refracted toward the normal when the speed decreases.

(b)

fast medium

incident wave front

θ_i

B

λ_1

A

θ_i

λ_2

θ_R

θ_R

normal

refracted wave front

slow medium

(c)

θ_i

air ($n = 1.00$)

glass ($n = 1.50$)

θ_R

normal

Partial Reflection–Partial Refraction

We have already seen from the ripple tank that waves partially reflect and partially refract whenever there is a change in speed, that the amount of partial reflection varies with the angle of incidence, that the reflection becomes total for angles of incidence greater than a critical angle, and that all these phenomena have parallels in optics. Recall that total internal reflection only occurs for waves travelling from a slow to a fast medium, as is the case for light (**Figure 8**).

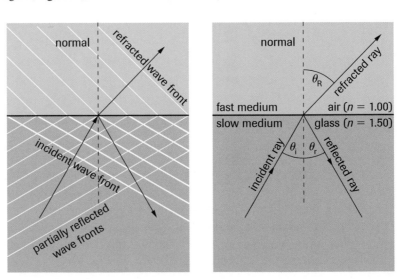

normal

refracted wave front

incident wave front

partially reflected wave fronts

normal

refracted ray

θ_R

fast medium

slow medium

air ($n = 1.00$)

glass ($n = 1.50$)

incident ray

θ_i θ_r

reflected ray

Figure 8
For waves and light refracted away from the normal when the speed increases, partial reflection also occurs.

Diffraction

Grimaldi had observed the diffraction of light when a ray was directed through two successive narrow slits. Newton had said that if light were a wave, then light waves should bend much more than was observed by Grimaldi. We saw in the previous section that diffraction only becomes easy to detect when the aperture is of approximately the same order of magnitude as the wavelength. If the wavelength is extremely small, diffraction will be minimal unless the aperature is extremely small, too.

Huygens' principle is consistent with diffraction around the edge of an obstacle, through a large aperture, and through an aperture whose size is on the same order of magnitude as the wavelength of the wave (**Figure 9**). Neither Newton nor Huygens had been able to determine what is now known, that the wavelengths of visible light are so incredibly small that diffraction effects must be very small as well. Both theories explained the diffraction phenomena known in their day. Once the minuteness of the wavelength of light was known, the wave theory was acknowledged to be superior.

(a)

(c)

(b)

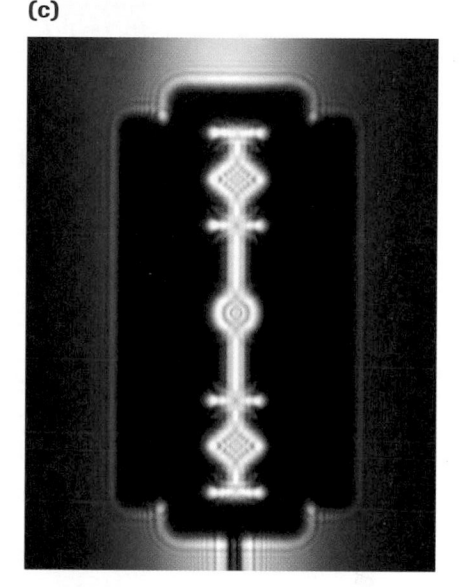

Figure 9
Diffraction patterns produced by
(a) a fine wire,
(b) a sharp edge
(c) a razor blade

Dispersion

Recall from Section 9.1 that long-wavelength waves were refracted a slightly different amount than short-wavelength waves when passing from one medium to another with a lower speed. Wave theory supporters used this fact to explain dispersion. They argued that white light is made up of the colours of the spectrum, each with a different wavelength. When white light passes through a prism, the violet wavelengths, for example, are refracted more than the red because they have different wavelengths. We will see later that the explanation is more complex, but with the knowledge available at the time, this wave explanation was satisfactory.

Rectilinear Propagation

The wave theory treats light as a series of wave fronts perpendicular to the paths of the light rays. Huygens thought of the rays as simply representing the direction of motion of a wave front. Newton felt that this did not adequately explain rectilinear propagation of light, since waves emitted from a point source spread out in all directions rather than travel in a straight line. At the time, Newton's corpuscular theory explained this property better than the wave theory.

In summary, Huygens' wave theory explained many of the properties of light, including reflection, refraction, partial reflection–partial refraction, diffraction, dispersion, and rectilinear propagation. The wave theory was more valid at that time than Newton's corpuscular theory, but because of Newton's reputation in other areas of physics, the corpuscular theory would dominate for 100 years, until Thomas Young provided new and definitive evidence in 1807.

SUMMARY   *Light: Wave or Particle?*

- Newton's particle theory provided a satisfactory explanation for four properties of light: rectilinear propagation, reflection, refraction, and dispersion. The theory was weak in its explanations of diffraction and partial reflection–partial refraction.

- Huygens' wave theory considered every point on a wave front as a point source of tiny secondary wavelets, spreading out in front of the wave at the same speed as the wave itself. The surface envelope, tangent to all the wavelets, constitutes the new wave front.

- Huygens' version of the wave theory explained many of the properties of light, including reflection, refraction, partial reflection–partial refraction, diffraction, and rectilinear propagation.

► Section 9.4 Questions

Understanding Concepts

1. In what ways does light behave like a wave? Draw diagrams to illustrate your answer.

2. When a real-life approximation to a particle, such as a steel ball, strikes a hard surface, its speed is slightly reduced. Explain how you know that the speed of light does not change when it is reflected.

3. Does Huygens' principle apply to sound waves? to water waves?

4. What experimental evidence suggests that light is a wave?

5. The index of refraction of one type of glass is 1.50. What, according to the particle theory of light, is the speed of light in glass? Explain your answer.

Applying Inquiry Skills

6. Newton hypothesized in his corpuscular theory that particles of light have very low masses. Design an experiment to show that if there are indeed particles of light possessing a low mass, then their mass cannot be high.

If light has wave properties, then two light sources oscillating in phase should produce a result similar to the interference pattern in a ripple tank for vibrators operating in phase (**Figure 1**). Light should be brighter in areas of constructive interference, and there should be darkness in areas of destructive interference.

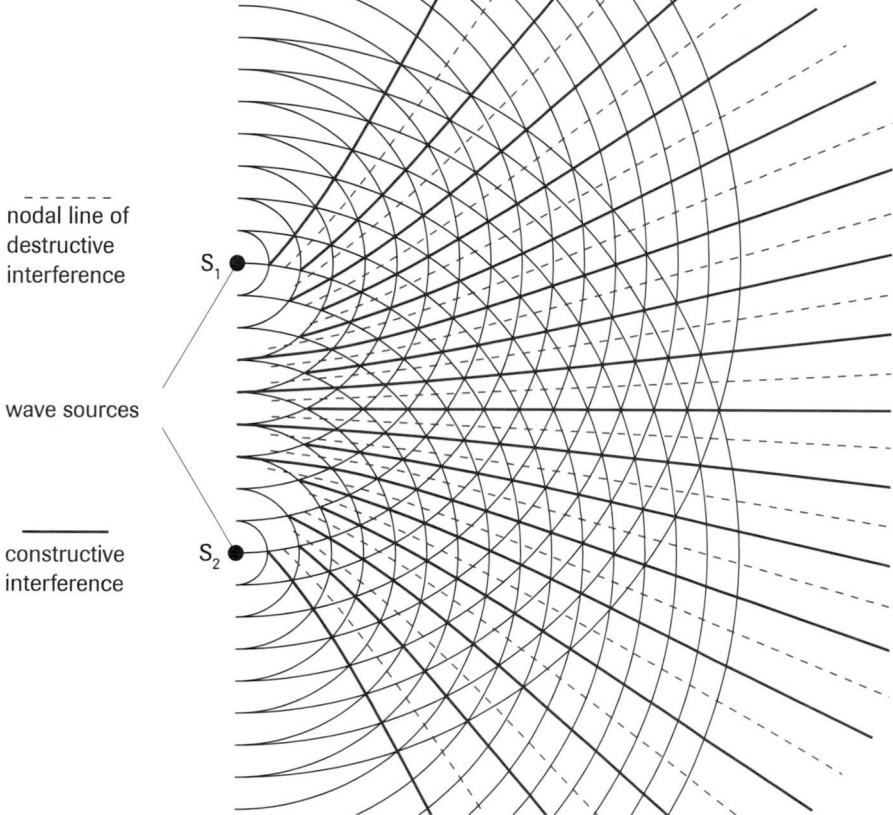

nodal line of destructive interference

S_1

wave sources

constructive interference

S_2

Figure 1
Interference of circular waves produced by two identical point sources in phase

Many investigators in the decades between Newton and Thomas Young attempted to demonstrate interference in light. In most cases, they placed two sources of light side by side. They scrutinized screens near their sources for interference patterns but always in vain. In part, they were defeated by the exceedingly small wavelength of light. In a ripple tank, where the frequency of the sources is relatively small and the wavelengths are large, the distance between adjacent nodal lines is easily observable. In experiments with light, the distance between the nodal lines was so small that no nodal lines were observed.

There is, however, a second, more fundamental, problem in transferring the ripple tank setup into optics. If the relative phase of the wave sources is altered, the interference pattern is shifted. When two incandescent light sources are placed side by side, the atoms in each source emit the light randomly, out of phase. When the light strikes the screen, a constantly varying interference pattern is produced, and no single pattern is observed.

In his experiments over the period 1802–1804, Young used one incandescent body instead of two, directing its light through two pinholes placed very close together. The light was diffracted through each pinhole, so that each acted as a point source of light. Since the sources were close together, the spacing between the nodal lines was large enough to make the pattern of nodal lines visible. Since the light from the two pinholes originated from the same incandescent body (Young chose the Sun), the two interfering beams of light were always in phase, and a single, fixed interference pattern could be created on a screen.

Young's experiment resolved the two major problems in observing the interference of light: the two sources were in phase, and the distance between sources was small enough that a series of light and dark bands was created on a screen placed in the path of the light. These bands of bright and dark are called **interference fringes** or **maxima** and **minima**. This experiment, now commonly called Young's experiment, provided very strong evidence for the wave theory of light.

The sense in which Young's experiment confirms the wave nature of light becomes evident in **Figure 2**, where water waves falling upon a barrier with two slits are diffracted and produce an interference pattern similar to that produced by two point sources vibrating in phase in a ripple tank.

interference fringes the light (**maxima**) and dark (**minima**) bands produced by the interference of light

(a)

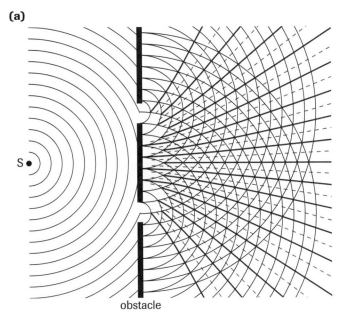

obstacle

(b)

Figure 2
(a) Interference in a ripple tank produced by waves from a single source passing through adjacent openings
(b) Photograph of interference in a ripple tank

Figure 3 shows light waves, in phase, emerging from slits S_1 and S_2, a distance d apart. Although the waves spread out in all directions after emerging from the slits, we will analyze them for only three different angles, θ. In **Figure 3(a)**, where $\theta = 0$, both waves reach the centre of the screen in phase, since they travel the same distance. Constructive interference therefore occurs, producing a bright spot at the centre of the screen. When the waves from slit S_2 travel an extra distance of $\frac{\lambda}{2}$ to reach the screen in **(b)**, the waves from the two sources arrive at the screen 180° out of phase. Destructive interference occurs, and the screen is dark in this region (corresponding to nodal line $n = 1$). As we move still farther from the centre of the screen, we reach a point at which the path difference is λ, as in **(c)**. Since the two waves are back in phase, with the waves from S_2 one whole wavelength behind those from S_1, constructive interference occurs (causing this region, like the centre of the screen, to be bright).

As in the ripple tank, we find destructive interference for appropriate values of the path difference, $d \sin \theta_n$:

$$\sin \theta_n = \left(n - \frac{1}{2}\right)\frac{\lambda}{d} \qquad \text{where } n = 1, 2, 3, \ldots$$

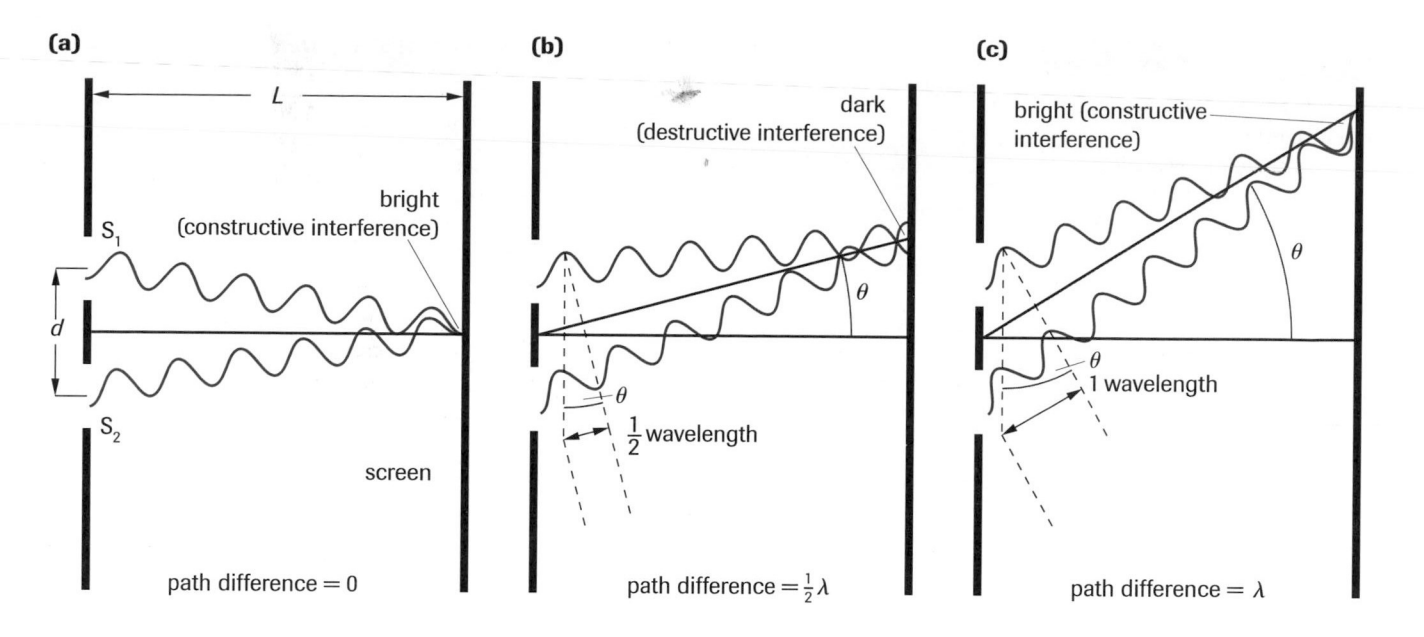

(a) bright (constructive interference)

path difference = 0

(b) dark (destructive interference)

θ

$\frac{1}{2}$ wavelength

path difference = $\frac{1}{2}\lambda$

(c) bright (constructive interference)

θ

1 wavelength

path difference = λ

Another set of values of $d \sin \theta$ yields constructive interference:

$$\sin \theta_m = \frac{m\lambda}{d} \qquad \text{where } m = 0, 1, 2, 3, \dots$$

Figure 3
(a) Path difference = 0
(b) Path difference = $\frac{1}{2}\lambda$
(c) Path difference = λ

Since the dark fringes created on the screen by destructive interference are very narrow in comparison with the bright areas, measurements are made with those nodal lines. Also, $\sin \theta_n$ is best determined not by trying to measure θ_n directly but by using the ratio $\frac{x}{L}$, where x is the distance of the nodal line from the centre line on the screen, and L is the distance to the screen from the midpoint between the slits.

In general, the equations used for the two-point interference pattern in the ripple tank can be used for light, that is,

$$\sin \theta_n = \frac{x_n}{L} = \left(n - \frac{1}{2}\right)\frac{\lambda}{d}$$

where x_n is the distance to the nth nodal line, measured from the right bisector, as in **Figure 4**.

> **LEARNING TIP**
>
> **A Good Approximation**
> Actually, $\frac{x_n}{L} = \tan \theta_n$. However, for $L \gg x$, $\tan \theta_n$ is very nearly equal to $\sin \theta_n$. Thus $\frac{x_n}{L}$ serves as a good approximation to $\sin \theta_n$ in this instance.

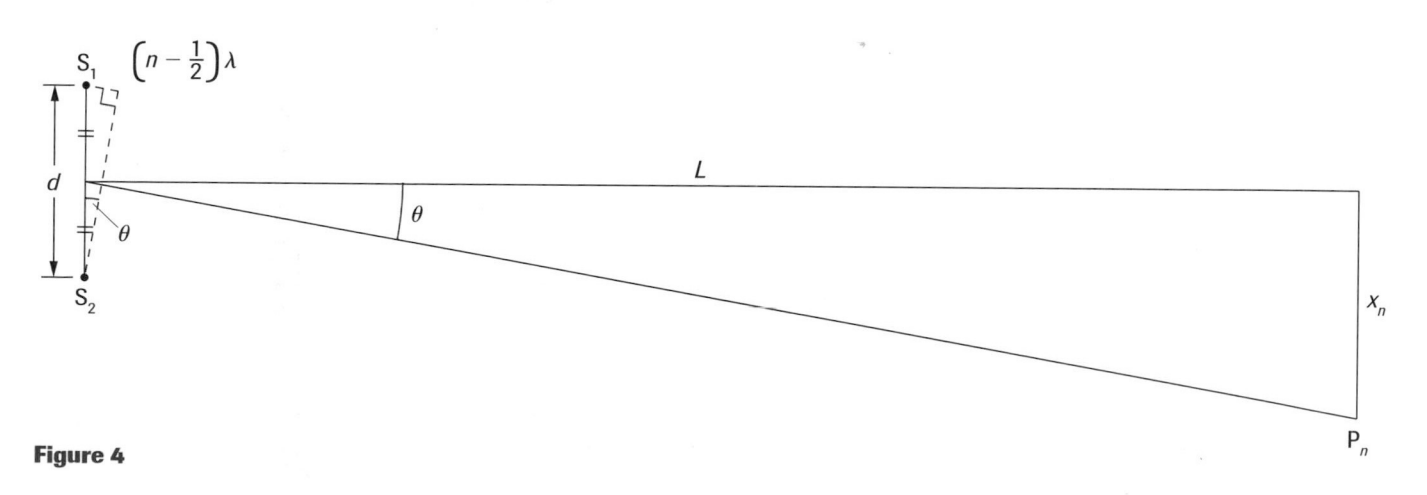

Figure 4

LEARNING TIP

The "Order" of Minima and Maxima

For a two-source, in-phase interference pattern, the nodal line numbers, or minima, can be called first-order minimum, second-order minimum, etc., for $n = 1, 2, ...$. The maximum numbers can be called zero-order maximum, first-order maximum, second-order maximum, etc., for $m = 0, 1, 2, ...$. The zero-order maximum is called the central maximum.

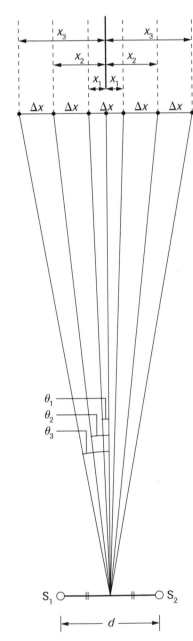

Figure 5

For each nodal line, we can derive a separate value for x (**Figure 4**) from this equation, as follows:

$$x_n = \left(n - \frac{1}{2}\right)\frac{L\lambda}{d}$$

$$x_1 = \left(1 - \frac{1}{2}\right)\frac{L\lambda}{d} = \frac{L\lambda}{2d}$$

$$x_2 = \left(2 - \frac{1}{2}\right)\frac{L\lambda}{d} = \frac{3L\lambda}{2d}$$

$$x_3 = \left(3 - \frac{1}{2}\right)\frac{L\lambda}{d} = \frac{5L\lambda}{2d}$$

etc.

Although L was different in the earlier equation, in this case L is so large compared to d and the values of L for the various nodal lines are so similar, that we can treat L as a constant, being essentially equal to the perpendicular distance from the slits to the screen.

Figure 5 shows that the displacement between adjacent nodal lines (Δx) is given by $(x_2 - x_1)$, $(x_3 - x_2)$, and $(x_1 + x_1)$. In each case the value is

$$\frac{\Delta x}{L} = \frac{\lambda}{d}$$

where Δx is the distance between adjacent nodal lines on the screen, d is the separation of the slits, and L is the perpendicular distance from the slits to the screen.

SAMPLE problem 1

You are measuring the wavelength of light from a certain single-colour source. You direct the light through two slits with a separation of 0.15 mm, and an interference pattern is created on a screen 3.0 m away. You find the distance between the first and the eighth consecutive dark lines to be 8.0 cm. At what wavelength is your source radiating?

Solution

$L = 3.0$ m

$\lambda = ?$

8 nodal lines $= 7\Delta x$

$\Delta x = \dfrac{8.0\,\text{cm}}{7} = 1.14\,\text{cm} = 1.14 \times 10^{-2}$ m

$d = 0.15$ mm $= 1.5 \times 10^{-4}$ m

$$\frac{\Delta x}{L} = \frac{\lambda}{d}$$

$$\lambda = \frac{d\Delta x}{L}$$

$$= \frac{(1.14 \times 10^{-2}\,\text{m})(1.5 \times 10^{-4}\,\text{m})}{3.0\,\text{m}}$$

$$\lambda = 5.7 \times 10^{-7}\,\text{m}$$

The wavelength of the source is 5.7×10^{-7} m, or 5.7×10^2 nm.

▶ **SAMPLE** problem **2**

The third-order dark fringe of 652-nm light is observed at an angle of 15.0° when the light falls on two narrow slits. How far apart are the slits?

Solution

$n = 3$ $\qquad\qquad\qquad\quad \theta_3 = 15.0°$

$\lambda = 652 \text{ nm} = 6.52 \times 10^{-7} \text{ m} \qquad d = ?$

$$\sin \theta_n = \left(n - \frac{1}{2}\right)\frac{\lambda}{d}$$

$$d = \frac{\left(n - \frac{1}{2}\right)\lambda}{\sin \theta_n}$$

$$= \frac{\left(3 - \frac{1}{2}\right)(6.52 \times 10^{-7} \text{ m})}{\sin 15.0°}$$

$$d = 6.30 \times 10^{-6} \text{ m}$$

The slit separation is 6.30×10^{-6} m.

▶ **Practice**

Understanding Concepts

1. A student performing Young's experiment with a single-colour source finds the distance between the first and the seventh nodal lines to be 6.0 cm. The screen is located 3.0 m from the two slits. The slit separation is 2.2×10^2 μm. Calculate the wavelength of the light.

2. Single-colour light falling on two slits 0.042 mm apart produces the fifth-order fringe at a 3.8° angle. Calculate the wavelength of the light.

3. An interference pattern is formed on a screen when helium–neon laser light ($\lambda = 6.3 \times 10^{-7}$ m) is directed toward it through two slits. The slits are 43 μm apart. The screen is 2.5 m away. Calculate the separation of adjacent nodal lines.

4. In an interference experiment, reddish light of wavelength 6.0×10^2 nm passes through a double slit. The distance between the first and eleventh dark bands, on a screen 1.5 m away, is 13.2 cm.
   (a) Calculate the separation of the slits.
   (b) Calculate the spacing between adjacent nodal lines using blue light of wavelength 4.5×10^2 nm.

5. A parallel beam of light from a laser, with a wavelength 656 nm, falls on two very narrow slits, 0.050 mm apart. How far apart are the fringes in the centre of the pattern thrown upon a screen 2.6 m away?

6. Light of wavelength 6.8×10^2 nm falls on two slits, producing an interference pattern where the fourth-order dark fringe is 48 mm from the centre of the interference pattern on a screen 1.5 m away. Calculate the separation of the two slits.

7. Reddish light of wavelength 6.0×10^{-7} m passes through two parallel slits. Nodal lines are produced on a screen 3.0 m away. The distance between the first and the tenth nodal lines is 5.0 cm. Calculate the separation of the two slits.

8. In an interference experiment, reddish light of wavelength 6.0×10^{-7} m passes through a double slit, hitting a screen 1.5 m away. The distance between the first and eleventh dark bands is 2.0 cm.
   (a) Calculate the separation of the slits.
   (b) Calculate the spacing between adjacent nodal lines using blue light ($\lambda_{blue} = 4.5 \times 10^{-7}$ m).

Answers

1. 7.3×10^{-7} m

2. 6.2×10^2 nm

3. 3.7 cm

4. (a) 68 μm
   (b) 1.0 cm

5. 3.4 cm

6. 7.4×10^{-2} mm

7. 3.2×10^{-4} m

8. (a) 1.5×10^{-3} m
   (b) 4.5×10^{-4} m

Further Developments in the Wave Theory of Light

In Section 9.3 we analyzed the interference pattern between two-point sources in a ripple tank and derived equations that permitted the calculation of the wavelength of the source. But with light, all we see are the results of light interference on a screen; we cannot see what is happening when the light passes through two slits. If Young's hypothesis is correct, we should be able to use the same equations to measure the wavelength of light. But we must have a source of light that has a fixed wavelength. There are a limited number of **monochromatic** (composed of only one colour and having one wavelength) sources of light. Traditionally the sodium vapour lamp was used for this purpose, but today we have lasers that emit a bright single wavelength light, usually in the red part of the spectrum. Investigation 9.5.1, in the Lab Activities section at the end of this chapter, gives you the opportunity to use a helium–neon laser or a light-emitting diode (LED) as your source and, based on the above analysis, predict the interference pattern using a procedure similar to that used by Young.

When Young announced his results in 1807, he reminded his audience that Newton had made several statements favouring a theory with some wave aspects. Nevertheless, Newton's influence was still dominant, and the scientific establishment did not take Young and his work seriously. It was not until 1818, when the French physicist Augustin Fresnel proposed his own mathematical wave theory, that Young's research was accepted. Fresnel's work was presented to a group of physicists and mathematicians, most of them strong supporters of the particle theory. One mathematician, Simon Poisson, showed that Fresnel's wave equations predict a unique diffraction pattern when light is directed past a small solid disk. If light really did behave like a wave, argued Poisson, the light diffracting around the edges of the disk should interfere constructively, producing a small bright spot at the exact centre of the diffraction pattern (**Figure 6**). (According to the particle theory, constructive interference at this position was impossible.) Poisson did not observe a bright spot and felt he had refuted the wave theory.

However, in 1818, Dominique Arago tested Poisson's prediction experimentally, and the bright spot was seen at the centre of the shadow (**Figure 7**). Even though Poisson refuted the wave theory, his prediction that there would be a bright spot at the centre of the shadow if the wave theory proved valid, led to this phenomenon being known as "Poisson's Bright Spot." (Note that there is also interference near the edge of the disk.)

By 1850, the validity of the wave theory of light had been generally accepted. For some time afterward, the mathematical consequences of the wave theory were applied to numerous aspects of the properties of light, including dispersion, polarization, single-slit diffraction, and the development of the electromagnetic spectrum, which we will discuss in the next section and in Chapter 10.

But the wave theory was not adequate to explain the movement of light through the vacuum of space, since waves required a material medium for their transmission. The power of the wave theory was now so great, however, that scientists theorized a "fluid" filling all space, from the space between atoms to the space between planets. They called it "ether." Many experiments were attempted to detect this ether, but none were successful (see Section 11.1).

monochromatic composed of only one colour; possessing only one wavelength

⚛ INVESTIGATION 9.5.1

Young's Double-Slit Experiment (p. 484)
Can you predict interference patterns using Young's method?

DID YOU KNOW ?

Augustin Fresnel

Augustin Fresnel (1788–1827) spent most of his life working for the French government as a civil engineer. His mathematical analysis provided the theoretical basis for the transverse wave model of light. Fresnel applied his analysis to design a lens of nearly uniform thickness for use in lighthouses as a replacement for the less efficient mirror systems of his day. Today, the Fresnel lens is found in a wide range of devices, including overhead projectors, beacon lights, and solar collectors.

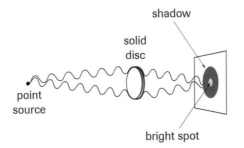

Figure 6
If light is a wave, a bright spot should appear at the centre of the shadow of a solid disk illuminated by a point source of monochromatic light.

Although in our exploration of the wave theory to this point, we have treated light as a transverse wave, in fact no evidence has been provided that it is a transverse, not a longitudinal, wave. One property of light not discussed previously is polarization. When we understand polarization and apply the wave theory in the next chapter we will have convincing evidence that validates the wave theory of light, leading to the study of electromagnetic waves.

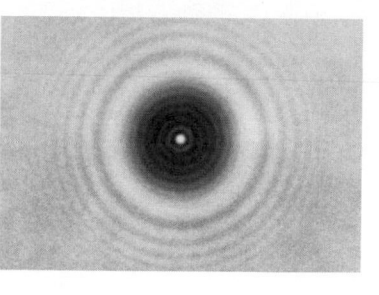

Figure 7
Poisson's Bright Spot

Wave Interference: Young's Double-Slit Experiment

- Early attempts to demonstrate the interference of light were unsuccessful because the two sources were too far apart and out of phase, and the wavelength of light is very small.

- Thomas Young's crucial contribution consisted of using one source illuminating two closely spaced openings in an opaque screen, thus using diffraction to create two sources of light close together and in phase.

- In Young's experiment a series of light and dark bands, called interference fringes, was created on a screen, placed in the path of light, in much the same way as those created in the ripple tank.

- The relationships $\sin \theta_n = \dfrac{x_n}{L} = \left(n - \dfrac{1}{2}\right)\dfrac{\lambda}{d}$ and $\dfrac{\Delta x}{L} = \dfrac{\lambda}{d}$ permit unknowns to be calculated, given any three of λ, Δx, L, θ, d, and n.

- Young's experiment supported the wave theory of light, explaining all the properties of light except transmission through a vacuum.

▶ Section 9.5 Questions

Understanding Concepts

1. Explain why the discoveries of Grimaldi were so important to Young's work.

2. Explain why the observation of the double-slit interference pattern was more convincing evidence for the wave theory of light than the observation of diffraction.

3. Monochromatic red light is incident on a double slit and produces an interference pattern on a screen some distance away. Explain how the fringe pattern would change if the red light source is replaced with a blue light source.

4. If Young's experiment were done completely under water, explain how the interference pattern would change from that observed in air, using the same equipment and experimental setup.

5. In a Young's double-slit experiment, the angle that locates the second dark fringe on either side of the central bright fringe is 5.4°. Calculate the ratio of the slit separation d to the wavelength λ of the light.

6. In measuring the wavelength of a narrow, monochromatic source of light, you use a double slit with a separation of 0.15 mm. Your friend places markers on a screen 2.0 m in front of the slits at the positions of successive dark bands in the pattern. Your friend finds the dark bands to be 0.56 cm apart.
   (a) Calculate the wavelength of the source in nanometres.

   (b) Calculate what the spacing of the dark bands would be if you used a source of wavelength 6.0×10^2 nm.

7. Monochromatic light from a point source illuminates two parallel, narrow slits. The centres of the slit openings are 0.80 mm apart. An interference pattern forms on a screen placed parallel to the plane of the slits and 49 cm away. The distance between two adjacent dark interference fringes is 0.30 mm.
   (a) Calculate the wavelength of the light.
   (b) What would the separation of the nodal lines be if the slit centre were narrowed to 0.60 mm?

8. Monochromatic light falls on two very narrow slits 0.040 mm apart. Successive nodal points on a screen 5.00 m away are 5.5 cm apart near the centre of the pattern. Calculate the wavelength of the light.

9. A Young's double-slit experiment is performed using light that has a wavelength of 6.3×10^2 nm. The separation between the slits is 3.3×10^{-5} m. Find the angles, with respect to the slits, that locate the first-, second-, and third-order bright (not dark) fringes on the screen.

Applying Inquiry Skills

10. A thin piece of glass is placed in front of one of the two slits in a Young's apparatus so that the waves exit that slit 180° out of phase with respect to the other slit. Describe, using diagrams, the interference pattern on the screen.

9.6 Colour and Wavelength

⚛ **INVESTIGATION 9.6.1**

**Wavelengths of Visible Light
(p. 485)**
What are the wavelengths of the
colours in visible light?

Table 1 The Visible Spectrum

Colour	Wavelength (nm)
violet	400–450
blue	450–500
green	500–570
yellow	570–590
orange	590–610
red	610–750

We know from the dispersion of white light in a prism that white light is made up of all of the colours in the visible spectrum. From our work in Section 9.5, we also know that helium–neon laser light has a wavelength of 630 nm. But what are some of the other wavelengths found in visible light? Investigation 9.6.1 in the Lab Activities section at the end of this chapter will give you the opportunity to use a white light source with filters to measure the wavelengths of red and green light. ⚛

Figure 1 shows three interference patterns: one for white, one for red, and one for blue light. You can see that the separation of the nodal lines is greater for red light than it is for blue. This is to be expected, since red light has a longer wavelength than blue. The relationship $\lambda = \dfrac{d\Delta x}{L}$ shows that the wavelength for red light is approximately 6.5×10^{-7} m and the wavelength for blue light is approximately 4.5×10^{-7} m. Similar determinations produce values for all the colours in the visible spectrum. Some of these are given in **Table 1**.

Figure 1
Interference of white, red, and blue light produced separately, using the same apparatus in all three cases

When white light passes through two narrow slits, the central bright areas in the interference patterns are white, whereas the spectral colours appear at the edges (**Figure 1**). If each spectral colour has its own band of wavelengths, each will interfere constructively at specific locations in the interference pattern. Thus, the colours of the spectrum are observed in the interference pattern because each band of wavelengths is associated with its own colour.

On passing through a prism, white light is dispersed, broken up into its components to form the spectrum. Each of the colours bends by a different amount and emerges from the prism at its own distinctive angle (**Figure 2**).

To explain dispersion, the wave theory must show that different frequencies (wavelengths) are bent by different amounts when they are refracted. Careful measurements in a ripple tank demonstrate this. Thus, if the frequency of a wave varies, the amount of refraction varies slightly as well, thereby explaining dispersion.

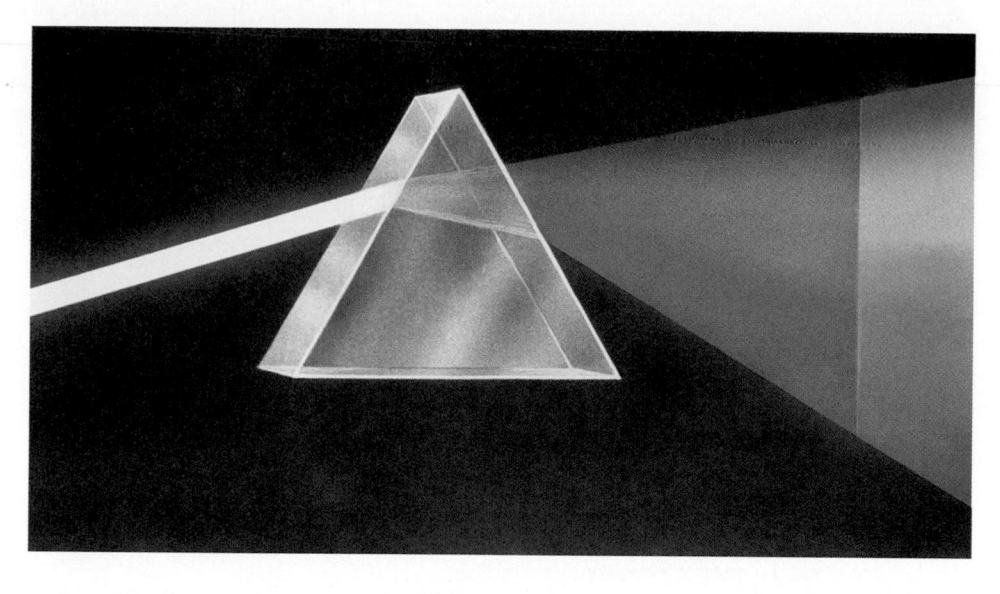

Figure 2
Dispersion of white light in a prism

Although the wavelength of the light does affect the amount of refraction, the behaviour is the reverse of what we encounter with water waves in a ripple tank. Shorter wavelengths, such as those at the violet end of the spectrum, are refracted more than the longer wavelengths in the red region of the spectrum. Each spectral colour, having a wavelength different from the others, is refracted a different amount. This explains the prism's separation of white light into the spectrum.

Since each of the wavelengths of visible light undergoes a slightly different amount of refraction by the prism, the glass must have a slightly different index of refraction for each colour. For example, the index of refraction of crown glass is 1.53 for violet light and 1.51 for red light. The speed of violet light in glass is slightly less than that for red.

The mathematical relationships governing waves in such media as ropes and water can be applied to optics:

$$v = f\lambda$$

$$\frac{\sin \theta_1}{\sin \theta_2} = n$$

$$n_1 \sin \theta_1 = n_2 \sin \theta_2$$

$$\frac{n_2}{n_1} = \frac{v_1}{v_2}$$

$$\frac{v_1}{v_2} = \frac{\lambda_1}{\lambda_2}$$

For example, we find from the equation $v = f\lambda$ that the frequency of red light, with a wavelength of 6.5×10^{-7} m, is

$$f = \frac{v}{\lambda}$$

$$= \frac{c}{\lambda}$$

$$= \frac{3.00 \times 10^8 \text{ m/s}}{6.5 \times 10^{-7} \text{ m}}$$

$$f = 4.6 \times 10^{14} \text{ Hz}$$

LEARNING _TIP_

The Speed of Light
The speed of light c equals 3.00×10^8 m/s.

Red light with a wavelength of 6.50×10^2 nm travels from air into crown glass ($n_2 = 1.52$).

(a) What is its speed in the glass?

(b) What is its wavelength in the glass?

Solution

(a) $\lambda = 6.50 \times 10^2$ nm

$n_2 = 1.52$ $n_1 = 1.00$

$v_2 = ?$ $v_1 = 3.00 \times 10^8$ m/s

$$\frac{n_2}{n_1} = \frac{v_1}{v_2}$$

$$v_2 = \frac{n_1}{n_2}v_1$$

$$= \frac{1.00}{1.52}(3.00 \times 10^8 \text{ m/s})$$

$$v_2 = 1.97 \times 10^8 \text{ m/s}$$

The velocity of red light in the glass is 1.97×10^8 m/s.

(b) $\lambda = ?$

$$\frac{v_1}{v_2} = \frac{\lambda_1}{\lambda_2}$$

$$\lambda_2 = \left(\frac{v_2}{v_1}\right)\lambda_1$$

$$= \left(\frac{1.97 \times 10^8 \text{ m/s}}{3.00 \times 10^8 \text{ m/s}}\right) 6.50 \times 10^2 \text{ nm}$$

$$\lambda_2 = 4.28 \times 10^2 \text{ nm}$$

The wavelength of red light in the crown glass is 4.28×10^2 nm.

▶ **Practice**

Understanding Concepts

Answers

1. 5.0×10^{14} Hz

2. 789 nm

3. 3.1×10^{-7} m

4. (a) 4.4×10^{-7} m

   (b) 26°

5. 4.5×10^{-7} m

6. 2.0×10^{-3} m

1. The wavelength of orange light is 6.0×10^{-7} m in air. Calculate its frequency.

2. Light from a certain source has a frequency of 3.80×10^{14} Hz. Calculate its wavelength in air, in nanometres.

3. A certain shade of violet light has a wavelength in air of 4.4×10^{-7} m. If the index of refraction of alcohol relative to air for violet light is 1.40, what is the wavelength of the violet light in alcohol?

4. The index of refraction of turpentine relative to air for red light is 1.47. A ray of red light ($\lambda_r = 6.5 \times 10^{-7}$ m) passes from air into turpentine with an angle of incidence of 40.0°.
   (a) Calculate the wavelength of the red light in the turpentine.
   (b) Calculate the angle of refraction.

5. A certain Young's apparatus has slits 0.12 mm apart. The screen is at a distance of 0.80 m. The third bright line to one side of the centre in the resulting interference pattern is displaced 9.0 mm from the central line. Calculate the wavelength of the light used. What colour was it?

6. Sunlight incident on a screen containing two narrow slits 0.20 mm apart casts a pattern on a white sheet of paper 2.0 m beyond. Find the distance separating the violet ($\lambda = 4.0 \times 10^2$ nm) in the first-order band from the red ($\lambda = 6.0 \times 10^2$ nm) in the second-order band.

Young's Experiment Today

It may be obvious to us now, but it was not obvious to the experimenters in the eighteenth and nineteenth centuries, that to produce an interference pattern, it is necessary to have two point sources of light in phase. Although the frequency of light sources is very high, what makes interference impossible is the way light is emitted from an incandescent source. The light from each source comes from a large number of individual atoms. Atoms send out light in time intervals of about 10^{-9} s. The probability that the atoms or groups of atoms in each source would emit their light waves in phase is nearly zero. Therefore, the interference pattern produced by two point sources changes in an irregular fashion every 10^{-9} s or so and is impossible for an observer to see. In recent years it has been possible to produce interference with two lasers. Laser light is monochromatic; in the case of helium–neon laser light, the wavelength is at the red end of the spectrum, 6.3×10^{-7} m. When two lasers have been made to operate in phase (they are then said to be "phase locked"), the interference fringes are seen. Since phase-locking is not perfect, some drifting of the pattern occurs. Even today, the easiest way to show the interference of light is to use Young's technique of putting a single emitter behind two apertures.

SUMMARY *Colour and Wavelength*

- White light is made of all of the colours found in the visible spectrum, each with its own range of wavelengths.

- Dispersion occurs because the refractive index of light is slightly dependent on the frequency of the light.

▶ *Section 9.6 Questions*

Understanding Concepts

1. For both converging and diverging lenses, explain how the focal length for red light differs from that for violet light.

2. When white light passes through a flat piece of window glass, it is not broken down into colours as it is by a prism. Explain why.

3. A certain shade of red light has a wavelength in air of 7.50×10^{-7} m. If the index of refraction of alcohol is 1.40, calculate the wavelength of this red light in alcohol.

4. The wavelengths of the visible spectrum range from 4.00×10^2 nm to 7.50×10^2 nm. Calculate the range of the frequencies of visible light.

5. Calculate the angle for the third-order maximum of 5.8×10^2 nm wavelength yellow light falling on double slits separated by 0.10 mm.

6. Determine the separation between two slits for which 6.10×10^2 nm orange light has its first maximum at an angle of 3.0°.

7. Using your calculations in questions 5 and 6, explain why it is difficult to observe and analyze the interference pattern produced by a double slit.

Making Connections

8. Explain why a rainbow is impossible just after sunrise and just before sunset.

INVESTIGATION 9.1.1

Transmission, Reflection, and Refraction of Water Waves in a Ripple Tank

Inquiry Skills

○ Questioning	○ Planning	● Analyzing
○ Hypothesizing	● Conducting	● Evaluating
○ Predicting	● Recording	● Communicating

The ripple tank is the equipment of choice for observing two-dimensional transverse waves. The objective of this investigation is to demonstrate the predicted behaviour of waves.

The ripple tank is a shallow, glass-bottomed tank on legs. Water is usually put in the tank to a depth of approximately 2 cm. Light from a source above the tank passes through the water and illuminates a screen on the table below. The light is made to converge by wave crests and to diverge by wave troughs (**Figure 1**), creating bright and dark areas on the screen. The distance between successive bright areas caused by crests is one wavelength, λ. Circular waves may be generated on the surface of the water by a point source like a finger, a drop of water from an eyedropper, or a single-source wave generator. Rolling a dowel, or running a straight wave generatgor produces straight waves.

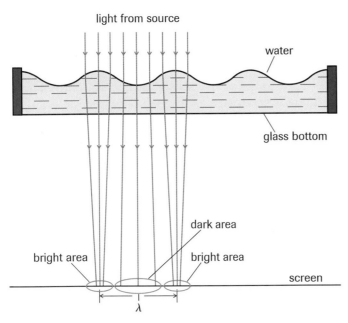

Figure 1
Ripple tank setup

Question

How are waves transmitted, reflected, and refracted in a ripple tank?

Prediction

Waves behave in a way similar to light and obey the same laws of transmission, reflection, and refraction.

Materials

ripple tank	straight wave generator
screen dampers	glass plate
(if necessary)	glass plate supports
wooden dowel	hand stroboscope
wax blocks	ruler

 Since the light source and generators are electrical, tape all wiring away from the water.

Since the lab will be dark, keep all bags, books, and other belongings out of the aisles and away from exits.

Procedure

Part 1: Transmission

1. Put water in the ripple tank to a depth of 1 cm. Level the tank to ensure that the water depth is uniform. (If necessary, place screen dampers at the perimeter of the tank to reduce reflection.)

2. Touch the surface of the water lightly at the centre of the tank with your finger. Observe the shadows on the screen. Make a sketch showing the wave and the source of the wave.

3. On your sketch, at four equally spaced points on the crest of the wave, draw arrows indicating the direction of wave travel.

4. Generate a straight wave with the dowel by rocking it back and forth across the surface. Draw a straight wave, showing the direction of its motion.

5. Generate continuous straight waves by rocking the dowel back and forth steadily. Use a sketch, with arrows, to indicate the direction of the wave movement.

Part 2: Reflection

6. Reduce the depth of the water to approximately 0.5 cm and ensure that the tank is still level.

INVESTIGATION 9.1.1 *continued*

7. Form a straight barrier at one end of the tank, using the wax blocks sitting on edge on the bottom. Send straight waves toward the barrier so that their wave fronts are parallel to the barrier. Make a diagram of your observations.

8. Arrange the barrier so that the waves strike it at an angle. To judge the angles, align rulers or other straight objects on the screen with the wave front images. Make a diagram showing incident wave fronts and reflected wave fronts and their directions of travel.

Part 3: Refraction

9. Position the generators at one end of the tank. Support a glass plate on the spacers so that it is approximately 1.5 cm above the bottom of the tank and about 15 cm from the wave generator. Its longest edge should be parallel to the generator. Put enough water in the tank to cover the glass plate to a depth of about 1 mm (**Figure 2**).

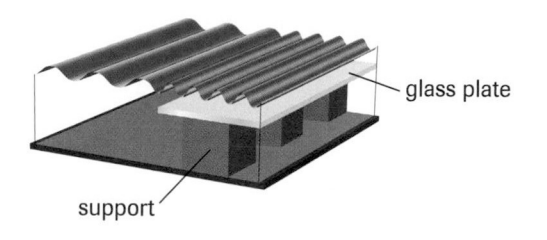

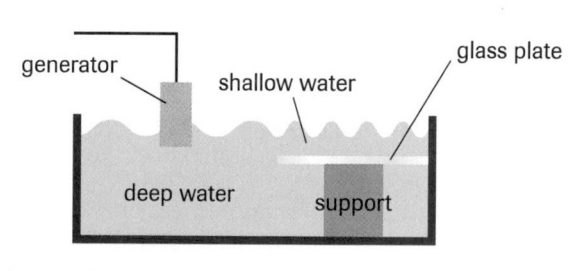

Figure 2
Creating two depths in a ripple tank

10. Adjust the height of the wave generator so the bottom of the vibrator is just below the surface of the water.

11. Adjust the frequency of the generator so that it produces waves with a long wavelength in the deep water. Sketch the pattern produced.

12. Look at the waves through a hand stroboscope, adjusting the stroboscope frequency so that waves in the deep water are "stopped."

13. Determine the shadow wavelength of the waves in both deep and shallow water by measuring the wavelengths of their projected images.

14. Set the edge of the glass plate at an angle of approximately 45° to the incoming waves. Note any changes that occur in the direction of travel of the waves. Draw a diagram showing a series of wave fronts and their directions of travel in both deep and shallow water.

15. Lay a ruler on the screen so that it is perpendicular (normal) to the boundary between the two depths of water. Lay a pencil along the line of incidence (the direction in which the incident wave is moving). Lay another pencil along the line of refraction. Measure the angle of incidence and the angle of refraction. Calculate the index of refraction for the two depths.

16. Repeat step 15 for a different angle of incidence.

Analysis

(a) How can you tell by the shape of the wave fronts that the speed of the wave is the same in all directions?

(b) How are the speed and wavelength of a wave affected by a change in frequency?

(c) As waves pass from the deep water to the shallow water, what changes occur in their speed, their direction of motion, and their wavelength?

(d) How does the value of the ratio $\dfrac{\lambda_{deep}}{\lambda_{shallow}}$ compare with the value determined using Snell's law?

(e) Explain how you could determine the ratio $\dfrac{v_{deep}}{v_{shallow}}$. How does this ratio compare with $\dfrac{\lambda_{deep}}{\lambda_{shallow}}$?

(f) Appraise the accuracy of the Prediction.

Evaluation

(g) Evaluate the prediction.

Synthesis

(h) When waves travel from deep to shallow water, why are they both "stopped" by the stroboscope?

(i) If the waves were passing from shallow to deep water

    (i) how would they be refracted?

    (ii) what relationships would predict their behaviour?

    (iii) what other phenomena would you expect to observe in the slower medium?

Diffraction of Water Waves

In this investigation, you are challenged to use your knowledge of ripple tanks to design your own procedure in response to the Question and Prediction posed. If you take care to produce a sharp shadow on the screen, your results should be excellent. Make sure you fully understand the relationship between wavelength and slit width.

Question

What factors affect the diffraction of a wave around an obstacle, by an edge, and through an opening?

Prediction

(a) Predict the two conditions that will maximize diffraction through an opening.

Materials

ripple tank and accessories
wave generator with a straight source
wax blocks of various sizes

 Since the light source and generators are electrical, tape all wiring away from the water.

Since the lab will be dark, keep all bags, books, and other belongings out of the aisles and away from exits.

Procedure

1. Some issues to address in your procedure include:
   (i) Do you require your wave fronts to change speed?
   (ii) How can you change your wave fronts from parallel to circular?
   (iii) How will you alter the wavelength of your waves?
   (iv) How will you use the wax blocks as barriers, and how will you create apertures in barriers?

Analysis

(b) How is the diffraction pattern behind the block affected when the wavelength is increased?

(c) Does diffraction around an edge increase or decrease when the wavelength increases?

(d) How must wavelength compare with aperture width if diffraction is to be kept small?

(e) Based on your prediction, what are the conditions for maximum diffraction through an opening?

(f) What value of $\frac{\lambda}{w}$ will produce noticeable diffraction?

(g) Answer the Question and appraise the accuracy of your prediction.

Evaluation

(h) Evaluate your design.

Interference of Waves in Two Dimensions

You have seen the pattern of interference of waves in two dimensions in photographs in this text and may also have observed the pattern in previous studies. Now, you will generate an interference pattern yourself and take some direct measurements. The purpose of this investigation is to test the theoretical analysis provided in the text and to apply the mathematical equations on an actual two-point interference pattern.

Question

What factors affect the patterns of interference produced by two identical water waves in a ripple tank?

Prediction

(a) Predict mathematically the wavelength of waves based on direct measurements of the interference pattern.

INVESTIGATION 9.3.1 *continued*

(b) Predict the two-point interference pattern produced using the diffraction of waves from a single wave source through two apertures.

Materials

ripple tank and accessories
wave generator with adjustable
    separation and phase control

2 point sources
wax blocks
hand stroboscope

🤚 **Since the light source and generators are electrical, tape all wiring away from the water.**

Since the lab will be dark, keep all bags, books, and other belongings out of the aisles and away from exits.

Procedure

1. Set up the ripple tank, making sure it is level. Fill it with water to a depth of approximately 1 cm.

2. Make a wave with one finger, then start a second wave some distance away. Observe the two waves as they pass through one another. Repeat the procedure for various points in the tank.

3. Connect the two point sources to the generator so that they are about 6.0 cm apart. Ensure that the two sources are in phase. (If your generator has a phase adjustment, set it at 0.)

4. Place the generator so that the two point sources are dipping equally into the water at one end of the tank. Generate waves with a frequency of approximately 10 Hz. Examine the pattern on the screen. Identify the nodal lines and the lines of constructive interference. Sketch the nodal line pattern.

5. Adjust the frequency of the generator. Record the effect of a change in frequency on the interference pattern.

6. Keeping the frequency constant, change the separation of the sources in steps, allowing the interference pattern to stabilize between changes. Record how the separation of the sources affects the interference pattern.

7. The relative phase of two sources also affects the interference pattern. Adjust the frequency of the generator so that a clearly visible pattern is produced on the screen. Place a pencil or other straight object on the screen so that it lies on a nodal line. Turn the phase control of the generator from 0 to $\frac{1}{2}$ (or 180°), then back to 0. Describe the changes in the interference pattern.

8. Stop the generator. On the screen, mark the positions of S_1 and S_2. Draw a line joining the sources. Next, draw the right bisector of this line, extending it across the screen (**Figure 1**).

9. Adjust the frequency of the generator so that three nodal lines are produced on either side of the right bisector. Choosing one nodal line, mark three nodal points (P_1, P_2, and P_3) on the screen. Make sure that one of these points is fairly close to S_1 and S_2 and that one is quite far away.

10. By making the appropriate measurements and calculations, predict the wavelength of the waves on the screen using two different mathematical relationships.

11. Repeat step 9 for three points on a different nodal line, on the other side of the right bisector.

12. Find an average calculated value for the wavelength of the waves.

13. Without changing the frequency of the waves, use a hand stroboscope to make the waves appear stationary. Measure the distance between three or four troughs or crests by placing markers on the screen. Calculate the wavelength. Compare your result with what you found in step 11.

(a)

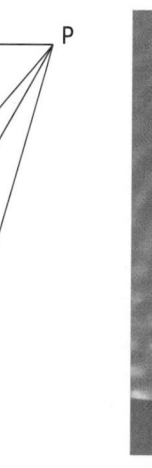

(b)

Figure 1
(a) Determining the path difference by measuring θ
(b) Measuring L and x on an interference pattern

14. Generate an interference pattern by using a single straight source and diffraction, as shown in **Figure 2**, by positioning your wax blocks so that two small openings are created, approximately 6.0 cm apart and 10.0 cm from the generator. Predict the result with a sketch.

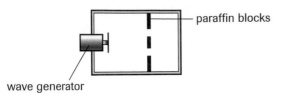

paraffin blocks

wave generator

Figure 2
Setup for step 14

15. With the generator operating, sketch the resulting interference pattern.

Analysis

(c) How does the interference pattern change when the frequency increases?

(d) How does the interference pattern change when the source separation increases?

(e) In what respects does the interference pattern change and in what respects does it stay constant when the relative phase of your sources changes from 0° to 180°?

Evaluation

(f) How does your Prediction compare with your results from step 14?

(g) How valid are the predicted wavelengths of the waves, based on mathematical wave interference relationships, when compared with direct measurements?

Synthesis

(h) The measurements for both the calculated and predicted values for the wavelength were done on the screen and are not the actual wavelengths of the water waves. Explain this. Why is this not a factor when validating the mathematical equations for a two-point interference pattern?

(i) If the relative phase of two identical sources were constantly changing, what effect would this have on the interference pattern?

(j) When a single source is used, why is the interference pattern more stable than that with two sources?

Young's Double-Slit Experiment

Young performed his experiment, as described in the text, with two pinholes in a piece of paper and the Sun as the light source. Today, we can use prepared double-slit plates of known separation and an intense monochromatic light source. This investigation applies the equations developed in Section 9.5 to measurements on a two-point interference pattern. You will determine the wavelength of laser light. You can check your results against the known wavelength of a helium–neon laser. But if you have a common LED, such as is found on pointers and key chains, you can use that instead, recreating the investigation at home if you wish.

Question

Is the double-slit interference pattern consistent with the wave theory of light?

Inquiry Skills

○ Questioning	○ Planning	● Analyzing
○ Hypothesizing	● Conducting	● Evaluating
○ Predicting	● Recording	● Communicating

Hypothesis

The wavelength of a certain source can be predicted using the mathematical relationship for a two-point interference pattern.

Materials

metre stick	white screen
support stand and clamp	helium–neon laser
multiple-slit plate	or red LED

 Low-power helium–neon laser light can cause temporary retinal damage. DO NOT look into the laser beam or into the reflection of the beam from a shiny surface.

INVESTIGATION 9.5.1 *continued*

Procedure

1. Direct the laser light through a double slit onto the screen located at least 3.0 m away (**Figure 1**). Describe the interference pattern.

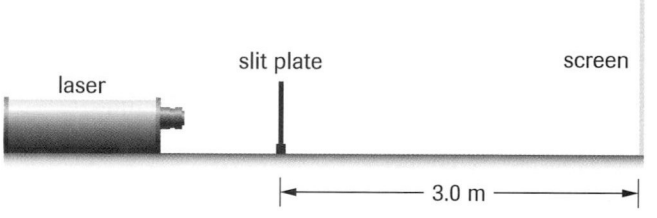

Figure 1
For step 1

2. Determine Δx by measuring the distance over at least seven bright points on the screen.

3. Predict the wavelength of the helium–neon laser light using the relationship $\dfrac{\Delta x}{L} = \dfrac{\lambda}{d}$.

4. Repeat steps 1 and 2 for two other pairs of slits that have different slit separations, d.

5. Your instructor will provide you with the wavelength of the light source. Compare this value with the average of your predictions in steps 2 and 3.

Analysis

(a) Compare the average results for the wavelength of the light source with the known value, and calculate the experimental error.

Evaluation

(b) What are the factors that contribute to the error in the measurement of the wavelength of laser light?

(c) Are there methods you might use to reduce error, given that the wavelength of the laser light is known to at least four significant figures?

Synthesis

(d) As you learned, the wavelength λ and the separation of the sources d affect the number of nodal lines produced. Using your results from steps 2 and 3, determine the effects of source separation on the nodal line structure for light.

(e) Compare your results with observations for water wave interference.

(f) Why does this investigation provide such strong support for the wave theory of light?

INVESTIGATION 9.6.1

Wavelengths of Visible Light

Inquiry Skills

○ Questioning	○ Planning	● Analyzing
○ Hypothesizing	● Conducting	● Evaluating
● Predicting	● Recording	● Communicating

If you have access to LEDs of different colours, this investigation is similar to 9.5.1. The wavelengths of various colours of visible light can be determined directly and accurately. As stated here (you can make adjustments if you have access to monochromatic LEDs), the procedure uses green and red filters with a white source. Sliders on a metre stick are used to measure the separation of the interference fringes. The measured distance from the slit to the sliders permits you to find the ratio $\dfrac{\Delta x}{L}$. Since you also know d, the slit separation, you can determine the wavelength. The purpose of this investigation is not to just measure the dominant wavelengths of your green and red filters, but to determine experimentally a range of wavelengths, and thus frequencies, for visible light.

Question

What are some of the wavelengths that constitute white light?

Prediction

(a) Predict the relationship between the wavelengths of red and green light.

Materials

clear showcase lamp
metre stick
retort stand and clamp
double-slit plate
white screen

red and green transparent
    filters
green-or blue light-emitting
    diode
paper sliders

The light bulb will become very hot. Allow it to cool before changing filters.

Procedure

1. Set up the apparatus as illustrated in **Figure 1**, ensuring that the slits are parallel to the filament of the lamp. View the clear lamp through the double slit. Describe the pattern seen on either side of the lamp filament.

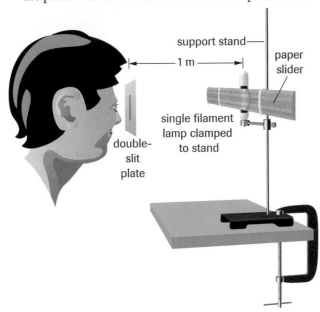

Figure 1
Setup for step 1

2. Cover the upper half of the bulb with the green filter and the lower half with the red filter, holding each in place with rubber bands. Compare the respective interference patterns for green and for red light.

3. Cover the lamp completely with the red filter. Using the ruler mounted in front of the light, count the number of nodal lines visible in a fixed distance. Paper sliders on the ruler can mark the distance.

4. Predict the relative wavelengths of red and green light.

5. Leaving the paper sliders in place, replace the red filter with the green filter. View the interference pattern from the same position as in step 3, and count the number of nodal lines visible between the paper sliders.

6. Using the number of nodal lines counted for the same viewing distance in steps 3 and 4, determine the ratio of the number of red lines to the number of green lines; determine the ratio $\frac{\lambda_{red}}{\lambda_{green}}$.

7. Cover the lamp completely with the red filter. View the red light through the double slit from a distance of exactly 1.0 m from the ruler. Adjust the paper sliders so that they are located on two nodal lines at opposite ends of the pattern. Count the number of bright lines between the markers. Measure the distance between the paper sliders, and calculate the average separation Δx of adjacent nodal lines.

8. Using the relationship $\frac{\Delta x}{L} = \frac{\lambda}{d}$, determine the wavelength of the red light. The value of d, the distance between the slits, is either recorded on your slit plate or available from your instructor. L is the perpendicular distance from the slits to the ruler (1.0 m).

9. Repeat steps 7 and 8 for green light.

10. Compare your results with those obtained by other groups.

11. If you have a green or blue LED, use the relationship $\lambda = \frac{d\Delta x}{L}$ to find the wavelength of each source.

Analysis

(b) Explain your observation for the source of white light in step 1.

(c) Why is the interference pattern for green light more closely spaced than the corresponding pattern for red light?

(d) Given the value of the ratio $\frac{\lambda_{red}}{\lambda_{green}}$ in step 6, which colour has the higher wavelength? the higher frequency?

(e) Compare your answer for (b) with your prediction.

(f) Compare your value for the ratio $\frac{\lambda_{red}}{\lambda_{green}}$ in step 6 with the ratio of the values for red and green light calculated in steps 8 and 9.

Evaluation

(g) What is the percentage difference for the values calculated for $\frac{\lambda_{red}}{\lambda_{green}}$?

(h) Why can you not expect all groups in your class to obtain the same wavelength for the red light?

Synthesis

(i) Why would the wavelengths for green and red light not vary significantly from group to group if LEDs were used as the sources for these colours?

Key Expectations

- analyze and interpret experimental evidence indicating that light has some characteristics and properties that are similar to those of mechanical waves and sound (9.1, 9.2, 9.6)
- identify the theoretical basis of an investigation, and develop a prediction that is consistent with that theoretical basis (e.g., predict diffraction and interference patterns produced in ripple tanks) (9.2, 9.3, 9.6)
- describe instances where the development of new technologies resulted in the advancement or revision of scientific theories (9.4)
- describe and explain the experimental evidence supporting a wave model of light (e.g., describe the scientific principles related to Young's double-slit experiment and explain how the results led to a general acceptance of the wave model of light) (9.4, 9.5)
- define and explain the concepts and units related to the wave nature of light (e.g., diffraction, reflection, dispersion, refraction, wave interference) (9.4, 9.5, 9.6)
- describe the phenomenon of wave interference as it applies to light in qualitative and quantitative terms, using diagrams and sketches (9.4, 9.5, 9.6)
- describe and explain the phenomenon of wave diffraction as it applies to light in quantitative terms, using diagrams (9.5, 9.6)
- collect and interpret experimental data in support of a scientific theory (e.g., conduct an experiment to observe the interference pattern produced by a light source shining through a double slit and explain how the data support the wave theory of light) (9.5, 9.6)
- analyze, using the concepts of refraction, diffraction, and wave interference, the separation of light into colours in various phenomena (9.6)

Key Terms

transverse wave

wave front

wave ray

angle of incidence

angle of reflection

refraction

normal

angle of refraction

absolute index of refraction

total internal reflection

diffraction

constructive interference

destructive interference

nodal lines

difference in path length

rectilinear propagation

Huygens' principle

interference fringes

minima

maxima

monochromatic

Key Equations

- $v = f\lambda$ universal wave equation   (9.1)

- $\dfrac{v_1}{v_2} = \dfrac{\lambda_1}{\lambda_2}$ (9.1)

- $\dfrac{\sin \theta_1}{\sin \theta_2} = \dfrac{\lambda_1}{\lambda_2}$ (9.1)

- $n_1 \sin \theta_1 = n_2 \sin \theta_2$ (9.1)

- $|P_nS_1 - P_nS_2| = \left(n - \dfrac{1}{2}\right)\lambda$ (9.3)

- $\sin \theta_n = \dfrac{x_n}{L} = \left(n - \dfrac{1}{2}\right)\dfrac{\lambda}{d}$ (9.3)

- destructive interference:

  $d \sin \theta_n = \left(n - \dfrac{1}{2}\right)\lambda$ where $n = 1, 2, 3, ...$ (9.5)

- constructive interference:

  $d \sin \theta_m = m\lambda$ where $m = 0, 1, 2, 3, ...$ (9.5)

- $\dfrac{\Delta x}{L} = \dfrac{\lambda}{d}$ (9.5)

▶ ***MAKE*** *a summary*

Set up a table in two columns, with the headings Particle Theory and Wave Theory. Label the rows with phrases for seven important optical phenomena. For each row, indicate how well each theory explains the given phenomenon.

Write numbers 1 to 10 in your notebook. Indicate beside each a number whether the corresponding statement is true (T) or false (F). If it is false, write a corrected version.

1. The universal wave equation, $v = f\lambda$, applies only to transverse waves.

2. Snell's law in the form $n = \dfrac{\sin \theta_1}{\sin \theta_2}$ holds for both waves and light.

3. Waves with shorter wavelength experience more diffraction than waves with a longer wavelength.

4. For a given slit, the amount of diffraction depends on the ratio $\dfrac{\lambda}{w}$. For observable diffraction, $\dfrac{\lambda}{w} \leq 1$.

5. In a two-point, in-phase interference pattern, increasing the wavelength of the two sources increases the number of nodal lines.

6. Decreasing the separation of the two-point interference pattern sources increases the number of nodal lines.

7. Newton's particle theory provided a satisfactory explanation for four properties of light: rectilinear propagation, reflection, refraction, and dispersion. It was weak in its explanation of diffraction and partial reflection–partial refraction.

8. Early attempts to demonstrate the interference of light were unsuccessful because the two sources were too far apart and out of phase and the frequency of light is very small.

9. Dispersion occurs because the refractive index of light is slightly higher for red light than it is for violet light.

10. Young's experiment validated the wave theory of light and explained all the properties of light.

Write numbers 11 to 23 in your notebook. Beside each number, write the letter corresponding to the best choice.

11. A beam of light travels from a vacuum ($c = 3.00 \times 10^8$ m/s) into a substance at an angle of 45°, with a frequency of 6.00×10^{14} Hz and a speed of 2.13×10^8 m/s. The index of refraction of the substance is
    (a) 0.707
    (b) 1.41
    (c) 1.50
    (d) indeterminable, but < 1
    (e) indeterminable, but > 1

12. You observe diffraction in a ripple tank (**Figure 1**). To increase the diffraction of the waves in the region beyond the barrier, you consider the following adjustments:
    (i)   decreasing the width of the opening
    (ii) decreasing the depth of the water
    (iii) decreasing the frequency of the source

    The best adjustment, or combination of adjustments, is
    (a) (i) only
    (b) (ii) only
    (c) (iii) only
    (d) (i) and (iii) only
    (e) (i), (ii), and (iii)

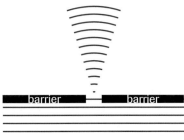

wave generator   **Figure 1**

13. Diffraction by a single slit in a ripple tank can be decreased by
    (a) increasing the frequency of the source
    (b) increasing the amplitude of the waves
    (c) decreasing the width of the slit
    (d) decreasing the distance between the wave generator and the slit
    (e) using a longer wavelength

14. Two point sources in a ripple tank vibrate in phase at a frequency of 12 Hz to produce waves of wavelength 0.024 m. The difference in path length from the two point sources to a point on the second nodal line is
    (a) 0.6 cm   (d) 3.6 cm
    (b) 1.2 cm   (e) 4.8 cm
    (c) 2.4 cm

15. Two point sources 4.5 cm apart are vibrating in phase in a ripple tank. You count exactly 10 nodal lines in the entire interference pattern. The approximate wavelength of the water waves in the tank is
    (a) 0.45 cm   (d) 10 cm
    (b) 1.0 cm   (e) insufficient data provided
    (c) 1.5 cm

16. You observe the wave pattern in **Figure 2** as you investigate periodic waves in a ripple tank. You draw the straight lines shown superimposed on the figure. The wavelength is

    (a) $\dfrac{x}{L}$ (b) $\dfrac{dx}{L}$ (c) $\dfrac{2dx}{L}$ (d) $\dfrac{2x}{3L}$ (e) $\dfrac{xd}{2L}$

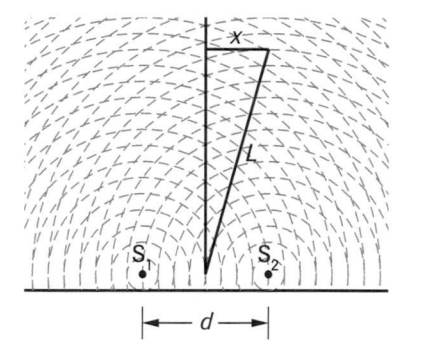

Figure 2
For questions 16, 17, and 18

17. You wish to continue the same pattern as in question 16, but contemplate making adjustments:
    (i)   increasing the frequency of the waves
    (ii) increasing the separation of the sources
    (iii) introducing a phase delay in S_1

    The adjustment, or combination of adjustments, that results in a larger number of nodal lines is
    (a) (i) only
    (b) (ii) only
    (c) (iii) only
    (d) (i) and (ii) only
    (e) (i), (ii), and (iii)

18. The adjustment, or combination of adjustments, in question 17 that results only in a shift of the nodal lines is
    (a) (i) only
    (b) (ii) only
    (c) (iii) only
    (d) (i) and (ii) only
    (e) (i), (ii), and (iii)

19. The particle theory is unable to account for the phenomenon of
    (a) radiation pressure
    (b) emission
    (c) interference
    (d) propagation
    (e) reflection

20. The statement regarding Young's experiment that is false is
    (a) Diffraction of light occurs at both slits.
    (b) Light waves leaving the two slits have a fixed phase.
    (c) The interference pattern from this experiment has a nodal line down the centre of the pattern.
    (d) The separation of the nodal lines is dependent on the wavelength of the light.
    (e) The particle theory was unable to give a satisfactory explanation of this phenomenon.

21. In a double-slit experiment, monochromatic light is used to produce interference fringes on a screen. The distance between the slits and the screen is 1.50 m. The bright fringes are separated by 0.30 cm. If the screen is moved so that it is 1.0 m from the slits, the average distance between adjacent dark fringes will be
    (a) 0.20 cm   (c) 0.45 cm   (e) 1.5 cm
    (b) 0.30 cm   (d) 0.67 cm

22. Ultraviolet light of wavelength 340 nm falls on a double slit. A fluorescent screen is placed 2.0 m away. The screen shows dark interference bands 3.4 cm apart. The distance between the slits is
    (a) 2.0 cm   (c) 0.020 cm   (e) none of these
    (b) 0.20 cm   (d) 0.0020 cm

23. **Figure 3** shows a double-slit pattern produced by a monochromatic source of pattern (**a**), which is changed to pattern (**b**). The following are possible adjustments:
    (i)   The frequency of the source was decreased.
    (ii) The frequency of the source was increased.
    (iii) The width of each slit was increased.
    (iv) The separation of the slits was increased.
    (v)   The separation of the slits was decreased.

    The adjustment, or combination of adjustments, that explains pattern (**b**) is
    (a) (iii) only
    (b) (v) only
    (c) (i) and (iii) only
    (d) (i) and (v) only
    (e) (ii) and (iv) only

(a)   **(b)**

Figure 3

NEL   An interactive version of the quiz is available online.
GO www.science.nelson.com

Waves and Light   **489**

Understanding Concepts

1. Explain why the wavelength of light decreases when it passes from a vacuum into a material. State which properties change and which stay the same.

2. List the similarities and differences between refraction and diffraction.

3. What is the ratio of thickness of crown glass and water that would contain the same number of wavelengths of light? ($n_g = 1.52$, $n_w = 1.33$)

4. Refraction was an area of difficulty for the particle theory of light. What phenomena of refraction were not known to Newton and his fellow supporters of the particle theory?

5. Describe and explain the experimental evidence collected up to the end of this chapter in support of the wave theory of light.

6. Explain why light from the two headlights of a car does not produce an interference pattern.

7. Young's experiment was a pivotal event in the history of science. Discuss the merits of this statement and summarize the basic concepts of the experiment.

8. Analysis of an interference effect in a clear material shows that within the material, light from a helium-neon laser of wavelength 6.33×10^{-7} m in air has a wavelength of 3.30×10^{-7} m. Is the material zircon or diamond? ($n_z = 1.92$, $n_d = 2.42$)

9. Light travels in water at three-quarters the speed it attains in air. If the angle of incidence in air were 10.0°, what would be the angle in water, according to a particle theorist?

10. Monochromatic light is incident on twin slits in a Young's double-slit experiment. The slits are separated by 0.50 mm. A screen located 6.50 m from the slits has nodal lines separated by 7.7 mm. Calculate the wavelength of the light.

11. In a Young's double-slit experiment, the angle that locates the second-order bright (not dark) fringe is 2.0°. The slit separation is 0.038 mm. Find the wavelength of the light.

12. Blue light ($\lambda = 482$ nm) is directed through parallel slits separated by 0.15 mm. A fringe pattern appears on a screen 2.00 m away. How far from the central axis on either side are the second-order dark bands?

13. A beam of light of wavelength 5.50×10^2 nm falls on a screen containing a pair of narrow slits separated by 0.10 mm. Calculate the separation between the two seventh-order maxima on a screen 2.00 m from the slits.

14. In Young's double-slit experiment, is it possible to see interference fringes only when the wavelength of the light is greater than the distance between the slits? Explain your answer.

15. A laser emitting at 632.8 nm illuminates a double slit. A screen is positioned 2.00 m from the slits. Interference fringes are observed with a separation of 1.0 cm.
    (a) Determine the separation of the slits.
    (b) Determine the angle of the first-order dark fringes.

16. In a Young's double-slit experiment, the angle for the second-order bright fringe is 2.0°; the slit separation is 3.8×10^{-5} m. Calculate the wavelength of the light.

17. Calculate the longest wavelength of light falling on double slits separated by 1.20×10^{-6} m for which there is a first-order maximum. In what part of the spectrum is this light?

18. A certain electromagnetic radiation has a frequency of 4.75×10^{14} Hz. Calculate its wavelength and, referring to **Table 1** in Section 9.6, state in which part of the spectrum this radiation is found.

19. In a double-slit experiment, blue light of wavelength 4.60×10^2 nm gives a second-order maximum at a certain location P on the screen. What wavelength of visible light would have a minimum at P?

20. Two slits are 0.158 mm apart. A mixture of red light ($\lambda = 665$ nm) and yellow-green light ($\lambda = 565$ nm) falls onto the slits. A screen is located 2.2 m away. Find the distance between the third-order red fringe and the third-order yellow-green fringe.

21. Light of wavelength 4.00×10^{-7} m in air falls onto two slits 5.00×10^{-5} m apart. The whole apparatus is immersed in water, including a viewing screen 40.0 cm away. How far apart are the fringes on the screen? ($n_{water} = 1.33$)

Applying Inquiry Skills

22. **Figure 1** in Section 9.6 is a two-point interference pattern for red, blue, and white light. Assuming that the photograph is enlarged four times, that the distance from the double slits is 1.00 m, and that the slit separation is 6.87×10^{-4} m, find the wavelengths of red and blue light.

23. In **Figure 1**, point P is on the third nodal line in a ripple tank interference pattern. The pattern, drawn to scale, was created by the two sources S_1 and S_2 vibrating in phase. Using a ruler, find the value of the wavelength of the interfering waves. (scale: 1.0 mm = 1.0 cm)

• P

• •   **Figure 1**
S_1 S_2 For question 23

Making Connections

24. Every autumn, some storms off Nova Scotia and the eastern seaboard of the United States create waves up to 35 m high. Often, rogue waves can appear from the storms hundreds of kilometres away, so their creation is not just the effect of high winds. Previous storms have been modelled to help marine forecasters better predict wave arrivals. Research the Internet for the latest research on how these waves are created and for the latest improvements in forecasting techniques. Present your findings in a creative way.

 www.science.nelson.com

25. The transmitting antenna for a radio station is 7.00 km from your house. The frequency of the electromagnetic wave broadcast by this station is 536 kHz. The station builds a second transmitting antenna that broadcasts an identical electromagnetic wave in phase with the first one. The new antenna is 8.12 km from your house. Show, with diagrams and calculations, whether constructive or destructive interference occurs at your radio.

26. A rock concert is being held in an open field. Two speakers are separated by 7.00 m. As an aid in arranging the seating, both speakers operate in phase and produce an 85-Hz bass tone simultaneously. A centre line is marked out in front of the speakers, perpendicular to the midpoint of the line between the speakers. Determine the smallest angle, relative to either side of this reference line, that locates places where the audience has trouble hearing the 85-Hz bass tone. (The speed of sound is 346 m/s.)

27. Two stereo speakers are placed 4.00 m apart against the east–west wall of a home theatre. A wiring error causes the speaker cones to vibrate 180° out of phase.

(a) What is the main problem with this arrangement if you are sitting at a point equidistant from the speakers?

(b) How far due east should you move along the opposite wall, 5.0 m away, to hear a peak in the intensity level of an 842-Hz sound? (The speed of sound is 346 m/s.)

28. Two 1.0-MHz radio antennas emitting in phase are separated by 585 m along a north–south line. A radio 19 km from each of the two transmitting antennas, on the east side of the line, picks up a fairly strong signal. How far north should the receiver be moved if it is again to detect a signal nearly as strong?

Extension

29. In a Young's double-slit experiment, using light of wavelength 488 nm, the angular separation of the interference fringes on a distant screen is measured to be 1.0°. Calculate the slit separation.

30. Light of wavelengths 4.80×10^2 nm and 632 nm passes through two slits 0.52 mm apart. How far apart are the second-order fringes on a screen 1.6 m away?

31. A police cruiser sets up a novel radar speed trap, consisting of two transmitting antennas at the edge of a main north–south road. One antenna is 2.0 m [W] of the other. The antennas, essentially point sources of continuous radio waves, are fed from a common transmitter with a frequency of 3.0×10^9 Hz. The trap is set for cars travelling south. A motorist drives a car equipped with a "radar detector" along an east–west road that crosses the main road at a level intersection 1.0×10^2 m [N] of the radar trap. The motorist hears a series of beeps upon driving west through the intersection. The time interval between successive quiet spots is 0.20 s as the car crosses the main road. How fast is the car moving?

🍎 Sir Isaac Newton Contest Question

32. You are carrying a small radio receiver that receives a signal from a transmitter located a few kilometres north of your position. You receive from the same transmitter a signal reflected from the aluminum siding on a house a few hundred metres south of your position. As you carry the receiver 9.0 m north, you notice that the sound level changes from a maximum to a minimum. What is the frequency of the radio transmitters? (Radio waves travel at the speed of light.)

🍎 Sir Isaac Newton Contest Question

10

Wave Effects of Light

▶ **In this chapter, you will be able to**

- describe polarized light in terms of its properties and behaviour and how it is applied in everyday applications

- explain single-slit diffraction and diffraction grating interference patterns, both qualitatively and quantitatively

- explain the operation of the spectroscope and the interferometer in terms of the wave properties of light

- describe how the wave properties of light are important in resolution of optical instruments and how these properties are applied in various applications of thin-film interference, for example, Newton's rings, colours in thin films, coated surfaces, CDs, and DVDs

- explain the basic concepts holography

- describe electromagnetic waves in terms of their properties and where they belong in the electromagnetic spectrum

Soap bubbles, colourful effects of oil on water, the visible spectrum, peacock feathers—this is a colourful chapter (**Figure 1**). You will learn how these effects are produced as well as how CDs (compact discs) and Polaroid sunglasses work. And our analysis of both visible and invisible electromagnetic waves will complete our exploration of the wave nature of light.

The commercial applications, which could not have been developed without an understanding of the wave theory of light, are very common in our everyday lives. Look at your digital watch or calculator display. These work because of the polarization of light. Notice the spectrum reflected from a CD or the shimmering effect on a bumper sticker. Light has been diffracted by a series of small slits or gratings. See the spectrum of colours on the pavement after a rain, look at the beauty of a large soap bubble in the bright sunlight, or admire the feathers of the peacock. All of these involve light interference in thin films. Answer your cell phone or watch moving images on your television that have been transmitted from all over the world by satellites. The development of these technologies required an understanding of electromagnetic waves. Even the manufacture of suntan lotion requires an understanding of electromagnetic radiation.

💡 REFLECT on your learning ▼

1. Why do you think polarizing sunglasses reduce glare?
2. Why do you think holding a CD in white light produces a rainbow effect?
3. Why does your camera lens have a purple glare?
4. Peacock feathers show brilliant colours, particularly in the green and blue parts of the spectrum (**Figure 2**). The colours are due, not to feather pigments, but to a wave effect of light. Can you explain the effect?

Figure 2
A peacock shows off his plumage.

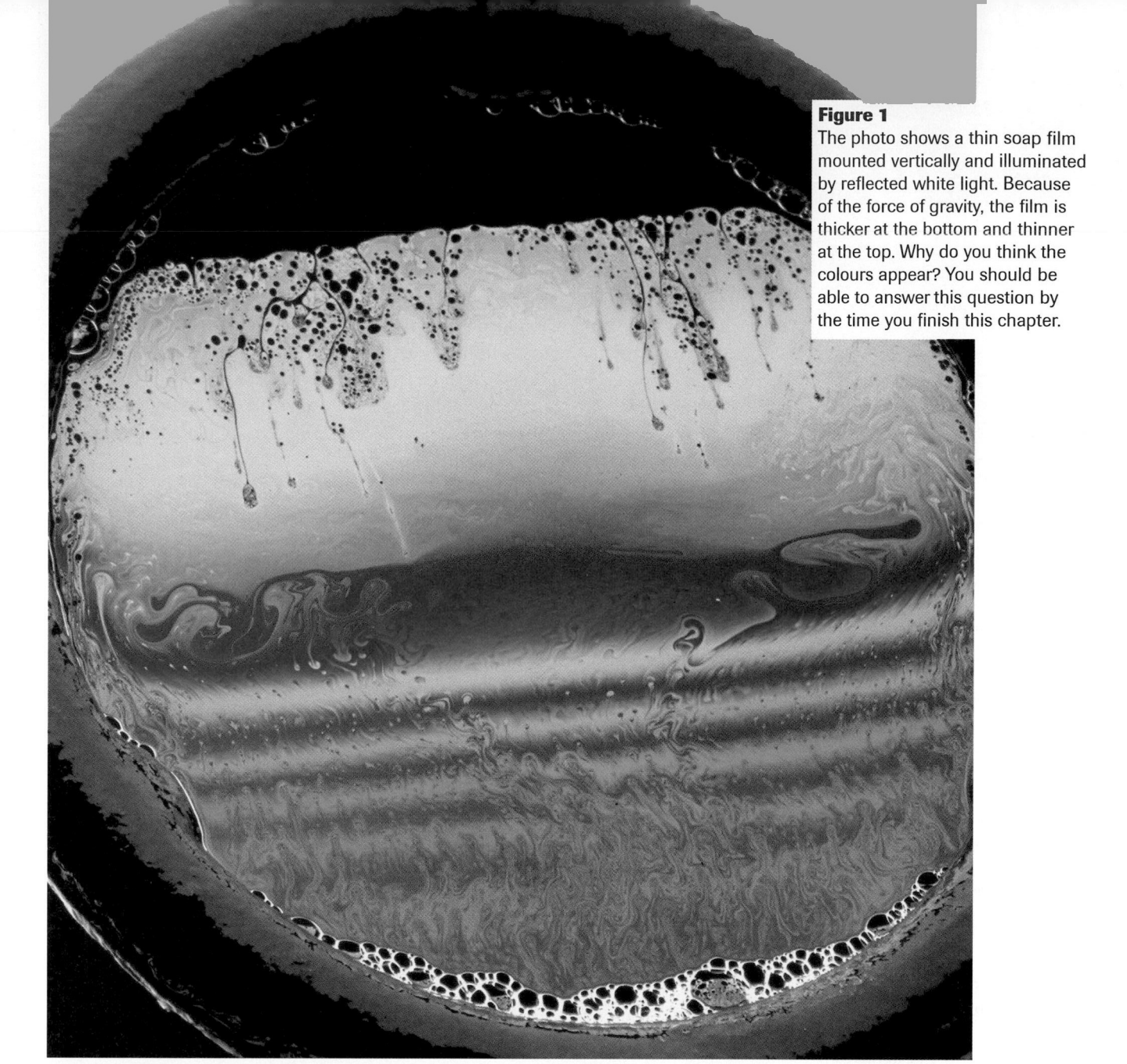

Figure 1

The photo shows a thin soap film mounted vertically and illuminated by reflected white light. Because of the force of gravity, the film is thicker at the bottom and thinner at the top. Why do you think the colours appear? You should be able to answer this question by the time you finish this chapter.

▶ **TRY THIS** activity **Thin Film on Water**

For this activity, you will need a piece of black cloth or a piece of black construction paper, a piece of plane glass, some kerosene or light machine oil, a bright light source, and red and blue filters.

- Spread the cloth or construction paper on a flat table.
- Place the plane glass on top of the black surface. Cover the surface of the glass with a thin layer of water.
- Place a few drops of light machine oil or kerosene on the water.

- Direct a bright white light source, such as a quartz reading light, at the surface. Darken the room. Note the interference pattern on the surface of the water.
- Place a red then a blue filter in front of the light, noting changes in the pattern.

(a) What do you think the dark areas in the oil film represent?

(b) What do you think caused the patterns you see?

(c) Why do you think the pattern changed when the colour of the light changed?

Interference in Young's experiment was a crucial test for the wave theory of light, but it gave no clue to whether light waves are transverse or longitudinal. Recall that it is possible to produce a two-source interference pattern with longitudinal sound waves in air as well as transverse water waves in a ripple tank.

In 1669, the Danish scientist Erasmus Bartholinus found that when he directed a beam of light into a crystal of Iceland spar (calcite), the ray was split into two beams. This effect can be observed if a calcite crystal is placed over a written word. **Figure 1** shows that the two rays create a double image. What causes the light to split into two rays travelling along different paths?

Let us hypothesize that the vibrations in a light wave are transverse and that they go in all directions, perpendicular to the direction in which the light is travelling. If such a transverse wave were to pass through a filter that allowed the vibrations to occur only in one plane, then the wave would be **plane-polarized**. We can illustrate this with a mechanical model. Transverse waves generated in a rope that is moved, in rapid succession, first up and down, then horizontally sideways, are **unpolarized** transverse waves. If the rope passes through a vertical slit, the transmitted waves vibrate only up and down, in the vertical plane. If these vertically polarized waves encounter a second slit, this time horizontal, the energy is absorbed or reflected, and the wave transmission will be almost completely stopped (**Figure 2**). This behaviour is also true for light.

Now that you have a basic understanding of **polarization**, we can study the effect of **polarizers**—natural and artificial—on light. How can the intensity of light be diminished or even appear to be cancelled? What type of wave is light, and how is light polarized by reflection and scattering? These are some of the questions we will be discussing.

Figure 1
This calcite crystal (shown in pink light) creates a double image.

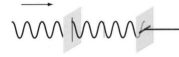

Figure 2
Vertically polarized waves in a rope are stopped almost completely by a horizontal polarizing slit.

plane-polarized a wave that can vibrate in one plane only

unpolarized a wave that vibrates in all directions perpendicular to the direction of travel

polarization confining the vibrations of a wave to one direction

polarizer a natural (e.g., clouds) or artificial (e.g., filters) means to achieve polarization

> ▶ **TRY THIS** activity   *Polaroid Sheets*
>
> 1. Hold a Polaroid sheet up to a light and rotate it 180°.
> 2. Hold two sheets of Polaroid up together, so light passes through both. Keeping one fixed, rotate the other 180°.
> 3. Using a bright light, create some glare on a flat surface such as a lab desk. Look at the glare through a single Polaroid sheet. Rotate the sheet.
> 4. Hold the Polaroid sheet against various regions of a clear blue sky. Rotate the sheet each time.
>
> **Never look directly at the Sun, even with polarizing filters; they do not protect your eyes from the damaging ultraviolet and infrared radiation.**

When light passes through a polarizing filter, the light waves are polarized in one plane. If the filter is oriented in such a way that the vibrations are horizontal, then we call the light horizontally polarized. If this horizontally polarized light falls on a second polarizing filter (the "analyzer") that polarizes light in the vertical plane, the light energy is almost completely absorbed (**Figure 3**). Such absorption occurs not just for vertical and horizontal orientations, but whenever the axes of the polarizing filters are at right angles to each other. When the axes of the two filters are parallel, the light polarized by the first filter passes through the second without further absorption (**Figure 4**).

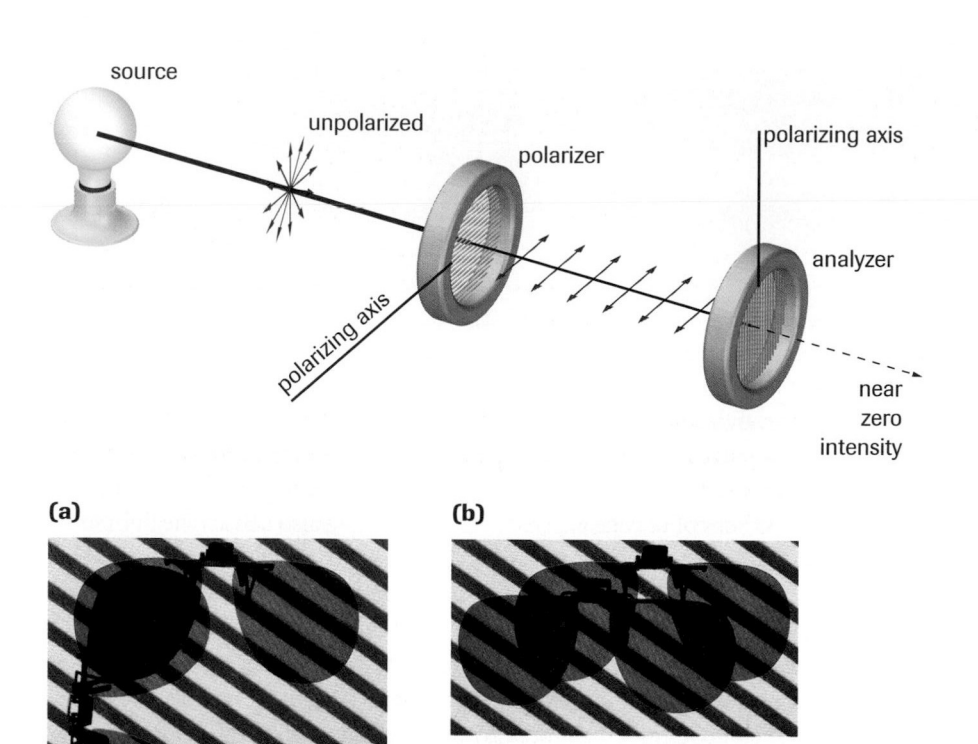

(a)

(b)

Figure 4
(a) Polarizing filters with axes perpendicular (no transmission of light)
(b) Polarizing filters with axes parallel (partial transmission of light)

Figure 3
After horizontally polarized light passes through the analyzer, the light energy is reduced significantly

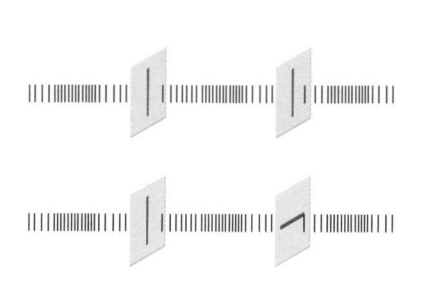

Figure 5
Longitudinal waves pass through polarizing filters unaffected.

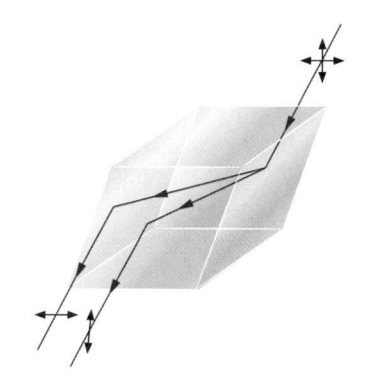

Figure 6
Polarization in a calcite crystal

double refraction the property of certain crystals (e.g., calcite) to split an incident beam of light into two

monochromatic of one colour, or one wavelength

Could these results be explained with longitudinal waves? If light travelled as a longitudinal wave, the vibrations could only be in only one direction, the direction in which the wave was travelling. Such a wave would pass through a pair of polarizing filters without being polarized (**Figure 5**). In other words, a longitudinal wave cannot be polarized. Light, which we have already decided behaves like a wave, must then behave like a transverse wave, not as a longitudinal wave.

Returning to the calcite crystal, why does it produce two beams? When a beam of unpolarized light strikes the calcite, it is separated by the crystal structure into two beams polarized at right angles, as in **Figure 6**, in a phenomenon called **double refraction**. Experimentally, it is found that one of the beams does not obey Snell's law in its simple form. For example, if **monochromatic** (i.e., light with only one wavelength) light with a wavelength of 590 nm strikes a calcite crystal, one beam behaves as though the crystal had a straightforward refractive index of 1.66, whereas the other beam behaves as though the crystal had a different index of refraction, varying from 1.49 to 1.66, depending on the angle of incidence. This difference suggests that the light beams travel through the crystal at different speeds, determined by the orientation of the planes within the crystal structure. The full explanation of the phenomenon, however, is too complex for us to consider in this text.

Polarization can be achieved four ways. The first is by double refraction, which we have just examined. The second is by reflection, when some absorption takes place at the point at which light is reflected off a smooth surface. Light waves reflected from a flat surface are partially polarized in the horizontal plane (**Figure 7**). Most glare comes from horizontal surfaces, such as a body of water, the hood of a car, or a paved road. The polarizing filters in Polaroid sunglasses are for this reason arranged in the vertical plane, reducing glare by absorbing the horizontally polarized light reflected from horizontal surfaces.

unpolarized   plane polarized

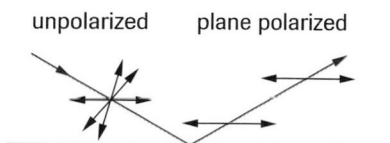

Figure 7
Light reflected by a nonmetallic surface is partially polarized in the horizontal plane.

scattering the change in direction of particles or waves as a result of collisions with particles

Polaroid a plastic, light-polarizing material

photoelasticity the property of a material that, when analyzed, reveals the material's stress distributions

▶ **TRY THIS** activity   *Polaroid Sunglasses*

Take a pair of Polaroid sunglasses and look at a shiny car in sunlight. Now rotate the lenses 90°. What do you see?

✋ **Never look directly at the Sun, even with polarizing filters; they do not protect your eyes from the damaging ultraviolet and infrared radiation.**

The third way is through **scattering**. Light from the Sun passes through our atmosphere and encounters small particles that scatter the light. Scattering causes the sky to appear blue, since the shorter wavelengths (shades of violet and blue) are scattered more than the longer wavelengths (shades of orange and red). This scattering also causes the light to be polarized. You can demonstrate polarization by looking at the sky through a rotating Polaroid sheet or through polarized sunglasses. The amount of polarization depends on the direction in which you look, being greatest at right angles to the direction of light from the Sun (**Figure 8**). Photographers use Polaroid filters to enhance photographs of the sky and clouds. Since large stretches of the sky are significantly polarized, the polarizing filter makes the clouds more prominent by reducing the glare (**Figure 9**).

The fourth method of polarizing is to use a polarizing filter. Calcite, tourmaline, and other naturally occurring polarizing crystals are scarce and fragile, keeping polarization a laboratory curiosity until 1928. In that year, Edwin Land developed the polarizing plastic he called **Polaroid**. Polaroid consists of long chains of polyvinyl alcohol impregnated with iodine, stretched so as to lie parallel to one another. (The original polarizer was made of microscopic, needle-like crystals of iodine.) Because Polaroid made it easy to produce polarized light, many everyday applications became feasible. Just as important, sheets of the new plastic could be used as convenient analyzers, making it easy to detect polarized light in nature and determine its plane of polarization.

Materials such as glass and Lucite (a transparent or translucent plastic), which become doubly refractive when subjected to mechanical stress, are said to have **photoelasticity**. When a photoelastic material is placed between polarizing and analyzing disks, the strain patterns (and thus the stress distributions) are revealed, as shown in **Figure 10**. Engineers analyzing stresses in objects such as trusses and gears build models in Lucite. When the models are placed under mechanical stress, areas of stress concentration are easily observable, allowing design changes to be made before the objects are constructed.

Figure 8
In being scattered from atmospheric particles, unpolarized light from the Sun becomes partially polarized.

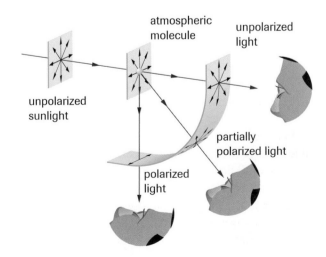

(a)

(b)

Figure 9
Cloud effects are enhanced when we add a polarizing filter to the camera.
(a) Without a filter
(b) With a polarizing filter

Polarization has been used to produce the illusion of three dimensions at the movies. Two overlapping pictures, shot by cinema cameras a few centimetres apart, in the manner of a pair of human eyes, are projected onto the theatre screen by a pair of projectors, each equipped with a Polaroid filter. The directions of polarization are chosen to be mutually perpendicular. The audience is provided cardboard-and-Polaroid spectacles, containing filters oriented to match the polarizing filters at the projector. The patron's left eye thus sees only the images taken in the film studio with the left-hand camera, the right eye only the images from the right-hand camera. Since the brain receives different left- and right-eye inputs, the screen looks like a window into a three-dimensional panorama.

To be able to detect polarized light, our eyes require an external polarizing filter. However, the eyes of certain creatures, for example, ants, horseshoe crabs, and spiders, are sensitive to polarized light; they use the polarized light from the sky, caused by scattering, as a navigational aid.

Many of the practical applications of polarization make use of the phenomenon of **optical activity**, the ability of some substances, such as sugar, turpentine, and insulin, to rotate the plane of polarization of a beam of light (**Figure 11**). Solutions of such substances rotate the plane of polarization in proportion to the concentration of the solution and to the length of the optical path through the substance. By placing a glass vessel between linear polarizers, we can measure the angle through which the plane of polarization has shifted, thereby obtaining a clue to the identity of the dissolved substance and the quantity present. The device used to measure the extent of polarization is called a *polarimeter*.

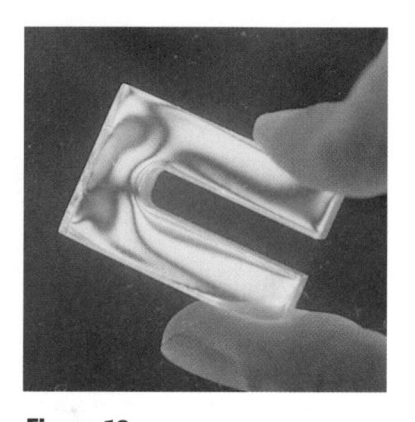

Figure 10
When placed between two polarizers, stresses on the Lucite are visible.

optical activity property of a substance whereby a transparent material rotates the plane of polarization of transmitted light

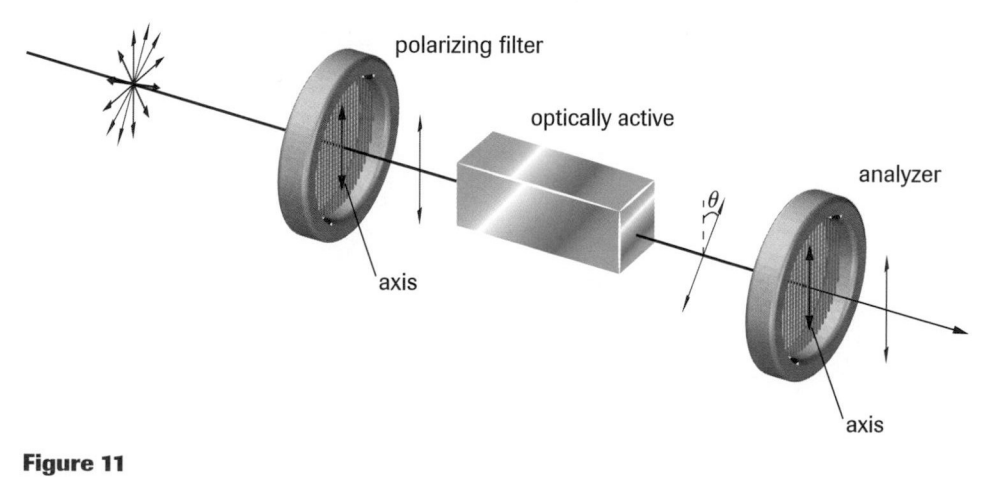

Figure 11
An analyzer reveals the ability of an optically active substance to rotate the plane of polarization.

- Polarization of light can be achieved in the following ways: double refraction, reflection, scattering, and a polarizing filter.
- Polarization provided the proof that light is a transverse wave.
- Polaroid can be used to detect the presence of polarized light and the orientation of the plane of polarization.
- Scattering occurs when light from the Sun passes through our atmosphere and encounters small particles that scatter the light.
- Polarizing filters have many uses, including glare reduction, stress analysis, and photography.
- The optical activity of certain materials can be used to help identify some substances.

▶ **Section 10.1** *Questions*

Understanding Concepts

1. Briefly describe how each method of polarization polarizes light.

2. Explain how a pair of Polaroid sheets can be used to change the intensity of a beam of light.

3. Just before the Sun sets, a driver encounters sunlight reflecting off the side of a building. Will Polaroid sunglasses stop this glare?

Applying Inquiry Skills

4. Many sunglasses, advertised as polarizing, are not. Describe two different ways to test sunglasses for polarizing capabilities.

5. You have placed a calcite crystal over the letter A on an otherwise blank piece of paper and have rotated the crystal so that two images are produced. If you were to view the images through a Polaroid filter, rotating the filter slowly through 180°, what would you see? Explain your answer.

Making Connections

6. Using the Internet or other resources, research the liquid crystal displays (LCDs) common in electronic screens, such as calculator and digital wristwatch readouts. Write a short report explaining how LCDs use polarization.

 www.science.nelson.com

7. Using the Internet and print sources, research optical activity and polarimeters and answer the following questions:

  (a) The first general use of the polarimeter was in the sugar-beet industry, in the early 1900s. What was the polarimeter called at the time? Why was it such an important innovation for farmers?

  (b) In what industries is the polarimeter in common use today and for what purposes?

 www.science.nelson.com

Light passing through a single, narrow slit is diffracted. The extent of the diffraction increases as narrower and narrower slits are used. However interference also occurs. **Figure 1** (and Investigation 10.2.1) shows that a pattern of bright and dark lines appears if a screen is placed on the far side of the slit. The pattern consists of a bright central region (the **central maximum**), with dark regions of destructive interference alternating with progressively less intense bright areas (the **secondary maxima**) on either side.

central maximum the bright central region in the interference pattern of light and dark lines produced in diffraction

secondary maxima the progressively less intense bright areas, outside the central region, in the interference pattern

Figure 1
Note the central maximum and secondary maxima.

Although the pattern bears some resemblance to Young's pattern, the spacing of the bright and dark areas is quite different. **Figure 2**, produced with white, blue, and red sources passing separately through the same slit, shows that here, as with Young's double-slit pattern, the wavelength of the source affects the extent of the diffraction.

Figure 2
Single-slit diffraction of white, blue, and red light

If you look carefully at the diffraction of water waves through a single opening, you see nodal lines (**Figure 3**), an indication that wave theory does predict interference for the single-slit diffraction pattern for light. To see how an interference pattern arises for light, we can analyze the wave behaviour of monochromatic light passing through a single slit. This can be done using mathematical analysis or hands-on experimentation in the form of Investigation 10.2.1 in the Lab Activities section at the end of this chapter.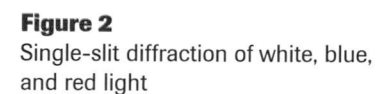

INVESTIGATION 10.2.1

Diffraction of Light in a Single Slit (p. 540)
What are the predicted patterns of diffraction and interference created by a slit or an obstacle? What relationship allows us to determine the wavelength of light, the size and location of the interference pattern, or the width of a slit?

Figure 3
Diffraction of water waves through
(a) a single wide opening
(b) a single narrow opening

(a)

(b)

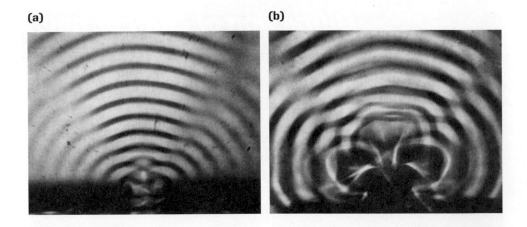

Fraunhofer Diffraction
The diffraction of light through a single slit is also called Fraunhofer diffraction, after Munich-born Joseph von Fraunhofer (1787–1826). Interest in light and optics led the 22-year-old Fraunhofer to become the first to measure the spectrum of sunlight and identify the absorption lines.

A single slit illuminated by monochromatic light may be considered a row of point sources of some reasonable, finite number—say, 12—close together and vibrating in phase. Each such source may be regarded as producing individual secondary circular waves as described by Huygens. A screen on the far side of the slit shows an interference pattern, the sum of the contributions from each of the point sources. The various point sources generate constructive and destructive interference because of the different phases of oscillations reaching the screen over different distances.

We will use wave rays to represent the direction of motion of the individual Huygens wavelets produced in the slit opening. First, let us consider the case for light rays that pass straight through the slit (**Figure 4**). Since the rays from all 12 point sources all start in phase and travel approximately the same distance to the screen, they arrive essentially in phase. Constructive interference produces a bright area on the screen, the central maximum.

Figure 4
Rays from all parts of the slit arrive at the centre of the screen, approximately in phase.

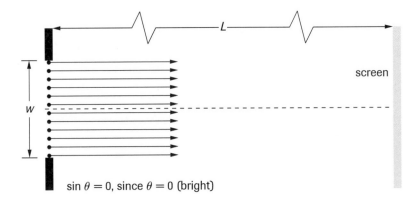

$\sin \theta = 0$, since $\theta = 0$ (bright)

LEARNING TIP

Applying Huygens' Principle
In applying Huygens' principle to analyze single slit diffraction, we have used 12 sources to show the derivation of the general equation. The true number of sources would be far greater than 12, but would be awkward to use in a derivation.

In the case of light diffracted downward through an angle (**Figure 5(a)**), waves from the top of the slit (point 1) travel farther than waves from the bottom (point 12). If the path difference is one wavelength, the light rays from the centre of the slit will travel one half-wavelength farther than those from the bottom of the slit. They will thus be out of phase, producing destructive interference. Similarly, waves slightly above the bottom (point 11) and slightly above the central point (point 5) will cancel. In fact, the ray coming from each point in the lower half of the slit will cancel the ray originating from a corresponding point in the upper half of the slit. As a result, the rays will interfere destructively in pairs, causing a dark band, or fringe, to appear on the screen. In the same manner, destructive interference occurs at an equal distance above the central maximum. As can be seen from **Figure 5(a)**, for the first minimum, the path difference of one wavelength is given

(a)

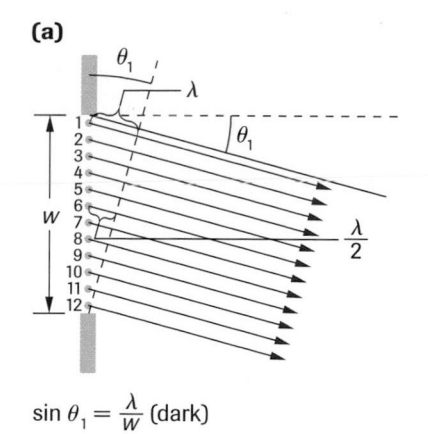

$\sin \theta_1 = \frac{\lambda}{w}$ (dark)

(b)

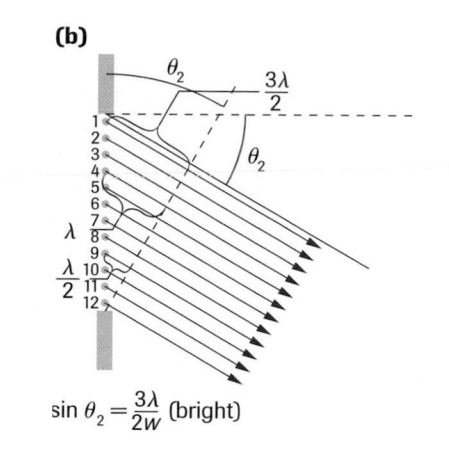

$\sin \theta_2 = \frac{3\lambda}{2w}$ (bright)

(c)

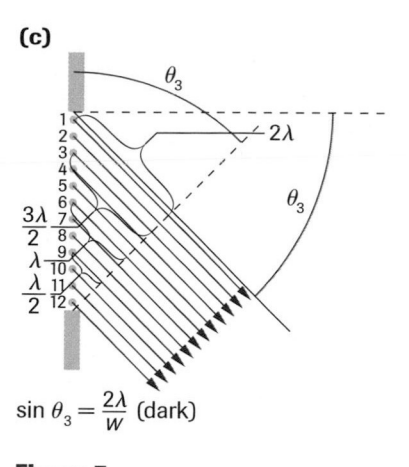

$\sin \theta_3 = \frac{2\lambda}{w}$ (dark)

Figure 5
(a) Formation of the first dark fringe
(b) Formation of the first bright fringe
(c) Formation of the second dark fringe

by $w \sin \theta_1 = \lambda$. Rearranging this equation, the angle θ_1 at which the first minimum appears is given by

$$\sin \theta = \frac{\lambda}{w} \quad \text{(first minimum)}$$

We now consider a larger angle θ_2 for which the path difference between the top and the bottom of the slit is $\frac{3}{2}\lambda$. We find that for each point source in the bottom third of the slit there exists a corresponding point source in the middle third that is $\frac{\lambda}{2}$ farther from the screen. These pairs of point sources to interfere destructively (**Figure 5(b)**). However, the waves from the top third of the slit still reach the screen roughly in phase, yielding a bright spot. The bright spot is not as intense as the central maximum, since most of the light passing through the slit at this angle, θ_2, as given by $\sin \theta_2 = \frac{3\lambda}{2w}$, will interfere destructively.

For an even larger angle, θ_3, the top waves travel a distance of 2λ farther than those from the bottom of the slit (**Figure 5(c)**). Waves from the bottom quarter cancel, in pairs, with those in the quarter just above, because their path lengths differ by $\frac{\lambda}{2}$. Those in the quarter above the centre cancel, in pairs, with those in the top quarter. At this angle, θ_3, given by $\sin \theta_3 = \frac{2\lambda}{w}$, a second line of zero intensity occurs in the diffraction pattern.

In summary, minima, or dark fringes, occur at

$$\sin \theta = \frac{\lambda}{w}, \frac{2\lambda}{w}, \frac{3\lambda}{w}, \dots$$

Or in general,

$$\sin \theta_n = \frac{n\lambda}{w} \quad \text{(minima)}$$

where θ is the direction of the fringe, λ is the wavelength, w is the width of the slit, and $n = 1, 2, 3, \dots$ is the order of the minimum.

Maxima, or bright fringes, occur at

$$\sin \theta = 0, \frac{3\lambda}{2w}, \frac{5\lambda}{2w}, \dots$$

Or in general,

$$\sin \theta_m = \frac{\left(m + \frac{1}{2}\right)\lambda}{w} \quad \text{(maxima)}$$

where θ is the direction of the fringe, λ is the wavelength, w is the width of the slit, and $m = 1, 2, 3, \ldots$ is the order of the maximum beyond the central maximum.

Since for each successive bright area more and more of the point light sources interfere destructively, in pairs, the intensity of the light decreases. The decrease is evident in **Figure 6**, a plot of intensity versus $\sin \theta$ for single-slit diffraction.

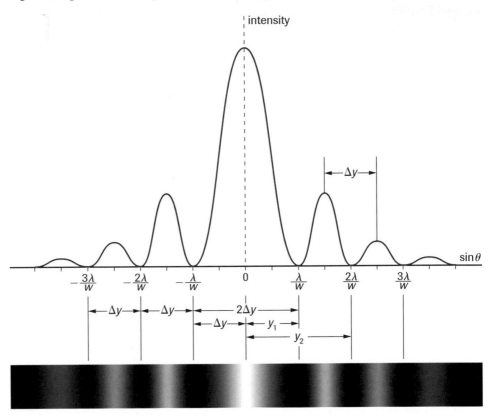

Figure 6
Graph of intensity versus $\sin \theta$ for diffraction through a single slit. The actual interference pattern is shown below.

As in the analysis of the double-slit interference pattern, the value of $\sin \theta_1$ can be determined from the ratio $\sin \theta_1 \simeq \tan \theta_1 = \frac{y_1}{L}$, where y_1 is the distance from the centre point in the diffraction pattern, and L is the perpendicular distance from the slit to the screen (**Figure 7**).

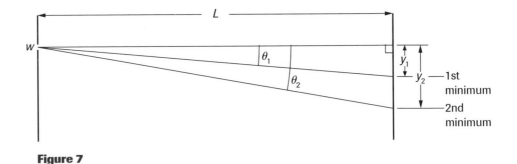

Figure 7

The width of the central maximum is defined by the first minima on either side of the centre line. For the position of the first minimum on the screen,

$$\sin \theta_1 = \frac{\lambda}{w}$$

$$\frac{y_1}{L} = \frac{\lambda}{w} \quad \text{(to a good approximation)}$$

$$\lambda = \frac{w y_1}{L}$$

Thus, the width of the central maximum is $y_1 + y_1$ (**Figure 6**). Since the separation of the maxima and minima (Δy), outside the central area, is the same as y_1, we may rewrite the relation $\lambda = \frac{w y_1}{L}$ as $\lambda = \frac{w \Delta y}{L}$. The latter equation is useful in analyzing the single-slit diffraction pattern, in finding the wavelength of the light, and in predicting the dimensions of the pattern and the positions of the fringes. A sample problem will illustrate.

▶ **SAMPLE** problem

Light from a laser pointer, with a wavelength of 6.70×10^2 nm, passes through a slit with a width of 12 μm. A screen is placed 30 cm away.

(a) How wide is the central maximum (i) in degrees and (ii) in centimetres?

(b) What is the separation of adjacent minima (excluding the pair on either side of the central maximum)?

Solution

(a) $\lambda = 6.70 \times 10^2$ nm $= 6.70 \times 10^{-7}$ m $\qquad n = 1$

$\quad w = 12 \ \mu$m $= 1.2 \times 10^{-5}$ m $\qquad \theta = ?$

$\quad L = 0.30$ cm

(i) On either side of the central line, the width of the central maximum is defined by the first-order dark fringes. Thus,

$$\sin \theta_1 = \frac{\lambda}{w}$$

$$= \frac{6.70 \times 10^{-7} \text{ m}}{1.2 \times 10^{-5} \text{ m}}$$

$$\sin \theta_1 = 5.58 \times 10^{-2}$$

$$\theta_1 = 3.2°$$

The angular width of the central maximum is $2 \times 3.2° = 6.4°$.

(ii) $\sin \theta_1 = \frac{y_1}{L}$

$$y_1 = L \sin \theta_1$$

$$= (0.30 \text{ m}) \sin 3.2°$$

$$y_1 = 1.67 \times 10^{-2} \text{ m, or } 1.7 \text{ cm}$$

The width of the central maximum is $2y_1$, or 2×1.67 cm $= 3.3$ cm.

(b) $\lambda = \frac{w \Delta y}{L}$

$$\Delta y = \frac{L \lambda}{w}$$

$$= \frac{(0.30 \text{ m})(6.70 \times 10^{-7} \text{ m})}{1.2 \times 10^{-5} \text{ m}}$$

$$\Delta y = 1.7 \times 10^{-2} \text{ m, or } 1.7 \text{ cm}$$

The separation of adjacent minima is 1.7 cm. The central maximum is exactly twice the width of the separation of other adjacent dark fringes.

As seen in the sample problem, the wave theory predicts that the width of the central maximum is twice the separation of adjacent minima. The photograph in **Figure 1** shows that the prediction is true. Our wave interpretation of both Young's experiment and single-slit diffraction appears to be correct, offering further support for the wave theory of light.

In Young's experiment, each individual slit produces its own single-slit diffraction pattern, the pattern centres being a distance *d* apart. The central maximum produced by each narrow slit covers a large lateral distance when it reaches the screen, relatively far away. As a result, the two central bright areas overlap and interfere. The double-slit interference pattern is, in reality, the resultant interference of two single-slit diffraction patterns. The other maxima of a single-slit diffraction pattern occur far out to the sides and are usually too weak to be seen. If wider slits are used, these maxima become more visible, as **Figure 8** demonstrates.

Figure 8
The top photograph illustrates the interference pattern produced by single, wide slits. The bottom photograph is an enlargement of the centre section of the top photograph. It is only the central region that is observed in most double-slit interference patterns, where narrow slits are used.

Answers

1. 49°
2. 2.2×10^{-6} m
4. 4.4 cm
5. 6.49×10^{-7} m
6. 6.6°
7. 0.67

▶ *Practice*

Understanding Concepts

1. Calculate the angle at which 7.50×10^2 nm light produces a second minimum if the single-slit width is 2.0 μm.

2. The first dark fringe in a certain single-slit diffraction pattern occurs at an angle of 15° for light with a wavelength of 580 nm. Calculate the width of the slit.

3. Red light passing through a single narrow slit forms an interference pattern. If the red light were replaced by blue, the spacing of the intensity maxima (where constructive interference takes place) would be different. In what way? Why?

4. Helium–neon laser light ($\lambda = 6.328 \times 10^{-7}$ m) passes through a single slit with a width of 43 μm onto a screen 3.0 m away. What is the separation of adjacent minima, other than those on either side of the central maximum?

5. Monochromatic light falls onto a slit 3.00×10^{-6} m wide. The angle between the first dark fringes on either side of the central maximum is 25.0°. Calculate the wavelength.

6. A single slit, 1.5×10^{-5} m wide, is illuminated by a ruby laser ($\lambda = 694.3$ nm). Determine the angular position of the second maximum.

7. The first dark fringe in the diffraction pattern of a single slit is located at an angle of $\theta_a = 56°$. With the same light, the first dark fringe formed with another single slit is located at $\theta_b = 34°$. Calculate the ratio $\dfrac{w_a}{w_b}$ of the widths of the two slits.

Resolution

Resolution is the ability to separate two closely spaced images. We have seen that light waves passing around an obstacle or through a small opening are diffracted and that the smaller the obstacle or opening, the greater the diffraction. This characteristic of diffraction is important in the design of microscopes and telescopes.

When light from two sources passes through the same small hole, not only is the light from each source diffracted, but the diffraction patterns overlap. The overlap makes the images fuzzy (**Figure 9**). If the hole is very small and the sources very close, the overlap may be extensive, making it impossible to distinguish the individual images.

resolution the ability of an instrument to separate two images that are close together

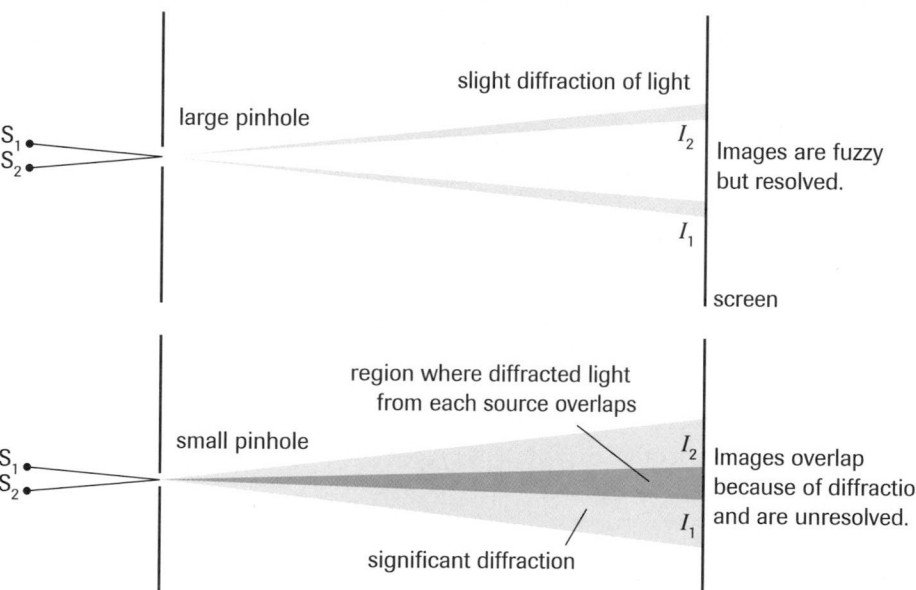
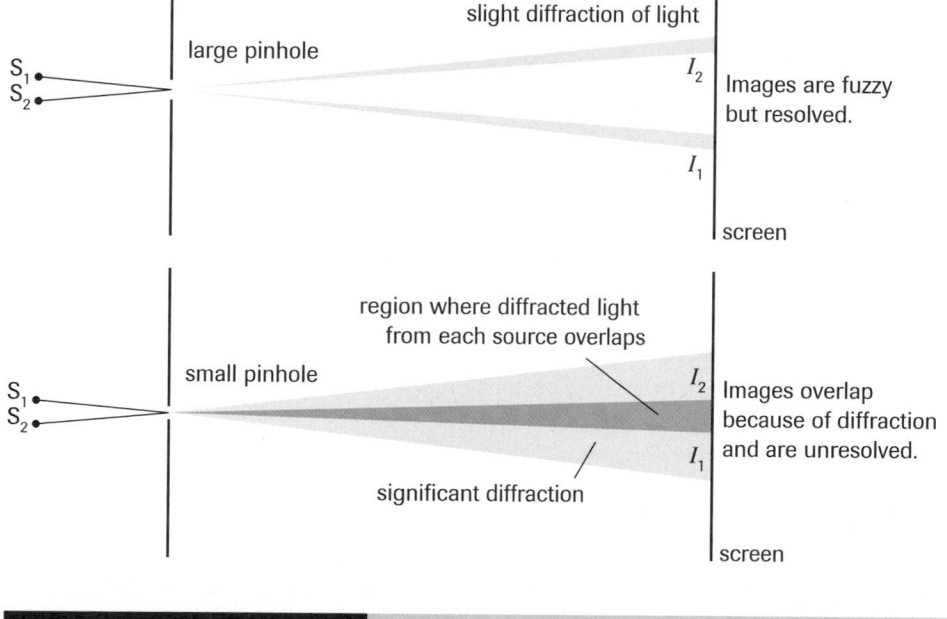

Figure 9
With a large pinhole, the images are fuzzy from diffraction but distinguishable. With a small pinhole, the diffraction patterns overlap so much that the two images cannot be resolved.

> ▶ **TRY THIS** activity   *Resolution*
>
> Set up two showcase lamps, almost touching, at one end of a dark room. Cut an opening in a piece of stiff paper board and tape a piece of aluminum foil over the opening. In the foil, poke three small holes with different diameters, starting with a pinhole. Place each hole, in succession, in front of one eye. Look at the two bulbs with the other eye closed. How does the size of hole affect your ability to clearly distinguish between both lamps? What is the relationship between the size of the opening and the resolution?

If we substitute a lens for the small hole, we define resolution as the ability of the lens to produce two sharp and separate images. Because light passes through a finite aperture when it goes through a lens, a diffraction pattern forms around the image. If the object is extremely small, the diffraction pattern appears as a central bright spot (called the Airy disk, after nineteenth-century British astronomer Sir George Airy) surrounded by concentric bright and dark circular interference fringes. If two objects are extremely close together, for example, a double star, the two diffraction patterns overlap. The bright fringes of one pattern fall on the dark fringes of the second pattern, causing the two objects to appear to merge and making it impossible to resolve. As with a hole, diameter matters: the smaller the diameter of the lens, the more difficult it is to separate two closely spaced objects. The photographs in **Figure 10** illustrate this behaviour for three lenses of different diameters. (Note that this discussion refers to the *entire* lens. In photography, the entire lens is not always used. The resolution is enhanced by using only the centre of the lens.)

  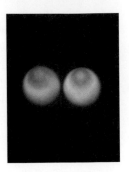

Figure 10
The view of two adjacent sources of light as seen, left to right, through a small-, medium-, and large-diameter lens. As the size of the lens increases, so does the resolution.

In a microscope, the objective lens has a small diameter. This limits even the best optical microscope to a maximum useful magnification of approximately 1000×, since even the finest objective lens can only resolve detail to a certain point. By decreasing the wavelength, we can increase the resolving power. For example, an ultraviolet microscope can detect much finer detail than a microscope operating with visible light. In Section 12.2, we will see that electron microscopes, with wavelengths approximately 10^{-5} that of light, can resolve objects down to 0.5 nm.

Observatory telescopes use large lenses or mirrors to increase the resolution. The largest telescopes are used to view the farthest distances in space, not only because they receive more light, but because they are able to resolve individual stars that appear very close together in the sky (**Figure 11**).

Figure 11
The Keck telescope in Hawaii is the largest diameter optical telescope in the world.

Diffraction of Light through a Single Slit

- Light passing through a single slit creates a diffraction pattern. The pattern consists of a bright central region with dark regions of destructive interference, alternating with progressively less intense areas of bright constructive interference.
- The smaller the slit width, the larger the distance between maxima and minima.

- The longer the wavelength, the greater the distance between maxima.
- Minima, or dark fringes, occur at $\sin \theta_n = \dfrac{n\lambda}{w}$ ($n = 1, 2, \dots$).
- Maxima, or bright fringes, occur at the centre of the pattern and also at

$$\sin \theta_m = \frac{\left(m + \dfrac{1}{2}\right)\lambda}{w} \quad (m = 1, 2, \dots).$$

- The separation Δy of adjacent maxima or minima is given by the relationship $\Delta y = \dfrac{\lambda L}{w}$, and the central maximum width is $2\Delta y$.
- Young's double-slit interference pattern results from the interference of two single-slit diffraction patterns.
- Resolution, or the ability of an instrument to separate two closely spaced images, is limited by the diffraction of light.

▶ *Section 10.2* *Questions*

Understanding Concepts

1. You are photographing a single-slit diffraction pattern from monochromatic light. How would your pattern differ if the wavelength were doubled? if the both the wavelength and slit width doubled at the same time?

2. Monochromatic light falls on a single slit with a width of 2.60×10^{-6} m. The angle between the first dark fringes on either side of the central maximum is 12°. Calculate the wavelength.

3. The ninth dark fringe in a single-slit diffraction pattern, from a source of wavelength 6.94×10^{-7} m, lies at an angle of 6.4° from the central axis. Calculate the width of the slit.

4. A single slit 2.25×10^{-6} m wide, illuminated with monochromatic light, produces a second-order bright fringe at 25°. Calculate the wavelength of the light.

5. A narrow, single slit with a width of 6.00×10^{-6} m, when illuminated by light of wavelength $\lambda = 482$ nm, produces a diffraction pattern on a screen 2.00 m away. Calculate (a) the angular width of the central maximum in degrees and (b) the width in centimetres.

6. What would be the angular width in question 5 if the entire setup were immersed in water ($n_w = 1.33$) instead of air ($n_a = 1.00$)?

7. A helium–neon laser operating at 632.7 nm illuminates a single slit 1.00×10^{-5} m wide. The screen is 10.0 m away. Calculate the separation of adjacent maxima, other than the central maximum.

8. A beam from a krypton ion laser ($\lambda = 461.9$ nm) falls on a single slit, producing a central maximum 4.0 cm wide on a screen 1.50 m away. Calculate the slit width.

9. Sodium-vapour light with an average wavelength of 589 nm falls on a single slit, 7.50×10^{-6} m wide.
   (a) At what angle is the second minimum?
   (b) What is the highest-order minimum produced?

10. Alcor and Mizar are two stars in the handle of the Big Dipper (Ursa Major). They look like one star to the unaided eye (unless the conditions are really good); through binoculars or a telescope they are easily distinguished as two. Explain why this is the case.

Applying Inquiry Skills

11. Predict what you will see if you hold a paper clip between your thumb and forefinger in the beam of a helium–neon laser. Try it!

 Do not let direct laser beams or reflected beams go straight into anyone's eyes.

12. Digital images are made up of "picture units," or pixels. The picture of the woman in **Figure 12** is 84 pixels wide and 62 pixels high. How could you improve the resolution? (*Hint:* Consider aperture and distance.)

Figure 12

diffraction grating device whose surface is ruled with close, equally spaced, parallel lines for the purpose of resolving light into spectra; transmission gratings are transparent; reflection gratings are mirrored

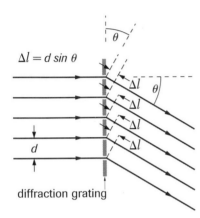

$$\Delta l = d \sin \theta$$

diffraction grating

Figure 1
Light rays passing through a diffraction grating

A **diffraction grating**, a device used for wave analysis, has a large number of equally spaced parallel slits, which act as individual line sources of light. The wave analysis of the pattern produced by these openings resembles the analysis we considered for the double slit. The waves passing through the slits interfere constructively on the viewing screen when $\sin \theta_m = \dfrac{m\lambda}{d}$, where $m = 0, 1, 2, 3 \ldots$ is the order of the bright line or maximum. This condition for constructive interference is derivable from the path difference $\Delta l = d \sin \theta$ between successive pairs of slits in the grating (**Figure 1**).

The double-slit and the multi-slit interference patterns differ, however, in important ways. First, since there are more slits in the grating, the multi-slit source delivers more light energy, yielding a brighter interference pattern. Second, the bright maxima are much sharper and narrower when produced by a diffraction grating. Third, since the slits in a diffraction grating are usually closer together, the separation between successive maxima is greater than in the typical double-slit setup, and the resolution is enhanced. For these reasons, the diffraction grating is a very precise device for measuring the wavelength of light.

There are two common types of diffraction grating: transmission and reflection. To produce a grating of either kind, fine lines, to a density in some cases exceeding 10 000/cm, can be ruled on a piece of glass with a diamond tip. In a transmission grating, the spaces between the lines transmit the light, the lines themselves being opaque. When the lined glass is used as a reflection grating, light falling on it is reflected only in the untouched segments. This reflected light effectively comes from a series of equally spaced sources that provide the diffraction grating interference pattern reflected onto the screen. Lined gratings on shiny metal can also be used as a reflection diffraction grating (**Figure 2**).

> **TRY THIS** activity　　**Grated Rulers**

Shine a laser pointer, at a small angle of incidence, onto a metal ruler with etched markings. Direct the reflected light onto a screen or white wall. What do you see? What causes this effect?

 Do not let direct laser beams or reflected beams go straight into anyone's eyes.

(a)

(b)

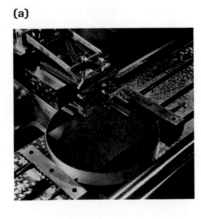

Figure 2
(a) A master grating being ruled by a diamond tip scribe
(b) A microscopic view of a ruled grating

▶ **SAMPLE** problem

At what angle will 638-nm light produce a second-order maximum when passing through a grating of 900 lines/cm?

Solution

$\lambda = 638 \text{ nm} = 6.38 \times 10^{-7} \text{ m}$ $d = \dfrac{1}{900 \text{ lines/cm}} = 1.11 \times 10^{-3} \text{ cm} = 1.11 \times 10^{-5} \text{ m}$

$m = 2$ $\theta = ?$

$$\sin \theta_m = \frac{m\lambda}{d} \quad \text{(for bright maxima)}$$

$$\sin \theta_2 = \frac{2(6.38 \times 10^{-7} \text{ m})}{1.11 \times 10^{-5} \text{ m}}$$

$$\sin \theta_2 = 1.15 \times 10^{-1}$$

$$\theta_2 = 6.60°$$

The angle to the second maximum is 6.60°.

▶ **Practice**

Understanding Concepts

1. A 4000-line/cm grating, illuminated with a monochromatic source, produces a second-order bright fringe at an angle of 23.0°. Calculate the wavelength of the light.

2. A diffraction grating with slits 1.00×10^{-5} m apart is illuminated by monochromatic light with a wavelength of 6.00×10^2 nm. Calculate the angle of the third-order maximum.

3. A diffraction grating produces a third-order maximum, at an angle of 22°, for red light (694.3 nm). Determine the spacing of the lines in centimetres.

4. Calculate the highest spectral order visible when a 6200-line/cm grating is illuminated with 633-nm laser light.

Crossed Gratings and the Spectroscope

If you look through a grating with the gratings perpendicular to the light source, you see a horizontal diffraction pattern. When you rotate the grating through 90°, you see a vertical pattern. If you look at a point source of light through two such gratings, you will get a pattern such as that seen in **Figure 3**, called a *crossed-grating* diffraction pattern.

LEARNING TIP

Exact Quantities
The quantity 900 lines/cm is a counted quantity, not a measured quantity, and thus is considered exact.

Answers

1. 4.88×10^{-7} m
2. 10.4°
3. 7.4×10^{-4} cm
4. $n = 2$

Figure 3
(a) A vertical grating produces a horizontal pattern.
(b) When the grating is horizontal, the pattern is vertical.
(c) Cross the gratings and the pattern is also crossed.
(d) A point source of light is viewed through crossed gratings.

(a)

(b)

(c)

(d)

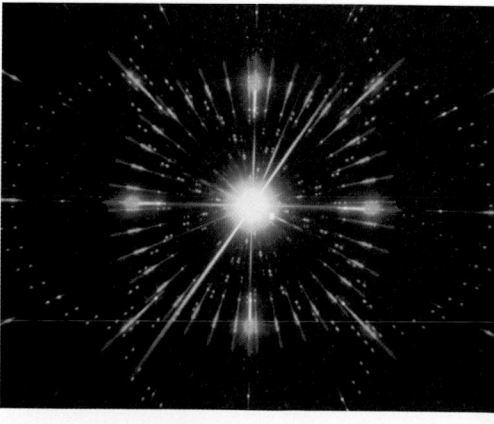

gratings vertical

gratings horizontal

crossed gratings

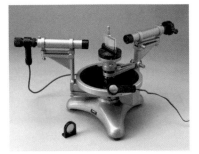
spectroscope an instrument that uses a diffraction grating to visually observe spectra

> ▶ **TRY THIS** activity   **Crossed Gratings**
>
> Take an ordinary handkerchief into a darkened room. Pull it taut and look at a distant point source of light through the fabric. (The point source should *not* be a laser beam.) In what way does the resulting diffraction pattern resemble **Figure 3**? Pull the cloth diagonally so that the mesh of the fabric is at an angle. How does the pattern change? Repeat with a coarser fabric, such as a tea towel, and with a finer fabric, such as a scrap of panty hose. What changes occur? Why? On a dark night, look at a bright star through an umbrella. Describe what you see.

If the light striking the grating is not monochromatic but a mixture of wavelengths, each wavelength produces a pattern of bright maxima at different locations on the viewing screen. This is what occurs when white light is directed through a diffraction grating. The central maximum will be a sharp white peak, but for each of the spectral colours, the maxima occur at different positions on the screen, giving the effect of a spectrum. The display is the same as when white light passes through a prism onto a viewing screen, except that the spectral pattern produced by a diffraction grating is much more widely spread out and easier to observe, making it an excellent device for spectral analysis. The instrument that performs this analysis is called a **spectroscope**.

In a spectroscope, light from a source is first directed through a collimator, a system of mirrors or lenses that makes the rays from the source essentially parallel. This parallel light passes through a diffraction grating. We view the resulting interference pattern with a small telescope. Since we can measure the angle θ quite accurately, we can determine the wavelength of the light to a high degree of accuracy (**Figure 4**).

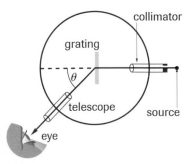

Figure 4
A spectroscope

> ▶ **TRY THIS** activity   **Using a Grating Spectroscope**
>
> View several gas discharge sources of light through a spectroscope, for example, hydrogen and neon, or use a fluorescent light (**Figure 5**). If you have the equipment, measure the angles for specific spectral lines for one of your sources, for example, hydrogen. Calculate their wavelengths, as directed by your teacher.

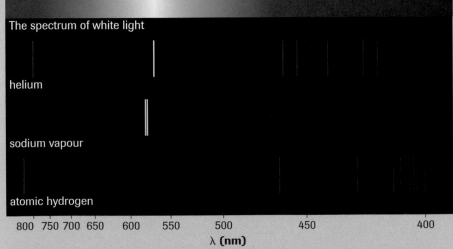

Figure 5
Spectra of white light, helium, sodium vapour, and hydrogen as produced by a spectroscope.

SUMMARY   *Diffraction Gratings*

- The surface of a diffraction grating consists of a large number of closely spaced, parallel slits.

- Diffraction gratings deliver brighter interference patterns than typical double-slit setups, with maxima that are narrower and more widely separated.

- Diffraction gratings are governed by the relationship $\sin \theta_m = \dfrac{m\lambda}{d}$, where d is the distance between adjacent gratings, and m is the order of the maxima.

▶ *Section 10.3 Questions*

Understanding Concepts

1. CDs reflect the colours of the rainbow when viewed under white light. What type of surface must be on the CD (**Figure 6**)? Explain your reasoning.

8318-2-R

Figure 6

2. At what angle will 6.50×10^2-nm light produce a second-order maximum when falling on a grating with slits 1.15×10^{-3} cm apart?

3. Light directed at a 10 000-line/cm grating produces three bright lines in the first-order spectrum, at angles of 31.2°, 36.4°, and 47.5°. Calculate the wavelengths of the spectral lines in nanometres. What are the colours?

4. The "Balmer α" and "Balmer δ" lines in the visible atomic-hydrogen spectrum have wavelengths of 6.56×10^2 nm and 4.10×10^2 nm, respectively. What will be the angular separation, in degrees, of their first-order maxima, if these wavelengths fall on a grating with 6600 lines/cm?

5. A diffraction grating gives a first-order maximum at an angle of 25.0° for 4.70×10^2-nm violet light. Calculate the number of lines per centimetre in the grating.

Applying Inquiry Skills

6. Fog a piece of glass with your breath and look at a point source of light in a darkened room. What do you see? Why? Where in the sky have you seen a similar effect? Explain your answer.

Making Connections

7. A certain spectroscope, while in vacuum, diffracts 5.00×10^2-nm light at an angle of 20° in the first-order spectrum. The same spectroscope is now taken to a large, distant planet with a dense atmosphere. The same light is now diffracted by 18°. Determine the index of refraction of the planet's atmosphere.

You have probably noticed the swirling colours of the spectrum that result when gasoline or oil is spilled on water. And you have also seen the colours of the spectrum shining on a soap bubble. These effects are produced through optical interference, when light is reflected by or transmitted through a thin film.

> ▶ **TRY THIS** activity **Soap Bubbles**
>
> Pour a small amount of bubble solution onto a clean plastic tray, such as a cafeteria tray. Use a straw to blow a bubble at least 20 cm in diameter. Direct a bright light onto the domed soap film. Note bright areas of constructive interference (different colours) and dark areas of destructive interference. These bright and dark areas correspond to variations in the thickness of the film and the movement of the water in the film.

Consider a horizontal film like a soap bubble that is extremely thin, compared to the wavelength of monochromatic light being directed at it from above, in air. When the light rays strike the upper surface of the film, some of the light is reflected, and some is refracted. Similar behaviour occurs at the lower surface. As a result, two rays are reflected to the eye of an observer: one (ray 1) from the top surface and another (ray 2) from the bottom (**Figure 1**). These two light rays travel along different paths. Whether they interfere constructively or destructively depends on their phase difference when they reach the eye.

Figure 1
Light waves have undergone a 180° phase change when reflected in **(a)**, but there is no phase change when reflected at **(b)**. Reflections from (a) and (b) are shown together in **(c)**. (We show an angle for clarity, but in reality all rays are vertical.)

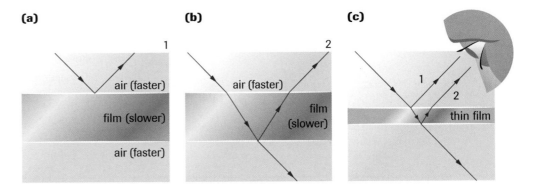

Recall that when waves pass into a slower medium, the partially reflected waves are inverted (so that a positive pulse is reflected as a negative). When the transition is from a slow medium to a fast medium, reflected waves are not inverted. Transmitted waves are never inverted. Since both rays originate from the same source, they are initially in phase. Ray 1 will be inverted when it is reflected, whereas ray 2 will not. Because the film is very thin ($t \ll \lambda$), the extra distance travelled by ray 2 is negligible, and the two rays, being 180° out of phase, interfere destructively (**Figure 2(a)**). For this reason, a dark area occurs at the top of a vertical soap film, where the film is very thin.

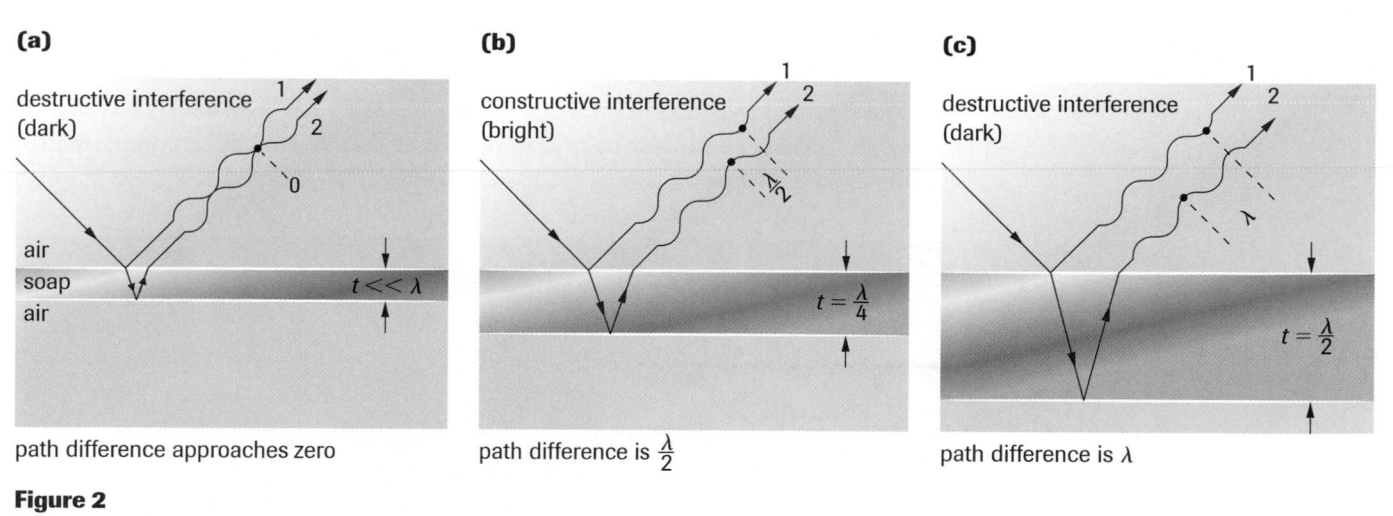

(a)

destructive interference (dark)

air
soap
air

$t \ll \lambda$

path difference approaches zero

(b)

constructive interference (bright)

$t = \frac{\lambda}{4}$

path difference is $\frac{\lambda}{2}$

(c)

destructive interference (dark)

$t = \frac{\lambda}{2}$

path difference is λ

Figure 2
When we replace the very thin film in **(a)** with thicker films, as in **(b)** and **(c)**, the two rays have a significant difference in path-length. (The diagrams are not drawn to scale.)

Let us now consider what happens if the soap film is a little thicker (**Figure 2(b)**). In this case, ray 2 will have an appreciable path difference in comparison with ray 1. If the thickness t of the film is $\frac{\lambda}{4}$, the path difference is $2 \times \frac{\lambda}{4}$, or $\frac{\lambda}{2}$, for nearly normal paths, yielding a 180° phase delay. The two rays, initially out of phase because of reflection, are now back in phase again. Constructive interference occurs, and a bright area is observed.

When the thickness of the film is $\frac{\lambda}{2}$ and the path difference is λ (**Figure 2(c)**), the two reflected rays are again out of phase and there is destructive interference.

There will thus be dark areas for reflection when the thickness of the film is $0, \frac{\lambda}{2},$ $\lambda, \frac{3\lambda}{2}, \dots$. For the same reason, bright areas will occur when the thickness is $\frac{\lambda}{4}, \frac{3\lambda}{4},$ $\frac{5\lambda}{4}, \dots$. In these conditions for destructive and constructive interference, λ is the wavelength of light *in the film*, which would be less than the wavelength in air by a factor of n, the index of refraction.

Interference in Soap Bubbles

Cover a clear showcase lamp with a red filter. Dip a wire loop into a soap solution. View the soap film by reflected red light, holding the loop in a vertical position for at least one minute. Remove the filter from the light so that white light strikes the soap film. Arrange the white light and the soap film so that the light passes through the film. Compare the respective patterns for transmitted and reflected light.

The effects of gravity on a vertical soap film cause the film to be wedge-shaped, thin at the top and thick at the bottom, with the thickness changing in a reasonably uniform way. The thickness changes uniformly, producing successive horizontal segments of dark and bright reflections, similar in appearance to the double-slit pattern under monochromatic light (**Figure 3**).

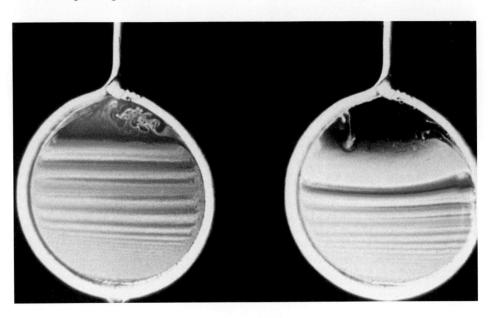

Figure 3
Interference in a thin soap film as seen by transmitted light and reflected light (far right)

When viewed under white light, the soap film produces a different effect. Since the spectral colours have different wavelengths, the thickness of the film required to produce constructive interference is different for each colour. For example, a thickness of $\frac{\lambda}{4}$ for red light is greater than the corresponding $\frac{\lambda}{4}$ thickness for blue light, since red light has a longer wavelength in the film than blue light. Blue light and red light will therefore reflect constructively at different film thicknesses. When white light is directed at the film, each colour of the spectrum is reflected constructively from its own particular film thickness, and the spectral colours are observed.

Interference also occurs when light is transmitted through a thin film. We will use the soap film as an example. When the thickness t of the film is essentially zero ($t << \lambda$), the transmitted light can be considered to consist of two rays: ray 1, transmitted without any phase change, and ray 2, reflected twice internally and likewise transmitted without a phase change. (Recall that for reflection from a slow medium to a fast medium there is no phase change.) Since the path difference is negligible, the two rays emerge in phase, yielding a bright area of constructive interference (**Figure 4(a)**). This is the opposite of the result for light reflected from the same thin film. Dark areas of destructive interference for transmission occur when the thickness is $\frac{\lambda}{4}, \frac{3\lambda}{4}, \frac{5\lambda}{4}, \ldots$ (**Figure 4(b)**). Bright transmission areas appear when the thickness is $0, \frac{\lambda}{2}, \lambda, \frac{3\lambda}{2}, \ldots$ (**Figure 4(c)**). (Remember that the path difference is twice the film thickness.) In all cases, λ is the wavelength of the light *in the film material*, which will be less than the wavelength of light in air by a factor of n, the index of refraction.

(a)

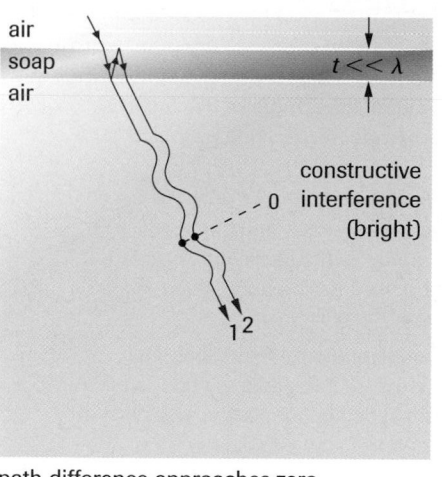

path difference approaches zero

(b)

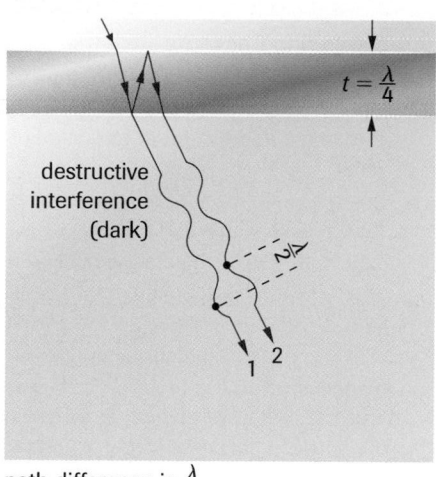

path difference is $\frac{\lambda}{2}$

(c)

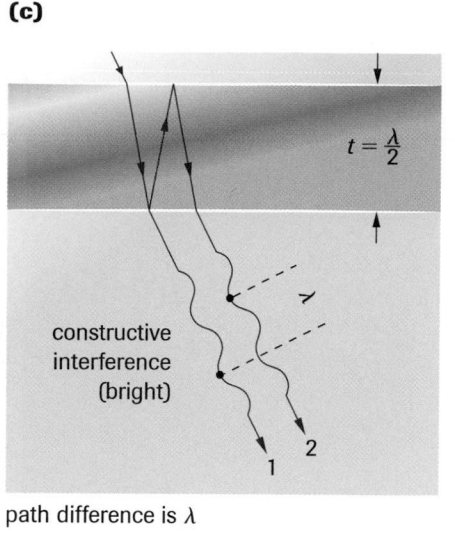

path difference is λ

Figure 4
(a) Rays 1 and 2 emerge in phase. Since there is no phase change for ray 2 and t is very small, constructive interference results.

(b) Ray 2 is delayed by $\frac{\lambda}{2}$ and interferes destructively with ray 1.

(c) Ray 2 is delayed by λ and interferes constructively with ray 1.

▶ **_SAMPLE_ problem 1**

In summer months, the amount of solar energy entering a house should be minimized. Window glass is made energy-efficient by applying a coating to maximize reflected light. Light in the midrange of the visible spectrum (at 568 nm) travels into energy-efficient window glass, as in **Figure 5**. What thickness of the added coating is needed to maximize reflected light and thus minimize transmitted light?

Solution

Reflection occurs both at the air–coating interface and at the coating–glass interface. In both cases, the reflected light is 180° out of phase with the incident light, since both reflections occur at a fast-to-slow boundary. The two reflected rays would therefore be in phase if there were a zero path difference. To produce constructive interference the path difference must be $\frac{\lambda}{2}$. In other words, the coating thickness t must be $\frac{\lambda}{4}$, where λ is the wavelength of the light in the coating.

$n_{coating} = 1.4$

$t = ?$

$$n_{coating} = \frac{\lambda_{air}}{\lambda_{coating}}$$

$$\lambda_{coating} = \frac{\lambda_{air}}{n_{coating}}$$

$$= \frac{568 \text{ nm}}{1.4}$$

$$\lambda_{coating} = 406 \text{ nm}$$

$$t = \frac{\lambda_{coating}}{4}$$

$$= \frac{406 \text{ nm}}{4}$$

$$t = 101 \text{ nm, or } 1.0 \times 10^{-7} \text{ m}$$

The required thickness for the coating is 1.0×10^{-7} m.

glass
$(n = 1.5)$

air
$(n = 1.0)$

coating
$(n = 1.4)$

Figure 5
For Sample Problem 1

> **Practice**

Understanding Concepts

1. What are the three smallest thicknesses of a soap bubble capable of producing reflective destructive interference for light with a wavelength of 645 nm in air? (Assume that the index of refraction of soapy water is the same as that of pure water, 1.33.)

2. A thin layer of glass ($n = 1.50$) floats on a transparent liquid ($n = 1.35$). The glass is illuminated from above by light with a wavelength, in air, of 5.80×10^2 nm. Calculate the minimum thickness of the glass, in nanometres, other than zero, capable of producing destructive interference in the reflected light. Draw a diagram as part of your solution.

3. A coating, 177.4 nm thick, is applied to a lens to minimize reflections. The respective indexes of refraction of the coating and of the lens material are 1.55 and 1.48. What wavelength in air is minimally reflected for normal incidence in the smallest thickness? Draw a diagram as part of your solution.

4. A transparent oil ($n = 1.29$) spills onto the surface of water ($n = 1.33$), producing a maximum of reflection with normally incident orange light, with a wavelength of 6.00×10^{-7} m in air. Assuming the maximum occurs in the first order, determine the thickness of the oil slick. Draw a diagram as part of your solution.

Mathematical Analysis of Interference in an Air Wedge

The soap film wedge, when held vertically and illuminated, produced bands of interference that were irregular. If an **air wedge** is created between two uniform pieces of glass and illuminated, a measurable pattern of constructive and destructive interference also results (**Figure 6**). This air wedge can be used to find the wavelength of the incident light. More importantly, it can be used to measure the size of very small objects.

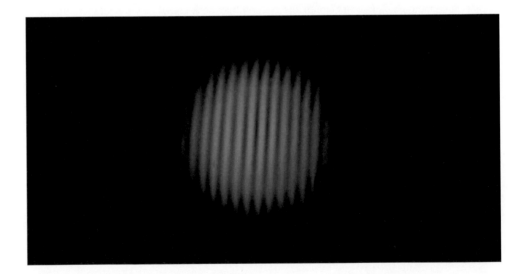

Figure 6
Interference in an air wedge illuminated by mercury light

The spacing of successive dark fringes in the reflection interference pattern of an air wedge may be calculated as follows (**Figure 7**):

Consider points G and F, where the glass-to-glass distances across the air wedge are $\frac{\lambda}{2}$ and λ, respectively. At point G, there is both transmission and reflection.

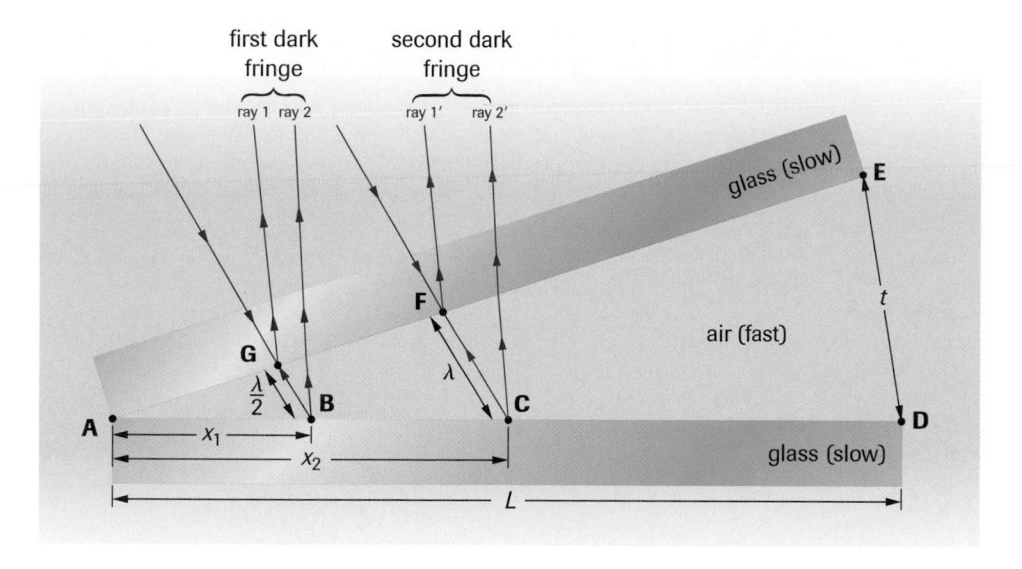

first dark fringe   second dark fringe

Figure 7
Interference in an air wedge. The diagram is not to scale, and although the rays are drawn at an oblique angle for clarity, the angle of incidence approaches zero.

Since the light is going from a slow to a fast medium, there is no phase change in ray 1. At point B, reflection is from a fast to a slow medium, yielding a phase change. But by the time ray 2 lines up with ray 1, it has travelled two widths of GB, or one wavelength, farther, keeping the phase change intact. The path difference between ray 1 and ray 2 is one wavelength, and ray 1 and 2 interfere destructively, since they are 180° out of phase. Similarly, destructive interference occurs at point F, because ray 1′ and ray 2′ are shifted 180° out of phase upon reflection and remain out of phase because ray 2′ has had to travel two wavelengths farther.

By similar triangles, we have, for the first dark fringe, $\triangle ABG \cong \triangle ADE$. Therefore,

$$\frac{x_1}{L} = \frac{\left(\frac{\lambda}{2}\right)}{t}$$

$$x_1 = \frac{L\lambda}{2t}$$

Similarly, for the second dark fringe, $\triangle ACF \cong \triangle ADE$.

$$\frac{x_2}{L} = \frac{\lambda}{t}$$

$$x_2 = \frac{L\lambda}{t}$$

Since $\Delta x = x_2 - x_1$

$$= \frac{L\lambda}{t} - \frac{L\lambda}{2t}$$

$$\Delta x = \frac{L\lambda}{t}\left(1 - \frac{1}{2}\right), \text{ or}$$

$$\Delta x = L\left(\frac{\lambda}{2t}\right)$$

where Δx is the distance between dark fringes, L is the length of the air wedge, t is the thickness of the base of the wedge, and λ is the wavelength of the light in the wedge. Try applying the theory by perfoming Invesigation 10.4.1 in the Lab Activities section at the end of this chapter, where you can measure the width of a strand of hair. ⚛️ ▮

⚛️ **INVESTIGATION 10.4.1**

Interference in Thin Films and Air Wedges (p. 542)
How can you precisely measure the widths of tiny objects, objects too tiny to use conventional measuring instruments? This investigation provides an opportunity to measure the wavelength of light as well as the width of a very thin object: a single strand of your own hair.

(a) An air wedge between two microscope slides, 11.0 cm long and separated at one end by a paper of thickness 0.091 mm, is illuminated with red light of wavelength 663 nm. What is the spacing of the dark fringes in the interference pattern reflected from the air wedge?

(b) How would the spacing change if the wedge were filled with water ($n = 1.33$)?

Solution

$L = 11.0$ cm $\qquad\qquad t = 0.091$ mm $= 9.1 \times 10^{-3}$ cm

$\lambda = 663$ nm $= 6.63 \times 10^{-5}$ cm $\qquad \Delta x = ?$

(a) In air:

$$\Delta x = L\left(\frac{\lambda}{2t}\right)$$

$$= 11.0 \text{ cm}\left(\frac{6.63 \times 10^{-5} \text{ cm}}{2(9.1 \times 10^{-3} \text{ cm})}\right)$$

$$\Delta x = 4.0 \times 10^{-2} \text{ cm}$$

The spacing between the dark fringes in air is 4.0×10^{-2} cm.

(b) If the air were replaced by water:

$$\frac{n_w}{n_a} = \frac{\lambda_{air}}{\lambda_{water}}$$

$$\lambda_{water} = \left(\frac{n_a}{n_w}\right)\lambda_{air}$$

$$= \frac{1.00}{1.33}(6.63 \times 10^{-5} \text{ cm})$$

$$\lambda_{water} = 4.98 \times 10^{-5} \text{ cm}$$

$$\Delta x = L\left(\frac{\lambda}{2t}\right)$$

$$= 11.0 \text{ cm}\left(\frac{4.98 \times 10^{-5} \text{ cm}}{2(9.1 \times 10^{-3} \text{ cm})}\right)$$

$$\Delta x = 3.0 \times 10^{-2} \text{ cm}$$

The spacing of the dark fringes in water would be 3.0×10^{-2} cm.

▶ Practice

Understanding Concepts

Answers

5. 6.9×10^{-5} cm

6. 1.3×10^{-3} cm

7. 1.8×10^{-3} cm

5. Two pieces of glass forming an air wedge 9.8 cm long are separated at one end by a piece of paper 1.92×10^{-3} cm thick. When the wedge is illuminated by monochromatic light, the distance between centres of the first and eighth successive dark bands is 1.23 cm. Calculate the wavelength of the light.

6. Light with a wavelength of 6.40×10^2 nm illuminates an air wedge 7.7 cm long, formed by separating two pieces of glass with a sheet of paper. The spacing between fringes is 0.19 cm. Calculate the thickness of the paper.

7. A piece of paper is placed at the end of an air wedge 4.0 cm long. Interference fringes appear when light of wavelength 639 nm is reflected from the wedge. A dark fringe occurs both at the vertex of the wedge and at its paper end, and 56 bright fringes appear between. Calculate the thickness of the paper.

Now that we have studied how the wave theory applies to thin films and the mathematics of air wedges, we can apply this knowledge in the next section to examine some real-world applications of thin films.

 **SUMMARY**   *Interference in Thin Films*

- For reflected light in thin films, destructive interference occurs when the thin film has a thickness of $0, \dfrac{\lambda}{2}, \lambda, \dfrac{3\lambda}{2}, \dots$, and constructive interference occurs at thicknesses of $\dfrac{\lambda}{4}, \dfrac{3\lambda}{4}, \dfrac{5\lambda}{4}, \dots$, where λ is the wavelength in the film.

- For transmitted light in thin films, destructive interference occurs at $\dfrac{\lambda}{4}, \dfrac{3\lambda}{4}, \dfrac{5\lambda}{4}, \dots$, and constructive interference occurs at $0, \dfrac{\lambda}{2}, \lambda, \dfrac{3\lambda}{2}, \dots$, where λ is the wavelength in the film.

- Air wedges can be used to determine the thicknesses of very small objects through the relationship $\Delta x = L\left(\dfrac{\lambda}{2t}\right)$.

▶ ***Section 10.4*** *Questions*

Understanding Concepts

1. When light is transmitted through a vertical soap film, the top of the film appears bright, not dark, as it is when viewed from the other side. Explain, using diagrams and the wave theory of light.

2. Explain why it is usually not possible to see interference effects in thick films.

3. What is the minimum thickness of an air layer between two flat glass surfaces (a) if the glass is to appear bright when 4.50×10^2-nm light is incident at 90°? (b) if the glass is to appear dark? Use a diagram to explain your reasoning in both cases.

4. A film of gasoline ($n = 1.40$) floats on water ($n = 1.33$). Yellow light, of wavelength 5.80×10^2 nm, shines on this film at an angle of 90°.
   (a) Determine the minimum nonzero thickness of the film, such that the film appears bright yellow from constructive interference.
   (b) What would your answer have been if the gasoline had been spread over glass ($n = 1.52$) rather than over water?

5. Two plane glass plates 10.0 cm long, touching at one end, are separated at the other end by a strip of paper 1.5×10^{-3} mm thick. When the plates are illuminated by monochromatic light, the average distance between consecutive dark fringes is 0.20 cm. Calculate the wavelength of the light.

6. Two plane glass plates 12.0 cm long, touching at one end, and separated at the other end by a strip of paper, are illuminated by light of wavelength 6.30×10^{-5} cm. A count of the fringes gives an average of 8 dark fringes per centimetre. Calculate the thickness of the paper.

Making Connections

7. Semiconductors, such as silicon, are used to fabricate solar cells. These cells are typically coated with a thin, transparent film to reduce reflection losses and increase the efficiency of the conversion of solar energy to electrical energy. Calculate the minimum thickness of the film required to produce the least reflection of light with a wavelength of 5.50×10^{-5} m when a thin coating of silicon oxide ($n = 1.45$) is placed on silicon ($n = 3.50$).

8. The national standards for new home construction may include thin-film coatings, called "E-coatings," on thermopane windows for energy conservation. Research this standard, and find out how E-coatings are used to reduce heat loss in winter and decrease heat gain in summer. Write a short report on your findings.

 www.science.nelson.com

Newton's Rings

When a curved glass surface is placed in contact with a flat glass surface and is illuminated by light, a series of concentric rings, called **Newton's rings** (**Figure 1**), appears. The pattern results from interference between the rays reflected by the top and bottom of the variable air gap, much like the interference in an air wedge between two flat glass sheets.

Newton's rings a series of concentric rings, produced as a result of interference between the light rays reflected by the top and bottom of a curved surface

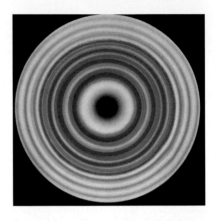

Figure 1
Newton's rings interference pattern

These interference effects are quite useful. For example, the surface of an optical part being ground to some desired curvature can be compared with the curvature of another surface, known to be correct, by observing interference fringes. Similarly, the surface of a metal block which is required to be perfectly flat can be tested by covering it with a flat piece of glass (an "optical flat"). In areas where the metal is not flat, air gaps form, creating interference patterns and revealing areas in need of further machining (**Figure 2**). With this machining technique, precisions to the order of a wavelength of light are achievable.

Oil on Water

The brilliant colours evident when light is reflected from a thin layer of oil floating on water come from interference between the rays reflected from the surface of the oil and those reflected from the surface of the water. The thickness of the oil film is subject to local variations. Further, the thickness of the film at any one place is subject to change over time, notably through evaporation of the oil. As with the soap bubble, different thicknesses produce constructive interference at different wavelengths. The colours of the spectrum reflected from oil on water constantly change position as the thickness of the oil film changes, and a swirling of the spectral colours results. In the case shown in **Figure 3**, both reflected rays are phase-inverted, at the air–oil interface in (**a**) and at the oil–water interface in (**b**), since $n_{air} < n_{oil} < n_{water}$.

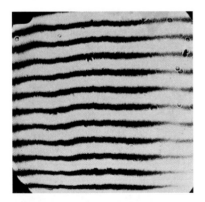

Figure 2
Interference caused by an optical flat

back-glare the reflection of light from the back of eyeglass lenses into the eyes

Eyeglasses and Lenses

A common problem with eyeglasses is **back-glare**, an effect occurring when light is reflected from the back of the glasses into the eyes. These reflections are significantly reduced if an antireflective coating is put on the surface of the lens. If the coating is about $\frac{\lambda}{4}$ thick, light reflected from the lens–coating interface interferes destructively

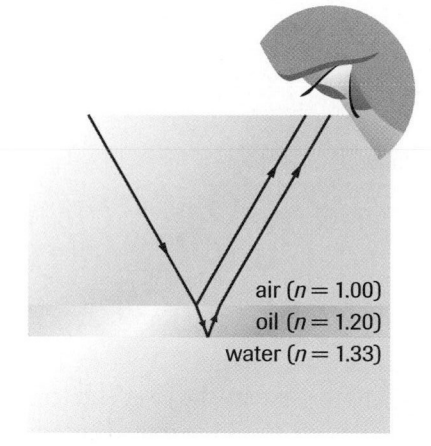

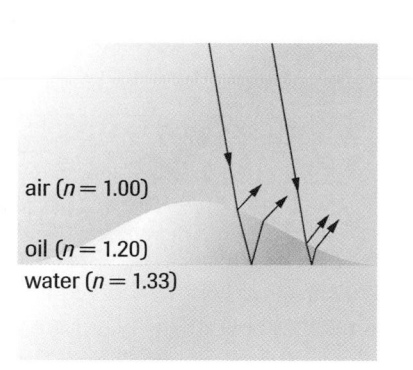

Figure 3
Light reflected from upper and lower surfaces of a
thin film of oil lying on water

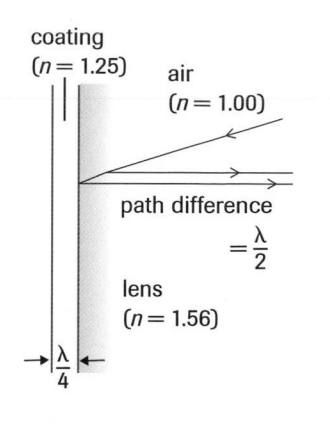

Figure 4
Back-glare of light in the mid-range
of the visible spectrum is reduced in
eyeglasses with a thin coating.

with light from the air–coating interface, minimizing the glare (**Figure 4**). Coatings are commonly used in sunglasses for the same reasons.

Several of the most serious eye problems are linked to damage caused by ultraviolet radiation (UV) from the Sun. For example, absorption of UV can eventually lead to cataracts or macular degeneration, the leading cause of blindness in older people. A coating of the appropriate thickness on the front surface of sunglasses can create destructive interference and eliminate some of the damaging wavelengths of UV. However, most UV blocking in sunglasses occurs in the lens itself. Sunglasses often have labels indicating how much protection from UV is provided.

Another important application of thin films is the coating of lenses for optical instruments. A glass surface reflects about 4% of the light passing through it. At each surface, internal reflections can create multiple or blurred images. Since a camera, for example, can contain up to 10 separate lenses, this is a problem that cannot be ignored. Applying a very thin coating on the surface of each lens reduces reflection. The thickness is selected to ensure that light reflected from both surfaces of the coating interferes destructively. A coating material is chosen with a refractive index midway between the indexes of air ($n = 1.0$) and glass ($n = 1.5$). The amount of reflection at the air–coating interface is then about equal to the amount at the coating–glass interface, and destructive interference upon reflection can occur for a specified wavelength, depending on the thickness of the film. The wavelength usually chosen is close to the midpoint of the visual spectrum (550 nm). Since reflected light near the violet and red extremes of the spectrum is not reduced very much, the surface of the coated lens reflects a mixture of violet and red light and appears purple. With multiple coatings, reflection can be minimized over a wider range of wavelengths. Reflected light cannot be eliminated entirely. Typically, a single coating reduces reflection to 1% of the incident light.

CDs and DVDs

A CD can store up to 74 minutes of music. But how can more than 783 megabytes (MB) of audio information be stored on a disc only 12 cm in diameter and 1.2 mm thick?

Most CDs consist of an injection-moulded piece of polycarbonate plastic. When the CD is manufactured, data are recorded as a series of bumps along spiral tracking, circling from the inside of the disc to the outside (**Figure 5**). Next, a very thin, clear layer of aluminum is put onto the disc, covering the bumps. This, in turn, is coated with a layer of

DID YOU KNOW ?

CD Formatting
Most CDs are formatted for
650 MB or 700 MB, leaving some
space for other data.

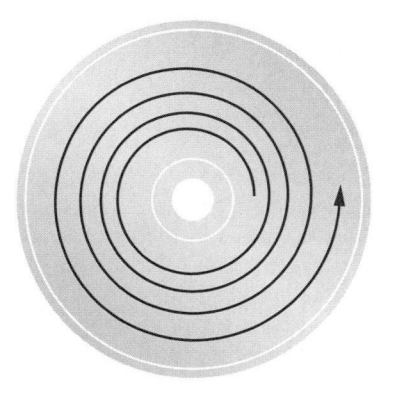

Figure 5
The track is only 0.5 μm wide; if
stretched into a straight line, this
track would be 5 km long.

Wave Effects of Light **521**

acrylic, which protects the aluminum. Finally, the label is printed onto the acrylic (**Figure 6**).

Figure 6
Coatings on a CD

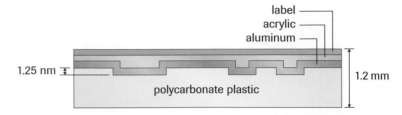

polycarbonate plastic

label
acrylic
aluminum
1.25 nm
1.2 mm
polycarbonate plastic

Reading the data stored on the disc requires great precision from the CD player. The three subsystems that operate the player are the drive motor system, the laser and lens system, and the tracking system (**Figure 7**). The drive motor spins the disc at speeds ranging from 200 to 500 rpm, depending on the track that is being "read." A diffraction grating, placed in front of the laser, produces three beams (**Figure 8**). The centre beam follows the data track, but the two first-order diffracted beams follow the smooth surface between adjacent tracks. Reflected light from the two diffracted beams keeps the laser correctly positioned on the data track of bumps and spaces. As the CD is played, the laser follows the track outward from the centre of the disc. Since the bumps must travel at a constant speed past the laser, the drive motor must slow down in a precisely prescribed way as the laser moves toward the edge.

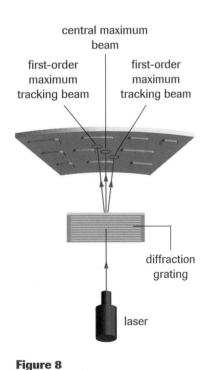

central maximum
beam

first-order
maximum
tracking beam

first-order
maximum
tracking beam

diffraction
grating

laser

Figure 8
Construction of the laser pickup assembly. A three-beam tracking method is often used in CD players to ensure that the laser follows the spiral track correctly. The three beams are created by a diffraction grating from a single laser beam.

Figure 7
Inside a CD player

Laser light is directed through a small lens onto the data track (**Figure 9**), where it is reflected from the aluminized bumps. The original laser beam is polarized vertically, so it is transmitted through the polarized beam splitter with no reflection. Because the beam is polarized, the beam splitter reflects nearly the entire beam into the photodiode detector. The depth of the spaces between the bumps is approximately one-quarter the wavelength of the laser light in the acrylic. In thin films, where the thickness is $\frac{\lambda}{4}$, the light reflected from the bottom surface and the light reflected from the top surface are 180° out of phase. It has also travelled $\frac{\lambda}{2}$ farther than the light from the bump. The resulting destructive interference produces a decrease in the intensity of the reflected light from the spaces. The variation in the intensity of the reflected laser light produces an electric signal having the same characteristics as the original etched on the disc at manufacture. The electronics in the player interprets these changes in intensity as bits comprising bytes. The digital data are converted to an analog signal and amplified to produce music. Other data encoded on the disc give the position of the laser on the track and encode additional information, such as music titles. Bytes are read in a similar way from a CD-ROM in a computer disk drive.

CDs produce better sound than magnetic tape and vinyl records because there is little background distortion or background noise, each note has unvaried pitch, and the dynamic range is wider than with tape and vinyl. Further, CDs are more durable than tape and vinyl because there is no reading head rubbing against the recorded surface.

CD writers are disc players that can also record data onto a blank CD. In the CD-R (read) format, the recording is permanent (comprising "read-only" data). Such CDs are used for data backup, for the permanent storage of computer software, and for the creation of music CDs. In the CD-RW ("read-write") format, information is stored in such a way that it can be erased, allowing the disc to be reused. The digital-video disc (DVD) superficially resembles a CD but has about seven times its capacity, permitting the storage of up to 133 minutes of high-resolution video. The DVD is consequently a popular format for viewing movies in the home. Although DVDs are physically the same size as CDs, to be able to record this much data they must be constructed differently: the tracks are narrower (320 nm in width, as opposed to 500 nm in the conventional CD) and closer together, and the laser used has a shorter wavelength (635 nm, as opposed to 780 nm with the CD). Another difference is the addition of a top semireflective layer of gold. The DVD laser can focus through the outer layer to the inner layer, receiving information from both layers. A DVD can record up to 4.7 GB on a single layer, 8.5 GB on a double layer, and 17 GB if both sides of the disc are used (**Figure 10**). Most DVD players can play CDs and CD-R discs as well since the physical mechanism is similar. DVD drives are now used in computers, replacing CD-ROMs, because of their much higher capacity.

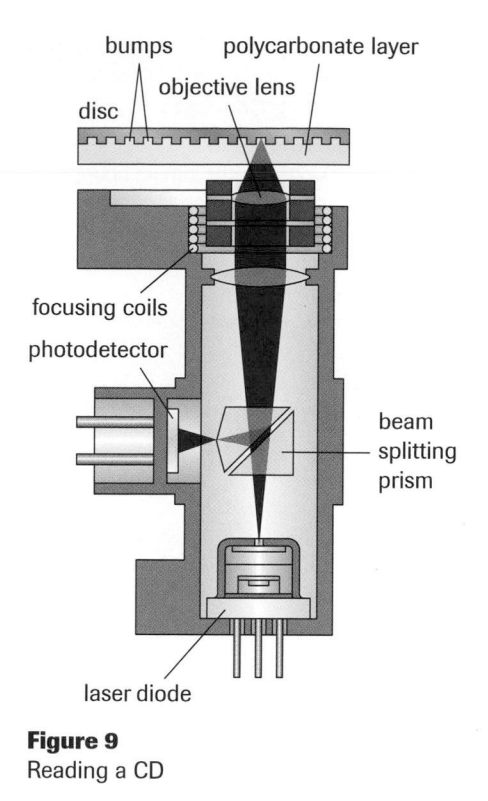

Figure 9
Reading a CD

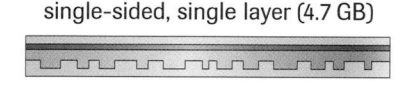

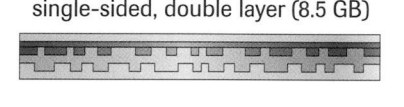

Figure 10
Different DVD formats

New advances in laser technology will further enhance the storage capacity of CDs and DVDs. For example, lasers using light in the blue range of the electromagnetic spectrum will allow the data tracks to be even closer together since the wavelength of light in that range is smaller than that currently used.

SUMMARY *Applications of Thin Films*

- Newton's rings can be used to determine the "flatness" of objects.
- Thinly coated lenses reduce or eliminate unwanted reflections and UV radiation. If the coating is $\frac{\lambda}{4}$ thick, destructive interference effectively reduces reflected light.
- CDs and DVDs use principles of thin-film interference and polarization.
- DVDs have a much higher capacity than CDs: their tracks are narrower; they can record data on two levels; and they use both sides of the disc.

Understanding Concepts

1. Explain why a dark spot appears at the centre of Newton's rings. Consider the phase changes that occur when light reflects from the upper curved surface and the lower flat surface.

2. Explain what causes the effect in **Figure 11**.

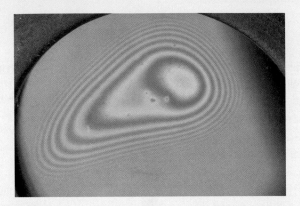

Figure 11

3. A plano-convex lens (flat on one side, convex on the other) rests with its curved side on a flat glass surface. The lens is illuminated from above by light of wavelength 521 nm. A dark spot is observed at the centre, surrounded by 15 concentric dark rings (with bright rings in between). How much thicker is the air wedge at the position of the 16th dark ring than at the centre?

4. Calculate the minimum thickness of a layer of magnesium fluoride ($n = 1.38$) on flint glass ($n = 1.66$) in a lens system, if light of wavelength 5.50×10^2 nm in air is to undergo destructive interference.

5. A lens appears greenish yellow ($\lambda = 5.70 \times 10^2$ nm is strongest) when white light reflects from it. What minimum thickness of coating ($n = 1.38$) was used on such a glass lens ($n = 1.50$) and why? Draw a diagram as part of your solution.

6. You are designing a lens system to be used primarily for red light (7.00×10^2 nm). What is the second thinnest coating of magnesium fluoride ($n = 1.38$) that would be nonreflective for this wavelength?

7. The index of refraction of the acrylic coating in a certain CD is 1.50. Calculate the heights of the bumps needed to produce destructive interference if the laser operates at a wavelength of 7.80×10^2 nm in air.

8. In terms of the tracking system, explain how CDs can be smaller than the standard 12 cm.

9. Explain how you can tell the difference between a regular DVD and an extended play DVD just by looking at it under white light.

Applying Inquiry Skills

10. Predict what you will see if you take two microscope slides, press them together so they "stick," and illuminate them at an angle under a point light source, such as a quartz-halogen reading lamp. Try it to verify your prediction.

Making Connections

11. Nonreflecting glass is used in picture frames to reduce glare. Explain, using the wave theory of light, how nonreflecting glass might be manufactured.

12. Research the Internet and other sources and write a short report on how CDs and DVDs are recorded on a computer. Pay particular attention to the operation of the laser and its effect on the recording surface.

 www.science.nelson.com

13. A thin layer of gold has been applied to the outside surface of the glass of the Royal Bank Tower in Toronto (**Figure 12**). Interference is not the prime reason for using a thin film in this application. What are other reasons?

Figure 12
Royal Bank Tower in Toronto

14. Thin-film technology is used in the manufacture of microchips and microprocessors as a means of measuring the thickness of the various applied layers. Research this application and write a short report on your findings.

 www.science.nelson.com

15. When information is scanned into a computer from an acetate sheet on a flatbed scanner, sometimes dark fringes appear in some areas of the computer image. Explain what may cause this effect.

When a photograph is taken of your face, the image is recorded on the photographic film. With the appropriate lens located at the correct distance from the film, a sharp image is obtained. But the lens only focuses the detail in one direction. To obtain a three-dimensional picture of your face, your camera would have to record countless different positions.

A technique for producing a three-dimensional image on a single film was discovered in 1947 by a Hungarian-born physicist, Dr. Dennis Gabor, working in London, U.K., at the Imperial College. Gabor was trying to improve the images produced by the electron microscope discussed in Section 12.2. Only small areas of the tiny object being viewed were in focus. He reasoned that the answer might lie not in taking a conventional electron microscope picture, but one that had all the information radiated from the illuminated object. The area of interest could then be sharpened by optical means. In other words, he envisioned a method whereby a picture would be taken, not of the scene itself, but of the *light* from the scene.

Gabor's theories assumed that light waves radiating from the various points on an illuminated object would interfere with each other, and the images recorded on the photographic film would be the resulting interference patterns. After the film had been developed and light passed through it, the original three-dimensional image would be reproduced. Gabor called such a film a **hologram** (from the Greek *holos*, for "whole," and *gramma*, "that which is drawn or written").

Gabor was able to demonstrate, using white light, that his ideas worked. However, the images, while three dimensional, were anything but sharp. The problem was that an ordinary white light source has a large range of frequencies. In addition, even at any one particular frequency, white light is "incoherent," being a mixture of waves, which over a short time interval, exhibit all possible phase shifts. The problem was overcome in 1960, with the development of lasers, light sources that are not only of high intensity and monochromatic but coherent.

E.N. Leith and Juris Upatnieks, two American physicists working at the University of Michigan, produced the first laser holograph in 1963. They illuminated an object with a laser beam that scattered the laser light onto a photographic film. From the first beam, they split off a second reference beam, using mirrors to direct it at the same film (**Figure 1**).

> **LEARNING TIP**
>
> **Holograph**
> A holograph is what you see when a hologram is illuminated.

hologram the three-dimensional image formed as a result of interference of (transmitted or reflected) coherent light

Figure 1
(a) Making a laser transmission holograph
(b) Viewing a holograph

(a)

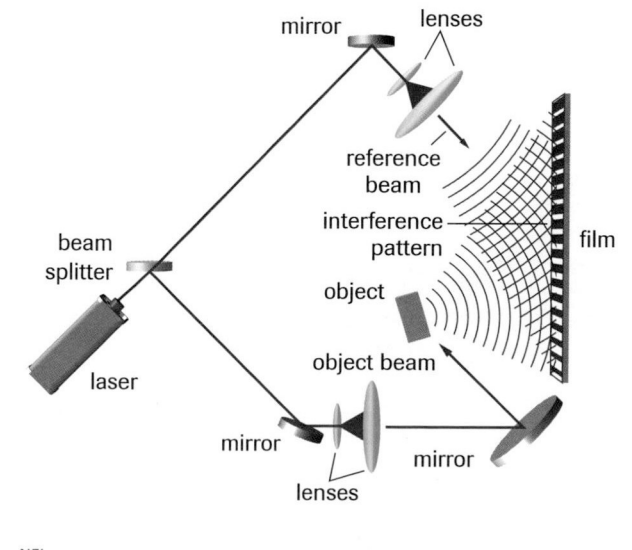

(b)

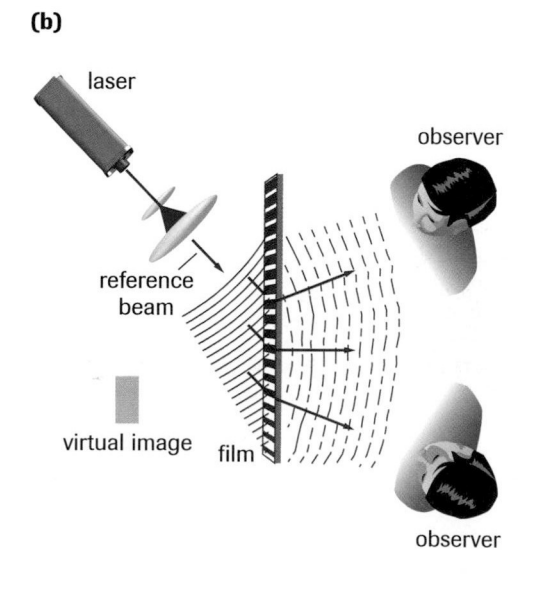

When light from the two beams interfered on its surface, the film recorded the interference pattern. To the naked eye in white light, the film appeared to contain grey smudges. But when these patterns were illuminated with the same laser light, a truly three-dimensional image was created. Nearly all scientific and commercial holographic images are now created in this same way (**Figure 2**). The implications of Dennis Gabor's work were recognized in 1971, when he was awarded the Nobel Prize in physics.

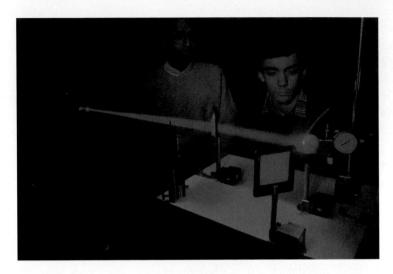

Figure 2
Producing a three-dimensional image of a golf ball with laser light

Holography already has numerous applications and may some day have many more. The ideas in optical holography have already, for example, been adapted to ultrasound, yielding three-dimensional images of the internal structures and organs of the human body. Holographic pictures appear on credit cards and printed money to discourage counterfeiters. The principles of holography are used to record the bars and stripes of the Universal Product Code (UPC) that identifies the groceries scanned by a laser at a checkout counter (**Figure 3**).

Figure 3
A low-powered laser bounces from a mirror to a rotating disc with 21 pie-shaped facets. Each facet is a separate hologram that directs the light in a unique direction, with a different angle, elevation, and focal length than the other facets. One of the sweeps will succeed in reaching the Universal Product Code (UPC) on the grocery item. Light from the successful sweep will be reflected back to a photodetector, which will convert the optical signal into electric pulses. A computer will interpret the pulses, recording the purchase and updating the inventory.

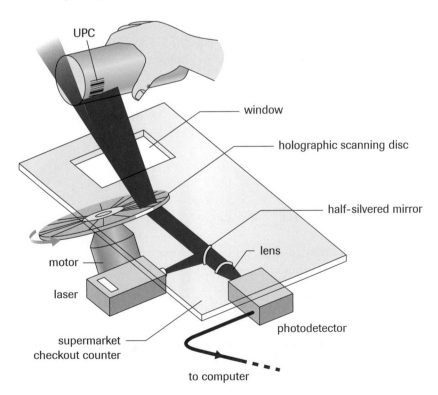

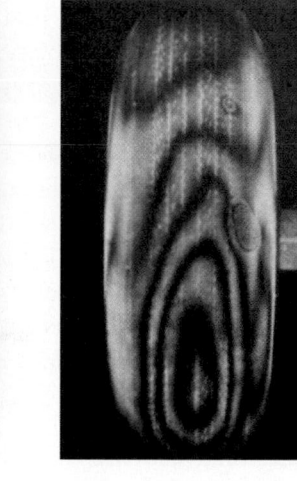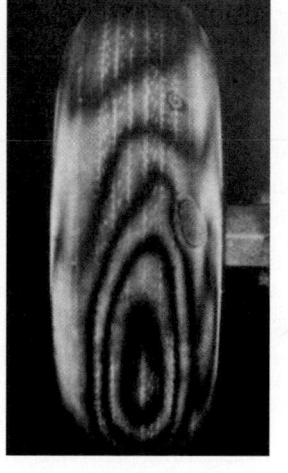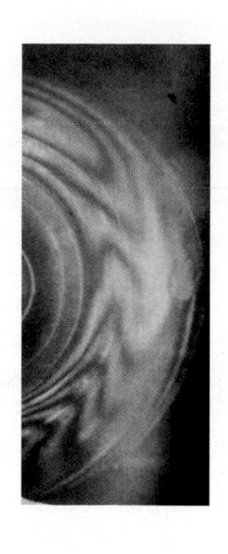

Figure 4
These holograms of a tire indicate any areas of tire separation.

Laser light and an apparatus similar to Michelson's interferometer (Section 10.7) are used to find invisible defects in such products as tires, pipes, aircraft parts, computer disk drives, and even tennis rackets (**Figure 4**). In the future, holograms taken with X-ray lasers could provide detailed images of microscopic objects. True three-dimensional cinema, television, and computer graphics will probably be produced by holography. Holographic memory holds the promise of storing the information from a thousand CDs in a crystal the size of a sugar cube.

 **Holography**

- Holography is the process of storing all of the light radiated from an object and then reproducing it.
- Holography is used for three-dimensional viewing, security, scanning, and quality control.

▶ **TRY THIS** activity

Viewing Holograms

Illuminate commercially prepared holograms with laser light. Use a magnifying glass to examine holograms on paper money and credit cards.

 **Do not let direct laser beams or reflected beams go straight into anyone's eyes.**

▶ **Section 10.6 Questions**

Understanding Concepts

1. Explain why the invention of the laser contributed to the technique of holography.

2. What is the difference between a hologram and a normal film negative?

3. Why does a hologram inspected in white light appear as a mixture of smudges?

Applying Inquiry Skills

4. The manager of a party supply store near your school has hired your science class and the art department to create a window display for Halloween. You are to design the part of the display that includes a hologram ghost. How will you proceed?

Making Connections

5. The words "hologram" and "holographic" have some special uses outside physics. Research what historians mean by "holographic document" and what lawyers mean by "holographic will," and write a report on your findings.

GO 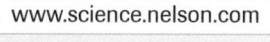 www.science.nelson.com

6. Research holographic computer memory and prepare a research paper on how it might work.

GO www.science.nelson.com

(a)

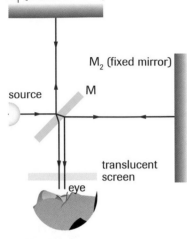

M₁ (movable mirror)

M₂ (fixed mirror)

source   M

translucent screen

eye

(b)

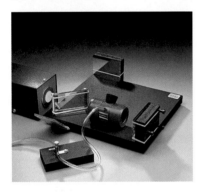

Figure 1
(a) Michelson's interferometer
(b) Using a Michelson interferometer

The German-born American physicist Albert Michelson (1852–1931) developed the *interferometer* (**Figure 1**), an instrument used to measure small distances. Monochromatic light strikes a half-silvered mirror M, which acts as a beam splitter. Half the light is reflected up to the movable mirror M₁, where it is reflected back to the observer. The other half is first reflected back by the fixed mirror M₂, then reflected by mirror M to the observer. If the two path lengths are identical, the two beams enter the eye in phase, yielding constructive interference. If the movable mirror (M₁) is moved a distance equal to $\frac{\lambda}{4}$, one beam travels an extra distance of $\frac{\lambda}{2}$, yielding destructive interference. If M₁ is moved farther, constructive or destructive interference occurs, depending on the path difference. If either M₁ or M₂ is tipped slightly, both constructive and destructive fringes appear, since the path lengths are different for different points on the surface of the tilted mirror.

As M₁ is moved through a distance of $\frac{\lambda}{2}$, a given fringe will change from dark to light and back to dark again. The overall effect will thus be that the fringe pattern has shifted one position. (One dark fringe is replaced by the next dark fringe, relative to a fixed reference point.) By counting the number of fringes that move laterally in this way, we can determine the total displacement of the movable mirror in terms of the source wavelength, since each fringe move represents movement in the mirror of $\frac{\lambda}{2}$. A sample problem will illustrate this concept.

> ### ▶ *SAMPLE* problem

You visit an optical engineering house in which an interferometer is illuminated by a monochromatic source of wavelength 6.4×10^{-7} m. You slowly and carefully move the movable mirror. You find that 100 bright fringes move past the reference point. How far did you move the mirror?

Solution

$\lambda = 6.4 \times 10^{-7}$ m

100 fringes = 50λ

The path difference is 50λ, or $(50)(6.4 \times 10^{-7}$ m$) = 3.2 \times 10^{-5}$ m.

The mirror has moved half this distance, or 1.6×10^{-5} m.

> ### ▶ Practice

Understanding Concepts

Answers

1. 2.50×10^2 nm
2. 0.319 mm
3. 679 nm

1. You are observing a system of straight vertical fringes in a Michelson interferometer using light with a wavelength of 5.00×10^2 nm. By how much must one of the mirrors be moved to cause a bright band to shift into the position previously occupied by an adjacent bright band?

2. One of the mirrors of a Michelson interferometer is moved, causing 1000 fringe pairs to shift past the hairline in a viewing telescope. The interferometer is illuminated by a 638-nm source. How far was the mirror moved?

3. You count 598 bright fringes upon displacing the moveable mirror in a Michelson interferometer through 0.203 mm. Calculate the wavelength of the light.

Using the Interferometer

Michelson used his interferometer to try to determine the length of the standard metre in terms of the wavelength of a red line in the cadmium spectrum. He was searching for a length standard that would be more precise than the existing "standard metre" (a pair of lines inscribed on a platinum-iridium bar near Paris) and would also be precisely reproducible anywhere in the world. Michelson's technique was accepted and the metre redefined but in terms of the wavelength of the orange-red line in the spectrum of krypton-86.

Another important historic use of the interferometer was the precise measurement of the speed of light in various media, achieved by placing the transparent medium into one beam of the interferometer. These measurements further illustrate the relationship between the refractive index of a material and the speed of light in it, another verification of the wave theory of light (see Section 9.5).

The most celebrated use of the instrument, however, was in Michelson and Morley's finding that the speed of light in vacuum is constant and independent of the motion of the observer. We will see in Chapter 11 that Einstein used these important findings in his 1905 special theory of relativity.

 **Michelson's Interferometer**

- Interferometers can measure distances as small as a wavelength of light, using interference fringes.

- Interferometers have been used to define the standard metre and to measure the speed of light in various media. Interferometers were used historically to verify that the speed of light is a constant.

Section 10.7 Questions

Understanding Concepts

1. Why are measurements with the Michelson interferometer so precise?

2. A micrometer is connected to the movable mirror of an interferometer. In the process of adjusting the micrometer to permit the insertion of a thin metal foil, 262 bright fringes move past the eyepiece crosshairs. The interferometer is illuminated by a 638-nm source. Calculate the thickness of the foil.

3. A Michelson interferometer is illuminated with monochromatic light. When one of its mirrors is moved 2.32×10^{-5} m, 89 fringe pairs pass by. Calculate the wavelength of the incident beam.

4. Calculate how far the mirror in Michelson's interferometer must be moved if 580 fringes of 589-nm light are to pass by a reference point.

5. You are working with Michelson's interferometer and a monochromatic source. You count 595 bright fringes upon moving the mirror 2.14×10^{-4} m. Calculate the wavelength of the light entering the interferometer.

Applying Inquiry Skills

6. Explain how an interferometer can be used to measure the index of refraction for liquids and gases.

Making Connections

7. Research the process used with an interferometer to define the length of a standard metre and write a brief summary.

8. How might an interferometer be used to determine minute movements in Earth's crust?

10.8 Electromagnetic Waves and Light

Once Oersted and Faraday had established the basic relationships between electricity and magnetism in the early nineteenth century, it was not long before others began to extend electromagnetic theory to closely related phenomena. One of the great scientific achievements of the nineteenth century was the discovery that waves of electromagnetic energy travel through space.

In 1864, the Scottish physicist and mathematician James Clerk Maxwell summarized his theories about electromagnetic fields as four basic relationships, appropriately known as Maxwell's equations of electromagnetism. Although the equations require mathematical notation beyond the scope of this text, we can summarize Maxwell's main ideas in words:

1. The distribution of electric charges, in space, produces an electric field.
2. Magnetic field lines are continuous loops without beginning or end. Electric field lines, on the other hand, begin and end on electric charges.
3. A changing electric field produces a magnetic field.
4. A changing magnetic field produces an electric field.

These statements should already be familiar to you, with the possible exception of 4. It is basically Faraday's law of electromagnetic induction, which, as you recall from Chapter 8, states that a changing magnetic field in the region of a conductor induces a potential difference in the conductor, causing a current to flow. For such an induced current to flow through a conductor, there must be an electric field present in the conductor, causing its charged particles to move.

These two converse phenomena—a changing electric field producing a magnetic field and a changing magnetic field producing an electric field—led Maxwell to an inevitable conclusion. He predicted that as they continuously changed, interacting electric and magnetic fields would actually travel through space in the form of electromagnetic waves. Further, Maxwell worked out the essential characteristics of such a wave:

- Electromagnetic waves are produced whenever electric charges are accelerated. The accelerated charge loses energy that is carried away in the electromagnetic wave.
- If the electric charge is accelerated in periodic motion, the frequency of the electromagnetic waves produced is exactly equal to the frequency of oscillation of the charge.
- All electromagnetic waves travel through a vacuum at a common speed ($c = 3.00 \times 10^8$ m/s), and obey the universal wave equation, $c = f\lambda$.
- Electromagnetic waves consist of electric and magnetic fields oscillating in phase, perpendicular to each other, and both at 90° to the direction of propagation of the wave, as depicted in **Figure 1**.
- Electromagnetic waves exhibit the properties of interference, diffraction, polarization, and refraction and can carry linear and angular momentum.
- All electromagnetic waves can be polarized, and radiation where the electric field vector is in only one plane is said to be plane-polarized. (The plane of polarization is the plane containing all of the changing electric field vectors.)

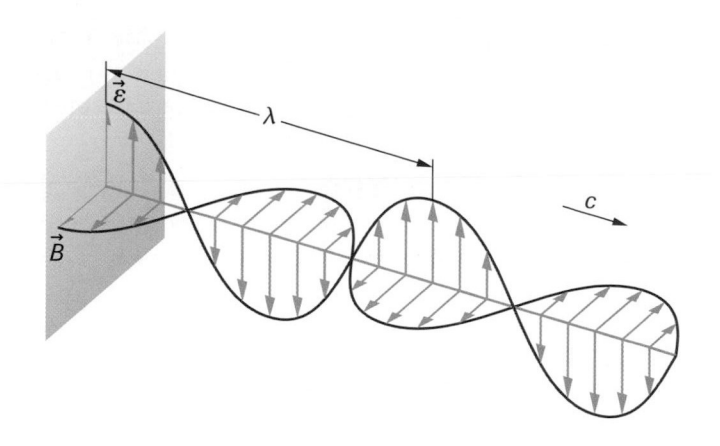

Figure 1
The electric and magnetic fields are perpendicular to one another and to the direction of radiation.

Such an electromagnetic wave was first produced and detected in the laboratory by the German physicist Heinrich Hertz (1857–1894) in 1887, not long after Maxwell's death. Using a spark gap, across which electric charges moved rapidly back and forth, Hertz was able to generate electromagnetic waves whose frequency was about 1 MHz. He detected these waves from some distance away, using as an antenna a loop of wire in which a current was produced when a changing magnetic field passed through (**Figure 2**).

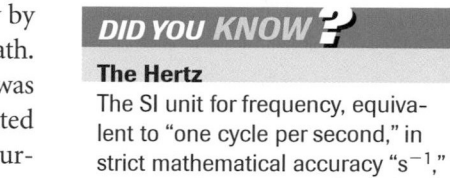

DID YOU KNOW

The Hertz
The SI unit for frequency, equivalent to "one cycle per second," in strict mathematical accuracy "s^{-1}," is named for Hertz: $1 \ s^{-1} = 1 \ Hz$.

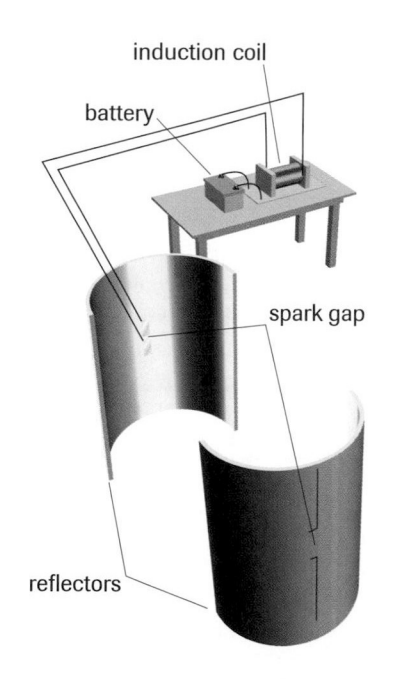

Figure 2
Hertz's experimental setup

Hertz was also able to show that these waves travelled at the speed of light in a vacuum and that they exhibited the characteristic wave phenomena: reflection, refraction, interference, and even polarization.

Hertz called his waves **radio waves**. His discovery lay the experimental foundation for engineering by Marconi and other radio pioneers, who first transmitted radio waves across the English Channel in 1889. Despite predictions that Earth's curvature would make long-distance communication by electromagnetic waves impossible, Marconi spanned the Atlantic in 1901. At what is now called Signal Hill, in St. John's, Newfoundland, he received a Morse code "S" sent from Cornwall, England, 3360 km away.

The prediction made by Maxwell, and its verification by Hertz, that electromagnetic waves travel at the speed of light was of paramount significance. Although it had been accepted for over half a century that light behaves as a wave, it had remained unclear

radio waves electromagnetic waves in the frequency range 10^4 to 10^{10} Hz; used in radio and TV transmission

what, in concrete physical terms, the wave was. Maxwell, on the basis of his calculated speed for electromagnetic waves, argued that light waves must be electromagnetic. After Hertz's discovery of radio waves, Maxwell's claim was soon widely accepted.

The Electromagnetic Spectrum

Visible light and radio waves occupy only two small ranges of all the frequencies possible for oscillating electric and magnetic fields. Today, we know that there is a broad range of frequencies of electromagnetic waves—the electromagnetic spectrum—all having the basic characteristics predicted by Maxwell. **Table 1** lists the names that have been given to the various regions of this spectrum and the approximate frequency range for each region, with a brief description of the type of accelerated charge that leads to the formation of each.

A sample problem will illustrate how traditional wave analysis can be used to solve problems using various regions of the spectrum.

Table 1 The Electromagnetic Spectrum

Type of Radiation	Frequency Range	Origin of Radiation	Applications or Effects of Radiation
low frequency AC	60 Hz	weak radiation emitted from conductors of AC power	causes interference in radio reception when passing near high-voltage transmission lines
radio, radar, TV	$10^4 - 10^{10}$ Hz	oscillations in electric circuits containing inductive and capacitive components	transmission of radio and TV communication signals; ship and aircraft navigation by radar; reception of radio waves from space by radio telescopes; control of satellites, space probes, and guided missiles
microwaves	$10^9 - 10^{12}$ Hz	oscillating currents in special tubes and solid-state devices	long-range transmission of TV and other telecommunication information; cooking in microwave ovens
infrared	$10^{11} - 4 \times 10^{14}$ Hz	transitions of outer electrons in atoms and molecules	causes the direct heating effect of the Sun and other radiant heat sources; is used for remote sensing and thermography
visible light	$4 \times 10^{14} - 8 \times 10^{14}$ Hz	higher-energy transitions of outer electrons in atoms	radiation that can be detected by the human eye, giving the sensation of "seeing"
ultraviolet	$8 \times 10^{14} - 10^{17}$ Hz	even higher energy transitions of outer electrons in atoms	causes fluorescence in some materials; causes "tanning" of human skin; kills bacteria; aids in the synthesis of vitamin D by the human body
X rays	$10^{15} - 10^{20}$ Hz	transitions of inner electrons of atoms or the rapid deceleration of high-energy free electrons	penetrate soft tissue easily but are absorbed by denser tissue, like bones and teeth, to produce X-ray images of internal body structures; used for radiation therapy and nondestructive testing in industry
gamma rays	$10^{19} - 10^{24}$ Hz	nuclei of atoms, both spontaneous and from the sudden deceleration of very high-energy particles from accelerators	treatment for localized cancerous tumours
cosmic rays	$> 10^{24}$ Hz	bombardment of Earth's atmosphere by very high-energy particles from space	responsible for auroras

▶ **SAMPLE** problem

Microwaves with a wavelength of 1.5 cm are used to transmit television signals coast to coast, through a network of relay towers.

(a) What is the frequency of these microwaves?

(b) How long does it take a microwave signal to cross the continent from St. John's, Newfoundland, to Victoria, British Columbia, a distance of approximately 5.0×10^3 km?

Solution

(a) $\lambda = 1.5$ cm

$v = c = 3.00 \times 10^8$ m/s

$f = ?$

$$f = \frac{c}{\lambda}$$

$$= \frac{3.00 \times 10^8 \text{ m/s}}{1.5 \times 10^{-2} \text{ m}}$$

$$f = 2.0 \times 10^{10} \text{ Hz}$$

The frequency is 2.0×10^{10} Hz.

(b) $\Delta d = 5.0 \times 10^3$ km $= 5.0 \times 10^6$ m

$\Delta t = ?$

$$\Delta d = v\Delta t$$

$$= c\Delta t$$

$$\Delta t = \frac{\Delta d}{c}$$

$$= \frac{5.0 \times 10^6 \text{ m}}{3.0 \times 10^8 \text{ m/s}}$$

$$\Delta t = 1.6 \times 10^{-2} \text{ s}$$

The time required is 1.6×10^{-2} s.

▶ **Practice**

Understanding Concepts

1. Calculate the wavelength of the signal radiated by an FM broadcast station with a frequency of 107.1 MHz.

2. Your class is touring a university physics lab. You notice an X-ray machine operating at 3.00×10^{17} Hz. What is the wavelength of the X rays produced?

3. Calculate the period of the light emitted by a helium–neon laser whose wavelength is 638 nm.

4. How many wavelengths of the radiation emitted by a 6.0×10^1 Hz electrical transmission line would it take to span the North American continent (a distance of approximately 5.0×10^3 km)?

Answers

1. 2.80 m

2. 1.00×10^{-9} m

3. 2.13×10^{-15} s

4. 1.0

In this unit, we started with a systematic inventory of the properties of light but came to the conclusion that light is just one of the many radiations in the electromagnetic spectrum, all possessing the same set of essential properties.

Electromagnetic Waves and Light

- Maxwell postulated and Hertz proved that light and all radiations travel as electromagnetic waves through space at the speed of light (3.00×10^8 m/s).

- Electromagnetic waves consist of electric and magnetic fields that oscillate in phase and perpendicular to each other and to the direction of wave propagation.

- Electromagnetic waves exhibit the properties of interference, diffraction, polarization, reflection, and refraction.

- The electromagnetic spectrum makes up all the radiations that originate from a source with a changing electric or magnetic field.

- The electromagnetic spectrum consists of radio waves (including microwaves), infrared waves, visible light, ultraviolet light, X rays, gamma rays, and cosmic rays.

▶ **Section 10.8 Questions**

Understanding Concepts

1. Calculate the quantity indicated for each of the following electromagnetic waves:
   (a) the frequency of an 1.80-cm wavelength microwave
   (b) the wavelength of a 3.20×10^{10}-Hz radar signal
   (c) the distance between adjacent maxima of magnetic field strength in the electromagnetic wave created by a 60.0-Hz transmission line
   (d) the frequency of red visible light, of wavelength 6.5×10^{-7} nm

2. Two football fans are listening to the Grey Cup game on the radio, one in Montreal, where the game is being played, the other in Inuvik, Northwest Territories, 6.00×10^3 km away. The distant signal is transmitted by microwave, through a communications satellite at an altitude of 3.6×10^4 km. Making whatever assumptions seem reasonable, determine how much sooner the fan in Montreal hears the results of any play.

3. A slit 6.0 cm wide is placed in front of a microwave source operating at a frequency of 7.5 GHz. Calculate the angle (measured from the central maximum) of the first minimum in the diffraction pattern.

4. The first radio amateurs used high-voltage electrical arcs, as Hertz did, to generate radio waves and communicate with one another. Why did this soon become an unworkable situation?

Applying Inquiry Skills

5. How could you use a small portable radio to locate a high-voltage leak in the ignition system of a car?

Making Connections

6. Why is it that when television correspondents are interviewed live on the other side of the planet, there is a short delay before their responses are heard?

7. Television and radio waves can reflect from nearby mountains or from airplanes. Such reflections can interfere with the direct signal from the station.
   (a) Determine what kind of interference will occur when 75-MHz television signals arrive at a receiver directly from a distant station and are also reflected from an airplane 134 m directly above the receiver. (Assume a $\frac{\lambda}{2}$ change in phase of the wave upon reflection.) Explain your reasoning.
   (b) Determine what kind of interference will occur if the plane is 42 m closer to the receiver. Explain your reasoning.

Some Applications of Electromagnetic Waves 10.9

Radio and Television Communications

Marconi first recognized the potential for transmitting information over long distances, using electromagnetic waves without any direct connection by wires. From his early dot–dash Morse code pulses evolved our present sophisticated radio and television networks.

Figure 1 shows the typical components of a modern communications transmitter. Sound waves are detected by a microphone and converted into a weak audio signal. This electrical signal is strengthened by an amplifier before passing into a modulator, where it either modulates the amplitude (in the case of AM) or creates slight perturbations in the frequency (in FM) of a radio-frequency (RF) carrier signal from the RF oscillator. This RF signal wavelength is different for each station.

DID YOU KNOW ?

TV Antennas

The receiving antenna could be an iron core wrapped with wire, a long wire, a metal rod, or a multi-element rooftop antenna. The signal could also enter your home by cable, either as range RF or in digital form. Your cable supplier has already received the signal with its equipment, thus replacing the antenna.

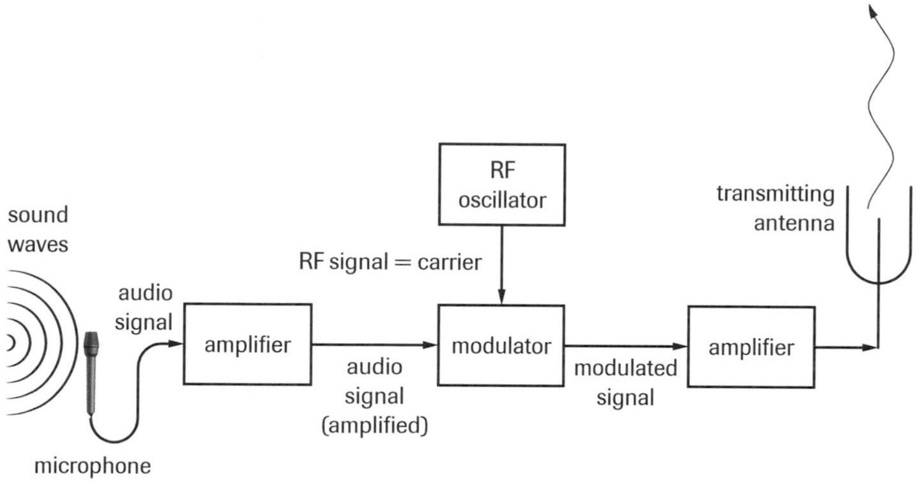

Figure 1
Transmitter circuit

The carrier frequency is the frequency you "tune" on your radio dial. The signal is then further amplified and supplied to a transmitting antenna, generating the electromagnetic wave. A television signal is produced in much the same way as audio radio, except that the carrier frequency is mixed with two signals: one for audio and the other for video. With both television and audio radio, electrons in the transmitting antenna oscillate back and forth at the carrier frequency. The accelerating charges produce the electromagnetic wave, which travels at the speed of light to your home receiver.

In the typical receiver shown in **Figure 2**, the receiving antenna detects incoming electromagnetic waves. The incoming, oscillating electromagnetic fields cause free electrons in the conducting material to move, creating a weak electric current in the antenna. The net effect is the production of a small electrical signal in the antenna, containing a mixture of frequencies from many different transmitting stations.

The first task for the receiver is to select a certain carrier frequency, or small range of frequencies, corresponding to a particular station. The selected RF signal is then amplified and sent into a demodulator, which separates the audio signal from the carrier signal. When this audio frequency (AF) signal has been successfully separated, it is amplified

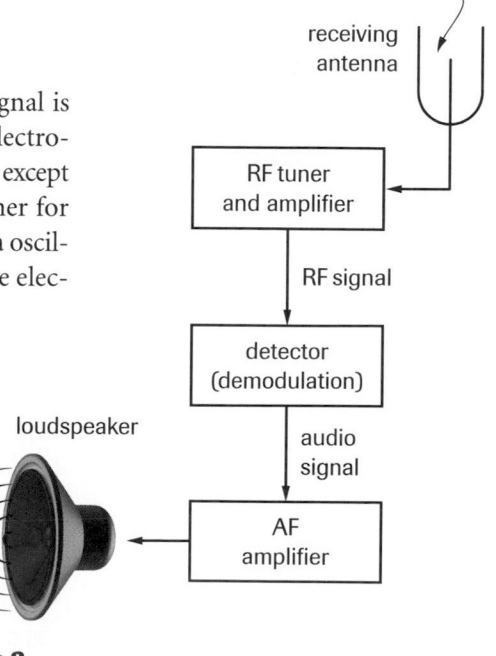

Figure 2
Receiver circuit

Figure 3
A microwave communications tower uses parabolic reflectors to both concentrate the electromagnetic radiation onto a small antenna when receiving a signal and to disperse the radiation from a small antenna when transmitting a signal.

incoherent light light of one or more wavelengths, out of phase (e.g., white light)

coherent light light of one wavelength, in phase (e.g., laser light)

and sent to the speaker for conversion into sound waves. In TV transmission, two distinct signals are demodulated, with the audio signal going to the speaker and the video signal to the picture tube.

In addition to radio and TV bands, frequency bands have been assigned for Citizens Band (CB) radio, ship-to-shore radio, aircraft, police, military, and amateur radio, cellular telephone, space and satellite communications, and radar (**Figure 3**).

Infrared

Infrared radiation (IR) occupies the region between microwaves and visible light. The frequencies range from about 1.0×10^{11} Hz to about 4×10^{14} Hz. We know that very hot objects emit electromagnetic radiation. At relatively low temperatures, we can feel the heat—infrared radiation—from an electric stove element. At higher temperatures, the element begins to glow red, indicating a range of emission in the visible region of the spectrum. At even higher temperatures, such as that of an incandescent light bulb filament, a white glow is observed. We can see that as the temperature of matter increases, the radiation it predominantly emits is of higher and higher frequency. But the lower frequencies are still there. A light bulb, for example, still gives off heat, noticeable even at a distance.

The most common detectors of infrared radiation are photographic film and television cameras sensitive to radiation in the infrared range. Full-colour pictures can show minute variations in the temperature of an object, as indicated by a different colour. For example, infrared photographs of the exterior of a house reveal "hot" spots around the doors and windows, areas in which heat is leaking out (**Figure 4**). Heat images of the human body reveal areas of infection and locations of tumours. Infrared satellite photographs reveal the type of crops being grown (**Figure 5**), the population density of urban areas, and the distribution of acid rain. Reconnaissance photographs of military installations reveal the locations of airport runways, camouflaged factories, and rocket launch sites.

Laser Radiation

Conventional light sources are either hot bodies or emitters of some sharply defined sets of wavelengths. The atoms in the tungsten filament of a common light bulb are agitated and excited to higher energy levels by high temperatures. Once excited, they emit light as they return to a lower energy state, over a wide spread of frequencies. In a gas lamp such as a fluorescent tube, it is the electron current passing through the gas that excites the atoms to high energy levels. The atoms give up this excitation energy by radiating it as light waves (see Section 12.4). Spontaneous emission from each single atom takes place independently of the emission from the others. The overall energy produced by either of these conventional light sources—the incandescent lamp or the fluorescent lamp—is a jumble of frequencies from numerous individual atoms. Each emission has its own phase that changes randomly from moment to moment and point to point. The light from conventional sources is therefore said to be **incoherent**.

In contrast, laser light is **coherent**. The emitted light waves are in phase, with almost all the crests and troughs in step for a substantial time. This coherence arises because the laser atoms do not emit at random but under stimulation (see Section 12.4 for a more detailed explanation). The light waves combine their energies in constructive interference to produce powerful and intense laser light. Since the emitted light has consistent wavelength or colour, laser light is said to be monochromatic. Finally, the light waves are emitted primarily in one direction.

These properties of coherence, intensity, and directionality make laser beams suitable for a wide range of scientific, commercial, medical, and military applications. Directionality ensures that a laser beam travels long distances in a straight line.

This property makes it useful for surveying, for establishing reference directions in the drilling of tunnels, for measuring the very small movement in the continents, for determining the speed of a baseball or a car, for guiding farmers in the laying of drainage tile, and for directing missiles. Further, since the light can be modulated, it is used in fibre optics, permitting thousands of wires to be replaced with a single optical fibre.

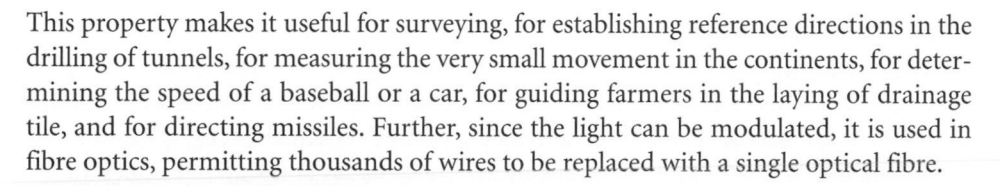

▶ *TRY THIS* activity   *Scattering Laser Light*

Most of the divergence of a laser beam is caused by the scattering of light by air particles. To increase the scattering and make the beam more visible, clap two chalk dusters together above a laser beam in a dark room. Why can you now see the laser beam?

 Do not let direct laser beams or reflected beams go straight into anyone's eyes.

If you are allergic or sensitive to chalk dust, use a light mist of water instead, from a spray bottle. Spray the water over the beam but keep the mist away from the laser.

The intensity of laser beams makes them useful in cutting and welding materials, including metals. An industrial laser can easily concentrate ten thousand million watts for short intervals. With no blades to break or bits to wear, lasers can make precise cuts in fabric for suits, cauterize and cut in various types of surgery (including plastic surgery), weld dishwasher doors, plate easily corroded metals, etch the patterns of microcircuits, and drill eyes in surgical needles (**Figure 6**).

Figure 4
This infrared photo reveals that the windows are much warmer than the surrounding structure. Replacing the windows with double or triple thermopane windows will decrease heat loss, conserving energy and reducing heating bills.

Figure 5
Land-use patterns are clearly seen in this infrared image of the Alberta and Montana border area. Thickly vegetated mountains and riverbanks appear red. Crops at different stages of growth in Montana (bottom half of image) appear in different colours.

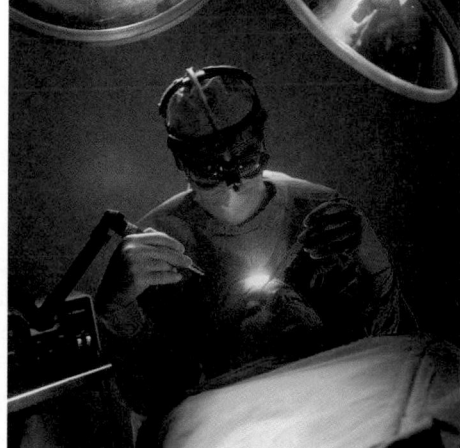

Figure 6
Lasers have many applications, such as cutting steel (left) and treating skin conditions (right).

Ultraviolet Radiation

Ultraviolet radiation (UV), also called ultraviolet light and sometimes "black light," is a band of frequencies lying between visible light and X rays, with a frequency range from 8.0×10^{14} Hz (violet light) to 10^{17} Hz. UV is emitted by very hot objects. Approximately 7% of the Sun's radiation is UV. It is this radiation that creates changes in the skin. Small amounts of UV are necessary for the production of vitamin D in the human body. But large amounts cause tanning and sunburn, which can increase the risk of skin cancer and cause cataracts. UV sources cause fluorescence in certain mineral ores and chemical substances such as dyes and paints, which are used to dramatic effect in posters and T-shirts.

Ionizing Radiation

ionizing radiation radiation at the limit at which ionization can occur, at frequencies higher than ultraviolet

nonionizing radiation radiation at or below the limit at which ionization can occur, at frequencies lower than ultraviolet

Radiation with frequencies higher than UV is **ionizing**. This radiation is so energetic that it causes atoms in a substance to become ionized, expelling one or more electrons. Both X rays and gamma rays are ionizing. Radiation with frequencies of UV and lower is **nonionizing**. Ionization can break chemical bonds, that is, break up molecules. In the human body, ionizing radiation can cause cell death or possible alteration in the cell causing illness and cancers. We will take a closer look at ionizing radiation in Unit 5.

▶ EXPLORE an issue

Cell Phones

The explosive worldwide growth in cell phone use has increased the public debate over possible health risks. Cell phones are small radio stations that send and receive microwaves. We noted in this section that radio waves, even microwaves, are nonionizing radiations. Does it follow that they are safe? Microwaves apparently do produce some heating effect on tissues, including the brain, near a cell phone. But it is not clear whether this could have measurable biological effects, such as an increased risk for cancer.

Most studies have concluded "that the use of hand-held cellular telephones is not associated with the risk of brain cancer." But the findings always have a caveat, such as "Further long-term studies are needed to account for longer usage, especially for slow-growing tumours."

Take a Stand
Is using a cell phone hazardous to your health?

Decision-Making Skills

● Define the Issue ● Analyze the Issue ● Research
● Defend the Position ○ Identify Alternatives ● Evaluate

Form an Opinion
Research the issue, citing the major studies done over the past three years. Make a note of the funding for each of the studies you examine.

- Evaluate the studies based on objective criteria.

- Summarize your findings and indicate to what extent the evidence objectively supports (or, as the case may be, is currently insufficient to support) a conclusion.

- State your personal conclusion, defending your position.

- Will your research lead you to modify your cell phone habits? Why or why not?

GO www.science.nelson.com

The Wave Theory of Light circa 1890

At the end of the nineteenth century, the wave theory of light was firmly established. Double- and single-slit interference strongly corroborated the theory, while additional interference phenomena and polarization raised confidence levels still higher. With the work of Maxwell and Hertz, the physics community was left in little doubt that light, and with it all other electromagnetic radiation, could be represented as transverse waves. Indeed, more radically, there was a sense that all the basic principles governing the physical universe were now known, leaving physics nothing more than a responsibility to clean up details.

This complacency disappeared as the 1890s wore on. In Germany, Wilhelm Roentgen discovered an unknown radiation, which he called "X rays," that were powerful enough to blacken a photographic plate after passing through flesh and wood. Shortly thereafter, in France, Henri Becquerel accidentally left a piece of a uranium ore in a drawer on top of a photographic plate. A few days later, he found that the plate was exposed by some strange radiation and deduced that radiation from the uranium must have passed through the thick cover. And in 1897, the electron was firmly identified as the carrier of electricity by Joseph John ("J.J.") Thomson in England.

However, soon thereafter, the complacent world of the scientists would be permanently disrupted. Radically new concepts of the physical world would emerge, questioning the wave theory of electromagnetic radiation and Newtonian mechanics. These are the topics of the next unit.

SUMMARY | *Some Applications of Electromagnetic Waves*

- Radio waves originate from an oscillating electric field in an antenna and involve a carrier wave modulated by an audio and/or a video wave.
- Infrared radiation originates from a hot object that radiates progressively higher-frequency light as its temperature rises.
- Infrared radiation can be detected photographically and with infrared-sensitive cameras.
- Ultraviolet light has a high enough frequency that the rays can damage human tissue.
- The electromagnetic spectrum is further divided into two parts: ionizing and nonionizing radiation.
- By 1890, it was firmly established that light is an electromagnetic wave that travels at 3.00×10^8 m/s in a vacuum.

> **DID YOU KNOW ?**
>
> **Frequencies of TV Channels and Radio Stations**
> Broadcast frequencies range from 500 kHz to 1600 kHz for medium-wave AM stations and from 88 MHz to 108 MHz for FM stations. TV carrier frequencies range from 54 MHz to 216 MHz for VHF channels 2 to 13 and from 470 MHz to 890 MHz for UHF channels.

▶ **Section 10.9** *Questions*

Understanding Concepts

1. Explain why medium-wave AM transmitters do not cast shadows (regions of no reception) behind obstacles such as buildings and hills, whereas TV and FM transmitters do.

2. An electromagnetic wave is travelling straight up, perpendicular to Earth's surface. Its electric field is oscillating in an east–west plane. What is the direction of oscillation of its magnetic field?

3. Explain why radio reception in a car is liable to distort when the car passes near high-voltage transmission lines or under steel-reinforced concrete.

Applying Inquiry Skills

4. Some laser beams can be modulated. How would you set up a laser and a receiver so that you could transmit the audio signal from a radio output across the room by laser light? Try out your idea if you have suitable equipment.

Making Connections

5. Suntan lotions are rated 15 to 45. What is the relationship between the rating and UV radiation?

6. Research the difference between UV-A and UV-B rays, labels commonly found on sunscreen lotion. Write a summary of your findings.

7. Research medical applications of infrared radiation. Choose two uses, one in diagnosis and the other in treatment, and write a short report on each (maximum 500 words).

8. Give several examples, both favourable and adverse, of ways in which electromagnetic radiation directly influences either our health or our more general well-being.

9. Explain why cell-phone use is forbidden in hospitals.

10. Infrared and ultraviolet light have different heating effects on the human skin. Explain how these effects differ and why.

11. The heating effect of microwaves was originally noticed by radar operators at the end of World War II. They found that they could reheat meals by placing them near the magnetron tubes generating the microwaves. This discovery eventually led to the microwave oven. Research the Internet and other sources and answer the following questions:
    (a) What are the wavelengths of the microwaves used in household microwave ovens?
    (b) What is their source?
    (c) How do microwaves heat food?
    (d) What types of food cannot be heated in a microwave oven?
    (e) Draw a labelled diagram showing the construction of a typical microwave oven. Comment on the safety features.
    (f) Why was the practice of the radar operators dangerous?

 GO www.science.nelson.com

INVESTIGATION 10.2.1

Diffraction of Light in a Single Slit

Inquiry Skills

○ Questioning	○ Planning	● Analyzing
○ Hypothesizing	● Conducting	● Evaluating
● Predicting	● Recording	● Communicating

This investigation has three parts. In the first part, you will explore single-slit diffraction, making qualitative observations about the effect of slit width on diffraction, the structure of the interference pattern, and how it is affected by slit width and wavelength (colour). In the second part, you will take measurements of the diffraction interference pattern using a helium–neon or LED laser. This will require you to review Section 10.2 first, since you will need to use mathematical relationships from that section. In Part 3, you will predict the diffraction pattern you would see when directing a laser beam onto a human hair. This investigation will greatly enhance your understanding of single-slit diffraction, providing you with a good base for future work with diffraction gratings and other interference effects.

Question

How do obstacles and single slits diffract light into defined patterns?

Hypothesis

Light is diffracted into predictable patterns that can be analyzed and used to determine variables, such as the wavelength of light and the width of a slit.

Prediction

(a) Predict the pattern of diffraction created by a human hair placed into a laser beam.

Materials

long-filament showcase lamp or halogen-quartz bulb
red and green transparent filters
elastic bands
single-slit plate
variable-slit plate
helium–neon or LED laser
razor blade
diverging lens
white screen
metric measuring tape
photometer or computer interface
microscope slides

Procedure

Part 1: Single-Slit Diffraction

 The showcase lamp will get very hot. Be careful not to touch it.

1. Set up the lamp so that the filament is vertical.

2. Press the pads of your two forefingers against each other, creating a small slit (**Figure 1**). Changing the pressure on your fingertips can change the slit width.

Figure 1
For steps 2 and 3

3. Position your finger slit so that it is parallel to the filament of the lamp. Vary the width of the slit, observing any changes in the light passing through.

4. View the long filament again, this time using a prepared slit. Record your observations in a simple sketch.

5. Cover the lamp completely with the red filter, held in place with an elastic band. View the red light through a series of single slits. Record the changes in the pattern as you increase the slit width w, while keeping the source wavelength and the separation between the source and the slit constant.

6. Viewing the light through a narrow, single slit, slowly move the slit away from the source, then back toward it. Record the changes in the pattern.

7. Cover the lamp with the red and green filters so that the upper half emits red light, the lower half green. Keeping the distance from the source fixed, compare the displacement y of the first minimum from the central line for red and for green light.

Part 2: Using a Laser as a Source of Monochromatic Light

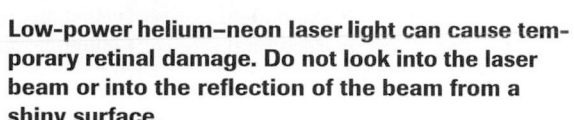 Low-power helium–neon laser light can cause temporary retinal damage. Do not look into the laser beam or into the reflection of the beam from a shiny surface.

Take care handling the razor blades.

8. Aim the helium–neon laser beam at a white screen approximately 1.0 m away. Slowly slide the edge of one razor blade into one side of the beam. Record the pattern on the screen.

9. Place the variable-slit plate into the laser beam. Slowly decrease the slit width, recording any changes in the pattern on the screen.

10. Pass the laser beam through a commercially prepared, narrow, single slit, then enlarge the beam with a diverging lens. Record the pattern on the screen.

11. Keeping the single slit and diverging lens in place, darken the room and move a sensitive photometer, or a probe connected to a computer interface, across the pattern produced on the screen, from one end to the other. Record the intensity variations at 5-mm intervals. Plot a graph of light intensity versus distance, fixing zero distance at the centre of the pattern.

12. With the screen still located 1.0 m in front of the laser aperture, remove the single slit. Mark on the screen the exact middle of the laser beam. Measure the distance L from the laser aperture to this point on the screen.

13. Place a single slit right in front of the laser beam so that a diffraction pattern is produced on the screen. You may have to adjust the slit somewhat to ensure that the exact middle of the central maximum is at the point you marked on the screen in step 12.

14. Measure the distances, on the screen, from the centre of the central maximum to the first nodal line on each side of the pattern. Find the average y_1 of these two distances.

15. Record the width w of the single slit. Using
$$\lambda = \frac{wy_1}{L},$$ determine the wavelength of the light.

16. Repeat steps 14 and 15 with a different slit. This time, since the wavelength of light is known, determine the width w of the slit.

Part 3: Diffraction by a Human Hair

17. Carefully attach a human hair to a microscope slide. Predict in a sketch what interference pattern will result when you insert your slide into the laser beam.

18. Mount the hair vertically in front of the laser beam. Focus a clear image of the hair onto the screen with a diverging lens. Sketch the pattern on the screen.

Analysis

(b) What width of single slit is required to produce diffraction? What does the width indicate about the wavelength? Explain your reasoning.

(c) You have compared the diffraction of red and green light. Which light does your comparison show to have the longer wavelength? Why?

(d) You have observed the effect of passing white light through the single slit. What do your observations indicate about the respective wavelengths of the spectral colours?

(e) (i) How does the slit width w affect the distance y_1 to the first nodal line? Write your answer as a proportion.

    (ii) What is the relationship between the distance y_1 from the central line to the first minimum and the distance L from the source to the first minimum? Write your answer as a proportion.

    (iii) What is the relationship between y and the wavelength λ? Write your answer as a proportion.

    (iv) Combine the proportionality statements in the last three steps into one proportionality statement involving y, L, w, and λ, making λ the dependent variable.

(f) Does the diffraction pattern you observed for the human hair agree with your prediction? Does your observation contain anything analogous to Poisson's Bright Spot (Section 9.5)?

Evaluation

(g) How does the graph of intensity versus distance compare with the graph in **Figure 6**, Section 10.2?

(h) Compare your value for the source wavelength with the accepted value of 6.328×10^{-7} m, stating your experimental error.

(i) Compare your value for slit width with the value provided by your teacher, stating your experimental error.

(j) Identify the most likely sources of error in your wavelength and slit-width determinations.

(k) What modifications could you make to get a more accurate wavelength determination?

(l) Evaluate the hypothesis.

Interference in Air Wedges

Interference effects in thin films were discussed in Section 10.4 but in a theoretical way. In this investigation you will apply the concepts of interference in an air wedge. You will determine the thickness of a human hair in wavelengths of light, comparing your measurements against those using more traditional methods. Since you have had experience with the laser and single-slit diffraction, you can apply the same approaches to an air wedge. The air wedge you will be using consists of two glass microscope slides held tightly together by an elastic band at one end, with a human hair between the slides at the other end, held in place by another elastic band (**Figure 1**). Your challenge is to design a procedure and report your results.

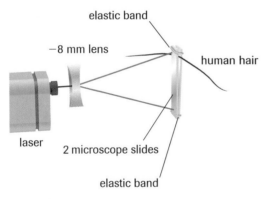

Figure 1
Setup for Investigation 10.4.1

Inquiry Skills

○ Questioning	● Planning	● Analyzing
○ Hypothesizing	● Conducting	● Evaluating
○ Predicting	● Recording	● Communicating

Question

How does the accuracy of the air wedge technique compare to other methods of measuring small objects?

Hypothesis

The air wedge technique is a more accurate procedure to use to measure the size of small objects.

Materials

diverging lens (–8 mm)
2 microscope slides
2 elastic bands
helium–neon laser
white screen
human hair
micrometer
microscope

Procedure

(a) Design your own investigation to determine the thickness of a human hair using an air wedge, a microscope, and a micrometer. Your report should include a statement of procedure, outlining the steps you plan to follow and all necessary safety procedures. The analysis section of your report should include all calculations for your methods, a comparison of the relative accuracies of the methods, and suggestions for modifications that may reduce your errors. Your report should include an evaluation.

There are many different types of careers that involve the study of the wave nature of light. Find out more about the careers described below or about some other interesting career based on the wave nature of light.

Lensmaker

Lensmakers learn their specialty through on-the-job training. Employers look for candidates with a high school diploma that includes a physics credit. Demonstrated interest in optics is helpful. Lensmakers use optical equipment, including radioscopes, lensometers, and computerized lathes, and also equipment for sterilization and polishing. Lensmakers work for private companies manufacturing spectacles and contact lenses. Good hand-eye coordination is essential.

Photonics Engineer

Photonics engineers deal with the properties and applications of light, especially as a medium for transmitting information. Individuals entering this diverse field include electrical engineers, university physics graduates, and college graduates in electronics and photonics. Specializations include research, design, repair and maintenance, manufacturing, and technical sales in areas such as telecommunications, photo imaging, medicine, printing, and consumer electronics. Photonics engineers work with different technologies including fibre optics, bar-code processing, CCD photography, and CD and DVD recording and playback, light-emitting diodes (LEDs), computer disk storage, flat screen displays, and lasers. With photonics poised for rapid growth, companies will require new employees who have the appropriate educational backgrounds and skills.

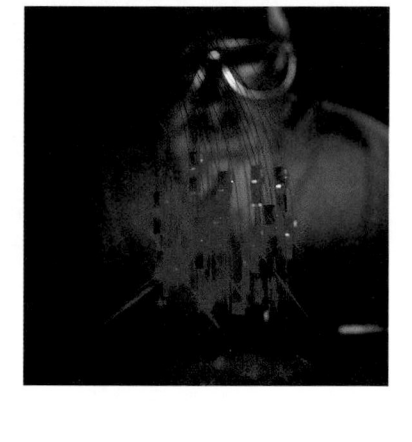

Astronomer

Astronomers use light to analyze astronomical data and attempt to understand the origin and evolution of the universe. They observe light from stars and the gas between stars, and individual galaxies or groups of galaxies. A Ph.D. in astronomy is required to do advanced work at a university or research facility, but many astronomers can work at observatories or in related fields with a bachelor's or master's degree in astronomy. Astronomers who do advanced research use a variety of telescopes including optical telescopes like the Hubble Space Telescope or the Canada-France-Hawaii Telescope. Some astronomers work as theorists and, while they don't use telescopes themselves, they take the results and develop theories using computers.

▶ **Practice**

Making Connections

1. Identify several careers that require knowledge about the wave nature of light. Select a career you are interested in from the list you made or from the careers described above. Imagine that you have been employed in your chosen career for five years and that you are applying to work on a new project of interest.

   (a) Describe the project. It should be related to some of the new things you learned in this unit. Explain how the concepts from this unit are applied in the project.

   (b) Create a résumé listing your credentials and explaining why you are qualified to work on the project. Include in your résumé
   - your educational background: what university degree or diploma program you graduated with, which educational institute you attended, postgraduate training (if any)
   - your skills
   - your duties in previous positions
   - your salary expectations

 www.science.nelson.com

Key Expectations

- analyze and interpret experimental evidence indicating that light has some characteristics and properties that are similar to those of mechanical waves and sound (10.1, 10.2)
- identify the theoretical basis of an investigation, and develop a prediction that is consistent with that theoretical basis (e.g., predict the effects related to the polarization of light as it passes through two polarizing filters; predict the diffraction pattern produced when a human hair is passed in front of a laser beam) (10.1, 10.2, 10.4)
- describe and explain the design and operation of technologies related to electromagnetic radiation (e.g., describe how information is stored and retrieved using compact discs and laser beams) (10.1, 10.5, 10.6, 10.9)
- describe instances where the development of new technologies resulted in the advancement or revision of scientific theories (10.1, 10.6, 10.7, 10.8)
- describe and explain the experimental evidence supporting a wave model of light (10.1, 10.2, 10.8)
- describe the phenomenon of wave interference as it applies to light in qualitative and quantitative terms, using diagrams and sketches (10.1, 10.2, 10.3, 10.4, 10.6, 10.7)
- define and explain the concepts and units related to the wave nature of light (e.g., diffraction, wave interference, polarization, electromagnetic radiation, electromagnetic spectrum) (10.1, 10.2, 10.3, 10.4, 10.6, 10.7, 10.8)
- describe and explain the phenomenon of wave diffraction as it applies to light in quantitative terms, using diagrams (10.2, 10.3)
- identify the interference pattern produced by the diffraction of light through narrow single slits and diffraction gratings, and analyze it (the pattern) in qualitative and quantitative terms (10.2, 10.3)
- analyze, using the concepts of refraction, diffraction, and wave interference, the separation of light into colours in various phenomena (e.g., the colours produced by thin films), which forms the basis for the design of technological devices (10.2, 10.3, 10.4, 10.5)
- describe, citing examples, how electromagnetic radiation, as a form of energy, is produced and transmitted, and how it interacts with matter (10.8, 10.9)

Key Terms

plane-polarized	resolution
unpolarized	diffraction grating
polarization	spectroscope
polarizer	air wedge
double refraction	Newton's rings
monochromatic	back-glare
scattering	hologram
Polaroid	radio waves
photoelasticity	incoherent light
optical activity	coherent light
central maximum	ionizing radiation
secondary maxima	nonionizing radiation

Key Equations

- $\sin \theta_n = \dfrac{n\lambda}{w}$ for dark fringes (single slit) (10.2)

- $\sin \theta_m = \dfrac{\left(m + \frac{1}{2}\right)\lambda}{w}$ for bright fringes (single slit) (10.2)

- $\sin \theta_m = \dfrac{m\lambda}{d}$ for bright spectral lines (gratings) (10.3)

- $\Delta x = L\left(\dfrac{\lambda}{2t}\right)$ for an air wedge (10.4)

- $c = f\lambda$ for all electromagnetic waves (10.8)

▶ *MAKE* a summary

Construct a four-column chart using the headings Property, Sound, Electromagnetic Waves, and Equations. Under the Property column, list all the wave properties you can think of. In the Sound and Electromagnetic Waves columns, specify the property as appropriate for sound and electromagnetic radiation, respectively. In the Equations column, write any equations relevant to each property.

(a) In a few sentences, summarize the similarities and differences between sound and electromagnetic radiation.

(b) Interference should be one of the properties listed. List five applications where the interference of electromagnetic waves plays an important role.

Write numbers 1 to 9 in your notebook. Indicate beside each question whether the statement is true (T) or false (F). If it is false, write a corrected version.

1. Polarization provided the proof that light is a longitudinal wave.

2. For single-slit diffraction,
   (a) the smaller the slit width, the smaller the distance between adjacent maxima and minima
   (b) the longer the wavelength, the greater the distance between maxima
   (c) minima, or dark fringes, occur at $\frac{\lambda}{w}, \frac{2\lambda}{w}, \frac{3\lambda}{w}, \ldots$

3. The smaller the aperture of an optical instrument, the better its resolution.

4. For transmitted light in thin films, destructive interference occurs for reflected light when the film has a thickness of $\frac{\lambda}{4}, \frac{3\lambda}{4}, \frac{5\lambda}{4}, \ldots$, where λ is the wavelength in the film.

5. In an interferometer, when the mirror moves so that four fringes are observed, the mirror has moved a distance of 2λ, where λ is the wavelength of the light source.

6. Hertz postulated and Maxwell proved that light and radio waves travel through space at the speed of light.

7. Radio waves originate from an oscillating electric field in an antenna.

8. Electromagnetic waves consist of electric and magnetic fields oscillating in phase, perpendicular to each other and to the direction of wave propagation.

9. Ionizing radiation originates in light with a wavelength longer than that of visible light.

Write numbers 10 to 16 in your notebook. Beside each number, write the letter corresponding to the best choice.

10. **Figure 1** shows a single slit, with lines marking the direction to a point P in the diffraction pattern; X and Y are the edges of the slit. The possible value for the path difference PY – PX that places P at the second intensity minimum from the central maximum is
    (a) $\frac{\lambda}{2}$ (b) λ (c) $\frac{3\lambda}{2}$ (d) 2λ (e) $\frac{5\lambda}{2}$

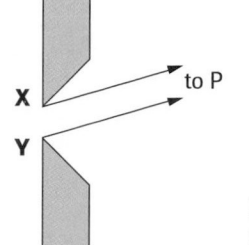

Figure 1
For questions 10 and 11

11. The possible value for the path difference PY – PX in **Figure 1** that places P at the intensity maximum nearest the central maximum is
    (a) $\frac{\lambda}{2}$ (b) λ (c) $\frac{3\lambda}{2}$ (d) 2λ (e) $\frac{5\lambda}{2}$

12. Colours are often observed when gasoline is poured onto water. This effect is primarily produced by
    (a) diffraction   (d) absorption
    (b) diffuse reflection   (e) incandescence
    (c) interference

13. **Figure 2** shows three experiments for studying the interaction of monochromatic light with thin films of glass of various thickness t. The eye represents the position of the observer. The observer sees constructive interference in
    (a) I only   (c) III only   (e) II and III only
    (b) II only   (d) I and III only

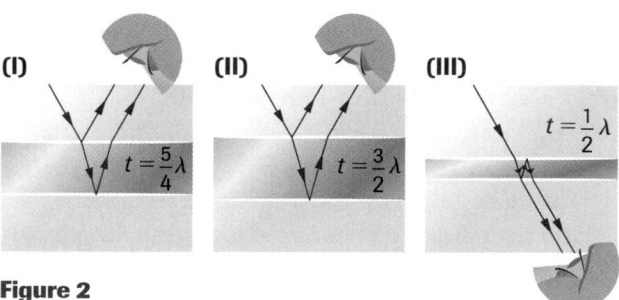

Figure 2

14. A thin coating, of refractive index 1.2, is applied to a glass camera lens, of refractive index $n > 1.2$, to minimize the intensity of the light reflected. The wavelength of the light is λ. The coating thickness required to minimize the intensity of reflected light is
    (a) $\frac{\lambda}{2}$ (c) $\frac{1.2\lambda}{4}$ (e) $\frac{\lambda}{4}$
    (b) $\frac{\lambda}{2 \times 1.2}$ (d) $\frac{\lambda}{4 \times 1.2}$

15. The type of electromagnetic radiation that travels at the greatest speed is
    (a) radio waves   (d) gamma rays
    (b) visible light   (e) They all travel at the
    (c) X rays   same speed.

16. The three types of radiation placed in order of increasing frequency are
    (a) gamma rays, radio waves, infrared radiation
    (b) radio waves, gamma rays, infrared radiation
    (c) infrared radiation, radio waves, gamma rays
    (d) gamma rays, infrared radiation, radio waves
    (e) radio waves, infrared radiation, gamma rays

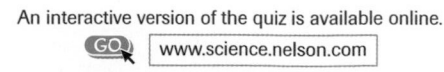

Understanding Concepts

1. Describe how you could use two large, circular Polaroid filters in front of a circular window as a kind of window shade.

2. A slit 4.30×10^{-5} m wide is located 1.32 m from a flat screen. Monochromatic light shines through the slit onto the screen. The width of the central fringe in the diffraction pattern is 3.8 cm. What is the wavelength of the light?

3. A diffraction grating, illuminated by yellow light at a wavelength of 5.50×10^2 nm, produces a second-order minimum at 25°. Determine the spacing between the lines.

4. Calculate the wavelength of light that produces its first minimum at an angle of 36.9° when falling on a single slit of width 1.00 μm.

5. A beam of parallel rays of red light from a ruby laser ($\lambda = 694.3$ nm), incident on a single slit, produces a central bright band, 42 mm wide, on a screen 2.50 m away. Calculate the width of the slit.

6. (a) What is the width of a single slit that produces its first minimum at 28.0° for 6.00×10^{-7}-m light?
   (b) What is the wavelength of light that has its second minimum at 67.0° for this same slit?

7. The first-order maximum produced by a grating is located at an angle $\theta = 18.0°$. What is the angle for the third-order maximum with the same light and the same slit width?

8. A transmission grating, with lines 3.00×10^{-6} m apart, is illuminated by a narrow beam of red light ($\lambda = 694.3$ nm) from a ruby laser. Bright spots of red light are seen on both sides of the central beam, on a screen 2.00 m away. How far from the central axis is each of the spots?

9. The wavelength of the laser beam used in a certain CD player is 7.80×10^2 nm. A diffraction grating creates two first-order tracking beams 1.2 mm apart, at a distance of 3.0 mm from the grating. Calculate the spacing between the slits of the grating.

10. A diffraction grating, ruled at 2400 lines/cm and illuminated by a monochromatic source, produces a first-order bright fringe 8.94×10^{-2} m away from the central bright fringe on a flat screen 0.625 m from the grating. Calculate the wavelength of the light.

11. When a certain transmission grating is illuminated at a wavelength of 638 nm, a third-order maximum forms at an angle of 19.0°. Calculate the number of lines per centimetre in the grating.

12. A certain transparent coating of thickness t, deposited on a glass plate, has a refractive index larger than the refractive index of the glass, not smaller, as with a typical nonreflective coating. For a certain wavelength within the coating, the thickness of the coating is $\frac{\lambda}{4}$. The coating improves the reflection of the light. Explain why.

13. A thin film of a material is floating on water ($n = 1.33$). When the material has a refractive index of $n = 1.20$, the film looks bright in reflected light as its thickness approaches zero. But when the material has a refractive index of $n = 1.45$, the film looks black in reflected light as its thickness approaches zero. Explain these observations with diagrams.

14. When looking straight down on a film of oil on water, you see the colour red. How thick could the film be to cause this effect? How thick could it be at another place where you see violet?

15. A thin layer of oil ($n = 1.25$) is floating on water ($n = 1.33$). How thick is the oil in the region that strongly reflects green light ($\lambda = 556$ nm)?

16. A soap film of refractive index 1.34 appears yellow ($\lambda = 5.80 \times 10^2$ nm) when viewed directly from the same side as the source of light. Calculate two possible values for the thickness of the film.

17. An oil slick 122 nm thick ($n = 1.40$), lying on water, is illuminated by white light incident perpendicular to its surface. What colour does the oil appear?

18. You are working with an apparatus for displaying Newton's rings, illuminated by a monochromatic source at 546 nm. One surface in your apparatus is fixed. The other is movable along the axis of the system. As you adjust that second surface, the rings appear to contract, with the centre of the pattern, initially at its darkest, becoming alternately bright and dark. The pattern passes through 26 bright phases, finishing at its darkest again. How far was the surface moved? Did it approach or recede from the fixed surface?

19. A film of magnesium fluoride ($n = 1.38$), 1.25×10^{-5} cm thick, is used to coat a camera lens ($n = 1.55$). Are any wavelengths in the visible spectrum intensified in the reflected light?

20. A thin layer of liquid methylene iodide ($n = 1.76$) is sandwiched between two flat parallel plates of glass ($n = 1.50$). Light with a wavelength of 689 nm in air is strongly reflected. Calculate the thickness of the liquid layer.

21. You are observing a fringe pattern in a Michelson interferometer. By how much must one of the mirrors be moved to cause a dark fringe to expand into the position previously occupied by a bright ring?

22. (a) A doorway is 81 cm wide. Calculate the angle locating the first dark fringe in the diffraction pattern formed when blue light ($\lambda = 489$ nm) passes through the doorway.
    (b) Repeat part (a) for a 512-Hz sound wave, taking the speed of sound to be 342 m/s.
    (c) Why are your answers for (a) and (b) so different?

Making Connections

23. Research the use of polarization as a navigation aid by spiders. Write a research paper on your findings.

 www.science.nelson.com

24. Bats use the reflections from ultra-high frequency sound to locate their prey. Estimate the typical frequency of a bat's sonar. Take the speed of sound to be 3.40×10^2 m/s, and a small moth, 3.00 mm across, to be a typical target.

25. Radio telescopes are used to map celestial radio-wave sources. In 1967, the Algonquin Radio Observatory (**Figure 1**), in Algonquin Park, Ontario, was linked to a radio telescope in Prince Albert, Saskatchewan, to increase the baseline (the distance between the two telescopes). This was the first successful experiment in very long baseline interferometry. Explain why such an arrangement is desirable.

26. The vivid iridescence of the peacock, comprising chiefly blues and greens, is caused by interference of white light upon reflection in the complex, layered surface of its feathers. This is called *biomimicry*.
    (a) Using the Internet and other sources, research biomimicry and report briefly on how this effect is produced in the peacock feather as well as similar effects seen in grackle and hummingbird plumage.
    (b) Why are investigators studying iridescent plumage?

 www.science.nelson.com

27. Photochromatic sunglasses have a coating that darkens when exposed to sunlight but returns to normal when not exposed. Explain how such sunglasses work.

28. The external surfaces of stealth bombers are covered with a thin coating. Explain how such a coating could protect the bombers from detection by radar. (Radar typically operates at wavelengths of a few centimetres.)

Extension

29. (a) If a single slit produces a first minimum at 13.8°, at what angle is the second-order minimum?
    (b) Calculate the angle of the third-order maximum.

30. Monochromatic light of wavelength 6.00×10^{-7} m falls normally onto a diffraction grating, producing a first-order maximum at an angle of 18.5°. When the same grating is used with a different monochromatic source, the first-order maximum is observed at an angle of 14.9°. Calculate the wavelength of the second source and the highest order observable with the second source.

31. A chamber with flat parallel windows is placed into one arm of a Michelson interferometer illuminated by 638-nm light. The length of the chamber is 8.0 cm as measured from the inside. The refractive index of air is 1.000 29. As the air is pumped out of the cell, how many fringe pairs will shift by in the process?

Figure 1
The dish at the Algonquin Radio Observatory is 46 m in diameter. (for question 25)

PERFORMANCE TASK

▶ **Criteria**

Process

- Choose appropriate research tools.
- Carry out the research and summarize your findings appropriately.
- Analyze the physical principles involved in the type of photography chosen.
- Process and display a photographic image or hologram.

Product

- Demonstrate an understanding of the related physics concepts in your report.
- Prepare a suitable research portfolio.
- Use terms, symbols, equations, and SI metric units correctly.
- Produce a final communication outlining the process followed and producing a tangible result.

Physical Optics Phenomena

As was stated at the beginning of Chapter 10, "Soap bubbles, colourful effects of oil on water, the visible spectrum, peacock feathers—this is a colourful chapter." It was interesting too, as you applied the physics of waves to understand everyday optical phenomena and applications that have changed our world. As you flip through the pages in this unit, you see many interesting photographs, taken in most cases by professional photographers. But, technology has advanced to the point that we can all use automatic cameras that take the properly focused and exposed pictures, and where you can see the results immediately or possibly an hour later. With digital cameras we can capture events at rest or moving immediately, and at much lower light levels.

For example, when studying polarization, materials such as glass and Lucite become doubly refractive when subjected to mechanical stress. When these materials are placed between polarizing and analyzing filters, the strain patterns, and thus the stress distributions, are revealed (**Figures 1** and **2**). You can take photographs like these.

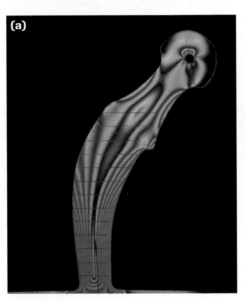

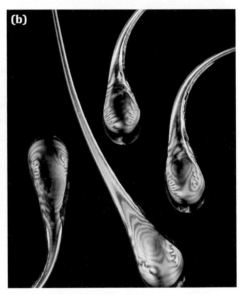

Figure 1
(a) Strain distribution in a plastic model of a hip replacement used in medical research. The pattern is produced when the plastic model is placed between two crossed polarizers.
(b) These glass objects, called Prince Rupert drops, are produced by dropping molten glass into water. The photograph was made by placing the objects between two crossed polarizers.

Figure 2
Optical stress analysis of a plastic lens placed between crossed polarizers.

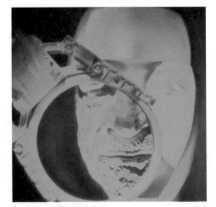

Figure 3
Holographic artists can achieve dramatic effects.

With the science of holography you can create your own images (holograms), now that inexpensive lasers are readily available and specially prepared photographic plates can be obtained outside of the laboratory. Holographic images can be a simple as that of a loonie or as artistically created as the image in **Figure 3**.

In this Performance Task you will choose one of two options. The first option is to take photographs that illustrate some phenomena of physical optics that you have studied. We have given you a dramatic example with photoelasticity, but it can be any of the effects discussed in this unit. Examples include wave properties in ripple tanks, refraction and dispersion effects, applications of polarization, diffraction effects in slits and diffraction gratings, thin film phenomena, etc. You may want to recreate photographs similar to those found in this text and other sources, or you may wish to create your own.

The second option is to set up and record a holographic image using a kit provided by your teacher. Since the kit utilizes an inexpensive laser pointer and specially prepared photographic plates, this option can be performed in the classroom or at home. The kit has been used extensively by students as young as 12, so don't be intimidated when considering this option.

Option 1: Photography of Physical Optical Phenomena

Begin by researching the images in this book, in other physics textbooks, and in science magazines such as *Scientific American*, *Discover*, and *Popular Science*. Photography and image marketing Web sites will provide other photographic examples. This research may help you select the physical optical phenomena you wish to record, or you may already have decided. Your teacher will indicate the physical resources available in your physics classroom. A digital camera is recommended. It may be made available to you, or you can bring one from home.

Task

Your task will be to set up and take a minimum of four photographic images of at least two different phenomena. The images will be mounted for display with a concise description of the underlying physics explained below the image. Your report will include at least three photographic images resulting from your research, a description of the process you followed to take your images, and the physical concepts and principles involved in all of the images in your report. As part of the research you will report the historical background and the people involved in the early discovery and/or application of the phenomena.

Option 2: Holography

Dennis Gabor, the inventor of holography, described his process as a "two-step method of optical imagery." The first step involves recording a set of light waves reflected off an object. The second step involves reconstructing those light waves to create an image. In other words, first you must record a hologram, then "play it back."

For this task, you will follow a procedure to record and reproduce a three-dimensional holographic image of a small object found in your house or classroom. After obtaining all the necessary materials, you will arrange them in a hologram recording set up. You will then record a hologram and process it. Shortly after, you will be able to see the result of your work: a holographic image of the object from which you made a hologram. The source of monochromatic, coherent light will be the semiconductor diode lasers used in laser pointers.

Your teacher will provide you with specific instructions and the materials to perform this task.

Task

- Research the operation of a semiconductor laser and write a simplified report on how it works, including diagrams as appropriate.
- Research and report on the silver halide process used to create a photographic image.
- Create and project a three-dimensional holograph.
- Evaluate the process and suggest ways to improve your image.
- Write a report outlining the procedure you followed, your analysis, and your evaluation of the process.

 **Do not let direct laser beams or reflected beams go straight into anyone's eyes.**

Assessment

Your report will be evaluated using the following criteria:

- the quantity and accuracy of your research
- the demonstration of the knowledge and understanding of the physics principles involved
- appropriate referencing and crediting
- a demonstrated ability to carefully follow instructions
- the quality of your manufactured hologram
- the quality of your written communication

Write numbers 1 to 8 in your notebook. Indicate beside each number whether the corresponding statement is true (T) or false (F). If it is false, write a corrected version.

1. Two ripple tank sources vibrating in phase produce an interference pattern. If the frequency of the two sources increases, the number of nodal lines increases.

2. The wave theory predicts that light slows down when it travels from air to glass, whereas the Newtonian particle theory predicts it will speed up.

3. All wave properties of light can be explained with the wave model.

4. Two rays of light from the same source interfere destructively if their path lengths differ by 3.5λ.

5. If a Young's double-slit apparatus, having operated in air, were to be submerged in water, the fringe pattern would become less spread out.

6. If a Young's double-slit apparatus, having operated with a monochromatic red source, were to be operated with a monochromatic blue source, the fringe pattern would become more spread out.

7. When using a single slit, the distance between adjacent dark fringes will increase if the slit width is decreased, all other factors being kept constant.

8. All waves have the same properties as electromagnetic waves.

Write the numbers 9 to 16 in your notebook. Beside each number, write the letter corresponding to the best choice.

9. In a ripple tank, the wavelength λ_1 of waves in the deep water is 2.0 cm. The wavelength λ_2 of waves in the shallow water is 1.2 cm. The wave generator has a frequency of 12 Hz. The speed of the waves in the deep water is
   (a) 2.0 cm/s
   (b) 6.0 cm/s
   (c) 12 cm/s
   (d) 14 cm/s
   (e) 24 cm/s

10. A narrow beam of light is transmitted through different media as shown in **Figure 1**. If v_1, v_2, and v_3 are the respective speeds of light in the three media, then
    (a) $v_1 > v_2 > v_3$
    (b) $v_3 > v_2 > v_1$
    (c) $v_3 > v_1 > v_2$
    (d) $v_2 > v_1 > v_3$
    (e) $v_1 > v_3 > v_2$

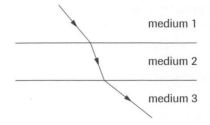

Figure 1

11. When a transverse wave travelling along a string reaches the junction with a lighter string, the wave is
    (a) totally reflected at the junction
    (b) partially transmitted, with a change of phase
    (c) transmitted, forming a standing-wave pattern in the lighter string
    (d) reflected so as to form a node at the junction
    (e) partially reflected without a change in phase

12. A nodal line pattern is produced by two point sources vibrating in phase in a ripple tank. A point P on the second nodal line is 37.0 cm from the one source and 28.0 cm from the other. The wavelength is
    (a) 18.0 cm
    (b) 13.5 cm
    (c) 9.0 cm
    (d) 6.0 cm
    (e) 4.5 cm

13. Monochromatic light in **Figure 2** passes through slit S in a cardboard sheet, then falls onto a metal sheet containing slits B and C, and finally produces an interference pattern, centred at P, onto a screen. All the slits are the same width.

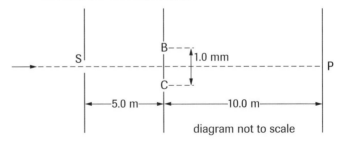

Figure 2

The intensity pattern on the screen will not change if
    (a) the separation between slits B and C is increased
    (b) the width of slits B and C is decreased
    (c) the distance from the metal sheet to the screen is decreased
    (d) the distance between the cardboard and metal sheets is increased
    (e) the wavelength is decreased

14. Of the five diagrams in **Figure 3**, choose the one which most accurately illustrates single-slit diffraction from a monochromatic source.

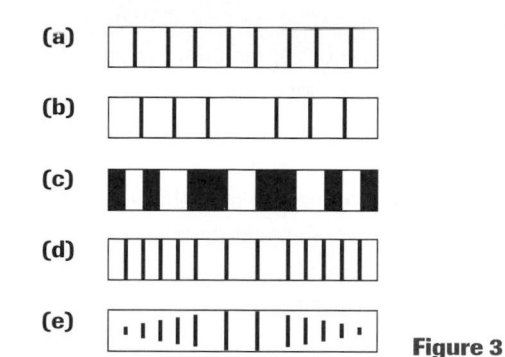

Figure 3

15. Red light, of wavelength λ in soapy water, is viewed through a thin soap film held vertically (**Figure 4**). At the second dark area from the top, the thickness of the film is

(a) λ (c) $\frac{1}{2}\lambda$ (e) very much less than λ

(b) $\frac{3}{4}\lambda$ (d) $\frac{1}{4}\lambda$

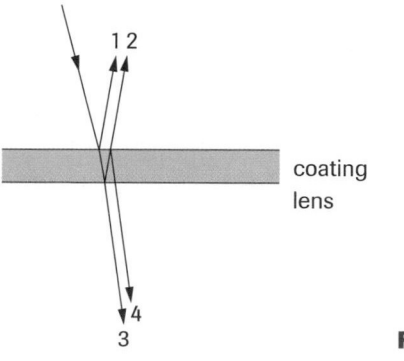

Figure 4

16. The condition necessary for maximum transmission of the light energy passing through the coating on the exterior of the lens in **Figure 5** is that
(a) rays 3 and 4 interfere constructively
(b) the coating be more transparent than the lens
(c) rays 1 and 2 interfere destructively
(d) the speed of light in the coating be less than the speed in the lens
(e) the total light energy reflected be a minimum

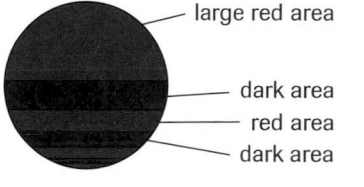

Figure 5

Write the numbers 17 to 28 in your notebook. Beside each number, place the word or phrase that best completes the statement.

17. At a constant speed, the wavelength of a wave is directly proportional to its ___?___ .

18. The frequency of a wave is determined by its ___?___ and does not change when the medium changes.

19. For a given slit, the amount of diffraction depends on the ratio ___?___ / ___?___ .

20. Increasing the separation of the sources in twin-source ripple tank diffraction increases the number of ___?___ lines.

21. Early attempts showing light interference were unsuccessful because the two sources were ___?___ and the ___?___ of light is very small.

22. The wave theory of light, as corroborated by Young's experiment, explained all the then-known properties of light except transmission through a(n) ___?___ .

23. Polarization showed that light is a(n) ___?___ wave.

24. For single-slit diffraction, the smaller the slit width, the ___?___ the distance between maxima and minima.

25. The position of minima, or dark fringes, in single-slit diffraction is given by the equation ___?___ .

26. The larger the aperture of an optical instrument, the ___?___ the resolution.

27. The higher the frequency, the ___?___ the energy of an electromagnetic wave.

28. **Table 1** lists scientists and discoveries or innovations important to the history of the wave theory of light. Match the scientist to the discovery or innovation discussed in this unit.

Table 1

Scientist	Discovery or Innovation
Gabor	diffraction of light
Grimaldi	diffraction of light around a small disk
Hertz	mathematical theory of electromagnetic waves
Huygens	holography
Land	interferometer
Marconi	particle theory of light
Maxwell	commercially viable polarizing filters
Michelson	transmission of radio signals
Newton	creation and detection of radio waves
Poisson	two-slit interference
Young	wavelet model for propagation of wave fronts

NEL   An interactive version of the quiz is available online.
GO www.science.nelson.com

The Wave Nature of Light   **551**

Understanding Concepts

1. List the successes and failures of the particle and wave models in accounting for the behaviour of light as follows:
   (a) Name four optical phenomena adequately accounted for by both models.
   (b) Name four phenomena not adequately accounted for by the particle model.
   (c) Name one phenomenon not adequately accounted for by the wave model.

2. If the index of refraction of silicate flint glass is 1.60, what is the wavelength of violet light in the glass, if its wavelength in air is 415 nm?

3. Sound and light are waves, yet we can hear sounds around corners but we cannot see around corners. Explain why.

4. In a ripple tank, one complete wave is sent out every 0.10 s. The wave is stopped with a stroboscope, and it is found that the separation between the first and sixth crests is 12 cm. Calculate (a) the wavelength and (b) the speed of the wave.

5. An interference pattern is set up by two point sources which are in phase and of the same frequency. A point on the second nodal line is 25.0 cm from one source and 29.5 cm from the other source. The speed of the waves is 7.5 cm/s. Calculate (a) the wavelength and (b) the frequency of the sources.

6. In Young's time, why was the observation of double-slit interference more convincing evidence for the wave theory of light than the observation of diffraction?

7. You are performing Young's experiment and measure a distance of 6.0 cm between the first and seventh nodal points on a screen located 3.00 m from the slit plate. The slit separation is 2.2×10^{-4} m.
   (a) Calculate the wavelength of the light being used.
   (b) Identify the colour of the light.

8. In a Young's double-slit experiment, the angle that locates the second dark fringe on either side of the central bright fringe is 5.2°. Find the ratio of the slit separation d to the wavelength λ of the light.

9. Monochromatic light falling on two slits 0.018 mm apart produces the fifth-order dark fringe at an angle of 8.2°. Calculate the wavelength of the light.

10. The third-order fringe of 638-nm light is observed at an angle of 8.0° when the light falls on two narrow slits. Calculate the distance between the slits.

11. Red light from a helium–neon laser ($\lambda = 633$ nm) is incident on a screen containing two very narrow horizontal slits separated by 0.100 mm. A fringe pattern appears on a screen 2.10 m away. Calculate, in millimetres, the distance of the first dark fringe above and below the central axis.

12. Monochromatic light falls on two very narrow slits 0.042 mm apart. Successive minima on a screen 4.00 m away are 5.5 cm apart near the centre of the pattern. Calculate the wavelength and frequency of the light.

13. A parallel beam of light from a laser, operating at 639 nm, falls on two very narrow slits 0.048 mm apart. The slits produce an interference pattern on a screen 2.80 m away. How far is the first dark fringe from the centre of the pattern?

14. Light of wavelength 656 nm falls on two slits, producing an interference pattern on a screen 1.50 m away. Each of the fourth-order maxima is 48.0 mm from the central bright fringe. Calculate the separation of the two slits.

15. Light of wavelengths 4.80×10^2 nm and 6.20×10^2 nm falls on a pair of horizontal slits 0.68 mm apart, producing an interference pattern on a screen 1.6 m away. How far apart are the second-order maxima?

16. Light of wavelength 4.00×10^2 nm falls on two slits 5.00×10^{-4} m apart. The slits are immersed in water ($n = 1.33$), as is a viewing screen 50.0 cm away. How far apart are the fringes on the screen?

17. When white light passes through a flat piece of window glass, it is not broken down into colours, as it is by a prism. Explain why.

18. Explain why polarization was important in validating the wave theory of light.

19. Explain, with diagrams, how Polaroid sunglasses reduce reflected glare.

20. Light shines through a single slit 5.60×10^{-4} m wide. A diffraction pattern is formed on a screen 3.00 m away. The distance between the middle of the central bright fringe and the first dark fringe is 3.5 mm. Calculate the wavelength of the light.

21. A diffraction pattern forms when light passes through a single slit. The wavelength of the light is 675 nm. Determine the angle that locates the first dark fringe when the width of the slit is (a) 1.80×10^{-4} m and (b) 1.80×10^{-6} m.

22. Light of wavelength 638 nm falls onto a single slit 4.40×10^{-4} m wide, producing a diffraction pattern onto a screen 1.45 m away. Determine the width of the central fringe.

23. (a) At what angle is the first minimum for 589-nm light falling on a single slit 1.08×10^{-6} m wide?
    (b) Does a second minimum appear? Explain your reasoning.

24. A narrow single slit is illuminated by infrared light from a helium–neon laser at 1.15×10^{-7} m. The centre of the eight dark bands lies at an angle of 8.4° off the central axis. Determine the width of the slit.

25. Light with a wavelength of 451 nm falls onto a slit 0.10 mm wide, casting a diffraction pattern onto a screen 3.50 m away. How wide is the central maximum?

26. A beam of 639-nm light is directed through a single slit 4.2×10^{-4} m wide onto a screen 3.50 m away. How far apart are the maxima?

27. The central bright fringe in a single-slit diffraction pattern has a width that is equal to the distance between the screen and the slit. Find the ratio $\dfrac{\lambda}{w}$ of the wavelength of the light to the width of the slit.

28. List the advantages of a diffraction grating over a prism in dispersing light for spectral analysis.

29. What would happen to the distance between the bright fringes produced by a diffraction grating if the entire interference apparatus (light source, grating, and screen) were immersed in water? Explain your answer.

30. The separation between the slits of a grating is 2.2×10^{-6} m. This grating is used with light whose wavelengths range from 412 nm to 661 nm. Rainbow-like spectra form on a screen 3.10 m away. How wide is the first-order spectrum?

31. Monochromatic light, falling onto a 5000-line/cm diffraction grating, produces a second maximum at 35.0°. Determine the wavelength of the light.

32. (a) Show that a 30 000-line/cm grating does not produce a maximum for visible light.
    (b) What is the longest wavelength for which this grating does produce a first-order maximum?

33. Two first-order spectral lines are measured by an 8500-line/cm spectroscope at angles, on each side of centre, of +26.6°, +41.1° and −26.8°, −41.3°. Calculate the wavelengths.

34. Calculate the minimum thickness of an oil slick on water that appears blue when illuminated by white light perpendicular to its surface (**Figure 1**). ($\lambda_{\text{blue}} = 482$ nm, $n_{\text{oil}} = 1.40$)

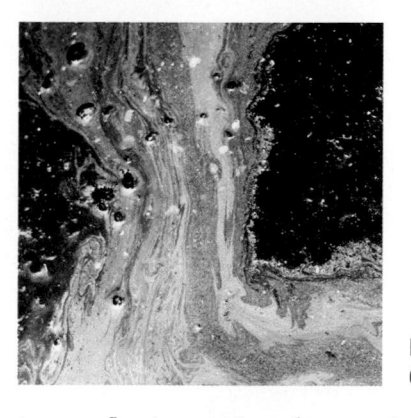

Figure 1
Oil slick on water

35. A nonreflective coating of magnesium fluoride ($n = 1.38$) covers the glass ($n = 1.52$) of a camera lens. If the coating prevents the reflection of yellow–green light ($\lambda = 565$ nm), determine the minimum nonzero thickness of the coating. Explain your calculations with a diagram.

36. A transparent coating ($n = 1.61$) on glass ($n = 1.52$) appears black when viewed in reflected light whose wavelength is 589 nm in vacuum. Calculate the two smallest possible nonzero values for the thickness of the coating.

37. A thin film of ethyl alcohol ($n = 1.36$) is spread on a flat glass plate ($n = 1.52$) and illuminated with white light, producing a colour pattern in reflection. If a region of the film reflects only green light (525 nm) strongly, how thick might it be?

38. A soap bubble is 112 nm thick and illuminated by white light whose angle of incidence is 90° (**Figure 2**). What wavelength and colour of light is most constructively reflected, assuming the same index of refraction as water?

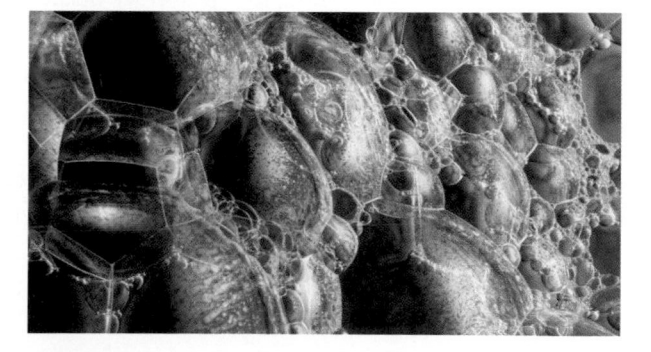

Figure 2
Soap bubbles illuminated by white light

39. A wire loop, dipped into soap solution, is viewed by the reflection of yellow light. At one instant, the appearance of the film is as in **Figure 3**.
    (a) Explain the large dark space at the top of the film.
    (b) As time goes on, what changes will occur in the pattern? Explain your answer.
    (c) Calculate the difference in thickness between adjacent bright bands. Express your answer in wavelengths.
    (d) Taking the wavelength of the yellow light in air to be 588 nm, calculate the thickness of the soap film ($n = 1.33$) in the lowest dark band.

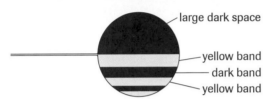

Figure 3

40. A fine metal foil separates one end of two pieces of optically flat glass. When the glass is illuminated, at essentially normal incidence, with 639-nm light, 38 dark lines are observed (with one at each end). Determine the thickness of the foil.

41. You have created a wedge-shaped air film between two sheets of glass, using a piece of paper 7.62×10^{-5} m thick as the spacer. You illuminate the wedge with 539-nm light, at essentially normal incidence. Determine the number of bright fringes you see across the wedge.

42. You form an air wedge with two glass plates, 15.8 cm long. At one end the glass plates are kept firmly together; at the other end the plates are separated by a strip of paper. You illuminate your wedge with light of wavelength 548 nm and observe the interference pattern in the reflected light. The average distance between two dark bands in the pattern is found to be 1.3 mm. Calculate the thickness of the paper strip separating the glass plates.

43. How far must the movable mirror of a Michelson interferometer, illuminated by a 589-nm source, be displaced for 2000 fringes to move past the reference point?

44. Monochromatic light is incident normally on a slit (**Figure 4**). A screen is located far away from the slit. The mirror produces a virtual image of the slit.
    (a) Is the virtual image *coherent* with the slit itself?
    (b) Is the pattern on the screen a double-slit interference pattern or a pair of single-slit diffraction patterns?
    (c) If the pattern is an interference pattern, is the fringe closest to the mirror surface bright or dark? Explain your answer. (This arrangement is known as Lloyd's mirror.)

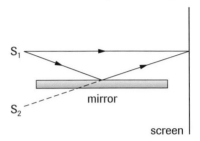

Figure 4

45. Compare radio, infrared, ultraviolet, and X rays under the following headings:
    (a) Nature of Source
    (b) Typical Means of Detection
    (c) Nonionizing or Ionizing

46. You have directed a parallel beam of microwaves at a metal screen with an opening 20.0 cm wide. As you move a microwave detector parallel to the plate, you locate a minimum at 36° from the central axis. Determine the wavelength of the microwaves.

Applying Inquiry Skills

47. Light from a small source in a certain lab passes through a single narrow slit to a distant screen, producing a diffraction pattern. **Figure 5(a)** is a graph of the intensity of light versus position on the screen. A second trial with the same equipment produced **Figure 5(b)**, drawn to the same scale. What change(s) could have produced the result? Explain your answer.

48. You are demonstrating single-slit diffraction using 10.5-GHz microwaves and a metal slit 2.0 cm wide. A screen is 0.50 m away from your microwave transmitter. Predict the numerical values for the quantities B and C in **Figure 6**.

(a)

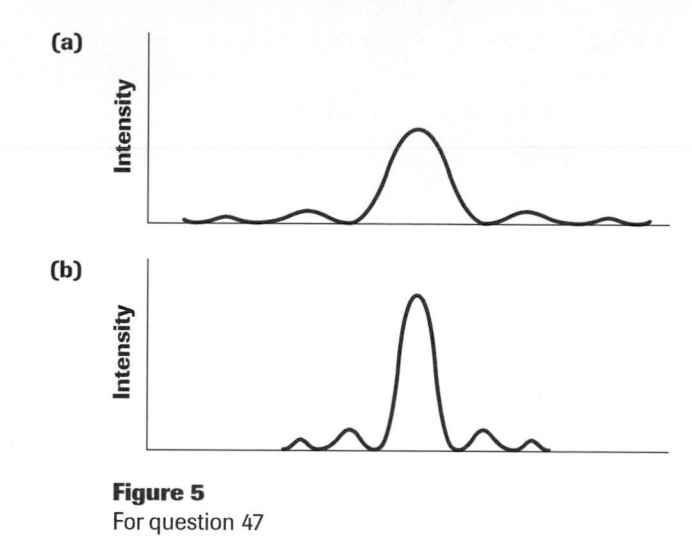

(b)

Figure 5
For question 47

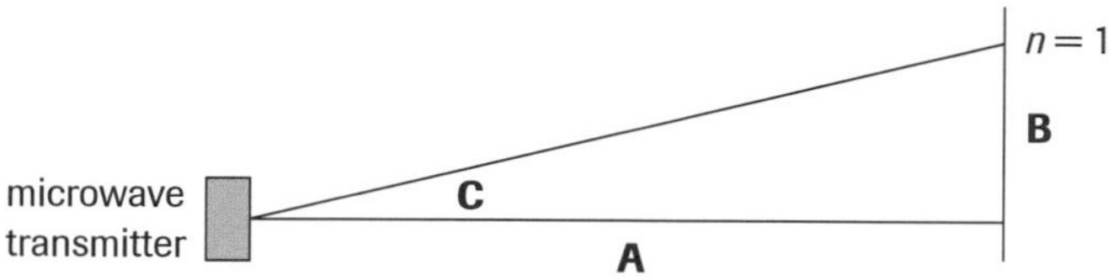

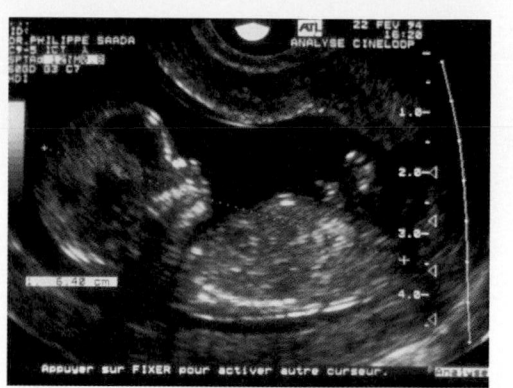

Figure 7

Figure 6
For question 48

Making Connections

49. Your favourite radio station, having broadcast with just one antenna, now adds a second antenna, radiating in phase with its first, at some new location. Are you guaranteed to enjoy better reception? Justify your answer.

50. A radio wave transmitter tower and a receiver tower are both 60.0 m above the ground and 0.50 km apart. The receiver can receive signals both directly from the transmitter and indirectly from signals that bounce off the ground. If the ground is level between the transmitter and receiver and a $\frac{\lambda}{2}$ phase shift occurs on reflection, determine the longest possible wavelengths that interfere (a) constructively and (b) destructively.

51. Ultrasonic waves are used to observe babies as they develop from fetus to birth (**Figure 7**). Frequencies typically range from 3.0×10^4 Hz to 4.5×10^4 Hz.
    (a) What would be the typical wavelengths if these were radio waves?
    (b) Calculate the actual wavelengths, in air, given that they are high-frequency sound waves with a speed of 3.4×10^2 m/s.

Extension

52. A sonar transmitter produces 14.0-kHz waves in water, creating the intensity pattern in **Figure 8**. The solid lines represent positions over which the intensity of the sound is constant. The intensity pattern is analogous to the effect of a single-slit interference pattern in optics. Taking the speed of sound in the water to be 1.40×10^3 m/s, calculate the width of the vibrating surface of the transmitter.

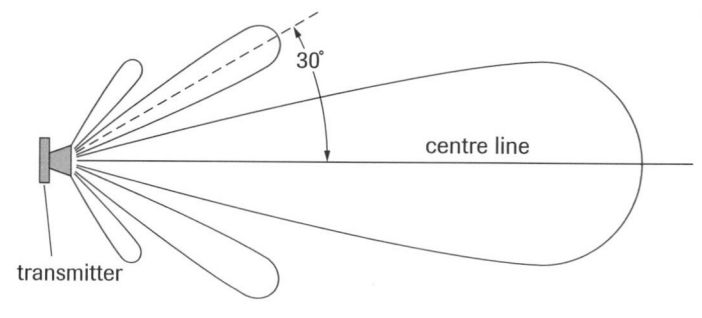

Figure 8

53. Two, and only two, full spectral orders can be seen on either side of the central maximum when white light is sent through a certain diffraction grating. Calculate the maximum possible number of lines per centimetre for this grating.

54. White light reflects normally from a soap film of refractive index 1.33, then falls upon the slit of a spectrograph. The slit illuminates a 500-line/mm diffraction grating with normal incidence. In the first-order spectrum a dark band is observed with minimum intensity at an angle of 18° to the normal. Determine the minimum possible thickness of the soap film.

55. A total of 31 dark Newton's rings (not counting the dark spot at the centre) appear when 589-nm light falls normally on a certain plano-convex lens resting on a flat glass surface. How much thicker is the centre than the edges?

Matter-Energy Interface

Dr. Art McDonald
Professor of Physics, Queen's University
Director, Sudbury Neutrino Observatory

Scientists have been studying the Big Bang Theory and its effects on the universe for many years. Dr. Art McDonald, a research scientist in the field of particle astrophysics, is fascinated with a particular elementary particle created from the Big Bang—the neutrino. As the director of the Sudbury Neutrino Observatory (SNO), his research focuses on changes in the properties of the neutrino when it travels from the Sun to Earth's surface. His research has helped to confirm theories about the nuclear processes that generate energy in the Sun.

To observe the properties of neutrinos, research must be conducted in an environment with low radioactivity and with little interference from the solar cosmic rays that hit Earth's surface. SNO achieves this ideal setting with a location two kilometres below Earth's surface. It houses sophisticated equipment including light sensors, electronic circuits, computers, and 1000 tonnes of heavy water (valued at $300 million), which was developed for use in CANDU nuclear reactors.

Many career opportunities in particle astrophysics involve academic or technical appointments at universities or research laboratories. These scientists push the frontiers of technology in an effort to answer some of the most fundamental questions we have about our universe.

▶ Overall Expectations

In this unit, you will be able to

- demonstrate an understanding of the basic concepts of Einstein's special theory of relativity and of the development of models of matter, based on classical and early quantum mechanics, that involve an interface between matter and energy

- interpret data to support scientific models of matter, and conduct thought experiments as a way of exploring abstract scientific ideas

- describe how the introduction of new conceptual models and theories can influence and change scientific thought and lead to the development of new technologies

ARE YOU READY?

Concepts

- describe the components and features of the electromagnetic spectrum
- apply fundamental laws, such as Newton's laws of motion, Coulomb's law, and the laws of conservation of energy and momentum

Skills

- analyze graphs
- analyze vectors
- manipulate algebraic equations
- apply basic trigonometric functions
- manipulate logarithms
- solve for an unknown
- use SI units
- define terms and use them in context
- communicate in writing, both verbally and mathematically
- conduct research from print resources and the Internet

Knowledge and Understanding

1. Draw a horizontal line. Label the segments of the line with the names of the various segments of the electromagnetic spectrum. Use an arrow above the line to mark the direction of increasing frequency. Use an arrow below the line to mark the direction of increasing wavelength. Use a broken arrow below the line to mark the direction of increasing energy.

2. Using the data in **Table 1**,
   (a) calculate the product of the frequency and the wavelength for each example of electromagnetic radiation
   (b) explain the significance of the results
   (c) name the segment of the electromagnetic spectrum to which each example of electromagnetic radiation belongs

Table 1 Data for Question 2

Frequency (Hz)	Wavelength (m)
5.0×10^{10}	6.0×10^{-3}
3.8×10^{14}	8.0×10^{-7}
1.2×10^{15}	2.5×10^{-7}
1.0×10^{18}	3.0×10^{-10}

3. Briefly state Maxwell's views on
   (a) the general source of all electromagnetic radiation
   (b) the properties of all types of electromagnetic radiation
   (c) the speed, in a vacuum, of all electromagnetic radiation

4. The crosses in **Figure 1** indicate that the direction of the magnetic field is into the page. How can you determine the charge of each particle from its motion?

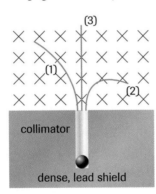

Figure 1
Charged particles in a magnetic field

5. An electron ($m_e = 9.11 \times 10^{-31}$ kg, $q = 1.60 \times 10^{-19}$ C) is accelerated from rest from one parallel plate to another. The potential difference between the plates is 258 V. Calculate the speed of the electron just before it hits the second plate.

6. State the law of conservation of energy.

7. (a) What two quantities are conserved in an elastic collision?
   (b) **Figure 2** shows two identical billiard balls before and after a glancing collision. Draw a vector diagram for the collision. Find the speed of ball 1 after the collision.

8. (a) What is the difference between the speed of light and a light-year?
   (b) Assuming you could travel in a spaceship at $0.50c$, how many days would it take you to travel to Alpha Centauri, which is 4.3 light-years from the Sun?
   (c) It takes, on average, 8.33 min for sunlight to travel from the Sun to Earth. How far away is the Sun from Earth?

9. Balance the following nuclear-reaction equations:

   (a) $^{226}_{88}\text{Ra} \rightarrow {}^{4}_{2}\text{He} + ?$ (b) $^{214}_{82}\text{Pb} \rightarrow {}^{0}_{-1}\text{e} + ?$

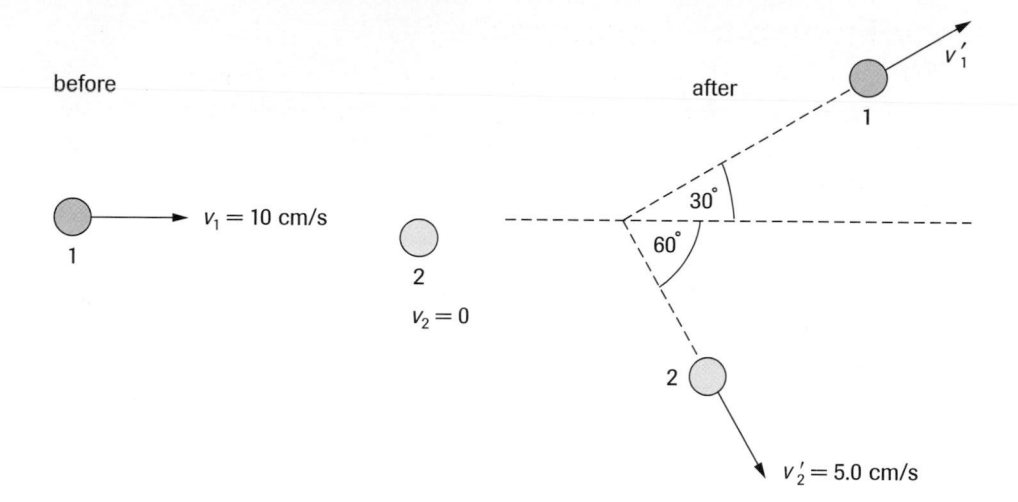

Figure 2
For question 7

Math Skills

10. Using the graph of energy versus frequency in **Figure 3**, answer the following questions:
    (a) What is the general equation of the family of curves to which this graph belongs?
    (b) What are the frequency and energy intercepts (including the units)?
    (c) What is the slope of the line on the graph (including the units)?
    (d) What is the equation of the line on the graph?

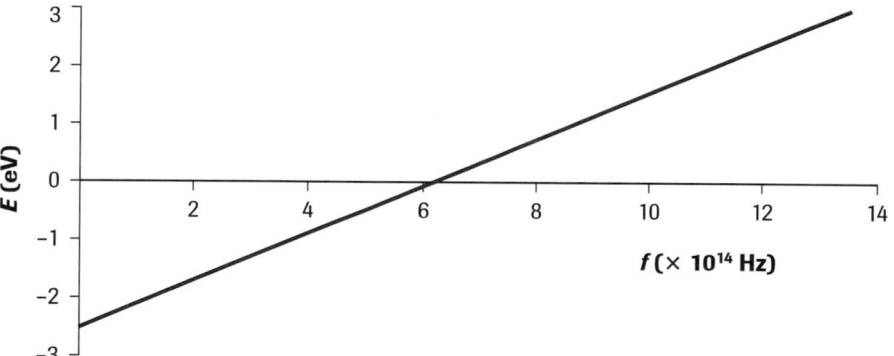

Figure 3
Graph of energy versus frequency

11. (a) Given that $x = 0.5y$ and $t_1 = 1.0$ h, solve for t_2 in seconds in the following equation:

$$t_2 = \frac{t_1}{\sqrt{1 - \dfrac{x^2}{y^2}}}$$

    (b) Solve for t in the following equation:

$$25 = 220\left(\frac{1}{2}\right)^{\frac{t}{4200}}$$

Technical Skills and Safety

12. What precautions are necessary when working with a source of ultraviolet light?

13. What precautions are necessary when using a high-voltage power supply?

11

Einstein's Special Theory of Relativity

▶ **In this chapter, you will be able to**

- state Einstein's two postulates for the special theory of relativity

- describe Einstein's thought experiments demonstrating relativity of simultaneity, time dilation, and length contraction

- state the laws of conservation of mass and energy, using Einstein's mass–energy equivalence

- conduct thought experiments involving objects travelling at different speeds, including those approaching the speed of light

By the end of the nineteenth century, physicists were well satisfied with their understanding of the physical world around them. Newtonian mechanics had been successful in explaining the motion of objects on Earth and in the heavens. Maxwell's theory of electromagnetism had consolidated knowledge about the special relationship between electric and magnetic forces and had predicted the existence of electromagnetic waves with properties similar to those of light—so similar, in fact, that light itself was assumed to be an electromagnetic wave. Physics as it was known up to this time is referred to as classical physics.

The puzzles that still remained—the structure of the atom and its nucleus—were expected to be solved by further applications of the currently accepted theories. Such was not to be the case, however. The solution to these puzzles required the proposal of two revolutionary and clever concepts: the theory of relativity and the quantum theory. These theories changed our understanding of the universe drastically; their development and application to the search for the structure of the atom are referred to as modern physics.

This and the remaining two chapters deal with the development of these theories and how they are applied to the problems of understanding atomic and nuclear structure.

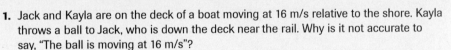

REFLECT on your learning

1. Jack and Kayla are on the deck of a boat moving at 16 m/s relative to the shore. Kayla throws a ball to Jack, who is down the deck near the rail. Why is it not accurate to say, "The ball is moving at 16 m/s"?

2. What do people mean when they say "It's all relative?"

3. The expressions "Time flies" and "This has been the longest day of my life" suggest that time does not flow equally in all situations. Can you describe any cases in which it is actually true that the flow of time is in some sense variable?

4. You are travelling on a spaceship moving, relative to Earth, at 90% the speed of light. You direct a laser beam in the same direction as the spaceship is travelling. How fast does the laser light travel relative to the ship? relative to Earth?

5. The law of conservation of mass tells us that the mass of all the reactants in a chemical reaction should be equal to the mass of all the products. Do the reactions inside the Sun or a nuclear reactor violate the law of conservation of mass?

6. One of the most famous of all equations is Einstein's $E = mc^2$. What do the symbols represent? What does the equation imply?

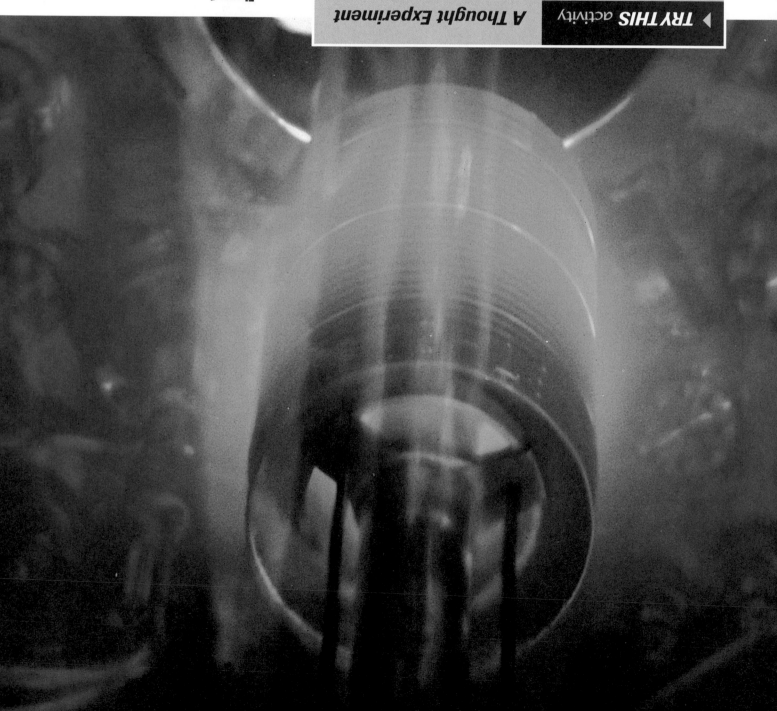

Figure 1

A radioactive fuel rod from a nuclear reactor is immersed in deep water. The intense blue glow surrounding the rod is an effect from electrons travelling at speeds greater than the speed of light in water. This is called the Cerenkov effect, named after the Russian physicist who discovered it. But nothing can travel faster than the speed of light, or can it?

▶ **TRY THIS** activity   **A Thought Experiment**

The study of relativity analyzes the properties of objects travelling near the speed of light. Obviously, direct observations and measurements cannot be made at these speeds, so to help us gain insights, we can create hypothetical situations called "thought experiments" to analyze these cases. The power of the thought experiment is the questions that arise, not necessarily the answers to the questions.

At the age of 16, Einstein showed the power of the thought experiment technique by imagining he could chase a beam of light until he was alongside it. Use the following questions to discuss Einstein's thought experiment:

(a) Could you catch up to the beam of light?
(b) If you could, would the beam remain stationary, relative to you?
(c) What would the beam consist of?
(d) According to Maxwell, why couldn't the beam remain stationary?
(e) Could you see the beam of light in a mirror?

Newton's laws of motion work very well at low speeds, that is, low compared to the speed of light. Einstein's special theory of relativity analyzes the effects of motion at high speeds, that is speeds approaching the speed of light. Further, as the word "relative" implies, the results of a measurement can depend on the frame of reference with respect to which the measurement is made. Before investigating motion at high speeds, we first review the concepts of relative motion for objects at low speeds.

Frames of Reference

In Unit 1, we saw that to describe and account for the motion of any object, we must adopt a frame of reference from which to view the motion—an arbitrary origin and set of axes from which to measure the changing position of a moving object. Most often we choose Earth as our frame of reference, assuming it to be stationary, and measure all positions of a moving object relative to some origin and set of axes fixed on Earth. It was, of course, in Earth's frame of reference that Newton's first law, the law of inertia, was discovered. Any frame of reference in which the law of inertia holds is called an **inertial frame of reference** (see Section 2.5); that is, if no net force acts on an object at rest, it remains at rest, or, if in motion, it continues to move in a straight line at a constant speed.

All of Newtonian physics, including gravitation theory and kinematics, holds as we make the transition from one inertial frame to another. Suppose (contrary to commonsense and highway safety laws) you are standing up in the back of a pickup truck, holding an apple. The truck is moving along a straight, level road at constant speed. If you drop the apple, you see it fall, relative to the truck body, straight down (**Figure 1(a)**). But to an observer at the side of the road, in what we will call the Earth frame of reference, the path of the apple is a curve (**Figure 1(b)**). How do the laws of Newtonian physics compare in the two frames?

In both cases, the force of gravity accelerates the apple straight down. The observed vertical trajectory of the apple in the frame of the truck is correctly predicted by classical

inertial frame of reference a frame of reference in which the law of inertia holds

Figure 1
An apple is dropped in a pickup truck.
(a) In the frame of reference of the truck, the apple falls straight down.
(b) In the frame of reference of Earth, the apple follows a parabolic path.

(a)
reference frame = pickup truck

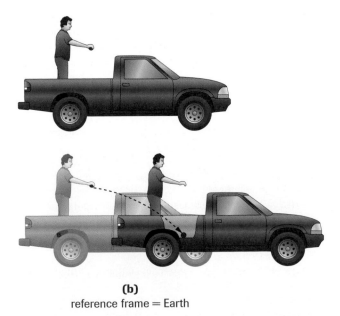

(b)
reference frame = Earth

kinematics, since the apple has an initial horizontal velocity of zero in that frame. The observed curved trajectory of the apple in the frame of Earth is again correctly predicted by classical kinematics, since the apple has a nonzero initial horizontal velocity, directed forward, in that frame. In other words, the laws of physics (Newton's laws and the equations of kinematics) are the same in both frames of reference, even though the paths are different. We can generalize to say that the Newtonian laws of physics are the same in all inertial frames of reference.

Our experiences of travel make us familiar with the behaviour of a **noninertial frame of reference**, or a frame accelerated with respect to an inertial frame. When a vehicle changes speed, or turns sharply while maintaining a constant speed, odd things appear to happen. Consider a ball at rest on the flat, smooth, level floor of a van moving in a straight line on a level road at a constant speed. As long as the van is an inertial frame of reference, Newton's first law applies, and the ball remains at rest (**Figure 2(a)**).

noninertial frame of reference
frame of reference that is accelerating relative to an inertial frame

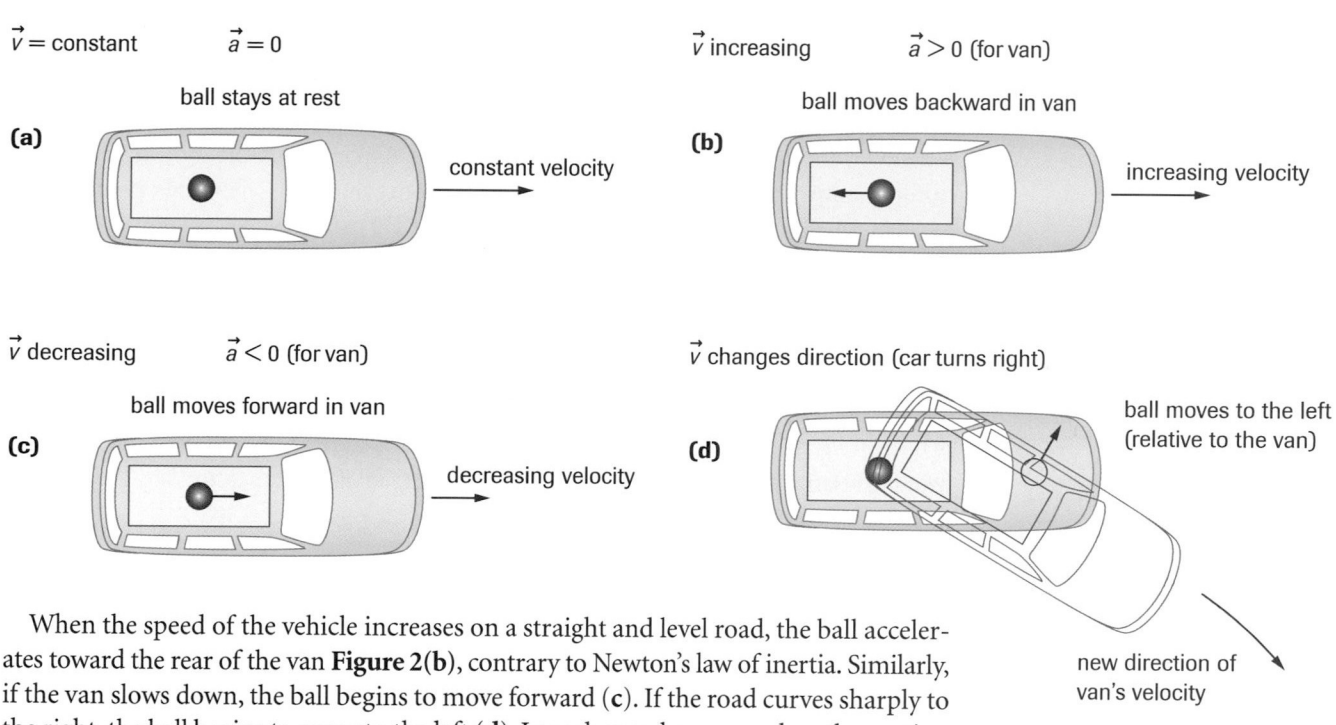

Figure 2
(a) The van moves with constant velocity, and the ball stays at rest relative to the vehicle.
(b) The van accelerates and the ball rolls backward relative to the vehicle.
(c) The van slows down, and the ball rolls forward relative to the vehicle.
(d) The ball rolls to the left relative to the vehicle.
In all cases the ball remains in uniform motion relative to Earth.

When the speed of the vehicle increases on a straight and level road, the ball accelerates toward the rear of the van **Figure 2(b)**, contrary to Newton's law of inertia. Similarly, if the van slows down, the ball begins to move forward (**c**). If the road curves sharply to the right, the ball begins to move to the left (**d**). In each case, however, when the motion is observed from the inertial frame of Earth, the ball is seen to obey the law of inertia—to continue moving in a straight line with a constant speed.

So firm is our belief in Newton's laws that we would rather invent a "fictitious force" to explain these strange motions in noninertial frames than abandon our belief in Newton's laws. In the previous example, we would have to assume a fictitious force in a direction opposite to that of the van's acceleration in order to explain the motion of the ball in each case. In the case where the van is turning, we make up a fictitious force, commonly called "centrifugal force," just to make intuitive sense. This is familiar to everyone who has taken a ride at an amusement park.

It is clear that the analysis of motion in noninertial frames is complicated. Looking at the same motion from any inertial frame provides a much simpler analysis, consistent with Newton's laws.

This leads us to three important statements about relative motion and frames of reference:

- In an inertial frame of reference, an object with no net force acting on it remains at rest or moving in a straight line with a constant speed.

- The laws of Newtonian mechanics are only valid in an inertial frame of reference.
- The laws of Newtonian mechanics apply equally in all inertial frames of reference; in other words, all inertial frames of reference are equivalent as far as adherence to the laws of mechanics is concerned.

One final point remains to be made in our review of Newtonian relative motion and frames of reference: there is no such thing as absolute velocity in Newtonian mechanics. Whether you drop a ball while in a vehicle moving with constant velocity east, or in a vehicle moving with a constant velocity west, or in a parked vehicle, the ball moves vertically in the frame of the vehicle. Thus you cannot use measurements of the motion of the ball to help you identify whether you are really moving. In general, for any two inertial frames moving with respect to each other, there is no physical meaning in the question, "Which of these two frames is really moving?"

Special Theory of Relativity

In Chapter 3, we learned how to calculate, by vector addition, relative velocities in moving frames of reference. We have just stressed in our review that Newton's laws of motion apply equally in all inertial frames. We now recall from Chapter 3 that the motion itself has a different appearance, depending on the frame from which it is viewed. For example, if a ball is rolled forward at 10 m/s in a car moving at 30 m/s, its speed is 40 m/s in Earth's frame of reference. Conversely, if the ball is rolled backward at the same speed in the same car, its speed relative to Earth is 20 m/s. Clearly, the speed with which the ball is observed to move depends on the frame of reference of the observer.

At the turn of the twentieth century, many physicists wondered whether the same vector-addition rules applied to the motion of light. If light has a speed c in a frame of reference of Earth, then would light emitted in the forward direction from a source moving relative to Earth at $\frac{1}{10}c$ have a measured speed of $\frac{11}{10}c$, measured by an observer in Earth's frame of reference? Would light emitted backward from the same source have a measured speed of $\frac{9}{10}c$ in Earth's frame? In other words, would the speed of light, like the speed of a ball rolling in a vehicle, depend on the frame of reference from which it is observed?

The first hint that light was somehow different from other phenomena came in the latter half of the nineteenth century, when Maxwell described light as an electromagnetic wave travelling in a vacuum at 3.00×10^8 m/s. Relative to what frame of reference would the speed of light have this value? Did the calculation presuppose some special, absolute frame?

Up to this time, physicists had always associated waves with a medium through which they travelled. It was natural, then, for them to assume that light must also travel through some kind of medium. Perhaps this medium was the absolute frame of reference in the universe and the speed Maxwell calculated for electromagnetic waves was relative to this frame. The supposed medium, called the **ether**, was thought to allow bodies to pass through it freely, to be of zero density, and to permeate all of space.

According to classical mechanics, the speed of light measured relative to any frame of reference moving through this ether should differ from 3.00×10^8 m/s by the magnitude of the velocity with which the frame is moving. It was assumed that Earth must be such a moving frame, since Earth is a planet orbiting the Sun. A number of very clever and complicated experiments were designed to measure the speed of Earth through the ether. The most successful of these was performed in 1887 by two Americans, A.A. Michelson (1852–1931) and E.W. Morley (1838–1923). While the details of the

LEARNING TIP

Shortcut Symbols
Since the speed of light is a constant, it is given the symbol c. Thus, $c = 3.00 \times 10^8$ m/s, so $\frac{1}{2}c$, or $0.5c$, is equal to $\frac{3.00 \times 10^8 \text{ m/s}}{2}$ or 1.50×10^8 m/s.

ether the hypothetical medium, regarded as not directly observable, through which electromagnetic radiation was thought to propagate

Michelson–Morley experiment can be left to a further course in physics, a brief description of their method and results is necessary for our understanding of special relativity.

In essence, Michelson and Morley compared the relative speeds of light in two perpendicular directions relative to Earth's motion through the ether (**Figure 3**). If Earth were travelling in the ether-absolute frame of reference with velocity $\vec{v}$, then in a frame on Earth the ether would be travelling at velocity $-\vec{v}$, producing an "ether wind." Michelson and Morley expected to find a difference in the measured speed of light dependent on the orientation of their apparatus in the ether wind. Just as the velocity, relative to the shore, of a boat with an outboard motor of constant power varies when the boat is directed first back and forth along the line of the river, then back and forth cross-stream, so the speed of light should differ when it is moving on the one hand back and forth along the line of the wind, and on the other hand perpendicular to the line. To detect the expected small difference in speed, Michelson and Morley used an interferometer, which generates an interference pattern between two parts of a split beam of light.

Figure 4(a) shows the setup of the apparatus. (See Section 10.7 for the operation of an interferometer.) The entire apparatus could be rotated to change the positions of the mirrors.

Any small difference in the velocity of light along the two paths would be indicated by a change in the interference pattern as the apparatus rotated. If the apparatus is rotated $90°$, the distance L_1 is now perpendicular to the ether wind and the distance L_2 is parallel to it (**Figure 4(b)**). Thus, the time taken to travel these distances should change as the apparatus is rotated. This should produce a phase change in the interference pattern.

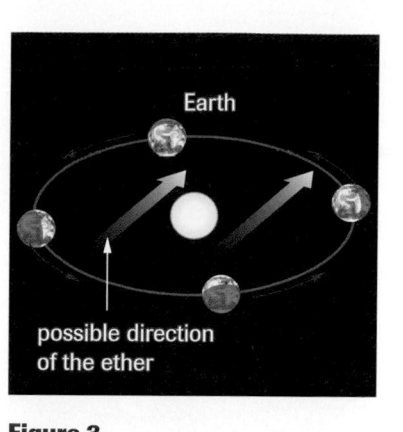

Figure 3
At most points during its orbit, Earth will be moving relative to the ether.

(a)   **(b)**

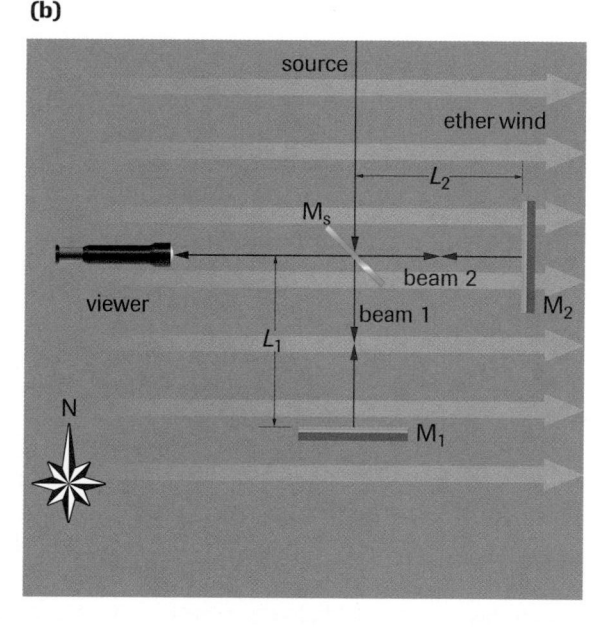

Figure 4
(a) A simplified view of an interferometer place in the hypothetical ether wind.
(b) The apparatus is rotated $90°$.

The importance of the experiment lies in its failure to show what was expected. Michelson and Morley performed their experiment over and over at different points in Earth's orbit but continued to get a null result: there was absolutely no change in the interference pattern. The speed of light was the same whether it travelled back and forth in the direction of the ether wind or at right angles to it. The relative velocity of the ether with respect to Earth had no effect on the speed of light. In other words, *the ether does not exist*. This null result was one of the great puzzles of physics at the turn of the twentieth century.

Many explanations were offered for the failure of the interference pattern to change. In 1905, Albert Einstein (1879–1955), then working in Switzerland as a junior patent clerk, proposed a revolutionary explanation in the form of the *special theory of relativity*. His theory rests on two postulates.

> **Special Theory of Relativity**
>
> 1. *The relativity principle:* all the laws of physics are valid in all inertial frames of reference.
> 2. *The constancy of the speed of light:* light travels through empty space with a speed of $c = 3.00 \times 10^8$ m/s, relative to all inertial frames of reference.

The first postulate is an easy-to-accept extension of the idea of Newtonian relativity, mentioned earlier. Einstein proposed that not only Newtonian mechanics but *all* the laws of physics, including those governing electricity, magnetism, and optics, are the same in all inertial frames. The second is more difficult to reconcile in our minds because it contradicts our commonsense notions of relative motion. We would expect two observers, one moving toward a light source and the other moving away from it, to make two different determinations of the relative speed of light. According to Einstein, however, each would obtain the same result, $c = 3.00 \times 10^8$ m/s. Clearly, our everyday experiences and common sense are of no help in dealing with motion at the speed of light.

By doing away with the notion of an absolute frame of reference, Einstein's theory solves the dilemma in Maxwell's equations: the speed of light predicted by Maxwell is not a speed in some special frame of reference; it is the speed in *any* inertial frame of reference.

We have seen that in Newtonian mechanics, while the laws of motion are the same in all inertial frames, the appearance of any one particular motion is liable to change from frame to frame. We shall see in the rest of this chapter that the position for Einstein is similar but more radical: the changes in the appearance of the world, as we move between inertial frames travelling at high speeds with respect to each other, are contrary to common sense.

Note that special relativity is a special case of the more general theory of relativity (not investigated in this text), published by Einstein in 1916. The general theory of relativity deals with gravitation and noninertial frames of reference.

The special and general theories of relativity and their many implications are now considered as much a part of physics as Newton's laws. The difference is this: to comprehend the many ramifications of the theories requires a great deal more mental flexibility and dexterity than was the case with Newtonian mechanics.

Simultaneity

We begin our examination of the consequences Einstein drew from his two postulates by considering time. In Newtonian mechanics, there is a universal time scale, the same for all observers. This seems right. Surely, a sequence of events that one observer measures to last 2.0 s would also last 2.0 s to an observer moving with respect to the first observer. But it is not always so! According to Einstein, time interval measurements depend on the reference frame in which they are made.

Simultaneity, the occurrence of two or more events at the same time, is also a relative concept, and we will make it our starting point, before proceeding to the relativity of a time interval. We will use a thought experiment to show that events that are simultaneous in one inertial frame are not simultaneous in other frames.

simultaneity the occurrence of two or more events at the same time

An observer O_s, stationary in the inertial frame of Earth, is standing on a railway platform at the midway point between two lampposts, L_1 and L_2 (**Figure 5**). The lampposts are connected to the same circuit, ensuring that, at least from the viewpoint of an iner-

(a)

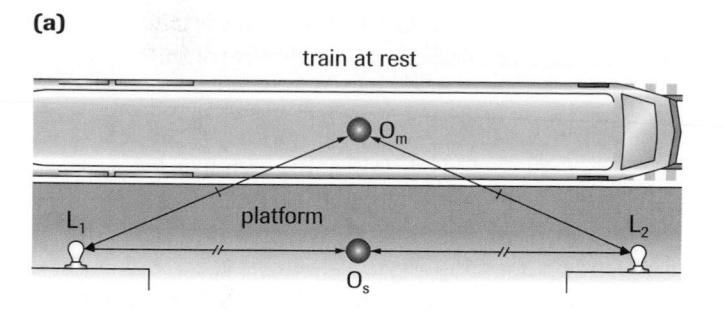

train at rest

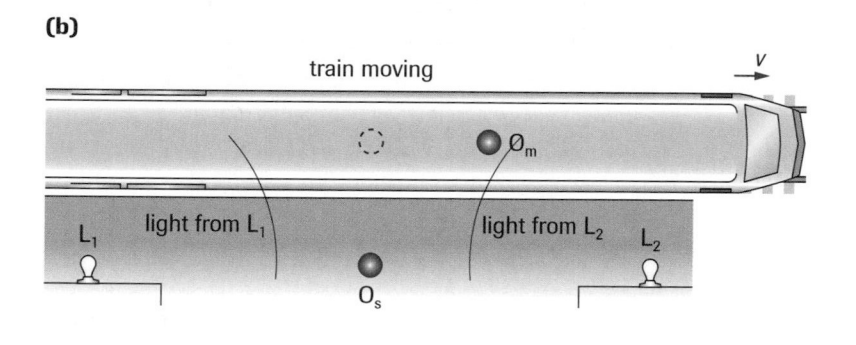

(b)

train moving

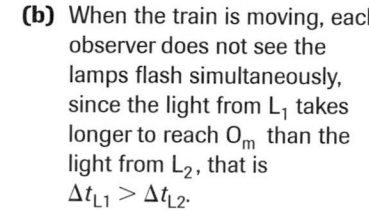

Figure 5
(a) When the train is at rest, each observer sees the lamps flash simultaneously, since each observer is halfway between the lamps.
(b) When the train is moving, each observer does not see the lamps flash simultaneously, since the light from L_1 takes longer to reach O_m than the light from L_2, that is $\Delta t_{L1} > \Delta t_{L2}$.

tial frame anchored in the railway platform, the lamps come on at the same time when the switch is closed. To make the experiment easy to follow, we assume that the lamps do not stay on when the current is applied but flash and explode, spewing out soot and broken glass. The light from each flash travels out in all directions at the speed of light, c. Since O_s is located at the midpoint between the lampposts, the distances the beams of light travel are equal, causing the arrival of light from the one lamp to be simultaneous with the arrival of light from the other lamp. Adjacent to O_s is a second observer O_m, sitting in a train on a straight track next to the platform. We make two trials in our thought experiment: in the first, keeping the train at rest relative to Earth, and in the second, making the train move with speed v relative to Earth.

If the train is at rest, O_m finds the arrival of the light from the first lamp to be simultaneous with the arrival of the light from the second lamp (**Figure 5(a)**). O_m then performs measurements of the soot marks left by the exploding lamps on his train: he is halfway between the soot marks, and light always travels at the same speed, c. Therefore, O_m is forced to conclude that the lamps flashed simultaneously. O_s reaches the same conclusion for the same reasons.

We now perform the second trial in the thought experiment, letting the train move by O_s at a high speed relative to the inertial frame of Earth but keeping everything else as before. In the time interval it takes for the flash of light to travel to O_s from each lamppost, O_m will have moved a short distance to the right (**Figure 5(b)**). In this time interval O_m will receive the flash of light from L_2 but not yet receive the flash of light from L_1. O_m thus sees the rear lamp flash a little later than the forward lamp. Having taken this observation, O_m now performs measurements, as in the first trial: he is halfway between the soot marks left on the train, and light always travels at the same speed, c. Therefore, O_m is forced to conclude that the two lamps did not flash simultaneously. We emphasize that the conclusion of nonsimultaneity relies on Einstein's second postulate. Since (as the placement of the soot marks reveals) the distances are equal, and since the light flashes travelled at the *same* speed from the two lamps, the fact that the flashes arrived at different times means that the lamps did not explode simultaneously. We thus reach the following conclusion:

> Two events that are simultaneous in one frame of reference are in general not simultaneous in a second frame moving with respect to the first; simultaneity is not an absolute concept.

In this thought experiment it is tempting to ask which observer's view of simultaneity is correct, O_s's or O_m's? Strangely enough they both are. Neither frame is better for judging simultaneity. Simultaneity is a relative concept rather than an absolute one. In everyday life, we are usually unaware of this effect; it becomes much more significant as the relative speed between the two observers increases to a significant fraction of c.

SUMMARY **Frames of Reference and Relativity**

- Any frame of reference in which the law of inertia holds is called an inertial frame of reference.
- A noninertial frame is one that is accelerating relative to an inertial frame.
- The laws of Newtonian mechanics are only valid in an inertial frame of reference and are the same in all inertial frames of reference.
- In Newtonian mechanics, no experiment can identify which inertial frame is truly at rest and which is moving. There is no absolute inertial frame of reference and no absolute velocity.
- Michelson and Morley's interferometer experiment showed that the ether does not exist.
- The two postulates of the special theory of relativity are: (1) all laws of physics are the same in all inertial frames of reference; (2) light travels through empty space with a speed of $c = 3.00 \times 10^8$ m/s in all inertial frames of reference.
- Simultaneity of events is a relative concept.

▶ *Section 11.1* Questions

Understanding Concepts

1. You are in a windowless car of a train that is either stationary or moving at a constant velocity with respect to Earth. Is there any experiment you can do in the train to determine whether you are moving? Explain your answer.

2. Distinguish between an inertial and a noninertial frame of reference, and give an example of each. How do we account for motions that occur, in seeming violation of the law of inertia, in noninertial frames?

3. You are travelling in a train that is slowing down upon approaching the station. You throw a heavy ball, aiming it directly at the ceiling above your chair. Relative to you, where will the ball fall? Explain your answer.

4. Describe the significance of the Michelson–Morley experiment. Why was its seeming failure a success?

5. State the two postulates of the special theory of relativity in such a way that they can be understood by a peer who does not study physics.

6. Is there a situation where two events that occur at the same time for one observer can be simultaneous to a second observer moving with respect to the first? Explain your answer.

Having introduced the consequences of Einstein's two postulates by demonstrating the relativity of simultaneity, we now draw a further, still more sweeping conclusion on time and overturn commonsense views on distance.

Time Dilation

For centuries philosophers have debated the concept of time. Does time proceed at the same rate everywhere in the world or, for that matter, on the Moon? We know time goes forward. Can it go backward? Despite thoughts to the contrary, it turns out that all time is relative, relative to the observer. There is no such thing as absolute time.

To illustrate, let us perform a thought experiment where two observers measure different time intervals for the same sequence of events. A spaceship contains two parallel mirrors (which we call "top" and "bottom") and a method of sending a pulse of light from the bottom mirror to the top, at right angles to the mirrors (**Figure 1(a)**). Inside the bottom mirror the astronaut has placed a clock that records a "tick" at the instant the pulse leaves the mirror and a "tock" when the pulse returns.

Figure 1

(a) The astronaut, stationary relative to the clock incorporated in the bottom mirror, measures a time interval $2\Delta t_s$ for the light to make a round trip and so infers Δt_s to be the duration of the upward journey.

(b) The time interval as measured by an observer on Earth, who records it as Δt_m.

(c) The distance triangle. (The stopwatches are drawn to depict the actual time dilation occurring for a spaceship travelling at $0.83c$.)

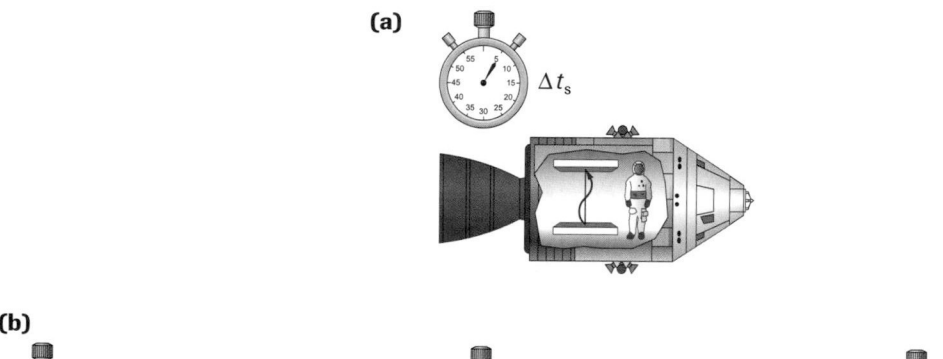

(a)

Δt_s

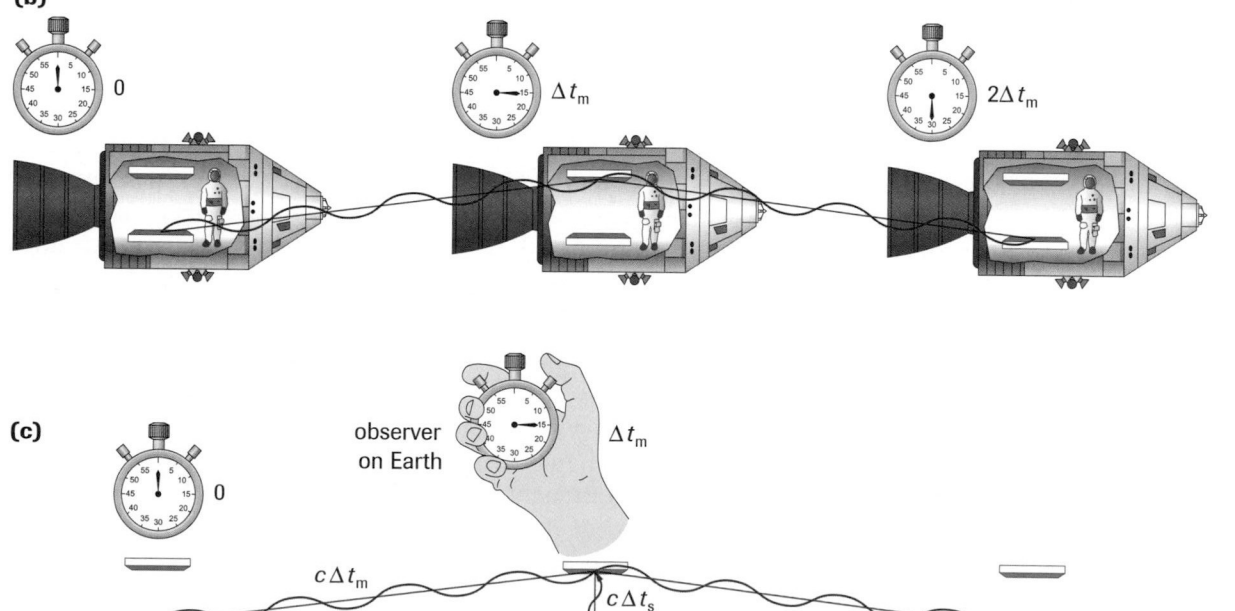

(b)

0 Δt_m $2\Delta t_m$

(c)

0

observer on Earth Δt_m

$c\Delta t_m$

$c\Delta t_s$

$v\Delta t_m$

To the astronaut, stationary with respect to the clock, the pulse goes up and down (causing the clock to register first a tick, then a tock) whether the spaceship is at rest relative to Earth or moving with a constant high velocity relative to Earth. We write $2\Delta t_s$ for the interval, in the inertial frame of the spaceship, separating tick from tock (with "s" for "stationary," as a reminder that the clock is stationary in the frame we have just chosen). The interval required for light to travel from the bottom mirror to the top is thus Δt_s and the distance between the mirrors is $c\Delta t_s$.

The spaceship is moving with a speed v relative to an observer on Earth. From the observer's viewpoint the pulse takes a longer interval Δt_m to travel the longer distance $c\Delta t_m$, where Δt_m is the time interval, in the frame of Earth, for light to travel from the bottom mirror to the top. We write "m" as a reminder that in this frame, the bottom mirror and top mirror are moving. In the same time that the pulse moves to the mirror, the spaceship moves a distance of $v\Delta t_m$ relative to the observer on Earth (**Figure 1(b)**). How can we determine if Δt_s and Δt_m are different? According to Einstein's second postulate, light has the same speed c for both observers. Using the distance triangle in **Figure 1(c)**, it follows from the Pythagorean theorem that

$$(c\Delta t_m)^2 = (v\Delta t_m)^2 + (c\Delta t_s)^2$$

We will isolate Δt_m to see how it compares with Δt_s.

$$(c\Delta t_m)^2 - (v\Delta t_m)^2 = (c\Delta t_s)^2$$
$$c^2(\Delta t_m)^2 - v^2(\Delta t_m)^2 = c^2(\Delta t_s)^2$$

Dividing both sides by c^2:

$$(\Delta t_m)^2 - \frac{v^2}{c^2}(\Delta t_m)^2 = (\Delta t_s)^2$$
$$(\Delta t_m)^2\left(1 - \frac{v^2}{c^2}\right) = (\Delta t_s)^2$$

Thus, rearranging to isolate $\Delta t_m{}^2$, and then taking the square root of both sides, we get:

$$\Delta t_m = \frac{\Delta t_s}{\sqrt{1 - \dfrac{v^2}{c^2}}}$$

where Δt_s is the time interval for the observer stationary relative to the sequence of events and Δt_m is the time interval for an observer moving with a speed v relative to the sequence of events.

This equation shows that, for any v such that $0 < v < c$, $\Delta t_m > \Delta t_s$. The time interval $2\Delta t_m$ seen by the Earthbound observer, moving relative to the mirrors, must be greater than the corresponding time interval $2\Delta t_s$ seen by the observer inside the spaceship, stationary with respect to the mirrors.

Another way of looking at this phenomenon is to consider the positions of the events between which the time interval is measured. The initial and final events in our thought experiment are the emission of the light from the bottom mirror (tick) and the detection of the light returning to the bottom mirror (tock). In the frame of reference of the spaceship, tick and tock occur at the same position. In the frame of reference of Earth, tick and tock occur at two positions that are separated by a distance of $2v\Delta t_m$. We can now identify the specific fact underlying the thought experiment: the time interval between events that occur at the same position in a frame of reference is less than the time interval between the same events as measured in any other frame of reference. In summary, "one position time" is less than "two position time" by a factor of

$$\frac{1}{\sqrt{1 - \dfrac{v^2}{c^2}}}$$ (for any speed v such that $0 < v < c$)

The duration of a process (in this example $2\Delta t_s$), as measured by an observer who sees the process begin and end in the same position, is called the **proper time**. The observation that time on a clock that is moving with respect to an observer is seen to run slower than time on the clock that is stationary with respect to that observer is called **time dilation**. Intuitively, we may think of time as "dilated" or "expanded" on the spaceship. How can this be, you may ask? Did we not find Δt_s to be less than Δt_m? But dilation, not contraction, is the right description. To the Earthbound observer, it seems that tick and tock are widely separated in time, so it seems that a supposedly swift process has slowed down.

This holds for any "clock," whether it is your watch, a bouncing spring, a pendulum, a beating heart, a dividing cell, or a galactic event. All time is relative to the observer. There is no absolute time.

Notice that in the equation above, Δt_s can be a real number only if the expression $1 - \dfrac{v^2}{c^2}$ is positive; that is,

$$1 - \frac{v^2}{c^2} > 0$$

$$\frac{v^2}{c^2} < 1$$

$$v^2 < c^2$$

and, finally, $v < c$

This is the famous "speed limit" proposed by Einstein. *No material object can have a speed that is equal to or greater than that of light.* We will address this again in the next section.

Time dilation effects have been measured. In 1971, four exceedingly accurate atomic clocks were flown around the world twice, on regularly scheduled passenger flights. The experimental hypothesis was that the clocks would have times that differed from a similar clock at rest at the U.S. Naval Observatory. Because of Earth's rotation, two trips were made, one eastward and one westward. Using the time dilation relationship, the predicted loss in time should have been 40 ± 23 ns for the eastward journey and 275 ± 21 ns for the westward journey. It was found that the clocks flying eastward lost 59 ± 10 ns, and the clocks flying westward lost 273 ± 7 ns. The theory of time dilation was consequently validated within the expected experimental error.

Muons, which we will encounter again in Chapter 13, are subnuclear particles that are similar to electrons but are unstable. Muons decay into less massive particles after an average "life" of 2.2 μs. In 1976, muons were accelerated to $0.9994c$ in the circular accelerator at CERN, in Switzerland. With a lifetime of 2.2 μs, the muons should last only 14 to 15 trips around the ring before they decay. In fact, because of time dilation, the muons did not decay until after 400 circuits, approximately 30 times longer. The mean life of the muons had increased by 30 times relative to Earth, or we could say that the time elapsed relative to Earth was longer; it was dilated. It's as if the muons were living life in slow motion. From this viewpoint, the moving muons will exist longer than stationary ones, but "the amount of life" the muons themselves will experience, relative to their own frame of reference, is exactly the same.

From the evidence provided by the life of a muon, we could reach the same conclusion for people moving in a spaceship at nearly the speed of light. The passengers would have a life expectancy of hundreds of years, relative to Earth. But from the standpoint of life on the spaceship, it's life as usual. From our perspective in the inertial frame of Earth, they are living life at a slower rate, and their normal life cycle takes an enormous amount of our time. A sample problem will illustrate this point.

proper time (Δt_s) the time interval between two events measured by an observer who sees the events occur at one position

time dilation the slowing down of time in a system, as seen by an observer in motion relative to the system

LEARNING *TIP*

Dilation
The word "dilation" means "widening." For example, the pupils in our eyes dilate to let more light in.

DID YOU *KNOW* **?**

Pretty Relative!
Einstein said, "When a man sits next to a pretty girl for an hour, it seems like a minute. But let him sit on a hot stove for one minute and it's much longer than an hour— that's relativity!"

DID YOU *KNOW* **?**

General Theory
Since the airliners validating time dilation were travelling above the surface of Earth, the gravitational field in flight was lower than at the U.S. Naval Observatory. Thus, the experimenters had to include general relativity as well as special relativity in their calculations.

An astronaut whose pulse frequency remains constant at 72 beats/min is sent on a voyage. What would her pulse beat be, relative to Earth, when the ship is moving relative to Earth at (a) $0.10c$ and (b) $0.90c$?

Solution

$c = 3.0 \times 10^8$ m/s

pulse frequency = 72 beats/min

pulse period at relativistic speed = Δt_m = ?

The pulse period measured on the spaceship (where pulses occur in the same position) is

$$\Delta t_s = \frac{1}{72 \text{ min}^{-1}}$$

$$\Delta t_s = 0.014 \text{ min}$$

(a) At $v = 0.10c$,

$$\Delta t_m = \frac{\Delta t_s}{\sqrt{1 - \dfrac{v^2}{c^2}}}$$

$$= \frac{0.014 \text{ min}}{\sqrt{1 - \dfrac{(0.10c)^2}{c^2}}}$$

$$= \frac{0.014 \text{ min}}{0.995}$$

$$\Delta t_m = 0.014 \text{ min, to 2 significant digists}$$

$$f = \frac{1}{T}$$

$$= \frac{1}{0.014 \text{ min}}$$

$$f = 72 \text{ beats/min}$$

The pulse frequency at $v = 0.10c$, relative to Earth, is to two significant digits unchanged, at 72 beats/min.

(b) At $v = 0.90c$,

$$\Delta t_m = \frac{0.014 \text{ min}}{\sqrt{1 - \dfrac{(0.90c)^2}{c^2}}}$$

$$= \frac{0.014 \text{ min}}{0.436}$$

$$\Delta t_m = 0.032 \text{ min}$$

$$f = \frac{1}{T}$$

$$= \frac{1}{0.032 \text{ min}}$$

$$f = 31 \text{ beats/min}$$

The pulse frequency at $v = 0.90c$, relative to Earth, is 31 beats/min. This result is much lower than the 72 beats/min that the astronaut would measure for herself on the ship.

> ▶ **Practice**

Understanding Concepts

1. Are airline pilots' watches running slow in comparison with clocks on the ground? Why or why not?

2. A beam of unknown elementary particles travels at a speed of 2.0×10^8 m/s. Their average lifetime in the beam is measured to be 1.6×10^{-8} s. Calculate their average lifetime when at rest.

3. A Vulcan spacecraft has a speed of $0.600c$ with respect to Earth. The Vulcans determine 32.0 h to be the time interval between two events on Earth. What value would they determine for this time interval if their ship had a speed of $0.940c$ with respect to Earth?

4. The K^+ meson, a subatomic particle, has an average rest lifetime of 1.0×10^{-8} s. If the particle travels through the laboratory at 2.6×10^8 m/s, by how much has its lifetime, relative to the laboratory, increased?

Answers

2. 1.2×10^{-8} s

3. 75.0 h

4. 2×

The Twin Paradox

One of Einstein's most famous thought experiments is the "twin paradox," which illustrates time dilation. Suppose that one of a pair of young identical twins takes off from Earth and travels to a star and back at a speed approaching c. The other twin remains on Earth. We may possibly expect, in view of our result in Sample Problem 1 concerning an astronaut's heartbeat, that the moving twin ages less than his Earthbound counterpart does.

But wouldn't the twin in the spaceship think the reverse, seeing his twin on Earth first receding at high speed and then returning? Would he not expect the Earthbound twin to have aged more for the same reason (**Figure 2**)? Is this not a paradox?

No! The consequences of the special theory of relativity only apply in an inertial frame of reference, in this case Earth. The twin on Earth is in the same frame of reference for the other twin's whole journey. Until now, the situations we have discussed have been symmetrical, with inertial observers moving relative to one another, seeing each other's clocks run slow. The travelling twin is in a frame of reference whose velocity relative to Earth must change at the turn-around position, which means it is a noninertial frame at that stage. Since the situation is not symmetrical, the observations can be different. It is indeed the twin in the spaceship who returns younger than his twin on Earth.

Figure 2
(a) As the twins depart, they are the same age.
(b) When the astronaut twin returns, he has aged less than the twin who stayed on Earth.

Length Contraction

Since time, once assumed to be absolute, is perceived differently by different observers, it seems natural to ask if length, another supposedly absolute concept, also changes.

Consider a spaceship making a trip from planet A to planet B, at rest with respect to each other and a distance L_s apart (relative to the planets) and at a speed v as measured by an observer on either planet (**Figure 3**). (Just as Δt_s was defined as the proper time, L_s is called the **proper length**.)

For the captain in the spaceship, the process (the departure of A, the arrival of B) occurs at one single place, the spaceship. The captain can thus assign a proper-time duration Δt_s to the process, using a single clock on the spacecraft. Since she sees A recede and B approach at the speed v, she finds the distance separating the two events to be $L_m = v\Delta t_s$. For observers on the planets, the process (the takeoff from A, the landing on B) occurs at two different places. Such observers can use a pair of synchronized clocks to assign a duration Δt_m to the two-event process consisting of the takeoff and the landing and would find the distance separating the events as $L_s = v\Delta t_m$. We can now argue as follows:

proper length (L_s) the length, in an inertial frame, of an object stationary in that frame

> **LEARNING TIP**
>
> **Proper Length**
> Note that "proper length" does not necessarily mean "correct length."

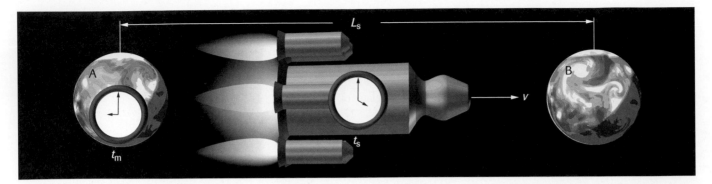

Figure 3

Planets A and B are at rest with respect to each other. The chart below summarizes the rotation used in this example:

Observer	Distance	Time
stationary observer	L_s	Δt_m
spacecraft observer	L_m	Δt_s

From the time dilation relationship

$$\Delta t_m = \frac{\Delta t_s}{\sqrt{1 - \frac{v^2}{c^2}}}$$

If we multiply both sides by v we obtain

$$v\Delta t_m = \frac{v\Delta t_s}{\sqrt{1 - \frac{v^2}{c^2}}}$$

But $L_m = v\Delta t_s$ and $L_s = v\Delta t_m$. Substituting above we obtain

$$L_s = \frac{L_m}{\sqrt{1 - \frac{v^2}{c^2}}} \quad \text{or}$$

$$L_m = L_s\sqrt{1 - \frac{v^2}{c^2}}$$

where L_s is the proper distance between A and B, directly measurable in the inertial frame in which A and B are at rest, and L_m is the distance—which we did not try to measure directly but deduced from kinematics—between A and B as seen in an inertial frame in which A and B are moving.

Since $\sqrt{1 - \frac{v^2}{c^2}} < 1$, $L_m < L_s$. In our example, occupants on-board the spaceship would measure the distance between planets as less than observers on either planet would measure it to be. The observers on the planets are not moving with respect to the space between planets, and therefore, measure the distance as L_s. The passengers on-board the spaceship are moving through that same space and measure its distance to be L_m. Our analysis shows that this **length contraction** occurs in the direction of motion. So, for example, a cylindrical spaceship 10 m in diameter, moving past Earth at high speed, is still 10 m in diameter in the frame of Earth (though shortened from tip to tail).

If you were in a spaceship flying by a tall, stationary building, at say, $0.9c$, the width of the front of the building will be much thinner but the height will be the same. You would notice that the building's sides are slightly curved in toward the middle since the light has travelled different distances to you, the observer, and you will see the sides of the building as you approach and recede from it. This description in words does not give you a true picture, nor will it be the same at different relativistic speeds. The best way to see what happens with length contraction is to view computer simulations of such events.

 www.science.nelson.com

DID YOU KNOW ?

The Lorentz Contraction

This relativistic change in length is known as the Lorentz contraction, named after the Dutch mathematician H.A. Lorentz, who created the same theoretical correction for Maxwell's electromagnetic equations before Einstein developed it independently 20 years later. As a result, the expression is also referred to as the Lorentz–Einstein contraction.

length contraction the shortening of distances in a system, as seen by an observer in motion relative to that system

▶ **SAMPLE** problem **2**

A UFO heads directly for the centre of Earth at 0.500c and is first spotted when it passes a communications satellite orbiting at 3.28 × 10³ km above the surface of Earth. What is the altitude of the UFO at that instant as determined by its pilot?

Solution

Before solving a problem in special relativity, we must work out which lengths or durations are proper. In this case, the UFO pilot is determining the length separating two events in a process *moving* through his frame (the first event being the arrival at the UFO of the satellite, the second the arrival at the UFO of the surface of Earth). The length that the pilot is determining is thus *not* a proper length so it can appropriately be called L_m. On the other hand, the given length of 3.28 × 10³ km is the length separating two events in a process *stationary* in the frame to which it is referred (the first event being the arrival of the UFO at the satellite, the second the arrival of the UFO at the surface of Earth). The given length is thus a proper length so it can appropriately be called L_s.

$v = 0.500c$

$L_s = 3.28 \times 10^3$ km

$L_m = ?$

$$L_m = L_s\sqrt{1 - \frac{v^2}{c^2}}$$

$$= (3.28 \times 10^3 \text{ km})\sqrt{1 - \frac{(0.500c)^2}{c^2}}$$

$$L_m = 2.84 \times 10^3 \text{ km}$$

The altitude as observed from the UFO is 2.84 × 10³ km.
Since the speed of the UFO is fairly slow, as far as relativistic events are concerned, the distance contraction is relatively small.

▶ **SAMPLE** problem **3**

A spaceship travelling past Earth with a speed of 0.87c, relative to Earth, is measured to be 48.0 m long by observers on Earth. What is the proper length of the spaceship?

Solution

Since the spaceship is moving relative to the observers on Earth, 48.0 m represents L_m.

$v = 0.87c$

$L_m = 48.0$ m

$L_s = ?$

$$L_m = L_s\sqrt{1 - \frac{v^2}{c^2}}$$

$$L_s = \frac{L_m}{\sqrt{1 - \frac{v^2}{c^2}}}$$

$$= \frac{48.0 \text{ m}}{\sqrt{1 - \frac{(0.87c)^2}{c^2}}}$$

$$L_s = 97.35 \text{ m, or } 97.4 \text{ m}$$

The proper length of the spaceship is 97.4 m.

DID YOU KNOW ?

The Fourth Dimension
Time is often thought of as the fourth dimension. An event may be specified by four quantities: three to describe where it is in space and the fourth to describe where it is in time. When objects move at speeds near that of light, space and time become intertwined. Each inertial frame of reference represents one way of setting up a coordinate system for space-time. Comparing measurements made by observers in different inertial frames requires a change of coordinates, the interwining of space and time.

Answers

5. 115 m

6. 6.0 ly

7. 3.95×10^2 m

8. (a) 37.7 ly

(b) 113 a

9. 0.89c

> ▶ **Practice**

Understanding Concepts

5. A spaceship passes you at the speed of 0.90c. You measure its length to be 50.0 m. What is its length when at rest?

6. You are a space traveller, moving at 0.60c with respect to Earth, on your way to a star that is stationary relative to Earth. You measure the length of your trajectory to be 8.0 light-years (ly). Your friend makes the same journey at 0.80c with respect to Earth. What does your friend measure the length of the trajectory to be?

7. A spacecraft travels along a space station platform at 0.65c relative to the platform. An astronaut on the spacecraft determines the platform to be 3.00×10^2 m long. What is the length of the platform as measured by an observer on the platform?

8. A star is measured to be 40.0 ly from Earth, in the inertial frame in which both star and Earth are at rest.
   (a) What would you determine this distance to be if you travelled to the star in a spaceship moving at 1.00×10^8 m/s relative to Earth?
   (b) How long would you determine the journey to take?

9. The proper length of one spaceship is twice the proper length of another. You, an observer in an inertial frame on Earth, find the two spaceships, travelling at constant speed in the same direction, to have the same length. The slower spaceship is moving with a speed of 0.40c relative to Earth. Determine the speed of the faster spaceship relative to Earth.

Relativistic Momentum

Momentum is one of the most important concepts in physics. Recall that Newton's laws can also be stated in terms of momentum and that momentum is conserved whenever there is no external, unbalanced force on a system. In subatomic physics (see Chapter 13), much of what we know involves the collision of particles travelling at relativistic speeds, so it is important to address relativistic momentum.

Using a derivation beyond the scope of this book but based on the Newtonian concept of conservation of momentum, Einstein was able to show that the momentum of an object is given by

$$p = \frac{mv}{\sqrt{1 - \dfrac{v^2}{c^2}}}$$

where p is the magnitude of the relativistic momentum, m is the mass of the object, and v is the speed of the object relative to an observer at rest.

The m in the equation is the mass of the object measured by an observer at rest relative to the mass. This mass is referred to as the **rest mass**.

rest mass mass measured at rest, relative to the observer

How do we measure rest mass? We measure it the same way we always have, using Newtonian physics. We either measure it in terms of inertia, using Newton's second law $\left(m = \dfrac{\Sigma F}{a}\right)$, or measure it gravitationally $\left(m = \dfrac{\Sigma F}{g}\right)$. For low-speed objects these inertial and gravitational masses are equivalent. When an object is accelerated to high speeds, the mass cannot be defined uniquely and physicists only use the rest mass.

In the next section we will see that rest mass can itself change, but only if the total energy of the system changes.

As with the relativistic equations for time and length, the nonrelativistic expression for the momentum of a particle ($p = mv$) can be used when v is very small in comparison with c. As a rule, anything travelling faster than about $0.1c$ can be called relativistic, and significant correction using the special relativity relationships is required.

The momentum equation predicts that as v approaches c, the quantity $\sqrt{1 - \dfrac{v^2}{c^2}}$

approaches 0, and, consequently, for an object of nonzero rest mass, p approaches infinity. Relativistic momentum would thus become infinite at the speed of light (**Figure 4**) for any object of nonzero rest mass. The unbounded increase of relativistic momentum reflects the fact that no body of nonzero (rest) mass can be accelerated from an initial speed less than c to a speed equal to or greater than c. (In Chapter 12, you will learn about photons, which act like particles of light. Since photons travel at the speed of light, they must have zero rest mass. Our relativistic momentum formula does not apply to this situation. In fact, it has been shown experimentally that photons do have well-defined momentum, even though they have no mass.)

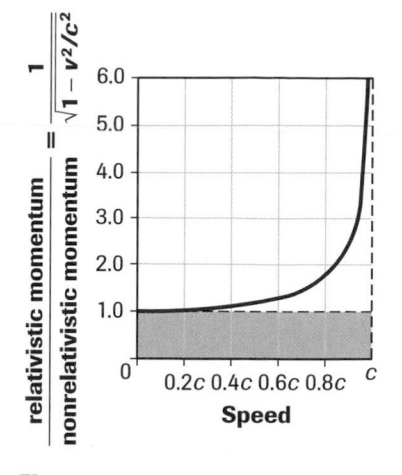

Figure 4
Relativistic momentum, here measured by taking the ratio of relativistic momentum to the nonrelativistic momentum (the product of speed and rest mass), increases without bound as the speed approaches c.

> ▶ **SAMPLE** problem **4**

Linear accelerators accelerate charged particles to nearly the speed of light (**Figure 5**). A proton is accelerated to $0.999\,994c$.

(a) Determine the magnitude of the relativistic momentum.

(b) Make an order-of-magnitude comparison between the relativistic and the nonrelativistic momenta.

Solution

(a) $v = 0.999\,994c$

$m = 1.67 \times 10^{-27}$ kg (from Appendix C)

$p = ?$

$$p = \frac{mv}{\sqrt{1 - \dfrac{v^2}{c^2}}}$$

$$= \frac{(1.67 \times 10^{-27}\ \text{kg})(0.999\,994c)}{\sqrt{1 - \dfrac{(0.999\,994c)^2}{c^2}}}$$

$$= \frac{5.010 \times 10^{-18}\ \text{kg·m/s}}{3.4641 \times 10^{-3}}$$

$$p = 1.45 \times 10^{-15}\ \text{kg·m/s}$$

The magnitude of the relativistic momentum of the proton is 1.45×10^{-15} kg·m/s. (This value agrees with the value that can be measured in the accelerator.)

(b) The magnitude of the nonrelativistic momentum, given by the classical Newtonian equation, is

$$p = mv$$

$$= (1.67 \times 10^{-27}\ \text{kg})(0.999\,994c)$$

$$= (1.67 \times 10^{-27}\ \text{kg})(0.999\,994)(3.00 \times 10^8\ \text{m/s})$$

$$p = 5.01 \times 10^{-19}\ \text{kg·m/s}$$

The nonrelativistic momentum is 5.01×10^{-19} kg·m/s. The relativistic momentum is more than three orders of magnitude larger than the nonrelativistic momentum.

Figure 5
A linear accelerator

▶ **Practice**

Understanding Concepts

10. What is the relativistic momentum of an electron moving at $0.999c$ in a linear accelerator? ($m_e = 9.11 \times 10^{-31}$ kg)

11. A small space probe of mass 2.00 kg moves in a straight line at a speed of $0.40c$ relative to Earth. Calculate its relativistic momentum in the Earth frame.

12. A proton is moving at a speed of $0.60c$ with respect to some inertial system. Determine its relativistic momentum in that system. ($m_p = 1.67 \times 10^{-27}$ kg)

SUMMARY *Relativity of Time, Length, and Momentum*

- Proper time Δt_s is the time interval separating two events as seen by an observer for whom the events occur at the same position.

- Time dilation is the slowing down of time in a system, as seen by an observer in motion relative to the system.

- The expression $\Delta t_m = \dfrac{\Delta t_s}{\sqrt{1 - \dfrac{v^2}{c^2}}}$ represents time dilation for all moving objects.

- Time is not absolute: both simultaneous and time duration events that are simultaneous to one observer may not be simultaneous to another; the time interval between two events as measured by one observer may differ from that measured by another.

- Proper length L_s is the length of an object, as measured by an observer at rest relative to the object.

- Length contraction occurs only in the direction of motion and is expressed as

$$L_m = L_s \sqrt{1 - \dfrac{v^2}{c^2}}.$$

- The magnitude p of the relativistic momentum increases as the speed increases according to the relationship $p = \dfrac{mv}{\sqrt{1 - \dfrac{v^2}{c^2}}}$.

- The rest mass m of an object is its mass in the inertial frame in which the object is at rest and is the only mass that can be uniquely defined.

- It is impossible for an object of nonzero rest mass to be accelerated to the speed of light.

Section 11.2 Questions

Understanding Concepts

1. The time dilation effect is sometimes misleadingly stated in the words "Moving clocks run slowly." Actually, this effect has nothing to do with motion affecting the functioning of clocks. What, then, does it deal with?

2. To whom does the elapsed time for a process seem to be longer, an observer moving relative to the process or an observer that is stationary relative to the process? Which observer measures proper time?

3. How would length and time behave if Einstein's postulates were true but with the speed of light infinite? (*Hint:* Would there be no relativistic effects, or would the relativistic effects be in some sense exceptionally severe?)

4. How would our lives be affected if Einstein's postulates were true but the speed of light were 100 km/h? (*Hint:* Consider simple specific examples, such as the nature of a highway journey at 60 km/h. What difficulty arises as we try to accelerate the car to 110 km/h?)

5. "Matter has broken the sound barrier but will not be able to exceed the speed of light." Explain this statement.

6. Muons created in collisions between cosmic rays and atoms high in our atmosphere are unstable and disintegrate into other particles. At rest these particles have an average lifetime of only 2.2×10^{-6} s.
   (a) What is the average lifetime in the laboratory inertial frame of muons travelling at $0.99c$ in that frame?
   (b) If muons did not experience a relativistic increase in lifetime, then through what average distance could they travel in the laboratory inertial frame before disintegrating, if travelling at $0.99c$ in that frame?
   (c) Through what average distance do muons travel in the laboratory frame, if moving through that frame at $0.99c$?

7. In 2000, a 20-year-old astronaut left Earth to explore the galaxy; her spaceship travels at 2.5×10^8 m/s. She returns in 2040. About how old will she appear to be?

8. A spaceship passes you at a speed of $0.90c$. You find the length of the ship in your frame to be 50.0 m. (The measurement is not easy: you have to arrange for a lamp to flash on the bow and the stern simultaneously in your frame, and then determine the distance between the flashes.) A few months later, the ship comes to the end of its mission and docks, allowing you to measure its length. (Now the measurement is easy: you can walk along the ship with a tape measure.) What length does your tape measure show?

9. A spaceship goes past a planet at a speed of $0.80c$ relative to the planet. An observer on the planet measures the length of the moving spaceship to be 40.0 m. The observer also finds that the planet has a diameter of 2.0×10^6 m.
   (a) The astronaut in the spaceship determines the length of the ship. What is this length?
   (b) The astronaut, while not in a position to actually measure the diameter of the planet, does succeed in computing a diameter indirectly. What is the resulting value?

(c) According to the observer on the planet, the spaceship takes 8.0 s to reach the next planet in the solar system. How long does the astronaut consider the journey to take?

10. A cube of aluminum 1.00 m $\times$ 1.00 m $\times$ 1.00 m is moving at $0.90c$, in the orientation shown in **Figure 6**. The rest density of aluminum is 2.70×10^3 kg/m^3.
    (a) Which of the three dimensions, a, b, or c, is affected by the motion?
    (b) Calculate the relativistic volume of the cube.
    (c) Calculate the relativistic momentum of the cube.

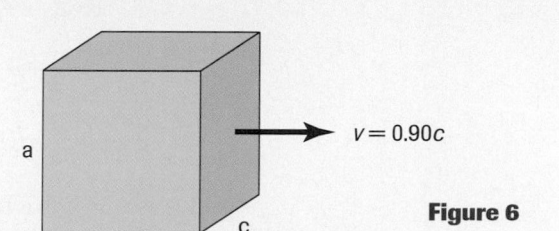

Figure 6

11. Calculate the relativistic momentum of a helium nucleus of rest mass 6.65×10^{-27} kg, moving in the laboratory frame at $0.400c$.

Applying Inquiry Skills

12. Generate the data for the first two columns in **Table 1** for values of $\frac{v}{c}$ from 0.05 to 0.95, in intervals of 0.05. Use these values to calculate Δt_m and L_m. The use of a computer spreadsheet, such as Excel, is recommended.

Table 1

$\frac{v}{c}$	$\sqrt{1 - \frac{v^2}{c^2}}$	Δt_s	Δt_m	L_s	L_m
0.05	?	100 s	?	100 m	?
0.10	?	100 s	?	100 m	?
0.15	?	100 s	?	100 m	?
0.20	?	100 s	?	100 m	?
0.25	?	100 s	?	100 m	?
⋮	⋮	⋮	⋮	⋮	⋮

(a) In what range of speeds is the time double the proper time?
(b) At what speed has the length of the object contracted by 10%?
(c) Based on the table, at what speed do relativistic effects become "noticeable"? What objects travel at these speeds?
(d) Plot graphs of Δt_m and L_m versus $\frac{v}{c}$.

In the previous section, we found that the definition of momentum has to be modified for relativistic speeds if we are to continue to have a conservation-of-momentum law. It similarly turns out that if we are to continue to have a conservation-of-energy law, we must revise the definition of energy.

When a force is applied to an object, work is done on it, increasing its kinetic energy. In Section 4.2 you learned that

$$\text{work done} = \Delta E_K$$
$$= E_{Kf} - E_{Ki}$$
$$= \frac{1}{2}mv_f^2 - \frac{1}{2}mv_i^2$$
$$\text{work done} = \frac{1}{2}m(v_f^2 - v_i^2)$$

We assumed that the object's mass remained constant and that any energy transferred to increase its kinetic energy resulted in an increase in speed only. Classically, we would expect this relation to continue to be valid as long as the force continues to act—the speed simply increases without bound. But this is not the case. As speeds become relativistic, the classical treatment of energy must be re-examined.

Einstein suggested that the total (relativistic) energy associated with an object of rest mass m, moving at speed v relative to an inertial frame is

$$E_{total} = \frac{mc^2}{\sqrt{1 - \dfrac{v^2}{c^2}}}$$

If the object happens to be at rest in this inertial frame, then v is zero and the total (relativistic) energy is simply

$$E_{rest} = mc^2$$

This is Einstein's famous $E = mc^2$. He proposed two things: rest mass is a form of energy that is associated with all massive objects, and there might be forces or interactions in nature that could transform mass into the more familiar types of energy or vice versa. In classical mechanics, mass and energy are conserved separately. In special relativity, these conservation laws are generalized to become one combined law, the **conservation of mass-energy**.

conservation of mass–energy
the principle that rest mass and energy are equivalent

Relativistic kinetic energy is the extra energy an object with mass has as a result of its motion:

$$E_{total} = E_{rest} + E_K$$
$$E_K = E_{total} - E_{rest}$$
$$E_K = \frac{mc^2}{\sqrt{1 - \dfrac{v^2}{c^2}}} - mc^2$$

For an object at rest in a given inertial frame ($v = 0$), its total energy in that frame is not zero but equals its rest energy, which is convertible to other forms of energy.

There are many instances when this conversion of mass into energy has been observed:

- The energy ΔE released by the fission of uranium in a nuclear reactor is accompanied by a decrease Δm in the rest mass of the reactants. Precise measurements of both have shown that $\Delta m = \dfrac{\Delta E}{c^2}$.

- When the π^0 meson (a subatomic particle) decays, it completely disappears, losing all of its rest mass. In its place appears electromagnetic radiation having an equivalent energy. (We will return to the π^0 meson in Chapter 13.)

- When hydrogen atoms react in the interior of the Sun, in a process called *fusion*, the tremendous energy released, ΔE, is accompanied by a corresponding loss of rest mass, Δm, given by $\Delta m = \dfrac{\Delta E}{c^2}$. In fact, the Sun is losing mass by this process at a rate of 4.1×10^9 kg/s.

Only with the technological advances of the twentieth century did physicists begin to examine the atomic and subatomic systems where matter-into-energy conversions and energy-into-matter conversions occur. Previously, mass and energy were seen to be conserved separately. It is believed that the equation $E = mc^2$ applies to most processes, although the changes are usually far too small to be measured.

For example, the heat of combustion of coal is approximately 3.2×10^7 J/kg. If 1.0 kg of coal is burned, what change would the release of energy in light and warmth make in the mass of the coal compared with the mass of the products of combustion? Using $\Delta E = (\Delta m)c^2$ for an original rest mass of 1.0 kg of coal:

$$\Delta m = \frac{\Delta E}{c^2}$$

$$= \frac{3.2 \times 10^7 \text{ J}}{(3.0 \times 10^8 \text{ m/s})^2}$$

$$\Delta m = 3.6 \times 10^{-10} \text{ kg}$$

As a percentage of the coal's original mass,

$$\frac{3.6 \times 10^{-10} \text{ kg}}{1.0 \text{ kg}} \times 100\% = 0.000\ 000\ 036\%$$

As you can see, this is an insignificant loss in mass, not detectable with even the best electronic balance.

However, this equation is a powerful theoretical tool that makes it possible to predict the amount of energy available from any process that results in a decrease in mass. For example, let us now calculate the energy available from the complete conversion of that same 1.0 kg of coal. Again, using $\Delta E = (\Delta m)c^2$ and $\Delta m = 1.0$ kg:

$$\Delta E = (\Delta m)c^2$$

$$= (1.0 \text{ kg})(3.0 \times 10^8 \text{ m/s})^2$$

$$\Delta E = 9.0 \times 10^{16} \text{ J}$$

DID YOU KNOW ?

Rest Mass and Energy Units
Physicists normally express the rest masses of subatomic particles in energy units. For example, the rest mass m_e of an electron is stated as 511 keV.

This is the same amount of energy that results from the combustion of approximately three billion kilograms of coal. It is no wonder that scientists are searching for methods of converting mass into energy. Even in the best nuclear fission reactors, only a fraction of one percent of the reacting mass is converted to energy, but the energy yield is enormous. One hope for solving the world's energy problems is the discovery of methods of converting some small fraction of normal mass into energy, without radioactive byproducts.

► SAMPLE problem 1

If the 0.50 kg mass of a ball at rest were totally converted to another form of energy, what would the energy output be?

Solution

$\Delta m = 0.50$ kg

$\Delta E = ?$

$$\Delta E = (\Delta m)c^2$$
$$= (0.50 \text{ kg})(3.00 \times 10^8 \text{ m/s})^2$$
$$\Delta E = 4.5 \times 10^{16} \text{ J}$$

The energy equivalent is 4.5×10^{16} J, or approximately half the energy emitted by the Sun every second.

► SAMPLE problem 2

In subatomic physics, it is convenient to use the electron volt, rather than the joule, as the unit of energy. An electron moves at $0.860c$ in a laboratory. Calculate the electron's rest energy, total energy, and kinetic energy in the laboratory frame, in electron volts.

Solution

$m = 9.11 \times 10^{-31}$ kg

$v = 0.860c$

$E_{rest} = ?$

$E_{total} = ?$

$E_K = ?$

$$E_{rest} = mc^2$$
$$= (9.11 \times 10^{-31} \text{ kg})(3.00 \times 10^8 \text{ m/s})^2$$
$$E_{rest} = 8.199 \times 10^{-14} \text{ J}$$

Converting to electron volts:

1.60×10^{-19} J $= 1$ eV

$$(8.199 \times 10^{-14} \text{ J}) \frac{1 \text{ eV}}{1.60 \times 10^{-19} \text{ J}} = 5.12 \times 10^5 \text{ eV}$$

This result is still a large number, so it is convenient to express the energy in mega electron volts (MeV), giving the result 0.512 MeV.

Reference books, however, show that the accepted rest energy of an electron is 0.511 MeV. Where did we go wrong? Our calculation assumed a value of 3.00×10^8 m/s for c. As noted earlier, a more precise value for c is $2.997\,924\,58 \times 10^8$ m/s. Using this value for c and taking the (measured) rest mass of an electron to be $9.109\,389 \times 10^{-31}$ kg, we find the rest energy of an electron to be 0.511 MeV, in agreement with the accepted value.

The total energy is given by the relationship

$$E_{total} = \frac{mc^2}{\sqrt{1 - \dfrac{v^2}{c^2}}}$$

But $mc^2 = 0.511$ MeV, therefore

$$E_{total} = \frac{0.511 \text{ MeV}}{\sqrt{1 - \dfrac{(0.860c)^2}{c^2}}}$$

$$E_{total} = 1.00 \text{ MeV}$$

The total energy of the electron is 1.00 MeV.

$$E_{total} = E_K + E_{rest}$$
$$E_K = E_{total} - E_{rest}$$
$$= 1.00 \text{ MeV} - 0.511 \text{MeV}$$
$$E_K = 0.489 \text{ MeV}$$

The kinetic energy of the electron is 0.489 MeV.

▶ *Practice*

Understanding Concepts

1. Calculate the rest energy of a proton in joules and in mega electron volts. ($m_p = 1.67 \times 10^{-27}$ kg)

2. The rest energy of a small object is 2.00×10^2 MJ. Calculate its rest mass.

3. A proton moves with a speed of $0.950c$ through a laboratory.
   (a) Calculate the total energy of the proton in the laboratory frame.
   (b) Calculate the kinetic energy of the proton in the laboratory frame.
   Give your answers in mega electron volts.

4. An electron is at rest in an inertial frame. Calculate the work needed to accelerate it to a speed of $0.990c$.

5. The total annual energy consumption of Canada is about 9.80×10^{18} J. How much mass would have to be totally converted to energy to meet this need?

6. The rest mass energies of a proton and a neutron are 938.3 MeV and 939.6 MeV, respectively. What is the difference in their rest masses in kilograms?

Answers

1. 1.50×10^{-10} J; 939 MeV

2. 2.22×10^{-9} kg

3. (a) 3.00×10^3 MeV
   (b) 2.07×10^3 MeV

4. 4.99×10^{-13} J

5. 1.09×10^2 kg

6. 2.31×10^{-30} kg

SUMMARY — Mass and Energy: $E = mc^2$

- Rest mass is the mass of an object at rest.
- Only the rest mass is used in relativistic calculations.
- Einstein's famous mass–energy equivalence equation is $E = mc^2$.
- The total energy of a particle is given by $E_{total} = \dfrac{mc^2}{\sqrt{1 - \dfrac{v^2}{c^2}}}$.
- Rest mass is a form of energy that is convertible into other more common and usable forms, for example, thermal energy.

▶ Section 11.3 Questions

Understanding Concepts

1. Explain how the equation $E = mc^2$ is consistent with the law of conservation of mass–energy.

2. Calculate how much energy can be produced by the complete annihilation of 1.0 kg of mass.

3. Earth, of mass 5.98×10^{24} kg, revolves around the Sun at an average speed of 2.96×10^4 m/s. How much mass, if converted into energy, could accelerate Earth from rest to that speed?

4. A nuclear generating plant produces electric power at an average rate of 5.0 GW, by converting a portion of the rest mass of nuclear fuel. How much fuel is converted to energy in one year, if the generation of electric power from the annihilated mass is 100% efficient? (*Hint:* Recall that a machine that delivers 1 W of power is delivering energy at the rate of 1 J/s.)

5. Calculate the energy required to accelerate a proton from rest to 0.90c. ($m_p = 1.673 \times 10^{-27}$ kg)

6. A hypothetical particle has a rest energy of 1.60 MeV and (in a certain inertial frame) a total energy of 3.20 MeV.
   (a) Calculate its rest mass.
   (b) Calculate its kinetic energy in the given frame.

Making Connections

7. How much would the rest energy in question 2 cost at the typical utility price of $0.15/kW·h?

8. It is reasonable to assume that 4 L of gasoline produces 1.05×10^8 J of energy and that this energy is sufficient to operate a car for 30.0 km. An Aspirin tablet has a mass of 325 mg. If the Aspirin could be converted completely into thermal energy, how many kilometres could the car go on a single tablet?

9. Deuteron, a heavy hydrogen nucleus ($^2_1$H), consists of a proton and a neutron. Its rest energy is 1875.6 MeV. How much energy is liberated, as kinetic energy and as a gamma ray, when a deuteron is created from a separate proton (a particle of rest mass energy 938.3 MeV) and a neutron (a particle of rest mass energy 939.6 MeV)?

The Life and Times of Albert Einstein

Albert Einstein (1879–1955) was born in the small town of Ulm, Germany, where he also received his early education. He showed little intellectual promise as a child, except in mathematics. He attended university in Switzerland but was not considered qualified to go on to graduate school or to secure a university post (**Figure 1**).

In 1901, he accepted a job as a clerk in the patent office in Berne, where he worked until 1909. In 1905, Einstein published papers that described three important new concepts in physics. The first, in quantum theory, was his explanation of the photoelectric effect (a phenomenon dealt with in Chapter 12). The second, published two months later, was his mathematical interpretation of the random motion of particles in a fluid, behaviour known as "Brownian movement." The third, his most celebrated, set out special relativity, profoundly revising our conceptions of time, length, and energy.

By 1909, Einstein's work had been widely recognized, and he was offered university posts, first at the University of Zurich and, in 1913, at the prestigious Kaiser Wilhelm Physical Institute in Berlin (later renamed the Max Planck Institute). In 1915, he published his general theory of relativity. This broader theory predicted further effects not forecast by Newtonian mechanics. In it, he proposed a theory of gravitation that treated Newton's theory of gravitation as only a special case of the more general situation. One of the consequences of the general theory is that a gravitational field can deflect light. This prediction was proved correct during the solar eclipse of 1919.

Einstein was then world famous. In the world of science, no investigator since Newton had been so esteemed in his own lifetime, or would be so esteemed in the decades following his death. Most scientists considered Newton and Einstein to be the "giants" of science, and this is still the case today. Although most laypeople did not understand his theories and their applications, he was respected and looked upon as the foremost scientist of the 20th century. In the world of popular culture, Einstein was frequently in the news, a folk figure, the butt of good-humoured Einstein jokes, much quoted as a source of wisdom on many topics. (The media attention once led him to list his occupation, good humouredly, as "photographer's model" (**Figure 2**)).

In 1930, Einstein went to California as a visiting professor. He subsequently chose to make his stay in the United States permanent because of the rise of Hitler and the Nazis in Germany. In 1933, he accepted a post at the Institute for Advanced Studies at Princeton, where he stayed until his death in 1955. For the last twenty-two years of his life, he searched in vain for a theory that would unite all gravitational and electromagnetic phenomena into a single, all-encompassing framework, a "unified field theory." Einstein never realized his dream, in large part because a number of essential properties of matter and the forces of nature were unknown at the time. As outlined partially in Chapter 13, scientific knowledge has expanded enormously over the past 50 years, and physicists are working on a framework tying everything together into a single theory that might describe all physical phenomena. One such theory is called the "superstring theory."

Einstein did not accept all the new ideas in physics, many of which originated with his theories of 1905. In particular, he was skeptical of the theories of Werner Heisenberg (see Section 12.5), which proposed that many of the properties of the subatomic universe were based on the laws of probability. He made statements such as "God may be subtle, but he is not malicious" and "God does not play at dice."

In 1939, Einstein was to see his famous prediction that mass could be changed into energy realized experimentally, with the achievement of nuclear fission by Otto Hahn and Lise Meitner in Germany. Various scientists persuaded Einstein, as the most influential

Figure 1
Albert Einstein as a young man in Bern

Ernst Mach
Ernst Mach (1818–1916), professor of physics in the University of Vienna (and the Mach in "Mach number"), wrote: "I can accept the theory of relativity as little as I can accept the existence of atoms and other such dogmas."

Figure 2
The Canadian photographer Joseph Karsh took this famous portrait of Einstein.

scientist in the United States, to write to President Franklin D. Roosevelt, urging him to pre-empt Nazi Germany in nuclear weapons research. The enormous Manhattan Project was begun, and atomic bombs were produced. When it was clear that the bomb had been built and worked, Einstein wrote again to Roosevelt, on behalf of a group of scientists, urging that the bomb not be used, except possibly as a demonstration to the Japanese. Roosevelt died three weeks later, leaving the decision to his successor, President Harry S. Truman. The Truman administration ignored Einstein's pleas, and two atomic bombs were dropped on Japan in 1945, ushering the world into a new nuclear era (**Figure 3**).

Ironically, Einstein was a confirmed pacifist, who had been opposed to Germany's invasions in both World Wars. He frequently expressed his views on social reform while in the United States, was a fervent Zionist, and was a lifelong proponent of total disarmament. When he died at his home in Princeton, New Jersey, on April 18, 1955, the world lost not only a great physicist but a great humanitarian. Shortly thereafter, a newly synthesized artificial element, with the atomic number 99, was named Einsteinium in his honour.

Figure 3
A thermonuclear explosion

▶ Practice

Making Connections

1. Einstein was probably the most famous scientist since Newton. Choose a topic of interest from below, collect information through the Internet and other sources, and write a report with a maximum of 500 words. Your report should include a description of Einstein as a person, some information about the people with whom he interacted, and some remarks on the prevailing scientific or (as relevant) social climate.
   (a) Einstein's intellectual development until the end of 1905
   (b) Einstein's work in physics beyond relativity
   (c) Einstein's relevance to the Manhattan Project
   (d) Einstein's efforts in the international diplomacy of the Cold War era
   (e) Einstein's efforts in a unified field theory

 www.science.nelson.com

Key Expectations

- state Einstein's two postulates for the special theory of relativity and describe related thought experiments relating to the constancy of the speed of light in all inertial frames of reference, time dilation, and length contraction (11.1, 11.2, 11.3)

- define and describe the concepts and units related to the present-day understanding of the mass–energy equivalence (11.1, 11.2, 11.3)

- outline the historical development of scientific views and models of matter and energy (11.1)

- conduct thought experiments as a way of developing an abstract understanding of the physical world (e.g., outline the sequence of thoughts used to predict effects arising from time dilation, length contraction, and increase of momentum when an object travels at several different speeds, including those that approach the speed of light) (11.2)

- apply quantitatively the laws of conservation of mass and energy, using Einstein's mass–energy equivalence (11.3)

Key Terms

inertial frame of reference

noninertial frame of reference

ether

special theory of relativity

simultaneity

proper time

time dilation

proper length

length contraction

rest mass

conservation of mass–energy

Key Equations

- $\Delta t_m = \dfrac{\Delta t_s}{\sqrt{1 - \dfrac{v^2}{c^2}}}$ (11.2)

- $L_m = L_s \sqrt{1 - \dfrac{v^2}{c^2}}$ (11.2)

- $p = \dfrac{mv}{\sqrt{1 - \dfrac{v^2}{c^2}}}$ (11.2)

- $E_{rest} = mc^2$ (11.3)

- $E_{total} = \dfrac{mc^2}{\sqrt{1 - \dfrac{v^2}{c^2}}}$ (11.3)

▶ *MAKE* a summary

Barnard's star, approximately 6 ly from Earth, is thought to have two Jupiter-class planets. You are the captain of a spaceship that will embark on a long trip at close to the speed of light to this system. You have one year to train your team of astronauts in all facets of the ship's operation, but before selecting the crew you need to brief them on certain topics to give them a clear understanding of what is involved before they make a commitment.

To begin, you should give them an overview of the relativistic effects involved in space travel. Using the following topics to guide you, summarize the facts you present to your group of astronauts:

(a) perceived ship time versus Earth time

(b) relationships with friends and relatives on Earth

(c) limitations on maximum speed

(d) energy conversions in the nuclear propulsion system

Write numbers 1 to 11 in your notebook. Indicate beside each number whether the corresponding statement is true (T) or false (F). If it is false, write a corrected version.

1. The speed of light in water is $\frac{c}{n}$, where $n = 1.33$ is the index of refraction of water. The speed of light in water is thus less than the speed of light in a vacuum. This fact violates the speed-of-light postulate of the special theory of relativity.

2. We customarily say that Earth revolves around the Sun. We can also say that the Sun revolves around Earth.

3. If events E_1 and E_2 are simultaneous in an inertial frame, then no observers stationary in the same frame will regard E_1 as occurring before E_2.

4. (a) Any two observers moving with a clock will agree on the rate at which it ticks.
   (b) Any two observers moving relative to each other, and simultaneously moving relative to a clock, will agree on the rate at which the clock ticks.
   (c) The observer moving with a clock, and measuring the time between ticks, measures the proper time between ticks.

5. Earth rotates on its axis once each day. To a person observing Earth from an inertial frame of reference in space, that is, stationary relative to Earth, a clock runs slower at the North Pole than at the equator. (Ignore the orbital motion of Earth about the Sun.)

6. A young astronaut has just returned to Earth from a long mission. She rushes up to an old man and in the ensuing conversation refers to him as her son. She cannot possibly be addressing her son.

7. (a) An object will be greater in length if the observer is moving with the object than if the object is moving relative to the observer.
   (b) An observer at rest relative to the moving object measures the object's proper length.

8. Relativistic effects such as time dilation and length contraction are for practical purposes undetectable in automobiles.

9. The total relativistic energy of an object is always equal to or greater than its rest mass energy.

10. Since rest mass is a form of energy, a spring has more mass when the coils are compressed than when relaxed.

11. The classical laws of conservation of energy and conservation of mass do not need to be modified for relativity.

Write numbers 12 to 23 in your notebook. Beside each number, write the letter corresponding to the best choice.

12. You are in a windowless spacecraft. You need to determine whether your spaceship is moving at constant nonzero velocity, or is at rest, in an inertial frame of Earth.
   (a) You can succeed by making very precise time measurements.
   (b) You can succeed by making very precise mass measurements.
   (c) You can succeed by making very precise length and time measurements.
   (d) You cannot succeed no matter what you do.
   (e) You are in a position not correctly described by any of these propositions.

13. You and your friend recede from each other in spacecraft in deep space without acceleration. In an inertial frame on your spaceship, your friend is receding at a speed of $0.9999c$. If you direct a light beam at your friend, and your friend directs a light beam at you, then
   (a) neither beam will reach the ship to which it is directed
   (b) you will see your friend's light arrive at a speed of $2c$, and your friend will see your light arrive at a speed of $2c$
   (c) you will see your friend's light arrive at a speed of c, and your friend will see your light arrive at a speed of c
   (d) one of you will see light arrive at a speed of c, and the other will see light arrive at $2c$
   (e) none of these propositions is true

14. Simultaneity is
   (a) dilated
   (b) absolute
   (c) invariant
   (d) relative
   (e) none of these

15. The Michelson–Morley experiment established that
   (a) there is no observable ether wind at the surface of Earth
   (b) the ether moves at c as Earth travels in its orbit
   (c) the ether is an elastic solid that streams over Earth
   (d) Earth does not move with respect to the Sun
   (e) none of these

16. A Klingon spaceship is approaching Earth at approximately $0.8c$ measured relative to Earth. The spaceship directs a laser beam forward directly through your physics classroom window. You measure the speed of this light to be
    (a) $1.8c$
    (b) $1.0c$
    (c) $0.9c$
    (d) $0.8c$
    (e) $0.2c$

17. You are an astronaut heading out toward a star. In the inertial frame of the star, you are steering directly for the star and are moving at constant speed. You can determine that you are in motion by
    (a) the slowing down of on-board clocks
    (b) the contraction of on-board metre sticks
    (c) your increase in mass
    (d) the increase in your heart rate
    (e) none of these

18. A clock, designed to tick each second, is moving past you at a uniform speed. You find the moving clock to be
    (a) ticking slowly
    (b) ticking quickly
    (c) accurate
    (d) running backward
    (e) none of these

19. The proper time between events E_1 and E_2 is
    (a) the time measured on clocks at rest with respect to E_1 and E_2
    (b) the time measured on clocks at rest in an inertial system moving properly with respect to E_1 and E_2
    (c) the time measured on clocks moving uniformly with respect to E_1 and E_2
    (d) the time between E_1 and E_2 as measured by a clock in a national-standards laboratory, such as the National Research Council in Ottawa
    (e) none of these

20. There are about 2.81×10^9 heartbeats in an average lifetime of 72 years. Space travellers who are born and die on a spaceship moving at a constant speed of $0.600c$ can expect their hearts to beat a total of
    (a) $(0.600)(2.81 \times 10^9)$ times
    (b) 2.81×10^9 times
    (c) $(0.800)(2.81 \times 10^9)$ times
    (d) $(1.25)(2.81 \times 10^9)$ times
    (e) none of these

21. A mass–spring system oscillates up and down with a period T when stationary in the inertial frame of an Earthbound observer. The same system is then moved past the Earthbound observer, with a velocity which in the observer's frame is constant and of magnitude $0.50c$. The observer now determines the period to be
    (a) $0.50T$
    (b) $0.87T$
    (c) $1.0T$
    (d) $1.2T$
    (e) $2.0T$

22. According to the effects of length contraction, from the viewpoint of an observer stationary with respect to a body moving at a uniform speed relative to the observer,
    (a) the body is not now contracted but would contract if it were to accelerate
    (b) the body contracts along the direction of motion
    (c) the time it takes for a clock incorporated in the body to tick contracts
    (d) the body contracts in some direction transverse to the direction of its motion
    (e) none of these

23. The energy output of the Sun is 3.7×10^{26} J/s. Matter is converted to energy in the Sun at the rate of
    (a) 4.1×10^9 kg/s
    (b) 6.3×10^9 kg/s
    (c) 7.4×10^1 kg/s
    (d) 3.7×10^9 kg/s
    (e) none of these

Understanding Concepts

1. Suppose you are standing at a railroad crossing, watching a train go by. Both you and a passenger in the train are looking at a clock on the train.
   (a) Which of you measures the proper time interval?
   (b) Which of you measures the proper length of the train car?
   (c) Which of you measures the proper length between the railroad ties under the track?

   Justify your answers.

2. A baseball player hitter pops a fly straight up; it is caught by the catcher at home plate. Identify which of the following observers is able to record the proper time interval between the two events:
   (a) a spectator sitting in the stands
   (b) a fan sitting on the couch and watching the game on TV
   (c) the shortstop running in to cover the play

   Explain your answer in each case.

3. When you are flying in a commercial jet, it appears to you that the airplane is stationary and Earth is moving beneath you. Is this point of view admissible? Discuss briefly.

4. Does time dilation mean that time actually passes more slowly in moving reference frames or that it only seems to pass more slowly? Discuss your answer.

5. Two identically constructed clocks are synchronized. One is put into orbit around Earth, and the other remains on Earth. When the moving clock returns to Earth, will the two clocks still be synchronized? Explain your answer.

6. Why is it that a pair of synchronized clocks, rather than a single clock, is needed for measuring any time interval other than a proper time?

7. Describe two instances in which the predictions of the special theory of relativity have been verified.

8. A spaceship passes you at a speed of $0.92c$. You measure its length to be 48.2 m. How long would the ship be when at rest?

9. The straight-line distance between Toronto and Vancouver is 3.2×10^3 km (neglecting the curvature of Earth). A UFO is flying between these two cities at a speed of $0.70c$ relative to Earth. What do the voyagers aboard the UFO measure for this distance?

10. A UFO streaks across a football field at $0.90c$ relative to the goal posts. Standing on the field, you measure the length of the UFO to be 228 m. The UFO later lands, allowing you to measure it with a metre stick. What length do you now obtain?

11. Two spaceships, X and Y, are exploring a planet. Relative to this planet, spaceship X has a speed of $0.70c$, while spaceship Y has a speed of $0.86c$. What is the ratio of the values for the planet's diameter that each spaceship measures, in a direction that is parallel to its motion?

12. An electron is travelling at $0.866c$ with respect to the face of a television picture tube. What is the value of its relativistic momentum with respect to the tube?

13. Nuclei of radium, an unstable element, disintegrate by emitting a helium nucleus with a kinetic energy, in the inertial frame of the laboratory, of about 4.9 MeV. Calculate the rest-mass equivalent of this energy.

14. A nuclear power reactor generates 3.00×10^9 W of power. In one year, what is the change in the mass of the nuclear fuel due to the energy conversion? (*Hint:* Recall that a 1-W power source delivers 1 J/s).

15. The electron and the positron each have a rest mass of 9.11×10^{-31} kg. In a certain experiment, an electron and a positron collide and vanish, leaving only electromagnetic radiation after the interaction. Each particle is moving at a speed of $0.20c$ relative to the laboratory before the collision. Determine the energy of the electromagnetic radiation.

16. The total energy of a certain muon, a particle with a rest energy of 105.7 MeV, is 106.7 MeV. What is its kinetic energy?

17. (a) Suppose the speed of light is only 47.0 m/s. Calculate the relativistic kinetic energy in an inertial frame of the road, which would be possessed by a car of rest mass 1.20×10^3 kg and moving at 28.0 m/s in that frame.
    (b) Calculate the ratio of this relativistic kinetic energy to the kinetic energy as computed in Newtonian mechanics.

18. The Big Bang, which is a theory predicting the origin of the universe, is estimated to have released 1.00×10^{68} J of energy. How many stars could half this energy create, assuming the average star's mass is 4.00×10^{30} kg?

19. A supernova explosion (**Figure 1**) of a star with a rest mass of 1.97×10^{31} kg, produces 1.02×10^{44} J of kinetic energy and radiation.
    (a) How many kilograms of mass are converted to energy in the explosion?
    (b) Calculate the ratio of the mass destroyed to the original mass of the star.

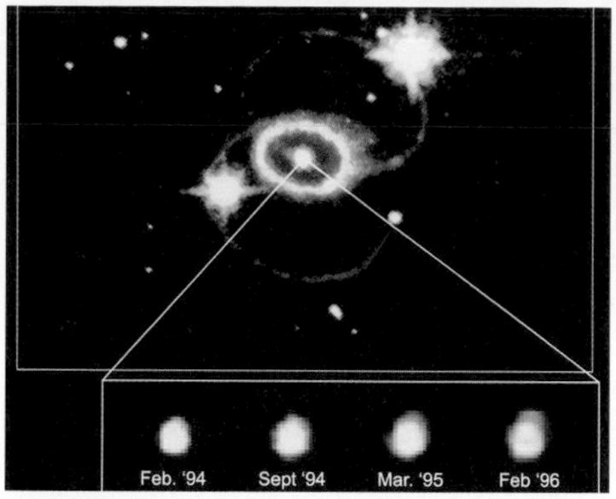

Figure 1
Supernova 1987A was discovered by Canadian Ian Shelton.

Making Connections

20. Describe several ways in which the authors of books on science fiction and space travel take the effects of special relativity into consideration.

21. In the introduction to this chapter there is a picture depicting the Cerenkov effect, in which particles emit light when travelling in a material, in this case water, at speed $v > \dfrac{c}{n}$, where n is the index of refraction of the material. (Consequently, $\dfrac{c}{n}$ is the speed of light in the material.) But it is impossible to exceed the speed of light. How is the Cerenkov effect possible?

22. Approximately 1.0×10^{34} J of energy is available from fusion of hydrogen in the world's oceans.
    (a) If 1.0×10^{33} J of this energy were utilized, what would be the decrease in mass of the oceans?
    (b) To what volume of water does this correspond?

23. Suppose you use an average of 485 kW·h of electric energy per month in your home.
    (a) How long would 1.00 g of mass converted to electric energy with an efficiency of 40.0% last you?
    (b) How many homes could be supplied with 485 kW·h each month for one year by the energy from the mass conversion?

Extension

24. An electron has, in a certain inertial frame, a total energy equal to five times its rest energy. Calculate its momentum in that frame.

25. Scientist Ludwig von Drake, while in his laboratory, measures the half-life of some radioactive material, which is in a bomb, approaching with speed v. Donald Duck, who is riding on the bomb, also measures the half-life. His answer is a factor of 2 smaller than Ludwig's. What is the value of v, expressed as a fraction of c?

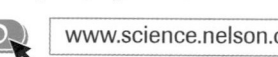

26. At what speed is the magnitude of the relativistic momentum of a particle three times the magnitude of the nonrelativistic momentum?

27. A rocket of rest mass 1.40×10^5 kg has, in a certain inertial frame, a relativistic momentum of magnitude 3.15×10^{13} kg·m/s. How fast is the rocket travelling?

28. As early as 1907, while Einstein and others explored the implications of his special theory of relativity, Einstein was already thinking about a more general theory. Could he extend the special theory to deal with objects in a noninertial frame of reference? Einstein saw a link between accelerated motion and the force of gravity. Galileo and Newton had found that all bodies, if released from the same height, would fall with exactly the same constant acceleration (in the absence of air resistance). Like the invariant speed of light on which Einstein had founded his special theory of relativity, here was an invariance that could be the starting point for another theory, the general theory of relativity. Research the Internet and other sources and answer the following questions:
    (a) What thought experiment could you use to connect accelerated motion and the force of gravity?
    (b) Briefly explain how the general theory of relativity describes how light moves under the force of gravity.
    (c) How did other others test his theory using a solar eclipse (**Figure 2**) in 1919?

GO www.science.nelson.com

Figure 2
A total solar eclipse

chapter

12

Waves, Photons, and Matter

▶ In this chapter, you will be able to

- define and describe the concepts and units related to the present-day understanding of the nature of the atom

- describe the photoelectric effect in terms of the quantum energy concept

- outline evidence that supports a photon model of light

- describe and explain the Bohr model of the hydrogen atom

- collect or interpret experimental data involving the photoelectric effect and the emission spectrum of hydrogen

- outline the historical development of models of matter and energy from 1890 to 1925

- describe how the development of quantum theory has led to scientific and technological advances

- describe some Canadian contributions to modern physics

Two major discoveries shook physics in the early part of the twentieth century. One was the special theory of relativity; the other was the quantum theory. Both led to significant changes in how we look at the physical world. The special theory of relativity was the creation of one man, Albert Einstein, in a single year, 1905. The quantum theory developed more slowly, over a period of thirty years, with contributions from many investigators. Quantum physics began in the 1890s with studies of blackbody radiation and reached its climax in the mid-1920s. At that time, Werner Heisenberg, Wolfgang Pauli, and Erwin Schrödinger used quantum theory to explain the behaviour of electrons in atoms.

In this chapter, we will examine the highlights of the development and application of the quantum theory as it relates to light, matter, and the energy of electrons in atoms. We will also look at a few practical applications, in photodetectors, digital cameras, electron microscopes, and lasers (**Figure 1**).

💡 REFLECT on your learning ▼

1. An ordinary light bulb becomes quite hot when turned on; a fluorescent lamp takes a moment before it comes on and is much cooler than an ordinary bulb. Why do they both produce white light, even though they have different temperatures?

2. In a colour photograph or poster, the reds and greens fade before the blues and violets (**Figure 2**). Why does this occur?

Figure 2

3. What do you think the term "quantum leap" means?

4. The caption to **Figure 1** says that the image was produced by an electron microscope. How do you think electrons can be used to create an image?

5. A satellite orbits Earth with a relatively constant radius.
   (a) What is the force holding the satellite in orbit?
   (b) What causes it to eventually crash into Earth?
   (c) An electron orbits a positively charged nucleus. What force holds it in orbit? Does it "crash" into the nucleus?

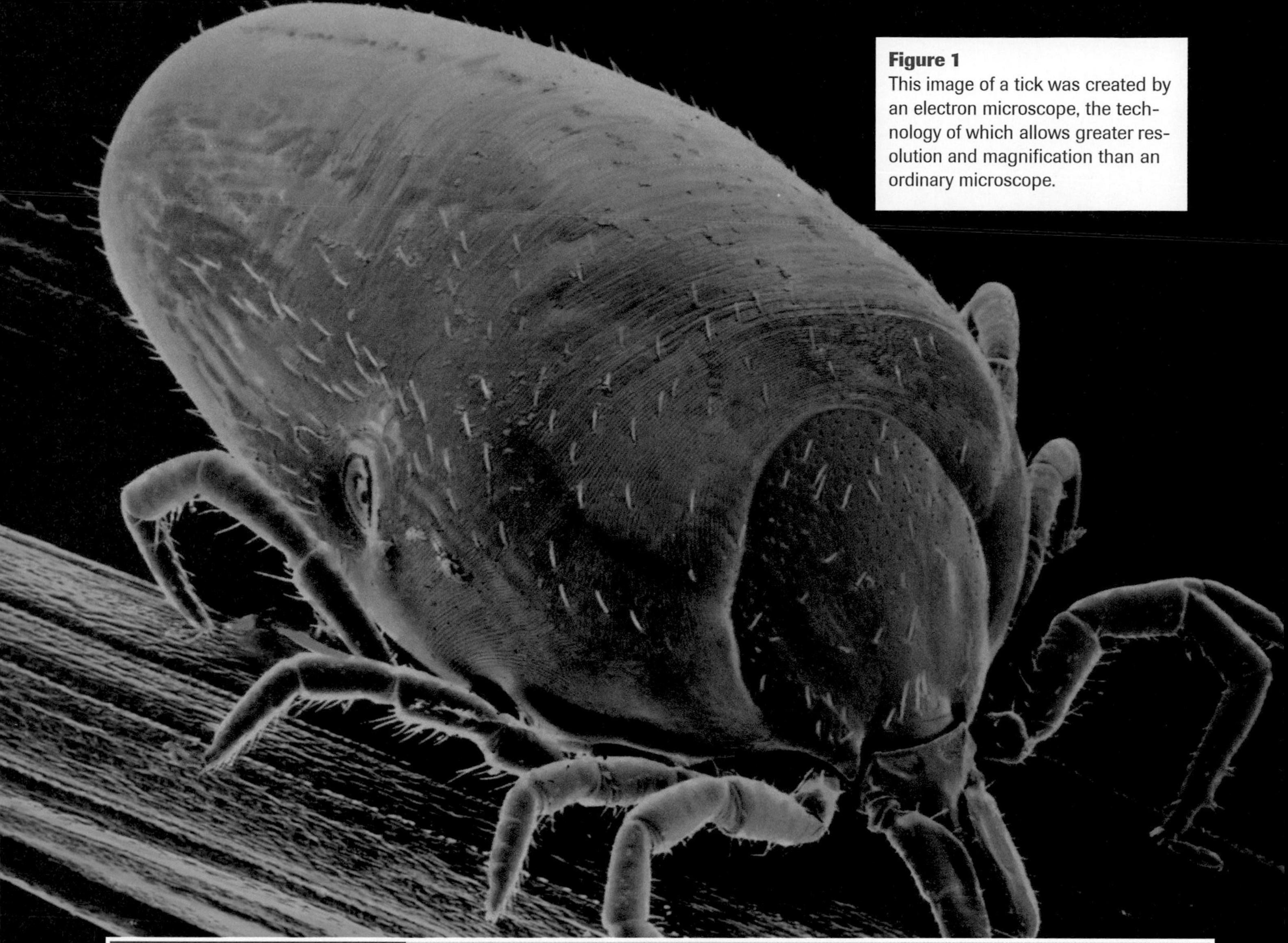

▶ TRY THIS activity   *Discharging with Light*

Do not look directly into a low-power ultraviolet lamp. High-power ultraviolet sources must be shielded.

For this activity, you will need a zinc plate, emery paper or steel wool, a metal-leaf electroscope, an insulated stand, ebonite and fur, electrical wire and clips, an ultraviolet lamp, and a glass plate.

- Polish one side of the zinc plate with emery paper or steel wool until it is shiny. Place it onto an insulated stand (**Figure 3**), and connect it to the knob of the electroscope.

- Charge the zinc plate negatively, using a charged ebonite rod. Allow the apparatus to stand for at least 2 min. Record the time required for the system to discharge.

- Place the zinc plate so that the polished side is facing the ultraviolet (UV) light. Position the glass plate as a filter between the polished zinc surface and the lamp. Turn on the lamp. Record the time required for the system to discharge.

- Repeat the discharging procedure, this time removing the glass plate.

- Compare the rate of change for the system with (i) no UV lamp, (ii) a UV lamp with glass filter, and (iii) a UV lamp without a glass filter.

  (a) For the negatively charged electroscope to change this way, what must have happened to the electrons on the zinc plate?

  (b) Propose an explanation for your observations.

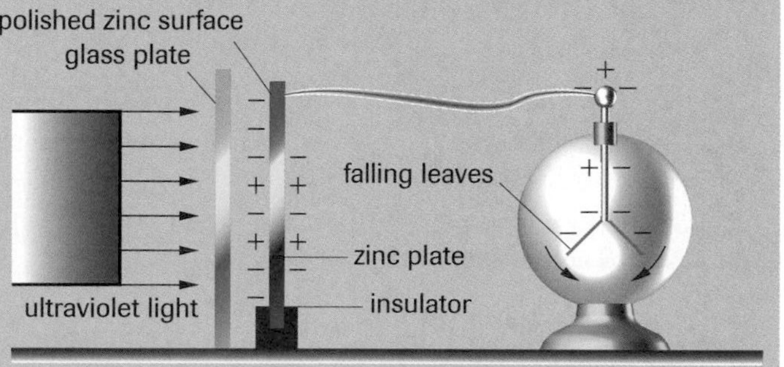

polished zinc surface
glass plate

falling leaves

zinc plate

ultraviolet light   insulator

metal-leaf electroscope, initially negatively charged

Figure 3

One of the major areas of research at the end of the nineteenth century was the spectral analysis of light emitted by hot solids and gases. In the study of blackbody radiation there was discrepancy between theory and experimental data that scientists could not reconcile. Many theories were put forward to explain and predict the details of the observed spectra, but none was adequate.

Blackbody Radiation

If a piece of steel is placed into the flame of a welding torch, the steel begins to glow: first dull red, then a brighter orange–red, then yellow, and finally white. At high temperatures (above 2000 K), the hot steel emits most of the visible colours of the spectrum as well as infrared radiation. If heated sufficiently, the steel can produce ultraviolet emissions as well. It has been found that this behaviour is similar for all incandescent solids, regardless of their composition. Thus, as the temperature increases, the spectrum of the emitted electromagnetic radiation shifts to higher frequencies (**Figure 1**). It has also been determined that the relative brightness of the different colours radiated by an incandescent solid depends mainly on the temperature of the material.

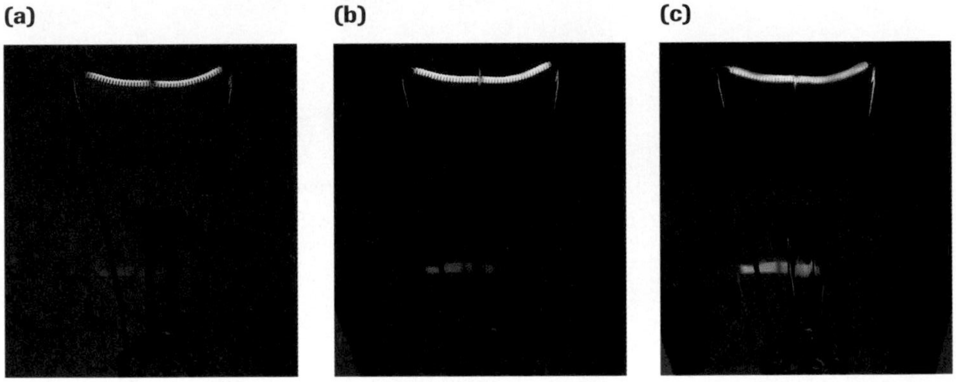

(a)   **(b)**   **(c)**

Figure 1
A hot filament and the spectra emitted for increasing temperatures, **(a)** to **(b)** to **(c)**. As the temperature increases, the spectrum spreads into the violet region.

The actual spectrum of wavelengths emitted by a hot object at various temperatures is shown in **Figure 2**. The curves illustrate two key points:

- At a given temperature, a spectrum of different wavelengths is emitted, of varying intensity, but there is a definite intensity maximum at one particular wavelength.

- As the temperature increases, the intensity maximum shifts to a shorter wavelength (higher frequency).

The curves in **Figure 2** represent the radiation from an object that approximates an ideal emitter or absorber of radiation. Such an object would absorb all wavelengths of light striking it, reflecting none. It would, therefore, appear black under reflected radiation and hence is called a **blackbody**. The detailed analysis of radiation absorption and emission shows that an object that absorbs all incoming radiation, of whatever wavelength, is likewise the most efficient possible emitter of radiation. The radiation emitted by a blackbody is called **blackbody radiation**.

Scientists in the 1890s were trying to explain the dependence of blackbody radiation on temperature. According to Maxwell's electromagnetic theory, the radiation originates from the oscillation of electric charges in the molecules or atoms of the material

blackbody an object that completely absorbs any radiation falling upon it

blackbody radiation radiation that would be emitted from an ideal blackbody

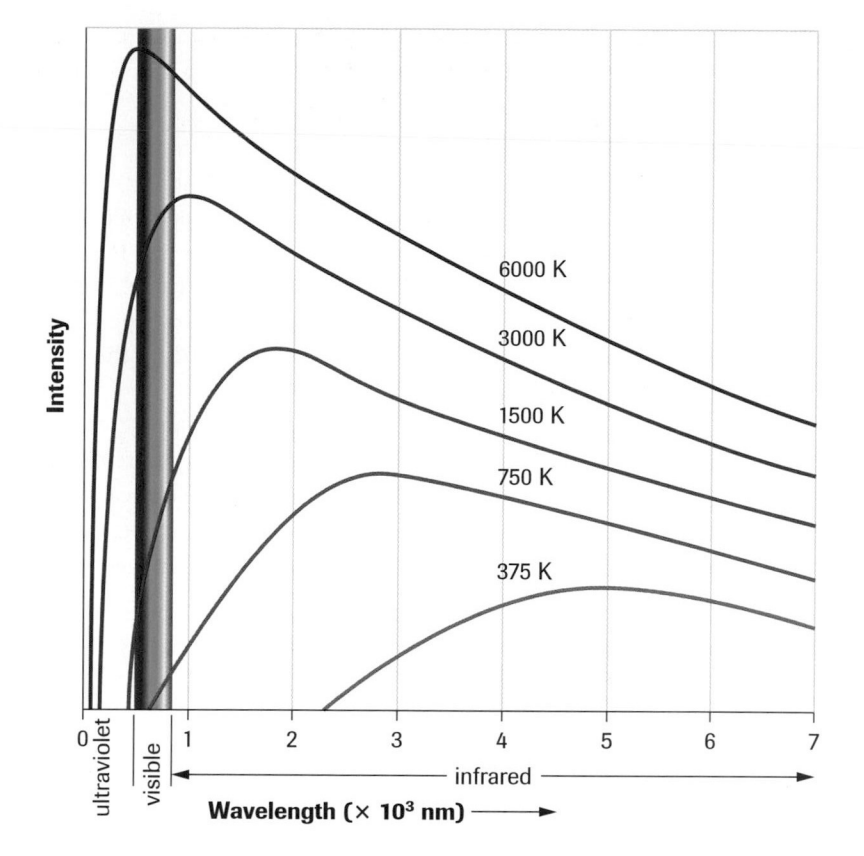

6000 K

3000 K

1500 K

750 K

375 K

Intensity

0

ultraviolet

visible

infrared

1   2   3   4   5   6   7

Wavelength (× 10³ nm) ⟶

(see Section 10.8). When the temperature increases, the frequency of these oscillations also increases. The corresponding frequency of the radiated light should increase as well. According to Maxwell's classical theory, the intensity versus wavelength must follow the dashed line in **Figure 3**. But this is not the case. The actual radiation follows the solid line. The region of the graph where theory and experimental data disagree is in the ultraviolet portion of the spectrum. Scientists in the 1890s referred to this problem as the ultraviolet catastrophe.

Planck's Quantum Hypothesis

In the early 1900s, the German physicist Max Planck proposed a new, radical theory to explain the data. He hypothesized that the vibrating molecules or atoms in a heated material vibrate only with specific quantities of energy. When energy radiates from the vibrating molecule or atom, it is not emitted in a continuous form but in bundles, or packets, which Planck called **quanta.** He further proposed that the energy of a single quantum is directly proportional to the frequency of the radiation:

$$E = hf$$

where E is the energy in joules, f is the frequency in hertz, and h is a constant in joule-seconds.

Planck estimated the value of the constant h by fitting his equation to experimental data. Today, the constant h is called **Planck's constant.** Its accepted value, to three significant digits, is

Planck's Constant

$h = 6.63 \times 10^{-34}$ J·s

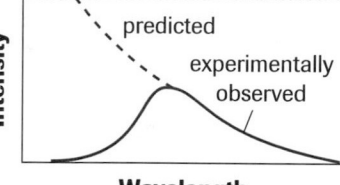

Intensity

predicted

experimentally observed

Wavelength

Figure 3
This graph illustrates the ultraviolet catastrophe. The predicted curve was quite different from the actual observations.

quanta packets of energy; one quantum is the minimum amount of energy a particle can emit

Planck's constant constant with the value $h = 6.63 \times 10^{-34}$ J·s; represents the ratio of the energy of a single quantum to its frequency

Figure 4
(a) On the ramp, the box can possess any one of a continuous range of values of gravitational potential energy.
(b) On the stairs, the box can possess only one of a set of discrete, or quantized, energies.

LEARNING TIP

Quantization
We have seen quantization in standing waves in a rope, where a stable pattern of nodes and antinodes, for a rope of a given length, can only be generated at specific frequencies. Also, resonance in air columns can only occur at specific column lengths.

Planck further hypothesized that the emitted energy must be an integral multiple of the minimum energy, that is, the energy can only be hf, $2hf$, $3hf$, … :

$$E = nhf \quad \text{where } n = 1, 2, 3, …$$

If light energy is quantized, and the energy of each bundle is determined by the relationship $E = hf$, the bundles in the red region will have low energy and the bundles in the ultraviolet region will have high energy. Using this quantum model and applying statistical methods beyond the level of this text, Planck explained the shape of the intensity versus wavelength graph for all areas of the spectrum, including the ultraviolet region, for a blackbody of any given temperature.

The concept of quantization can be clarified with a simple analogy: compare the change in gravitational energy as a box is pushed up a ramp, with the progress of the same box, to the same final elevation, by stairs (**Figure 4**). According to classical physics, the box on the ramp takes on a continuous range of gravitational potential energies as it is pushed up the ramp. According to the quantum model, the box that moves up the stairs does so in discrete, quantized "steps" of energy.

(a)   **(b)**

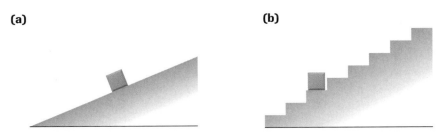

The concept of quantized values was not new. Dalton, in his theory of the atom ninety years before, had proposed that the structure of matter was based on the smallest indivisible particle, the atom, and this was well accepted in 1900. Also, it had been shown by Thomson that the electric charge is quantized: the smallest charge found in nature is the charge on the electron. Nevertheless, the idea that energy is quantized was not easy to accept.

Planck's quantum idea was revolutionary for two reasons:

- It challenged the classical wave theory of light by proposing that electromagnetic waves do not transmit energy in a continuous manner but, instead, transmit energy in small packages, or bundles.

- It challenged the classical physics of Newton, since it proposed that a physical object is not free to vibrate with any random energy; the energy is restricted to certain discrete values.

Planck, himself, was initially skeptical about his own theory. He was not ready to reject the classical theories that were so well accepted by the scientific community. He even stated that, although his hypothesis worked in explaining blackbody radiation, he hoped a better explanation would come forth.

More experimental evidence for the quantum theory was required. Quantization of energy remained generally unaccepted until 1905. In that year Einstein argued persuasively on its behalf, showing how it helped explain the *photoelectric effect*, as light ejects electrons from a metal in a frequency-dependent manner. (The photoelectric effect is discussed later in this chapter.) So drastic, in retrospect, was the change ushered in by Planck's quantum hypothesis that historians established a sharp division; physics prior to 1900 became known as classical physics, and physics after 1900 was called modern physics. Since Planck's work was so important historically, Planck's honour and respect in the scientific community were second only to Einstein's in the first half of the 20th century (**Figure 5**).

▶ ***SAMPLE*** problem ***1***

Calculate the energy in joules and electron volts of

(a) a quantum of blue light with a frequency of 6.67×10^{14} Hz

(b) a quantum of red light with a wavelength of 635 nm

Solution

(a) $f = 6.67 \times 10^{14}$ Hz

$h = 6.63 \times 10^{-34}$ J·s

$$E = hf$$
$$= (6.63 \times 10^{-34} \text{ J·s})(6.67 \times 10^{14} \text{ Hz})$$
$$E = 4.42 \times 10^{-19} \text{ J}$$

1.60×10^{-19} J $= 1$ eV

$$\frac{4.42 \times 10^{-19} \text{ J}}{1.60 \times 10^{-19} \text{ J/eV}} = 2.76 \text{ eV}$$

The energy is 4.42×10^{-19} J, or 2.76 eV.

(b) $\lambda = 635$ nm $= 6.35 \times 10^{-7}$ m

$h = 6.63 \times 10^{-34}$ J·s

$$E = hf$$

But $v = f\lambda$ or $c = f\lambda$, and $f = \dfrac{c}{\lambda}$, where c is the speed of light $= 3.00 \times 10^8$ m/s.

$$E = \frac{hc}{\lambda}$$
$$= \frac{(6.63 \times 10^{-34} \text{ J·s})(3.00 \times 10^8 \text{ m/s})}{6.35 \times 10^{-7} \text{ m}}$$
$$E = 3.13 \times 10^{-19} \text{ J}$$

1.60×10^{-19} J $= 1$ eV

$$\frac{3.13 \times 10^{-19} \text{ J}}{1.60 \times 10^{-19} \text{ J/eV}} = 1.96 \text{ eV}$$

The energy is 3.13×10^{-19} J, or 1.96 eV.

▶ **Practice**

Understanding Concepts

1. Explain which of the following quantities are discrete: time, money, matter, energy, length, scores in hockey games.

2. Determine the energy, in electron volts, for quanta of electromagnetic radiation with the following characteristics:
   (a) wavelength = 941 nm (infrared radiation)
   (b) frequency = 4.4×10^{14} Hz (red light)
   (c) wavelength = 435 nm (violet light)
   (d) frequency = 1.2×10^{18} Hz (X rays)

Figure 5
Max Karl Planck (1858–1947) worked at the University of Berlin. His initial influential work on black-body radiation dates from 1889. In 1918, Planck's discovery of energy quanta was recognized with the Nobel Prize in physics. Stimulated by Planck's work, Einstein became an early proponent of the quantum theory. The celebrated Max Planck Society in Germany runs research institutes similar to those maintained by the National Research Council in Canada.

LEARNING TIP

Electron Volts
It is more common to use electron volts in quantum mechanics. Recall that $\Delta E = q \, \Delta V$; to convert joules to electron volts, use the relationship 1 eV = 1.60×10^{-19} J.

Answers

2. (a) 1.32 eV
   (b) 1.8 eV
   (c) 2.86 eV
   (d) 5.0×10^3 eV

Answers

3. 622 nm

4. 5.43×10^{14} Hz

5. 3.33:1

6. 10^{18}

photoelectric effect the phenomenon in which electrons are liberated from a substance exposed to electromagnetic radiation

photoelectrons electrons liberated in the photoelectric effect

cutoff potential smallest potential difference sufficient to reduce the photocurrent to zero

3. Calculate the wavelength, in nanometres, of a quantum of electromagnetic radiation with 3.20×10^{-19} J of energy. What colour is it? (See Section 9.6 for reference.)

4. Calculate the frequency of a 2.25-eV quantum of electromagnetic radiation.

5. Compare the respective energies of a quantum of "soft" ultraviolet radiation ($\lambda = 3.80 \times 10^{-7}$ m) and a quantum of "hard" ultraviolet radiation ($\lambda = 1.14 \times 10^{-7}$ m), expressing your answer as a ratio.

Making Connections

6. As you read this text, your body may be bombarded with quanta from radio waves ($\lambda = 10^2$ m) and quanta of cosmic rays, energetic particles, rather than electromagnetic waves, which nevertheless prove in quantum theory to have a wave aspect ($\lambda = 10^{-16}$ m). How many quanta of radio waves would it take to impart the same amount of energy as a single quantum of cosmic radiation? Comment on the relative biological hazards posed by these two sources of energy.

Einstein and the Photoelectric Effect

German physicist Heinrich Hertz was testing Maxwell's theory of electromagnetic waves in 1887 when he noticed that certain metallic surfaces lose their negative charges when exposed to ultraviolet light. He demonstrated the charge loss by wiring an insulated, polished zinc plate to a gold-leaf electroscope, as in **Figure 3** in the chapter introduction. Incident ultraviolet light somehow caused the zinc plate to release electrons, as indicated by the falling leaves of the electroscope. Hertz's phenomenon was called the **photoelectric effect** (since it involved both light and electricity), and the emitted electrons were called **photoelectrons**. Today we can easily demonstrate the photoelectric effect with visible light and a photocell (**Figure 6**).

Figure 7 also illustrates the photoelectric effect. A photosensitive cathode is illuminated by light of frequency f and intensity i, causing the emission of photoelectrons from the cathode. These photoelectrons travel across the vacuum tube toward the anode, due to the applied, external potential difference, and so constitute a photocurrent, I, measured by the microammeter (**Figure 7(a)**). But the circuit also contains a variable source of electrical potential, which can make the anode negative. This has the effect of reducing the photocurrent by causing all but the faster photoelectrons to be "turned back" (**Figure 7(b)**). If the anode is made gradually more negative relative to the cathode, a potential difference, the **cutoff potential**, is reached which is just large enough to reduce the current to zero. This cutoff potential corresponds to the maximum kinetic energy of the photoelectrons.

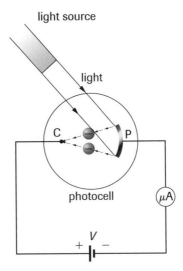

Figure 6
When light strikes the photoelectric surface (P), electrons are ejected and flow to the collector (C). Notice that the flow of photoelectrons is opposite in direction to conventional current.

Figure 7
(a) When the anode is positive, a current flows through the tube, provided light shines on the photosensitive surface (cathode).
(b) If the anode is made gradually more negative, a potential difference (the cutoff potential) sufficient to reduce the current to zero is eventually reached.

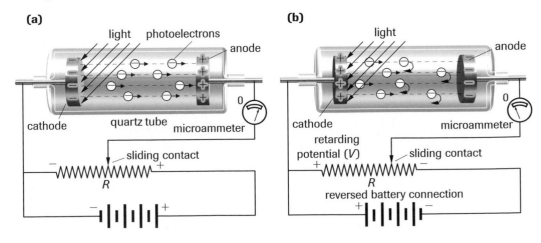

Many scientists repeated Hertz's experiment with similar apparatus. Their results not only gave some support to Planck's theories but also provided the basis for Einstein's analysis of the photoelectric effect. You can explore the effect by performing Lab Exercise 12.1.1 in the Lab Activities section at the end of this chapter.

Here are some of the more significant findings:

1. Photoelectrons are emitted from the photoelectric surface when the incident light is above a certain frequency f_0, called the **threshold frequency**. Above the threshold frequency, the more intense the light, the greater the current of photoelectrons (**Figure 8(a)**).

2. The intensity (brightness) of the light has no effect on the threshold frequency. No matter how intense the incident light, if it is below the threshold frequency, not a single photoelectron is emitted (**Figure 8(b)**).

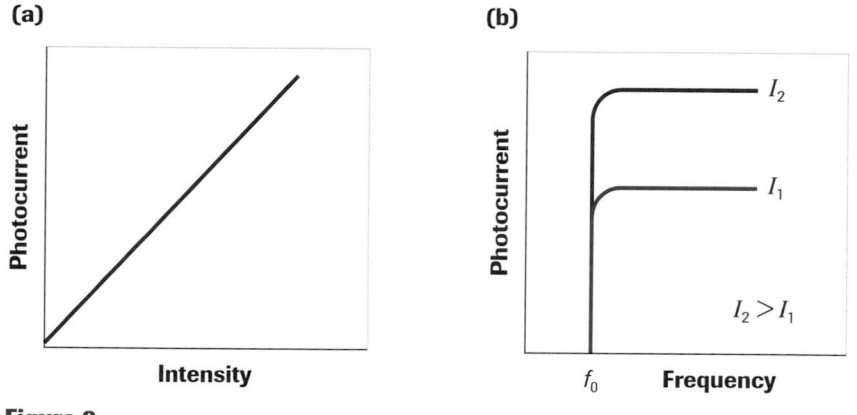

(a)

(b)

Figure 8
(a) Photocurrent versus intensity of light
(b) Photocurrent versus frequency of light for two intensities, I_1 and I_2

3. The threshold frequency, at which photoelectric emission first occurs, is different for different surfaces. For example, light that causes photoelectric emission from a cesium cathode has no effect on a copper cathode (**Figure 9**).

4. As the retarding potential applied to the anode is increased, the photocurrent I decreases, regardless of the intensity of the light. The photoelectrons are thus emitted with different kinetic energies. A value V_0 of the retarding potential is eventually reached, just sufficient to make the photocurrent zero. Even the fastest photoelectrons are now prevented from reaching the anode, being turned back by the retarding potential (**Figure 10**).

5. If different frequencies of light, all above the threshold frequency, are directed at the same photoelectric surface, the cutoff potential is different for each. It is found that the higher the frequency of the light, the higher the cutoff potential. The cutoff potential is related to the maximum kinetic energy with which photoelectrons are emitted: for a photoelectron of charge e and kinetic energy E_K, cut off by a retarding potential V_0, $E_K = eV_0$. (This follows from the definition of potential difference in Chapter 7.) By illuminating several photoelectric surfaces with light of various frequencies and measuring the cutoff potential obtained for each surface, values are obtained for the graph shown in **Figure 11**. Although each surface has a different threshold frequency, each line has the same slope.

LAB EXERCISE 12.1.1

Analyzing the Photoelectric Effect (p. 654)
What effect do the frequency and intensity of a light source have on the emission of photoelectrons? Do all materials used as the photoelectric surface behave the same? If not, how are they different and why? This lab exercise provides data that you can use to simulate photocathode experiments. Your analysis of the results may well lead you to the same conclusions as Einstein.

threshold frequency (f_0) the minimum frequency at which photoelectrons are liberated from a given photoelectric surface

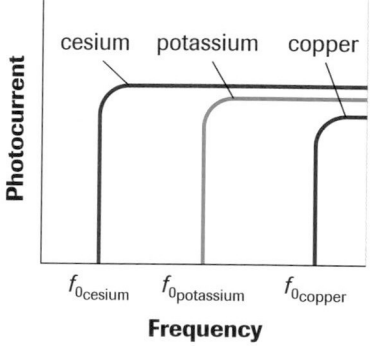

Figure 9
Photocurrent versus frequency of incident light for three surfaces. Cesium has a lower threshold frequency than potassium and copper.

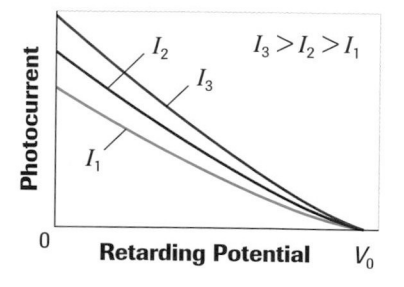

Figure 10
Cutoff potential is constant for the same material for any value of intensity, for light of a given frequency.

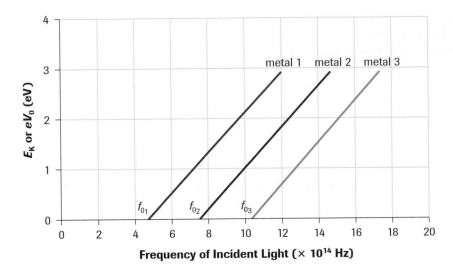

Figure 11
Graph of kinetic energy of the photoelectrons versus frequency for three metals. The lines all have the same slope but show different cutoff frequencies.

6. During photoemission, the release of the electron is immediate, with no appreciable delay between illumination and photoelectron emission, even for extremely weak light. It appears that the electron absorbs the light energy immediately: no time is required to accumulate sufficient energy to liberate the electrons.

Of these various experimental findings, only the first could be explained on the basis of the classical electromagnetic theory of light. In particular, according to classical wave theory, there is no reason why an intense beam of low-frequency light should not be able to produce a photoelectric current or why the intensity of the beam should not affect the maximum kinetic energy of the ejected photoelectrons. The classical wave theory of light could not properly explain the photoelectric effect at all.

As an analogy, consider a boat in a harbour. As long as the incoming water waves have a small amplitude (i.e., are of low intensity), the boat will not be tossed up on the shore, regardless of the frequency of the waves. However, according to the above observations, even a small-amplitude (low-intensity) wave can eject a photoelectron if the frequency is high enough. This is analogous to the boat being hurled up on the shore by a small wave with a high enough frequency, certainly not what classical wave theory would predict.

Einstein was well aware of these experiments and Planck's blackbody hypothesis. He also knew about Newton's particle theory of light, some aspects of which he resurrected to make a radical proposal: the energy of electromagnetic radiation, including visible light, is not transmitted in a continuous wave but is concentrated in bundles of energy called **photons**. Einstein further proposed that the energy in each of his photons was constrained to be one of a set of discrete possible values, determined by Planck's equation, $E = hf$. He used his photon theory of light to explain some of the experimental results of the photoelectric effect and predicted new effects as well.

Einstein reasoned that if an electron, near the surface of a metal, absorbs a photon, the energy gained by the electron might be great enough for the electron to escape from the metal. Some of the absorbed energy would be used to break away from the metal surface, with the remainder showing up as the kinetic energy of the electron (**Figure 12**). Since the energy of a photon is given by hf, the higher the frequency, the greater the kinetic energy of the ejected photoelectron.

This behaviour also explained why there is a threshold frequency. The electron has to receive a minimum amount of energy to escape the attractive forces holding it to the metal. When the frequency of the incident light is too low, the photon does not provide the absorbing electron with sufficient energy, and it remains bound to the surface.

photon the quantum of electromagnetic energy whose energy is hf

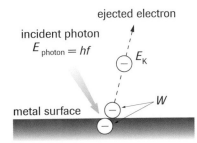

Figure 12
Part of the energy of the incident photon goes to releasing the surface electron. (W is the energy binding the electron to the surface.) The remainder provides the kinetic energy of the ejected electron.

The intensity (brightness) of the light is only a measure of the rate at which the photons strike the surface, not of the energy per photon. This helps explain why the kinetic energy of the emitted photoelectrons and the threshold frequency are independent of the intensity of the incident light.

To summarize: when a photon hits a photoelectric surface, a surface electron absorbs its energy. Some of the energy is needed to release the electron, while the remainder becomes the kinetic energy of the ejected photoelectron. This is what one would expect based on the conservation of energy. Einstein described this mathematically as follows:

$$E_{photon} = W + E_K$$

where E_{photon} is the energy of the incident photon, W is the energy with which the electron is bound to the photoelectric surface, and E_K is the kinetic energy of the ejected photoelectron.

Rearranging the equation, we obtain

$$E_K = E_{photon} - W$$

Upon rewriting E_{photon} in terms of the frequency of the incident photon, we have *Einstein's photoelectric equation:*

$$E_K = hf - W$$

The value W (the energy needed to release an electron from an illuminated metal) is called the **work function** of the metal. The work function is different for different metals (**Table 1**) and in most cases is less than 1.6×10^{-18} J (equivalently, less than 10 eV).

When surface electrons absorb the photons, many interactions occur. Some absorbing electrons move into the surface and do not become photoelectrons at all. Others either emerge immediately at a large angle to the normal or undergo inelastic collisions before emerging. Still others emerge immediately at small angles to the normal, moving more or less directly toward the anode. The net effect is that only a small number of the more energetic photoelectrons come close to reaching the anode. They are further inhibited as the retarding voltage approaches the cutoff potential. Therefore, only the most energetic electrons reach the anode. As a result, the cutoff potential V_0 measures the maximum possible kinetic energy of the photoelectrons (represented by E_K in the equation $E_K = hf - W$).

The same mathematical relationship may be derived from the same three surfaces in **Figure 13**, except the vertical axis has been extended to include the negative intercept.

work function the energy with which an electron is bound to a photoelectric surface

Table 1 Approximate Photoelectric Work Functions for Various Metals

Metal	Work Function (eV)
aluminum (Al)	4.20
barium (Ba)	2.52
cesium (Cs)	1.95
copper (Cu)	4.48
gold (Au)	5.47
iron (Fe)	4.67
lead (Pb)	4.25
lithium (Li)	2.93
mercury (Hg)	4.48
nickel (Ni)	5.22
platinum (Pt)	5.93
potassium (K)	2.29
rubidium (Rb)	2.26
silver (Ag)	4.74
sodium (Na)	2.36
tin (Sn)	4.42
zinc (Zn)	3.63

Source: *CRC Handbook of Chemistry and Physics,* 81st ed. (CRC Press, Boca Raton, FL, 2000).

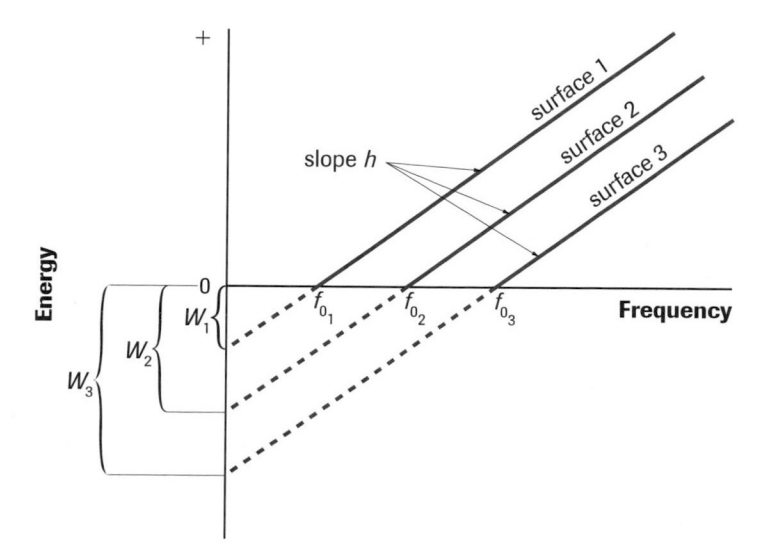

Figure 13
Energy of photoelectrons versus frequency of incident light for three surfaces

For each photoelectric surface, the graph is a straight line of the form $y = m(x - a)$, where m is the slope and a is the horizontal intercept.

In this case,

$$eV_0 = mf - mf_0$$

since the intercept on the frequency-axis is f_0.

But we have already stated that eV_0 is equal to the kinetic energy of the emitted photoelectron. Thus, the equation becomes

$$E_K = mf - mf_0$$

which matches Einstein's equation if m, the slope of the line on the graph, equals Planck's constant h, and $W = hf_0$.

Further, if the straight line is extended (dashed lines in **Figure 13**) until it crosses the vertical axis, the equation $E_K = hf - W$ is seen to be of the form $y = mx + b$, with the absolute value of the vertical intercept b giving the work function W for that surface.

Note that on a graph of E_K (or eV_0) versus f, each photosurface has the same slope (h, or Planck's constant), but each has its own unique horizontal intercept (f_0, or threshold frequency) and vertical intercept ($-W$, or work function) (**Figure 14**).

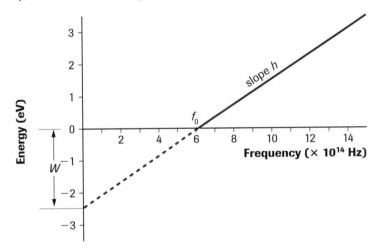

Figure 14
For sodium, the threshold frequency f_0 is 6.0×10^{14} Hz, and the work function W is -2.5 eV. These values represent the intercepts on the frequency and energy axes, respectively.

Einstein's photoelectric equation agreed qualitatively with the experimental results available in 1905, but quantitative results were required to find out if the maximum kinetic energy did indeed increase linearly with the frequency and if the slope of the graph, h, was common to all photoelectric substances.

Oxidization impurities on the surfaces of metal photocathodes caused difficulties for the experimentalists. It was not until 1916 that Robert Millikan designed an apparatus in which the metallic surface was cut clean in a vacuum before each set of readings. Millikan showed Einstein's explanation and prediction to be correct. Millikan also found the numerical value h, as the slope of his plots, to be in agreement with the value Planck had calculated earlier, using a completely different method. It was for his explanation of the photoelectric effect, based on the photon theory of light, that Albert Einstein received the 1921 Nobel Prize in physics (not, as is sometimes claimed, for his still more celebrated work on relativity).

> ▶ **SAMPLE** problem 2

Orange light with a wavelength of 6.00×10^2 nm is directed at a metallic surface with a work function of 1.60 eV. Calculate

(a) the maximum kinetic energy, in joules, of the emitted electrons

(b) their maximum speed

(c) the cutoff potential necessary to stop these electrons

Solution

(a) $\lambda = 6.00 \times 10^2$ nm $= 6.00 \times 10^{-7}$ m

$h = 6.63 \times 10^{-34}$ J·s

$E_K = ?$

$$W = 1.60 \text{ eV}$$
$$= (1.60 \text{ eV})(1.60 \times 10^{-19} \text{ J/eV})$$
$$W = 2.56 \times 10^{-19} \text{ J}$$

$$E_{K,max} = \frac{hc}{\lambda} - W$$

$$= \frac{(6.63 \times 10^{-34} \text{ J·s})(3.00 \times 10^8 \text{ m/s})}{6.00 \times 10^{-7} \text{ m}} - 2.56 \times 10^{-19} \text{ J}$$

$$E_{K,max} = 7.55 \times 10^{-20} \text{ J}$$

The maximum kinetic energy of the emitted photons is 7.55×10^{-20} J.

(b) $v = ?$

$m_e = 9.11 \times 10^{-31}$ kg (from Appendix C)

$$E_K = \frac{1}{2}mv^2$$

$$v = \sqrt{\frac{2E_K}{m}}$$

$$= \sqrt{\frac{2(7.55 \times 10^{-20} \text{ J})}{9.11 \times 10^{-31} \text{ kg}}}$$

$$v = 4.07 \times 10^5 \text{ m/s}$$

The maximum speed of the emitted electrons is 4.07×10^5 m/s.

(c) $V_0 = ?$

$$E_K = eV_0$$

$$V_0 = \frac{E_K}{e}$$

$$= \frac{7.55 \times 10^{-20} \text{ J}}{1.60 \times 10^{-19} \text{ C}}$$

$$V_0 = 0.472 \text{ V}$$

The cutoff potential necessary to stop these electrons is 0.472 V.

The answer to (c) could also have been determined from (a), as follows:

$$7.55 \times 10^{-20} \text{ J} = \frac{7.55 \times 10^{-20} \text{ J}}{1.60 \times 10^{-19} \text{ J/eV}} = 0.472 \text{ eV}$$

photodiode a semiconductor in which electrons are liberated by incident photons, raising the conductivity

charge-coupled device (CCD) a semiconductor chip with an array of light-sensitive cells, used for converting light images into electrical signals

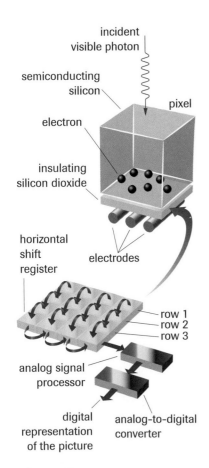

Figure 15
A CCD array captures images using the photoelectric effect.

Photodiodes and Digital Cameras

In addition to its theoretical role in confirming the photon view of light, the photoelectric effect has many practical applications, for the most part in semiconductors known as **photodiodes**. The absorption of a photon liberates an electron, which changes the conductivity of the photodiode material. Burglar alarms, garage doors, and automatic door openers often incorporate photodiodes. When a beam of light is interrupted, the drop in current in the circuit activates a switch, triggering an alarm or starting a motor. An infrared beam is sometimes used because of its invisibility. Remote controls for some televisions and video machines work in much the same way. Many smoke detectors use the photoelectric effect: the particles of smoke interrupt the flow of light and alter the electric current. Photocell sensors in cameras measure the level of light, adjusting the shutter speed or the aperture for the correct exposure. Photocells are used in a host of other devices, such as outdoor security lights and automatic street lights.

An important application of the photoelectric effect is the **charge-coupled device** (CCD). An array of these devices is used in digital cameras to capture images electronically.

A CCD array is a sandwich of semiconducting silicon and insulating silicon dioxide, with electrodes. The array is divided into many small sections, or pixels, as in **Figure 15** (where, for simplicity, we show a 16-pixel array, even though some cameras' arrays have over three million). The blow-up in **Figure 15** shows a single pixel. Incident photons of visible light strike the silicon, liberating photoelectrons as a result of the photoelectric effect. The number of electrons produced is proportional to the number of photons striking the pixel. Each pixel in the CCD array thus accumulates an accurate representation of the light intensity at that point on the image. In some applications, prisms or red, green, or blue filters are used to separate the colours.

The CCD was invented in 1969 by Willard S. Boyle (**Figure 16**), a Canadian, and George Smith, at Bell Research Laboratories in the United States. Their invention has not only brought digital photography, including video recording, to the consumer marketplace, but has triggered a revolution in astronomical image-processing.

 ▶ **Practice**

Making Connections

17. The photoelectric effect has many applications. Choose one, either from this text or from a search of the Internet or other media. Prepare a research paper, using the following as a guide:
  (a) Explain in detail, with the help of labelled diagrams, how your chosen device detects light using the photoelectric effect.
  (b) Explain how your device uses information from the photoelectric detector.
  (c) Identify at least three other devices that operate in a similar manner.

GO www.science.nelson.com

Figure 16
Willard S. Boyle (1924–) was born in Amherst, Nova Scotia, and took all his physics degrees at McGill University in Montreal. Before developing the CCD, which won him and Smith numerous awards, he also invented the first continuously operating ruby laser in 1962. Also in the 1960s, while director of Space Science and Exploratory Studies at Bellcomm, a Bell subsidiary that provided technological support for the Apollo space program, Boyle helped NASA select a lunar landing site.

Momentum of a Photon: The Compton Effect

In 1923, the American physicist A.H. Compton (1892–1962) directed a beam of high-energy X-ray photons at a thin metal foil. The experiment was similar to the photoelectric experiments, except that high-energy X-ray photons were used instead of light. Compton not only observed ejected electrons, as was to be expected from the theory of the photoelectric effect, but also detected an emission of X-ray photons, lower in energy, and therefore lower in frequency, than the photons in the bombarding beam. He also noted that electrons were scattered at an angle to the X-ray photons. This scattering of lower-frequency X-ray photons from foil bombarded by high-energy photons is known as the **Compton effect** (**Figure 17**).

A whole series of experiments, using different metal foils and different beams of X rays, produced similar results that could not be explained using electromagnetic-wave theory. Compton proposed that the incident X-ray photon acts like a particle that collides elastically with an electron in the metal, emerging with lower energy. The electron flies off with the kinetic energy it gained in the collision. Compton's data indicated that energy was indeed conserved.

If energy were conserved in the collision (see **Figure 18**), the following would be true:

$$E_{\text{X ray}} = E'_{\text{X ray}} + E_{\text{electron}}$$

$$hf = hf' + \frac{1}{2}mv^2$$

Compton's stroke of genius was to inquire whether momentum is conserved, as in ordinary collisions. It is not, at first, clear in what sense momentum could be associated with a bundle of energy with no mass, travelling at the speed of light. Compton solved this problem by using Einstein's $E = mc^2$ equation from special relativity. A body with energy E has a mass equivalence of $\frac{E}{c^2}$ (see Section 11.3). Compton's solution was the following: the magnitude of the momentum p of a body is defined as the product of mass m and speed v, $p = mv$. If we replace m with its mass equivalent, $\frac{E}{c^2}$, and replace v with c, we can write

$$p = \left(\frac{E}{c^2}\right)v \quad \text{or} \quad p = \frac{E}{c}$$

as an expression for p in which mass does not explicitly appear.

Compton effect the scattering of photons by high-energy photons

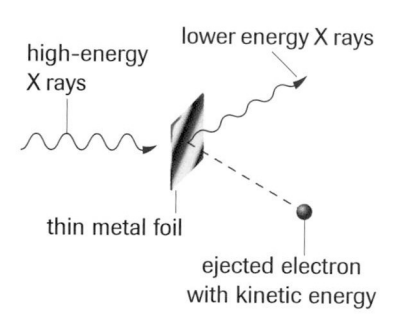

high-energy X rays

lower energy X rays

thin metal foil

ejected electron with kinetic energy

Figure 17
The Compton effect

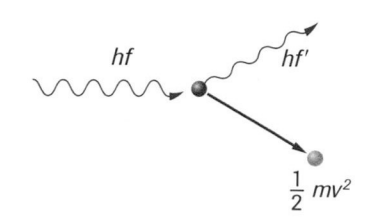

hf hf'

$\frac{1}{2}mv^2$

Figure 18

Now from the photon's energy $E = hf$ and the universal wave equation $c = f\lambda$, E and c are replaced to give $p = \dfrac{hf}{f\lambda}$, or

$$p = \frac{h}{\lambda}$$

This relation gives the magnitude of the **momentum of a photon**, where p is the magnitude of the momentum, in kilogram-metres per second, h is Planck's constant with a value of 6.63×10^{-34} J·s, and λ is the wavelength, in metres.

Using this definition for photon momentum, Compton found that the conservation of momentum did hold for X-ray scattering collisions, as seen in **Figure 19** and expressed in the vector equation

$$\vec{p}_{photon} = \vec{p}'_{photon} + \vec{p}'_{electron}$$

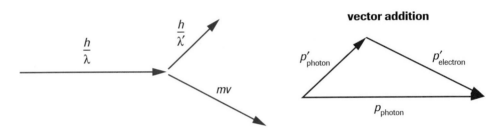

Figure 19
Law of conservation of momentum

Compton's experiments clearly demonstrated the particle-like aspects of light, for not only can a discrete energy, hf, be assigned to a photon, but also a value of momentum, $\dfrac{h}{\lambda}$. His work provided conclusive evidence for the photon theory of light. As a result, Compton was awarded the Nobel Prize for physics in 1927.

DID YOU KNOW ?

Energy in the Compton Effect
In the Compton effect, the energy of the incident X-ray photons is so high (5.0×10^4 eV) in comparison to the work function (<10 eV) that the work function is not considered in the energy calculations involved in the collision. In fact, most of the energy of the incident photon appears again in the "deflected" photon.

momentum of a photon defined as $p = \dfrac{h}{\lambda}$

DID YOU KNOW ?

Photon
The word "photon" is similar to the names given to various other particles: electron, proton, neutron.

> **SAMPLE problem 3**

What is the magnitude of the momentum of a photon with a wavelength of 1.2×10^{-12} m?

Solution

$\lambda = 1.2 \times 10^{-12}$ m

$h = 6.63 \times 10^{-34}$ J·s

$p = ?$

$$p = \frac{h}{\lambda}$$

$$= \frac{6.63 \times 10^{-34} \text{ J·s}}{1.2 \times 10^{-12} \text{ m}}$$

$$p = 5.5 \times 10^{-22} \text{ kg·m/s}$$

The magnitude of the momentum of the photon is 5.5×10^{-22} kg·m/s.

> ▶ *Practice*

Understanding Concepts

18. Show that the units of $\frac{h}{\lambda}$ are units of momentum.

19. Calculate the magnitude of the momentum of a photon whose wavelength is 5.00×10^2 nm.

20. Calculate the magnitude of the momentum of a photon whose frequency is 4.5×10^{15} Hz.

21. Calculate the magnitude of the momentum of a 1.50×10^2 eV photon.

22. Calculate the wavelength of a photon having the same momentum as an electron moving at 1.0×10^6 m/s.

Answers

19. 1.33×10^{-27} kg·m/s

20. 9.9×10^{-27} kg·m/s

21. 8.00×10^{-26} kg·m/s

22. 0.73 nm

> **LEARNING TIP**
>
> **Photon Pressure**
> If a surface is highly reflective, each photon undergoes twice as great a change in momentum as it would in absorption, and the radiation pressure on the surface is twice as great as the radiation pressure on an absorptive surface. This is analogous to comparing a bouncing ball with a chunk of sticky putty.

Interactions of Photons with Matter

If an intense beam of light is directed at the surface of an absorbing material, the energy of the photons is mostly absorbed by that surface. As a result, the surface heats up. But the Compton effect shows that photons transfer momentum as well. The sum of the impacts on the surface of all of the photons per unit of time results in pressure on the surface. This pressure is not normally discernible. (We do not feel the pressure of light when we walk out into sunlight or stand under a strong lamp.) Today, however, using very sensitive equipment, we can actually measure the pressure of light on a surface and confirm that the relationship $p = \frac{h}{\lambda}$ is a valid expression for the momentum of an individual photon.

We have seen, with both the photoelectric effect and the Compton effect, that when a photon comes into contact with matter, there is an interaction. Five main interactions are possible:

1. The most common interaction is simple reflection, as when photons of visible light undergo perfectly elastic collisions with a mirror.

2. In the case of the photoelectric effect, a photon may liberate an electron, being absorbed in the process.

3. In the Compton effect, the photon emerges with less energy and momentum, having ejected a photoelectron. After its interaction with matter, the photon still travels at the speed of light but is less energetic, having a lower frequency.

4. A photon may interact with an individual atom, elevating an electron to a higher energy level within the atom. In this case, the photon completely disappears. All of its energy is transferred to the atom, causing the atom to be in an energized, or "excited," state. (We will examine the details of this interaction later in this chapter.)

5. A photon can disappear altogether, creating two particles of nonzero mass in a process called **pair production** (see Section 13.1). Pair production requires a photon of very high energy (> 1.02 MeV) and, correspondingly, a very short wavelength (as with X-ray and gamma-ray photons). When such a photon collides with a heavy nucleus, it disappears, creating an electron ($_{-0}e$) and a particle of equal mass but opposite charge, the positron ($_{+0}e$) (**Figure 20**). This creation of mass from energy obeys Einstein's mass–energy equivalence equation $E = mc^2$.

pair production the creation of a pair of particles (an electron and a positron) as a result of a collision of a high-energy photon with a nucleus

before

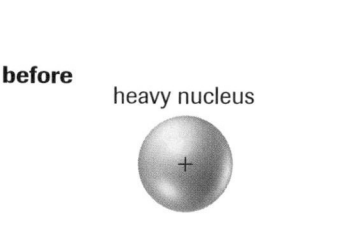

heavy nucleus

photon

after

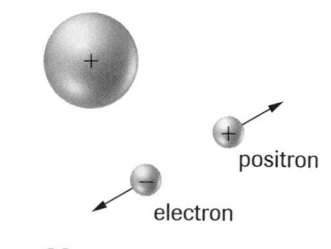

positron

electron

Figure 20
Representation of pair production

- A blackbody of a given temperature emits electromagnetic radiation over a continuous spectrum of frequencies, with a definite intensity maximum at one particular frequency. As the temperature increases, the intensity maximum shifts to progressively higher frequencies.

- Planck proposed that molecules or atoms of a radiating blackbody are constrained to vibrate at discrete energy levels, which he called quanta. The energy of a single quantum is directly proportional to the frequency of the emitted radiation, according to the relationship $E = hf$, where h is Planck's constant.

- Photoelectrons are ejected from a photoelectric surface when the incident light is above a certain frequency f_0, called the threshold frequency. The intensity (brightness) of the incoming light has no effect on the threshold frequency. The threshold frequency is different for different surfaces.

- The cutoff potential is the potential difference at which even the most energetic photoelectrons are prevented from reaching the anode. For the same surface the cutoff potential is different for each frequency, and the higher the frequency of the light, the higher the cutoff potential.

- The energy of light is transmitted in bundles of energy called photons, whose energy has a discrete, fixed amount, determined by Planck's equation, $E = hf$.

- When a photon hits a photoelectric surface, a surface electron absorbs its energy. Some of the absorbed energy releases the electron, and the remainder becomes its kinetic energy of the liberated electron, according to the photoelectric equation $E_K = hf - W$.

- In the Compton effect, high-energy photons strike a surface, ejecting electrons with kinetic energy and lower-energy photons. Photons have momentum whose magnitude is given by $p = \dfrac{h}{\lambda}$.

- Interactions between photons and matter can be classified into reflection, the photoelectric effect, the Compton effect, changes in electron energy levels within atoms, and pair production.

Section 12.1 Questions

Understanding Concepts

1. List the historical discoveries and interpretations that led to the confirmation of the photon theory of light.

2. Use Planck's quantum theory to suggest a reason why no photoelectrons are released from a surface until light of sufficiently high frequency is incident on the surface.

3. List at least five devices in your home that operate using the photoelectric effect.

4. State which physical quantities are represented by the symbols in the photoelectric equation $E_K = hf - W$.

5. Compare and contrast the photoelectric effect and the Compton effect.

6. Describe five interactions between photons and matter.

7. The average temperature in the visible incandescent layers of the Sun is about 6000 K. An incandescent light has a temperature of 2500 K.
   (a) Why do artificial sources of light not provide proper illumination when exposing a colour film designed to be used in sunlight?
   (b) Why does a xenon flash (operating at about 6000 K) provide proper illumination for the same daylight film?

8. Calculate the energy of an ultraviolet photon, of wavelength 122 nm, in both joules and electron volts.

9. The relationship $E = \dfrac{1.24 \times 10^3}{\lambda}$, where E is the energy of a photon in electron volts and λ is its wavelength in nanometres, is a handy form of the equation $E = \dfrac{hc}{\lambda}$. The relationship is quite useful in quantum-mechanics calculations, since many measurements with subatomic particles and photons involve electron volts and nanometres. Substitute in $E = \dfrac{hc}{\lambda}$, and make any necessary unit conversions, to show that $E = \dfrac{1.24 \times 10^3}{\lambda}$ is valid for nanometres and electron volts.

10. How does the pair of curves in **Figure 8(b)** show that the maximum speed of the photoelectrons is independent of the intensity of the light directed at the photoelectric surface?

11. Locate sodium and copper in **Table 1**. Does it take more energy to remove a photoelectron from sodium or from copper? Which has the higher threshold frequency, potassium or barium? Explain your answers.

12. Find the minimum frequency of the light required to eject photoelectrons from a metallic surface whose work function is 7.2×10^{-19} J.

13. What wavelength of light is required for ejecting photoelectrons from a tungsten surface ($W = 4.52$ eV) if the maximum kinetic energy of the electrons is 1.68 eV?

14. When light of wavelength of 482 nm falls onto a certain metallic surface, a retarding potential of 1.2 V proves just sufficient to make the current passing through the phototube fall to zero. Calculate the work function of the metal.

15. (a) Calculate the frequency of a photon whose wavelength is 2.0×10^{-7} m.
    (b) Calculate the energy of the same photon, in both joules and electron volts.
    (c) Calculate the momentum of the same photon.

16. (a) Calculate the momentum of a photon of wavelength 2.50×10^{-9} m.
    (b) Calculate the speed of an electron having the same momentum as the photon in (a). ($m_e = 9.11 \times 10^{-31}$ kg).
    (c) Calculate the kinetic energy of the electron. How does it compare with the energy of the photon?

17. Calculate, in electron volts, the energies of the photons emitted by radio stations of frequencies 5.70×10^2 kHz and 102 MHz.

Applying Inquiry Skills

18. Photosynthesis is the chemical change of carbon dioxide and water into sugar and oxygen, in the presence of light and chlorophyll. The graph in **Figure 21** shows that the rate of the reaction depends on the wavelength of the incident light. Using the photon theory and the graph, explain
    (a) why leaves containing chlorophyll appear green in white light

(b) why pure green light does not produce photosynthesis
(c) why an incandescent lamp, operating at 2500 K, does not produce sufficient photosynthesis to maintain the health of a green plant

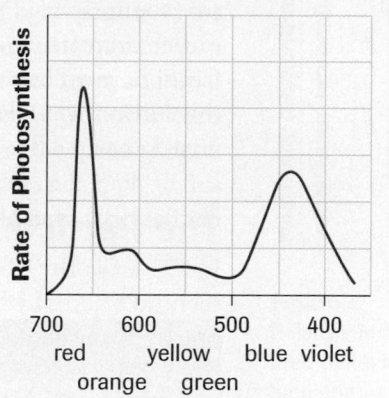

Figure 21
Rate of photosynthesis versus wavelength of incident light

Making Connections

19. Suggest some ways life would be different if Planck's constant were much larger or much smaller than its actual value.

20. A certain solar-powered calculator receives light with an average wavelength of 552 nm, converts 15% of the incoming solar energy into electrical energy, and consumes 1.0 mW of power. Calculate the number of light quanta needed by the calculator each second.

21. (a) Calculate the energy of a single microwave quantum of wavelength of 1.0 cm.
    (b) Calculate how many quanta of 1.0-cm microwave energy would be required to raise the temperature of 250.0 mL of water from 20°C to the boiling point, given that the specific heat capacity of water is 4.2×10^3 J/kg·°C.

22. Research the Internet to learn how astronomers use photodetectors on NASA's Hubble Space Telescope to produce galactic images such as the one at the beginning of Chapter 9.

GO   www.science.nelson.com

23. Ultraviolet light can kill skin cells, as it does when you are sunburned. Infrared light, also from the Sun, only warms skin cells. Explain this difference in behaviour using the photon theory.

The photoelectric effect and the Compton effect revealed that light and X rays have a particle nature; that is, photons act like particles with a given energy and momentum. In earlier chapters, however, we saw that for the properties of reflection, refraction, diffraction, interference, and polarization, electromagnetic radiation acts like a wave. In this section, we will see how quantum theory reconciles these two apparently opposing viewpoints.

The Particle Nature of Electromagnetic Waves

In 1910, Geoffrey Taylor, a young student at Cambridge University, set up an experiment to find out whether the interference patterns of light resulted from the interactions of many photons or whether the behaviour of individual photons could be predicted from their wave properties. The basic equipment he used is illustrated in **Figure 1(a)**.

Light from a small lamp passed first through a slit, then through a series of dimming filters, which reduced the intensity of the light. After passing through another single slit, the light was diffracted by a vertical needle, and the resulting image was recorded on a photographic plate (**Figure 1(b)**). Taylor adjusted the dimensions of the box and its contents so that diffraction bands around the shadow of the needle were plainly visible in bright light, without any filters. Then he reduced the intensity of light by adding filters. He found that progressively longer exposures were needed to get a well-exposed photographic plate, since fewer and fewer photons passed through the slit per second as he made his stack of dimming filters progressively thicker. Finally, Taylor made a very weak exposure that lasted three months. Even on this plate, the diffraction interference fringes were perfectly clear. By calculation, Taylor was able to show that with such a dim source, two or more photons would rarely, if ever, be in the box at the same time. In other words, the behaviour of a single photon was governed by the wave theory.

Figure 1
(a) Lightproof box
(b) Diffraction pattern created by a needle

(a)

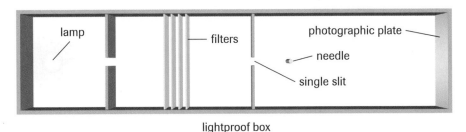

lightproof box

(b)

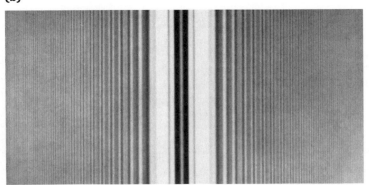

One way of visualizing the relationship between a photon and its electromagnetic wave is to consider that the electromagnetic wave acts as a "guide" that predicts the probable behaviour of the photon. The electromagnetic wave determines the chance, or probability, that a photon will be at a certain position in space at a given instant. For a classical particle the probability of being in certain places is either 100% (if it is there) or 0% (if it is not). We do not have this exactness for photons. We only know the probabilities determined by the electromagnetic wave. Quantum theory assumes that, at any instant, the photon has a probability of being in any position. The probability is greater in those regions where the amplitude of the electromagnetic wave interference pattern is greater and smaller in those regions where the amplitude of the electromagnetic wave interference pattern is smaller.

If an intense beam of light is directed through two adjacent slits, as in Young's experiment (Section 9.6), a series of alternating bands of constructive and destructive interference is created on the screen. The photons pass through the two slits, and it is the probability of their arrival on the screen that is predicted by their electromagnetic waves. If two electromagnetic waves interfere destructively, the amplitude is smaller than either of the original waves, so the probability of a photon arriving is reduced. When conditions are such that the resultant amplitude is zero, as it is on a nodal line, the probability of finding a photon is zero. On the other hand, if the two electromagnetic waves interfere constructively, the resultant amplitude is larger and the probability is high that a photon will be in that position; that is, a bright area is found.

If a photographic film replaces the screen, the particle nature of photons becomes evident. A photographic film may be constructed of plastic film on which has been deposited a thin layer of very small silver bromide crystals. Each photon absorbed by a silver bromide crystal gives up a fixed amount of energy, freeing the silver, and producing a bright area on the resulting picture (**Figure 2**). The electromagnetic wave gives the probability of its falling on any part of the film. However, since a photon's chance of registering in areas of constructive interference is high, many silver bromide crystals are

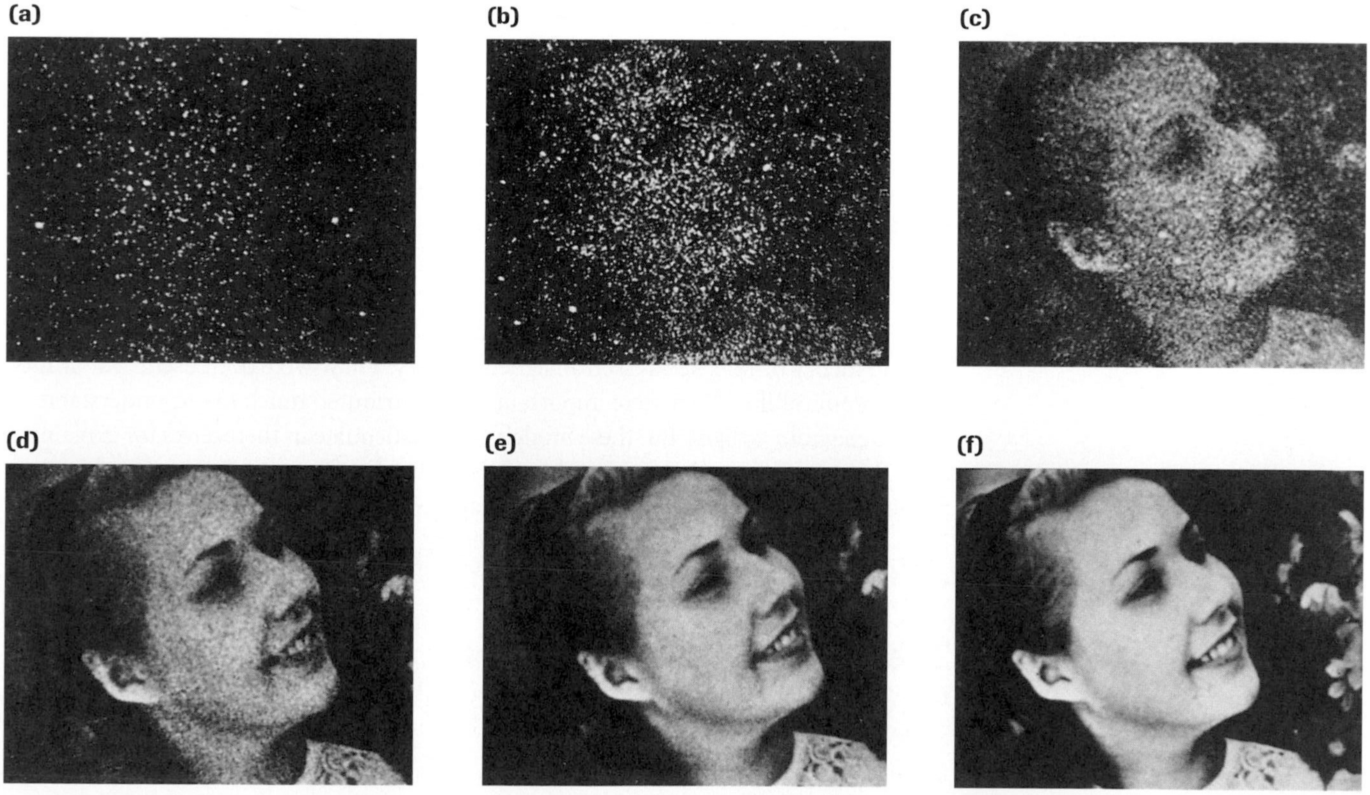

Figure 2
When a photograph is taken, the individual photons cause changes in the silver bromide molecules. As more and more photons strike the film, the image is gradually created. The number of photons applied to form each reproduction of the same image in this sequence of photos is as follows:
(a) 2×10^3 photons
(b) 1.2×10^4 photons
(c) 9.3×10^4 photons
(d) 7.6×10^5 photons
(e) 3.6×10^6 photons
(f) 2.8×10^7 photons

(a)

(b)

(c)

(d)

(e)

(f)

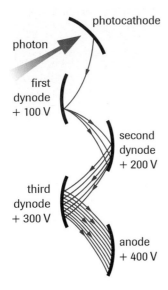

Figure 3
A photomultiplier is an instrument that takes a small amount of light energy and, using a series of electron-emitting surfaces, amplifies the signal many thousands of times. This is a three-stage photomultiplier.

wave–particle duality the property of electromagnetic radiation that defines its dual nature of displaying both wave-like and particle-like characteristics

changed in these areas, and a bright area will be recorded on the image. In areas of near-total destructive interference, fewer crystals are changed, and a relatively dark area will be recorded on the image. On the nodal lines, no crystals change at all.

Today, using a photomultiplier (**Figure 3**), photon experiments can be performed with much greater speed and sensitivity than in Geoffrey Taylor's time. By placing the photomultiplier at various locations in an interference pattern, the number of individual photons arriving at the photocathode can be measured. All the results point to the same conclusion: even though the photons arrive one at a time, their distribution on the detecting screen is predicted by their wave properties.

The experimental evidence forces us to conclude that light does not have just a wave nature but also the nature of a stream of particles: photons with momentum. Physicists refer to this dual nature as **wave–particle duality**.

The two aspects of light complement one another, and understanding both aspects is essential to having a full understanding of light. Niels Bohr (1885–1962), the great Danish physicist, partially clarified the situation by proposing his *principle of complementarity*:

Principle of Complementarity
To understand a specific experiment, one must use either the wave theory or the photon theory but not both.

To understand how light interferes after it passes through two parallel slits, we must use the wave theory, as illustrated in Young's experiment, not the particle theory. To understand the photoelectric effect or why a photographic plate is exposed as it is, we must use the photon, or particle nature of light, not the wave theory. As a general rule, when light passes through space or through a medium, its behaviour is best explained using its wave properties. But when light interacts with matter, its behaviour is more like that of a particle. The limitations of human experience make it difficult for us to understand the dual nature of light. It is very difficult, if not impossible, for us to visualize this duality. We are used to creating wave pictures, or images, in some applications and particle pictures in others, but never both at the same time.

In the study of light, particularly as it transfers energy from place to place, we must base our knowledge on indirect experiments. We cannot see directly how light energy is transmitted as a wave or a particle. All we can observe are the results of the interaction of light and matter. Our knowledge is limited to indirect information. Therefore, to describe light's dual nature, we cannot use visual means. Further study of quantum mechanics uses mathematical models, not visual models.

The wave–particle model of light that we use today is much more subtle than Newton's particle theory or Maxwell's electromagnetic theory. These were both useful but limited in their applicability. They were important and contributed much to our understanding of the behaviour of light. But these models were inadequate in themselves for explaining all of the properties of light. Like all models or theories, they can be enhanced or even replaced when new information becomes available. This is the case with the two classical theories of light. They have been superseded by the wave–particle model of light, the only theory that we find acceptable today for a full understanding of the nature of light.

The Wave Nature of Matter

In 1923, Louis de Broglie (**Figure 4**), a young graduate student at the University of Paris, proposed a radical idea: he hypothesized that since the momentum of a photon was given by the relationship $p = \dfrac{h}{\lambda}$, any particle with momentum might also be expected to have an associated wavelength. He further suggested that this wavelength could be determined from the Compton relationship as follows: if $p = \dfrac{h}{\lambda}$ for photons, then for particles having nonzero mass,

$$\lambda = \frac{h}{p} = \frac{h}{mv}$$

This wavelength is known as the **de Broglie wavelength**. Since the wavelength is associated with particles having nonzero mass, they have become known as **matter waves**. The concept was so radical at the time that de Broglie's graduation was held up for one year. (Since Einstein supported the hypothesis, de Broglie duly graduated, in 1924.) Before discussing the implications of his hypothesis, it is important to determine the magnitudes of the associated wavelengths of a macroscopic object and a subatomic particle.

Figure 4
Prince Louis-Victor de Broglie (1892–1987) originally applied his hypothesis to the special case of the electron, using it to analyze the energy levels in hydrogen (see Section 12.5). He was awarded the 1929 Nobel Prize in physics for his electron analysis.

▶ **SAMPLE** problem **1**

What de Broglie wavelength is associated with a 0.10 kg ball moving at 19.0 m/s?

de Broglie wavelength the wavelength associated with the motion of a particle possessing momentum of magnitude p: $\lambda = \dfrac{h}{p}$

matter waves the name given to wave properties associated with matter

Solution

$m = 0.10$ kg

$v = 19.0$ m/s

$\lambda = ?$

$$\lambda = \frac{h}{mv}$$

$$= \frac{6.63 \times 10^{-34} \text{ J·s}}{(0.10 \text{ kg})(19.0 \text{ m/s})}$$

$$\lambda = 3.5 \times 10^{-34} \text{ m}$$

The de Broglie wavelength of the ball is 3.5×10^{-34} m.

We see from this example that for macroscopic objects the wavelength is extremely small, even by subatomic standards (being a million-billion-billionth the approximate diameter of a typical atom).

▶ **SAMPLE** problem **2**

What de Broglie wavelength is associated with an electron that has been accelerated from rest through a potential difference of 52.0 V?

Solution

$m = 9.11 \times 10^{-31}$ kg

$\Delta V = 52.0$ V

$\lambda = ?$

$$\Delta V = \frac{\Delta E_e}{q}$$

$$\Delta E_e = q\Delta V$$

The loss of electric potential energy is equivalent to the gain in the electron's kinetic energy.

$$\Delta E_K = \Delta E_e$$

For an electron

$$E_K = e\Delta V$$

$$= (1.60 \times 10^{-19}\ C)(52.0\ J/C)$$

$$E_K = 8.32 \times 10^{-18}\ J$$

But $E_K = \frac{1}{2}mv^2$

$$v = \sqrt{\frac{2E_K}{m}}$$

$$= \sqrt{\frac{2(8.32 \times 10^{-18}\ J)}{9.11 \times 10^{-31}\ kg}}$$

$$v = 4.27 \times 10^6\ m/s$$

Then $\lambda = \frac{h}{mv}$

$$= \frac{6.63 \times 10^{-34}\ J\cdot s}{(9.11 \times 10^{-31}\ kg)(4.27 \times 10^6\ m/s)}$$

$$\lambda = 1.70 \times 10^{-10}\ m$$

The de Broglie wavelength of the electron is 1.70×10^{-10} m.

We see from this example that while for a low-momentum subatomic particle such as an electron the de Broglie wavelength is still small, it is no longer very small. For example, the diameter of a hydrogen atom is approximately 1.0×10^{-10} m, that is, *less* than the de Broglie wavelength associated with an electron. This is an issue of great importance, to which we will return in Section 12.5.

▶ Practice

Understanding Concepts

1. Calculate the de Broglie wavelength associated with each of the following:
   (a) a 2.0-kg ball thrown at 15 m/s
   (b) a proton accelerated to 1.3×10^5 m/s
   (c) an electron moving at 5.0×10^4 m/s

2. Calculate the associated wavelengths, in metres, of a 3.0-eV photon and a 5.0-eV electron.

3. Calculate the de Broglie wavelength associated with an artillery shell having a mass of 0.50 kg and a speed of 5.00×10^2 m/s.

4. Calculate the energy, in electron volts, required to give an electron an associated de Broglie wavelength of 0.15 nm.

5. An electron is accelerated through a potential difference of 1.00×10^2 V. Calculate the associated de Broglie wavelength.

6. (a) Calculate the momentum of an electron that has an associated de Broglie wavelength of 1.0×10^{-10} m.
   (b) Calculate the speed of the same electron.
   (c) Calculate the kinetic energy of the same electron.

Answers

1. (a) 2.2×10^{-35} m

   (b) 3.0×10^{-12} m

   (c) 1.5×10^{-8} m

2. 4.1×10^{-7} m; 5.5×10^{-10} m

3. 2.7×10^{-36} m

4. 67 eV

5. 1.23×10^{-10} m

6. (a) 6.6×10^{-24} kg·m/s

   (b) 7.3×10^6 m/s

   (c) 2.4×10^{-17} J, or 1.5×10^2 eV

Matter Waves

We saw in the preceding problems that the matter wavelengths of most ordinary objects, such as baseballs, are exceedingly small, even on atomic scales. We also saw that the matter wavelengths of objects such as electrons are small on macroscopic scales but appreciable on atomic scales (being comparable, in fact, with the wavelengths of some X rays). Recall that the wave nature of light was elusive until the time of Young because light has such short wavelengths. The matter wavelengths of macroscopic objects are so small they preclude detection. For subatomic particles, the matter wavelengths are still small enough to make detection challenging.

In 1927, two physicists in the United States, C.J. Davisson and L.H. Germer, showed that de Broglie's matter waves do exist. Earlier, in Britain, W.H. Bragg (1862–1942) and his son, W.L. Bragg (1890–1971), had developed equations that predicted the diffraction of X rays upon scattering by thin crystals. The intensity of the scattered radiation produced a maximum at a series of regularly spaced angles, as in **Figure 5(a)**. Davisson and Germer used the Bragg analysis to show that a beam of electrons could be diffracted in much the same way, thereby demonstrating the wavelike properties of particles. When they directed a beam of electrons at a single crystal of nickel, the observed diffraction pattern was in almost perfect agreement with calculations made using the de Broglie wavelength of the electrons. **Figure 5(b)** shows how the Davisson–Germer experiment gave convincing support to de Broglie's hypothesis.

Figure 5
The wave nature of photons and electrons
(a) X-ray diffraction due to a crystal of nickel
(b) Diffraction of electrons due to a gold film

(a)

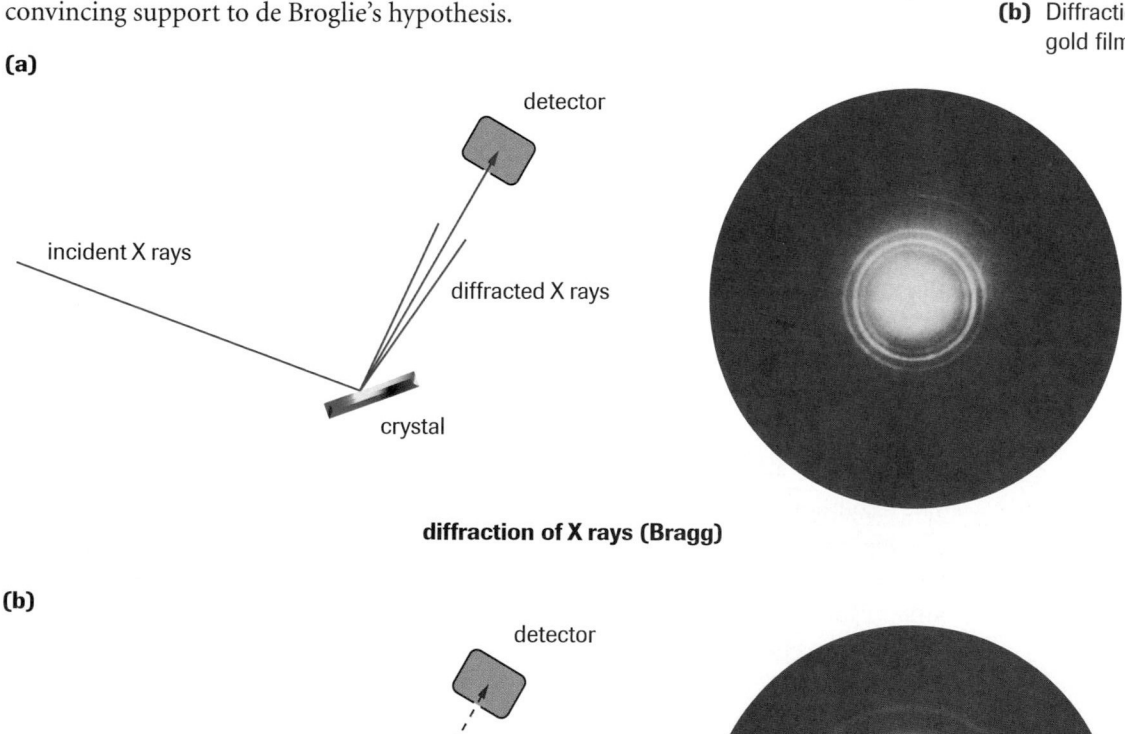

incident X rays

detector

diffracted X rays

crystal

diffraction of X rays (Bragg)

(b)

incident electrons

detector

diffracted electrons

crystal

diffraction of electrons (Davisson and Germer)

In the same year, 1927, G.P. Thomson, in Britain, passed a beam of electrons through a thin metal foil. The diffraction pattern was the same as for X rays, once the correct wavelength was taken into account. The Davisson–Germer and Thomson experiments left little doubt that particles exhibit wavelike properties. Later experiments using protons, neutrons, helium nuclei, and other particles produced similar results. **Quantum mechanics**, the mathematical interpretation of the structure and interactions of matter based on the concept that particles have a wave nature, was vindicated.

The wave–particle duality for small particles matched the wave–particle duality for the photon, as worked out by Compton. The principle of complementarity thus applies to matter as well as to radiation. We may now ask, as we did for light, under what general conditions does matter reveal its wavelike properties? Recall that for the wave property of diffraction to be evident in optics, an aperture comparable to the wavelength of light is needed. Otherwise, the light behaved like a beam of particles moving in a straight line through an opening or past an obstacle, showing little diffraction or interference. A similar requirement holds for matter waves.

Ordinary objects, such as baseballs, have associated matter waves whose wavelength is extremely short compared with the dimensions of other objects or openings that they encounter. Therefore, they act like particles, concealing their wave nature. Subatomic particles such as electrons, by contrast, have associated matter waves whose wavelength is of the same order of magnitude as the objects with which they interact. As a result, they produce diffraction patterns large enough to be observed.

What about the conceptual interpretation of matter waves? Like electromagnetic waves, matter waves predict the probability that a particle will follow a particular path through space. It is important to note that matter waves do not carry energy. They only predict behaviour. The particle carries the energy.

The fact that wave–particle duality exists for both matter and light reinforced Einstein's contention (Section 11.4) that mass is interconvertible with energy, under the relationship $E = mc^2$. By 1927, the concept that mass and energy were interrelated did not seem as astonishing as it had when Einstein proposed it in 1905. Furthermore, the wave characteristics of the electrons orbiting the nucleus of an atom could now be examined using quantum mechanics (see Section 12.5).

Electron Microscopes

The resolution of an ordinary microscope is limited by the wavelength of the light used. The highest useful magnification obtainable, with an oil-immersion objective, is 2000×, with the best resolution approximately 2.0×10^{-7} m (about one-half the wavelength of visible light). On the other hand, a beam of electrons having an associated de Broglie wavelength of less than 1.0 nm could produce a resolution of approximately 0.5 nm. This means that if one could get electrons to behave as light does in a microscope, the magnification could be increased to as high as 2 million times or more.

Technological developments in the 1920s that involved the focusing of electron beams by means of magnetic coils permitted the development of a crude electron microscope in Germany, in 1931. The first North American electron microscope, and the first of immediate practical application anywhere, was designed and built in the winter of 1937–38 by James Hillier (**Figure 6**) and Albert Prebus, two young graduate students at the University of Toronto. By the summer of 1938, they were producing microphotographs with a magnification of 20 000× and a resolution of 6.0 nm (30 atomic diameters). The electronics manufacturer RCA soon used their design in the first commercial electron microscope.

A **transmission electron microscope** is similar in operation to an ordinary light microscope, except that magnetic "lenses" replace the glass lenses (**Figure 7**). The magnetic "lenses" are constructed of circular electromagnetic coils that create strong magnetic fields. These fields exert forces on the moving electrons, focusing them in much the same way that a glass lens focuses light. Electrons emitted from a hot cathode filament are accelerated by an anode through an electrical potential of 50 kV to 100 kV or more. The electrons are focused into a parallel beam by a condensing lens before they pass through the specimen, or object, being imaged. For transmission to take place, the specimen must be very thin (approximately 20 to 50 nm); otherwise, the electrons would be slowed down too much or scattered, and the resulting image would be blurred.

Next, the beam of electrons passes through the objective coil and finally through the projector coil (corresponding to the eyepiece in an optical microscope). The beam is projected onto a fluorescent screen or photographic plate, creating a two-dimensional image of the specimen. Since the powerful beam of electrons can degrade the specimen, short exposure times are necessary. Further, it is necessary to operate the whole system of coils, beams, and specimen in a high vacuum, to avoid scattering of the electron beam by collisions with air molecules.

Figure 6
In this 1944 photograph, a young James Hillier (standing) demonstrates an early electron microscope at RCA Laboratories where he was a research engineer. When he retired in 1978, he was executive vice-president and senior scientist at RCA Labs. Born in Brantford, Ontario, he received his physics Ph.D. in 1941, from the University of Toronto. A generation later, more than 2000 electron microscopes, some capable of magnifying more than 2 million times, were in use in laboratories around the world.

(a)

(b)

light source

condenser lens

object

objective lens

image formed by objective lens

eyepiece (projection lens)

final image

screen or photographic plate

electron source

condenser coil

object

objective coil

image formed by objective coil

projector coil

final image

fluorescent screen or photographic plate

transmission electron microscope a type of microscope that uses magnetic lenses fashioned from circular electromagnetic coils creating strong magnetic fields

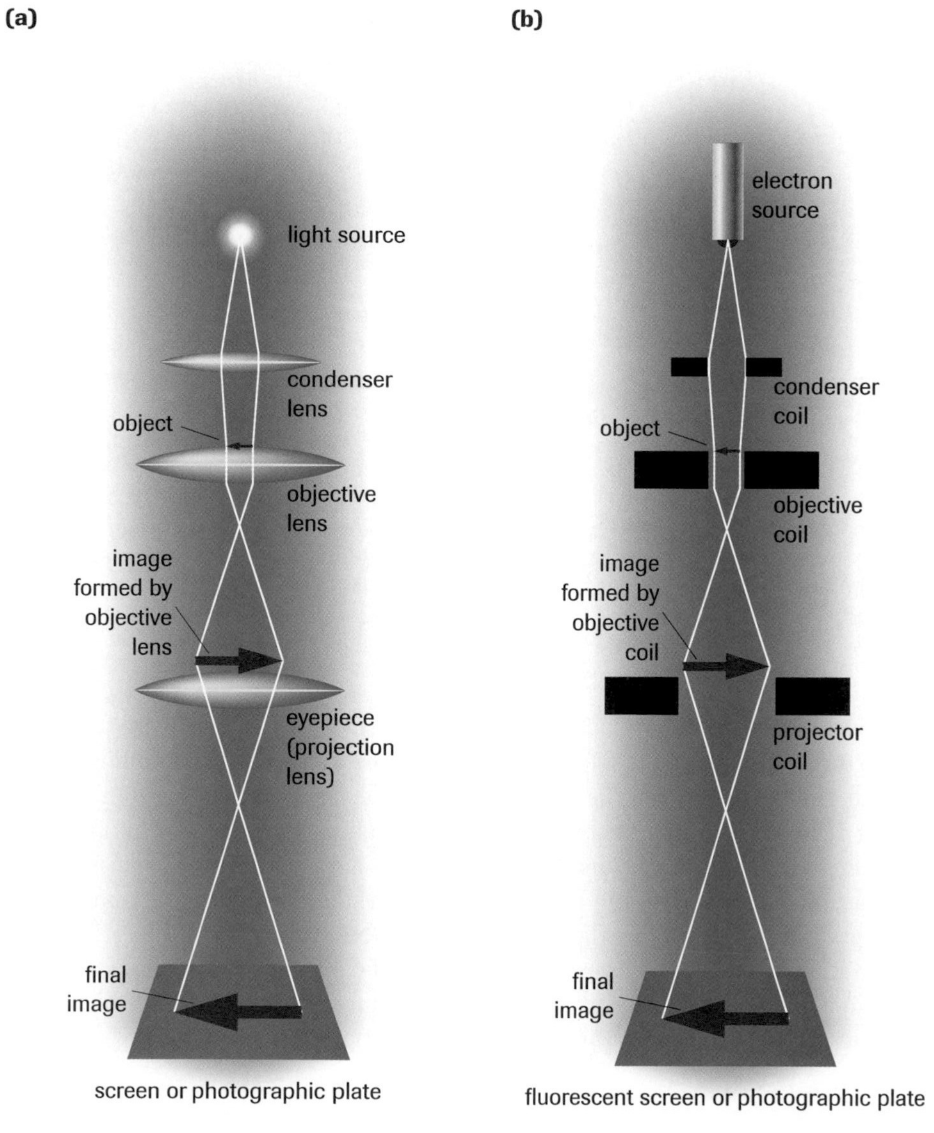

Figure 7
Design similarities of **(a)** a compound optical microscope and **(b)** an electron microscope. To help make the similarities evident, the optical microscope is depicted upside down.

scanning electron microscope a type of microscope in which a beam of electrons is scanned across a specimen

scanning tunnelling electron microscope a type of microscope in which a probe is held close to the surface of the sample; electrons "tunnel" between the sample and the probe, creating a current

Unlike the more traditional transmission electron microscope, with the **scanning electron microscope** three-dimensional, contoured images are possible. In this type of microscope, a carefully directed beam of electrons is moved across the specimen (**Figure 8(a)**). At each position on the specimen, the secondary electrons emitted from the surface are collected, controlling the intensity (brightness) of a picture element in a monitor. As a result, as the beam "sweeps" the specimen, a corresponding magnified, three-dimensional image is created on the monitor. Since the beam of electrons will damage a biological specimen, the time of exposure is generally limited. Further, it is usually necessary to coat the specimen with a thin layer of gold so that it does not accumulate negative charges from the electron beam. (Accumulated charge would repel the beam as it sweeps across the specimen, distorting the image.)

(a)

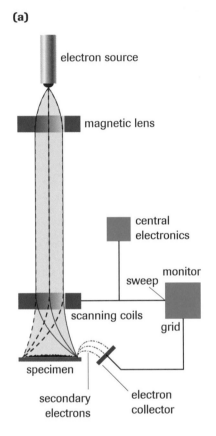

(b)

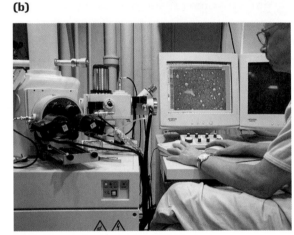

Figure 8
(a) Scanning electron microscope (SEM). Scanning coils move an electron beam back and forth across the specimen. The secondary electrons are collected. The resulting signal is used to modulate the beam in a monitor, producing an image.
(b) Operator using an SEM

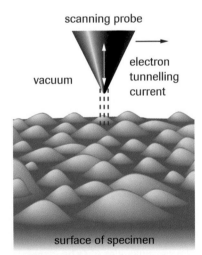

Figure 9
The tip of a probe in a scanning tunnelling electron microscope moves up and down to maintain a constant current, producing an image of the surface.

The **scanning tunnelling electron microscope** uses the tip of a probe, a few atoms thick, to scan very close to the specimen surface (**Figure 9**). During the scanning, a small potential difference between the tip and the surface causes surface electrons to leave, creating a current through the probe in a process called "tunnelling." This current is used to create a three-dimensional image, recording surface features as fine as the size of atoms. In fact, the images can actually "picture" the distribution of electrons; one of the images in **Figure 10** shows the structure of the DNA molecule.

Electron microscopes have extended the frontiers of research in the microscopic world. Although biological specimens produce some of the most dramatic images, microscopy of atomic and molecular structure holds even greater promise.

(a)

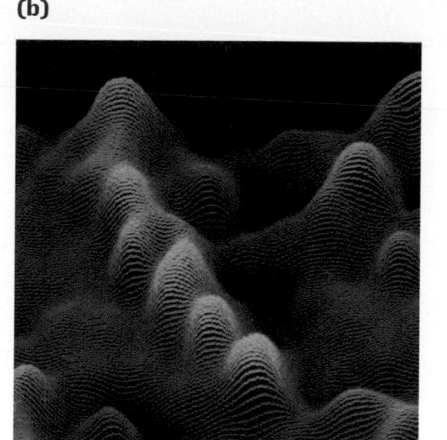

(b)

(c)

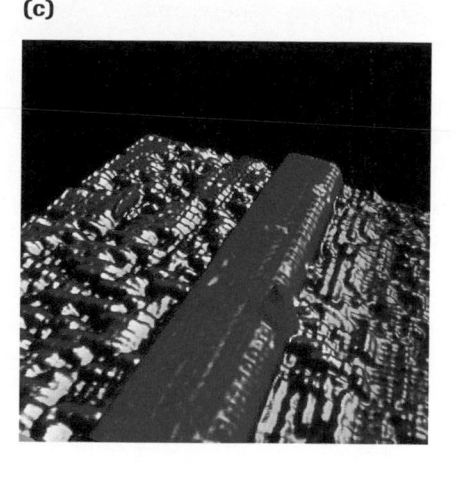

Figure 10
False-coloured images from a scanning tunnelling microscope
(a) Atoms and electron bonds in a crystal of silicon. The black spots are the individual silicon atoms in a single "unit cell." The bright regions between them show the position of electron bonds that hold the structure together.
(b) A strand of DNA
(c) This nanowire, just 10 atoms wide, could be used in a computer operating at the limits of miniturization. The wire is made of a rare-earth metal (lanthanide) combined with silicon.

SUMMARY *Wave–Particle Duality*

- The behaviour of a single photon was predicted by the wave theory. The electromagnetic wave predicts the probability that a photon will register at a certain position on a detecting surface at a given instant.

- Light is not just a wave and not just a particle but exhibits a "wave–particle duality."

- Understanding both the wave and the particle properties of light is essential for a complete understanding of light; the two aspects of light complement each other.

- When light passes through space or through a medium, its behaviour is best explained using its wave properties; when light interacts with matter, its behaviour is more like that of a particle.

- The wave–particle model of light has superseded Newton's particle theory and Maxwell's electromagnetic theory, incorporating elements of both.

- A particle of nonzero mass has a wavelike nature, including a wavelength λ, found by de Broglie to equal $\dfrac{h}{mv}$.

- Matter wavelengths of most ordinary objects are very small and thus unnoticeable.

- Matter waves predict the probability that a particle will follow a particular path through space. The diffraction of electrons revealed these wave characteristics.

- Electron microscopes use the principles of quantum mechanics and matter waves to achieve very high magnifications, in some cases exceeding 2 million times.

Understanding Concepts

1. Describe one type of evidence for
   (a) the wave nature of matter
   (b) the particle nature of electromagnetic radiation

2. Explain how the equations for single-slit diffraction can be used to predict the behaviour of a photon passing through a single slit.

3. Compare and contrast a 2-eV electron and a 2-eV photon, citing at least four properties of each.

4. Calculate the associated de Broglie wavelength of
   (a) a neutron travelling at 1.5×10^4 m/s
       $(m_n = 1.67 \times 10^{-27}$ kg$)$
   (b) an electron travelling at 1.2×10^6 m/s
       $(m_e = 9.11 \times 10^{-31}$ kg$)$
   (c) a proton with kinetic energy 1.0×10^9 eV
       $(m_p = 1.67 \times 10^{-27}$ kg$)$

5. An electron beam in a certain electron microscope has electrons with individual kinetic energies of 5.00×10^4 eV. Calculate the de Broglie wavelength of such electrons.

6. Calculate the momentum and the equivalent mass of a 0.20 nm X-ray photon. (This does not imply a photon has mass!)

7. A certain microscopic object has a speed of 1.2×10^5 m/s. Its associated de Broglie wavelength is 8.4×10^{-14} m. Calculate its mass.

8. What would the slit width have to be before the matter wave effects would be noticeable for a 5.0-eV electron passing through the single slit?

9. A proton emerges from a Van de Graaff accelerator with a speed that is 25.0% the speed of light. Assuming, contrary to fact, that the proton can be treated nonrelativistically, calculate
   (a) the associated de Broglie wavelength
   (b) the kinetic energy
   (c) the potential difference through which the proton was accelerated if it started essentially from rest

10. In a television picture tube, electrons are accelerated essentially from rest through an appreciable anode-cathode potential difference. Just before an electron strikes the screen, its associated de Broglie wavelength is 1.0×10^{-11} m. Calculate the potential difference.

Making Connections

11. Research the use of tunnelling electron microscopes to determine the electron distribution in atoms. Write a short report on your findings.

 www.science.nelson.com

12. Research electron microscopes and find out what precautions are necessary to protect the sample from damage.

 www.science.nelson.com

13. In Sections 12.1 and 12.2 you read about two significant accomplishments by Canadian scientists: Willard Boyle and the CCD, and James Hillier and the first commercial electron microscope. Choose one of these Canadian scientists (or another of your choosing who has contributed to modern physics), and prepare a summary that includes biographical information, the technology, background to the development of the technology, the physics behind it, and how it contributed to the respective field(s) of science and to society. Your summary can be in the form of a research paper, a web site, or a pamphlet designed to sell the technology.

 www.science.nelson.com

As early as 400 B.C., the Greek philosopher Democritus theorized that matter was composed of tiny, indivisible particles called atoms (*atomos* is Greek for "uncuttable"). His theory was based on philosophical reasoning rather than on experiment. Laboratory evidence for the existence of atoms was not found until much later, early in the nineteenth century, by the British chemist John Dalton (1766–1844). Dalton proposed that atoms are like tiny, solid, billiard balls, capable of joining together into small, whole-numbered combinations to produce various compounds. Some clue to the internal structure of the atom was provided around the turn of the twentieth century by J.J. Thomson, who suggested that the atom was a sphere of positive charge with negative electrons embedded throughout it, like raisins in a bun. By this time, physicists were convinced that the atom did have internal structure, and they were busy finding ways to reveal it.

Our modern concept of the structure of the atom relies heavily on the detective work of Ernest Rutherford (**Figure 1**) in the early years of the twentieth century, culminating in his 1911 proposal of an atomic model.

By the end of the nineteenth century, it was known that the negative charge in an atom is carried by its electrons, whose mass is only a very small fraction of the total atomic mass. It followed, then, that the rest of the atom should contain an equal amount of positive charge (the atom was known to be neutral) and most of the mass. But how are mass and positive charge distributed within the atom?

A possible answer lay in a creative experiment proposed by Rutherford, when he was director of the research laboratory at the University of Manchester. His associates, Hans Geiger and Eric Marsden, performed the experiment between 1911 and 1913. The essence of their experimental technique was to show how small, high-speed particles could be scattered by the unknown internal structure of the atom.

A simple example illustrates the principles in a scattering experiment. Imagine that we are given a large black box, of known size and mass, but are unable to see how mass is distributed inside it. The box might be completely filled with some substance of uniform density, such as wood. It might, on the other hand, be filled with a mixture of inflated balloons and steel ball bearings. How can we determine which model best represents the actual distribution of mass within the box?

We could shoot a stream of bullets into the box, all with the same speed and in the same direction. If all the bullets were to emerge in the same direction, with only a slightly reduced speed, we would believe the box to be filled with some uniform, low-density substance (like wood), incapable of causing the bullets to change direction (i.e., to scatter), but able to just slow them down slightly. On the other hand, if we found that while most of the bullets had emerged from the box with their original speed and direction, a few had emerged with drastic deflections, we would conclude that these few had bounced off some small, very dense, widely dispersed material in their paths. Then, by studying the distribution of bullets scattered by the box (in both direction and speed), it would be possible to learn much about the distribution of mass within the box.

The Rutherford Experiment

Rutherford proposed using high-speed α particles from a radioactive polonium source as the bullets and a very thin sheet of gold foil as the black box. **Figure 2** shows his experimental setup.

Figure 1
Ernest Rutherford (1871–1937). After studying at the University of New Zealand, Rutherford went to Cambridge University, working under J.J. Thomson. He began his work on α-particle scattering while at McGill University, Montreal (1898–1907), and continued it when he returned to the University of Manchester in 1907. He received the 1908 Nobel Prize in chemistry for his work in radioactivity and was knighted in 1914. He returned to Cambridge in 1919 as professor of physics.

A narrow beam of α particles was created by a hole drilled in a lead shield (called a collimator) surrounding the polonium. These α particles struck a very thin sheet of gold foil within a vacuum chamber. (The thinnest gold foil available to Rutherford was about 10^{-7} m thick. Even such a thin foil contains about 400 layers of gold atoms.) After being scattered by the gold foil, the α particles were detected by a scintillation counter placed at an angle θ to the beam. The scintillation counter was a screen coated with a thin zinc sulphide film. When an α particle struck this screen, a tiny flash of light, or scintillation, is given off by the zinc sulphide and observed through a microscope. The experiment consisted of moving the scintillation counter through all possible values of θ from 0° to nearly 180° and counting the number of α particles detected at each scattering angle θ (**Figure 2(b)**).

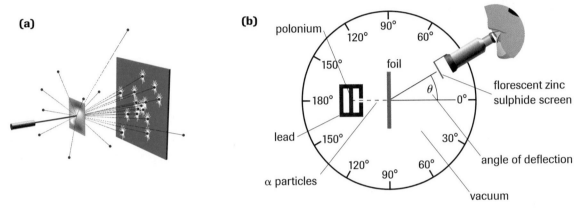

(a)

(b)

Figure 2
Rutherford's experimental setup
(a) When α particles strike a metallic foil, some are deflected.
(b) The scintillation screen is used to count the scattered α particles.

Geiger and Marsden performed their scattering experiments with great care for nearly two years. In 1913, they were able to report the following results:

1. The great majority of α particles passed through the gold foil with virtually no deviation from their original path.

2. Very few α particles were scattered through sizable angles (with only 1 in 10 000 deflected by more than 10°).

3. In extremely rare cases, an α particle was deflected by nearly 180°, back along its original path.

4. After a period of exposure to the beam, the foil acquired a positive charge.

In interpreting these results, Rutherford formulated a model of atomic structure, using classical mechanics that includes the following features:

1. The greatest proportion of an atom's volume is empty space.

This would account for the observation that most α particles passed through this great volume of empty space and were undeflected.

2. The atom has a positively charged, very small but extremely dense central region—the nucleus—containing all of the atom's positive charge and most of its mass.

Rutherford reasoned that the force of electric repulsion from this small, positive nucleus deflected a positive α particle only when it very closely approached the nucleus. Since so very few particles were deflected by any appreciable angle, the nucleus must be so small that most α particles did not approach it closely enough to be deflected. This would account for the observation that most α particles passed through this great volume of empty space and were undeflected.

3. The greatest proportion of an atom's volume is empty space and, within this empty space, a number of very light, negatively charged electrons move in orbits around the nucleus.

As the α particles passed undeflected through the empty space of the atom, occasionally one of them would encounter an electron, capture it by the force of electrostatic attraction, and move on, essentially undeflected by the very slight mass of the acquired electron. The gold atom, having lost an electron, would now be a positive ion.

How did the electrons in the vicinity of the nucleus, uncaptured by an incoming α particle, behave? Rutherford suggested that those electrons were moving around the positive nucleus, held in orbit by the force of electric attraction, much like planets moving around the Sun under the influence of gravity. (If the electrons were at rest, they would be captured by the nucleus, neutralizing it and making it incapable of deflecting α particles.)

As a result of these assumptions, Rutherford's model became known as the "planetary model." With a few modifications and additional features, it is roughly how we view the atom today (**Figure 3**).

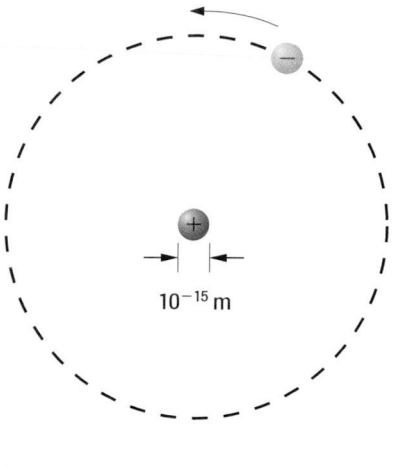
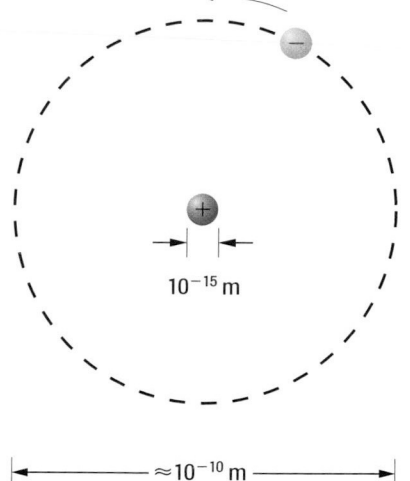

Figure 3
Rutherford's model of the atom (not to scale). Electrons orbit a very small positive nucleus.

Information from α-Particle Scattering Experiments

Rutherford and his colleagues continued to analyze α-particle scattering closely and were able to reach further conclusions regarding atomic structure.

1. The Trajectory of the α Particles

Rutherford started by asking what force was acting between the stationary gold nucleus and the incoming α particle causing it to be scattered. He knew that α particles are positively charged. His model suggested that all of the atom's positive charge was concentrated within the nucleus. He hypothesized that the force causing the scattering was electrostatic repulsion between the α particle and the nucleus as given by Coulomb's law. Thus, the magnitude of the force is inversely proportional to the square of the distance between the α particle and the nucleus: $F = \dfrac{kq_1q_2}{r^2}$.

It was then necessary to obtain some experimental evidence that this assumption about the Coulomb force was valid. Using mathematics beyond the scope of this book, Rutherford showed that the path taken by any incoming α particle, in the presence of a Coulomb force field, must be a hyperbola, with the initial and final directions of the α particle representing its asymptotes and the nucleus at one of its foci. **Figure 4** depicts some of these hyperbolic paths, showing that the eccentricity (amount of bending) of each hyperbola depends on the distance of the initial path to the line of direct hit.

Geiger and Marsden confirmed that, within experimental limits, their scattering force obeyed Coulomb's law. It is of great importance in understanding atomic structure to know that Coulomb's law applies to the electric force between small charged particles even at subatomic distances.

2. The Charge on the Nucleus

The explanation we have used to account for the scattering of α particles by gold nuclei could apply equally well to any other nucleus. Other nuclei would differ from gold nuclei in only two respects: mass and charge. Since Rutherford assumed that the scattering nucleus was essentially fixed in position, a nucleus of a different mass would have no significant effect on the trajectory of the α particle. A different nuclear charge would, however, affect the magnitude of the Coulomb force experienced by the incoming

LEARNING TIP

Simulation Software
There is software available that can simulate α-particle scattering.

GO ▸ www.science.nelson.com

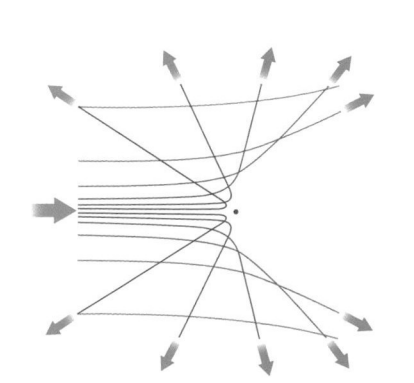

Figure 4
The scattering of α particles by an atomic nucleus: the closer the incoming α particle is to the line of direct hit, the larger the scattering.

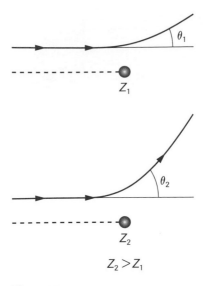

Figure 5
The charge on the nucleus affects the scattering angle of the α particle.

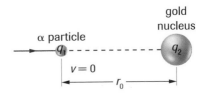

Figure 6

α particle and, hence, would affect the scattering angle. **Figure 5** shows how two α particles of the same energy are scattered by two different nuclei, of charges Z_1 and Z_2. (The charge on a nucleus, represented by Z, is its atomic number—79 in the case of gold.)

In the example shown, Z_2 is greater than Z_1, causing a stronger force to be exerted on the α particle, leading to a greater deflection. Detailed computations, based on Newton's laws of motion and Coulomb's law and taking into account the geometry of the scattering interaction, showed that the number of α particles scattered at a given angle θ is proportional to the square of the nuclear charge Z^2. These results were verified experimentally by comparing the scattering data when α particles of the same energy were fired at foils composed of different atoms.

3. The Size of the Nucleus

The fact that an occasional α particle can be stopped by a gold nucleus and returned along its initial path provides us with a way of estimating an upper limit for the size of the nucleus.

Alpha particles come closest to a nucleus when aimed directly at its centre. An α particle of mass m, charge q_1, and speed v_0, a very great distance away from a stationary nucleus of mass m_{nucleus} and charge q_2, has only kinetic energy, given by

$$E_{K0} = \frac{1}{2}mv_0^2$$

As the particle approaches the nucleus, it encounters the electric field of the nucleus, thereby losing kinetic energy and gaining electric potential energy E_E. However, the total energy E_{K0} of the particle remains constant at any point along its hyperbolic path:

$$E_{\text{total}} = E_K + E_E = E_{K0} \quad \text{(constant)}$$

An α particle making a direct hit will be brought to rest a distance r_0 from the nucleus, at which point all of its energy will have been momentarily converted from kinetic energy into electric potential energy (**Figure 6**).

To determine that position, r_0, we begin with the equation

$$E_{\text{total}} = E_E = E_{K0} = \frac{1}{2}mv_0^2$$

But for two charges, q_1 and q_2, a distance r_0 apart, so that

$$E_E = \frac{kq_1q_2}{r_0}$$

$$\frac{kq_1q_2}{r_0} = \frac{1}{2}mv_0^2$$

$$r_0 = \frac{2kq_1q_2}{mv_0^2}$$

A polonium source produces α particles with a speed of 1.6×10^7 m/s. The charge and mass of an α particle are 3.2×10^{-19} C and 6.6×10^{-27} kg, respectively. The charge on a gold nucleus, of atomic number 79, is $+79e$, or 1.3×10^{-17} C. Therefore,

$$r_0 = \frac{2(9.0 \times 10^9 \text{ N·m}^2/\text{C}^2)(3.2 \times 10^{-19} \text{ C})(1.3 \times 10^{-17} \text{ C})}{(6.6 \times 10^{-27} \text{ kg})(1.6 \times 10^7 \text{ m/s})^2}$$

$$r_0 = 4.2 \times 10^{-14} \text{ m}$$

This represents the closest distance at which an α particle moving with an initial speed of 1.6×10^7 m/s can approach a gold nucleus and thus serves as an upper limit for the radius of the gold nucleus. If the nucleus were any larger than 4.2×10^{-14} m, the α particle would make a contact collision, and the scattering would not conform to the predictions based on Coulomb's law.

Other measurements of the distance between adjacent gold atoms yield a value of about 2.5×10^{-10} m. This gives a value for the atomic radius of about 1.2×10^{-10} m. We can therefore calculate the ratio of the volume of the gold atom to the volume of its nucleus:

$$\frac{V_{atom}}{V_{nucleus}} = \left(\frac{r_{atom}}{r_{nucleus}}\right)^3$$

$$= \left(\frac{1.2 \times 10^{-10} \text{ m}}{4.2 \times 10^{-14} \text{ m}}\right)^3$$

$$\frac{V_{atom}}{V_{nucleus}} = 2.3 \times 10^{10}$$

In everyday terms, if the nucleus were the size of the head of a straight pin (about 1 mm in diameter), the atom would be about the size of small car.

SUMMARY   *Rutherford's Model of the Atom*

- The α-scattering experiment revealed that the great majority of α particles passed straight through the gold foil; only a few α particles were scattered by sizable angles; a very few were deflected by 180°.

- Rutherford's model proposed that the atom consists of a small, extremely dense positive nucleus that contains most of its mass; the atom's volume is mostly empty space; and the Coulomb force holds the electrons in orbit.

- Further work on α scattering revealed that Coulomb's law, $F_e = \dfrac{kq_1q_2}{r^2}$, applies

  to the electric force between small charged particles even at distances smaller than the size of atoms; the positive charge on the nucleus is the same as the atomic number.

▶ *Section 12.3* *Questions*

Understanding Concepts

1. What does the α-particle scattering pattern indicate about the nucleus of an atom?

2. According to Rutherford's planetary model of the atom, what keeps electrons from flying off into space?

3. Calculate the ratio of the gravitational force between the proton and electron of a hydrogen atom to the electrical force between them for an orbital radius of 5.3×10^{-11} m. Are either of the forces negligible? Explain your answer.

4. Calculate the closest distance a 4.5-MeV α particle, of mass 6.6×10^{-27} kg, can approach a fixed gold nucleus, of charge $+79e$.

5. Calculate the ratio of the distances an α particle of a given energy can approach an aluminum nucleus ($Z_{Al} = 13$) and a gold nucleus ($Z_{Au} = 79$).

Applying Inquiry Skills

6. Describe how you could use disc magnets (with N-poles on the top surface) to simulate Rutherford's gold foil experiment in two dimensions. Describe limitations of the simulation.

Making Connections

7. Rutherford was recognized early in his career for his outstanding skills as an experimentalist and for his ability to inspire and stimulate those around him. Two examples are his relationships with Frederick Soddy while at McGill University and with Hans Geiger while at the University of Manchester. Research Rutherford's life on the Internet or using other sources, and report on how these personal skills enabled Rutherford and his colleagues to accomplish so much.

 www.science.nelson.com

Long before Rutherford proposed his planetary model for atomic structure, it was known that matter, when heated intensely, gives off light. Solids, liquids, and very dense gases gave off light with a continuous spectrum of wavelengths. On the other hand, the light emitted when a high voltage was applied to a rarefied gas was quite different. The special behaviour of incandescent rarefied gases, studied for half a century before Rutherford, was now to provide a valuable clue to the structure of the atom.

continuous spectrum a spectrum showing continuous (not discrete) changes in intensity

emission spectrum a spectrum that a substance emits with its own specific set of characteristic frequencies

The **continuous spectrum**, such as that from white light, usually originates from a heated solid and results from the interactions between each atom or molecule and its close-packed neighbours. By contrast, in a hot, rarefied gas, the atoms are far enough apart to ensure that any light emitted comes from individual, isolated atoms. It is for this reason that an analysis of the light emitted by a rarefied gas provides a clue to the structure of the gas atoms themselves.

As early as the beginning of the nineteenth century, it was known that the radiation from electrically "excited" gases was discrete rather than continuous; that is, an excited gas gives off only specific frequencies of light. When this light is passed through a spectroscope, a *bright-line emission spectrum* is observed, containing lines of light of the various frequencies given off by that gas. Each gas emits its own specific set of characteristic frequencies, called its **emission spectrum**, making spectroscopy a particularly accurate method for identifying elements (**Figure 1**).

Figure 1
(a) Schematic of a gas discharge tube
(b) Hydrogen is the gas used in this discharge tube.

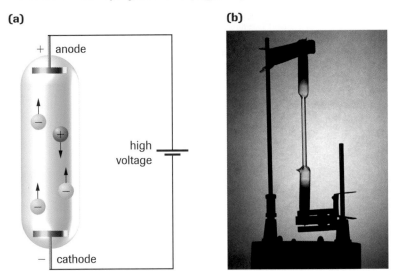

For example, if a sample of hydrogen gas under low pressure in a vacuum tube is excited by a high electric potential applied between electrodes at the ends of the tube, a pink-purple glow is produced. If this pink-purple light is passed through a spectroscope (Section 10.3), it is found to consist of numerous discrete wavelengths. Four of these are visible in the ordinary school laboratory in the red, blue–green, blue, and violet parts of the spectrum. An additional ten or so lines in the near ultraviolet are discernible by photography with a modest spectrograph. **Figure 2** shows the formation of a typical emission spectrum and the apparatus needed to create it. **Figure 3(a)** shows the visible line spectra of three gases.

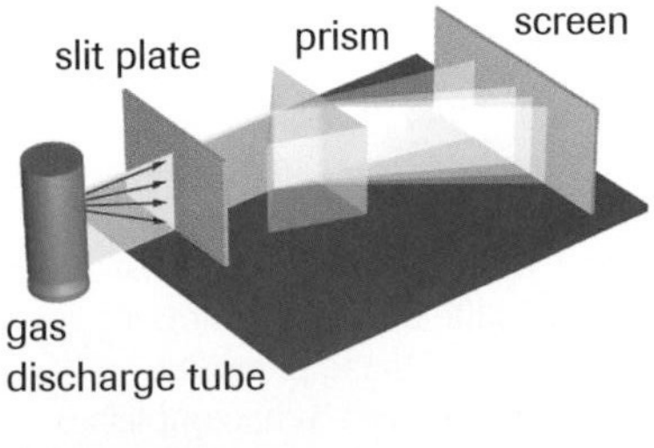

Figure 2
Apparatus used to produce an emission spectrum

A still more extensive examination of the hydrogen emission spectrum, using photographic film sensitive to infrared and far ultraviolet radiation, would reveal that it also contains a number of frequencies in these regions of the electromagnetic spectrum.

It can also be shown that if white light is allowed to pass through a gas, and the transmitted light is analyzed with a spectroscope, dark lines of missing light are observed in the continuous spectrum at exactly the same frequencies as the lines in the corresponding emission spectrum. This so-called **absorption spectrum** is created by light absorbed from the continuous spectrum as it passes through the gas (**Figure 3(b)**).

absorption spectrum the lines of missing colour in a continuous spectrum, at the same frequencies as would be emitted by an incandescent gas of the same element

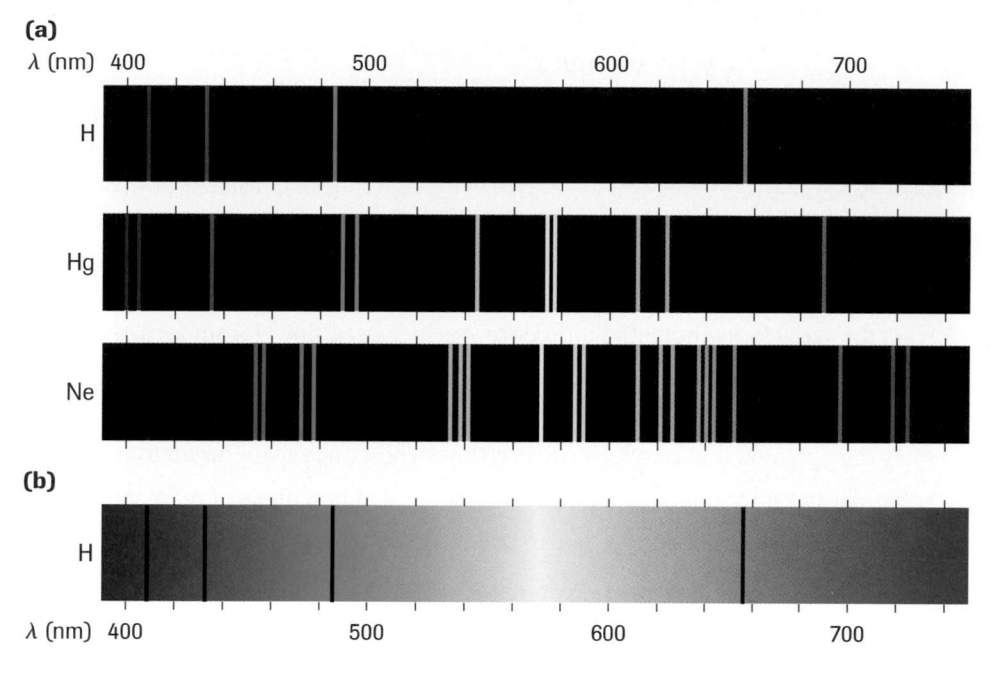

(a)

(b)

Figure 3
Visible spectra
(a) Line spectra produced by emissions from hydrogen, mercury, and neon
(b) Absorption spectrum for hydrogen. The dark absorption lines occur at the same wavelengths and frequencies as the emission lines for hydrogen in **(a)**.

It is evident that atoms absorb light of the same frequencies as they emit. Our model of the atom must be capable of explaining why atoms only emit and absorb certain discrete frequencies of light; in fact, it should be able to predict what these frequencies are. Since Rutherford's planetary model made no attempt to account for discrete emission and absorption spectra, modifications were needed.

The Franck–Hertz Experiment

In 1914, a team of two German physicists, James Franck and Gustav Hertz (**Figure 4**), provided another significant contribution to our understanding of atomic structure. They devised an experiment to investigate how atoms absorb energy in collisions with fast-moving electrons.

(a)   **(b)**

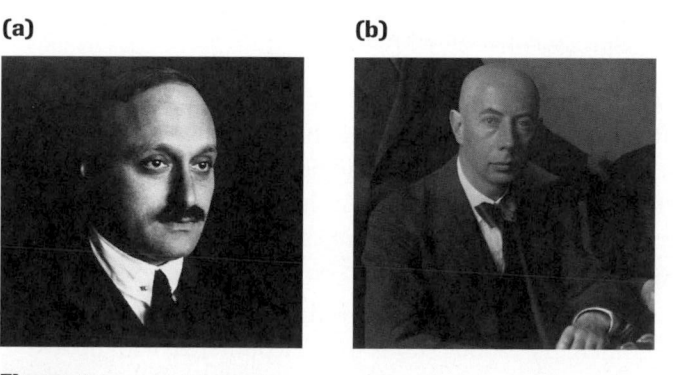

Figure 4
(a) James Franck (1882–1964) and **(b)** Gustav Hertz (1887–1975) received the 1925 Nobel Prize in physics. When the Nazis came to power in Germany, Franck was forced to flee to the United States. In order to carry his gold Nobel Prize medal with him, he dissolved it in a bottle of acid. He later precipitated the metal and recast it.

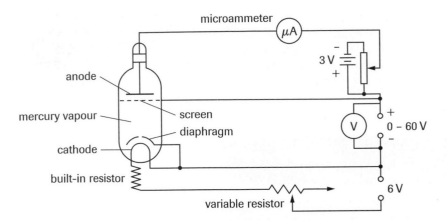

Figure 5
Apparatus used by Franck and Hertz to determine how atoms absorb energy

Franck and Hertz used an apparatus similar to that shown in **Figure 5**. Free electrons emitted from a cathode were accelerated through low-pressure mercury vapour by a positive voltage applied to a wire screen anode, or "grid." Most of the electrons missed this screen and were collected by a plate maintained at a slightly lower voltage. These collected electrons constituted an electric current, measured by a sensitive ammeter.

The experiment consisted of measuring the electric current for various accelerating electrical potential differences. Franck and Hertz found the following:

- As the accelerating potential difference was increased slowly from zero, the current increased gradually as well.
- At a potential of 4.9 V, the current dropped dramatically, almost to zero.
- As the potential was increased further, the current once again began to increase.
- Similar but minor decreases in current occurred at potentials of 6.7 V and 8.8 V.
- Another significant decrease in current occurred at a potential of 9.8 V.

A graph of collected current transmitted through the mercury vapour versus electron accelerating potential difference is shown in **Figure 6**.

Figure 6
Collected current versus accelerating potential difference

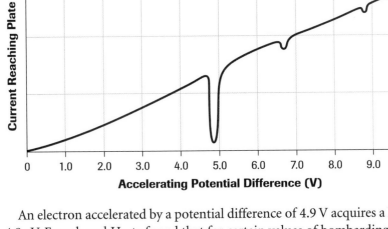

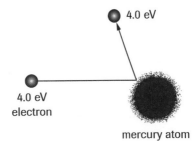

Figure 7
An incident electron with kinetic energy less than 4.9 eV bounces off the mercury atom with no loss of kinetic energy.

An electron accelerated by a potential difference of 4.9 V acquires a kinetic energy of 4.9 eV. Franck and Hertz found that for certain values of bombarding-electron kinetic energy (4.9 eV, 6.7 eV, 8.8 eV, 9.8 eV, ...) the electrons did not pass through the mercury vapour and contribute to the measured plate current. At these specific values, the electrons lost their kinetic energy to collisions with mercury vapour atoms.

Franck and Hertz proposed an explanation that was simple yet elegant:

- Whenever the kinetic energy of the incident electrons was less than 4.9 eV, they simply bounced off any mercury vapour atoms they encountered, with no loss of kinetic energy, and continued on as part of the current (**Figure 7**). These were elastic collisions with little loss of energy from the electrons, so they still passed between the screen wires, reaching the plate.

- Those electrons with a kinetic energy of 4.9 eV that collided with a mercury atom transferred all their kinetic energy to the mercury atom (**Figure 8**). With no energy remaining, they did not reach the plate, being instead drawn to the positive wire screen.
- At kinetic energies greater than 4.9 eV, electrons colliding with mercury atoms could give up 4.9 eV in the collision, with enough kinetic energy left over to let them reach the plate (**Figure 9**).
- At electron energies of 6.7 eV and 8.8 eV, collisions once again robbed the bombarding electrons of all their kinetic energy. However, these collisions were less likely to occur than those at 4.9 eV, so the effect on the current was less severe.
- At the 9.8 V accelerating potential, the electrons reached the 4.9-eV kinetic energy at the halfway point in their flight. There was a good chance the electrons would lose their kinetic energy in a collision with a mercury atom. The electrons were then reaccelerated. Just before they reached the grid, they lost their energy in a second collision, causing the current to dip at 9.8 V.

In a collision between a moving and a stationary puck (Chapter 4), the target puck can absorb any amount of energy from the moving puck in the collision. When the mass of the moving puck is very small in comparison with the stationary puck (as would be the case for a moving electron and a stationary mercury atom), almost no kinetic energy is transferred to the stationary puck, so that the moving puck bounces off with almost all its original kinetic energy. In the electron–mercury atom collision, by contrast, the mercury atom does absorb all of the electron's energy at certain discrete values (4.9 eV, 6.7 eV, 8.8 eV, ...), not what we would expect from classical mechanics. This is the significance of the Franck–Hertz experiment: atoms can change their *internal* energy as a result of collisions with electrons, but only by specific, discrete amounts.

A mercury atom that has not absorbed any extra internal energy as a result of a collision with an electron is normally found in its **ground state**. When it has absorbed 4.9 eV, the smallest amount of energy it is capable of absorbing— its **first excitation energy**—we say the atom is in its *first excited state*. Other greater amounts of internal energy are the second and third excitation energies, respectively. These successive values of internal energy that an atom can possess are called its **energy levels** and can be depicted on an energy-level diagram, such as the one shown in **Figure 10**.

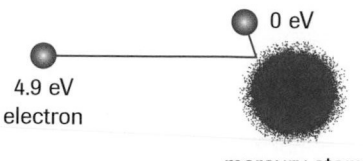

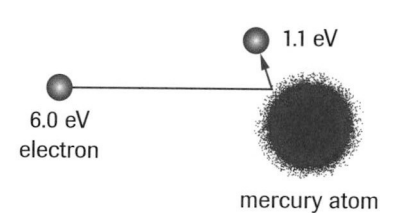

Figure 8
An incident electron with kinetic energy 4.9 eV collides with the mercury atom and loses all its energy.

Figure 9
The incident electron with kinetic energy greater than 4.9 eV collides with the mercury atom, losing 4.9 eV of kinetic energy but retaining enough energy to be able to reach the plate.

ground state the lowest energy state of an atom

first excitation energy the smallest amount of energy an atom is capable of absorbing

energy levels the various discrete values of internal energy that an atom can possess

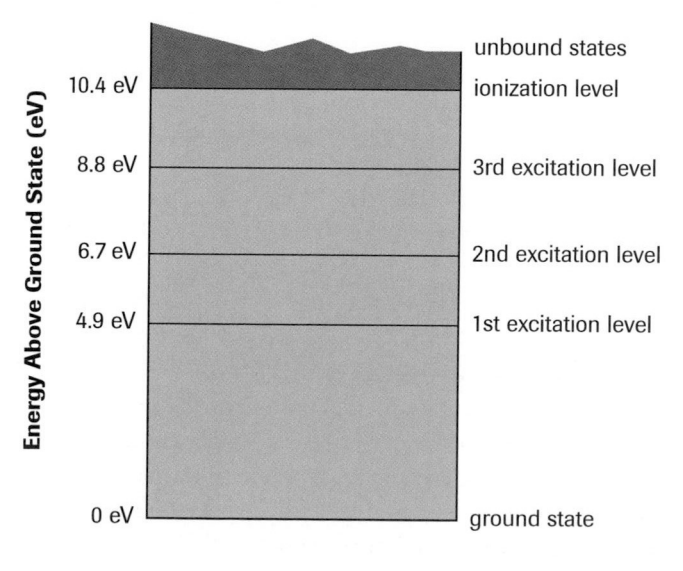

Figure 10
Energy-level diagram for mercury. Although only three excitation levels are shown, there are many more above the third level, spaced progressively closer together up to the ionization level. Beyond the ionization level, electrons are not bound to the nucleus of an atom.

An important difference occurs, though, when the absorbed energy is 10.4 eV or greater. The structure of the mercury atom itself changes. The 10.4 eV of internal energy is too great to be absorbed without the ejection of an electron from the mercury atom, leaving a positive ground-state mercury ion behind. The ejected electron can carry away with it any excess kinetic energy not needed for its release. In this way, the atom can absorb any value of incident energy greater than 10.4 eV. For mercury, 10.4 eV is called its **ionization energy**. The energy-level diagram is a continuum above this energy, rather than a series of discrete levels.

Other elements can be studied with similar electron-collision experiments. Each different electrically neutral element is found to have its own unique ionization energy and set of internal energy levels.

ionization energy the energy required to liberate an electron from an atom

---

▶ **SAMPLE** problem **1**

Electrons with a kinetic energy of 12.0 eV collide with atoms of metallic element X, in the gaseous state. After the collisions, the electrons are found to emerge with energies of 4.0 eV and 7.0 eV only. What are the first and second excitation levels for atoms of element X?

Solution

Since energy is conserved in the interaction between a free electron and an electron bound to an atom in its ground state,

$$E_n = E_{K,initial} - E_{K,final}$$
$$E_1 = 12.0 \text{ eV} - 7.0 \text{ eV} = 5.0 \text{ eV}$$
$$E_2 = 12.0 \text{ eV} - 4.0 \text{ eV} = 8.0 \text{ eV}$$

The first and second excitation levels are 5.0 eV and 8.0 eV, respectively.

▶ **Practice**

Understanding Concepts

1. An electron with a kinetic energy of 3.9 eV collides with a free mercury atom. What is the kinetic energy of the electron after the collision?

2. **Figure 10** is the energy-level diagram for mercury. An electron with a kinetic energy of 9.00 eV collides with a mercury atom in the ground state. With what energies can it scatter?

3. The following data were collected when a gaseous sample of a metallic element was bombarded with electrons of increasing kinetic energy:
   (i)   Electrons with $E_K < 1.4$ eV collided elastically with the gas atoms.
   (ii) Electrons with $E_K = 1.8$ eV scattered with $E_K = 0.3$ eV.
   (iii) Electrons with $E_K = 5.2$ eV scattered with $E_K = 3.7$ eV or $E_K = 1.9$ eV.

   What are the most likely values for the first two energy levels of this element?

Answers

1. 3.9 eV

2. 4.14 eV; 2.33 eV; 0.16 eV

3. 1.5 eV; 3.3 eV

Analyzing Atomic Spectra

Another Franck–Hertz observation provides more information about the internal energy levels in atoms. When bombarded with electrons whose energy is less than 4.9 eV, the mercury vapour gave off no light. But for electron energies just greater than 4.9 eV, light was emitted. When this light was examined with a spectroscope, it was found to consist of a single frequency of ultraviolet light, of wavelength 254 nm.

It seems that when atoms absorb energy in collisions with electrons, they quickly emit this excess energy in the form of light. Recall from Section 12.1 that Planck's hypothesis stated that light consists of photons whose energy and wavelength are related by the equation

$$E_p = \frac{hc}{\lambda}$$

Thus, ultraviolet light from mercury vapour consists of photons of energy

$$E_p = \frac{(6.63 \times 10^{-34} \text{ J·s})(3.00 \times 10^8 \text{ m/s})}{2.54 \times 10^{-7} \text{ m}}$$

$$E_p = 7.83 \times 10^{-19} \text{ J} = 4.89 \text{ eV}$$

This was a significant discovery. Atoms that will only absorb energy in 4.89-eV packages re-emit the energy in the form of photons of exactly the same energy. In other words, mercury atoms raised to their first excitation level by collisions with electrons de-excite, returning to their ground state by emitting a photon whose energy is equal to the difference between the energy of the first excited state and the ground state.

What would we expect to find upon analyzing light from the same mercury atoms when the energy of the bombarding electrons is increased above the second excitation level, say to 7.00 eV? There should be a line in the spectrum composed of photons emitted when the atom de-excites from its second excitation level, of 6.67 eV, to the ground state. The expected wavelength is

$$\lambda = \frac{hc}{E_p}$$

$$= \frac{(6.63 \times 10^{-34} \text{ J·s})(3.00 \times 10^8 \text{ m/s})}{(6.67 \text{ eV})(1.60 \times 10^{-19} \text{ J/eV})}$$

$$\lambda = 1.86 \times 10^{-7} \text{ m, or 186 nm}$$

Although this line is more difficult to observe in the spectrum of mercury, since its wavelength is too short to be detected on normal photographic film (let alone with the naked eye), special film, sensitive to ultraviolet radiation, does confirm its presence.

There are, however, additional lines in the spectrum of mercury that do not correspond to de-excitations from the various excited states to the ground state. Apparently there are other photons emitted as the atom gives off its excess energy in returning from the second excited level to the ground state. A line observed at a wavelength of 697 nm provides a clue. The energy of these photons is

$$E_p = \frac{hc}{\lambda}$$

$$= \frac{(6.63 \times 10^{-34} \text{ J·s})(3.00 \times 10^8 \text{ m/s})}{6.97 \times 10^{-7} \text{ m}}$$

$$E_p = 2.85 \times 10^{-19} \text{ J, or 1.78 eV}$$

Since the first excitation level (and hence the lowest) in mercury is 4.89 eV, this photon cannot correspond to a transition from any excited state to the ground state. A careful examination of the energy levels of mercury shows the difference between the first and second excitation levels to be

$$E_2 - E_1 = 6.67 \text{ eV} - 4.89 \text{ eV}$$

$$E_p = 1.78 \text{ eV}$$

Cecilia Payne-Gaposchkin

Based on absorption spectra from sunlight, it was assumed that all of the elements found on Earth were present in the Sun and other stars. In 1925, the British-born astronomer Cecilia Payne-Gaposchkin, while working at Harvard, found that stellar atmospheres are composed primarily of helium and hydrogen. Her discovery formed the basis of the now-accepted theory that the heavier elements are synthesized from hydrogen and helium.

It thus appears that a mercury atom can de-excite from the second excitation level to the ground level in two stages, first emitting a 1.78-eV photon to decrease its energy to the first excitation level, then emitting a 4.89-eV photon to reach the ground state. Further examination of the complete spectrum of mercury reveals other lines corresponding to downward transitions between higher excitation levels.

In general, for the emission spectrum of any element, we can write

$$E_p = E_i - E_f$$

where E_p is the energy of the emitted photon, E_i is the energy of the higher energy level, and E_f is the energy of the lower energy level.

In terms of the wavelength of the spectral line,

$$\lambda = \frac{hc}{E_h - E_l}$$

> ### SAMPLE problem 2

An unknown substance has first and second excitation levels of 3.65 eV and 5.12 eV, respectively. Determine the energy and wavelength of each photon found in its emission spectrum when the atoms are bombarded with electrons of kinetic energy (a) 3.00 eV, (b) 4.50 eV, and (c) 6.00 eV.

Solution

(a) Since the first excitation energy is 3.65 eV, no energy is absorbed, and there is no emission spectrum.

(b) With incident electrons of energy 4.50 eV, only upward transitions to the first excitation level are possible.

$$E_p = ?$$
$$\lambda = ?$$

$$E_p = E_i - E_f$$
$$= 3.65 \text{ eV} - 0 \text{ eV}$$
$$E_p = 3.65 \text{ eV}$$

$$\lambda = \frac{hc}{E_p}$$
$$= \frac{(6.63 \times 10^{-34} \text{ J·s})(3.00 \times 10^8 \text{ m/s})}{(3.65 \text{ eV})(1.60 \times 10^{-19} \text{ J/eV})}$$
$$\lambda = 3.41 \times 10^{-7} \text{ m or 341 nm}$$

The energy and wavelength of each photon are 3.65 eV and 341 nm, respectively.

(c) With incident electrons of energy 6.00 eV, excitation to both the first and second levels is possible. Thus, in addition to the photon emitted in (b), we can have

$$E_p = E_h - E_l \qquad \text{and} \qquad E_p = E_h - E_l$$
$$= 5.12 \text{ eV} - 0 \text{ eV} \qquad\qquad\qquad = 5.12 \text{ eV} - 3.65 \text{ eV}$$
$$E_p = 5.12 \text{ eV} \qquad\qquad\qquad\qquad E_p = 1.47 \text{ eV}$$

The energies of the photons are 1.47 eV and 5.12 eV. The wavelengths, calculated with the same equation as in (b), are 243 nm and 846 nm, respectively. (None of these photons would be visible to the naked eye because one is infrared and the other two are ultraviolet.)

> **Practice**

Understanding Concepts

4. Calculate the energy difference between the two energy levels in a sodium atom that gives rise to the emission of a 589-nm photon.

5. An atom emits a photon of wavelength 684 nm, how much energy does it lose?

6. A substance has its second energy level at 8.25 eV. If an atom completely absorbs a photon (λ = 343 nm), putting the electron into the third energy level, what is the energy for this level?

7. Electrons are accelerated in a Franck–Hertz experiment through mercury vapour, over a potential difference of 7.0 V. Calculate the energies of all the photons that may be emitted by the mercury vapour.

8. A spectroscope is used to examine white light that has been passed through a sample of mercury vapour. Dark lines, characteristic of the absorption spectrum of mercury, are observed.
   (a) Explain what eventually happens to the energy the mercury vapour absorbs from the white light.
   (b) Explain why the absorption lines are dark.

Answers

4. 2.11 eV

5. 1.82 eV

6. 11.9 eV

7. 4.9 eV; 6.7 eV; 1.8 eV

DID YOU KNOW ?

Energy-Level Problems
The energy levels used in some of the problems are illustrative only and do not necessarily correspond to actual elements or the laws that govern them.

Analysis of Absorption Spectra

As you learned earlier, examination of emission spectra is not the only way in which the internal energy levels of an atom can be probed. Similar information is learned if a beam of white light passes through a sample of the substance. Photons absorbed by the atoms are missing from the transmitted light, causing dark lines (gaps) to appear in the continuous spectrum.

The absorption of the photons by the atoms causes transitions from a lower internal energy level (normally the ground state) to some higher level (an excited state), but only if the energy of the photon is *exactly* equal to the difference between the two energy levels. The relationship between the energy of the photons absorbed and the internal energy levels of the atom is the same as for an emission spectrum, except that the order of the process is reversed, the initial energy level being lower and the final level higher:

$$E_p = E_f - E_i$$

For example, in the absorption spectrum of sodium, dark gaps appear at (ultraviolet) wavelengths of 259 nm, 254 nm, and 251 nm. What energy difference between internal energy levels corresponds to each of these absorption bands?

For the 259-nm line, the energy of the absorbed photon is given by

$$E_p = \frac{hc}{\lambda}$$

$$= \frac{(6.63 \times 10^{-34} \text{ J·s})(3.00 \times 10^8 \text{ m/s})}{2.59 \times 10^{-7} \text{ m}}$$

$$E_p = 7.68 \times 10^{-19} \text{ J, or 4.80 eV}$$

Thus, the energy levels in sodium are 4.80 eV apart. Photons of that energy are absorbed from the incoming light, causing electrons in the sodium atoms to jump from the lower to the higher level. Similarly, for the other two lines, the energy differences are 4.89 eV and 4.95 eV, respectively.

DID YOU KNOW ?

Gerhard Herzberg

Dr. Gerhard Herzberg (1904–1999) was born and educated in Germany, where he studied molecular spectroscopy. There he discovered the so-called "Herzberg bands" of oxygen in the upper atmosphere, explaining such phenomena as the light in the night sky and the production of ozone. He left Germany before World War II, settling at the University of Saskatchewan. Although Herzberg considered himself a physicist, his ideas and discoveries did much to stimulate the growth of modern chemical development. He was awarded the 1971 Nobel Prize in chemistry. The Herzberg Institute of Astrophysics in Ottawa is named after him.

This analysis of absorption spectra explains why most gases, including mercury vapour, are invisible to the eye at room temperature. Even the most energetic photons in visible light (deep violet ~3 eV) do not have sufficient energy to excite a mercury atom from the ground state to its first excitation level (4.87 eV) and be absorbed from the white light. Thus, all the photons in the visible light pass through the mercury vapour without being absorbed, rendering the vapour invisible.

You may wonder why the re-emission of photons does not act to fill in the missing spaces in the absorption spectrum. To a limited extent it does. However, the re-emitted photons are radiated in all directions at random, with only a few travelling in the direction of the original beam. Also, for absorption to other than the first excitation level, the de-excitation mode may result in a series of photons, different from the ones absorbed, being emitted.

The emission spectrum of any element contains more lines than its absorption spectrum does. As we saw, lines in an emission spectrum can correspond to downward transitions between two excited states as well as to transitions from any excited state to the ground state. On the other hand, since most atoms are normally in their ground state, only absorptions from the ground state to an excited state are likely. Atoms do not remain in an excited state for a sufficiently long time to make a further absorption to an even higher excited state probable. For example, the emission and absorption spectra of sodium vapour are shown in **Figure 11**.

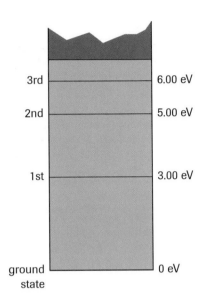

Figure 12
Energy-level diagram for hypothetical element X in question 11

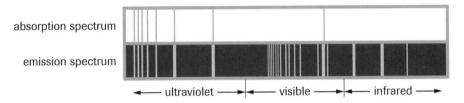

Figure 11
The absorption and emission spectra of sodium vapour

> ▶ **Practice**

Understanding Concepts

9. Atoms can receive energy in two different ways. Describe each way, and provide an example.

10. The emission spectrum of an unknown substance contains lines with the wavelengths 172 nm, 194 nm, and 258 nm, all resulting from transitions to the ground state.
    (a) Calculate the energies of the first three excited states.
    (b) Calculate the wavelengths of three other lines in the substance's emission spectrum.

11. **Figure 12** is the energy-level diagram for hypothetical element X. Calculate all of the wavelengths in both the emission and the absorption spectra.

Fluorescence and Phosphorescence

When an atom absorbs a photon and attains an excited state, it can return to the ground state through a series of intermediate states. The emitted photons will have lower energy, and therefore lower frequency, than the absorbed photon. The process of converting high-frequency radiation to lower-frequency radiation by this means is called **fluorescence**.

The common fluorescent light applies this principle. Electrons are liberated in the tube as a filament at the end is heated. An applied anode-cathode potential difference accelerates the electrons, which then strike atoms of gas in the tube, exciting them. When the excited atoms return to their normal levels, they emit ultraviolet (UV) photons that

Answers

10. (a) 4.82 eV; 6.41 eV; 7.22 eV
    (b) 518 nm; 782 nm; 152 nm

11. 1240 nm; 414 nm; 207 nm;
    622 nm; 249 nm; 249 nm;
    414 nm; 207 nm

fluorescence the process of converting high-frequency radiation to lower-frequency radiation through absorption of photons by an atom; when the light source is removed, the fluorescence stops

strike a phosphor coating on the inside of the tube. The light we see is a result of this material fluorescing in response to the bombardment of UV photons. Different phosphors emit light of different colours. "Cool white" fluorescent lights emit nearly all the visible colours, while "warm white" fluorescent lights have a phosphor that emits more red light, thereby producing a "warmer" light.

The wavelength for which fluorescence occurs depends on the energy levels of the bombarded atoms or molecules. Because the de-excitation frequencies are different for different substances, and because many substances fluoresce readily (**Figure 13**), fluorescence is a powerful tool for identification of compounds. Sometimes the simple observation of fluorescence is sufficient for the identification of a compound. In other cases spectrometers must be used.

Lasers and fluorescence are often used in crime detection. The radiation from an argon laser causes the perspiration and body oils in fingerprints to fluoresce. In this technique a laser beam illuminates a darkened region where fingerprints are suspected. The forensic technician wears glasses that filter the laser light but allow the fluorescence of the fingerprints to pass through.

Another class of materials continues to glow long after light is removed. This property is called **phosphorescence**. An excited atom in a fluorescent material drops to its normal level in about 10^{-8} s. By contrast, an excited atom of a phosphorescent material may remain in an excited state for an interval ranging from a few seconds to as long as several hours, in a so-called **metastable** state. Eventually, the atom does drop to its normal state, emitting a visible photon. Paints and dyes made from such substances are used on the luminescent dials and hands of watches and clocks and in the luminescent paints applied as a safety measure to doors and stairways.

Lasers

The principle of the **laser** was first developed for microwave frequencies in the *maser* (the "m" stands for microwaves), developed by the American physicist Charles H. Townes in the 1950s. (Townes shared the 1964 Nobel Prize in physics with Basov and Prochorov for this work.) The first maser used ammonia gas. Subsequently, other substances, including ruby, carbon dioxide, argon, and a mixture of helium and neon, were found to have "masing" or "lasing" action. Although there are several different types of lasers, the general principles involved can be illustrated in the action of the helium–neon laser, the type most commonly used in classroom and laboratory demonstrations.

An excited atom can emit photons either through **spontaneous emission** or through **stimulated emission**. The absorption of a quantum of energy by a helium atom raises an electron to a higher energy level. The electron usually moves spontaneously to a lower energy level in a relatively short time ($\sim 10^{-8}$ s), emitting a photon. There is no amplification in spontaneous emission, since the energy absorbed by the atoms is nearly equal to what is radiated.

First predicted by Einstein, stimulated emission can produce amplification, but only under certain conditions. If a photon passes an excited neon atom, it may stimulate the atom to emit a photon additional to the incident photon and identical to it. Consequently, although one photon approaches the atom, two identical photons leave. For stimulated emission to take place, the incident photon must have exactly the same frequency as the photon emitted by the atom. The two photons leaving the atom then not only have the same frequency and wavelength but also travel in the same direction, exactly in phase, and with the same polarization properties. In other words, the emitted light exhibits **coherence**.

Suppose there is a large group of atoms with more atoms in the excited state than in the ground state, and suppose that the energy-level difference for the atoms is exactly the same as the energy of the photons in the incident light beam. A first photon interacting

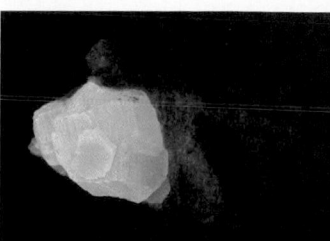

(a)

(b)

Figure 13
(a) When ultraviolet light is directed at certain rocks—in this case, witherite attached to a piece of barite—they fluoresce.
(b) When the light source is removed, the fluorescence stops.

phosphorescence the property of some materials that allows them to emit light after excitation has been removed

metastable state of sustained excitation by electrons in which they can remain excited for comparatively long times

laser acronym for Light Amplification by Stimulated Emission of Radiation; source of monochromatic, coherent light

spontaneous emission emission of a photon by an electron as a result of the absorption of a quantum of energy by an atom; the electron moves spontaneously to a lower energy level in a relatively short time ($\sim 10^{-8}$ s)

stimulated emission process in which an excited atom is stimulated to emit a photon identical to a closely approaching photon

coherence property of light in which photons have the same frequency and polarization, travel in the same direction, and are in phase

with an excited atom could produce a second photon; these two photons could stimulate the emission of two more; and those four, four more. A chain reaction would quickly occur, amplifying the light. Unfortunately, however, the number of atoms in the ground state is, under normal conditions, greater than in the excited state.

When more atoms are in a metastable condition than are in the ground state, we say there is a **population inversion**. For laser action to take place, both population inversion and the conditions for stimulated emission must exist in the lasing medium.

The red light of the helium–neon laser is produced in a narrow glass tube (capillary tube) containing a mixture of 85% helium and 15% neon, at low pressure. A metal cathode is outside the tube and an anode inside one end of the tube. A potential difference of approximately 8 kV creates a strong electric field that provides a continuous source of energy for the laser, much like a gas discharge tube. Fused to the capillary tube at one end is a 99.9% reflective flat mirror. At the other end, another mirror reflects 99% of the light, transmitting 1%. It is this transmitted light that is the output of the laser (**Figure 14**).

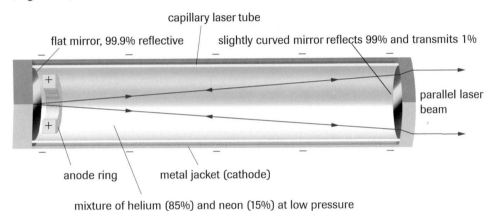

Figure 14
Structure of a helium–neon laser

The strong electric field along the length of the laser tube causes free electrons to gain kinetic energy as they are accelerated toward the positive anode. There is a high probability that an energetic electron will collide with a helium atom before reaching the anode, putting the atom into its excited state as one of its electrons jumps to a higher energy level. The thermal motions of the excited helium atoms result in collisions with neon atoms in the laser tube. During such collisions, a helium atom may revert to its ground state, passing energy to the neon atom. Conveniently, helium has exactly the same energy in its excited state as the neon atom requires to raise it to its metastable state. When an excited neon electron makes a downward transition (**Figure 15**),

Figure 15
Energy absorption, collision transfer, and spontaneous emission of neon light

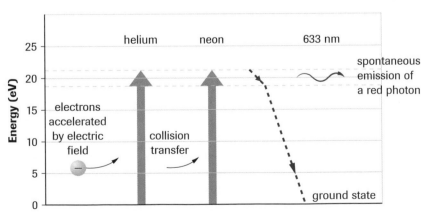

1.96 eV of energy is released, and a photon with a wavelength of 633 nm is created. Since there is a population inversion in the tube, this photon stimulates the emission of an identical photon from an adjacent neon atom that, in turn, produces more stimulations along the tube. To strengthen the output of coherent light, the mirrors at each end of the tube reflect the light along the axis of the tube, back and forth through the laser medium. Further reinforcement is achieved with each passage of photons along the tube as a multitude of neon atoms are stimulated to produce 633-nm photons. The mirrors reflect most, but not all, of the light. They transmit a small percentage of the light with each reflection, sufficient to produce the bright laser beam emerging from the laser aperture (**Figure 16**).

The type of laser described above is a *continuous* laser. In such a laser, when the atoms are stimulated and fall down to a lower energy level, they are soon excited back up, making the energy output continuous. In a *pulsed* laser, on the other hand, the atoms are excited by periodic inputs of energy, after which they are stimulated to fall to a lower state. The process then recycles, with another input of excitation energy.

Lasers are used in a wide variety of medical applications: in eye surgery (**Figure 17**), for the destruction of tissue, for the breaking up of gallstones and kidney stones, for optical-fibre surgery, for the removal of plaque from clogged arteries, for cancer treatment, and for cauterization during conventional surgery. In addition, lasers are useful in research into the functions of the cell. In industry, lasers are used for the welding and machining of metals, for the drilling of tiny holes, for the cutting of garment cloth, for surveying and distance measurements, for fibre-optics communication, and for holography.

SUMMARY *Atomic Absorption and Emission Spectra*

- A continuous spectrum given off by a heated solid is caused by the interactions between neighbouring atoms or molecules. An emission spectrum or line spectrum is emitted from electrically "excited" gases.

- An absorption spectrum occurs when some of the light from a continuous spectrum is absorbed upon passing through a gas. Atoms absorb light of the same frequencies that they emit.

- The Franck–Hertz experiment showed that the kinetic energy of incident electrons is absorbed by mercury atoms but only at discrete energy levels.

- An atom is normally in its ground state. The excited states or energy levels are given by the discrete amounts of energy the atom can internally absorb.

- Ionization energy is the maximum energy that can be absorbed internally by an atom, without triggering the loss of an electron.

- In the emission spectrum, the energy of the emitted photon equals the change in the internal energy level: $E_p = E_h - E_l$.

- When a photon is absorbed, its energy is equal to the difference between the internal energy levels: $E_p = E_h - E_l$.

- Atoms can receive energy in two ways: by collisions with high-speed particles, such as electrons, and by absorbing a photon.

- Once raised to an excited state, an atom can emit photons either through spontaneous emission or through stimulated emission. Light amplification requires stimulated emission.

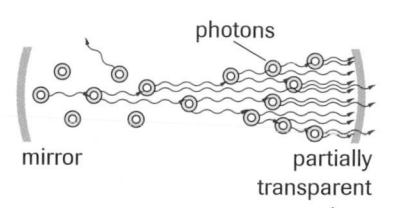

Figure 16
The chain-reaction effect of stimulated emissions in the laser tube

Figure 17
Laser being used in eye surgery

- Some substances or combinations of substances have metastable excited states. A population inversion occurs when more atoms are in a metastable condition than in the ground state.

- For laser action to take place, both population inversion and the conditions for stimulated emission must exist in the lasing medium.

- Lasers are of two types: continuous and pulsed.

▶ Section 12.4 Questions

Understanding Concepts

1. Compare and contrast continuous, line, and absorption spectra.

2. Explain why the Franck–Hertz experiment was so important in the development of the quantum model of the atom.

3. Compare spontaneous emission with stimulated emission.

4. In what ways does laser light differ from, and in what ways does it resemble, light from an ordinary lamp?

5. Explain how a 0.0005-W laser beam, photographed at a distance, can seem much stronger than a 1000-W street lamp.

6. A certain variation of a helium–neon laser produces radiation involving a transition between energy levels 3.66×10^{-19} J apart. Calculate the wavelength emitted by the laser.

7. A laser suitable for holography has an average output power of 5.0 mW. The laser beam is actually a series of pulses of electromagnetic radiation at a wavelength of 632.8 nm, lasting 2.50×10^{-2} s. Calculate
   (a) the energy (in joules) radiated with each pulse
   (b) the number of photons per pulse

Applying Inquiry Skills

8. The energy-level diagram of atom X is shown **Figure 18**. Assuming that atom X is in its ground state, what is likely to occur when
   (a) a 9.0-eV electron collides with the atom
   (b) a 9.0-eV photon collides with the atom
   (c) an 11.0-eV photon collides with the atom
   (d) a 22.0-eV electron collides with the atom

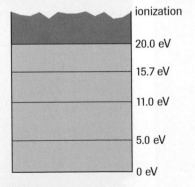

Figure 18
Energy levels for atom X

9. Outline a method in which an astronomer can determine the approximate average temperature of the surface of a star by analyzing its spectrum.

Making Connections

10. What can the absorption spectrum of sunlight tell you about the composition of the gases at the Sun's surface?

11. The emission line spectrum for hydrogen from a distant star is shifted toward the red end of the visible spectrum. What conclusion can be drawn about the star?

 www.science.nelson.com

12. In addition to the gas lasers, there are many other types: solid-state, excimer, dye, and semiconductor. One of the most powerful lasers used to cut metal and other dense surfaces is the carbon dioxide (CO_2) gas laser. Research the Internet and other sources, and find out how the CO_2 gas laser works and how it has been applied. Present your findings in a creative way.

 www.science.nelson.com

13. A missile shield for North America that uses lasers to knock out incoming missiles has been researched and tested since the 1980s. Research this technology and answer the following questions:
   (a) How would the shield work? In particular, what types of lasers have been proposed?
   (b) What are some of the major technical challenges?
   (c) Why do some consider that the production of these devices could provoke the proliferation of missiles?

 www.science.nelson.com

The Energy Levels of Hydrogen

As early as the middle of the nineteenth century, it was known that hydrogen was the lightest and simplest atom and thus an ideal candidate for the study of atomic structure. Its emission spectrum was of particular interest. The spacing of spectral lines in the visible region formed a regular pattern. In 1885, this pattern attracted the attention of J.J. Balmer, a Swiss teacher who devised a simple empirical equation from which all of the lines in the visible spectrum of hydrogen could be computed. He found that the wavelengths of the spectral lines obeyed the equation

$$\frac{1}{\lambda} = R\left(\frac{1}{2^2} - \frac{1}{n^2}\right)$$

where R is a constant, later called the Rydberg constant, whose value Balmer found to be $1.097 \times 10^7 \text{ m}^{-1}$, and n is a whole number greater than 2. Each successive value of n (3, 4, 5, ...) yields a value for the wavelength of a line in the spectrum.

Further studies of the hydrogen spectrum carried out over the next three or four decades, using ultraviolet and infrared detection techniques, revealed that the entire hydrogen spectrum obeyed a relationship generalizing the one devised by Balmer. By replacing the 2^2 term in Balmer's expression with the squares of other integers, a more general expression was devised to predict the wavelengths of all possible lines in the hydrogen spectrum:

$$\frac{1}{\lambda} = R\left(\frac{1}{n_l^2} - \frac{1}{n_u^2}\right)$$

where n_l is any whole number 1, 2, 3, 4, ... , and n_u is any whole number greater than n_l. The choice of subscripts l for "lower" and u for "upper" reflects the idea of a transition between energy levels.

This expression can be related to the energy of the emitted photons by isolating $\frac{1}{\lambda}$ from $E_p = \frac{hc}{\lambda}$ and substituting. Also, the energy of the emitted photon E_p is determined from the difference in energy of the energy levels involved in the transition producing the photon, that is $E_p = E_u - E_l$. This yields

$$\frac{1}{\lambda} = \frac{E_p}{hc}$$

$$\frac{1}{\lambda} = \frac{E_u - E_l}{hc}$$

$$\frac{E_u - E_l}{hc} = R\left(\frac{1}{n_l^2} - \frac{1}{n_u^2}\right)$$

$$E_u - E_l = Rhc\left(\frac{1}{n_l^2} - \frac{1}{n_u^2}\right)$$

$$E_l - E_u = Rhc\left(\frac{1}{n_l^2} - \frac{1}{n_u^2}\right)$$

Now, when n_u becomes very large, E_u approaches the ionization state. If we choose the ionization state to have zero energy, then $E_u \to 0$ and $\frac{1}{n_u^2} \to 0$ and the formula for the energy levels becomes

$$E_l = \frac{-Rhc}{n_l^2}$$

LEARNING TIP

Abbreviations
Note that *l* stands for lower, but I, as in E_I, stands for ionization.

Rutherford's planetary model proposed that the hydrogen atom consists of a single proton nucleus (the Sun) and a single orbiting electron (a planet). In this model, the Coulomb force of attraction binds the electron to its nucleus in much the way Earth is bound to the Sun by the gravitational force. When we studied such a gravitational system earlier (Section 6.3), we found it useful to choose the zero level of energy as the point where the two masses are no longer bound to each other. This zero level of energy denotes the borderline between the bound and the free condition of the system. If an object has a total energy greater than zero, it can reach an essentially infinite distance, where its potential energy is near zero, without coming to rest. For the hydrogen atom, this situation corresponds to ionization: the electron is no longer bound to its nucleus, as part of the atom, but is liberated. Thus, if we choose $E_I = 0$ when *n* approaches infinity, then the expression for the energy levels of hydrogen becomes even simpler:

$$E_n = E_I - \frac{Rhc}{n^2}$$

$$= 0 - \frac{(1.097 \times 10^7 \text{ m}^{-1})(6.63 \times 10^{-34} \text{ J·s})(3.00 \times 10^8 \text{ m/s})}{n^2}$$

$$E_n = -\frac{2.18 \times 10^{-18}}{n^2} \text{ J}$$

Then, converting from joules to electron volts, we have

$$E_n = -\frac{13.6}{n^2} \text{ eV} \quad \text{where } n = 1, 2, 3, \ldots$$

INVESTIGATION 12.5.1

The Energy Levels of Hydrogen (p. 656)
You can measure the wavelengths and calculate the energies for the first four lines in the Balmer series, then compare your results with the theoretical values.

Using this equation, we can calculate the values of all the energy levels of the hydrogen atom, as in **Table 1**. The values can be represented graphically on an energy-level diagram (**Figure 1**), showing both the energy above the ground state (on the right) and the energy below ionization (on the left).

By performing Investigation 12.5.1 in the Lab Activities section at the end of this chapter, you can measure the line spectra in hydrogen. ◈▮

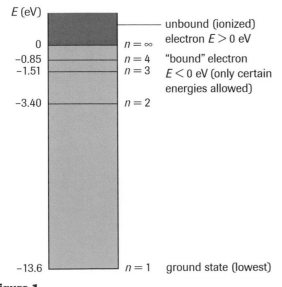

Figure 1
Energy levels of hydrogen

Table 1 Energy Levels of Hydrogen

Level	Value of *n*	Energy	Energy Above Ground State
ground state	1	−13.6 eV	0
1st excited state	2	−3.4 eV	10.2 eV
2nd excited state	3	−1.51 eV	12.1 eV
3rd excited state	4	−0.85 eV	12.8 eV
4th excited state	5	−0.54 eV	13.1 eV
⋮			
ionization state	∞	0	13.6 eV

▶ *SAMPLE* problem *1*

Calculate the energy of the $n = 6$ state for hydrogen, and state it with respect to the ground state.

Solution

$n = 6$

$E = ?$

$$E = -\frac{13.6 \text{ eV}}{n^2}$$

$$= -\frac{13.6 \text{ eV}}{6^2}$$

$$E = -0.38 \text{ eV}$$

The $n = 6$ energy level is -0.38 eV, or -13.6 eV $- (-0.38$ eV$) = 13.2$ eV, above the ground state.

▶ *SAMPLE* problem *2*

If an electron in a hydrogen atom moves from the $n = 6$ to the $n = 4$ state, what is the wavelength of the emitted photon? In what region of the electromagnetic spectrum does it reside?

Solution

$\lambda = ?$

From Sample Problem 1, the energy of the $n = 6$ state is -0.38 eV.

The energy of the $n = 4$ state is

$$E = -\frac{13.6 \text{ eV}}{4^2}$$

$$E = -0.85 \text{ eV}$$

energy change $= -0.38$ eV$- (- 0.85$ eV$)$
energy change $= 0.47$ eV

0.47 eV $= (0.47 \text{ eV})(1.60 \times 10^{-19} \text{ J/eV}) = 7.5 \times 10^{-20}$ J

The wavelength is calculated from the relationship

$$E = \frac{hc}{\lambda}$$

$$\lambda = \frac{hc}{E}$$

$$= \frac{(6.63 \times 10^{-34} \text{ J·s})(3.00 \times 10^8 \text{ m/s})}{7.52 \times 10^{-20} \text{ J}}$$

$$\lambda = 2.6 \times 10^{-6} \text{ m, or } 2.6 \times 10^2 \text{ nm}$$

The wavelength of the emitted photon is 2.6×10^2 nm, in the ultraviolet region of the spectrum.

▶ **Practice**

Understanding Concepts

1. What values of n are involved in the transition that gives rise to the emission of a 388-nm photon from hydrogen gas?

2. How much energy is required to ionize hydrogen when it is in
   (a) the ground state?
   (b) the state for $n = 3$?

3. A hydrogen atom emits a photon of wavelength 656 nm. Between what levels did the transition occur?

4. What is the energy of the photon that, when absorbed by a hydrogen atom, could cause
   (a) an electron transition from the $n = 3$ state to the $n = 5$ state?
   (b) an electron transition from the $n = 5$ state to the $n = 7$ state?

DID YOU KNOW ?

Collapse Time
Detailed calculations beyond the scope of this text suggest that the collapse of an atom would occur within 10^{-8} s.

Figure 2
Niels Bohr (1885–1962) received his Ph.D. from the University of Copenhagen in 1911 but worked at Manchester University with Rutherford until 1916, when he returned to Copenhagen to take up a professorial chair in physics. He was awarded the 1922 Nobel Prize in physics for his development of the atomic model. An avid supporter of the peaceful uses of atomic energy, Bohr organized the first Atoms for Peace Conference in 1955 and in 1957 was honoured with the first Atoms for Peace Award.

The Bohr Model

The Rutherford planetary model of the atom had negatively charged electrons moving in orbits around a small, dense, positive nucleus, held there by the force of Coulomb attraction between unlike charges. It was very appealing, although it did have two major shortcomings. First, according to Maxwell's well-established theories of electrodynamics, any accelerating electric charge would continuously emit energy in the form of electromagnetic waves. An electron orbiting a nucleus in Rutherford's model would be accelerating centripetally and, hence, continuously giving off energy in the form of electromagnetic radiation. The electron would be expected to spiral in toward the nucleus in an orbit of ever-decreasing radius, as its total energy decreased. Eventually, with all its energy spent, it would be captured by the nucleus, and the atom would be considered to have collapsed. On the basis of classical mechanics and electromagnetic theory, atoms should remain stable for only a relatively short time. This is, of course, in direct contradiction to the evidence that atoms exist on a seemingly permanent basis and show no such tendency to collapse.

Second, under certain conditions, atoms do emit radiation in the form of visible and invisible light, but only at specific, discrete frequencies. The spiralling electron described above would emit radiation in a continuous spectrum, with a gradually increasing frequency until the instant of arrival at the nucleus. Furthermore, the work of Franck and Hertz plus the analysis of emission and absorption spectra had virtually confirmed the notion of discrete, well-defined internal energy levels within the atom, a feature that Rutherford's model lacked.

Shortly after the publication of Rutherford's proposals, the young Danish physicist Niels Bohr (**Figure 2**), a post-doctoral student in Rutherford's laboratory, became intrigued with these problems inherent in the model. He realized that the laws of classical mechanics and electrodynamics might fail to apply within the confines of the atom. Inspired by the Planck–Einstein introduction of quanta into the theory of electromagnetic radiation, Bohr proposed a quantum approach to the motion of electrons within the atom.

His paper, released in 1913 after two years of formulation, sent shock waves through the scientific community. In making the following three postulates about the motion of electrons within atoms, he defied the well-established classical laws of mechanics and electromagnetism:

- Of all the possible circular and elliptical orbits for electrons around a nucleus, only a very special few orbits are physically "allowed." Each allowed orbit is characterized by a different specific amount of electron energy.

- When moving in an allowed orbit, an electron is exempt from the classical laws of electromagnetism and, in particular, does not radiate energy as it moves along its orbital path. Each such orbit is consequently called a **stationary state**.

- Electrons "jump" from a higher energy orbit to a lower energy orbit, with the energy difference between these two stationary states given off in the form of a single photon of electromagnetic radiation. Similarly, an atom can only absorb energy if that amount of energy is equal to the energy difference between a lower stationary state and some higher one.

stationary state the orbit of an electron in which it does not radiate energy

To summarize: Bohr's idea was that atoms only exist in certain stationary states characterized by certain allowed orbits for their electrons, which move in these orbits with only certain amounts of total energy, the so-called energy levels of the atom. But what made these allowed orbits different from all the other disallowed orbits?

Bohr believed, drawing on the work of Planck, that something in the model of the atom must be quantized. Although he actually chose angular momentum, the picture is clearer if we leap ahead a decade and borrow the concept of wave–particle duality from de Broglie. Let us suppose that electrons can only exist in stable orbits if the length of the orbital path is a whole number of de Broglie electron wavelengths. Recall that an electron of mass m and speed v has a de Broglie wavelength given by

$$\lambda = \frac{h}{mv}$$

where h is Planck's constant (6.63×10^{-34} J·s).

The standing-wave pattern for an electron in a stable orbit might then, for example, be three wavelengths, as in **Figure 3(a)**. Similar conditions hold for the standing-wave interference pattern for a string fixed at both ends (**Figure 3(b)**).

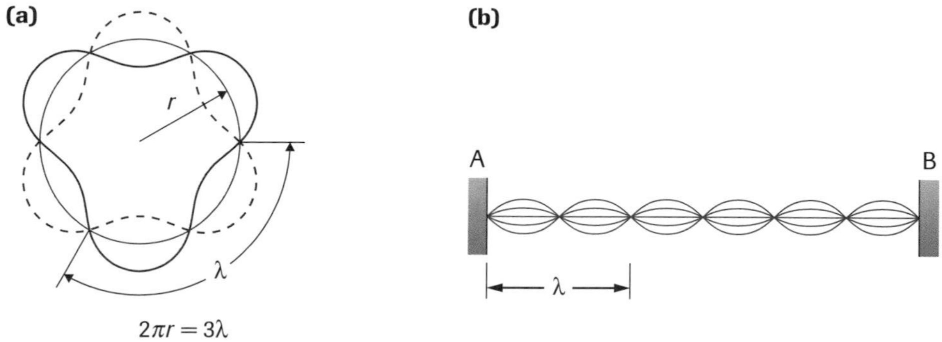

(a)

$$2\pi r = 3\lambda$$

(b)

Figure 3
(a) The standing-wave pattern for an electron wave in a stable orbit of hydrogen, here chosen to have exactly three wavelengths
(b) The standing-wave pattern for a string fixed at both ends

If the orbits are essentially circular, and if the first allowed orbit has a radius r_1 and is occupied by an electron moving with a speed v_1, the length of the orbital path will be one wavelength:

$$2\pi r_1 = \lambda$$
$$2\pi r_1 = \frac{h}{mv_1}$$

Similarly, for the second allowed orbit,

$$2\pi r_2 = 2\lambda$$

More generally, for the nth allowed orbit,

$$2\pi r_n = n\lambda = n\left(\frac{h}{mv_n}\right)$$

Thus, according to Bohr, the allowed orbits are those determined by the relationship

$$mv_n r_n = n\left(\frac{h}{2\pi}\right) \quad (n = 1, 2, \dots)$$

The whole number n appearing in this equation, which represents the number of de Broglie wavelengths in the orbital path, is called the "quantum number" for the allowed orbit (**Figure 4**). The equation itself, named "Bohr's quantum condition," provides the key to an explanation of atomic structure more complete than Rutherford's.

The Wave-Mechanical Model of the Hydrogen Atom

With the formulation of Bohr's quantum hypothesis about the special nature of the allowed orbits, it became possible to combine classical mechanics with quantum wave mechanics to produce an elegant model of atomic structure, satisfactory for hydrogen (but overhauled a few years later to generalize the electron orbits of all elements).

A hydrogen atom consists of a stationary proton of mass m_p and charge $+1e$ and a moving electron of mass m_e and charge $-1e$. The electron moves in a circular orbit of radius r_n at a constant speed v_n in such a way that n complete de Broglie wavelengths fit exactly into each orbital path. The Coulomb force of electrical attraction between the proton and the electron provides the force necessary to sustain the circular orbit; that is,

$$F_c = F_e$$
$$\frac{m_e v_n^2}{r_n} = \frac{ke^2}{r_n^2}$$

or more simply,

$$m_e v_n^2 = \frac{ke^2}{r_n} \qquad \text{Equation (1)}$$

Applying Bohr's quantum hypothesis,

$$mv_n r_n = n\left(\frac{h}{2\pi}\right) \qquad \text{Equation (2)}$$

Solving Equation (2) for v_n, we have

$$v_n = \frac{nh}{2\pi m_e r_n} \qquad \text{Equation (2a)}$$

Substituting this value for v_n into Equation (1), we have

$$m_e\left(\frac{nh}{2\pi m_e r_n}\right)^2 = \frac{ke^2}{r_n}$$

$$\frac{n^2 h^2}{4\pi^2 m_e r_n^2} = \frac{ke^2}{r_n}$$

$$r_n = \frac{n^2 h^2}{4\pi^2 m_e ke^2} \qquad \text{Equation (3)}$$

as an expression for the radius of the nth circular allowed orbit in the hydrogen atom.

(a)

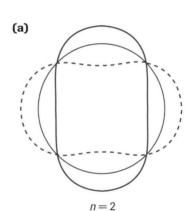

$n = 2$

(b)

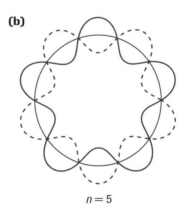

$n = 5$

Figure 4
Standing circular waves for **(a)** two and **(b)** five de Broglie wavelengths. The number of wavelengths n is also the quantum number.

By substituting known values for the constants, we can evaluate this radius:

$$r_n = n^2 \left[\frac{(6.63 \times 10^{-34} \text{ J·s})^2}{4\pi^2 \, (9.1 \times 10^{-31} \text{ kg})(9.0 \times 10^9 \text{ N·m}^2/\text{C}^2)(1.6 \times 10^{-19} \text{ C})^2} \right]$$

$$r_n = 5.3 \times 10^{-11} n^2 \text{ m}$$

The radius of the smallest orbit in hydrogen (when $n = 1$) is 5.3×10^{-11} m, sometimes called the Bohr radius. It is a good estimate of the normal size of a hydrogen atom. The radii of other orbits, given by the equation above, are

$$r_2 = 2^2 r_1 = 4r_1 = 4(5.3 \times 10^{-11} \text{ m}) = 2.1 \times 10^{-10} \text{ m}$$

$$r_3 = 3^2 r_1 = 9r_1 = 4.8 \times 10^{-10} \text{ m} \qquad \text{(and so on)}$$

Recall that, according to Bohr, an electron can only exist in one of these allowed orbits, with no other orbital radius being physically possible.

To find the speed v_n with which the electron moves in its orbit, we rearrange Equation (2a) to get

$$v_n = \frac{nh}{2\pi m_e \left(\dfrac{n^2 h^2}{4\pi^2 k m_e e^2} \right)}$$

$$v_n = \frac{2\pi k e^2}{nh} \qquad \text{Equation (4)}$$

Again substituting known values, we have

$$v_n = \frac{1}{n} \left[\frac{2\pi (9.0 \times 10^9 \text{ N·m}^2/\text{C}^2)(1.6 \times 10^{-19} \text{ C})^2}{6.63 \times 10^{-34} \text{ J·s}} \right]$$

$$v_n = \frac{1}{n}(2.2 \times 10^6) \text{ m/s}$$

so that

$$v_1 = 2.2 \times 10^6 \text{ m/s}$$

$$v_2 = \frac{1}{2} v_1 = 1.1 \times 10^6 \text{ m/s}$$

$$v_3 = \frac{1}{3} v_1 = 7.3 \times 10^5 \text{ m/s} \qquad \text{(and so on)}$$

Just as with a satellite orbiting Earth, the electron has a definite, characteristic energy, given by the sum of its kinetic and electrical-potential energies. Thus, in its nth orbit the total energy of the electron is

$$E_n = E_K + E_e$$

$$E_n = \frac{1}{2} m_e v_n^2 + \left(-\frac{ke^2}{r_n} \right)$$

Substituting values for v_n from Equation (4) and for r_n from Equation (3), we have

$$E_n = \frac{1}{2} m_e \left(\frac{2\pi k e^2}{nh} \right)^2 - \frac{ke^2}{\left(\dfrac{n^2 h^2}{4\pi^2 k m_e e^2} \right)}$$

$$= \frac{2\pi^2 m_e k^2 e^4}{n^2 h^2} - \frac{4\pi^2 m_e k^2 e^4}{n^2 h^2}$$

$$E_n = -\frac{2\pi^2 m_e k^2 e^4}{n^2 h^2}$$

Again substituting values for the constants, we have

$$E_n = -\frac{1}{n^2}\left[\frac{2\pi^2(9.1 \times 10^{-31} \text{ kg})(9.0 \times 10^9 \text{ N·m}^2/\text{C}^2)^2(1.6 \times 10^{-19} \text{ C})^4}{(6.63 \times 10^{-34} \text{ J·s})^2}\right]$$

$$= -\frac{2.17 \times 10^{-18}}{n^2} \text{ J}$$

$$E_n = -\frac{13.6}{n^2} \text{ eV}$$

Thus, the energy levels for the allowed orbits of hydrogen are

$$E_1 = -\frac{13.6}{1^2} = -13.6 \text{ eV}$$

$$E_2 = -\frac{13.6}{2^2} = -3.40 \text{ eV}$$

$$E_3 = -\frac{13.6}{3^2} = -1.51 \text{ eV} \qquad \text{(and so on)}$$

This model verifies, exactly, the hydrogen atom energy levels previously established on the basis of the hydrogen emission spectrum. Although all the energy levels are negative, as is characteristic of a "bound" system, the energy of the outer orbits is less negative, and hence greater, than the energy of the inner orbits. The orbit closest to the nucleus ($n = 1$) has the lowest energy (-13.6 eV), the smallest radius (0.53×10^{-10} m), and the greatest electron speed (2.2×10^6 m/s).

It is now possible to draw a complete and detailed energy-level diagram for the hydrogen atom (**Figure 5**).

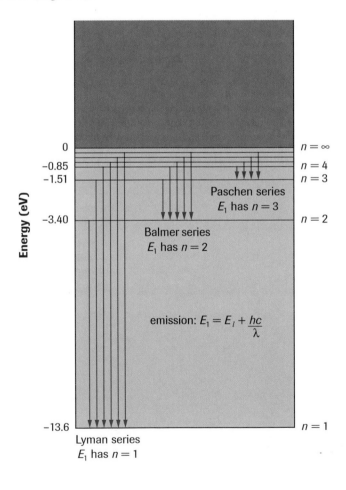

Figure 5

Energy-level diagram for the hydrogen atom

The lone electron of the hydrogen atom normally resides in the ground state ($n = 1$). However, in absorbing energy from photons or during collisions with high-speed particles, it may be boosted up to any of the excited states ($n = 2, 3, 4, ...$). Once in an excited state, the electron will typically jump down to any lower energy state, giving off the excess energy by creating a photon. The arrows in **Figure 5** represent downward transitions giving rise to the various lines found in the hydrogen emission spectrum. They are grouped together in series, according to their common lower state; the series are named after famous spectroscopists whose work led to their discovery. The **Lyman series** is the set of transitions from higher energy levels to the ground state ($n = 1$); the **Balmer series** is the set of downward transitions to $n = 2$; and the **Paschen series** is the set of downward transitions to $n = 3$.

A sample problem illustrates how we can identify these spectral lines.

Lyman series series of wavelengths emitted in transitions of a photon from higher energy levels to the $n = 1$, or ground, state

Balmer series series of wavelengths emitted in transitions of a photon from higher energy levels to the $n = 2$ state

Paschen series series of wavelengths emitted in transitions of a photon from higher energy levels to the $n = 3$ state

▶ SAMPLE problem 3

Determine, with the help of **Figure 5**, the wavelength of light emitted when a hydrogen atom makes a transition from the $n = 5$ orbit to the $n = 2$ orbit.

Solution

$\lambda = ?$

For $n = 5$, $\quad E_5 = -\dfrac{13.6}{5^2}$ eV $= -0.54$ eV

For $n = 2$, $\quad E_2 = -\dfrac{13.6}{2^2}$ eV $= -3.40$ eV

$E_p = E_5 - E_2$

$\quad = -0.54$ eV $- (-3.40$ eV$)$

$E_p = 2.86$ eV

Thus,

$\lambda = \dfrac{hc}{E_p}$

$\quad = \dfrac{(6.63 \times 10^{-34} \text{ J·s})(3.00 \times 10^8 \text{ m/s})}{(2.86 \text{ eV})(1.60 \times 10^{-19} \text{ J/eV})}$

$\lambda = 4.35 \times 10^{-7}$ m, or 435 nm

The wavelength of light emitted is 435 nm. (This is a violet line in the visible spectrum, the third line in the Balmer series.)

▶ Practice

Understanding Concepts

5. How does the de Broglie wavelength of the electron compare with the circumference of the first orbit?

6. Calculate the energies of all the photons that could possibly be emitted by a large sample of hydrogen atoms, all initially excited to the $n = 5$ state.

7. In performing a Franck–Hertz type experiment, you accelerate electrons through hydrogen gas at room temperature over a potential difference of 12.3 V. What wavelengths of light could be emitted by the hydrogen?

8. Calculate the wavelength of the line in the hydrogen Balmer series for which $n = 4$.

Answers

6. 0.31 eV; 0.65 eV; 0.96 eV; 1.9 eV; 2.6 eV; 2.86 eV; 10.2 eV; 12.1 eV; 12.8 eV; 13.1 eV

7. 122 nm; 103 nm; 654 nm

8. 488 nm

9. Calculate the wavelengths of (a) the most energetic and (b) the least energetic photon that can be emitted by a hydrogen atom in the $n = 7$ state.

10. Calculate the energy and wavelength of the least energetic photon that can be absorbed by a hydrogen atom at room temperature.

11. Calculate the longest wavelengths in (a) the hydrogen Lyman series ($n = 1$) and (b) the hydrogen Paschen series ($n = 3$).

12. What value of n would give a hydrogen atom a Bohr orbit of radius 1.0 mm? What would be the energy of an electron in that orbit?

Success of the Bohr Model

Although based on theoretical assumptions designed to fit the observations rather than on direct empirical evidence, Bohr's model was for many reasons quite successful:

- It provided a physical model of the atom whose internal energy levels matched those of the observed hydrogen spectrum.

- It accounted for the stability of atoms: Once an electron had descended to the ground state, there was no lower energy to which it could jump. Thus, it stayed there indefinitely, and the atom was stable.

- It applied equally well to other one-electron atoms, such as a singly ionized helium ion.

The model was incomplete, however, and failed to stand up to closer examination:

- It broke down when applied to many-electron atoms because it took no account of the interactions between electrons in orbit.

- With the development of more precise spectroscopic techniques, it became apparent that each of the excited states was not a unique, single energy level but a group of finely separated levels, near the Bohr level. To explain this splitting of levels, it was necessary to introduce modifications to the shape of the Bohr orbits as well as the concept that the electron was spinning on an axis as it moved.

Even though the Bohr model eventually had to be abandoned, it was a triumph of original thought and one whose basic features are still useful. It first incorporated the ideas of quantum mechanics into the inner structure of the atom and provided a basic physical model of the atom. In time, scientific thought would replace it by moving into the less tangible realm of electron waves and probability distributions, as discussed in the next section.

SUMMARY   *The Bohr Model of the Atom*

- Balmer devised a simple empirical equation from which all of the lines in the visible spectrum of hydrogen could be computed: $\frac{1}{\lambda} = R\left(\frac{1}{n_l^2} - \frac{1}{n_u^2}\right)$.

  His equation allowed the energy levels for hydrogen to be predicted as

  $E_n = -\frac{13.6 \text{ eV}}{n^2}$ $(n = 1, 2, 3, \ldots)$.

- The work of Franck and Hertz, and the analysis of emission and absorption spectra had confirmed that there are discrete, well-defined internal energy levels within the atom.

- Bohr proposed that atoms only exist in certain stationary states with certain allowed orbits for their electrons. Electrons move in these orbits with only certain amounts of total energy, called energy levels of the atom.

- Bohr made the following three postulates regarding the motion of electrons within atoms:

  1. There are a few special electron orbits that are "allowed," each characterized by a different specific electron energy.

  2. When moving in an allowed stationary orbit, an electron does not radiate energy.

  3. Electrons may move from a higher-energy orbit to a lower-energy orbit, giving off a single photon. Similarly, an atom can only absorb energy if that energy is equal to the energy difference between a lower stationary state and some higher one.

- Bohr combined classical mechanics with quantum wave mechanics to produce a satisfactory model of the atomic structure of hydrogen.

- The lone electron of a hydrogen atom normally resides in the ground state ($n = 1$). By absorbing energy from photons, however, or from collisions with high-speed particles, it may be boosted up to any of the excited states ($n = 2, 3, 4, …$). Once in an excited state, the electron quickly moves to any lower state, creating a photon in the process.

- Bohr's model was quite successful in that it provided a physical model of the hydrogen atom, matching the internal energy levels to those of the observed hydrogen spectrum, while also accounting for the stability of the hydrogen atom.

- Bohr's model was incomplete in that it broke down when applied to many-electron atoms.

▶ Section 12.5 Questions

Understanding Concepts

1. In the hydrogen atom, the quantum number n can increase without limit. Does the frequency of possible spectral lines from hydrogen correspondingly increase without limit?

2. A hydrogen atom initially in its ground state ($n = 1$) absorbs a photon, ending up in the state for which $n = 3$.
   (a) Calculate the energy of the absorbed photon.
   (b) If the atom eventually returns to the ground state, what photon energies could the atom emit?

3. What energy is needed to ionize a hydrogen atom from the $n = 2$ state? How likely is such ionization to occur? Explain your answer.

4. Determine the wavelength and frequency of the fourth Balmer line (emitted in the transition from $n = 6$ to $n = 2$) for hydrogen.

5. For which excited state, according to the Bohr theory, can the hydrogen atom have a radius of 0.847 nm?

6. According to the Bohr theory of the atom, the speed of an electron in the first Bohr orbit of the hydrogen atom is 2.19×10^6 m/s.
   (a) Calculate the de Broglie wavelength associated with this electron.
   (b) Prove, using the de Broglie wavelength, that if the radius of the Bohr orbit is 4.8×10^{-10} m, then the quantum number is $n = 3$.

7. Calculate the Coulomb force of attraction on the electron when it is in the ground state of the Bohr hydrogen atom.

Heisenberg's Uncertainty Principle

Once scientists had abandoned the well-established realm of classical Newtonian mechanics and entered the new, uncharted world of quantum mechanics, many phenomena were discovered that were both strange and difficult to visualize. In classical mechanics, objects we identify as particles always behave like particles, and wave phenomena always exhibit pure wave properties. But the quantum hypotheses of Planck, Einstein, and Bohr created a new dilemma: light, which had traditionally been viewed as a wave phenomenon, was apparently composed of photons possessing distinct particle characteristics. Electrons, to this point thought of as tiny particles with a definite charge and mass, behaved like waves with a definite wavelength, as they moved in orbits within the atom and interacted with objects of atomic dimensions. Clearly, a new way of looking at particle and wave phenomena was needed.

The equations in Section 12.5 suggest that we can be very precise about the properties of an electron in the hydrogen atom. We can determine an orbiting electron's exact location using the equation for r_n and can likewise determine its exact speed and energy. In 1927, the German physicist Werner Heisenberg (**Figure 1**) proposed that there was always some inherent uncertainty in the determination of these quantities. It was not a question of accuracy in measurements. The uncertainty was inherent and originated from the quantum-mechanical nature of subatomic particles. Let us consider an illustration of Heisenberg's position.

Suppose we are measuring the temperature of a cup of hot coffee with a laboratory thermometer. When the room-temperature thermometer is immersed in the coffee, it extracts some heat from the coffee. Therefore, the temperature registered is that of the system and not just the original temperature of the coffee. A smaller thermometer will disturb the temperature of the coffee less, thereby yielding a more precise reading. In the limiting situation, an infinitely small thermometer would produce an infinitely precise result. There is no inherent lower limit to the size of the thermometer that would limit the precision of the temperature determination.

Imagine, next, that we are trying to determine the position of an electron within an atom. To do this, we bombard the atom with highly energetic electromagnetic radiation of a given wavelength (**Figure 2**). A photon of wavelength λ will have a

Figure 1
Werner Heisenberg (1901–1976) was awarded the 1932 Nobel Prize in physics for developing the uncertainty principle.

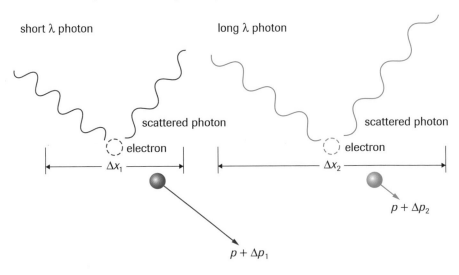

Figure 2
The more accurately we try to locate the electron, the less precisely we know its momentum.

momentum $\frac{h}{\lambda}$. We know from our analysis of the Compton effect (Section 12.3) that this photon will transfer some of its momentum to the electron when they interact. Thus, the electron will acquire a new and unknown value of momentum just as a consequence of being located by the photon. The more accurately we try to locate the electron by selecting a photon of smaller wavelength, the less precisely we know its momentum. If we use a photon of longer wavelength to be more precise about the momentum of the electron, we must be content with being less certain of its location.

As a result, we are unable to measure both the position and the momentum of the electron with unlimited accuracy. Heisenberg was able to determine the limits of these inherent uncertainties and to express them mathematically, in a formulation known as *Heisenberg's uncertainty principle:*

> **Heisenberg's Uncertainty Principle**
>
> If Δx is the uncertainty in a particle's position, and Δp is the uncertainty in its momentum, then
>
> $\Delta x \Delta p \geq \dfrac{h}{2\pi}$ where h is Planck's constant

To appreciate the significance of Heisenberg's principle, let us look at examples from both the macroscopic and the microscopic worlds. For a large particle of mass 1.0 kg, whose momentum p is given by the equation $p = mv$,

$$\Delta x \Delta p = \Delta x m \Delta v \geq \frac{h}{2\pi}$$

$$\Delta x \Delta v \geq \frac{h}{2\pi m}$$

$$\geq \frac{6.63 \times 10^{-34} \text{ J·s}}{2\pi (1.0 \text{ kg})}$$

$$\Delta x \Delta v \geq 1.1 \times 10^{-34} \text{ J·s/kg}$$

Thus, if we can know the position of the particle to within an uncertainty Δx of $\pm 10^{-6}$ m, we are permitted to know its speed to within an uncertainty Δv of $\pm 10^{-28}$ m/s (since the product of $\Delta x \Delta v$ cannot be smaller than 10^{-34} J·s/kg). Such small uncertainties are of no consequence when dealing with macroscopic objects.

On the other hand, for an electron of mass 9.1×10^{-31} kg,

$$\Delta x \Delta v \geq \frac{h}{2\pi m}$$

$$\geq \frac{6.63 \times 10^{-34} \text{ J·s}}{2\pi (9.1 \times 10^{-31} \text{ kg})}$$

$$\Delta x \Delta v \geq 1.2 \times 10^{-4} \text{ J·s/kg}$$

If we confine the uncertainty in the location of the electron to $\pm 10^{-10}$ m (about the size of an atom), we cannot know its speed within an uncertainty of less than $\pm 10^6$ m/s. These uncertainties are significant enough to invalidate Bohr's picture of a finite electron moving in a well-defined orbit. Clearly, a new look is needed at just what an electron is. We will leave this discussion to Chapter 13.

Probability and Determinism

The Newtonian view of mechanics was deterministic. If the position and speed of an object at a particular time were known, its position and speed for all future time could be determined simply by knowing the forces acting on it. More than two centuries of success in describing the macroscopic world had made the deterministic view of nature convincing. Bohr had no reason to believe that the motion of electrons within atoms would be any different.

However, because of the uncertainty in measuring an electron's position and speed, it becomes impossible to say, for any individual electron, where it is now or where it will be at any future time. Because of its inherent wave properties, an electron in an atom cannot be visualized as a Newtonian particle. Rather than saying where it is, we must be satisfied with describing its location by stating the probability that it will be found near any point.

One way of visualizing this situation is to think of the electron existing as a cloud of negative charge distributed around the atom rather than as a particle moving in a circular orbit (**Figure 3**). The cloud is denser in areas of high probability and less dense in areas where the electron is less likely to be found. For the first Bohr orbit of the hydrogen atom ($n = 1$), the cloud is most dense in a spherical shell of radius 5.3×10^{-11} m, the first Bohr radius. Even though this is where the electron is most likely to be, it does have a small statistical probability of being anywhere else.

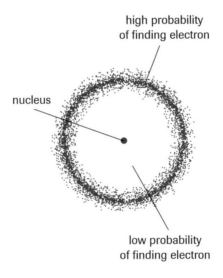

high probability
of finding electron

nucleus

low probability
of finding electron

Figure 3
The electron cloud, or probability distribution, for the ground state of the hydrogen atom. The cloud is most dense—corresponding to the highest probability—at a distance from the nucleus of 5.3×10^{-11} m, which is what the Bohr model predicts for the radius of the first orbit. But modern quantum mechanics departs from the Bohr model in telling us that the electron can be within or beyond that distance at any given time.

The "probability cloud" for other allowed Bohr orbits takes on different shapes and dimensions in ways that can be determined mathematically. In 1925, working independently, Heisenberg and Erwin Schrödinger devised equivalent mathematical equations whose solutions gave the probability distributions for virtually any problem in quantum mechanics. The expressions became known as the Schrödinger equations and have been immensely successful in solving atomic structure problems. They provide a mathematical interpretation of the physical situation, yielding the values of all measurable quantities such as momentum and energy, as well as the probability for all positions that the particle can occupy. Physicists have spent countless hours applying these techniques to a seemingly endless array of problems, with success in almost every instance. One example is the whole field of solid-state physics, from which semiconductors, the backbone of modern electronics, have developed.

 **Probability versus Determinism**

- In classical mechanics, the objects we identify as particles always behave like particles, while wave phenomena always exhibit pure wave properties.

- In quantum mechanics, light is composed of photons possessing distinct particle characteristics, and electrons behave like waves with a definite wavelength.

- Heisenberg proposed that an inherent uncertainty exists in the simultaneous determination of any measured quantity due to the quantum-mechanical wave aspect of particles.

- We are unable to measure both the position and the momentum of the electron with unlimited accuracy. Heisenberg was able to determine the limits of these inherent uncertainties and to express them mathematically as $\Delta x \Delta p \geq \dfrac{h}{2\pi}$.

- Physics now considers the electron in an atom as a probability cloud of negative charge distributed around the nucleus rather than as a particle moving in a circular orbit. The cloud is denser in areas of high probability and less dense in areas where the electron is less likely to be found.

- An electron's position and velocity are impossible to predict; we only know the *probability* that the electron will be found near any point. The shapes and dimensions of these probability distributions can be determined mathematically.

▶ **Section 12.6 Questions**

Understanding Concepts

1. In what sense does Bohr's model of the atom violate the uncertainty principle?

2. How accurately can the position and speed of a particle be known, simultaneously?

3. A 12.0-g bullet leaves a rifle with a speed of 1.80×10^2 m/s.
   (a) Calculate the de Broglie wavelength associated with the bullet.

   (b) If the position of the bullet is known to an accuracy of 0.60 cm (radius of the rifle barrel), what is the minimum uncertainty in momentum?

4. If Planck's constant were very large, what would be the effect on shooting an arrow at a stationary target? What would be the effect with a moving target, such as a deer?

✐ LAB EXERCISE 12.1.1

Analyzing the Photoelectric Effect

Inquiry Skills

○ Questioning	○ Planning	● Analyzing
○ Hypothesizing	○ Conducting	○ Evaluating
○ Predicting	○ Recording	● Communicating

Since most schools do not have access to a phototube, data from an actual experiment are provided for analysis. Working with these data will acquaint you with most of the important concepts you require to understand the photoelectric effect and its relationship to the photon theory of light.

When a phototube is used commercially, the collector is positive, and the photoelectric current flows at any time that light of sufficiently high frequency shines on the photoelectric surface. In this lab exercise, however, the collector will usually be negative, impeding the current in the phototube. At a sufficiently negative collector potential, V_0, the current will stop altogether. At this point, the retarding potential difference between the electrodes represents the maximum possible kinetic energy of the ejected photoelectrons (see Section 12.1). If the potential difference is expressed in volts, this maximum kinetic energy of the electrons can be found in joules, from the relationship $E = qV_0$. Light with different colours (wavelengths) is directed at the photoelectric surface during the experiment (**Figure 1**).

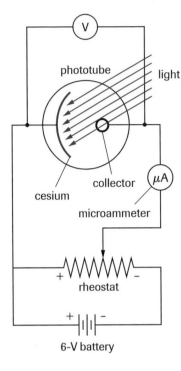

Figure 1
Either the voltmeter must have a very high resistance or a correction must be made in the measured current to allow for voltmeter leakage.

Evidence

(a) Refer to the data in **Table 1**.

Analysis

(b) For each of the light sources used, plot a graph of photocurrent versus retarding potential. Choose the scales of the axes in such a way that all five graphs fit onto the same set of axes.

(c) State the relationship between the maximum electric current and the intensity of the incident light.

(d) Which colour of light is associated with the largest cutoff potential? Do the two graphs for violet light reveal that the intensity of the incident light affects the cutoff potential?

(e) The cutoff potential is a measure of the maximum kinetic energy of the electrons ejected from the photoelectric surface. Using a chart similar to **Table 2**, determine the maximum kinetic energy of the photoelectrons, in both electron volts and joules. Which colour of light has the highest-energy photons? Explain your reasoning.

(f) Using the relationship $c = f\lambda$, determine the frequency of each colour. Plot a graph of the maximum kinetic energy of the ejected electrons, in joules, versus the frequency of the photons, in hertz. The energy axis should have a negative axis equal in magnitude to the positive axis, and the frequency should begin at zero. To simplify your graph, use scientific notation for the scales on both axes. How are the two variables related?

(g) Find the slope of the energy-versus-frequency graph. The accepted value for this slope is Planck's constant $(6.63 \times 10^{-34} \text{ J·s})$. Calculate your experimental error.

(h) You can see from your work in (f) that if the graph line is extrapolated, it has intercepts on both the energy and frequency axes. The magnitude of the negative intercept on the energy axis represents the work function W, which is the energy required to release the electron from the photoelectric surface (see Section 12.1). What is the work function for cesium? What is the significance of the negative value of the intercept?

Table 1 Observation Chart

Colour	Yellow	Green	Blue	Violet	
Wavelength	**578 nm**	**546 nm**	**480 nm**	**410 nm (low intensity)**	**410 nm (high intensity)**
Retarding Potential (V)	**Photo-current (μA)**	**Photo-current (μA)**	**Photo-current (μA)**	**Photo-current (μA)**	**Photo-current (μA)**
0.00	3.2	10.4	11.2	8.5	14.8
0.05	2.3	8.7	10.1	8.1	14.0
0.10	1.3	7.1	9.0	7.6	13.3
0.15	0.6	5.5	8.0	7.2	12.6
0.20	0.2	4.0	7.0	6.7	11.9
0.25	0	2.4	6.0	6.2	11.1
0.30	0	1.0	4.9	5.7	10.4
0.35		0.2	3.8	5.3	9.6
0.40		0	2.8	4.8	8.9
0.45		0	1.7	4.4	8.2
0.50			1.2	3.9	7.0
0.55			0.7	3.4	6.7
0.60			0.4	3.0	6.0
0.65			0.1	2.5	5.2
0.70			0	2.0	4.5
0.75			0	1.6	3.7
0.80				1.1	3.0
0.85				0.9	2.3
0.90				0.7	1.7
0.95				0.5	1.2
1.00				0.3	0.8
1.05				0.2	0.4
1.10				0.1	0.1
1.15				0	0
1.20				0	0

Table 2

Colour of Light	Wavelength of Light (nm)	Cutoff Potential (V)	Maximum E_K of Ejected Electrons (eV)	(J)	Frequency of Light (Hz)
yellow	578	?	?	?	?
green	546	?	?	?	?
blue	480	?	?	?	?
violet (low intensity)	410	?	?	?	?
violet (high intensity)	410	?	?	?	?

(i) The intercept on the frequency axis represents the threshold frequency f_0, or the minimum frequency of the photons that will cause electrons to be ejected from a cesium surface. What are the threshold frequency and the threshold wavelength for cesium?

(j) Using the slope and intercept values above, write a general equation describing the graph in the mathematical form $y = mx + b$.

(k) Write an energy-conservation equation using the variables E_{photon}, E_K, and W. Rearrange it so that it is in the same form as the equation in (j). You will need to recall the equation relating the energy and the frequency of a photon.

(l) **Table 3** gives data for two other photoelectric surfaces. Having made appropriate calculations, plot the data on the graph you used in step (f).

Table 3

Barium Frequency ($\times 10^{14}$ Hz)	Barium Cutoff Potential (V)	Calcium Frequency ($\times 10^{14}$ Hz)	Calcium Cutoff Potential (V)
6.25	0.10	8.50	0.20
6.55	0.25	9.25	0.50
7.00	0.40	10.0	0.80
7.50	0.65	11.0	1.25

(m) Using the two new graph lines, determine the threshold frequencies and work functions for both barium and calcium. Which of the three substances used in this lab exercise would not produce photoelectric emission for the visible range of the spectrum?

(n) Compare the slopes of the three graphs. What can you infer about Planck's constant?

The Energy Levels of Hydrogen

Inquiry Skills

○ Questioning	○ Planning	● Analyzing
○ Hypothesizing	● Conducting	● Evaluating
○ Predicting	● Recording	● Communicating

In Section 12.4, we discussed emission and absorption spectra and performed some calculations involving energy levels. When studying that section, you may have been able to look through a spectroscope at the emission spectra of a number of electrically excited gases, including hydrogen, in discharge tubes. In this investigation, you will use your knowledge of diffraction gratings and the spectroscope (Section 10.3) to take measurements and determine the wavelengths of visible emission lines of hydrogen. Your exact procedure will depend, to a degree, on the sophistication of the spectroscope you are provided. Even with a simple spectroscope, however, your values should be close to the theoretical values.

Question

What are the wavelengths of the visible lines in the emission spectrum of hydrogen?

Prediction

The measured wavelengths and energies for the first four lines in the Balmer series are the same as the calculated theoretical values.

Materials

diffraction-grating spectroscope
high-potential source (transformer or induction coil)
hydrogen gas discharge tube
metric ruler

Procedure

Note: The following procedure is for a simple spectroscope. If the spectroscope can measure the diffraction angles of the spectral lines, steps 2, 5, 6, and 7 can be omitted.

1. Examine the apparatus that has been set up for you by your teacher. Note each part, drawing a labelled diagram. Do not move the collimator and telescope from their mounts. (The adjustment and focus can be quite time-consuming.)

2. Tape a piece of paper under the telescope mount, ensuring that the mount can move freely.

3. Move the gas discharge tube, touching the holder only, so that it is lined up as closely as possible with the slit in the collimator. Place the black shield so that only light going through the collimator enters the telescope. Turn on the high-potential source.

 Do not touch any part of the gas tube, holder, leads, or power source, except the on/off switch.

4. Turn off the room lights. Adjust the telescope mount so that the telescope is in a direct line with the slit. Sight the telescope carefully, so that the eyepiece hairline aligns with the central maximum (a bright line). A slight adjustment of the gas-discharge tube may be necessary to obtain accurate alignment.

5. Move the telescope to one side, locating the three brightest lines (whose colours are violet, greenish-blue, and red). If you have good eyesight, your room is very dark, and your equipment is adjusted properly, you may see a fainter violet line adjacent to the bright violet line. Move the telescope to the other side of the central maximum, locating the same set of spectral lines.

6. Return to the central line, making a mark with a sharp pencil in the notch on your paper. Move the telescope to one side, making similar marks at the positions of each of the spectral lines you locate. Make corresponding marks for the other side of the central maximum.

7. Turn off the power.

8. Measure the distance from the central line to the mark you have made for each spectral line. Average the distances on either side of the central maximum.

9. Using your knowledge of diffraction gratings (Section 10.3) and the value of d, the separation of the slits, calculate the wavelengths corresponding to the three spectral lines.

Analysis

(a) Calculate the wavelength of the photons in each spectral line observed.

(b) Express the energy, in electron volts, of the photons comprising each spectral line observed.

(c) Calculate the energies of the electrons in each of the first six allowed energy levels for hydrogen using the relationship $E_n = -\dfrac{13.6 \text{ eV}}{n^2}$.

(d) Determine the energy of the first four photons in the Balmer series (the series in which electrons descend to the $n = 2$ state from higher states).

(e) Determine the specific energy levels involved in the transitions leading to each of the spectral lines observed.

Evaluation

(f) Evaluate the prediction by comparing the energy of each photon, as calculated from the measurements done with the spectroscope, with its theoretical value.

Synthesis

(g) Describe a procedure you would follow to find the energy of the visible photons emitted by neon gas.

Chapter 12 *SUMMARY*

Key Expectations

- define and describe the concepts and units related to the present-day understanding of the nature of the atom including quantum theory, photoelectric effect, matter waves, wave–matter duality, energy levels in the atom, and uncertainty (12.1, 12.2, 12.3, 12.4, 12.5, 12.6)
- describe the photoelectric effect in terms of the quantum energy concept, and outline the experimental evidence that supports a particle model of light (12.1)
- describe and explain in qualitative terms the Bohr model of the hydrogen atom as a synthesis of classical and early quantum mechanics (12.5)
- collect and interpret experimental data in support of the photoelectric effect and, in the case of the Bohr model of the atom, an analysis of the emission spectrum of hydrogen (12.1, 12.5)
- outline the historical development of scientific views and models of matter and energy that led up to Bohr's model of the hydrogen atom (12.1, 12.3, 12.5, 12.6)
- describe how the development of the quantum theory has led to scientific and technological advances that have benefited society (12.1, 12.2, 12.4)
- describe examples of contributions of Canadians to the development of modern physics (12.1, 12.2)

Key Terms

blackbody

blackbody radiation

quanta

Planck's constant

photoelectric effect

photoelectrons

cutoff potential

threshold frequency

photon

Einstein's photoelectric equation

work function

photodiode

charge-coupled device

Compton effect

momentum of a photon

pair production

wave–particle duality

principle of complementarity

de Broglie wavelength

matter waves

quantum mechanics

transmission electron microscope

scanning electron microscope

scanning tunnelling electron microscope

continuous spectrum

emission spectrum

absorption spectrum

ground state

first excitation energy

energy levels

ionization energy

fluorescence

phosphorescence

metastable

laser

spontaneous emission

stimulated emission

coherence

population inversion

stationary state

Lyman series

Balmer series

Paschen series

Heisenberg's uncertainty principle

Key Equations

- $E = hf$ (12.1)
- $h = 6.63 \times 10^{-34}$ J·s   Planck's constant   (12.1)
- $E_K = E_{photon} - W$ Einstein's photoelectric equation   (12.1)
- $E_K = hf - W$ (12.1)
- $p = \dfrac{h}{\lambda}$ (12.1)
- $\lambda = \dfrac{h}{p} = \dfrac{h}{mv}$ de Broglie wavelength   (12.2)
- $E_p = E_i - E_f$ photon emission   (12.4)
- $E_p = E_f - E_i$ photon absorption   (12.4)
- $E_n = -\dfrac{13.6}{n^2}$ eV   hydrogen   (12.5)
- $\Delta x \Delta p \geq \dfrac{h}{2\pi}$ Heisenberg's uncertainty principle   (12.6)

▶ *MAKE* a summary

Construct a concept map of the scientific ideas that contributed to the development of the quantum theory and its application to the hydrogen atom, beginning with Planck and ending with Bohr. Include as many key terms, equations, and concepts from this chapter as possible.

Write numbers 1 to 11 in your notebook. Indicate beside each number whether the corresponding statement is true (T) or false (F). If it is false, write a corrected version.

1. Planck proposed that energy is radiated in bundles he called quanta. The energy of a single quantum is directly proportional to its wavelength.

2. At the cutoff potential, even the most energetic photoelectrons are prevented from reaching the anode.

3. For a given photoelectric surface, the longer the wavelength of light incident on it, the higher the cutoff potential.

4. In the Compton effect, high-energy photons strike a surface, ejecting electrons with kinetic energy and lower-energy photons.

5. Photons have momentum whose value is given by
$$p = \frac{hc}{\lambda}.$$

6. When light passes through a medium, its behaviour is best explained using its particle properties, whereas when light interacts with matter, its behaviour is best explained using its wave properties.

7. The diffraction of electrons revealed that particles have wave characteristics.

8. Electrically "excited" gases produce a continuous spectrum, while an emission spectrum or line spectrum is emitted from a heated solid.

9. An atom is normally in its ground state. The excited states or energy levels are the amounts of energy the atom can internally absorb.

10. The analysis of emission and absorption spectra confirmed that there are discrete, well-defined internal energy levels within the atom.

11. In the atom we think of the electron as a particle moving in a circular orbit whose wave properties predict its exact position and velocity.

Write numbers 12 to 24 in your notebook. Beside each number, write the letter corresponding to the best choice.

12. In the photoelectric effect, increasing the frequency of the light incident on a metal surface
    (a) decreases the threshold frequency for the emission of photoelectrons
    (b) decreases the number of photoelectrons emitted
    (c) increases the threshold frequency for the emission of photoelectrons
    (d) increases the kinetic energy of the most energetic photoelectrons
    (e) does not affect the kinetic energy of the photoelectrons

Use **Figure 1** to answer questions 13 to 15. **Figure 1** shows the results of an experiment involving the photoelectric effect. The graph shows the currents observed in the photocell circuit as a function of the potential difference between the plates of the photocell when light beams A, B, C, and D, each with its own wavelength, were each directed at the photocell.

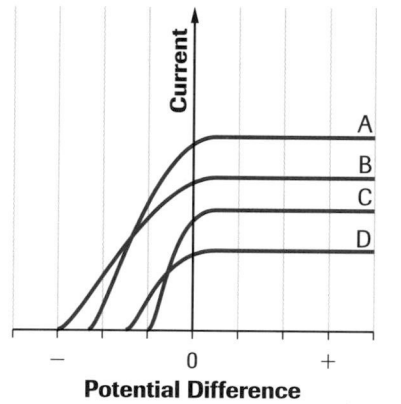

Figure 1
Graph of current versus potential difference for four different beams of light (for questions 13, 14, 15)

13. Which of the beams of light had the highest frequency?
    (a) A   (c) C   (e) They all had the same
    (b) B   (d) D   frequency.

14. Which of the beams of light had the longest wavelength?
    (a) A   (c) C   (e) They all had the same
    (b) B   (d) D   wavelength.

15. Which of the beams of light ejected photoelectrons having the greatest momentum?
    (a) A   (d) D
    (b) B   (e) They all ejected photoelectrons
    (c) C   having the same momentum.

Use **Figure 2** to answer questions 16 and 17. Here, electrons of a single energy are focused into a thin pencil-like beam incident at 90° on a very thin crystalline film of gold. On the other side of the film, a pattern of circular rings is observed on a fluorescent screen.

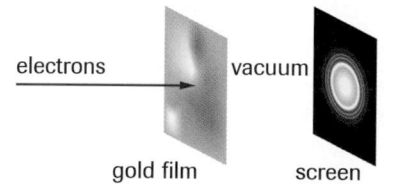

electrons   vacuum

gold film   screen

Figure 2
For questions 16 and 17

NEL   An interactive version of the quiz is available online.
GO www.science.nelson.com

Waves, Photons, and Matter   **659**

16. This experiment provides evidence for
    (a) the wave nature of matter
    (b) the high speed of electrons
    (c) circular electron orbits around nuclei
    (d) the spherical shape of the gold atom
    (e) none of these

17. If the energy of the electrons were increased, the rings would
    (a) assume the shape of an increasingly eccentric ellipse
    (b) remain essentially unchanged
    (c) become less intense
    (d) increase in width
    (e) decrease in size

Use **Figure 3** to answer questions 18 to 20. **Figure 3** shows a Franck–Hertz experiment performed using an accelerating potential of 8.00 V in a tube containing mercury vapour.

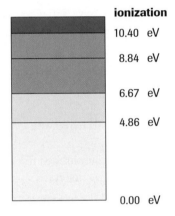

ionization

10.40 eV

8.84 eV

6.67 eV

4.86 eV

0.00 eV

Figure 3
Energy levels for mercury (for questions 18, 19, 20)

18. After passing through the gas, the electrons can have energies
    (a) of 4.86 eV and 6.67 eV only
    (b) of 1.33 eV and 8.00 eV only
    (c) of 0.84 eV, 2.40 eV, and 8.00 eV only
    (d) of 3.14 eV, 1.33 eV, and 8.00 eV only
    (e) in a continuum of values from 0 to 8.00 eV

19. An electron of kinetic energy 9.00 eV collides with a mercury atom that is in the ground state. The mercury atom
    (a) can only be excited to an energy of 8.84 eV
    (b) can only be excited to an energy of 1.40 eV
    (c) can only be excited to an energy of 0.16 eV
    (d) can be excited to any of the 4.86 eV, 6.67 eV, or 8.84 eV energy levels
    (e) cannot be excited by this electron

20. A photon of energy 9.00 eV collides with a mercury atom in the ground state. The mercury atom
    (a) can only be excited to an energy of 8.84 eV
    (b) can only be excited to an energy of 1.40 eV
    (c) can only be excited to an energy of 0.16 eV
    (d) can be excited to any of the 4.86 eV, 6.67 eV, or 8.84 eV energy levels
    (e) cannot be excited by this photon

21. Consider the following predictions made on the basis of the Rutherford model of the atom:
    I. Electrons in an atom spiral into the nucleus.
    II. The nuclei of atoms scatter α particles in a Coulomb interaction.
    III. De-exciting atoms will emit light in a continuous spectrum, rather than in a discrete set of colours.

    Of these predictions,
    (a) only I is contradicted by observation
    (b) only II is contradicted by observation
    (c) only I and II are contradicted by observation
    (d) only I and III are contradicted by observation
    (e) none are consistent with observations

For questions 22 to 24, recall that $c = 3.00 \times 10^8$ m/s, $h = 6.63 \times 10^{-34}$ J·s, and 1 eV $= 1.6 \times 10^{-19}$ J, and assume further that the following are energy levels for a hydrogen-like atom:

$n = \infty$ ...	18 eV
$n = 5$ ...	17 eV
$n = 4$ ...	15 eV
$n = 3$ ...	12 eV
$n = 2$ ...	8 eV
$n = 1$ ...	0 eV

22. The ionization potential of this atom is
    (a) 0 V
    (b) 8 V
    (c) 10 V
    (d) 18 V
    (e) impossible to compute from the data given

23. The energy of the photon emitted when this atom de-excites from the state $n = 3$ to the state $n = 2$ is
    (a) 4 eV   (c) 8 eV   (e) 12 eV
    (b) 6 eV   (d) 10 eV

24. An electron of kinetic energy 10 eV bombards this atom in its ground state. A possible value for the kinetic energy of this electron *after* this interaction is
    (a) 0 eV   (c) 8 eV   (e) 28 eV
    (b) 2 eV   (d) 18 eV

Understanding Concepts

1. Explain, using the photon theory, why we cannot see in the dark.

2. In a photographer's darkroom light is very damaging to the sensitive film emulsions, ruining photographs. However, we may use red light bulbs when working with some types of film. Using the photon theory, explain why red light does not affect the photographic film.

3. When monochromatic light illuminates a photoelectric surface, photoelectrons with many different speeds, up to some maximum value, are ejected. Explain why there is a variation in the speeds.

4. Calculate the longest wavelength of light that can eject electrons from a surface with a work function of 2.46 eV.

5. Light with the wavelength 6.0×10^2 nm strikes a metal having a work function of 2.3×10^{-19} J. Calculate the maximum kinetic energy, in joules, of the emitted electrons and the potential difference required to stop them.

6. Light with wavelength 4.30×10^2 nm falls onto a photoelectric surface. The maximum kinetic energy of the photoelectrons is 1.21 eV. Calculate the work function of the surface.

7. Calculate the momentum of a 4.10×10^2-nm photon of violet light.

8. Calculate the energy, in electron volts, required to give an electron an associated de Broglie wavelength of 7.5×10^{-10} m.

9. An electron is accelerated from rest through a potential difference of 1.50×10^4 V. Calculate its associated de Broglie wavelength.

10. An electron is fired at a metal target, reaching a speed of 1.00×10^6 m/s. On impact, it rapidly decelerates to half that speed, emitting a photon in the process. Calculate the wavelength of the photon.

11. (a) Calculate the wavelength of a photon that has the same magnitude of momentum as an electron moving with a speed of 2.52×10^6 m/s.
    (b) Calculate the de Broglie wavelength associated with the electron.

12. How does the diffraction of electrons by a thin nickel foil illustrate the concept of wave–particle duality?

13. Identify the major discrepancies between observation and Rutherford's explanations of the emission of light by atoms.

14. Why is it difficult for an observer on Earth to determine by spectral analysis whether the atmospheres of Venus and Mars contain oxygen? Briefly explain your reasoning.

15. When light of a continuous mix of wavelengths, ranging from the deep ultraviolet to the deep infrared, passes through hydrogen gas at room temperature, only the Lyman series of absorption lines is observed. Explain why we do not observe any of the other series.

16. Suppose the electron in a hydrogen atom obeyed classical mechanics rather than quantum mechanics. Explain why such a hypothetical atom should emit a continuous spectrum.

17. Explain why deep ultraviolet and X rays are called ionizing radiation.

18. State the principle of complementarity.

19. Explain the differences and similarities between the interference of water waves and the interference of electrons.

20. Compare how particles are viewed in quantum mechanics versus how they are viewed in classical mechanics.

21. Assuming that the hydrogen atom is spherical, by what factor is its volume greater when in its first excited state than when in its ground state?

22. What experimental evidence supported Bohr's postulate concerning the existence of discrete energy levels in the hydrogen atom?

23. Describe the change in each of the following quantities as an electron passes from one Bohr orbit to the next higher energy orbit:
    (a) speed   (c) energy
    (b) orbital radius (d) de Broglie wavelength

24. According to the Bohr theory, what is the radius of the second excited state of the hydrogen atom?

25. The average solar power received at ground level in Toronto and Montreal is about 1.0 kW/m².
    (a) If the average wavelength of sunlight is 5.50×10^2 nm, how many photons per second strike an area of 1.0 cm²? Assume that the light rays strike the surface at 90°.
    (b) Calculate how many photons you would find in a thimble with a volume of 1 cm³.

26. How does the principle of uncertainty apply to an electron orbiting a nucleus?

27. Can an object ever be truly at rest? Use the uncertainty principle to explain.

Applying Inquiry Skills

28. Create a graph of electric current versus accelerating potential that represents the findings of the Franck–Hertz experiment.

29. The graph in **Figure 1** shows the kinetic energy of the most energetic photoelectrons as a function of the frequency of light falling on the cathode in a photoelectric cell.
    (a) According to the graph, what potential difference would be required to stop all the emitted electrons if the incident light had a frequency of 7.5×10^{14} Hz?
    (b) What is the physical significance of the intercept of the graph with the frequency axis (x-axis)?
    (c) What is the physical significance of the intercept obtained when the graph is extrapolated back to the kinetic energy axis (y-axis)?
    (d) Use the graph to determine a value for Planck's constant.

30. You used a spectroscope with a 5000-line/cm grating to determine the wavelength of the green line of mercury. **Figure 2** gives your measurements. Calculate the wavelength of the first-order green line of mercury.

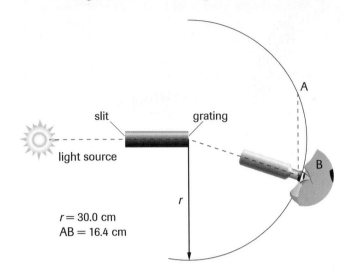

$r = 30.0$ cm
$AB = 16.4$ cm

Figure 2

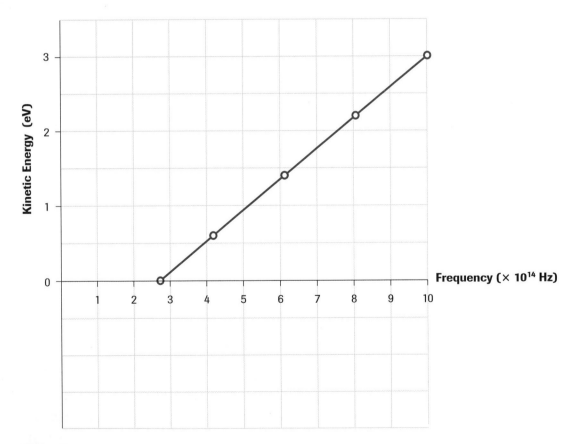

Figure 1
Maximum kinetic energy versus frequency (for question 29)

Making Connections

31. One of the most important applications of the photo-electric effect is the solar cell (**Figure 3**). Research the Internet and other sources and answer the following questions:

    (a) How do solar cells use the photoelectric effect?

    (b) Comment on their efficiency, identifying measures taken to enhance it.

    (c) List the significant advantages and disadvantages of solar cells in comparison with other forms of electrical generation.

    (d) Describe three applications of the solar cell on Earth and two in space.

    (e) Suggest how solar cells may be used in the future.

 www.science.nelson.com

Figure 3
The Hubble Space Telescope uses solar cells to generate power.

32. A high-speed neutron liberated in a nuclear reactor has a speed of approximately 4×10^6 m/s. When such a neutron approaches a uranium nucleus, instead of hitting the nucleus and causing fission (splitting the atom into two relatively equal parts, with a release of energy), the neutron tends to diffract around it. For this reason, a moderator, such as heavy water or graphite, slows the neutrons down to approximately 2×10^3 m/s, making fission-producing collisions more likely. Using your knowledge of matter waves, explain why a moderator is necessary to enhance the probability of fission. Using your knowledge of elastic collisions, explain how the moderator achieves its design objective.

33. Some of the vocabulary of physics has found its way into the vernacular. For example, "quantum leap" is used to describe significant changes in anything, and "polarization" is used with reference to opinions, political views, and philosophies. Describe the use of two or more other words from the world of physics that have become part of the vernacular.

Extension

34. In a Young's double-slit experiment performed with electrons in place of photons, the angle locating the first-order bright fringes is $\theta_1 = 1.6 \times 10^{-4\circ}$ when the magnitude of the electron momentum is $p_1 = 1.2 \times 10^{-22}$ kg·m/s. What momentum magnitude p_2 is necessary with this same pair of slits if an angle $\theta_2 = 4.0 \times 10^{-4\circ}$ is to locate the first-order bright fringe?

35. An electron and a proton are accelerated to equal kinetic energies, attaining speeds low enough to keep relativistic effects negligible. Find the ratio of their de Broglie wavelengths.

36. The neutrons in a parallel beam, each having a speed of 8.75×10^6 m/s, are directed through two slits 5.0×10^{-6} apart. How far apart will the interference maxima be on a screen 1.0 m away?

37. The kinetic energy of a certain particle is equal to the energy of a photon. The particle moves at 5.0% the speed of light. Find the ratio of the photon wavelength to the de Broglie wavelength of the particle.

38. The total number of protons in the known universe is estimated to be about 10^{81}; the radius of a proton is about 10^{-15} m. What is the order of magnitude of the radius of the sphere, in metres, that would contain all these protons if they were tightly packed together?

📱 Sir Isaac Newton Contest Question

13

Radioactivity and Elementary Particles

Curiosity drives scientific research. At the heart of every scientific investigation is a question that usually begins with how or why. How do stars like the Sun produce the enormous amounts of heat and light that radiate through space? Why will a sample of uranium expose photographic film in the dark? Why does the universe appear to be expanding? Ultimately, scientists would like to know how all of the matter and energy in the universe came to be.

In their search for answers to the great questions of science, scientists have constructed grand theories that attempt to explain the nature of very large entities, such as planets, stars, and galaxies, and very small things, such as atoms, protons, and electrons. Two of the most fundamental theories of science—the theory of relativity and quantum mechanics—stand in stark contrast to one another. Einstein's general theory of relativity explains the nature of gravity and its effects on very large objects and the quantum theory describes the nature of very small objects. Since protons, electrons, planets, and galaxies are all forms of matter that interact through the four fundamental forces of nature, it seems reasonable that a single theory should exist that explains the nature of everything.

For the last thirty years of his life, Einstein tried—and failed—to devise an all-encompassing view of the universe by attempting to unify relativity and quantum mechanics. It almost seems as if the universe obeys two sets of rules: one for the very large and one for the very small.

How much progress has been made since Einstein's death in 1955? We now have steadily improving models that describe *what* happens at the level of the fundamental building blocks of matter. This, in turn, may shed light on the more fundamental question of *why* matter behaves as it does. It is possible that physics will, in your lifetime, discover a theory that unites everything.

💡 REFLECT on your learning ▼

1. Define or describe radioactivity.

2. Many discoveries in archaeology depend on radiocarbon dating. How is this related to radioactivity?

3. (a) What are the four fundamental forces of nature?
   (b) Which of these forces causes a stationary golf ball to move when it is hit with a club?
   (c) Which of these forces hold the neutrons and protons together in a nucleus?

4. (a) What is antimatter?
   (b) What happens when antimatter collides with matter?

5. If a substance has a half-life of two days, what percentage of a sample of the material will there be after four days?

6. What are elementary particles and how are they classified?

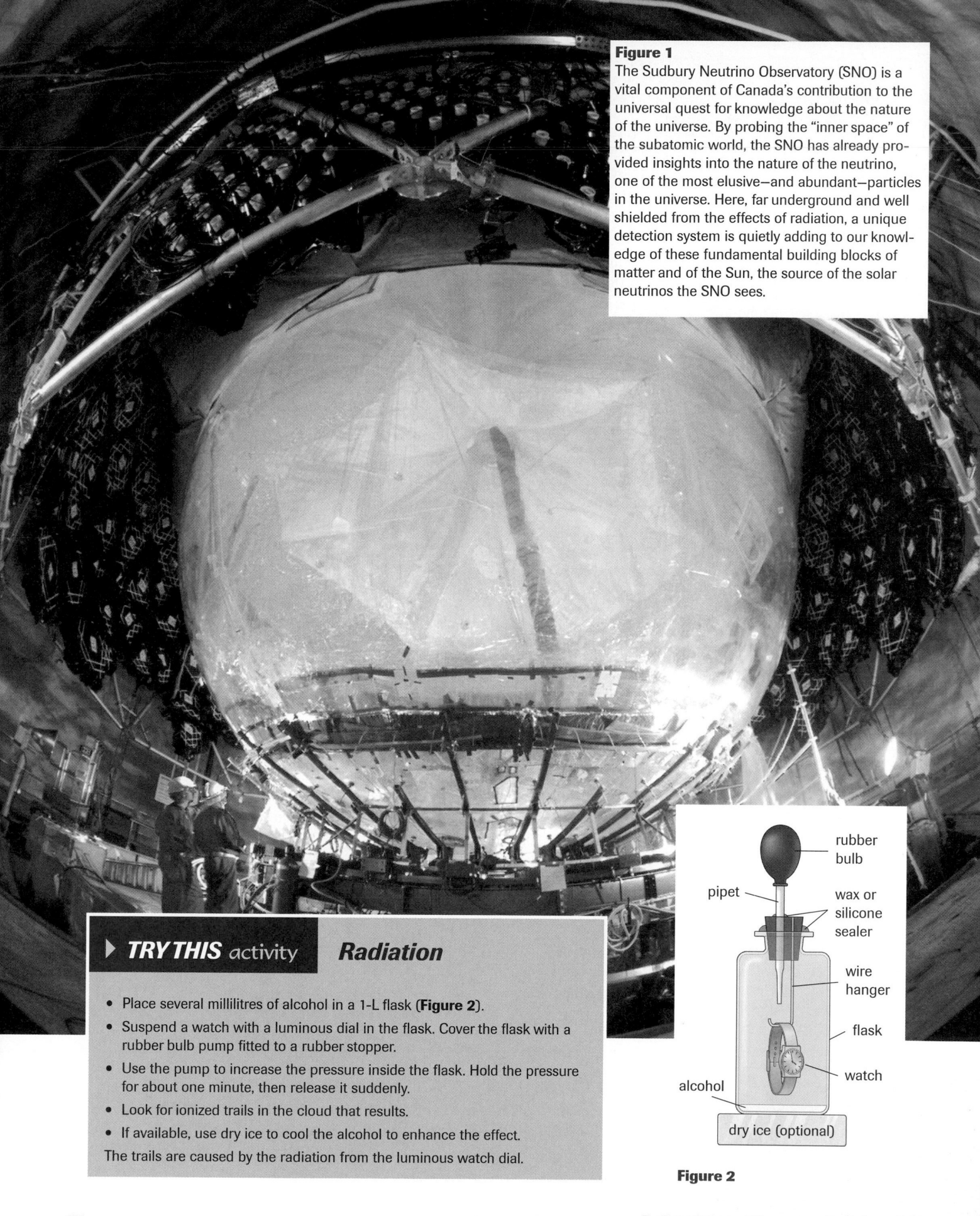

Figure 1
The Sudbury Neutrino Observatory (SNO) is a vital component of Canada's contribution to the universal quest for knowledge about the nature of the universe. By probing the "inner space" of the subatomic world, the SNO has already provided insights into the nature of the neutrino, one of the most elusive—and abundant—particles in the universe. Here, far underground and well shielded from the effects of radiation, a unique detection system is quietly adding to our knowledge of these fundamental building blocks of matter and of the Sun, the source of the solar neutrinos the SNO sees.

▶ **TRY THIS** activity   *Radiation*

- Place several millilitres of alcohol in a 1-L flask (**Figure 2**).
- Suspend a watch with a luminous dial in the flask. Cover the flask with a rubber bulb pump fitted to a rubber stopper.
- Use the pump to increase the pressure inside the flask. Hold the pressure for about one minute, then release it suddenly.
- Look for ionized trails in the cloud that results.
- If available, use dry ice to cool the alcohol to enhance the effect.

The trails are caused by the radiation from the luminous watch dial.

rubber bulb

pipet

wax or silicone sealer

wire hanger

flask

watch

alcohol

dry ice (optional)

Figure 2

radioactivity the spontaneous emission of electromagnetic (gamma) radiation or particles of nonzero mass by a nucleus

LEARNING *TIP*

Isotopes
An isotope is a form of an element in which the atoms have the same number of protons as all other forms of that element but a different number of neutrons. The designation ^4_2He is a way of representing an atom, in this case, helium; 4 is the atomic mass number (equal to the number of protons and neutrons), and 2 is the atomic number (equal to the number of protons). The following symbols are all accepted ways of representing the isotope of helium containing two protons and two neutrons: ^4_2He, helium-4, He-4, and ^4He.

alpha (α) particle a form of radiation consisting of two protons and two neutrons, emitted during α decay

Radioactivity

Unexpected observations tend to trigger flurries of research. These, in turn, can lead science into new and exciting directions. The discovery by Henri Becquerel (1852–1908) in 1896 is a fascinating example: while studying phosphorescence, Becquerel noticed that an ore containing uranium had the ability to darken a photographic plate even when the plate was completely covered and protected from light. Shortly afterward, other scientists, including Pierre (1859–1906) and Marie (1867–1934) Curie, isolated other substances exhibiting this property.

Unlike other properties, such as magnetism and electrical conductivity, this new property was different. It was unaffected by physical treatments, such as heating and cooling, and it remained even after the strongest chemical treatment. Clearly, **radioactivity**, as it was eventually named, appeared to be a fundamental property of the atom. The nucleus of a radioactive atom emits radiation as it decomposes (decays).

New discoveries were imminent. Intense research by Rutherford and his colleagues, most of it done at McGill University in Montreal, revealed radioactive emissions to be of three types, initially referred to as alpha particles, beta particles, and gamma rays.

In alpha (α) decay, nuclei emit positively charged objects, α particles, at speeds perhaps as high as 1.6×10^7 m/s (**Figure 1**). An α-particle beam from a typical natural source, such as pitchblende, a source of uranium, can penetrate only about 5 cm of air and is stopped with just a few sheets of paper.

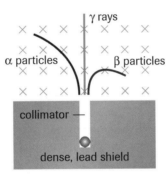

Figure 1
Alpha particles, beta particles, and gamma rays in a magnetic field. The collimator acts like a gun barrel to ensure that the particles are initially travelling in a straight line. The crosses indicate that the direction of the magnetic field is into the page of this book.

The particles emitted in beta (β) decay are primarily negatively charged particles (**Figure 1**). In some cases, the particles may be positively charged. Beta particles from a typical radioactive source travel at less than the speed of light but faster than α particles. A β particle beam can pass through 3 mm to 6 mm of aluminum.

Unlike α and β particles, gamma (γ) decay produces a form of electromagnetic radiation called γ rays. These are photons that travel at the speed of light (**Figure 1**). A beam of γ rays from a typical radioactive source can pass through a lead barrier as thick as 30 cm. Photons do not have an electric charge.

Alpha Decay

The **alpha (α) particles** detected by Rutherford were found to consist of two protons and two neutrons. Since the nucleus of the most abundant isotope of helium consists of these particles, the α particle is often designated $^4_2$He and may be viewed as equivalent to a helium nucleus. When a radioactive material emits an α particle, the nucleus of one if its atoms loses two protons and two neutrons. The loss of two protons changes the atom from one type of element to another. This process is called **transmutation**. The nucleus of the new atom is called the **daughter nucleus**. Alpha particles are put to work in a smoke detector (**Figure 2**). Here, a small quantity of americium dioxide emits α particles that ionize air molecules, causing a small current to flow between two plates in a circurt. Smoke interferes with the ionization process, reducing the current between the plates. This activates the alarm circuit which sounds the alarm.

If an atom of element X transmutes into element Y by emitting an α particle, we say that a nuclear reaction has occurred. The total number of protons and neutrons is conserved. The nuclear reaction can be represented symbolically in an equation as

$$^{A}_{Z}X \rightarrow {}^{4}_{2}He + {}^{A-4}_{Z-2}Y$$

where A is the atomic mass number (the number of particles, or *nucleons*, in the nucleus) and Z is the atomic number (the number of protons).

> ### ▶ *SAMPLE* problem *1*
>
> An unstable polonium atom spontaneously emits an α particle and transmutes into an atom of some other element. Show the process, including the new element, in standard nuclear-reaction notation.
>
> #### Solution
>
> X = new element
>
> $$^{218}_{84}Po \rightarrow {}^{4}_{2}He + {}^{A-4}_{Z-2}X$$
>
> $$^{218}_{84}Po \rightarrow {}^{4}_{2}He + {}^{218-4}_{84-2}X$$
>
> $$^{218}_{84}Po \rightarrow {}^{4}_{2}He + {}^{214}_{82}X$$
>
> Every element has a unique atomic number. The periodic table shows the new element to be lead (Pb). The finalized equation can now be written:
>
> $$^{218}_{84}Po \rightarrow {}^{4}_{2}He + {}^{214}_{82}Pb$$
>
> In the nuclear reaction, polonium transmutes into lead by α decay.

Recall that α particles emitted in nuclear decay have the ability to penetrate 5 cm of air and to penetrate a few sheets of paper. They must therefore possess some kinetic energy. Since energy is a conserved quantity, we may ask where the kinetic energy comes from. The theory of *binding energy* and the *strong nuclear force* give a satisfactory answer.

The protons within the nucleus repel one another through the electric force. A stable nucleus must therefore be held together by a force that is—at least over short distances—stronger than the electric force. This force is called the **strong nuclear force**. The strong nuclear force is only effective over distances on the order of about 1.5×10^{-15} m, which is about the radius of a small nucleus. Since the strong nuclear force is attractive, work must be done to break the nucleus apart.

Binding Energy

Studies have shown that the mass of an atomic nucleus is always less than the sum of the masses of its constituent neutrons and protons. The energy equivalent of the mass difference is the **binding energy**, or (positive) work that would have to be done to break a nucleus apart.

transmutation the process of changing an atom of one element into another as a result of radioactive decay

daughter nucleus the nucleus of an atom created as a result of radioactive decay

(a) Normal operation

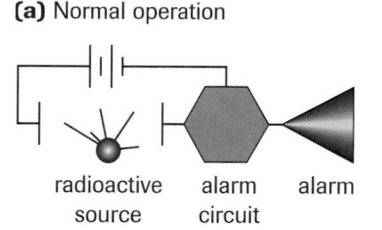

radioactive source   alarm circuit   alarm

(b) Smoke present

radioactive source   alarm circuit   alarm

Figure 2
A smoke detector is a life-saving device that uses a radioactive material in part of its circuitry.
(a) A tiny quantity of radioactive americium dioxide emits α particles, which ionize air molecules and, consequently, permit a small current to flow between the plates.
(b) Smoke particles absorb the radiation and cause the current to drop significantly, thus activating an alarm circuit.

strong nuclear force the force that binds the nucleus of a stable atom

binding energy the energy required to break up the nucleus into protons and neutrons

Recall that the relation $E = mc^2$ relates the mass of an object in kilograms to the energy of the object in joules. If the mass is given in atomic mass units (u), then the following conversion to electron volts can be made:

$$1\,u = 1.66054 \times 10^{-27}\,kg$$

$$E = mc^2$$
$$= (1.66054 \times 10^{-27}\,kg)(2.9979 \times 10^8\,m/s)^2$$
$$E = 1.4923 \times 10^{-10}\,J$$

$$1\,eV = 1.6022 \times 10^{-19}\,J$$
$$E = 1.4923 \times 10^{-10}\,J \times \frac{1\,eV}{1.6022 \times 10^{-19}\,J}$$
$$= 9.315 \times 10^8\,eV$$
$$E = 931.5\,MeV$$

$$E = mc^2$$
$$m = \frac{E}{c^2}$$
$$E = 931.5\,MeV/c^2$$

Since $m = u$,

$$u = 931.5\,MeV/c^2$$

Therefore, $1\,u = 931.5\,MeV/c^2$.

The Meaning of MeV/c^2

MeV/c^2 is a unit of mass commonly used in physics.

$1\,MeV/c^2 = 1.782\,663 \times 10^{-30}\,kg$

▶ *SAMPLE* problem 2

Molecules of "heavy water," used both in CANDU nuclear reactors and in the Sudbury Neutrino Observatory, contain an oxygen atom, an ordinary hydrogen atom, and an atom of the rare hydrogen isotope *deuterium*. A *deuteron* is the name given to the nucleus of a deuterium atom. It is composed of a proton and a neutron. Calculate the binding energy per nucleon in a deuteron.

Solution

$$m_d = 2.013553\,u\ \text{(from Appendix C)}$$
$$m_p = 1.007276\,u$$
$$m_n = 1.008665\,u$$

$$E = ((m_p + m_n) - m_d)c^2$$
$$= ((1.007276\,u + 1.008665\,u) - 2.013553\,u)c^2$$
$$E = (0.002388\,u)c^2$$

Since $1\,u = 931.5\,MeV/c^2$,

$$E = (0.002338\,u)c^2 \left(\frac{931.5\,MeV/c^2}{1\,u}\right)$$
$$= 2.18\,MeV$$
$$E = 2.18 \times 10^6\,eV$$

The deuteron has two nucleons (a proton and a neutron; therefore,

$$E_n = \frac{E}{2}$$
$$= \frac{2.18 \times 10^6\,eV}{2}$$
$$E_n = 1.09 \times 10^6\,eV$$

The binding energy per nucleon is $1.09 \times 10^6\,eV$.

Figure 3 is a graph of the average binding energies per nucleon for all the elements. The average binding energy per nucleon is a maximum when the mass number is 56 (which is the case for iron) and decreases steadily afterward. Nuclei near the middle of the periodic table are thus held together more strongly than other nuclei.

Why is it that the middle elements have the highest binding energies? The nucleus is a battleground between the strong nuclear and electromagnetic forces. As we move in the periodic table toward iron, we find the nuclei have more nucleons, all pulling inward on each other. The binding energy therefore rises. As we move farther away from the middle elements, we have still more nucleons. Now, however, some pairs of nucleons are so widely separated that they can no longer experience the mutual attraction due to the (short-range) strong nuclear force. The proton pairs among these nucleon pairs continue to feel the repulsion of the infinite-range electromagnetic force. For the really massive elements, for example, radium, polonium, and uranium, the binding energy is so low that the nucleus is not stable at all. Once in a while, two protons and two neutrons get together and form an α particle inside the nucleus. The α particle has kinetic energy and is released in its creation.

When we compare the mass of the parent nucleus with the sum of the masses of the daughter nucleus and an α particle, we find that the products of the nuclear decay are less massive (**Figure 4**). This missing mass appears as the increased kinetic energy of the products.

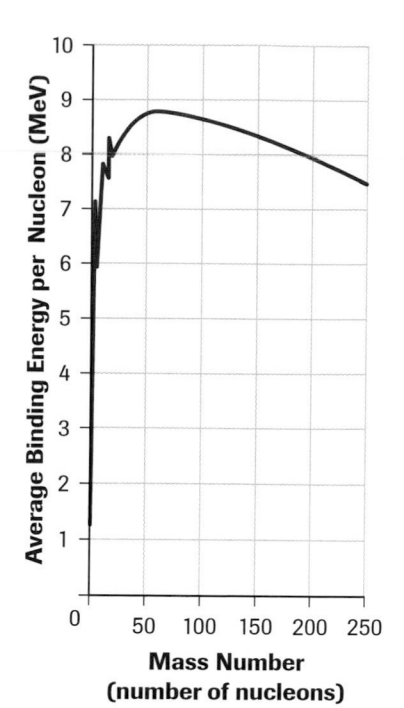

Figure 3
Average binding energy per nucleon versus mass number

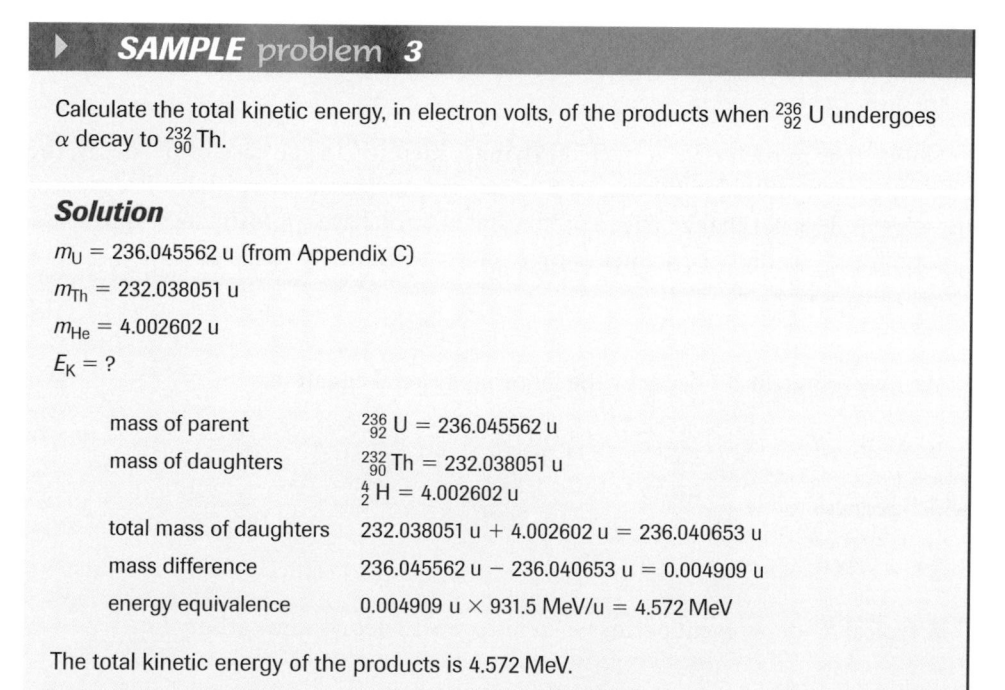

▶ *SAMPLE* problem **3**

Calculate the total kinetic energy, in electron volts, of the products when $^{236}_{92}$ U undergoes α decay to $^{232}_{90}$ Th.

Solution

$m_U = 236.045562$ u (from Appendix C)

$m_{Th} = 232.038051$ u

$m_{He} = 4.002602$ u

$E_K = ?$

mass of parent	$^{236}_{92}$ U $= 236.045562$ u
mass of daughters	$^{232}_{90}$ Th $= 232.038051$ u
	$^{4}_{2}$ H $= 4.002602$ u
total mass of daughters	232.038051 u $+ 4.002602$ u $= 236.040653$ u
mass difference	236.045562 u $- 236.040653$ u $= 0.004909$ u
energy equivalence	0.004909 u $\times 931.5$ MeV/u $= 4.572$ MeV

The total kinetic energy of the products is 4.572 MeV.

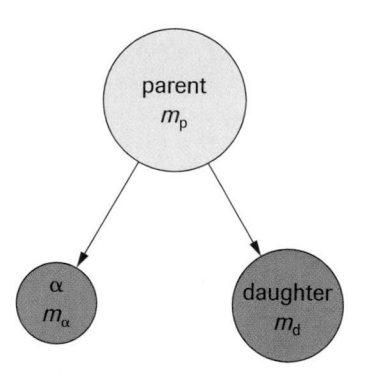

Figure 4
According to conservation of mass, we should have $m_p = m_\alpha + m_d$. However, $m_p > m_\alpha + m_d$. The missing mass is converted into kinetic energy according to the relationship $E = mc^2$.

Although both products share the liberated kinetic energy, they do not share it equally. Recall that momentum is a conserved quantity. If an object, stationary in some inertial frame, breaks into two fragments, conservation of momentum requires that the two fragments fly off in opposite directions in that frame, with the vector sum of their momenta equalling zero. The recoil velocities of the fragments depend on their relative masses. When you jump from a small boat stationary with respect to the shore, you and the boat move in opposite directions relative to the shore. Because you are much less massive than the boat, you move faster than the boat does, making your momentum, $m_1\vec{v}_1$, equal and opposite to the momentum $m_2\vec{v}_2$ of the boat.

We can apply this analysis to the α decay of uranium into thorium. Consider a thorium nucleus at rest in an inertial frame of reference. Since $m_{\text{Th}} >> m_\alpha$, after emitting an α particle, the thorium atom's recoil velocity will be much smaller than the speed of the emitted α particle since momentum and energy are conserved.

Beta Decay

The **beta (β) particles** emitted in some forms of radioactive decay may be negatively charged electrons or positively charged electrons, called **positrons**. A positron is a particle like an electron in every way except that it is positively charged. When the β decay releases electrons, it is called β^- decay; when it releases positrons, it is called β^+ decay. The β particle is symbolized as $_{-1}^{0}e$ if it is an electron and $_{+1}^{0}e$ if it is a positron. β^- decay is much more common than β^+ decay.

It is important to note that the electron released in β^- decay is not one of the electrons in the orbitals of an atom that participates in chemical bonding. The β^- particle is produced in the nucleus of the radioactive atom. Although the mechanism of its production is complex, it can be likened to the conversion of a neutron into a proton and an electron:

$$_{0}^{1}n \rightarrow \, _{1}^{1}p + \, _{-1}^{0}e$$

β^+ decay can be considered the equivalent of a proton changing into a neutron and a positron:

$$_{1}^{1}p \rightarrow \, _{0}^{1}n + \, _{+1}^{0}e$$

Notice that in each case, a nucleon changes identity. In the case of β^- decay, the nucleus gains a proton; in the case of β^+ decay, the nucleus loses a proton. The mass of the nucleus does not change since a proton and neutron have approximately equal mass.

A typical β^- decay occurs when carbon-14 decays into nitrogen-14:

$$_{6}^{14}C \rightarrow \, _{7}^{14}N + \, _{-1}^{0}e$$

We may represent β^- decay by the following general equation:

$$_{Z}^{A}X \rightarrow \, _{Z-(-1)}^{A}Y + \, _{-1}^{0}e$$

which reduces to

$$_{Z}^{A}X \rightarrow \, _{Z+1}^{A}Y + \, _{-1}^{0}e$$

A typical β^+ decay event occurs when nitrogen-12 decays into carbon-12:

$$_{7}^{12}N \rightarrow \, _{6}^{12}C + \, _{+1}^{0}e$$

In general,

$$_{Z}^{A}X \rightarrow \, _{Z-(+1)}^{A}Y + \, _{-1}^{0}e$$

which reduces to

$$_{Z}^{A}X \rightarrow \, _{Z-1}^{A}Y + \, _{+1}^{0}e$$

β^+ decay occurs in isotopes that have too few neutrons in comparison with their number of protons.

beta (β) particle negatively charged particles emitted during β^- decay (electrons); positively charged electrons (positrons) emitted in β^+ decay

positron a particle identical to an electron but with a positive charge; also called an antielectron

> ▶ **SAMPLE** problem **4**

An atom of sodium-24 can transmute into an atom of some other element by emitting a β^- particle. Represent this reaction in symbols, and identify the daughter element.

Solution

$$^{24}_{11}\text{Na} \rightarrow {}^{A}_{Z+1}\text{Y} + {}^{0}_{-1}\text{e}$$

$$^{24}_{11}\text{Na} \rightarrow {}^{24}_{11+1}\text{Y} + {}^{0}_{-1}\text{e}$$

$$^{24}_{11}\text{Na} \rightarrow {}^{24}_{12}\text{Y} + {}^{0}_{-1}\text{e}$$

The periodic table reveals the new element to be magnesium:

$$^{24}_{11}\text{Na} \rightarrow {}^{24}_{12}\text{Mg} + {}^{0}_{-1}\text{e}$$

When sodium-24 undergoes β^- decay, magnesium-24 is produced.

As was the case for α decay, an understanding of the equation $E = mc^2$ helps us calculate a theoretical value for the energy released in a single β decay.

> ▶ **SAMPLE** problem **5**

Calculate the energy released by the reaction in Sample Problem 4.

Solution

$m_{\text{Na}} = 23.990961 \text{ u}$ (from Appendix C)

$m_{\text{Mg}} = 23.985042 \text{ u}$

$$\Delta m = m_{\text{Na}} - m_{\text{Mg}}$$
$$= (23.990961 \text{ u} - 23.985042 \text{ u})$$
$$\Delta m = 0.005937 \text{ u}$$

Since $1 \text{ u} = 931.5 \text{ MeV}$,

$$\Delta E = (0.005937 \text{ u})(931.4 \text{ MeV/u})$$
$$\Delta E = 5.5297 \text{ MeV}$$

The energy released is 5.5297 MeV.

> **LEARNING TIP**
>
> **Masses**
> Sample Problem 5 illustrates that you can use the mass of the neutral atom since it contains the same components as the products of the interaction.

Recall that the mass of the electron is approximately 2000 times less than that of the proton. The mass of the β particle is therefore much, much less than that of the daughter nucleus. Due to the law of conservation of momentum, the recoil velocity of the daughter nucleus should be practically zero. Based on this, you would expect almost 100% of the energy released in the reaction to be found in the β particle.

Unfortunately this was found not to be the case. When experiments were done with atoms that decayed by releasing α particles, the α particles produced all had the same kinetic energy (as measured by their penetrating power), and this energy agreed closely with its calculated value. The β particles, on the other hand, tended to have a range of kinetic energies, all of them less than the law of conservation of energy required. (Typical kinetic energies were just one-third of the value predicted.)

Further, the law of conservation of momentum appeared to be violated. If the reaction really produced just two particles—the daughter nucleus and the β particle—the law of conservation of momentum would require that the decay products move off in opposite directions (in a given inertial frame of reference). This did not occur. Instead, the two particles were found to be ejected at angles other than 180°. Compounding this was the notion that angular momentum also did not seem to be conserved. Recall from Chapter 5 that linear momentum is a quantity of motion, calculated as the product $m\vec{v}$. Like energy, momentum is a conserved quantity. In a similar way, rotating objects also have a quantity of motion called *angular momentum*, which is also a conserved quantity. On the quantum scale, this quantity is called *spin*. (You will learn more about spin in Section 13.5.) Interestingly, the calculations based on the emitted β particles seemed to indicate that this quantity was not conserved.

In 1930, Wolfgang Pauli (1900–1958) suggested an explanation. Perhaps there was another product in the reaction. The third particle would have zero charge and zero, or nearly zero, mass. This particle could carry off the unaccounted kinetic energy, momentum, and angular momentum. Enrico Fermi (1901–1954), who devised a comprehensive theory of β decay, called the particle the "little neutral one," or *neutrino*. The neutrino is represented by the Greek letter nu (ν). When the conservation laws for β decay were recalculated, it was discovered that this particular reaction required an *antineutrino* ($\overline{\nu}$), an "antiparticle" related to the neutrino as the positron (an antielectron), $_{+1}^{0}e$, is related to the electron, $_{-1}^{0}e$. (These are two instances of the distinction between matter and "antimatter," which we shall examine later in this section.) Neutrinos are extremely difficult to detect. The existence of the neutrino was not confirmed until 1956, when some indirect evidence was found. Even today, this particle remains an elusive entity since it has an extremely small probability of reacting with matter.

> ▶ **TRY THIS** activity   ***Neutrinos***
>
> 1. Place your hand on this page.
> 2. Look at your hand and count to 3.
> 3. About 1.5×10^{15} neutrinos just went through your hand.

A more correct equation for the decay process in Sample Problem 4 is thus

$$_{11}^{24}\text{Na} \rightarrow {}_{12}^{24}\text{Mg} + {}_{-1}^{0}e + \overline{\nu}$$

A more correct equation for β^+ decay includes the production of a neutrino as in the following example of the decay of chromium-46 into vanadium-46:

$$_{24}^{46}\text{Cr} \rightarrow {}_{23}^{46}\text{V} + {}_{+1}^{0}e + \nu$$

Therefore, the general equations representing β^- decay and β^+ decay are

$$_{Z}^{A}X \rightarrow {}_{Z+1}^{A}Y + {}_{-1}^{0}e + \overline{\nu} \quad (\beta^- \text{ decay})$$
$$_{Z}^{A}X \rightarrow {}_{Z-1}^{A}Y + {}_{+1}^{0}e + \nu \quad (\beta^+ \text{ decay})$$

Recall that α decay was explained with reference to the strong nuclear force, which binds nucleons together. Neither this force nor the two more familiar fundamental forces—gravity and the electromagnetic force—give a satisfactory explanation of β decay. It was therefore necessary to acknowledge the presence of a fourth force, the *weak nuclear force*, which we will consider later in this chapter. Altogether, we recognize four fundamental forces in nature: the force of gravity, the electromagnetic force, and the strong and weak nuclear forces.

Gamma Decay

Unlike α and β decay, γ decay results in the production of photons that have zero mass and no electric charge. This type of decay occurs when a highly excited nucleus—probably the product of another nuclear reaction—drops to a lower energy state while emitting a photon of energy. If an atom of material Y emits a γ ray (γ photon), then the nuclear reaction can be represented symbolically as

$$^A_Z Y \rightarrow {}^A_Z Y + \gamma$$

Notice that a transmutation does not occur. Gamma decays frequently occur simultaneously with α or β decays. For example, the β^- decay process by which lead-211 transmutes to bismuth-211 is usually accompanied by γ decay as the excited bismuth-211 nucleus drops to a lower state. The reaction is correctly written as follows:

$$^{211}_{82} Pb \rightarrow {}^{211}_{83} Bi + {}^{0}_{-1} e + \overline{\nu} + \gamma$$

In reality, **gamma (γ) rays** are similar to X rays. Typical γ rays are of a higher frequency and thus higher energy than X rays; however, the range of frequencies for both types of rays overlaps. For most practical purposes physicists distinguish between the two based on how they are produced. The rays produced when high-energy electrons interact with matter are normally called X rays, while those produced from within the nucleus are usually called γ rays.

gamma (γ) ray high-frequency emission of (massless, chargeless) photons during γ decay

---

▶ **SAMPLE** problem **6**

Give the value of x and y in each reaction. Classify each as α, β, or γ decay.

(a) $^{212}_{82} Pb \rightarrow {}^{212}_{x} Bi + {}^{0}_{-1} e$

(b) $^{210}_{84} Po \rightarrow {}^{y}_{x} Pb + {}^{4}_{2} He$

(c) $^{227}_{89} Ac \rightarrow {}^{227}_{90} Th + x$

(d) $^{226}_{88} Ra \rightarrow {}^{y}_{x} Ra + \gamma$

Solution

(a) $x = 83$. Since ${}^{0}_{-1} e$ is by definition a β^- particle, the reaction is β^- decay.

(b) $x = 82$, $y = 206$. The reaction is α decay since 2 protons and 2 neutrons are emitted as one particle.

(c) $x = {}^{0}_{-1} e$. The increase by 1 in the atomic number and the lack of change in the mass number together indicate that a proton appeared; therefore this is β^- decay.

(d) $x = 88$, $y = 226$. Since the process is γ decay, neither the atomic number nor the atomic mass number is changed.

▶ **Practice**

Understanding Concepts

1. Give the values of x and y in each of the following equations:

(a) $^{212}_{x} Pb \rightarrow {}^{212}_{83} Bi + y$

(b) $^{214}_{83} Bi \rightarrow {}^{x}_{y} Po + {}^{0}_{-1} e$

(c) $^{x}_{y} Ra \rightarrow {}^{222}_{86} Rn + {}^{4}_{2} He$

(d) $^{215}_{84} Po \rightarrow {}^{211}_{82} Pb + x$

(e) $^{3}_{1} H \rightarrow x + \gamma$

Answers

1. (a) $x = 82$; $y = {}^{0}_{-1} e$

(b) $x = 214$; $y = 84$

(c) $x = 226$; $y = 88$

(d) $x = {}^{4}_{2} He$

(e) $x = {}^{3}_{1} H$

Radiation Detectors

When decay particles pass through a gas, they cause extensive ionization. The α and β particles are charged and have very high kinetic energy (of the order of 1 MeV, compared with the 10 eV or so required for ionization). Consequently, they have little difficulty pulling or knocking orbital electrons loose. The uncharged γ particles can also cause some ionization through either the photoelectric effect or the Compton effect.

A **Geiger-Mueller tube** (Geiger counter) takes advantage of ionization to detect radiation. The device consists of a partially evacuated tube containing a copper cylindrical cathode (negatively charged electrode) and a thin wire anode (positively charged electrode) inside the copper cylinder (**Figure 5**). The potential difference across the electrodes is barely below the point at which a spark will jump across.

Geiger-Mueller tube an instrument that detects and measures the ionization from α and β particles

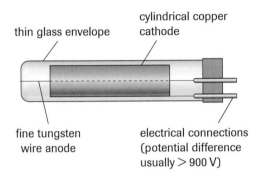

thin glass envelope

cylindrical copper cathode

fine tungsten wire anode

electrical connections (potential difference usually > 900 V)

Figure 5
A Geiger-Mueller tube

scintillation tube an instrument that detects and measures the energy delivered to a crystal by incoming γ photons

When a particle enters the tube, it ionizes many gas molecules. The electrons accelerate toward the anode, the positive ions toward the cathode. The ions collide with neutral molecules in their path and cause even more ionization. The net result is a cascade of negative charge into the anode and positive charge into the cathode, producing a short-lived current. The pulse is then amplified. A resistor in the circuit dissipates the current. The tube then stabilizes until another α or β particle causes another cascade.

Since γ rays do not cause nearly as much ionization as α and β particles, they are difficult to detect with a Geiger-Mueller tube. In their case, the **scintillation tube** (**Figure 6**) is used. The incoming γ photon strikes a scintillation crystal in the tube, giving up much of its energy. The crystal emits this captured energy as a lower-energy photon. When the photon strikes the first of several electrodes, several electrons are released. These, in turn, accelerate toward the second electrode. Each of the impinging, newly liberated electrons causes further releases. The net result is a cascade of electrons striking a final electrode. This small current pulse is amplified and can be used to drive a counter as in some Geiger-Mueller detectors. Since the pulses are proportional to the amount of energy originally deposited by the γ photon in the crystal, they can be used to measure γ-ray energy.

A third type of detector, in common use, uses a semiconductor diode. The semiconductor allows a transient current to flow when a particle strikes it.

incoming photon

photon

light-sensitive cathode

scintillation crystal

+200 V
+400 V
+600 V
+800 V
+1000 V
+1200 V
+1400 V
+1600 V

photomultiplier tube

output pulse

Figure 6
A scintillation tube

Pair Production and Pair Annihilation

In the early 1930s, Carl Anderson (1905–1991) made an intriguing observation. When high-energy radiation from deep space passed through a detector, pairs of particles were produced spontaneously. The incoming radiation (for the most part high-energy X rays) seemed to disappear. In its place pairs of particles appeared. The motion of the particles indicated that they had equal masses and speeds; therefore, they had momenta of equal magnitude and opposite charges of the same magnitude. One of the particles was the familiar electron; the other was called an antielectron, or positron (**Figure 7**). Anderson's observation was in agreement with the mass–energy equivalence from special relativity.

The opposite of this process has also been observed. When electrons and positrons interact, they annihilate one another, usually producing a pair of photons, each with an energy of 0.511 MeV (the rest-mass energy of an electron). The production of two photons, rather than one, is in accordance with conservation of momentum (**Figure 8**).

Antimatter

We have seen that sodium undergoes β^- decay according to the reaction $^{24}_{11}\text{Na} \rightarrow ^{24}_{12}\text{Mg} + ^{0}_{-1}\text{e} + \overline{\nu}$ and that the reaction products include an antineutrino. Current theory holds that every particle has its own antiparticle. In a few cases, the particle is its own antiparticle. Most notably, a photon is its own antiparticle. Think of an antiparticle as a sort of opposite or mirror image of the given particle; for example, the particle and antiparticle are opposite in charge, if they happen to be charged.

The existence of antimatter was first proposed because of the fact that equations with even exponents have more than one root. In the late 1920s the brilliant theoretician Paul Dirac proposed a theory that combined the concepts of special relativity with those of quantum mechanics. Dirac's equation incorporated the wave nature of electrons and the relativity of motion; however there was one peculiarity. With Dirac's new theory the relation between mass and energy was expressed as $E^2 = m^2c^4$. This, in turn, yielded two separate relationships: the now-familiar $E = mc^2$ and a second equation, $E = -mc^2$.

The second equation indicates that the energy of the electron could be negative. Because most physical systems tend to seek the lowest possible energy, the idea has a disturbing consequence: the energy of the electron could, in theory, continue to become more and more negative, without lower bound. This does not make sense.

Dirac's solution to this impossibility called upon the **Pauli exclusion principle**, which says that no more than one particle can occupy any one quantum state. He reasoned that the negative energy states might already be occupied by electrons. Since they had never been observed, Dirac's reasoning asserted that they were invisible.

He went on to contend that if one of the invisible electrons absorbed sufficient energy, it could make a transition to a positive energy state, entering the observable realm. The transition would, in turn, leave behind a "hole" in the realm of particles with negative energy. If the negative-energy particles were invisible, the hole left by the absence of such a particle must be visible. This new particle would resemble an electron in almost all respects, except in being positively charged. This means, overall, that when an electron appeared, it would be accompanied by its opposite, an antielectron, or (as it became known) a positron.

The presence of these particles was confirmed in the early 1930s through studies of radiation from deep space. Some particles, which resembled electrons in all other ways, curved the wrong way in a magnetic field. These had to be the elusive positrons. Many other types of antiparticles, such as antiprotons, antineutrons, and antineutrinos, have since been observed, produced, and even stored.

Later developments in quantum theory solved the problem of preventing electrons from falling into ever-increasing negative energy states. The "negative energy" portion of Dirac's mass–energy relation is still accepted, however. This part of the equation predicts that all types of particles should have a corresponding antiparticle. The holes in the negative energy spectrum were later reinterpreted as positive energy antiparticles.

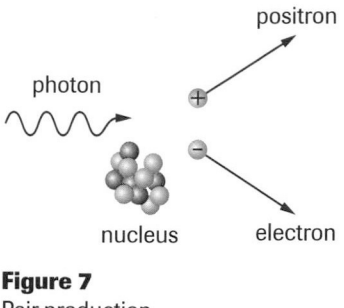

Figure 7
Pair production

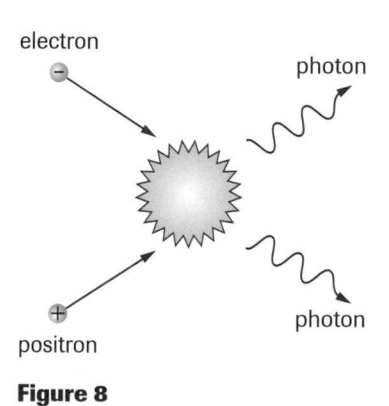

Figure 8
Pair annihilation

Pauli exclusion principle states that no more than one particle can occupy any one quantum state

Radiation and Radioactive Decay

- Alpha decay occurs when an unstable nucleus emits a particle, often denoted as $^4_2$He, which consists of two protons and two neutrons. The resulting daughter nucleus is of a different element and has two protons and two neutrons fewer than the parent.

- Beta decay assumes two forms. In β^- decay, a neutron is replaced with a proton and a β^- particle (a high-speed electron). In β^+ decay, a proton is replaced with a neutron and a β^+ particle (a high-speed positron).

- The analysis of β decays reveals that additional particles, either antineutrinos or neutrinos, must be produced to satisfy the conservation of energy and linear and angular momentum.

- Gamma decay is the result of an excited nucleus that has emitted a photon and dropped to a lower state.

- The twin phenomena of pair production and pair annihilation demonstrate mass–energy equivalence.

▶ *Section 13.1* *Questions*

Understanding Concepts

1. Prepare a table comparing the three types of radioactive emission. Classify each type under the following headings: Type of Emission, Mass, Charge, Speed, Penetrating Power, Ionization Ability.

2. In each of the following equations, identify the missing particle and state whether the element has undergone α or β decay. (Do not include γ emissions.)
   (a) $^{222}_{86}\text{Rn} \rightarrow ^{218}_{84}\text{Po} + ?$
   (b) $^{141}_{57}\text{La} \rightarrow ^{141}_{58}\text{Ce} + ?$
   (c) $^{238}_{92}\text{U} \rightarrow ^{234}_{90}\text{Th} + ?$
   (d) $^{141}_{56}\text{Ba} \rightarrow ^{141}_{57}\text{La} + ?$
   (e) $^{35}_{17}\text{Cl} \rightarrow ^{35}_{18}\text{Ar} + ?$
   (f) $^{212}_{82}\text{Pb} \rightarrow ^{212}_{83}\text{Bi} + ?$
   (g) $^{226}_{88}\text{Ra} \rightarrow ^{222}_{86}\text{Rn} + ?$
   (h) $^{215}_{84}\text{Po} \rightarrow ^{211}_{82}\text{Pb} + ?$

3. Give the value of x and y in each of the following equations:
   (a) $^{212}_{x}\text{Pb} \rightarrow ^{212}_{83}\text{Bi} + y$
   (b) $^{214}_{83}\text{Bi} \rightarrow ^{x}_{y}\text{Po} + ^{0}_{-1}\text{e}$
   (c) $^{x}_{y}\text{Ra} \rightarrow ^{222}_{86}\text{Rn} + ^{4}_{2}\text{He}$
   (d) $^{215}_{84}\text{Po} \rightarrow ^{211}_{82}\text{Pb} + x$
   (e) $^{3}_{1}\text{H} \rightarrow x + \nu$
   (f) $^{141}_{58}\text{Ce} \rightarrow ^{x}_{59}\text{Pr} + ^{0}_{-1}\text{e}$

4. (a) Generally speaking, which tend to be more unstable, small or large nuclei? Explain your answer.
   (b) What implication does this have for elements with large atomic mass numbers?

5. The particles produced when any given isotope undergoes α decay all have the same kinetic energy. The particles produced when a given isotope undergoes β decay, on the other hand, can have a range of values of kinetic energy. Explain the differences.

6. Calculate the total binding energy and the average binding energy per nucleon of carbon-14. See Appendix C for the atomic masses of carbon-14, the neutron, and the proton.

7. Carbon-14 decays by β^- emission.
   (a) Express the reaction in symbols.
   (b) The daughter nucleus produced in the reaction has an atomic mass of 14.003074 u. Calculate the energy released in one decay.

8. Explain why a sample of radioactive material is always slightly warmer than its surroundings.

Making Connections

9. Make an inventory of all of the devices in your home that contain a radioactive substance. Explain the purpose of the radioactive material in the device. Then search the Internet to find out how the consumer products in **Figure 9** use radiation in their manufacture.

(a)

(b)

(c)

Figure 9
(a) Cosmetics are sterilized with radiation to remove allergens.
(b) Nonstick pans are treated with radiation to fix the nonstick coating to the pan.
(c) Computer disks "remember" data better when they are treated with radioactive materials.

Half-Life

The probability that any given nucleus will undergo decay depends on the nature of the nucleus. Some nuclei are more unstable than others and are therefore more likely to decay in any given period of time. It is not possible to determine the exact time that any particular nucleus will undergo radioactive decay.

Because atoms are so small, any significant quantity of material will contain an enormous number of them. When viewed on this scale, probabilistic determinations of the behaviour of the material can be made with great accuracy. Consider this analogy: if a coin is tossed, you have no way to predict, with accuracy, whether the outcome will be heads or tails. On the other hand, if one billion coins were tossed, you could predict, with almost full accuracy, that 50% of the outcomes would be heads. In a similar way, if you have a measurable quantity of a given radioactive substance, you can make an accurate prediction, on the macroscopic scale, about the level of radioactivity at any future instant.

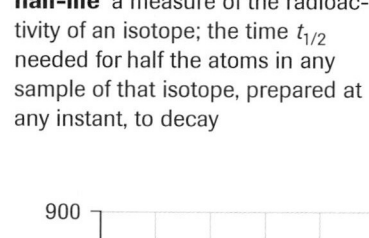

> ▶ **TRY THIS** activity

Modelling Radioactive Decay

Assume that 40 coins represent 40 unstable atoms and that they have two states: decayed or not. Place all the coins in a jar, shake the jar, and empty the coins onto a paper plate. Assume that the coins showing tails have not yet decayed. Record this number and remove these coins from the plate. Discard the coins that came up heads. Place the nondecayed (tails) coins back in the jar and repeat the process. Again, record the number of coins that have not decayed. Continue until all of the coins have decayed. Graph the results and compare the shape of the line to the one shown in **Figure 1**. Comment on the similarity.

The concept of **half-life**, first used by Rutherford, is a useful mathematical tool for modelling radioactive decay. This is based on the premise that the rate at which nuclei decay is related to the number of unstable nuclei present. This reasoning has a powerfully simple outcome: the time needed for one-half of the unstable nuclei to decay will always be a constant.

half-life a measure of the radioactivity of an isotope; the time $t_{1/2}$ needed for half the atoms in any sample of that isotope, prepared at any instant, to decay

---

▶ **SAMPLE** problem **1**

The half-life of carbon-14 is 5730 a. The mass of a certain sample of this isotope is 800 μg. Graph the activity for the first 5 half-lives.

Solution

$m = 800\ \mu g$

$t_{1/2} = \text{half-life} = 5730\ a$

After 5730 a, the amount of carbon-14 remaining will be one-half the original amount, or 400 μg. In another 5730 a, it will be one-half as much again. This reasoning allows you to make the calculations summarized in **Table 1** and construct a plot (**Figure 1**).

Table 1

Time (a)	0	5730	11 460	17 190	22 920	28 650
Amount Remaining (μg)	800	400	200	100	50	25

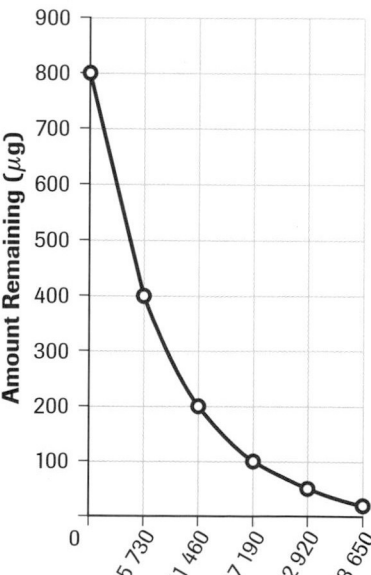

Figure 1
For Sample Problem 1

> ▶ **Practice**

Understanding Concepts

1. Using the information in Sample Problem 1,
   (a) estimate the amount remaining after 1.00×10^4 a
   (b) predict the time at which the amount remaining will be 3.00×10^3 μg

2. A small sample has 5.0×10^{-3} g of radium, the half-life of which is 1600 a.
   (a) Prepare a graph showing the amount remaining for the first 6 half-lives.
   (b) Determine, from your graph, the amount remaining after 5.00×10^3 a.
   (c) At what time will the amount remaining be 1.0×10^3 g?

Applying Inquiry Skills

3. According to **Figure 1**, when will the amount of carbon-14 be zero? Explain whether you think the model is reasonable.

Using an Equation to Model Radioactive Decay

The level of radioactivity in a substance can be thought of as the number of nuclear decays per unit time. A highly radioactive substance is thus one in which the decay is rapid; the half-life would be correspondingly short.

If a sample initially has N unstable nuclei, then the rate of decay can be written as $\dfrac{\Delta N}{\Delta t}$. This quantity is normally called the *activity, A*, stated in decays per second. As we have already noted, the rate of decay is proportional to the number N of unstable nuclei ($A \propto N$):

$$A = \frac{\Delta N}{\Delta t} = -\lambda N$$

decay constant the proportionality constant that relates the rate of decay of a radioactive isotope to the total number of nuclei of that isotope

where A is the activity of the sample (SI, s^{-1}), and λ is the **decay constant** of the isotope (also s^{-1}). Each isotope has its own decay constant.

Quantities whose rate of decay depends upon the amount of substance present are said to undergo *exponential decay*. In this instance, the amount N of radioactive substance left after some time t has elapsed is given by

$$N = N_0\left(\frac{1}{2}\right)^{\frac{t}{t_{1/2}}}$$

where N_0 is the initial quantity, and $t_{1/2}$ is the half-life. In a similar way, the activity A of a sample after some time t is given by

$$A = A_0\left(\frac{1}{2}\right)^{\frac{t}{t_{1/2}}}$$

where A_0 is the initial activity.

becquerel (Bq) the SI unit for radioactivity; 1 Bq = 1 s^{-1}

The SI unit for radioactivity is the **becquerel**, Bq. In SI base units, 1 Bq = 1 s^{-1}. This is a very small unit. For example, 1.0 g of radium has an activity of 3.7×10^{10} Bq. Therefore, the kilobecquerel (kBq) and the megabecquerel (MBq) are commonly used, so we would say that the activity of 1.0 g of radium is 3.7×10^4 MBq.

> ▶ **SAMPLE** problem 2

The half-life for carbon-14 is 5730 a. A specimen of peat from an ancient bog presently contains 800 μg of carbon-14.
(a) What will be the amount of carbon-14 remaining after 10 000 a?
(b) At what time will the amount remaining be 300 μg?

Solution

(a) $N_0 = 800.0$ μg $t = 10\ 000$ a

   $t_{1/2} = 5730$ a $N = ?$

$$N = N_0\left(\frac{1}{2}\right)^{\frac{t}{t_{1/2}}}$$

$$= 800\left(\frac{1}{2}\right)^{\frac{10\,000}{5730}}$$

$$N = 240$$

After 10 000 a, the amount remaining will be 240 μg.

(b) $N_0 = 400\ \mu g$ $\quad t_{1/2} = 5730\ a$
$\quad N = 300\ \mu g$ $\quad\quad t = ?$

$$N = N_0\left(\frac{1}{2}\right)^{\frac{t}{t_{1/2}}}$$

$$300 = 800.0\left(\frac{1}{2}\right)^{\frac{t}{5730}}$$

$$\frac{3}{8} = \left(\frac{1}{2}\right)^{\frac{t}{5730}}$$

$$\log\left(\frac{3}{8}\right) = \log\left(\frac{1}{2}\right)^{\frac{t}{5730}}$$ (where we arbitrarily choose logarithms of any desired base)

$$\log\left(\frac{3}{8}\right) = \frac{t}{5730}\log\left(\frac{1}{2}\right)$$

$$t = 5730\,\frac{\log\left(\frac{3}{8}\right)}{\log\left(\frac{1}{2}\right)}$$

$$t = 8100\ a$$

After 8100 a, the amount of radioactive material remaining will be 300 μg.

> **LEARNING TIP**
>
> **Logarithms**
> Recall the following property of logarithms: $\log x^y = y \log x$.

▶ **SAMPLE** problem **3**

The half-life of cobalt-60 is 5.2714 a. At a certain medical-supply house specializing in radiotherapy, a particular sample of this isotope currently has an activity of 400.00 kBq. How much time will have passed before the activity drops to 40.000 kBq?

Solution

$t_{1/2} = 5.2714\ a$ $\quad\quad A = 40.000\ kBq$
$A_0 = 400.00\ kBq$ $\quad\quad t = ?$

$$A = A_0\left(\frac{1}{2}\right)^{\frac{t}{t_{1/2}}}$$

$$40.000 = 400.00\left(\frac{1}{2}\right)^{\frac{t}{5.2714}}$$

$$\frac{40.000}{400.00} = \left(\frac{1}{2}\right)^{\frac{t}{5.2714}}$$

$$\log\left(\frac{40.000}{400.00}\right) = \log\left(\frac{1}{2}\right)^{\frac{t}{5.2714}}$$

$$\log(0.1) = \frac{t}{5.2714}\log\left(\frac{1}{2}\right)$$

$$t = 5.2714\,\frac{\log(0.1)}{\log\left(\frac{1}{2}\right)}$$

$$t = 17.511\ a$$

The radioactivity will drop to 40.000 kBq after 17.511 a.

Answers

4. (a) 4.4 mg
   (b) 164 a
5. (a) 496 μg
   (b) 2^{-45}, or $\approx 2.8 \times 10^{-14}$
   (c) 1280 h

> ▶ **Practice**

Understanding Concepts

4. A mass of contaminated soil from the site of a 1950s nuclear-weapons test contains 5.0 mg of strontium-90. This radioactive isotope has a half-life of 29.1 a.
   (a) Calculate the quantity of radioactive material remaining after 5.00 a.
   (b) Calculate the time needed for the quantity to decay to 0.100 mg.

5. The thyroid gland gathers and concentrates iodine from the bloodstream. The radioactive isotope I-131, with a half-life of 193 h, can consequently be used as a marker in determining how well the thyroid gland is functioning. An initial amount of 5.00×10^2 μg is given to a patient.
   (a) The patient is tested 2.00 h after the I-131 is taken. How much of the material is left in the patient's body?
   (b) What fraction of the original quantity is left after one year?
   (c) How much time is required for the amount to fall to $\dfrac{1}{100}$ of the original quantity?

6. A Geiger-Mueller tube is irradiated by a gram of C-14 ($t_{1/2}$ = 5730 a). An identical tube is irradiated by a gram of I-131 ($t_{1/2}$ = 8.04 d). The two sources are the same distance from their respective detectors. Which detector gives the higher reading? Explain your answer.

radioactive dating a technique using known properties of radioactive materials to estimate the age of old objects

Radioactive Dating

Archaeologists and geologists use **radioactive dating** to estimate the age of ancient objects. One common procedure uses carbon-14.

Neutrons in the constant stream of high-energy particles from deep space react with atmospheric nitrogen atoms, knocking one proton from the nucleus of $^{14}_{7}$N. The neutron is absorbed, resulting in the creation of a $^{14}_{6}$C atom (**Figure 2**). This carbon atom can combine with oxygen in the atmosphere to produce a CO_2 molecule. Plants can thus absorb some of this radioactive carbon in the normal photosynthetic process by which they produce their food. Likewise, the animals that eat those plants can ingest radioactive carbon (**Figure 3**).

The proportion of the total amount of carbon that is carbon-14 is very small, about 1.3×10^{-12}. Nonetheless the amount is measurable. As long as the creature is alive, it will continue to absorb and collect this radioactive material. Once the creature dies, no further carbon-14 will be ingested, and the proportion of carbon-14 will start to decline. A measurement of the activity present can therefore be used to estimate the age of the specimen. Carbon-14 is most useful for dating materials less than 60 000 a old. After about four half-lives have elapsed, the fraction, $\dfrac{1}{16}$, of the remaining C-14 is too small to be measured accurately.

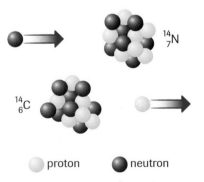

Figure 2
An interaction with a high-speed neutron can cause a nitrogen atom to transmute to a carbon-14 atom.

○ proton   ● neutron

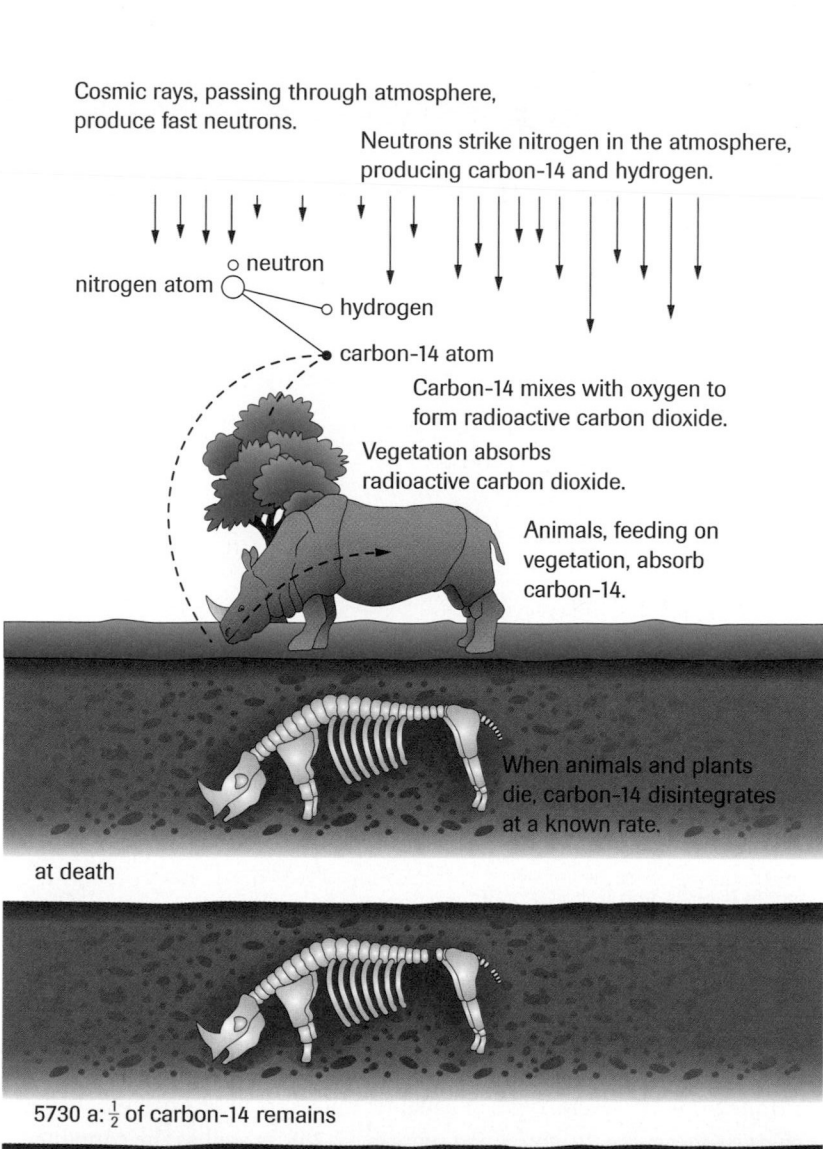

Cosmic rays, passing through atmosphere, produce fast neutrons.

Neutrons strike nitrogen in the atmosphere, producing carbon-14 and hydrogen.

neutron

nitrogen atom

hydrogen

carbon-14 atom

Carbon-14 mixes with oxygen to form radioactive carbon dioxide.

Vegetation absorbs radioactive carbon dioxide.

Animals, feeding on vegetation, absorb carbon-14.

When animals and plants die, carbon-14 disintegrates at a known rate.

at death

5730 a: $\frac{1}{2}$ of carbon-14 remains

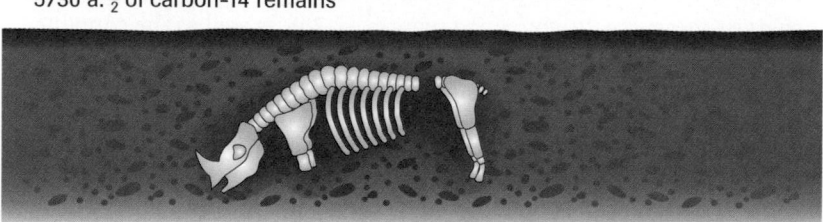

11 460 a: $\frac{1}{4}$ of carbon-14 remains

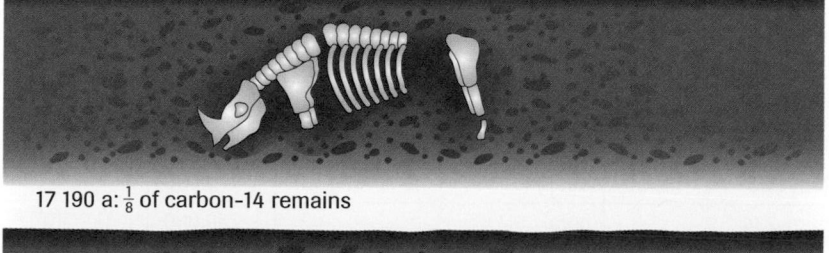

17 190 a: $\frac{1}{8}$ of carbon-14 remains

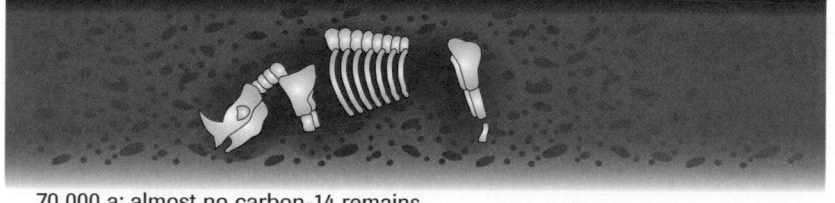

70 000 a: almost no carbon-14 remains

Figure 3

Radiocarbon dating is possible because plant and animal life absorb radioactive carbon-14 through their intake of CO_2. When an organism dies, the carbon-14, disintegrating at a rate determined by the carbon-14 half-life of 5730 a, is not replaced. At any stage, the proportion of carbon-14 that is left in a specimen indicates its age.

A piece of wood from an ancient burial site has an activity of 3.00×10^1 Bq. The original activity is estimated to be 2.4×10^2 Bq. What is the estimated age of the wood?

Solution

$A = 3.00 \times 10^1$ Bq $\qquad t_{1/2} = 5730$ a

$A_0 = 2.4 \times 10^2$ Bq $\qquad t = ?$

$$A = A_0 \left(\frac{1}{2}\right)^{\frac{t}{t_{1/2}}}$$

$$3.00 \times 10^1 = 2.4 \times 10^2 \left(\frac{1}{2}\right)^{\frac{t}{5730}}$$

$$\frac{3.00 \times 10^1}{2.4 \times 10^2} = \left(\frac{1}{2}\right)^{\frac{t}{5730}}$$

$$\log\left(\frac{3.00 \times 10^1}{2.4 \times 10^2}\right) = \log\left(\frac{1}{2}\right)^{\frac{t}{5730}}$$

$$\log\left(\frac{3.00 \times 10^1}{2.4 \times 10^2}\right) = \frac{t}{5730} \log\left(\frac{1}{2}\right)$$

$$t = 5730 \frac{\log\left(\frac{3.00 \times 10^1}{2.4 \times 10^2}\right)}{\log\left(\frac{1}{2}\right)}$$

$$t = 1.7 \times 10^4 \text{ a}$$

The sample is estimated to be 1.7×10^4 a old.

DID YOU KNOW ?

Keeping Earth Warm
The most abundant radioactive isotopes in Earth's crust and mantle are potassium-40, uranium-235, uranium-238, and thorium-238. Their half-lives are long, and they generate enough heat to keep the interior of Earth quite hot.

Materials with relatively longer half-lives can be used to determine the absolute age of geologic formations. Uranium-238, for example, with a half-life of 4.5×10^9 a, can be used to date even the oldest deposits on Earth. Since U-238 decays several times, eventually becoming Pb-206, several types of daughter nuclei are to be expected. To date a rock, the geochemist measures the contained mass of U-238 as well as the contained masses of the expected daughter isotopes. The relative amounts of U-238 and daughter isotopes can then be used to estimate the age of the rock. Samples found near Sudbury have been determined with this method to be in excess of 3.5×10^9 years old, making them among the oldest rocks in the world.

Table 2 lists some of the isotopes commonly used in radioactive dating.

Table 2 Some Isotopes Commonly Used in Radioactive Dating

Radioactive Substance	Material Tested	Half-Life (a)	Potential Range (a)
carbon-14	wood, charcoal, shell	5 730	70 000
protactinium-231	deep sea sediment	32 000	120 000
thorium-230	deep sea sediment, coral shell	75 000	400 000
uranium-234	coral	250 000	10^6
chlorine-36	igneous and volcanic rocks	300 000	500 000
beryllium-10	deep-sea sediment	2.5 billion	800 000
helium-4	coral shell	4.5 billion	—
potassium-40	volcanic ash (containing decay product argon-40)	1.3 billion	—

> ▶ *Practice*

Understanding Concepts

7. An ancient piece of bark is estimated to have originally contained 2.00 μg of carbon-14. Measurements reveal that it currently has 0.25 μg of carbon-14. Estimate its age.

8. L'Anse Aux Meadows, in Northern Newfoundland, is the only confirmed viking settlement in North America. Suppose that a sample of charcoal (a form of pure carbon) is found at the site and the measured activity is currently 7.13 Bq. The original activity is estimated to be 8.00 Bq. Estimate the age of the settlement.

9. A sample of a uranium ore is estimated to have originally contained 772 mg of uranium-238. Analysis reveals the sample to contain 705 mg of uranium-238. What is its estimated age? (Refer to Appendix C for the half-life of U-238.)

10. An ancient burial site contains a piece of parchment and the blade of a knife. Can carbon-14 dating determine the date of both items, of neither, or of just one? Explain your answer.

Answers

7. 1.7×10^4 a

8. 9.5×10^2 a

9. 5.9×10^8 a

Decay Series

Uranium-238 decays by emitting an α particle. The daughter isotope, Th-234, being itself unstable, decays to Pa-234 by emitting a β^- particle. In fact, as many as 14 transmutations can occur before a stable daughter, Pb-206, is created. **Figure 4** shows several series of transmutations by which U-238 can decay. The decay yields unstable isotopes (such as radium-226, with a half-life of 1600 a) that would have long disappeared from Earth if they were present only when Earth was formed, 4 or 5 billion years ago, and were not somehow replenished in recent times.

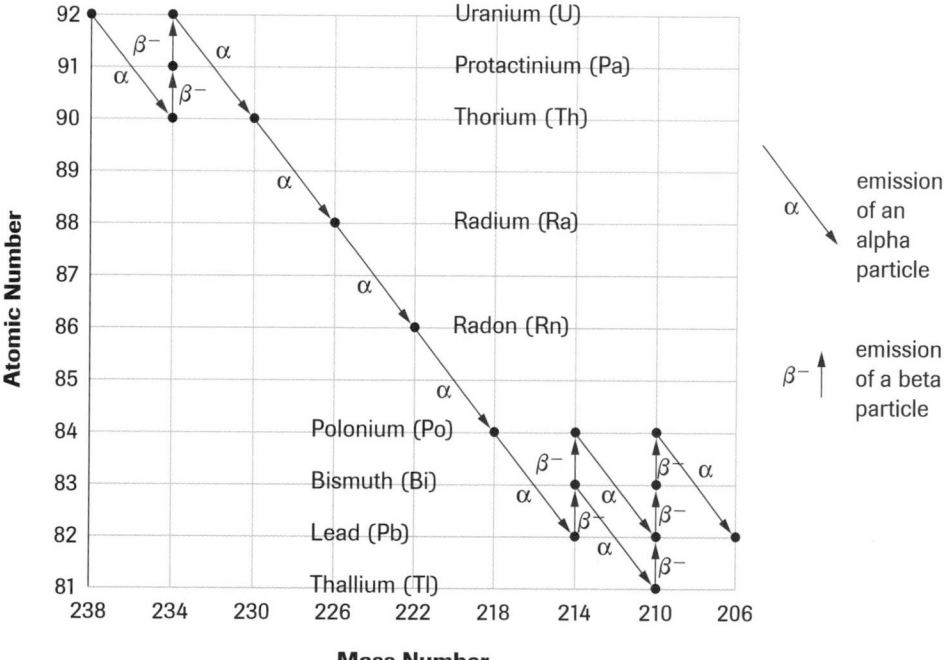

Figure 4

A *nuclide chart* shows all the decay products of a given radioisotope. In nuclear physics, nuclide charts are more useful than the periodic table. The last isotope in a nuclide chart is usually stable. This is illustrated in the chart for uranium-238, where lead-206 is not radioactive and thus stable.

Medical Applications of Radioactivity

Recall from Section 13.1 that the α and β particles released in nuclear decays ionize the molecules of the substances they pass through. For example, fast-moving β particles can knock electrons in the air molecules from their orbitals. This is even more so the case for α particles, which carry twice the charge. The particles emitted in radioactive decay processes have relatively high kinetic energies, on the order of 10^4 eV to 10^7 eV. Since a kinetic energy on the order of 10 eV is enough to ionize an atom or a molecule, a single particle can produce a very large number of ionizations. In addition, photons produced by γ decay can ionize atoms and molecules, through Compton scattering and the photoelectric effect.

Ionization is a disadvantage for any living tissue bombarded by α particles, β particles, or γ rays. The ionized molecules can cause harmful chemical reactions within the cells harbouring them. Damage to DNA can cause even more serious harm. If the radiation is sufficiently intense, it will destroy molecules faster than replacement copies can be made, killing the cell. Even worse, the damage to the cell's DNA might be such that altered cells could survive and continue to divide. Such a condition could lead to one of many forms of cancer.

Fortunately, the damaging effects of radiation on living tissue can be put to good use, since the processes that kill healthy cells are even more liable to kill the rapidly growing cancerous cells. Radiotherapists concentrate the radiation on the place where it is needed, minimizing the effect on the healthy surrounding tissue. One process localizes the damage by moving the source of the radiation around the body while directing a thin beam of particles at the cancerous tissue. A second process localizes the effect by using very small, rice-like radioactive particles, embedded close to the cancer (**Figure 5**).

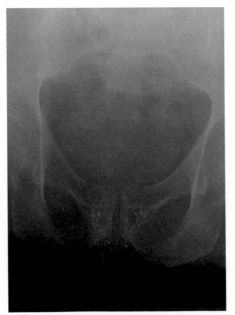

Figure 5
The white dots on this X-ray are radioactive implants used to treat prostate cancer.

Radiation has applications in diagnosis as well. Sodium-24, for example, which is soluble in blood, is injected into the body to measure kidney function. The isotope $^{99}_{43}$Tc (technetium), with a half-life of 6 h, is a vital part of many of the more popular radioactive tracers in current use. Because the isotope can combine with many other materials, tracer compounds can be designed that are tailored to many different body systems and functions. These advanced tracers can then be coupled with equally advanced detectors—gamma cameras—to produce real-time data for studies.

Gamma cameras can also be used with chemicals containing positron emitters to help form three-dimensional scans in *positron emission tomography* (PET). When the emitters undergo β^+ decay within the body, the resulting positron typically travels only a short distance before colliding with an electron. Two γ photons of opposite momenta are emitted and recorded by gamma camera detectors on opposite sides of the patient. The location of the annihilations, which are along the line between the two γ photons, can be traced once the differences in arrival times are calculated (**Figure 6**).

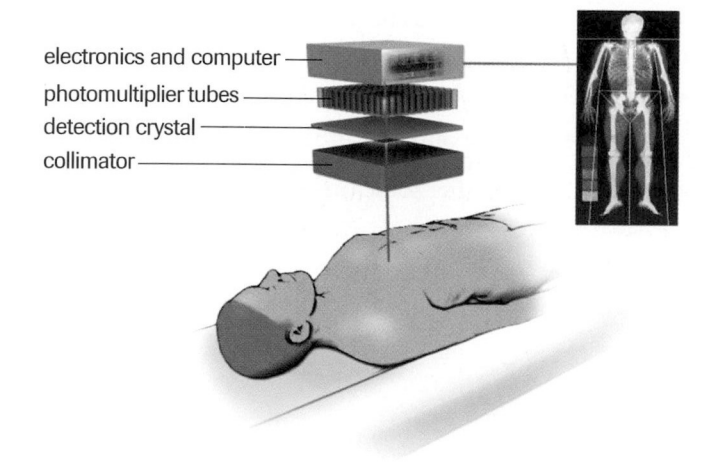

electronics and computer
photomultiplier tubes
detection crystal
collimator

DID YOU KNOW ?

The Cobalt Bomb

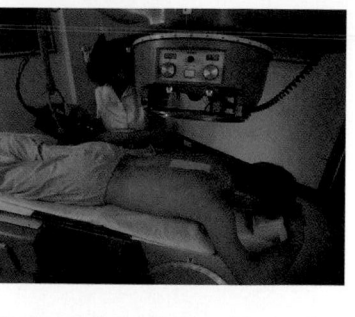

The "cobalt bomb," used to treat cancer, directs very high-energy γ and β radiation, produced from the decay of cobalt-60, onto affected areas. The apparatus is designed and marketed by Atomic Energy of Canada Limited (AECL).

Figure 6
A gamma camera assembly. The photons emitted in the patient's body are detected by the photomultiplier tubes. A computer monitor displays the image computed from the photomultiplier signals.

Continuous advances in the speed and sophistication of PET electronics have produced a steady improvement in image resolution (**Figure 7**). In addition, PET imaging makes use of a much higher percentage of the nuclear decays than do most other such techniques. This allows the administered dose of radiation to be much lower, making the devices inherently safer than the alternatives, such as the X-ray-based CAT (computerized axial tomography) scanners.

(a)

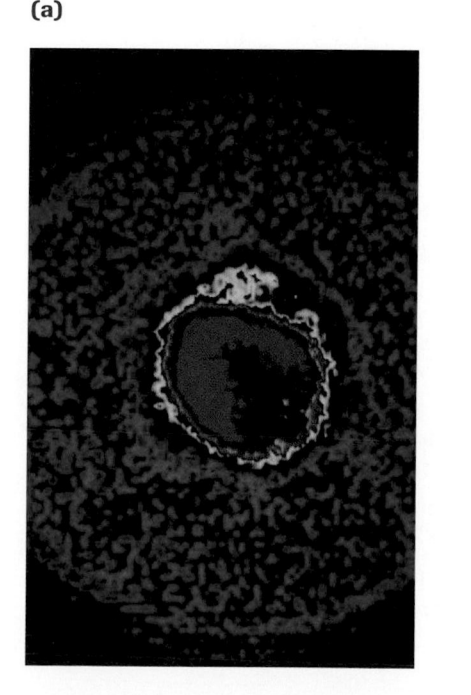

(b)

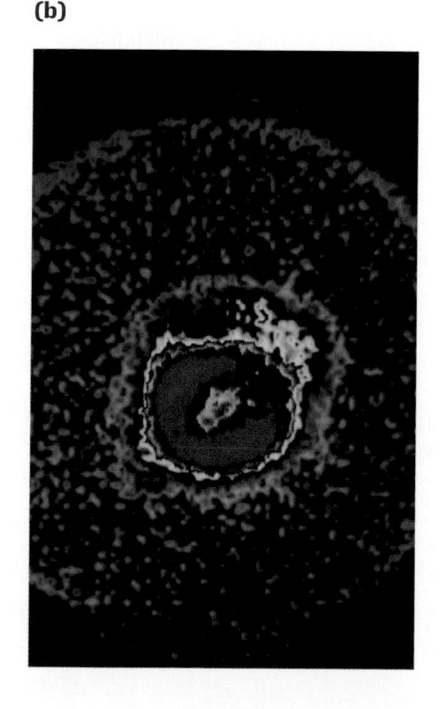

Figure 7
PET imaging helps identify problems such as tumours and damage to organs.
(a) A healthy heart
(b) A heart that has suffered a myocardial infarction

Rate of Radioactive Decay

- The half-life, which is unique to any given isotope, is the time required for one-half of the original to decay.
- The activity A, in decays per second (Bq), is proportional to the number N of unstable nuclei present.
- The amount of radioactive substance N left after some time t is given by $N = N_0 \left(\frac{1}{2}\right)^{\frac{t}{t_{1/2}}}$, where N_0 is the initial quantity and $t_{1/2}$ is the half-life.
- The activity, A, in becquerels, after some time t is given by $A = A_0 \left(\frac{1}{2}\right)^{\frac{t}{t_{1/2}}}$, where A_0 is the original activity.
- If the half-life of a radioactive isotope, the level of radioactivity, and the original activity or amount are known, then the age of a material can be estimated.

▶ *Section 13.2 Questions*

Understanding Concepts

1. Uranium-238 has a half-life of 4.5×10^9 a. A material specimen presently containing 1.00 mg of U-238 has an activity of 3.8×10^8 Bq.
   (a) Calculate the activity of the specimen after 1.00×10^6 a.
   (b) How many years will pass before the amount of U-238 remaining is 0.100 mg?

2. The activity of a specimen containing some hypothetical radioactive isotope X is initially measured to be 1.20×10^3 Bq. One hour later, the activity has fallen to a value of 1.00×10^3 Bq. Calculate the half-life of X.

3. Mass spectrometry of a mineral specimen originally composed mainly of U-238 reveals that 9.55% of the metallic content is consistent with daughter products from the decay of this isotope. Estimate the age of the specimen.

4. A bone fragment of carbon is found to have an activity of 4.00 Bq. The initial activity is estimated to be 18.0 Bq. Estimate the age of the fragment.

5. It is quite likely that transuranium elements (elements with atomic numbers greater than 92) were present in Earth's crust shortly after the planet formed. Suggest reasons why these elements are not presently found in minerals.

6. You have unearthed a clay tablet in your back yard. Why would C-14 dating be inappropriate? Suggest a reasonable alternative.

Applying Inquiry Skills

7. Thorium-232 undergoes the following series of decays before a stable daughter is produced: β^-, β^-, α, α, α, α, β^-, β^-, α. Construct a graph similar to **Figure 4** to depict the series.

Making Connections

8. Radioactive dating has helped determine that life first appeared on Earth approximately 3 billion years ago. Suggest how this estimate could have been made.

9. Research the costs of purchasing and maintaining a PET scanner. Draw conclusions about the cost-effectiveness of such a purchase.

10. Research the methods used in mining radioactive substances, such as uranium. Briefly describe some of the safeguards taken to protect the health of the miners.

 www.science.nelson.com

Suppose you challenge two friends to identify an object concealed from their view, a golf ball. You allow your friends to fire a large number of probing particles, from any angle, and to measure the trajectories upon rebound, as in Rutherford's α-scattering investigation. You equip your friends with two sizes of probe, one much smaller than the other (**Figure 1**). Which friend will get more precise information about the object being bombarded?

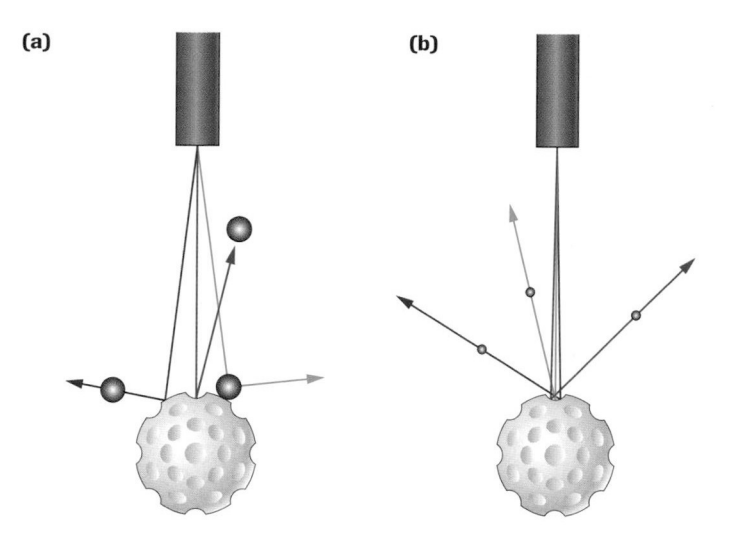

(a)   **(b)**

Figure 1
(a) A golf ball appears spherical when probed with steel balls 4 mm in diameter.
(b) With steel balls 1 mm in diameter, some of its dimples are revealed.

The friend using the smaller probing particles would be able to resolve the surface dimples. In a similar way, physicists probe the atom with particle beams of the highest possible resolving power, as determined by the de Broglie wavelength.

Recall from Chapter 12 that the de Broglie wavelength associated with any moving object of nonzero mass is $\lambda = \dfrac{h}{mv}$. It follows that the wavelength associated with a particle decreases when the speed increases (disregarding relativistic effects), being inversely proportional to the square root of the kinetic energy. Therefore, high-energy particles are preferred for probing unknown nuclei.

In Chapter 12 we saw that the probing of the nucleus began in Rutherford's laboratory with α particles from a natural radioactive source. By the 1930s, experimentalists began constructing accelerating machines, in search of higher energies. This search continues into the twenty-first century.

The Cyclotron and Synchrocyclotron

It is evident that charged particles can be accelerated through high potentials, such as are achievable with a Van de Graaff machine. However, in the 1930s, problems in working with very high voltages stimulated the American, Ernest Lawrence, to consider accelerating particles by means of a large number of small increases in electrical potential rather than with one large increase. Lawrence suggested magnetically deflecting the particles into a circular orbit. The key to the operation of his device, the *cyclotron* (**Figure 2**), is the fact that the orbits of charged particles in a uniform magnetic field are **isochronous**: the time taken for particles with the same mass and charge to make one complete cycle is the

Figure 2
Ernest O. Lawrence holding his first cyclotron

isochronous recurring at regular intervals even when some variable changes; for example, the period of a pendulum is isochronous with respect to variations in the mass of the bob

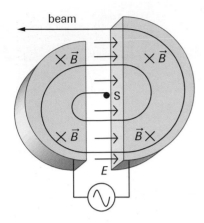

Figure 3
A cyclotron. The crosses indicate that the magnetic field is downward, through the dees. The oscillating electric field across the gap between the dees gives the particle a small boost of energy each time it crosses the gap. The magnetic field, acting down through the dees, keeps the particle moving in a circular path but with increasing radius. What would happen if the direction of the magnetic field were reversed?

same at any speed. Since the radius of the circular path increases exactly as the speed, the time for any orbit stays constant. This makes it possible for a modest potential difference, reversing in polarity at constant frequency, to accelerate a charged particle many times.

The most obvious feature of the cyclotron is a pair of "dees," hollow, D-shaped electrodes that cause the accelerating particles (usually protons) to move in a spiral path. **Figure 3** shows that a magnetic field is directed downward through the dees to cause the deflection. An AC potential is applied to opposite dees. The period of the variation in potential is timed to coincide with the period of the circular motion of the particles. In this way, the strong electric field in the gap between the dees causes the particles to accelerate each time they jump over.

The increased speed results in ever-increasing radii for the circular motion. After some number of revolutions, the particles are so energetic they miss the second dee when they cross the gap, leaving the apparatus in a high-energy beam that can be used in collision experiments.

At nonrelativistic speeds the mechanics are simple. The design task is to find the right AC frequency, given the charge on the particles and the strength of the magnetic field. This is straightforward, since the charge of the proton and the α particle is precisely known, and the magnetic field strength can be calculated from the geometry and current load of the electromagnet.

The kinetic energy of the emitted particles is independent of the potential difference across the dees. A very high voltage causes an enormous acceleration across the gap, leading to a spiral pattern that grows quickly, with the particle exiting after only a few cycles. A lower voltage, on the other hand, produces less acceleration across the gap, leading to a spiral pattern that grows slowly, with the particle exiting after many cycles. The same total work is done in both cases, ensuring that the charged particle exits with the same kinetic energy in both cases.

However, at relativistic speeds the mechanics of the cyclotron are not simple. Like duration and length, momentum is affected by high speeds. As the speed of the particle approaches the speed of light, the momentum approaches infinity. This steady relativistic increase in momentum causes the cyclotron frequency to lose synchronization with the circling particles at high energies and therefore sets an upper limit on the energy that can be imparted.

A *synchrocyclotron*, or *frequency-modulated (FM) cyclotron*, is a modified classic cyclotron in which the frequency of the alternation in electric potential is changed during the accelerating cycle. This allows the particles to stay in phase with the alternating electrical field even when the relativistic momentum increase becomes significant. As a result, relativity does not impose as low a limit on the energy of the accelerated particles as with the classic cyclotron.

We can illustrate this concept with protons. In the early part of the acceleration, when the speed is lower, a conceivable frequency for proton acceleration is 32 MHz. By the time the proton has acquired an energy of 400 MeV, the required frequency has fallen to 20 MHz. This change in frequency takes approximately 10 ms. As a result, the accelerated protons are delivered in bunches, one for each frequency-modulation cycle. After the delivery of a bunch of protons, the frequency must return to 32 MHz so that the machine can pick up another batch of protons.

Since the beam is not continuous but comes in bursts, its intensity is much lower than in a classic cyclotron. To compensate, there are now very large synchrocyclotrons, with huge magnets, in many countries. The size and cost of the magnets presently set an upper limit of 1 GeV to the energy achievable in a synchrocyclotron. Superconducting magnets may, however, increase this limit by making smaller magnets feasible.

The TRIUMF Cyclotron

In the 1970s, several new versions of the synchrocyclotron appeared, designed to improve both the intensity of the proton beam and the length of the duration of the bursts. In these machines, it is the magnetic field rather than the frequency of the alternation in potential difference that is varied to compensate for the relativistic momentum effect. Adjustments had to be made in the magnetic field as problems in focusing developed. It was found that if the electromagnets were segmented, this problem was partially resolved. The TRIUMF cyclotron at the University of British Columbia is an example of a synchrocyclotron with segmented magnets, or, as they are now called, *sector-focused cyclotrons* (**Figure 4**).

The TRIUMF cyclotron is of a type often called a "meson factory." It is so named because it is particularly well-suited to the production of short-lived particles called *pions*, which belong to a class of particles called *mesons*.

The negatively charged hydrogen ions accelerated by the TRIUMF reach speeds of about $0.75c$. At this point, the ions have energies of about 520 MeV and are directed out of the cyclotron into areas where they are used for research. Using a stripping foil inside the cyclotron, electrons can be removed from the ions, thus leaving proton beams with varying energies, which can also be used for research. The proton beams can be directed into pipes called *beam lines*, where electromagnets guide them to where they are needed, either in the proton hall, where the beam can be used directly, or the meson hall. The protons then collide with targets, producing the short-lived pions.

Figure 4
The TRIUMF is the world's largest cyclotron. (TRIUMF stands for tri-university meson facility, although now there are 11 universities involved.)

Linear Accelerators

Cyclotrons and synchrocyclotrons have a number of disadvantages. Since the particles are contained by a magnetic field, the ejection of a high-energy beam is difficult and inefficient. Therefore, using internal targets limits the kinds of experiments that can be performed. Also, in the case of high-energy electrons, there are severe losses of energy through synchrotron radiation.

The *linear accelerator*, or *linac*, is designed to overcome some of these limitations. The linac is a long, evacuated tube containing a large number of *drift tubes*. Alternate drift tubes are connected to opposite sides of a high-frequency generator through transmission lines running the length of the accelerator (**Figure 5(a)**). If a negatively charged

Figure 5
(a) A linear accelerator. Charged particles accelerate as they are attracted by the alternately charged drift tubes.
(b) The Stanford Linear Accelerator

(a)

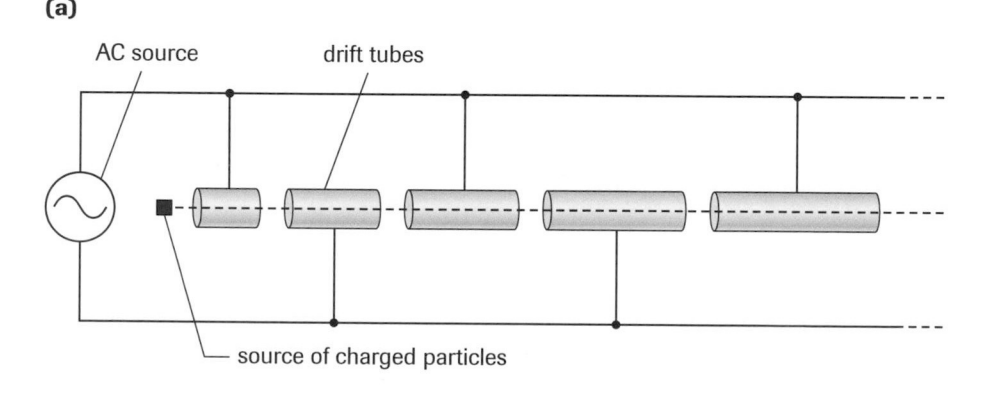

AC source   drift tubes

source of charged particles

(b)

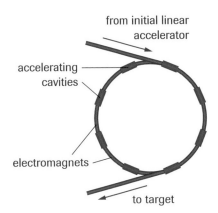

Figure 6
A simplified schematic of a synchrotron

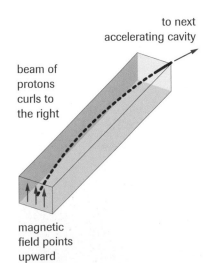

Figure 7
Segmented bending magnet

particle is injected when the potential of the first drift tube is positive, the particle accelerates to it, acquiring kinetic energy. Once it is in the first tube, it does not accelerate further but moves at a constant "drift" velocity. (Inside a drift tube, as inside any container with walls at a spatially constant potential, the electric field is zero at all times, even if the potential of the walls happens to vary over time.) If, by the time the particle reaches the end of the first drift tube the electrical potential difference between alternate drift tubes has reversed, the particle accelerates between the tubes. The particle drifts more quickly through the second tube, which is longer. It is further accelerated in the space between the second and third tubes, since the potential difference has reversed again. The process continues through a succession of progressively longer drift tubes, with the kinetic energy of the particles increasing upon each transition.

The Stanford Linear Accelerator (SLAC), completed in 1961, is 3.2 km long and contains 240 drift tubes (**Figure 5(b)**). It is designed to accelerate electrons to energies of approximately 20 GeV. At this energy, the relativistic momentum increase gives the electron a mass 40 000 times its rest mass. The highest-energy proton linac is located at Los Alamos, New Mexico. Completed in 1973, it accelerates protons to 800 MeV.

The intense pulses of high-energy protons from proton linacs make these devices ideal as injectors for proton synchrotrons. Used on their own, however, they serve primarily to produce mesons in the bombardment of targets.

Synchrotrons

Strong progress in nuclear research was made possible by raising the energies of protons in successively larger accelerators of the designs we have considered so far. This had to stop, however, because of the rising cost of the magnets, some of which had to have masses as great as 40 000 t.

Higher energies are reached by combining some design ideas from the linac and the synchrocyclotron. In a *synchrotron*, in place of one large magnet a series of smaller magnets keeps the accelerated beam in a circular path. Between successive electromagnets are radio-frequency accelerating devices called *cavities*, which work much like the short sections of a linear accelerator. Protons are first accelerated by a linear accelerator, then directed into a circular vacuum chamber running through a succession of electromagnets (**Figure 6**). The electromagnets are designed in such a way that the field increases with increasing radius, confining the beam of protons to a relatively small cross-section. This beam can be used directly to strike targets outside the ring. Alternatively, a target can be placed in the beam, so that secondary particles are ejected from it. In either case, special magnets direct the particles out of the ring.

While electrons are sometimes used in synchrotrons (e.g., the Canadian Light Source, discussed later), usually protons are the particles used. Why? Charged particles emit photons—synchrotron radiation—when accelerated. Since the particles in the synchrotron undergo circular motion, they are constantly accelerated not only by the accelerating cavities but also by the bending magnets (**Figure 7**). The net result is that much of the work done on the particles is radiated away, without increasing the kinetic energy. Because the amount and intensity of the synchrotron radiation depend on the speed of the particles and the magnetic field strength, the emission increases enormously at relativistic speeds. Specifically, the output of synchrotron radiation increases with the cube of the ratio of a particle's energy to its rest-mass energy (the product of rest mass and c^2). Because this ratio tends to be much higher for lighter particles, heavier particles are preferred. The energy of the protons is increased by a series of accelerators before the protons are injected into a "main ring" in a synchrotron. The so-called Tevatron, the synchrotron at the Fermi National Accelerator Laboratory (Fermilab) in Batavia, Illinois, illustrates this arrangement. In the Tevatron main ring are 1000 superconducting magnets (each costing $40 000), with coils of niobium and titanium cooled to −268° by liquid helium. At this temperature, the coils lose nearly all their electrical resistance, minimizing power demands.

Accelerated particles are stored in a second ring, ready for collision with accelerated particles in the first ring. When a moving particle strikes a target, which in the inertial frame of the laboratory is essentially at rest, only a small portion of the resulting energy is available for interaction with another particle. For particles moving at close to the speed of light the effect is significant. For example, if a proton with an energy of 400 GeV strikes a proton in a target at rest, only 27.4 GeV is available for the interaction. If, on the other hand, the two particles are moving in opposite directions and collide, then all the energy is available for the interaction (**Figure 8**). For example, if two 31.4 GeV protons collide, 62.8 GeV is available for the interaction.

A similar arrangement is available with the Large Electron-Positron Collider (LEP) at CERN (European Organisation for Nuclear Research) in Geneva, Switzerland. Beams of particles are accelerated in two rings, moving clockwise in one, counterclockwise in the other. When the beams meet, some of the particles interact. A team under the direction of Carlo Rubbia used colliding beams of protons and antiprotons in a CERN accelerator to confirm the existence of three particles, the W^+, W^-, and Z particles, known as *bosons*. (We will return to bosons later in this chapter.)

Synchrotrons are enormous in size and cost. The synchrotron at Fermilab has a circumference of 6.3 km. The LEP has a circumference of 27 km. A giant superconducting supercollider was planned for Waxahachie, Texas. The device would have used a ring 87 km in circumference and could have produced collisions with energies of 40 TeV. Nicknamed the Desertron, since its huge size could only be accommodated in a large expanse like the American desert, it was cancelled in 1993 because of its cost. Apparently the magnitude and costs of high-energy particle research have reached levels exceeding what can be accommodated by national governments acting alone.

Despite the challenges in funding, several large-scale projects are underway. Upgrades are constantly in progress at Fermilab's Tevatron. There are also plans for the construction of a very large hadron collider near Fermilab. This device will collide muons (heavy cousins of the electron) with about 50 times the energy available at the Tevatron. The promising outlook for international cooperation in particle physics is illustrated by the Large Hadron Collider (LHC) at CERN, expected to enter production, using the existing LEP tunnel, in the first decade of this century. Energies as high as 7 TeV should be possible (**Figure 9**).

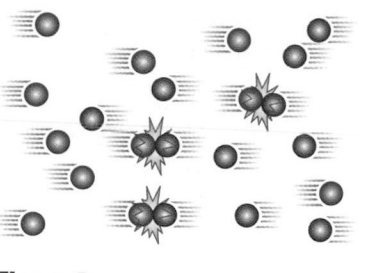

Figure 8
Colliding beams of particles

Figure 9
(a) CERN's new Large Hadron Collider
(b) The giant Collider Detector at Fermilab

(a)

(b)

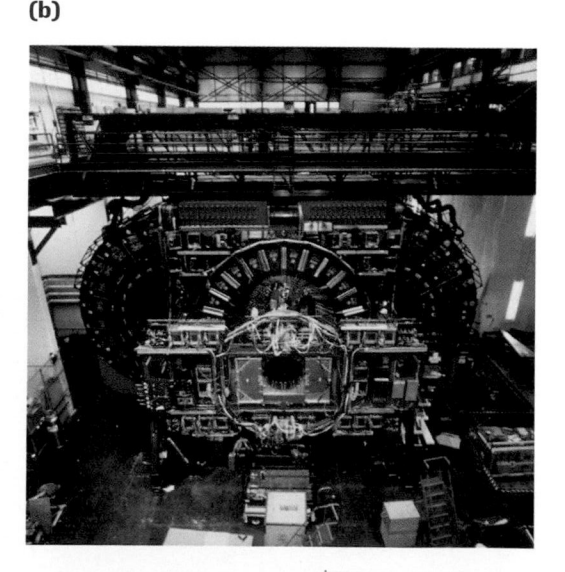

▶ EXPLORE an issue

Funding Research on Elementary Particles

Decision-Making Skills

- ● Define the Issue
- ● Analyze the Issue
- ● Research
- ○ Defend the Position
- ○ Identify Alternatives
- ○ Evaluate

Progress in particle physics goes hand in hand with particle-accelerator technology. The rapid but expensive process through which the atomic bomb was developed suggested to the policy-makers of the day that the new physics, if coupled with sufficient funding, could readily be put to military use. After World War II, physics enjoyed lavish funding, particularly in the United States. The funding climate soon produced the hydrogen bomb and encouraged the development of increasingly powerful particle accelerators. Thanks to the accelerators, the zoo of known particles expanded greatly, and theoretical predictions were put to effective test.

By the end of the 1980s, however, the easing of Cold War tensions reduced the perceived need in the West to invest in physics as a guarantor of national security. One of the first major projects affected was the Desertron, cancelled in 1993. At the same time, construction of the international LHC at CERN went ahead. The message was clear: the future of large-budget particle physics lay in international cooperation.

Understanding the Issue

1. Search the Internet using key words such as "particle physics" and "particle accelerators." Visit the Web sites at Brookhaven, CERN, Fermilab, TRIUMF, and Stanford to get an idea of the megaprojects currently underway.

GO www.science.nelson.com

2. Imagine that you are in charge of building the next generation of superaccelerator. You have settled on a synchrotron 100 km in circumference.
   (a) From which organizations would you seek funding? What would be the basis for your proposal?
   (b) What opposition would you expect to encounter? How would you deal with it?
3. What recommendations regarding future directions for elementary particle research would you make to the international research community?

Form an Opinion

4. On the strength of your research and your answers to the above questions, form an opinion on the appropriate level of public funding for research in particle physics. Present your opinion verbally to the class.

Synchrotron Radiation: The Canadian Light Source

Table 1 Relative Brightness of Various Light Sources

Source	Intensity $\left(\frac{\text{photons/s}}{\text{mm}^2}\right)$
CLS synchrotron	10^{19}
sunlight	10^{13}
candle	10^{9}
medical X ray	10^{7}

Synchrotron radiation, more commonly known in Canada as *synchrotron light*, can be put to good use as a tool used in microscopy. The Canadian Light Source (CLS) synchrotron, located in Saskatoon, has been specifically designed to produce intense beams of light at various wavelengths, particularly those in the X-ray range. The extremely small wavelength of the light, coupled with its great intensity (**Table 1**), makes it an ideal probe with which to examine the most minute of structures.

Initiated in 1999, the majority of the CLS's beam lines are expected to be in operation by 2007 (**Figure 10**). The total funding in the amount of $173.5 million for the CLS comes from a variety of sources, both public and private (**Table 2**).

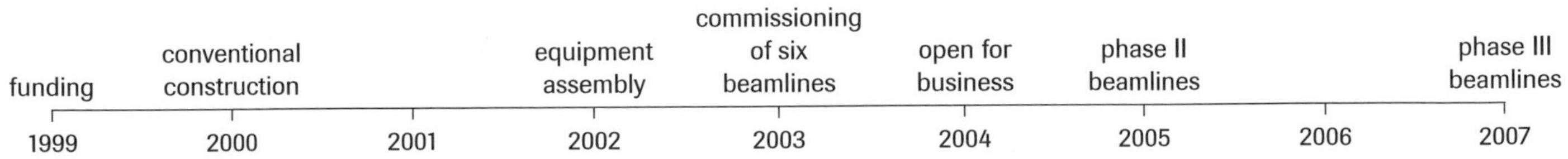

funding
conventional construction
equipment assembly
commissioning of six beamlines
open for business
phase II beamlines
phase III beamlines
1999
2000
2001
2002
2003
2004
2005
2006
2007

Figure 10
Timeline for completion of the CLS beam lines

The CLS is actually a series of integrated systems. First, the combination of an electron gun and a linac accelerates electrons to close to the speed of light, where they attain a kinetic energy of approximately 0.3 GeV. Next, the particles are injected into the booster ring where their kinetic energy is increased, by a factor of approximately 10, to 2.9 GeV. From here, the high-energy electrons are transferred to the 54 m diameter storage ring, where the synchrotron light is produced.

Beam lines then direct the synchrotron light to an area called the *optics hutch* where the full spectrum is separated into several discrete bands, including infrared and soft and hard X rays. These beams are then available for research at the experimental hutch and at various stations in the facility (**Figure 11**).

There are many uses for synchrotron light (**Table 3**). Medical science, for example, can benefit from the extremely detailed images that the light can produce. In particular, researchers expect to use the facility to study the finer structures of the heart and brain. In addition, chemical researchers can also benefit from the intensity of the light by using it to produce nanosecond-by-nanosecond representations of molecular interactions. This information can then be put to use in the design of pharmaceuticals that have much more predictable results. Other applications to chemistry will include the design of advanced materials.

Table 2 Funding for the CLS

Source	Millions of Dollars
"In kind" contributions	32.6
Canada Foundation for Innovation	56.4
Federal Government	28.3
Saskatchewan Provincial Government	25
Ontario Synchrotron Consortium	9.4
University of Saskatchewan	7.3
City of Saskatoon	2.4
SaskPower	2.0
University of Alberta	0.3
University of Western Ontario	0.3 + in kind
Other	9.5

Table 3 Research Applications

Type	Sample Applications
infrared	Studying the behaviour of biological molecules advanced materials design
soft X rays	Studying the chemical structure of materials
hard X rays	Studying materials at the molecular level

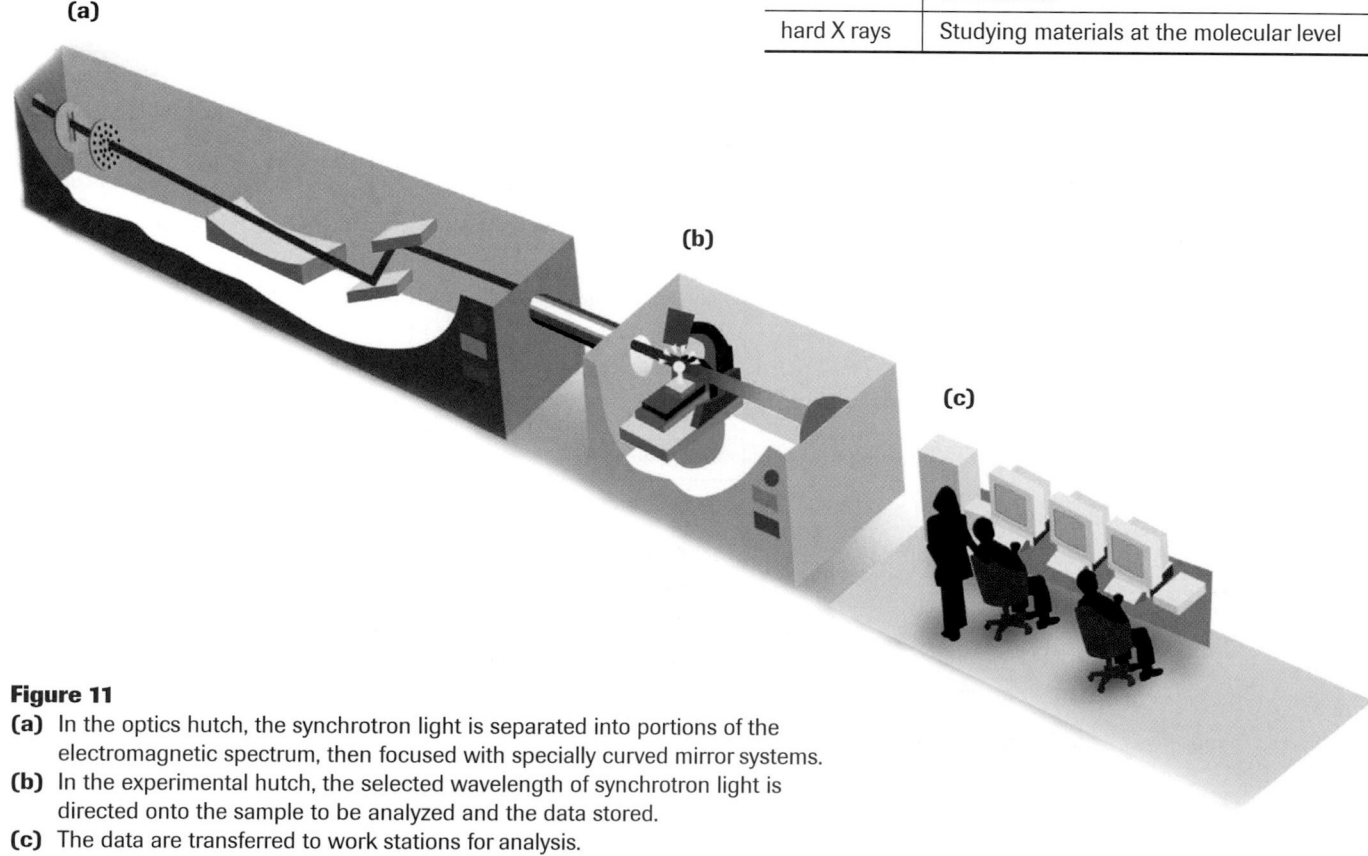

(a)

(b)

(c)

Figure 11
(a) In the optics hutch, the synchrotron light is separated into portions of the electromagnetic spectrum, then focused with specially curved mirror systems.
(b) In the experimental hutch, the selected wavelength of synchrotron light is directed onto the sample to be analyzed and the data stored.
(c) The data are transferred to work stations for analysis.

Understanding Concepts

1. Simple mathematical models can only be applied to particle accelerators when the energies and speeds are relatively low. Why does the situation become so much more complicated in practice?

2. Why is TRIUMF called a "meson factory"?

3. TRIUMF uses hydrogen ions or protons. Suggest a reason why the electron is the particle of choice for the CLS synchrotron.

4. Suggest reasons why the operators of the CLS refer to synchrotron light rather than the conventional term, synchrotron radiation.

Particle Detectors

Subatomic particles are far too small and move far too quickly to be observed and measured directly. Further, most elementary particles are exceedingly short-lived, typically decaying into other particles within a nanosecond. The particle detectors used to observe the subtle products of high-energy accelerators are in some ways as impressive as the accelerators themselves. For example, we must be able to photograph the effects of a subatomic particle that remains in the detector for just 10^{-11} s.

For a detector to sense a particle, there must be an interaction between the particle and the detector material. The interaction is typically the emission of light, the ionization of the medium, or a phase or chemical change in the medium. **Table 4** summarizes the various devices used to detect subatomic particles. We will first examine two of the detectors traditionally used in high-energy research, the cloud chamber and the bubble chamber, and then briefly consider more contemporary instrumentation.

Table 4 Some Properties of Particle Detectors

Primary Response	Type of Device	Sensitive Material	Time Resolution	Space Resolution
ionization	solid-state detector	solid	10^{-6} to 10^{-7} s	size of detector
	ionization chamber proportional counter Geiger counter	gas		
	spark chamber			1 mm
light emission	scintillation counter	gas, liquid, or solid	10^{-9} s	size of detector
	Cerenkov counter			
	scintillation chamber	solid	10^{-8} s	1 mm
phase or chemical change	cloud chamber	gas	none	0.1 mm
	bubble chamber	liquid		
	nuclear emulsion	gel		1 μm
	solid-state track detectors	solid		

Cloud Chambers

The cloud chamber was devised in 1911 by Charles Wilson (1869–1959) in England. Wilson found that in a gas supersaturated with a vapour, condensation forms along the trajectories of charged ions, leaving trails of droplets, which can be photographed.

A simple cloud chamber can be made with a glass or plastic cylindrical container, open at one end. A piece of black cloth saturated with alcohol is placed onto a block of dry ice and then covered by the container. The container soon fills with alcohol vapour. A supersaturated layer of alcohol forms just above the black cloth. If a radioactive source, emitting α or β particles, is put into the container, the moving particles leave behind vapour trails, reminiscent of jet-airplane sky trails, as they condense the alcohol vapour. (A strong source of light from the side, such as the beam from a 35-mm slide projector, helps make the trails visible.)

Argon and ethyl alcohol are common in the more sophisticated cloud chambers used in serious research. In the detector in **Figure 12**, compressed air forces a piston forward when valve A is opened. When valve B is opened to the atmosphere, the piston is forced backward, the pressure decreases, and the vapour expands to a supersaturated state, making droplet growth possible. When charged particles pass through the chamber, they attract nearby molecules, creating tiny droplets that form small vapour trails in the chamber. A high-speed strobe camera, triggered by the passage of a particle, records any trails present in the chamber, including any trails representing collisions.

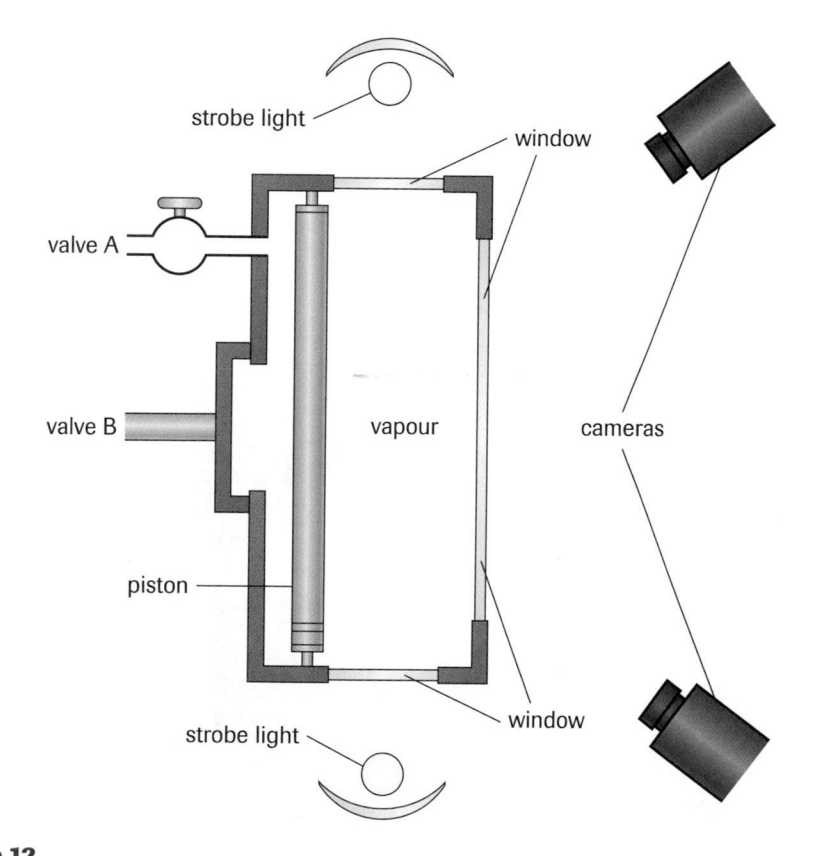

Figure 12
Schematic of a cloud chamber

Bubble Chambers

Bubble chambers (**Figure 13**) use liquefied gas, for example, propane, hydrogen, helium, or xenon, with liquid hydrogen the most common choice. The hydrogen must be kept

Figure 13
The bubble chamber holds a liquefied gas close to its boiling point for the particular pressure applied. The liquid is then superheated by allowing the pressure to drop slightly. The bubbles that form are made visible on the diffusing surface and are photographed in stereo.

below −252.8°C to remain liquid at a typical operating pressure. If the pressure is suddenly lowered, the liquid boils. If a high-speed charged particle passes through the hydrogen as the pressure is lowered, hydrogen ions form. The hydrogen boils a few thousandths of a second sooner around these ions than in the rest of the container. Carefully timed photographs record the resulting bubble trails. A magnetic field is frequently applied across the chamber, causing the paths of positively charged particles to curve in one direction, the paths of negatively charged particles to curve in the other. By measuring the curvature of their paths and knowing the strength of the magnetic field, we can determine the ratio of the momentum to the charge (as a useful first step in working out the mass). Further, since a hydrogen atom is simply a proton and an electron, if the chosen medium is hydrogen, collisions between accelerated protons and the protons in the tank could occur and be recorded. One such collision can be clearly seen at the bottom left of the bubble chamber photograph in **Figure 14(a)**. Bubble chambers are quite large and complex (**Figure 14(b)**).

Figure 14
(a) A bubble chamber photograph
(b) A hydrogen bubble chamber

(a)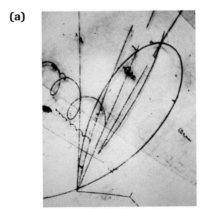

(b)

Tracking Detectors and Calorimeters

The detectors at supercolliders consist of several devices, each testing for different events caused by a collision.

The *tracking detector* uses a series of wire grids (**Figure 15**). Particles pass through each grid and produce an electrical signal. The pattern through many grids can be used to reconstruct the trajectory through the detector. If a magnetic field has been applied and the incoming particle is charged, the shape of the trajectory supplies clues regarding the type of particle and its energy. Photons are invisible to this detector.

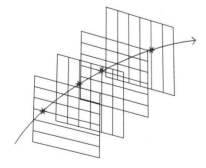

Figure 15
Tracking detector

Electromagnetic calorimeters are usually constructed of slabs of absorbent material sandwiched between light-sensitive detectors (**Figure 16**). These detectors give an indication of the kinetic energy possessed by the incoming particles, since both the degree to which the particles penetrate the material and the amount of light produced are determined by the energy. Typically, photons and electrons, which lose energy quickly, are stopped in the inner layers of the detectors. Jets produced by particles descended from protons and neutrons travel farther. Muons (high-energy particles produced by collisions in accelerators) penetrate the farthest.

These various types of detectors are often combined into one unit. **Figure 17** depicts one such device. But one key component of the contemporary detector is not pictured. Any given experiment will produce several million particle interactions per second. The detector produces data at a rate of 20 Mb/s. The computer is therefore an essential part of the detection system. Data are typically analyzed with hundreds of PCs "clustered" into a supercomputer.

- tracking
- e.m. calorimeter
- hadron calorimeter
- muon chamber

Figure 16
Particle detector. Particles and antiparticles are made to collide in the tube at the centre. Collision products, whether photons of electromagnetic radiation, hadrons (a family of particle we will examine shortly), or muons, are detected in the surrounding cylinders.

| **SUMMARY** | ***Working with Particles*** |

- We gain much of our information about the atom through collision experiments in which high-energy particles are made to collide with stationary atoms or with one another.

- Particle accelerators are used to accelerate charged particles, such as protons and electrons, to very high kinetic energies.

- The cyclotron, an early high-energy accelerator, operates by accelerating particles as they cross the gap between two hollow electrodes.

- Synchrocyclotrons impart higher kinetic energies than the classic cyclotron by varying the frequency of the accelerating voltage in compensation for relativistic mass increase.

- Linear accelerators use electric fields to accelerate charged particles on a straight path through many sets of oppositely charged electrodes.

- Synchrotrons accelerate objects in a circle with constant radius. Both the frequency of the radio-frequency accelerating cavity and the strength of the bending magnets are adjusted to compensate for the relativistic mass increase.

- Synchrotrons typically collide oppositely moving particles, thereby greatly increasing the energies of the collisions.

- High-energy particles in synchrotrons such as the CLS emit a full spectrum of electromagnetic waves. This synchrotron light is well suited to the task of probing the fine structure of matter.

- Particle detectors work in tandem with accelerators to provide information about elementary particles.

- Cloud chambers and bubble chambers display the trajectories of charged particles as trails of vapour. Strong electromagnetic fields can be applied to deflect the charged particles, which provide clues to masses and kinetic energies.

- The detectors in contemporary accelerators are often integrated units, comprising a tracking detector and electromagnetic calorimeters.

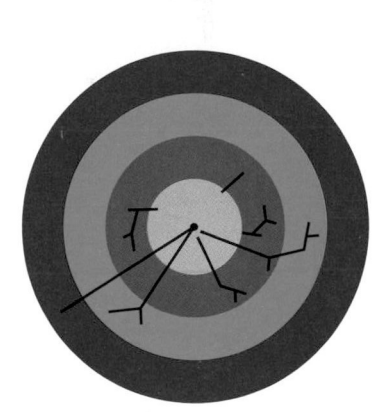
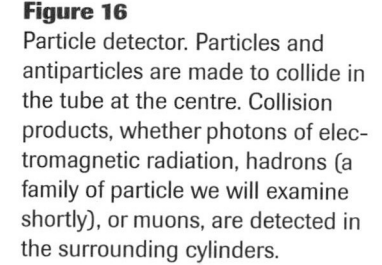
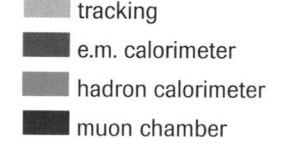

- tracking
- e.m. calorimeter
- hadron calorimeter
- muon chamber

Figure 17
Cross-section of a complex particle detector. The forked-lightning appearance of some trajectories tells us that particles decay into daughter particles, with the daughters themselves liable to decay. The lines that seem to appear from nowhere represent photons, visible to the electromagnetic calorimeter but invisible to the tracking detector deeper in the interior of the apparatus.

Understanding Concepts

1. Explain why there is an upper limit on the amount of energy that a cyclotron can impart to a particle. How do circular-path accelerators, more sophisticated than the cyclotron, overcome this limitation?

2. Explain why a neutron inside the Stanford linac would not be accelerated.

3. Protons enter a hypothetical synchrotron, 1.0 km in radius, with an initial energy of 8.0 GeV. The protons gain 2.5 MeV with each revolution. Assume that although the protons complete each revolution at essentially the speed of light, the relativistic mass increase can be neglected.
   (a) Calculate the distance travelled by the protons before reaching 1.0 TeV.
   (b) Calculate the time it takes the protons to travel this distance.

Applying Inquiry Skills

4. You have constructed a simple cloud chamber from a side-illuminated viewing cylinder resting on dry ice. You have placed a radioactive source in your chamber. How could you now determine whether the particles you are observing are neutral or charged, and if charged, whether charged positively or negatively?

5. You are working with a radioactive source emitting particles of several kinds, all positively charged, not necessarily of the same mass. How could you determine whether all the particles have the same charge?

Making Connections

6. Some microwave communications dishes are not formed from sheet metal but from steel mesh. (The mesh reduces low-velocity wind loading.) Use your understanding of particle energy and resolving power to help explain why these dishes reflect microwaves just as effectively as ones fashioned from sheet metal.

7. Recall from Chapter 12 that every object of nonzero mass m, moving at nonzero speed v, has an associated de Broglie wavelength $\lambda = \dfrac{h}{mv}$. Consider a proton that has been accelerated to 1 TeV. Neglecting the relativistic mass increase and comparing the de Broglie wavelength of the proton under this assumption with the wavelength of visible light, explain why high-energy particles are promising tools for resolving the finer details of the workings of atoms.

8. **Table 5** compares some of the particle accelerators discussed in this section. Copy and complete the table.

Table 5

Name	Method for Accelerating Particles	Particles Accelerated	Energies Achieved
cyclotron	?	?	?
synchrocyclotron	?	?	?
linac	?	?	?
synchrotron	?	?	?

9. **Table 6** summarizes some of the basic research that can be done using various types of particle accelerators. Copy the table and complete the missing entries. For "Resolving Ability," make an estimate based on the de Broglie wavelength.

Table 6

Experiment	Typical Particle Energies	Resolving Ability	Types of Questions Addressed by Experiment
gold-foil α scattering	?	?	?
early experiments with cyclotrons	?	?	?
experiments with synchrocyclotrons	?	?	?
experiments with linacs	?	?	?
Tevatron experiments	?	?	?
CERN LHC experiments	?	?	?

10. In this section, you learned that sophisticated computers are needed to process the data from particle experiments. Visit the TRIUMF Web site and learn about new microchips created for this purpose. Briefly report on your findings.

 www.science.nelson.com

The idea that matter is composed of elementary building blocks originated with Democritus, around 500 B.C. By the early 1800s, with the acceptance of Dalton's atomic theory, the atom was considered elementary. By the early part of the twentieth century, the discovery of the electron and the basic subatomic structure of the atom suggested that the electron, proton, and neutron were the elementary particles. By the mid-1930s, the photon, positron, and neutrino were also considered elementary. Since that time, hundreds of additional particles have been discovered and are still being discovered. The question arises then, What particles are elementary? It is this question that challenges participants in the field of physics known as *elementary particle physics*.

The Electromagnetic Force

British theoretician Paul Dirac (**Figure 1**) laid much of the foundation for elementary particle physics. In 1927, Dirac worked out the quantum mechanics of electromagnetic fields, explaining the formation and absorption of photons in the atom and, as we saw in Section 13.1, postulating the existence of the positron.

As previously discussed, it is the electromagnetic force that attracts the electron to the positive nucleus and in fact holds matter together. In studies of objects in collision, certain interactions are often described as involving forces that act at a distance, whereby two objects interact without physical contact, with an interchange of energy and momentum. How, then, is the transfer of energy and momentum achieved?

In examining wave–particle duality, we saw that an electromagnetic wave (such as γ radiation or visible light) can be considered a stream of photons, each photon having energy and momentum. Using the work of Dirac, this quantum approach can be applied to the effects caused when one particle's electromagnetic field acts on the electromagnetic field of another particle. In a sense, we consider an electromagnetic field to be composed of particles. When one electromagnetic field acts on another, the two fields exchange photons with each other during the interaction. In other words, photons are the carriers, or transfer agents, that carry the electromagnetic force from one charged particle to another.

As an analogy, consider a girl and a boy standing facing each other on a nearly frictionless ice surface, each holding a hockey puck. If the girl throws her puck to the boy, the girl will move backward (action–reaction and impulse). The boy will also move backward when he catches the puck. Their movements demonstrate repulsive force. On the other hand, if they exchange pucks by grabbing them from each other, they will be pulled together—the equivalent of an attractive force.

Another way is to say that the particles exchanged in this manner convey messages. Typically the message will be "come closer" or "move away." In fact, physics often refers to particles like the photon as *messenger particles*.

Because of the uncertainties inherent in quantum mechanics, it is impossible to directly observe the types of exchanges we have outlined. It is possible, however, to describe them. In the 1940s, Richard Feynman (**Figure 2**) and Julian Schwinger developed a complete theory of the exchanges, called **quantum electrodynamics** (QED). Since then, numerous experiments have demonstrated the ability of QED to describe, in detail, the subtle interactions possible between particles in terms of virtual photons.

Feynman also developed the concept of a particular kind of space-time diagram, the **Feynman diagram**, to illustrate such electrodynamic interactions. The simplest case occurs when only one photon is exchanged. Consider the interaction of two electrons.

Figure 1
Paul Dirac (1902–1984)

Figure 2
Richard Feynman (1918–1988)

quantum electrodynamics the study of interactions of charged particles in terms of virtual photons

Feynman diagram a space-time diagram that depicts the interactions of charged particles

One electron may be considered to create a photon, the other to absorb the photon. Each electron undergoes changes in energy and momentum because of the exchange. Since a change in momentum is caused by a force, the electrons repel each other (**Figure 3**). This concept was applied to many other electromagnetic interactions, and it was concluded that the exchange of a photon, or photons, is responsible for all electromagnetic interactions between charged particles. The exchange photon, being for a variety of reasons unobservable, is called a **virtual photon** to distinguish it from a real photon.

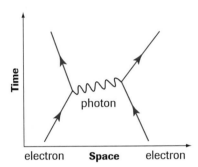

Figure 3
A Feynman diagram depicting the electromagnetic force. The vertical axis represents time and the horizontal axis represents position (Feynman diagrams can be drawn with or without the time/space axes.) The red wavy line represents a virtual photon exchanged between the two electrons. The photon transmits momentum and energy from one electron to the other. Since the transfer is not quite instantaneous (the speed of the photon, c, is finite), the line is not quite horizontal.

We have just considered the exchange of a single virtual photon. Alternatively, two or more photons may be exchanged. The probability of these more elaborate situations, however, decreases with the number of exchanges, as does the strength of the interaction.

The Strong Nuclear Force

In the nucleus of a stable atom, protons and neutrons are bound together by the strong nuclear force. In 1935, the Japanese physicist Hideki Yukawa (1907–1981) proposed that just as the photon is the particle transferring the electromagnetic force, some particle transfers the strong nuclear force between the nucleons in the nucleus. Yukawa predicted that this new particle would have a rest mass midway between the electron and the proton. The postulated particle was consequently called the **meson**, which means "in the middle."

Let us consider the hypothetical interaction in **Figure 4**. The particle that carries the interaction must have been created from the quantum vacuum. According to the uncertainty principle, the apparent violation of mass conservation implies that

meson the elementary particle originally predicted to be responsible for the strong nuclear force; now a class of particles

$$(\Delta E)(\Delta t) \approx \frac{h}{2\pi}$$

$$(\Delta E) \approx \frac{h}{2\pi(\Delta t)}$$

$$mc^2 \approx \frac{h}{2\pi\left(\dfrac{d}{c}\right)}$$

$$mc^2 \approx \frac{hc}{2\pi d}$$

Using the known values of h and c as well as the value $d = 1.5 \times 10^{-15}$ m (a typical diameter of the nucleus of a small atom), we obtain an estimate for ΔE of 2.2×10^{-11} J, or approximately 130 MeV. Comparing this with the energy equivalent of the electron rest mass, 0.511 MeV, we estimate the meson to be a little over 250 times more massive than the electron ($250m_e$).

Using similar reasoning, Yukawa calculated that the meson would have a rest mass of $270m_e$. He further theorized that just as photons not only are the unseen participants in electromagnetic interactions but can also be observed as free particles, so too a free meson is observable. At the time, the most obvious place to look for this particle was the sky, through an examination of the particles created by collisions resulting from incoming

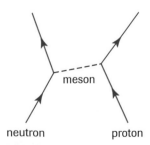

Figure 4
The strong nuclear force. The virtual particle exchanged this time is the carrier of the strong nuclear force rather than the photon, which carries the electromagnetic force.

cosmic rays from deep space. In 1936, a new particle was discovered, of mass $207m_e$. At first it was thought to be the elusive meson, but closer study revealed otherwise: not only was its mass too low; its interactions with matter were too weak. For instance, these particles were found in deep mines, having passed unaffected through several kilometres of earth. But the meson, as the carrier of the strong force, would have to interact strongly with matter. The new particles were called mu (μ) mesons, or **muons**. They exist in two forms: positive and negative.

Finally, in 1947, Yukawa's particle was found by British physicist Patrick Blackett (1897–1974). The observations were made from cosmic rays, which typically contain very few mesons. Blackett therefore only observed a small number of the sought-after particles, so he could not be sure whether his observations were simply due to chance. Fortunately, a 4.7-m cyclotron had just been completed at the Lawrence Berkeley Laboratory. This instrument, coupled with a photographic method developed by British physicist Cecil Powell (1903–1969), confirmed the observations. Blackett's particle was later found to be one of a family of mesons and was named the pi (π) meson, or **pion**. Pions were also found to exist in two varieties, π^+ and π^- (positive and negative), and to have a rest mass of $274m_e$, as Yukawa had predicted. Later, a third π meson, the neutral π^0, was discovered, with a slightly smaller mass of $264m_e$.

The π mesons exhibited strong interactions with matter. It was generally accepted that mesons transmit, or mediate, the strong nuclear force in much the same way as photons transmit the electromagnetic force. Free π mesons (pions) are unstable and quickly decay (in 10^{-8} s) into μ mesons (muons). In fact, the muons observed in cosmic radiation are probably produced from the decay of pions. Since the discovery of the pion, a number of other mesons have been discovered, and these also appear to mediate the strong nuclear force (**Figure 5**).

Recent developments in physics have greatly enhanced this picture. Today, the carriers of the strong nuclear force are thought to be the gluons (see Section 13.5).

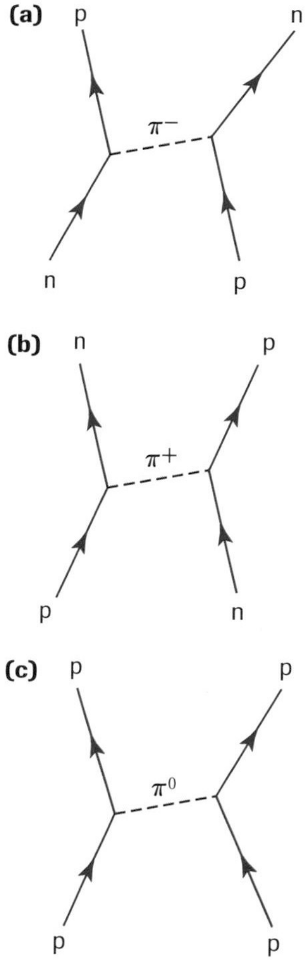

> ▶ **Practice**
>
> **Understanding Concepts**
>
> 1. A positron and an electron can annihilate one another, producing γ photons. Draw a Feynman diagram showing this process.
>
> 2. Recall from Chapter 12 that in the photoelectric effect, a photon striking a metal surface with sufficient energy can liberate electrons from that surface. Draw a Feynman diagram showing the interaction.

The Weak Nuclear Force

We have already seen that the process of β decay cannot be explained in terms of the electromagnetic force or the strong nuclear force. A reasonable theory of this process required a third force, which came to be known as the **weak nuclear force**.

A modern explanation of the β decay process assumes that the proton and the neutron are not elementary particles. Instead, each is composed of combinations of smaller elementary particles called quarks. There are several types of quarks including the up quarks and down quarks. Protons are assumed to be composed of two up quarks and one down quark, and neutrons are assumed to be composed of one up quark and two down quarks. (We will examine quarks in detail in Section 13.5.)

muon an elementary particle; a mu meson

pion an elementary particle; a pi meson

Figure 5
Feynman diagrams of nucleon–nucleon interactions through the exchange of virtual pions
(a) neutron–proton interaction
(b) proton–neutron interaction
(c) proton–proton interaction

weak nuclear force the weak force in a nucleus thought to be associated with β decay

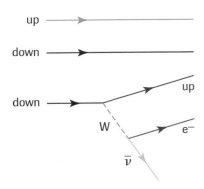

Figure 6
A Feynman diagram depicting β decay. Only one quark is affected. The result is a particle with two up quarks and one down (a proton) as well as a β particle and an antineutrino.

In the process of β^- decay, a neutron disappears and is replaced by a proton, a β particle, and an antineutrino. The theory of quarks offers the following description of the process: a particle consisting of one up quark and two down quarks is changed when one of the down quarks disappears and is replaced with an up quark and a quite massive particle, a virtual **W boson**. This virtual W boson, like any virtual particle, has an exceedingly short life, decaying almost at once to produce the more familiar β-decay products: the β particle and the antineutrino (**Figure 6**). It is one of the carriers of the weak force.

The *electroweak theory*, which sought to unite the electromagnetic force with the weak force, predicted a second particle, later called the **Z boson**. These particles are difficult to observe directly. However, careful examination of many interactions revealed some events that could not be explained without their existence. Direct evidence was later found in 1983, when very high-energy particle accelerators caused collisions that produced both W and Z bosons.

Gravity: The Odd One Out

Since the other forces can be explained in terms of particle exchange, it makes sense to assume that the same can be done with gravity. In recent years, much work has been done on the **graviton**, the hypothetical carrier of the gravitational force. The particle is as yet unseen; many think it will never be seen. Therefore, theory will have to provide clues about its nature.

It is assumed that, like photons, gravitons travel at the speed of light. Unlike photons, however, which do not directly interact with one another, gravitons can interact. Two intersecting beams of photons, for example, will pass through one another unscathed. Gravitons, on the other hand, will scatter when they interact. This self-interaction is perhaps the chief barrier preventing scientists from formulating a quantum theory of gravity. This implies that two gravitons can exchange a third graviton while simultaneously interacting with particles. These multiple exchanges make the interactions much too complicated and uncertain to describe.

Despite these challenges, work is ongoing on the theory of quantum gravity, for it will be necessary to complete this before we can completely understand the big bang theory. At the Big Bang, when it is thought that the whole universe was an unbelievably dense object, the strength of the gravitational force was comparable to that of the other types of interactions.

Table 1 summarizes the four fundamental forces and their carriers.

Table 1 Forces and Their Carriers

Force	Carriers	Symbol	Charge	Mass
electromagnetic	photon	γ	0	0
strong	gluon	g	0	0
weak	W boson	W^+	+	80.1 GeV
		W^-	−	80.6 GeV
	Z boson	Z	0	91.2 GeV
gravitational	graviton	G	0	0

Presently the most promising research in this area views particles as closed loops, or strings, rather than as point-like entities. Some important features of the emerging string theories will be described in Section 13.7.

> ▶ **Practice**
>
> **Understanding Concepts**
>
> **3.** Briefly describe the process by which the mass of the meson can be estimated.
>
> **4.** How was it determined that the muon, discovered in 1936, was not the much-sought meson?

The Sudbury Neutrino Observatory

In a way, you can consider the accelerators and detectors discussed in Section 13.3 as active observatories in which scientists probe elementary particles. The observatories are active in the sense that they produce their own particles that are used for observation. This is not the only possible approach. The earlier observatories made use of cosmic rays. These observatories could therefore be considered passive because they worked using particles that had been created elsewhere.

Several passive observatories exist today. One of the most recent, and exciting, is the Sudbury Neutrino Observatory (SNO), operated by an 80-member collaboration of scientists from Canada, the United States, and Great Britain. Located 2 km underground, near Sudbury, Ontario, in the deepest section of Inco's Creighton Mine, the SNO measures neutrinos that come from the energy-releasing core of the Sun. The observatory, begun in 1990 and completed in 1998 at a cost of $78 million, has been in almost continuous use since 1999.

The heart of the observatory is located in a ten-storey-high cavern where a 12-m spherical acrylic container holds 1000 t of deuterium oxide, D_2O, or "heavy water." This is placed in a water-filled cavity measuring 22 m in diameter and 34 m high. Outside the acrylic sphere is a geodesic sphere containing 9456 light sensors or phototubes capable of detecting the tiny amounts of the blue-violet Cerenkov light that is formed when neutrinos are stopped or scattered by the D_2O molecules (**Figure 7**). The D_2O is ideal for the detection of neutrinos because all three types react with it, and with three separate reactions, the SNO is unique in its ability to look for a conversion, or "oscillation," of the one type of neutrino produced in the Sun's core into the other two types. Several thousand interactions per year are recorded at the observatory.

Previous neutrino detectors have recorded far fewer interactions than expected, based on models that explain the energy production in the Sun, so one of the purposes of the SNO is to try and determine why. One explanation that has been put forward centres on the neutrino's possible ability to transmute from one type to another. This, in turn, suggests that the particle has mass. Unlike the other operating observatories, which see a single neutrino reaction, the SNO sees three types of neutrino interactions and can determine the presence of neutrinos of all three types.

In 2001, SNO scientists announced that they had found the cause of a 30-year old mystery—why only about one-third of the neutrinos expected from solar models had been detected in previous neutrino detectors. SNO has found that the other two-thirds of the neutrinos had indeed been changed to the other two types of neutrinos not seen by the other labs. From these results, a small mass can be assigned to the neutrino (previously thought to be massless), and its effect on the expansion of the universe could be estimated. The results attracted world-wide attention and were rated among the top discoveries in 2001.

Figure 7
The SNO detectors are held in place on an 18-m sphere, which surrounds the container of heavy water.

Particle Interactions

- The electromagnetic force can be seen as a particle exchange. The particle, a virtual photon, is invisible.
- The theory of quantum electrodynamics describes interactions in terms of the exchange of particles.
- A Feynman diagram is a shorthand way of depicting particle interactions. The two-dimensional diagrams can be seen in terms of space and time.
- The meson, originally thought to be the carrier of the strong nuclear force, was predicted in 1935 by Yukawa and finally detected in 1947 by Blackett.
- The weak nuclear force can be explained in terms of an exchange of particles. The carriers of this force, the W and Z bosons, though difficult to observe, were detected in 1983.
- Gravitons are the hypothetical carriers of the gravitational force; they are capable of self-interaction, so the formulation of a theory of quantum gravity is proving difficult.
- The Sudbury Neutrino Observatory detects the three types of neutrinos; it is able to accomplish this by detecting the radiation emitted when a neutrino is scattered or stopped by a D_2O molecule.

▶ Section 13.4 Questions

Understanding Concepts

1. In what sense is "element" now an outdated term?

2. Explain how an interaction can be attractive when particles exchange particles.

3. Explain why we call the photon involved in the electromagnetic force virtual.

4. Some electromagnetic interactions involve the exchange of more than one photon. How do these typically differ from interactions involving the exchange of one photon?

5. (a) What nuclear process made it clear that there was a force in addition to the electromagnetic, gravitational, and strong nuclear forces?
   (b) Name the carriers of this fourth force.

6. (a) Draw a Feynman diagram depicting β decay.
   (b) A proton and an antiproton can annihilate one another, in a process producing two pions. Draw a Feynman diagram showing the process.

7. (a) In what ways is it true that gravity is "the odd one out"?
   (b) Explain why it is difficult to formulate a quantum theory of gravity.

8. In which of the four force interactions does each of the following particles play a role?
   (a) electron   (c) proton   (e) neutrino
   (b) positron   (d) neutron

9. Recall that the description of the process that could estimate the mass of the Yukawa particle resulted in the approximation $mc^2 \approx \dfrac{hc}{2\pi d}$. The masses of the W and Z bosons are assumed to be 80.3 GeV/c^2 and 91.2 GeV/c^2. Use the approximation equation to estimate the range of the weak force.

Making Connections

10. Visit the SNO Web site and answer the following questions:
   (a) Approximately how many people were involved in constructing the facility?
   (b) How has the facility been funded?
   (c) Briefly describe one of the three ways in which neutrinos are detected in the SNO.
   (d) Briefly describe some research results from the facility.

 www.science.nelson.com

Particle Classification

More than 150 years ago, scientists recognized that elements could be arranged in groups according to their chemical properties. The periodic table of elements resulted. As more and more subatomic particles were discovered, it was found that they too could be organized into groupings according to their properties. A table of subatomic particles was first proposed by Murray Gell-Mann (**Figure 1**) and the Japanese physicist Kazuhiko Nishijima (1912–), working independently.

The original tables were based chiefly on mass, but as more particles were discovered, investigators discovered other properties.

Many puzzling observations about light emitted and absorbed by matter could be explained if electrons were assumed to have some magnetic properties. Remember that a charged particle that moves about some axis forms an electric current loop and therefore forms a magnetic dipole. It appeared as if rotational motion could account for these magnetic properties. Based on this, in 1925 the Dutch physicists G.E. Uhlenbeck and S. Goudsmit stated that the electron must revolve and rotate. This resulted in a realization that a new quantum number, **spin**, was needed.

Subsequent work by other scientists revealed that all elementary particles have a spin number attached. There are two things to be pointed out about this quantity. First, since it is a quantum number, it cannot take a range of values; only certain discrete amounts are possible. Second, spin is a property that is intrinsic to the particle; that is, any given type of particle has one unique value of spin. All electrons, for example, have spin $\frac{1}{2}$. It is impossible for the electron to have any other value of spin.

This new quantum number is best understood as a representation of the angular momentum that the object has. For example, when we say that the electron has spin $\frac{1}{2}$, what we are really saying is that its angular momentum is $\frac{1}{2}\hbar$, where $\hbar = \frac{h}{2\pi}$.

Spin and mass are two of the keys to the grouping of particles. **Table 1** presents the current major classifications. In simple terms, the current scheme first distinguishes *gauge bosons*, *leptons*, and *hadrons* and then makes subdivisions among the hadrons.

- **Gauge bosons** are so named because *gauge theory* makes them mediators of interactions. (We will see later that this theory unites the electromagnetic force with the weak force into a single electroweak force.) The particles in the gauge boson category include the photon, which carries the electromagnetic force, and the W and Z bosons, which carry the weak nuclear force.

- **Leptons** are particles that interact through the weak nuclear force and do not interact through the strong nuclear force. The leptons comprise three charged particles, each existing in both a positive and a negative form—the electron, the muon, the tau (also called the tauon)—and neutrinos of three corresponding types—the electron neutrino, the muo neutrino, and the tau neutrino.

- **Hadrons** are particles that interact chiefly through the strong nuclear force. They include the neutron, the proton, the pion, and other particles with larger rest masses. Hadrons are further divided by mass and spin into the mesons and the heavier baryons.

So many particles had been discovered that by the 1950s some physicists referred to the collection as a particle zoo. The well-known nuclear physicist Enrico Fermi remarked that he would have been like a botanist had he the ability to remember all the names. Fortunately, simplification was on the way.

Figure 1
Murray Gell-Mann (1929–)

spin the quantum property of particles denoting rotational motion; each particle has its own spin number

gauge bosons the class of particles that interact through the electroweak force; contains the photon and the W and Z bosons

leptons the class of particles that interact through the weak nuclear force; contains the electron, the muon, the tauon, and the three types of neutrino

hadrons the class of particles that chiefly interact through the strong nuclear force; contains the neutron, the proton, the pion, and other particles of large mass

DID YOU KNOW ?

Magnetism and Spin
A modern theory of magnetism proposes that electron spin is responsible for the magnetism we see in macroscopic pieces of matter. If the electrons of a substance are equally divided in spin, the magnetic fields around the electrons cancel each other and the substance is unmagnetized. When the division is unequal, the macroscopic specimen is magnetized.

Table 1   Some Subatomic Particles

Name	Symbol	Antiparticle	Rest Mass (MeV/c^2)	Spin	Lifetime (s)
Gauge Bosons					
photon	γ	self	0	1	stable
W	W^+	W^-	80.3×10^3	1	3×10^{-25}
Z	Z^0	Z^0	91.2×10^3	1	3×10^{-25}
Leptons					
electron	e^-	e^+	0.511	$\frac{1}{2}$	stable
muon	μ	$\overline{\mu}$	105.7	$\frac{1}{2}$	2.2×10^{-6}
tau	τ	$\overline{\tau}$	1777	$\frac{1}{2}$	2.91×10^{-13}
neutrino (e)	ν_e	$\overline{\nu}_e$	$< 7.0 \times 10^{-6}$	$\frac{1}{2}$	stable
neutrino (μ)	ν_μ	$\overline{\nu}_\mu$	< 0.17	$\frac{1}{2}$	stable
neutrino (τ)	ν_τ	$\overline{\nu}_\tau$	< 24	$\frac{1}{2}$	stable
Hadrons					
Some Mesons					
pion	π^+	π^-	139.6	0	2.60×10^{-8}
	π^0	self	135.0		0.84×10^{-16}
kaon	K^+	K^-	493.7	0	1.24×10^{-8}
					0.89×10^{-10}
	K^0_S	$\overline{K}^0_S$	497.7	0	5.17×10^{-8}
	K^0_L	$\overline{K}^0_L$	497.7		
eta	η^0	self	547.5	0	5×10^{-19}
Some Baryons					
proton	p	$\overline{p}$	938.3	$\frac{1}{2}$	stable
neutron	n	$\overline{n}$	939.6	$\frac{1}{2}$	stable
lambda	Λ^0	$\overline{\Lambda}^0$	1115.7	$\frac{1}{2}$	2.63×10^{-10}
sigma	Σ^+	$\overline{\Sigma}^-$	1189.4	$\frac{1}{2}$	0.80×10^{-10}
	Σ^0	$\overline{\Sigma}^0$	1192.6	$\frac{1}{2}$	7.4×10^{-20}
	Σ^-	$\overline{\Sigma}^+$	1197.4	$\frac{1}{2}$	1.48×10^{-10}
xi	Ξ^0	self	1314.9	$\frac{1}{2}$	2.90×10^{-10}
	Ξ^-	$\overline{\Xi}^+$	1321.3	$\frac{1}{2}$	1.64×10^{-10}
omega	Ω^-	Ω^+	1672.5	$\frac{3}{2}$	0.82×10^{-10}

Strangeness and the Eightfold Way

At the start of the 1960s, Murray Gell-Mann, in the United States, drew conclusions from the unusual behaviour of certain hadrons, including the kaon, the lambda, and the sigma. For one thing, the decay rates of these particles were unexpectedly long, as would be expected for particles interacting through the weak rather than the strong nuclear force. Further, it appeared that reactions always produced these particles in pairs, so that if, for example, a certain reaction produced a kaon particle, it could be guaranteed to produce some variant of another kaon, or perhaps a lambda or sigma.

Gell-Mann explained many of the unexpected observations by assigning a new quantum number, appropriately called **strangeness**. The unusually long decay times were explained by making a further imaginative leap. The strangeness number was not exactly conserved. Instead, the strange particles, which primarily interacted through the strong nuclear force, were postulated to decay through the relatively slower weak nuclear force.

Gell-Mann then went on to prepare another classification scheme for the hadrons, based on octets (eight-member groupings) of baryons, mesons, and spin numbers. Not all the slots in the scheme could be filled immediately, since they described unknown particles. With characteristic self-confidence, Gell-Mann suggested that research would fill the missing slots.

Gell-Mann's eightfold classification scheme was particularly well accepted in the 1960s (**Table 2**). Later findings, however, such as the discovery of a family of hadrons with 10, not 8, members, cast some doubt on its overall usefulness. His fame was unblemished, however; he again rose to prominence for his work with quarks, which are discussed next.

DID YOU KNOW ?

Nobel Prize Winner
In 1969, Gell-Mann received the Nobel Prize for his work with the concept of strangeness and the development of the eightfold way of classification.

strangeness a property of certain particles that chiefly interact through the strong nuclear force yet decay through the weak nuclear force

Table 2 The Hadrons Classified According to Gell-Mann's Eightfold Way

	Mesons								Baryons			
Spin	0				1				$\frac{1}{2}$			
Name	pion	kaon	anti-kaon	eta	rho	hyper-kaon	antihy-perkaon	omega	sigma	proton/neutron	xi	lambda
Charge	1, 0, −1	1, 0	0, −1	0	1, 0, −1	1, 0	0, −1	0	1, 0, −1	1, 0	0, −1	0
Strangeness	0	1	−1	0	0	1	−1	0	−1	0	−2	−1

> ▶ **Practice**

Understanding Concepts

1. On what basis is a particle called (a) a gauge boson, (b) a lepton, and (c) a baryon?

2. Explain what is meant by the property "strange."

3. Consider what Gell-Mann did to organize the hadrons according to strangeness. Would you say that his work was entirely logical, entirely imaginative, or both? Explain your answer.

Three Quarks …

The particles discovered in the 1960s and 1970s were all hadrons. It became apparent that the four then-known leptons (the electron, the muon, and the two corresponding neutrinos) were truly elementary particles, since they did not appear to break down into smaller particles. Hadrons, on the other hand, did.

Evidence that hadrons were not fundamental began to mount in the late 1960s. Jerome Friedman, Henry Kendall, and Canadian-born Richard Taylor found evidence that the particles within the nucleus were, themselves, composed of subparticles.

At this time Gell-Mann, at the California Institute of Technology, was attempting to classify all known particles, seeking a general substructure. He proposed that a pattern he discerned in the hadrons could be explained by building hadrons up from six subparticles (organized into three particle–antiparticle pairs), which he called **quarks**.

Gell-Mann distinguished his three quarks (**Table 3**) on the basis of a property he called their **flavour**: up, down, and sideways (abbreviated u, d, and s). Later on it became apparent that sideways had to do with strangeness, so the term "strange" became more common than "sideways."

quarks elementary particles making up hadrons

flavours categories of quarks: up, down, and strange

baryon number a property of an elementary particle; quarks have a baryon number of $\frac{1}{3}$

law of conservation of baryon number the total baryon number before a particle interaction equals the total baryon number after

Table 3 Quarks, As Originally Conceived

Name	Symbol	Charge	Spin	Baryon Number	Strangeness
Quarks					
up	u	$+\frac{2}{3}$	$\frac{1}{2}$	$\frac{1}{3}$	0
down	d	$-\frac{1}{3}$	$\frac{1}{2}$	$\frac{1}{3}$	0
strange	s	$-\frac{1}{3}$	$\frac{1}{2}$	$\frac{1}{3}$	-1
Antiquarks					
up	$\bar{u}$	$-\frac{2}{3}$	$\frac{1}{2}$	$-\frac{1}{3}$	0
down	$\bar{d}$	$+\frac{1}{3}$	$\frac{1}{2}$	$-\frac{1}{3}$	0
strange	$\bar{s}$	$+\frac{1}{3}$	$\frac{1}{2}$	$-\frac{1}{3}$	$+1$

Particle interactions have been observed to conserve the number of baryons present; hence the introduction of another quantum number, the **baryon number**, and the **law of conservation of baryon number**. Quarks are assigned a baryon number of $\frac{1}{3}$, since three quarks are required to construct a baryon. **Table 4** gives the baryon numbers of other particles.

As **Table 3** indicates, quark theory makes the imaginative proposal that the charge of a quark is not an integer but a fractional multiple of the elementary charge (with the up quark having charge $+\frac{2}{3}$ and the down and strange each having $-\frac{1}{3}$). These fractional assignments allow combinations of two or three quarks to have charge values of ± 1 or 0.

Each hadron was pictured as being composed of three quarks. For example, a neutron would consist of the three quarks u, d, and d. The charges on these three quarks add to zero, the baryon numbers to 1, and the strangenesses to 0. The spins of up and down quarks were postulated to be opposite, giving the neutron a total spin of $\frac{1}{2}$. In other words, the properties of the quarks added up to those of the neutron (**Figure 2**).

Table 4 Baryon Numbers

Particle	Baryon Number
baryon	$+1$
antibaryon	-1
mesons	0
leptons	0
gauge bosons	0
quarks	$\frac{1}{3}$
antiquarks	$-\frac{1}{3}$

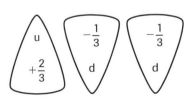

Figure 2
Quark model of a neutron. The three charges add up to 0, making the particle neutral. The baryon numbers, strangenesses, and spins likewise add up to the values expected of a neutron.

Construct and draw a quark model of a proton.

Solution

The charge of a proton is +1. **Table 1** shows the proton's spin to be $\frac{1}{2}$, and **Table 2** shows the proton's strangeness to be 0. Since the proton is composed of three quarks, each having baryon number $\frac{1}{3}$, the baryon number is 1. To satisfy these constraints, we need three quarks, in some combination of u and d. **Table 3** shows that the combination uud has a total charge of +1. We may therefore proceed to check the other quantum numbers:

baryon number: $\frac{1}{3} + \frac{1}{3} + \frac{1}{3} = 1$ (correct)

spin: one up and one down cancel, leaving $\frac{1}{2}$ (correct)

strangeness: $0 + 0 + 0 = 0$ (correct)

Since the sums for the other quantum numbers are correct, the combination uud is correct (**Figure 3**).

With this system, Gell-Mann was able to show the makeup of each baryon by using its three quarks; he was also able to construct each meson by pairing a quark with an antiquark.

Construct and draw a quark model of a π^+ pion.

Solution

From **Table 1** we see that the π^+ pion has spin 0; from **Table 2** we see that the π^+ pion has charge +1 and strangeness 0. Since the π^+ pion is a meson, the baryon number is 0. To obtain all the properties of a π^+, we need a quark and an antiquark. **Table 3** shows that we cannot include the strange quark: if we included it, we would have to pair it with its antiparticle to obtain a spin of 0. But this would yield charge 0, which is incorrect. The remaining possibilities are then $u\bar{u}$, $d\bar{d}$, $u\bar{d}$, and $d\bar{u}$. The first two possibilities are excluded because they yield the charge 0. The combination $d\bar{u}$ is excluded because it also yields an incorrect charge $\left(-\frac{1}{3}\right) + \left(-\frac{2}{3}\right) = -1$. This leaves the combination $u\bar{d}$ as the only candidate. To confirm the correctness of this combination, we check the other quantum numbers:

baryon: $\frac{1}{3} + \left(-\frac{1}{3}\right) = 0$ (correct)

spin: u and d have opposite spins, yielding a sum of 0   (correct)

strangeness: $0 + 0 = 0$ (correct)

The quark model of the π^+ pion is $u\bar{d}$ (**Figure 4**).

Understanding Concepts

4. Using **Table 3**, calculate the charge of each of the following hypothetical particles:
   (a) uuu   (b) u$\bar{u}$ (c) $\bar{d}$du   (d) ds

5. Construct quark models for each of the following hadrons:
   (a) antiproton   (b) antineutron   (c) neutral pion (π^0)   (d) K^- kaon

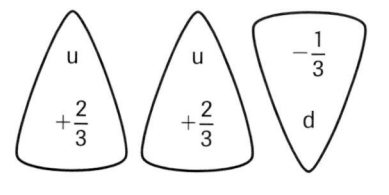

Figure 3
Quark model of a proton. The charges have a sum of +1. Baryon number, spin, and strangeness likewise add up to the values expected of a proton.

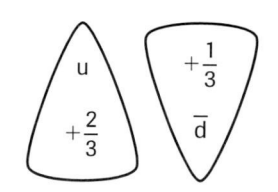

Figure 4
Quark model of a π^+ pion. The net charge is +1, and the other quantum numbers likewise have the values expected of a π^+. Because the meson is composed of a particle and an antiparticle, it decays rapidly.

(a)

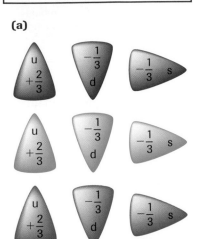

(b)

Figure 5
(a) Sheldon Glashow proposed that quarks had another property, which he called colour. The result was then 9 quarks and 9 corresponding anti-quarks. The antiquarks, which are not pictured, are assumed to have opposite colour: antired, antigreen, and antiblue.
(b) Sheldon Glashow

colour property assigned to quarks, keeping them in different quantum states to avoid violation of the Pauli exclusion principle

gluons hypothetical chargeless, massless particles believed to carry the strong nuclear force

quantum chromodynamics (QCD) theory that describes the strong interaction in terms of gluon exchanges on the part of quarks and antiquarks

The Colour Force

There was one problem with Gell-Mann's original model. According to the Pauli exclusion principle, two identical particles with identical sets of quantum numbers cannot occur together in the same atomic or subatomic system. Each quark, however, has a half-spin, and quarks with identical flavours exist in the same particle. For example, the proton has two u quarks and one d quark, and an omega (Ω) particle (a baryon) has three s quarks.

To solve this problem, the Danish-American physicist Sheldon Glashow suggested that quarks had another property, which he called **colour** (**Figure 5**). He proposed that every quark and antiquark had one of three possible values of this property, which he called red, green, and blue. He further proposed that the three quarks making up baryons all have a different colour, making each baryon colourless. In particular, the three s quarks in the Ω particle were of different colours, consistent with the Pauli exclusion principle.

How does colour work with mesons? They are made up of a quark and an antiquark. Since the quark and the antiquark already have different quantum states, they do not need to be of different colour. Instead, the theory proposes that they rapidly change colour from red to green to blue, with the change in colour so rapid that the colours balance out, making the meson colourless.

The Strong Nuclear Force Revisited

Taylor's observations that nucleons were composed of subparticles could not be completely explained in terms of quarks. Nuclei also seemed to contain uncharged particles—not quarks, which all have some fractional charge. Glashow believed that the quark colour had to do with the strong nuclear force and that quarks exchanged particles, **gluons**. According to this theory, it was the exchange of gluons (of colour) in the interactions between quarks, and not (as previously proposed) the exchange of mesons, that was the origin of the strong force.

The theory of the colour force and the interactions of particles due to gluons is **quantum chromodynamics**, or QCD. Quantum chromodynamics is similar to Feynman's quantum electrodynamics, with colour analogous to electric charge and the gluon analogous to the photon.

We can illustrate QCD by considering how quarks behave in the neutron, which has quark composition udd. According to Glashow, all three particles must have different colours to maintain the white quality of the colour force. Six of the eight possible gluons that are exchanged have colour charge, giving them the ability to change the colours of quarks and keeping the constituent quarks together while ensuring that the entire three-quark assemblage remains colourless (**Figure 6**).

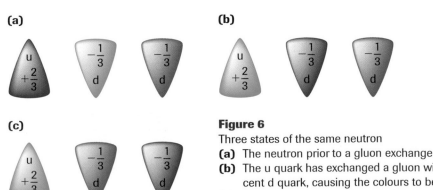

Figure 6
Three states of the same neutron
(a) The neutron prior to a gluon exchange
(b) The u quark has exchanged a gluon with the adjacent d quark, causing the colours to be permuted.
(c) The first and second d quarks have exchanged a gluon. Once again, the colours have been permuted. One quark of each colour is present at all times.

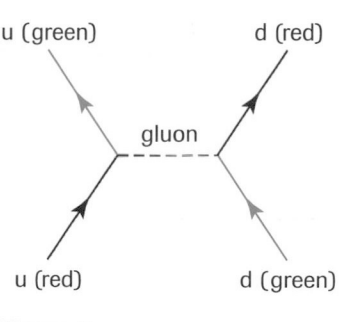

Understanding Concepts

6. In **Figure 6(a)**, suppose that the u quark exchanges a colour-charged gluon with the rightmost d quark. Sketch the result.

7. Recall that the root word *chromos* refers to colour. Explain why, in light of this, the term "quantum chromodynamics" is appropriate.

8. **Figure 7** is a Feynman diagram depicting the gluon exchange that produces **(b)** from **(a)** in **Figure 6**. Draw the Feynman diagram depicting the exchange that produces **(c)** from **(b)**.

Figure 7
A Feynman diagram depicting the colour-force exchange in the transition from **(a)** to **(b)** in **Figure 6**.

The Full Quark Family Tree

In the years leading up to 1970, Glashow as well as Steven Weinberg and Abdus Salam completed the work of unifying the electromagnetic and weak nuclear forces. The **electroweak**, or **gauge**, **theory** showed that the two forces became one at extremely high temperatures and pressures. (Gauge theories are theories in which forces arise from underlying symmetries.) As expected, the theory was successful in making predictions about the behaviour of leptons, the particles one would expect to be acted on. There was a startling addition, however, in that the theory predicted a fourth quark—postulated because the hadrons were also, to some degree, subject to the weak force. Since the electroweak force was derived from four particles, symmetry suggested that the family of leptons should likewise be constructed from four particles. Glashow accordingly predicted a fourth quark, **charm** (symbol c). To the great surprise of the physics community, who seriously doubted the work of Glashow, Weinberg, and Salam, Samuel Ting and Burton Richter discovered the particle in 1974.

In 1975, Martin Perl and his associates started a third family of leptons by discovering a fifth lepton, the tau (also known as the taon). Symmetry now required that the hadrons have a third family, with two new quarks. Perl's team accordingly proposed a fifth and sixth quark, which came to be known as **top** and **bottom** in North America (and as truth and beauty in Europe). The bottom quark was discovered at Fermilab in 1977 in a composite quark–antiquark (b$\bar{\text{b}}$) particle called upsilon, Υ.

The sixth quark, top, was the most elusive. Although its presence was long expected, it remained undiscovered until 1995, when a team using the high-energy collider at Fermilab found conclusive, even if indirect, evidence of its existence. Top decays rapidly, producing bottom and a W boson. The W, in turn, decays to pairs of quarks or into a lepton and a neutrino. Specialized detectors showed evidence of the descendants from top and of the particles that subsequently evolve from them, supporting the conclusion that a top had been present originally (**Figure 8**).

In the 1970s and early 1980s, physics arrived at the conviction that the fundamental, or elementary, particles are the quarks and the leptons. Of the three taken as fundamental earlier in the twentieth century—the proton, the neutron, the electron—only the electron survives as fundamental.

The question arises: "What importance do quarks have to the materials we use in the everyday world?" The only leptons needed to explain commonplace weak interactions are the electron and its companion neutrino. The up and down quarks are needed to form the two commonplace nucleons, the proton and the neutron. The muon, its neutrino, and the strange quark, on the other hand, only appear in the high-energy world of cosmic rays, high above Earth. Similarly, the charm, bottom, and top quarks only appear in the explorations of particle accelerators. It seems that quarks do not have much relevance for us. Yet these phantom particles apparently have a purpose in nature's scheme. The problem remains to determine just what this purpose is.

electroweak (gauge) theory
theory that unifies the electromagnetic and weak nuclear forces

charm the fourth type of quark

top the fifth type of quark

bottom the sixth type of quark

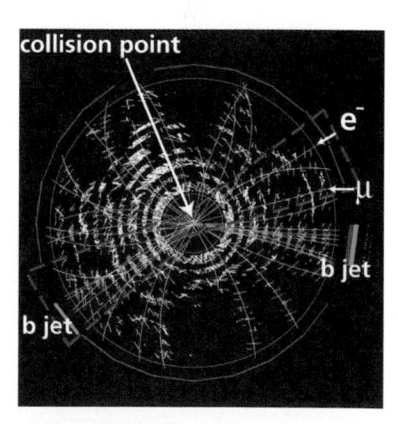

Figure 8
The discovery of the top quark was an international process involving almost 1000 scientists in 22 countries. The "b jet" in the photograph means "bottom jet"; quarks (and gluons) appear as a narrow spray of particles called a jet.

- Elementary particles have been organized into groups according to their fundamental properties, including mass and spin.
- One classification scheme treated particles as gauge bosons, leptons, and hadrons.
- The hadrons are further divided, by mass and spin, into two subclasses: the mesons and the baryons.
- When some hadrons were observed to behave strangely, in having unexpectedly long decay times, the spin quantum number was supplemented with a number for strangeness.
- Gell-Mann used the new quantum number to organize the hadrons into three distinct groups, each with eight particles, based on spin.
- Hadrons were found not to be elementary particles. Three new fundamental particles called quarks—up, down and strange, with charges $+\frac{2}{3}, -\frac{1}{3},$ and $-\frac{1}{3},$ and strangenesses $0, 0,$ and -1—were accordingly proposed.
- Baryons are assumed to consist of three quarks, and mesons to consist of a quark and an antiquark. The various quantum numbers of a complex particle are the sums of the quantum numbers of its constituents.
- The colour force was devised as a possible solution to the problem of applying the Pauli exclusion principle to quarks. It is assumed that each flavour of quark comes in three different colours. Baryons contain all three colours. Mesons cycle rapidly through the colours.
- The strong force carrier is no longer believed to be the meson. Instead, the mediators of the strong force are believed to be gluons.
- The original three quarks have been supplemented with an additional three: charm, bottom, and top.

Section 13.5 Questions

Understanding Concepts

1. Identify the particle corresponding to each of the following quark combinations:
   (a) $s\bar{u}$ (c) uds
   (b) $d\bar{u}$ (d) uus

2. Since quarks each have spin $\frac{1}{2}$, explain how a combination of three of them can still result in a particle—a baryon— with spin $\frac{1}{2}$.

3. Is it possible to produce a proton using two red up quarks and one blue down quark? Explain your answer.

4. Explain how mesons can be colour-neutral and yet composed of two quarks.

5. What is the role of a gluon in contemporary theory? What particle was previously thought to play the role?

6. (a) Briefly describe each of the types of quark.
   (b) Explain why scientists are now confident that all the possible quarks have been observed.

7. Identify the quark combination that would produce each of the following particles:
   (a) kaon +   (b) sigma 0

Applying Inquiry Skills

8. Draw a Feynman diagram depicting a gluon interaction between any two quarks in a proton.

Making Connections

9. How many different elementary particles are there in a CO_2 molecule?

 www.science.nelson.com

Case Study: Analyzing Elementary Particle Trajectories 13.6

The Bubble Chamber

The bubble chamber was developed in 1952 by Donald Glaser (**Figure 1**), who won the Nobel Prize in physics in 1960 for his invention. It was the most commonly used particle detector from about 1955 to the early 1980s. Although they are incompatible with the functions of modern particle accelerator systems, bubble chambers have provided physicists with a wealth of information regarding the nature of elementary particles and their interactions.

Many of the properties of fundamental particles may be determined by analyzing the trails they create in a bubble chamber. Using measurements made directly on bubble chamber photographs (like the one on the front cover of this textbook), we can often identify the particles by their tracks and calculate properties such as mass, momentum, and kinetic energy. In a typical experiment, a beam of a particular type of particle leaves an accelerator and enters a bubble chamber, which is a large, liquid hydrogen-filled vessel, as described in Section 13.3. **Figure 2** shows a bubble chamber apparatus.

The liquid hydrogen is in a "superheated" state and boils in response to the slightest disturbance. As fast-moving subatomic particles stream through the liquid hydrogen, they leave characteristic "bubble trails" that can be photographed for analysis. The chamber is placed in a strong magnetic field, which causes charged particles to travel in curved trajectories.

In the bubble chamber photographs we will examine, the magnetic field points out of the page so positively charged particles curve to the right (clockwise), and negatively charged particles curve to the left (counterclockwise) (**Figure 3**).

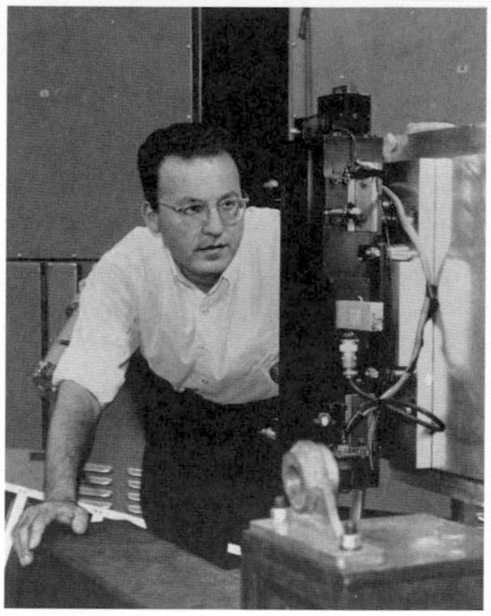

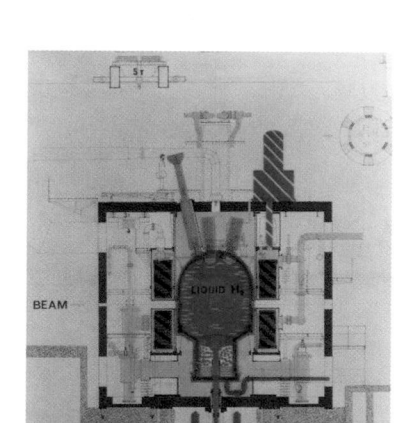

Figure 1
Donald Glaser

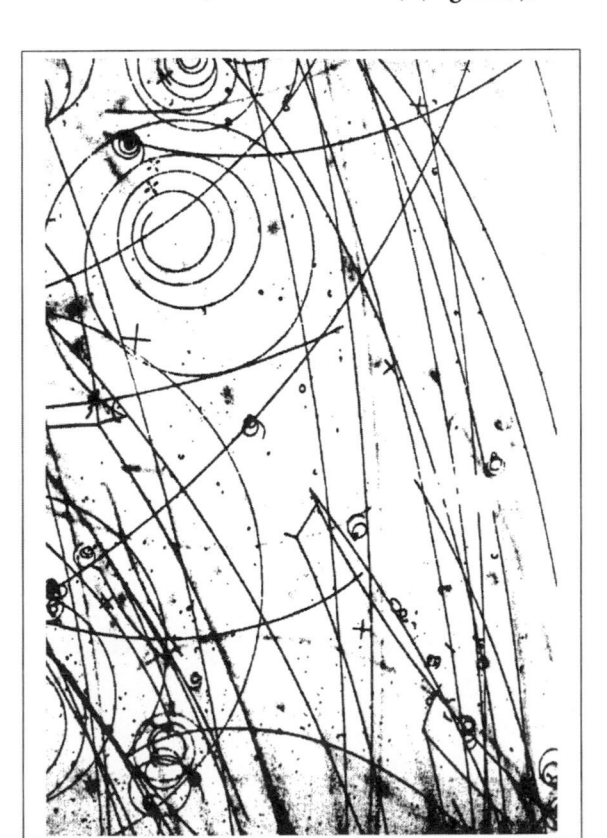

Figure 2
Bubble chamber apparatus

Figure 3
The particles enter the chamber from the bottom of the photograph. This will be true of all bubble chamber photos that appear in this case study. Note that to determine the sign of a particle's charge, it is necessary to know in which direction the particle travelled along the track.

In this case study, we will be analyzing the following four subatomic particles: proton (p), kaon (K), pion (π), and sigma (Σ). Of these, the proton is positively charged and is a stable component of ordinary matter. The other three are short-lived and may be positive, negative, or neutral (**Table 1**).

Table 1 Some Elementary Particles and Their Charges

Particle Name	Charge		
	Positive	*Negative*	*Neutral*
proton	p^+	no particle	no particle
kaon	K^+	K^-	K^0
pion	π^+	π^-	π^0
sigma	Σ^+	Σ^-	Σ^0

Particle Reactions

When a beam of one type of particle collides with a target, various interactions are observed. The photograph in **Figure 4** shows a number of kaons entering the chamber from the bottom. Since the magnetic field $\vec{B}$ points out of the page, the counterclockwise curvature of the tracks indicates that the particles are negatively charged. If we follow a K^- track, we will notice that many of these particles pass through the chamber without incident. However, some interact with a hydrogen nucleus (a proton) and start a number of reactions. The simplest type of interaction between two particles is called *elastic scattering*, and can be considered analogous to a billiard ball collision. We represent the elastic scattering of a K^- particle and a proton (p^+) symbolically as follows:

$$K^- + p^+ \rightarrow K^- + p^+$$

Notice that in this case, no change occurs in the identities of the interacting particles—they collide and bounce off each other unaffected. However, in some cases, an incident K^- particle reacts in such a way that new particles are created. In many cases, the created particles live for only 10^{-10} s or less and then disintegrate (decay) into other particles which may themselves undergo further decay. We will focus on the Σ^- production reaction, which may be symbolized as follows:

$$K^- + p^+ \rightarrow \Sigma^- + \pi^+$$

Notice in the above equation that the K^- particle and the proton disappear, and a sigma minus particle (Σ^-) and a pi plus particle (π^+) are created. The Σ^- particle is the most unstable product of the interaction and, in about 10^{-10} s, disintegrates into a π^- particle and a neutral particle we will call X^0, which leaves no trail in the bubble chamber. (Note that unlike Σ^- and π^+, X^0 is not the symbol of a known subatomic particle; it is a generic symbol we are using to denote an invisible, uncharged particle produced in this event.) We symbolize the Σ^- decay reaction as follows:

$$\Sigma^- \rightarrow \pi^- + X^0$$

The overall interaction can be shown as a two-step process:

$$K^- + p^+ \xrightarrow{(1)} \Sigma^- + \pi^+$$
$$\quad\quad\quad\quad {}_{(2)}\!\!\longrightarrow \pi^- + X^0$$

where (1) represents Σ^- production and (2) symbolizes Σ^- decay.

Recognizing Events On a Bubble Chamber Photograph

Bubble chamber photographs may appear confusing at first; however, they become easier to understand when you know what to look for. It is relatively easy to locate events in the photograph. An *event* is a change in a particle's characteristics or a particle interaction that is visible in the photograph.

K^- mesons travel with sufficiently low energy that many of them slow down and come to rest. For a Σ^- production reaction to take place, the K^- meson and the proton must be approximately 10^{-15} m apart. Although there is a force of attraction between the positively charged proton and the negatively charged K^- meson, the interaction is more likely to occur when the K^- particle is moving slowly or is at rest. We know that the initial momentum of the K^-/p^+ system is zero. Thus, the law of conservation of momentum requires that the Σ^- and π^+ particles have equal and opposite momenta. This makes the Σ^- and p^+ tracks appear to be a single track. The Σ^- production reaction liberates energy because the combined rest mass of the K^-/p^+ system is greater than the combined rest mass of the Σ^-/π^+ system. **Figure 4** is a bubble chamber photograph that contains a Σ^- production/decay event; the event is circled.

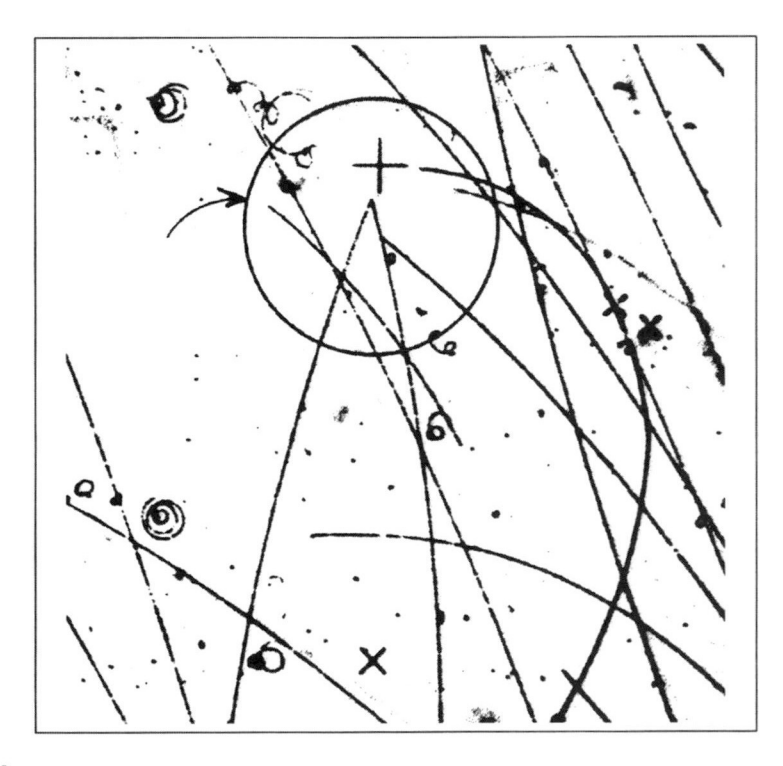

Figure 4
A bubble chamber photograph showing a K^-/p^+ interaction (circled event)

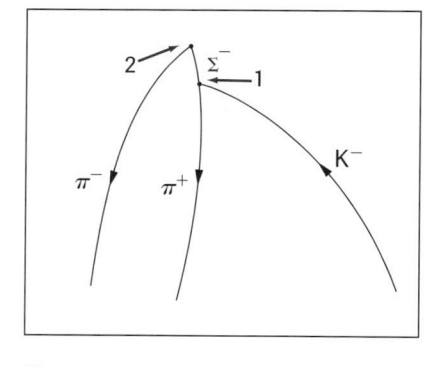

Figure 5
Schematic diagram of the K^-/p^+ interaction in **Figure 4**

Figure 5 is a schematic drawing of this event; it shows the particle identities and directions of motion. Notice how the Σ^- and π^+ tracks appear to be a single track. We interpret this to mean that the Σ^- production reaction occurred after the K^- came to rest (at point 1). You will also notice a sharp bend in the Σ^- track less than 1.0 cm from where it was created (point 2). It is at this sharp bend that the Σ^- particle decayed into a π^- meson and the invisible (neutral) X^0 particle. The length of the Σ^- track will be short due to the Σ particle's relatively short lifetime. Look at each of the photographs in **Figures 6** and **7** and see if you can identify individual events; each photograph has one or more events.

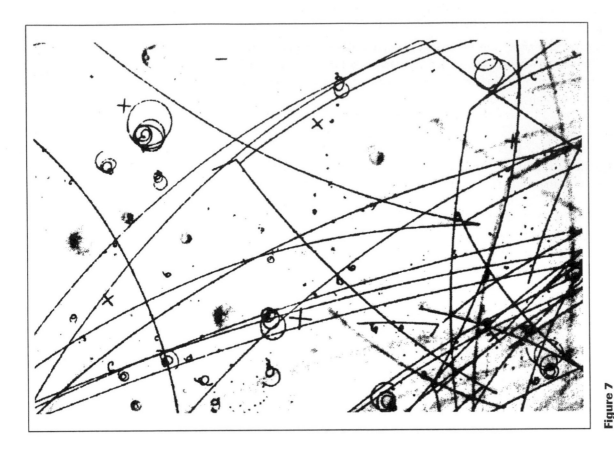

Figure 7
Another obvious event is near the bottom of the photograph.

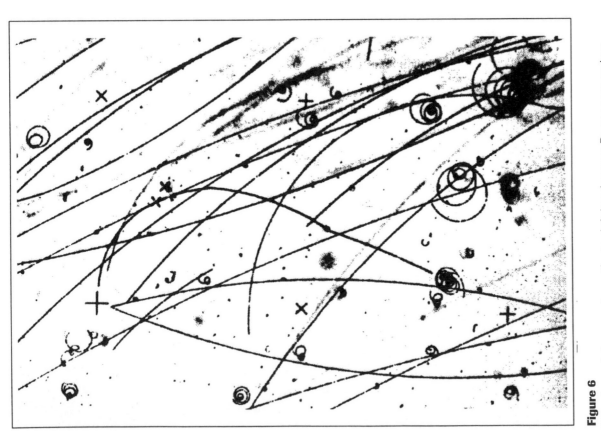

Figure 6
There is an obvious event near the top left-hand corner. Do you see any less obvious events?

Quantitative Analysis of Bubble Chamber Events

Careful measurements made of the length, direction, and curvature of the tracks in bubble chamber photographs reveal much more information about the particles and their interactions than a simple visual inspection of the photographs provides. Quantitative analysis of the particles that are seen in the photographs can also lead to the discovery of invisible particles such as X^0.

This case study will be divided into parts A and B. In part A you will analyze the trajectory of a π^- particle ($p_\pi-$) and determine its charge-to-mass ratio and rest mass. You will then evaluate the calculated rest mass by comparing its value to the accepted value as given in a standard reference table (**Table 2**). In part B, you will determine the rest mass of the invisible X^0 particle that is formed in the Σ^- event.

Table 2 Rest Masses for π^- and Σ^-

Particle	Rest Mass m (MeV/c^2)
π^-	139.6
Σ^-	1197.4

Part A: Determination of the Charge-to-Mass Ratio and the Rest Mass of the π^- Particle Formed in Σ^- Decay

Recall that a particle of charge q and mass m, moving perpendicular to a uniform magnetic field of magnitude B, has a charge-to-mass ratio $\dfrac{q}{m}$ given by $\dfrac{q}{m} = \dfrac{v}{Br}$.

Assuming that charged (long-lived) subatomic particles travel at the speed of light ($c = 3.0 \times 10^8$ m/s) through a bubble chamber, we can determine the charge-to-mass ratio by measuring the radius of curvature r of the tracks. In the bubble chamber photographs we will examine, the magnetic field points out of the page and has a magnitude B equal to 1.43 T. Therefore,

$$\frac{q}{m} = \frac{c}{Br}$$

$$= \frac{3.00 \times 10^8 \text{ m/s}}{(1.43 \text{ T})r} \quad (1 \text{ T} = 1 \text{ kg/C·s})$$

$$\frac{q}{m} = \frac{1.98 \times 10^8 \text{ C·m/kg}}{r}$$

If the radius of curvature of the particle track is measured in metres, the charge-to-mass ratio will be calculated in coulombs per kilogram (C/kg). If the charge of the particle is known, then its mass can also be calculated. Since all known (long-lived) subatomic particles possess a charge q that is the same as that of an electron ($e = 1.6 \times 10^{-19}$ C), we can use this value to calculate the rest mass of the π^- particle.

Calculating the Radius of Curvature by the Sagitta Method

For a curved track, the radius of curvature r cannot be measured directly since the centre of the circular arc is not known. However, if we draw a chord on the track and measure both the length of the chord l and the length of the sagitta s (the *sagitta* is the distance from the midpoint of an arc to the midpoint of its chord), the radius r can then be found in terms of l and s (**Figure 8**). As you can see in **Figure 8**, the Pythagorean theorem gives the following relation between the radius r, chord length l, and sagitta s:

$$r^2 = (r - s)^2 + \left(\frac{l}{2}\right)^2$$

Solving for r:

$$r^2 = r^2 - 2rs + s^2 + \frac{l^2}{4}$$

$$2rs = s^2 + \frac{l^2}{4}$$

$$r = \frac{l^2}{8s} + \frac{s}{2}$$

It is best to draw the longest possible chord subtending the track arc in order to obtain the greatest possible accuracy for the value of *r*.

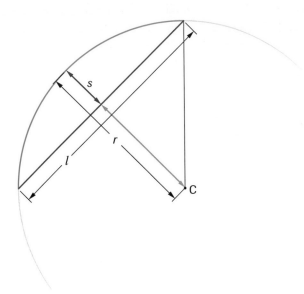

Figure 8
The sagitta method for calculating the radius of curvature *r*

Summary: Part A

To determine the charge-to-mass ratio of the π^- particle in Σ^- decay, we use the following steps:

1. Identify a Σ^- event on the bubble chamber photograph and isolate the π^- track.

2. Determine the radius of curvature *r* by measuring the chord length *l* and sagitta *s* and substituting into the equation $r = \dfrac{l^2}{8s} + \dfrac{s}{2}$.

3. Calculate the charge-to-mass ratio by substituting the value of *r* into the equation $\dfrac{q}{m} = \dfrac{1.98 \times 10^8 \text{ C·m/kg}}{r}$.

4. Since the charge *q* of the π^- particle equals the elementary charge, 1.6×10^{-19} C, this value can be used to calculate the mass of the π^- particle in kilograms from the charge-to-mass ratio.

▶ **SAMPLE problem 1**

A sigma decay event is identified in the bubble chamber photograph in **Figure 9**.

(a) Calculate the rest mass of the π^- particle.

(b) Evaluate your answer in (a) by comparing this calculated rest mass with the accepted value ($m_{\pi^-} = 2.48 \times 10^{-28}$ kg). Calculate the percent difference.

Solution

(a) Measurements taken from the schematic (**Figure 10**):

$l_{\pi^-} = 6.8$ cm

$s_{\pi^-} = 0.20$ cm

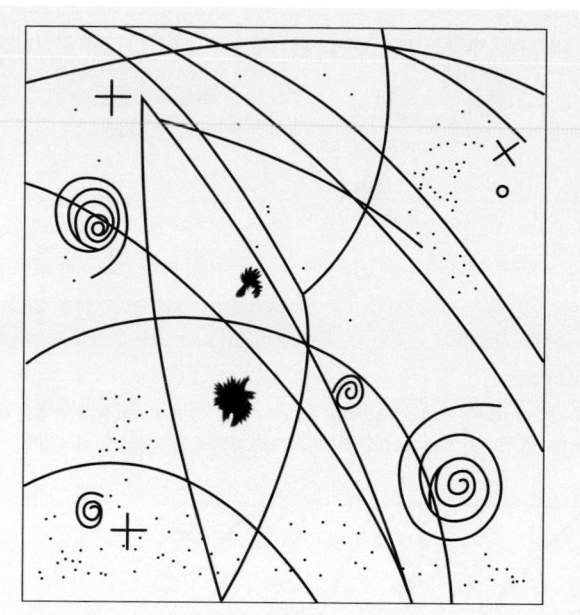

Figure 9

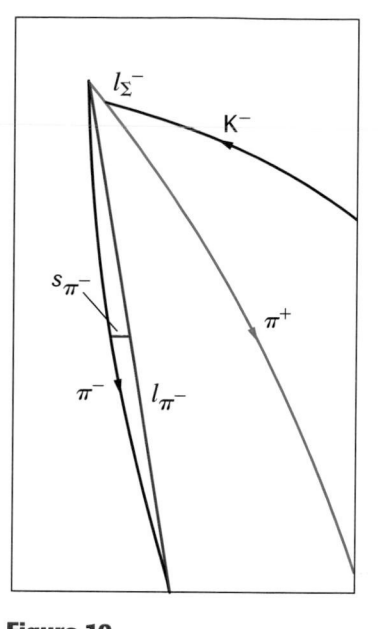

Figure 10

First, calculate the radius of curvature r for the π^- particle:

$$r = \frac{l^2_{\pi-}}{8s_{\pi-}} + \frac{s_{\pi-}}{2}$$

$$= \frac{(6.8 \text{ cm})^2}{8(0.20 \text{ cm})} + \frac{0.20 \text{ cm}}{2}$$

$$r = 29 \text{ cm, or } 0.29 \text{ m}$$

Now to calculate the charge-to-mass ratio of the π^- particle, substitute the value of r into the equation:

$$\frac{q}{m} = \frac{1.98 \times 10^8 \text{ C·m/kg}}{r}$$

$$= \frac{1.98 \times 10^8 \text{ C·m/kg}}{0.29 \text{ m}}$$

$$\frac{q}{m} = 6.6 \times 10^8 \text{ C/kg}$$

Notice that the charge-to-mass ratio of the π^- particle (6.6×10^8 C/kg) is smaller than that of the electron (1.76×10^{11} C/kg). Since the two particles carry the same charge, we may predict that the π^- particle has a larger mass.

We calculate the mass of the π^- particle by substituting the value of the elementary charge ($e = 1.6 \times 10^{-19}$ C) for q:

Since $q = 1.6 \times 10^{-19}$ C, then

$$\frac{q}{m} = 6.6 \times 10^8 \text{ C/kg}$$

$$m = \frac{q}{6.6 \times 10^8 \text{ C/kg}}$$

$$= \frac{1.6 \times 10^{-19} \text{ C}}{6.6 \times 10^8 \text{ C/kg}}$$

$$m = 2.42 \times 10^{-28} \text{ kg}$$

The calculated mass of the π^- particle is 2.42×10^{-28} kg. The mass is indeed larger than the mass of the electron (9.1×10^{-31} kg).

(b) Now calculate the percent difference between the calculated value and the accepted value:

$$\% \text{ difference } = \frac{\left| \text{calculated value } - \text{ accepted value} \right|}{\text{accepted value}} \times 100\%$$

$$= \frac{\left| (2.42 \times 10^{-28} \text{ kg}) - (2.48 \times 10^{-28} \text{ kg}) \right|}{2.48 \times 10^{-28} \text{ kg}} \times 100\%$$

$$\% \text{ difference } = 2.3\%$$

▶ **Practice**

Understanding Concepts

1. Given the bubble chamber photograph of a beam of kaons in **Figure 11**, calculate (a) the charge-to-mass ratio and (b) the rest mass of the π^{-} particle.

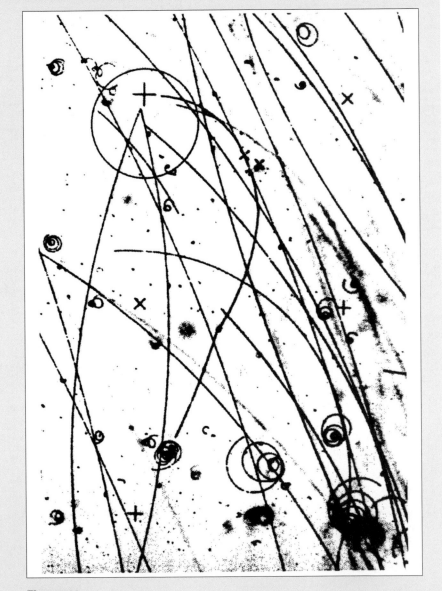

Figure 11

Part B: Determination of the Identity of the X^0 Particle

To determine the identity of the invisible X^0 particle, we must calculate the following values:

A. the momentum of the π^- particle ($p_{\pi-}$)

B. the momentum of the Σ^- particle ($p_{\Sigma-}$)

C. the angle θ between the π^- and Σ^- momentum vectors at the point of decay

D. the rest mass of the X^0 particle

We can use these values to compare the calculated rest mass to the rest masses of known (neutral) subatomic particles as they appear in a standard table, such as **Table 3**.

We will now describe each of the four calculations that need to be performed.

A. Calculating the Momentum of the π^- Particle

A particle of charge q and momentum of magnitude p, moving perpendicular to a uniform magnetic field of magnitude B, travels in a circular arc of radius r, given by the equation

$$r = \frac{p}{qB}$$

We can rearrange the equation to solve for the magnitude of the momentum of a π^- particle:

$$p = qBr$$

The charge q on all known long-lived subatomic particles is constant ($q = 1.6 \times 10^{-19}$ C) and the value of B is also constant for a particular bubble chamber setting. If the radius of curvature r is measured in centimetres, the momentum equation becomes:

$$(6.86 \text{ MeV}/c \cdot \text{cm})r$$

This equation may be used to calculate the momentum of the π^- particle using the bubble chamber photographs in this case study.

B. Calculating the Momentum of the Σ^- Particle

The momentum of the Σ^- particle cannot be determined from its radius of curvature because the track is much too short. Instead, we make use of the known way that a particle loses momentum as a function of the distance it travels. In each event in which the K$^-$ particle comes to rest before interacting, the law of conservation of energy requires that the Σ^- particle have a specific momentum of 174 MeV/c. The relatively massive Σ^- particle loses energy rapidly, so its momentum at the point of its decay is significantly less than 174 MeV/c, even though it travels only a short distance.

It is known that a charged particle's range d, which is the distance it travelled before coming to rest, is approximately proportional to the fourth power of its initial momentum, (i.e., $d \propto p^4$). For a Σ^- particle travelling in liquid hydrogen, the constant of proportionality is such that a particle of initial momentum 174 MeV/c has a maximum range of 0.597 cm, before it decays and becomes invisible. However, in most cases, the Σ^- particle decays before it comes to rest, so the distance it travels, $l_{\Sigma-}$, is less than its maximum range, $d_0 = 0.597$ cm. Therefore, the equation

$$d = 0.597 \text{ cm} \left(\frac{p_{\Sigma-}}{174 \text{ MeV}/c} \right)^4$$

will give the correct range for the Σ^- particle.

Table 3 Rest Masses of Several Known (Neutral) Subatomic Particles

Particle	Rest Mass (MeV/c^2)
π^0	135.0
K^0	497.7
n^0	939.6
Λ^0	1115.7
Σ^0	1192.6
Ξ^0	1314.9

The difference between the maximum range d_0 and the actual Σ^- particle track length l_{Σ^-} is called the *residual range*. Thus, the relationship between the residual range $(d_0 - l_{\Sigma^-})$ and the momentum of the Σ^- particle is

$$d_0 = 0.597 \left(\frac{p_{\Sigma^-}}{174 \text{ MeV/}c} \right)^4$$

$$p_{\Sigma^-} = 174 \text{ MeV/}c \sqrt[4]{\frac{d_0}{0.597 \text{ cm}} - \frac{l_{\Sigma^-}}{0.597 \text{ cm}}}$$

Since $d_0 = 0.597$ cm

$$p_{\Sigma^-} = 174 \text{ MeV/}c \sqrt[4]{1 - \frac{l_{\Sigma^-}}{0.597 \text{ cm}}}$$

Note that when $l_{\Sigma^-} = 0.597$ cm, $p_{\Sigma^-} = 0$ as would be expected.

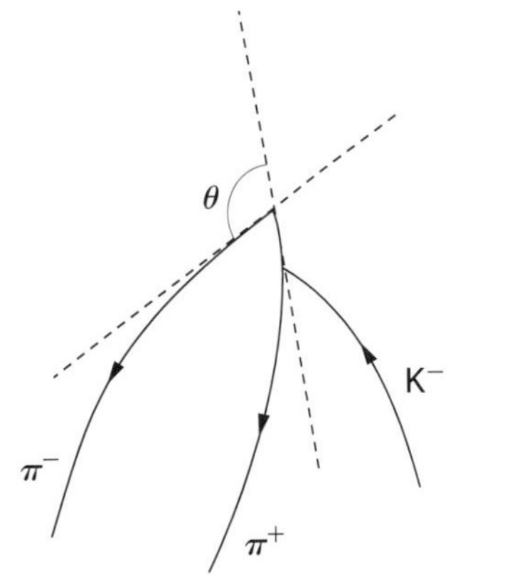

C. Measuring the Angle θ between the π^- and Σ^- Momentum Vectors at the Point of Decay

The angle θ between the π^- and Σ^- momentum vectors at the point of decay can be measured directly by drawing tangents to the π^- and Σ^- tracks at the point where the Σ^- decay occurs (**Figure 12**). We then measure the angle between the tangents using a protractor.

Calculating the Mass of the Invisible X⁰ Particle

Although we cannot see bubble chamber tracks left by the X⁰ particle, its mass can be calculated from measurements made directly on bubble chamber photographs. To do this, we use the values of p_{π^-}, p_{Σ^-}, and angle θ, determined in the previous three parts, to calculate the energy and momentum of the particles that participate in the Σ decay process (π^- and Σ^-). We then use the law of conservation of energy and the law of conservation of momentum to calculate the energy and momentum of the invisible X⁰ particle. These values are used to calculate the mass of the invisible particle. Finally, the identity of the particle can be determined by comparing the calculated mass to a table that lists the masses of known particles.

Since the particles that participate in the Σ decay event travel at speeds close to the speed of light c, all calculations must be done using relativistic equations. The two equations we will use are

$$E = mc^2 \qquad \text{and} \qquad E^2 = p^2c^2 + m^2c^4$$

where E is the total energy of the particle in MeV, m is the rest mass of the particle in MeV/c^2, and p is the momentum of the particle in MeV/c.

When performing calculations, use the values for the rest masses of the Σ^- and π^- particles shown in **Table 2**.

Remember that the invisible particle X⁰, whose mass we want to find, is produced in the Σ^- decay process according to the equation

$$\Sigma^- \rightarrow \pi^- + X^0$$

The law of conservation of momentum requires the X⁰ particle to have a momentum $\vec{p}_{X^0}$ given by the equation

$$\vec{p}_{X^0} = \vec{p}_{\Sigma^-} - \vec{p}_{\pi^-}$$

Figure 12
Measuring the angle θ between the π^- and Σ^- momentum vectors

LEARNING TIP

The relativistic equation $E^2 = p^2c^2 + m^2c^4$ was introduced in Chapter 11 as, $p = \dfrac{mv}{\sqrt{1 - \dfrac{v^2}{c^2}}}$.

With a little effort, you should be able to convert one into the other. Assume that $m_0 = m$ in this case.

The law of conservation of energy requires the X^0 particle to have energy E_{X^0} given by

$$E_{X^0} = E_{\Sigma^-} - E_{\pi^-}$$

Since $E^2 = p^2c^2 + m^2c^4$, then

$$mc^2 = \sqrt{E^2 - p^2c^2}$$

Therefore, we calculate the rest mass m of the X^0 particle as follows:

$$m_{X^0} = \sqrt{(E_{\Sigma^-} - E_{\pi^-})^2 - (p_{\Sigma^-}c^2 - p_{\pi^-}c^2)^2}$$

Expanding the $(p_{\Sigma^-}c^2 - p_{\pi^-}c^2)^2$ term we obtain

$$m_{X^0}c^2 = \sqrt{(E_{\Sigma^-} - E_{\pi^-})^2 - (p_{\Sigma^-}^2c^4 - 2p_{\Sigma^-}p_{\pi^-}c^4 + p_{\pi^-}^2c^4)}$$

This equation can be used to calculate the rest mass of the invisible X^0 particle from measurements made on a bubble chamber photograph. The X^0 particle can be identified by comparing its calculated rest mass with the masses of known particles in a reference table such as **Table 3**.

Summary: Part B

To measure the rest mass of the invisible X^0 particle formed in a Σ decay event, you will need to use all of the concepts and equations discussed in part B of this case study. Here are the steps you should follow:

1. Analyze the bubble chamber tracks on a bubble chamber photograph and identify a Σ^- decay event.

2. (a) Identify the π^- track.
   (b) Draw the longest chord possible subtending the π^- track arc.
   (c) Measure the length of the arc l_{π^-} and the saggita s_{π^-} in centimetres. Use these values to calculate the radius of curvature r_{π^-} of the π^- track, and then substitute this value into the equation $p_{\pi^-} = (6.86 \text{ MeV}/c \cdot \text{cm})r$ to calculate the momentum of the π^- particle in MeV/c.
   (d) Substitute the value of p_{π^-} and the value of m_{π^-} (140.0 MeV/c^2) into the equation $E_{\pi^-}^2 = p_{\pi^-}^2c^2 + m_{\pi^-}^2c^4$ to calculate the total energy E_{π^-} of the π^- particle in MeV.

3. (a) Identify the Σ^- track.
   (b) Measure the Σ^- particle track length, l_{Σ^-}, in centimetres, and substitute this value into the equation $d = 0.597 \text{ cm} \left(\dfrac{p_{\Sigma^-}}{174 \text{ MeV}/c} \right)^4$ to calculate the Σ^- particle's momentum in MeV/c.
   (c) Substitute the value of p_{Σ^-} and the value of m_{Σ^-} (1197.0 MeV/c^2) into the equation $E_{\Sigma^-}^2 = p_{\Sigma^-}^2c^2 + m_{\Sigma^-}^2c^4$ to calculate the total energy E_{Σ^-} of the Σ^- particle in MeV.

4. Draw tangents to the π^- and Σ^- trajectories and use a protractor to measure the angle θ.

5. Substitute the values for p_{π^-}, E_{π^-}, p_{Σ^-}, E_{Σ^-}, and θ into the equation
$$m_{X^0}c^4 = \sqrt{(E_{\Sigma^-} - E_{\pi^-})^2 - (p_{\Sigma^-}{}^2 c^4 - 2p_{\Sigma^-}p_{\pi^-}c^4 + p_{\pi^-}{}^2 c^4)}$$ to calculate the mass of X^0 in MeV/c^2.

6. Determine the identity of particle X^0 by comparing its calculated rest mass with the masses of known particles in a reference table such as **Table 3**.

▶ **SAMPLE** problem **2**

The bubble chamber photograph in **Figure 13** shows a circled Σ^- decay event.

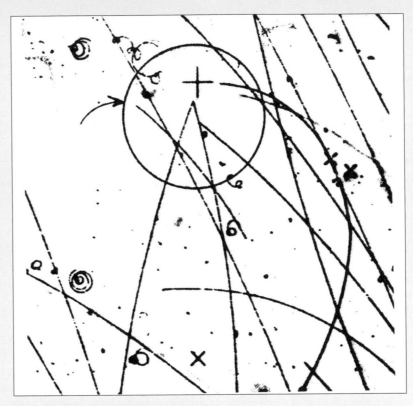

Figure 13
Bubble chamber photograph

(a) Calculate the rest mass of the invisible X^0 particle formed in the interaction.

(b) Identify the X^0 particle by comparing its calculated rest mass with the masses of the known particles in **Table 3**.

Solution

(a) To calculate the rest mass of the X^0 particle, we will have to measure l_{π^-}, s_{π^-}, l_{Σ^-}, and θ directly on the bubble chamber photograph. See the schematic diagram of the Σ^- event in **Figure 14**.

4. Calculate the momentum of the Σ^- particle.

$$p_{\Sigma^-} = 174 \text{ MeV}/c \sqrt[4]{1 - \frac{l_{\Sigma^-}}{0.597 \text{ cm}}}$$

$$= 174 \text{ MeV}/c \sqrt[4]{1 - \frac{0.6 \text{ cm}}{0.597 \text{ cm}}}$$

$$\doteq 174 \text{ MeV}/c \sqrt[4]{1 - 1}$$

$$p_{\Sigma^-} \doteq 0 \text{ MeV}/c$$

5. Calculate the energy of the Σ^- particle.

$$E_{\Sigma^-}^2 = p_{\Sigma^-}^2 c^2 + m_{\Sigma^-}^2 c^4$$

$$E_{\Sigma^-}^2 = 0 \text{ MeV}^2 + (1197.0 \text{ MeV}^2/c^4)c^4$$

$$E_{\Sigma^-} = 1.197 \times 10^3 \text{ MeV}$$

6. Measure the angle between the π^- and Σ^- trajectories (π^- and Σ^- momentum vectors) $\theta = 137°$

7. Calculate the rest mass of the invisible X^0 particle.

$$m_{X^0}c^2 = \sqrt{(E_{\Sigma^-} - E_{\pi^-})^2 - (p_{\Sigma^-}^2 c^4 - 2p_{\Sigma^-}p_{\pi^-}c^4 + p_{\pi^-}^2 c^4)}$$

$$= \sqrt{(1.1970 \times 10^3 \text{ MeV} - 2.3 \times 10^2 \text{ MeV})^2 - (0 - 0 + (3.4 \times 10^4 \text{ MeV}^2/c^4)c^4)}$$

$$= \sqrt{(9.7 \times 10^2 \text{ MeV})^2 - (3.4 \times 10^4 \text{ MeV}^2)}$$

$$= \sqrt{(9.4 \times 10^5 \text{ MeV}^2) - (3.4 \times 10^4 \text{ MeV}^2)}$$

$$m_{X^0}c^2 = 9.5 \times 10^2 \text{ MeV}$$

$$m_{X^0} = 9.5 \times 10^2 \text{ MeV}/c^2$$

(b) The X^0 particle's rest mass (9.5×10^2 MeV/c^2) corresponds best with the rest mass of the n^0 (nu) particle (940 MeV/c^2). Therefore, we assume that the invisible neutral particle produced in the sigma event is the n^0 particle

SUMMARY — Case Study: Analyzing Elementary Particle Trajectories

- Some properties of fundamental particles can be identified by analyzing bubble chamber photographs.
- In the analysis of the π and Σ particles, we determine the momenta of the two particles and the angle θ between the momentum vectors at the point of decay. This leads to calculation of the mass of the invisible particle, which can then be compared with a table of known masses to identify the particle.

The Standard Model

The **standard model**, which has evolved from the work begun in particle physics in the early part of the twentieth century, unites quantum chromodynamic (QCD) theory with the electroweak theory. The model is a complete and sophisticated theory that sees the universe as composed of two essential types of particles: **fermions** and **bosons**. The fermions, which all have spin $\frac{1}{2}$, are assumed to be the fundamental particles from which matter is composed. These particles, in turn, are subdivided into the leptons and the quarks. The bosons are assumed to be the particles that carry interactions and to be responsible for the fundamental forces of nature.

Table 1 summarizes the particles of the standard model. Because quarks are assumed to exist in three colours, there are 18 quarks, not 6. This gives a total of 24 fermions. When you add each fermion and its antiparticle, you can account for no fewer than 48 fundamental particles from which matter is formed.

standard model the theory that unites quantum chromodynamics with the electroweak theory; it holds that all matter is composed of fermions and bosons

fermions according to the standard model, the particles from which all matter is composed; subdivided into leptons and quarks

bosons according to the standard model, the particles responsible for the fundamental forces of nature

Table 1 The Standard Model

Fermions building blocks of matter; spin $= \frac{1}{2}$					
Leptons			**Quarks**		
Name	*Charge*	*Mass* (m_e)	*Name*	*Charge*	*Mass* (m_e)
electron	-1	1	up	$\frac{2}{3}$	20
electron neutrino	0	~0	down	$-\frac{1}{3}$	20
muon	-1	200	charm	$\frac{2}{3}$	3 000
muon neutrino	0	~0	strange	$-\frac{1}{3}$	300
tau	-1	3 600	top	$\frac{2}{3}$	350 000
tau neutrino	0	~0	bottom	$-\frac{1}{3}$	11 000

Bosons carriers of forces		
Name	*Spin*	*Force*
photon	1	electromagnetic force
W^+, W^0, and Z bosons	1	weak nuclear force
gluons (8 different types)	1	strong nuclear force
graviton	2	gravitational force

The fermions are organized into three distinct families, each containing two leptons and two quarks. The *first family*, consisting of the electron, its neutrino, and the u and d quarks, composes the matter that exists at everyday energies. The other two families are assumed to be more prevalent at very high energies.

DID YOU KNOW ?

Symmetry in Physics
Symmetry has frequently been used in the formulation of physical principles:

- Galileo visualized the laws of physics as symmetrical in the sense of remaining unchanged when we transform ourselves mathematically from one frame to another, provided the frames have a constant relative velocity.

- Einstein used special relativity to generalize Galileo's idea, exhibiting even electrical phenomena as the same in all inertial frames (with a magnetic field analyzed as an electric field in a moving frame).

- Mathematician Emmy Noether showed that the conservation laws can be seen as symmetric with respect to time.

- Feynman suggested that the electron and positron could be viewed as symmetric with respect to time, with the positron actually moving backward in time.

grand unified theory (GUT) a theory that attempts to combine the strong, weak, and electromagnetic forces into a single theory

unification scale the limit $(10^{-30}$ m) specified by the GUT below which only one force is predicted to exist, in place of the separate electromagnetic and strong and weak nuclear forces

The standard model has been called the most sophisticated and complete theory ever developed. It is the culmination of over a century of research and experimentation by many thousands of individuals. With the exception of the graviton, every particle predicted by the model has been discovered.

Despite this, the model has sometimes been described as crude in that it lacks the simplicity of Newton's idea of universal gravitation and the mathematical elegance of Maxwell's and Einstein's field equations. Because it is so tied to experimental results, it tends to concentrate more on the "what" than on the "why," leaving questions such as the following unanswered:

- What is so special about the number three? (For instance, why are there three families of leptons and quarks?)

- If the number three is so special, then why are there only two types of matter particles?

- Why do the masses increase so much from family to family, without any precise ratio?

- What is the underlying feature whose presence endows a particle with mass and whose absence makes the particle massless?

- How do the four forces fit together? (In particular, how does gravity interact with the other three forces at the quantum level?)

- Why do the various parameters, such as the masses of the particles, have to be decided by experiment? Why can they not be predicted?

Grand Unified Theories

For decades physics has been seeking a standpoint more comprehensive than the theoretical unification of the weak and electromagnetic forces into the electroweak force. We may distinguish two enterprises, one more ambitious than the other: there is the attempt to unite the strong, weak, and electromagnetic forces as aspects of a single force; this is called the quest for a **grand unified theory** (GUT). There is also the attempt to find a still higher abstraction based on the idea that *all* the laws of nature flow from one fundamental law. This is the search for unification of the strong, weak, electromagnetic, and gravitational forces, sometimes described as a *theory of everything* (TOE).

Let us begin by considering the current status of the quest for a GUT. A successful unification must account for all the various force-mediating bosons. The task is made difficult by the fact that the three forces behave in radically different ways. In particular, the strong nuclear force actually *increases* with distance.

Sheldon Glashow and his associates tackled the GUT problem by applying symmetry to the conservation of charge and spin. For example, the electron and the positron are symmetric with respect to charge. **Figure 1** shows that if the first-family fermions are seen as vertices on a cube, the various particles become symmetric with respect to one another. The GUTs extended the symmetries already in the standard model by unifying the three forces and the particles that they acted upon. At the so-called **unification scale**, with distances shorter than 10^{-30} m, the three forces were assumed to be one superforce, symmetrical and incapable of distinguishing between charge and spin. At distances greater than the unification scale, the symmetry was held to break, with distinctions appearing between the three forces.

Using symmetry, several things were accomplished. The unification of the strong, weak, and electromagnetic forces was achieved not only on the unification scale but also at very high energies. An explanation was reached for the arrangement of quarks and leptons in the three great fermion families and for the quantization of charge.

The unification predicted a new fundamental force field. The mediating particle for the field, X, the **Higgs boson**, is massive, perhaps as much as 10^{14} times more massive than the proton. Recall that force-mediating particles are virtual, not real; that they arise, in an apparent creation from nothing, out of the "quantum vacuum" because Heisenberg $\Delta E \Delta t$ uncertainty allows very short-lived violations of conservation of energy; and that the same $\Delta E \Delta t$ uncertainty that allows them to live makes their existence so fleeting they cannot be observed. It follows from these ideas that the life of a virtual particle is inversely proportional to its mass. Therefore, the life of the massive Higgs particle is very fleeting indeed, about 10^{-35} s, or sufficient time for travelling at most 10^{-23} m.

According to GUTs, if elementary particles approach one another at distances of about 10^{-30} m, it will be possible for them to exchange an X particle. At these distances, the X particle would allow radical transmutations, perhaps even making quarks and leptons interchangeable. In accordance with the assumed conservation of baryon number, the probability of this happening is unlikely. Because of their huge mass, X particles have an extremely small probability of spontaneously appearing from the quantum vacuum, even at the tremendously high energies that can be achieved in particle accelerators.

A Disturbing Consequence of Unification

Because of quantum uncertainty, it is possible that the Higgs boson can spontaneously appear for a very short time inside a proton. This raises an issue that must be dealt with if GUTs are to survive the test of experiment. Suppose that, during its brief appearance inside the proton, the Higgs boson encounters one of the three quarks. Suppose, further, that this quark subsequently makes a close approach to a second of the three. The Higgs boson in this scenario may be exchanged, causing the two quarks to change into two new particles: an antiquark and a positron. The positron will be ejected. The antiquark, for its part, will unite with the remaining (third) quark to form a pion. The pion will subsequently decay into photons.

Given an enormous period of time, it is possible that all the protons in the universe could decay in this way, leaving only photons, positrons, and electrons. The latter two, being mutual antiparticles, will also annihilate one another, leaving only photons.

This chain of events—possible, according to GUTs, although of exceedingly low probability—has a radical effect on our conception of matter, since it means that the proton, and hence every atom, is inherently unstable. But these events are so unlikely that the expected life of a proton is around 10^{32} years.

Quantum uncertainty, the cause of proton decay, is taken advantage of in the search for evidence for it. Because the decay is described in terms of probabilities, there is a tiny probability that any given proton will decay in a finite period of time. Experiments have therefore been initiated to take advantage of this. The methodology is simple. Massive quantities of a nonradioactive substance are examined over long periods of time to see if proton decay can be detected. To date, no such decay has been detected. This lack of evidence, although not sufficient to discredit the unified theories, has sparked the development of other creative theoretical avenues, for example, string theory.

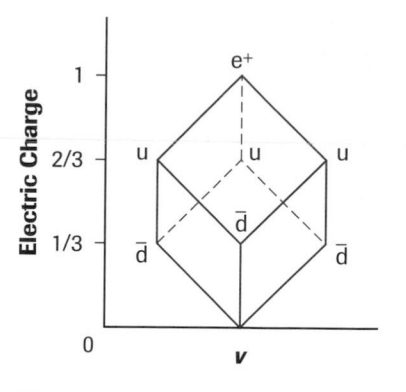

Figure 1
A cube showing the symmetry of the first family of quarks and leptons. There are three of each type of quark, since each is assumed to have three colours.

Higgs boson the theoretical particle X predicted to carry a fourth fundamental force field in the GUT unification of the electromagnetic and strong and weak nuclear forces

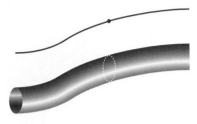

Figure 2
A hypertube. A hose is really a cylinder. When viewed from a distance, however, a cross-section looks like a point on a line. Similarly, a particle may be a tiny circle in the fourth dimension.

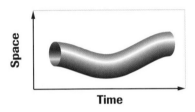

Figure 3
Closed-loop string. When viewed in space-time, such a string appears as a tube.

Physics on a String

Shortly after Einstein published his general relativity theory, the German mathematician Theodor Kaluza developed a geometrical representation of electromagnetism. His theory envisioned the electromagnetic field as a warp or ripple in a fourth spatial dimension. If Einstein's theory of gravitation is formulated in Kaluza's framework, the result is a five-dimensional universe, incorporating four-dimensional gravity with Maxwell's equations.

The Swedish-born Oskar Klein extended upon Kaluza's theory by suggesting that the extra spatial dimension was invisible, being curled up in the manner of a coil of rope. According to Klein, particles are, in fact, tiny circles moving in four-dimensional space (**Figure 2**). The circles were calculated to be incredibly small—approximately one-billionth the size of the nucleus—and therefore invisible for all practical purposes.

The Kaluza-Klein theory faded from prominence, since it failed to incorporate the two newcomers to dynamics: the strong and weak nuclear forces. In the 1980s, however, the theory resurfaced and was regarded as appropriate for some complexities in the two newcomers. In its reformulation, string theory dealt with the complications of the strong and weak nuclear forces by putting strings into many extra dimensions rather than into the single extra dimension originally introduced for the electromagnetic force.

The new theory saw fundamental particles as strings that could be open or closed (**Figure 3**). Each fundamental particle was assumed to be a different vibrating mode on the same string.

As in the original Kaluza-Klein model, the strings were assumed to be small (on the order of 10^{-33} m) and therefore appear as pointlike particles even from the perspective of giant accelerators. Since the strings were assumed to obey Einstein's equations in space-time, there was a prospect of their uniting quantum mechanics with general relativity.

Initial work with strings caused great interest. The fact that the graviton would emerge as the lowest form of energy for a string gave some indication that gravity might soon be united with the other three forces. Unfortunately, the mathematics soon became much too complicated, since the model had to place the strings into 26 dimensions. This, coupled with strong developments in GUTs, caused research to slow down.

In 1984, Michael Green and John Schwartz simplified the mathematical model to 10 dimensions. Of these, 6 are "curled up," making them invisible and leaving 4 for inspection. The resulting *superstring* theory rekindled interest, by accommodating *supersymmetry*, allowing fermions and bosons to be rotated into one another. Each fermion was now paired with a boson called a sparticle, and each boson paired with a fermion called a bosino.

Around the time the work of Green and Schwartz was becoming noticed, there was another favourable development. String theory unexpectedly suggested the existence of a particle not known to exist in the nucleus. The particle was massless and travelled at the speed *c*. Furthermore its spin number was 2. It was suggested that the particle was one already known to theory but not known in the nucleus: the graviton. In this way, string theory started to become a theory that also described gravity.

The extra dimensions intrinsic to string theory continue to raise possibilities that are intriguing but difficult to test. String sizes are typically one billion-billion times smaller than the nucleus. As we saw in Chapter 12, quantum theory associates distance (or the de Broglie wavelength associated with the particle probing that distance) with energy. Examining those minuscule distances will therefore require probing particles with enormous energies, beyond the capability of any conceivable accelerator.

In fact, the only event involving these types of energies is the theoretical big bang. If superstring theory is correct, then the extra dimensions may have been fundamental to that event. In fact, it may well have been that at the time of the big bang, all the dimensions existed as equal partners, with three of the dimensions then greatly expanding, drawing the remainder out of sight. Although still in existence, the extra dimensions are only seen through their effects on the internal processes at the subnuclear level.

Gravity, still the "odd one out," therefore remains as the only force that can be associated with the space-time we perceive.

Strange as all of this may seem, the symmetry inherent in the theory suggests an even stranger consequence. The full theory expects the full unification of all interactions twice over. This, in turn, hints at the possible existence of a parallel, shadow universe, able to interact with ours only through gravity. A low-mass object from that universe would appear invisible to objects in this one because the only interaction would be through gravity. A massive object from that universe (say, with the mass of a planet or star) would, on the other hand, be noticeable from its gravitational effects. Such an object, if it came into close contact with a body in our universe, would cause the body to behave erratically, suffering a strong gravitational pull without a detectable source.

We may now speculate that stars, planets, and other large objects could form from this invisible matter. When observed from Earth, they would be indistinguishable from black holes formed from the inward collapse of large quantities of matter in the universe to which we have spatial access. Perhaps this would account for some of the so-called dark matter evidently existing in our universe and betraying its existence through gravitational effects.

Of course, superstring theory is speculative, perhaps destined to rise eventually to the eminence now enjoyed by quantum theory or to go the route of the ether.

Conclusion

Many see science as a quest for understanding the nature of the universe. While this may well be true, most then take this reasonable observation to a naive conclusion. They assume that, at some time in the not-too-distant future, all will be known. This is not just true today. Near the end of the nineteenth century, after Maxwell's equations had been published, many scientists assumed that most of the truths about the physical world had been revealed. All that remained was to fill in some pieces here and there.

Now more than one hundred years later, we can look back and see how naive this idea was. Quantum theory demolished the concept that the nature of the everyday world was scalable down to the sizes of the atom. Logical laws describing behaviour were soon replaced with individual quirkiness that could only be understood statistically. Through the twentieth century the situation grew increasingly more complex as interaction after interaction was discovered.

Today, in the early part of the twenty-first century, the best theories that we have—and the standard model is very good—leave us with more questions than answers. When one begins to develop an appreciation for all of this, one is forced to conclude that we may never find the truth that we seek. It may be forever beyond our grasp.

In your study of physics, you have seen theories proposed, tested, and refined or abandoned. Through this continual upheaval, one thing has remained constant. We constantly crave a physical understanding of the universe and use all our tools to this end. Perhaps this is the greatest lesson of all. Science, and indeed life, should be seen as an unceasing interplay between need, technological innovation, and theory. If our craving for physical insight is destined never to be fully satisfied, we may still experience a selfless joy in directing our finite intellects to a reality exceeding our intellectual limitations. Perhaps it's the process that counts, not the end result.

The Standard Model and Grand Unified Theories

- The standard model, sometimes referred to as the most complete and well-developed model in the history of science, describes the universe in terms of two classes of particles: fermions, the matter makers, and bosons, the force carriers. Fermions are further divided into two subclasses: the leptons and the quarks.

- The standard model, although well developed, is not mathematically elegant and leaves several important questions unanswered.

- Grand unified theories have generally exploited symmetry in an attempt to reconcile the electroweak and strong nuclear forces. At very small distances, the carrier of this unified force is thought to be the extremely massive X, the Higgs boson.

- The interactions of the X boson, when coupled with concepts of quantum mechanics, result in a small, but not zero, probability that a proton will decay and so lead to a view of matter as inherently unstable.

- Attempts to observe proton decay have been unsuccessful. This, in turn, has increased interest in other types of theories, particularly those relating to strings.

- The currently preferred version of string theory, superstring theory, takes the fundamental entities in the universe to be extremely tiny, multi-dimensional strings. Although strings are regarded as composed of 10, or perhaps more, dimensions, only 3 of the spatial dimensions are visible.

- According to superstring theory, the three currently observed dimensions increased in importance immediately after the theoretical big bang, causing the remainder to be hidden from view.

▶ **Section 13.7** *Questions*

Understanding Concepts

1. **Table 1** lists 16 fundamental particles according to the standard model.
   (a) Explain how you can say that there are 48 different fermions.
   (b) How many different particles exist in the standard model?

2. Construct a table similar to **Table 1** but include only the particles that would be relevant to the first family, that is, the particles thought to constitute the matter that exists in the everyday world that we live in.

3. In what way(s) is the standard model crude?

4. (a) What is unified by the GUTs?
   (b) Briefly describe the typical means of achieving this unification.

5. Explain why the X particle is difficult to observe.

6. How does the nature of the X particle suggest that matter may be unstable?

7. Why are many scientists and other thinkers still developing alternatives to GUTs?

8. Why do strings, in superstring theory, appear as particles?

9. If there is only one type of string, then how can the large variety of observed particles be accounted for?

10. Estimate the particle energies that would typically have to be produced to observe strings and the X boson.

11. Use either the uncertainty principle or de Broglie's equation to show that the unification distance corresponds to an energy level of about 10^{17} MeV.

There are many different types of careers that involve the study of matter and energy. Find out more about the careers described below or about some other interesting career related to matter and energy.

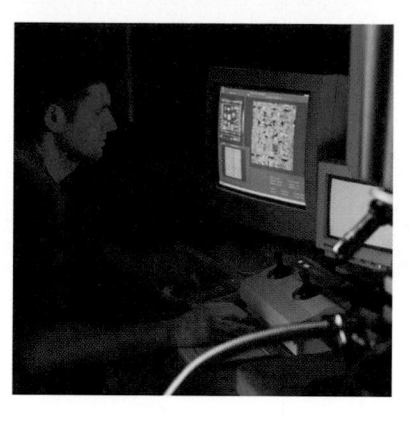

Nanoscientist

Nanoscientists design and build their own sophisticated tools, including scanning tunnelling microscopes, which are capable of imaging surfaces at the atomic level. In many instances, tool construction involves Computer Aided Design (CAD) and close cooperation with skilled machinists. The nanoscientist's ultimate goal is the assembly of useful structures from individual atoms or molecules. These scientists used to be called condensed matter physicists. Nanoscience is an emerging field and only a few companies, for example, IBM and Hewlett-Packard, actively employ researchers in this area. This field is expected to expand, however, and soon many new start-up companies will be employing nanoscientists. Basic research requires a bachelor of science with a concentration in physics. Senior positions require post-graduate degrees.

Physics Teacher

After graduating from high school with a strong background in physics and mathematics, physics teachers will study for three or four years to obtain a bachelor of science degree. They must proceed to a bachelor of education from an accredited teachers' college or university to become a certified teacher. Physics teachers use a range of equipment, including computers, graphing calculators, projectile launchers, timers, motion sensors, multimeters, and power supplies. Physics teachers work in the public and private school systems and, occasionally, as tutors.

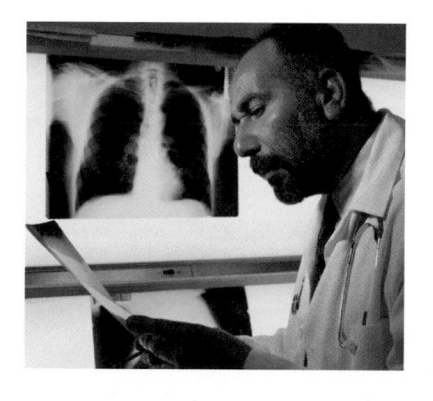

Radiologist

Radiologists begin university with at least two years in a science-intensive undergraduate program, then proceed to an M.D., before taking a four-year residency in radiology. Radiologists find themselves in a rapidly evolving field, requiring a firm grasp of nuclear science. Technologies applied include Computed Axial Tomography (CAT) scanning and Magnetic Resonance Imaging (MRI), as well as traditional X-ray and ultrasound imaging. Contemporary radiologists not only diagnose conditions such as fractures and tumours but investigate such delicate phenomena as activity levels in the functioning brain. Essentially all hospitals and many private clinics employ radiologists. Opportunities for professional advancement include specialization in nuclear medicine.

▶ **Practice**

Making Connections

1. Identify several careers that require knowledge about matter and energy. Select a career you are interested in from the list you made or from the careers described above. Imagine that you have been employed in your chosen career for five years and that you are applying to work on a new project of interest.
   (a) Describe the project. It should be related to some of the new things you learned in this unit. Explain how the concepts from this unit are applied in the project.

(b) Create a résumé listing your credentials and explaining why you are qualified to work on the project. Include in your résumé
   - your educational background: what university degree or diploma program you graduated with, which educational institute you attended, post-graduate training (if any)
   - your skills
   - your duties in previous positions
   - your salary expectations

 GO www.science.nelson.com

Key Expectations

- define and describe the concepts and units related to the present-day understanding of the atom and elementary particles (13.1, 13.2, 13.3, 13.4, 13.5, 13.6, 13.7)
- describe the principal forms of nuclear decay and compare the properties of alpha particles, beta particles, and gamma rays in terms of mass, charge, speed, penetrating power, and ionizing ability (13.1, 13.2)
- analyze images of the trajectories of elementary particles to determine the mass-versus-charge ratio (13.6)
- describe the standard model of elementary particles in terms of the characteristic properties of quarks, leptons, and bosons, and identify the quarks that form familiar particles such as the proton and the neutron (13.4, 13.5, 13.7)
- compile, organize, and display data related to the nature of the atom and elementary particles, using appropriate formats and treatments (13.2, 13.6, 13.7)
- describe examples of Canadian contributions to modern physics. (13.3, 13.4, 13.7)

Key Terms

radioactivity

alpha (α) particles

transmutation

daughter nucleus

strong nuclear force

binding energy

beta (β) particles

positron

gamma (γ) rays

Geiger-Mueller tube

scintillation tube

Pauli exclusion principle

half-life

decay constant

becquerel

radioactive dating

isochronous

quantum electro-dynamics

Feynman diagram

virtual photon

meson

muon

pion

weak nuclear force

W boson

Z boson

graviton

spin

gauge bosons

leptons

hadrons

strangeness

quarks

flavours

baryon number

law of conservation of baryon number

colour

gluons

quantum chromo-dynamics

electroweak (gauge) theory

charm

top

bottom

standard model

fermions

bosons

grand unified theory (GUT)

unification scale

Higgs boson

Key Equations

- $E = mc^2$ (13.1)

- $E = 931.5 \text{ MeV}/c^2 \times m$ (13.1)

- ${}^{A}_{Z}X \rightarrow {}^{4}_{2}He + {}^{A-4}_{Z-2}Y$ α decay   (13.1)

- ${}^{A}_{Z}X \rightarrow {}^{A}_{Z+1}Y + {}^{0}_{-1}e + \overline{\nu}$ β^- decay   (13.1)

- ${}^{A}_{Z}X \rightarrow {}^{A}_{Z-1}Y + {}^{0}_{+1}e + \nu$ β^+ decay   (13.1)

- ${}^{A}_{Z}Y \rightarrow {}^{A}_{Z}Y + \gamma$ γ decay   (13.1)

- $N = N_0\left(\dfrac{1}{2}\right)^{\frac{t}{t_{1/2}}}$ amount of radioactive   (13.2)
  substance remaining

- $A = A_0\left(\dfrac{1}{2}\right)^{\frac{t}{t_{1/2}}}$ radioactivity level   (13.2)

▸ *MAKE* a summary

Construct a concept map of the scientific ideas that contributed to the development of the quantum theory, beginning with Planck and ending with the standard model. If you completed the concept map in the Chapter 12 Make A Summary, make it the basis of your present map, adding appropriate concepts from this chapter.

Write numbers 1 to 9 in your notebook. Indicate beside each number whether the corresponding statement is true (T) or false (F). If it is false, write a corrected version.

1. The amount of energy released in a particular α or β decay is found by determining the mass difference between the products and the parent. A mass–energy equivalence calculation then gives the energy.

2. The average binding energy per nucleon decreases with increasing atomic mass number.

3. The half-life for the decay shown in **Figure 1** is 250 a.

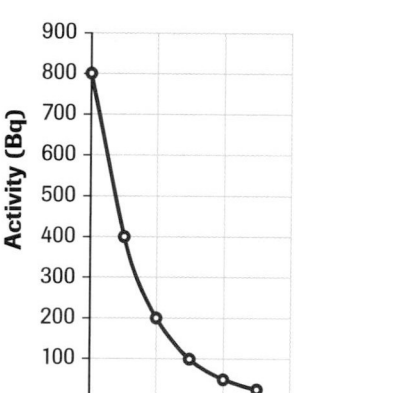

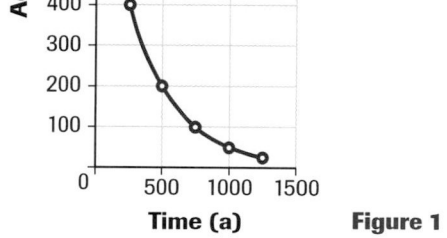

Time (a)   **Figure 1**

4. Both α and β decay can be explained in terms of the strong nuclear force.

5. The fact that gravitons can interact with one another is one of the principal obstacles impeding the development of a quantum theory of gravity.

6. In Murray Gell-Mann's eightfold way of classification, each of the three sets of eight particles has a unique spin number.

7. Electrons, which normally have a spin of $\frac{1}{2}$, can take on other values of spin if they acquire enough energy.

8. According to quark theory, two quarks are needed to form a hadron, and two quarks are needed to form a meson.

9. When a quark absorbs or emits a gluon, its mass changes.

Write numbers 10 to 16 in your notebook. Beside each number, write the letter corresponding to the best choice.

10. The process represented by the nuclear equation
$^{230}_{90}\text{Th} \rightarrow {}^{226}_{88}\text{Ra} + {}^{4}_{2}\text{He}$ is
(a) annihilation   (d) γ decay
(b) α decay   (e) pair production
(c) β decay

11. The values of x and y that correctly complete the equation $^{214}_{82}\text{Pb} \rightarrow {}^{x}_{y}\text{Bi} + {}^{0}_{-1}\text{e} + \overline{\nu}$ are
(a) $x = 214$, $y = 81$
(b) $x = 214$, $y = 82$
(c) $x = 214$, $y = 83$
(d) $x = 215$, $y = 83$
(e) $x = 212$, $y = 81$

12. A sample of coal initially contains 10.0 mg of carbon-14. This isotope has a half-life of 5730 a. The amount of carbon-14 remaining in the sample after 573 a is
(a) 0.00 mg   (d) 9.30 mg
(b) 1.00 mg   (e) 9.99 mg
(c) 5.00 mg

13. If the mass of the particle being accelerated in a cyclotron were to double, the cyclotron frequency would have to
(a) decrease by a factor of 2
(b) decrease by a factor of 4
(c) increase by a factor of 2
(d) increase by a factor of 4
(e) undergo no change, since the frequency is independent of mass

14. Modern synchrotrons perform colliding-beam experiments because
(a) the resulting collisions are more energetic
(b) it is easier to contain the resulting particles
(c) only colliding-beam arrangements conserve momentum
(d) collisions with stationary targets do not produce particles
(e) none of the above

15. The need to bring quark theory into agreement with the Pauli exclusion principle prompted existing ideas to be modified by
(a) postulating the s quark
(b) postulating a second family of quarks
(c) postulating a third family of quarks
(d) endowing quarks with a fractional charge
(e) introducing a quantum number for colour

16. Attempts to develop a grand unified theory have encountered particularly grave difficulties in uniting
(a) the strong nuclear force with the weak and electromagnetic forces
(b) the weak nuclear force with the electromagnetic force
(c) the strong nuclear force with gravity
(d) the strong nuclear force with the electromagnetic force
(e) the weak nuclear force with the strong nuclear force

NEL   An interactive version of the quiz is available online.
GO   www.science.nelson.com

Radioactivity and Elementary Particles   **735**

Understanding Concepts

1. Summarize the properties of α, β, and γ radiation in a table under the following headings: composition, penetrating ability, and charge.

2. Give the values for x and y in each of the following equations:
   (a) $^{x}_{y}\text{Pb} \rightarrow ^{212}_{83}\text{Bi} + ^{0}_{-1}\text{e}$
   (b) $^{238}_{92}\text{U} \rightarrow ^{x}_{y}\text{Th} + ^{4}_{2}\text{He}$
   (c) $^{215}_{84}\text{Po} \rightarrow ^{211}_{x}\text{Pb} + ^{4}_{2}\text{He}$
   (d) $^{116}_{49}\text{In} \rightarrow ^{y}_{x}\text{In} \rightarrow \gamma$
   (e) $^{30}_{15}\text{P} \rightarrow ^{30}_{14}\text{Si} + ^{y}_{x}z + \nu$
   (f) $^{13}_{7}\text{N} \rightarrow ^{y}_{x}z + ^{0}_{+1}\text{e} + \nu$

3. Compare and contrast the strong nuclear force and the electric force.

4. Is it possible for $^{2}_{1}\text{H}$ to undergo α decay? Explain your reasoning.

5. Plutonium-239 decays to uranium-235 by α emission.
   (a) Express the reaction in a balanced nuclear equation.
   (b) Calculate the amount of energy released by one decay. (Refer to Appendix C for atomic masses of plutonium-239, uranium-235, and an α particle.)

6. A sample initially contains 22.0 mg of lead-212.
   (a) How much lead-212 will remain after 24 hours?
   (b) How much time will elapse before the amount of lead-212 left is 5.0 mg?

7. A chunk of carbon, assumed to be ashes from an ancient fire, has an activity of 89 Bq. The initial activity is estimated to be 105.4 Bq. Estimate the age of the sample.

8. Briefly describe two medical applications of radioactivity.

9. (a) Explain why there is an upper limit on the amount of energy that a cyclotron can impart to a particle.
   (b) How do synchrocyclotrons and synchrotrons overcome this upper limit?

10. Why is it easier for a synchrotron to accelerate protons to very high energies than to accelerate electrons to very high energies?

11. You are designing a very high-energy particle accelerator. Why would you be more likely to obtain extremely high energies from a synchrotron than from a linear accelerator?

12. Why do the detectors used in modern particle accelerators typically have several integrated parts?

13. Two sufficiently energetic colliding protons can produce a neutral pion (π^0) from the released kinetic energy, in the process $\text{p} + \text{p} \rightarrow \text{p} + \text{p} + \pi^0$. Draw a Feynman diagram for this interaction.

14. Two protons moving with equal speeds and in opposite directions collide. The collision produces a neutral pion (π^0). Use the masses of the particles to calculate the minimum kinetic energy required of each proton.

15. Identify the particles associated with each of the following quark combinations:
    (a) uss
    (b) $u\bar{u}$

16. In what sense is it appropriate to call a boson a "messenger" particle?

17. Distinguish between
    (a) fermions and bosons
    (b) leptons and hadrons
    (c) mesons and baryons

18. Fermions are organized into families (groupings distinct from those that appear in the previous question).
    (a) Explain what is meant by a "family" of fermions.
    (b) Prepare a table that organizes the particles of each family.

19. Briefly explain what is meant by each of the following quantum variables:
    (a) spin
    (b) strangeness

20. A Σ^- event was identified on a bubble chamber photograph in which the values of s and l for the π^- track are measured to be 0.6 cm and 11 cm, respectively. Calculate
    (a) the charge-to-mass ratio of the π^- particle
    (b) the mass of the particle

21. Sketch a helium atom, assuming with quark theory that its constituents are u, d, and e^-.

22. (a) Identify the respect(s) in which the standard model is a sophisticated and complete theory.
    (b) Identify the respect(s) in which the standard model is crude.

23. How does the X boson attempt to reconcile all the fundamental particles into one particle?

24. Copy **Figure 1** into your notebook. Complete the diagram by filling in the names of the fundamental forces and the names of the unification theories.

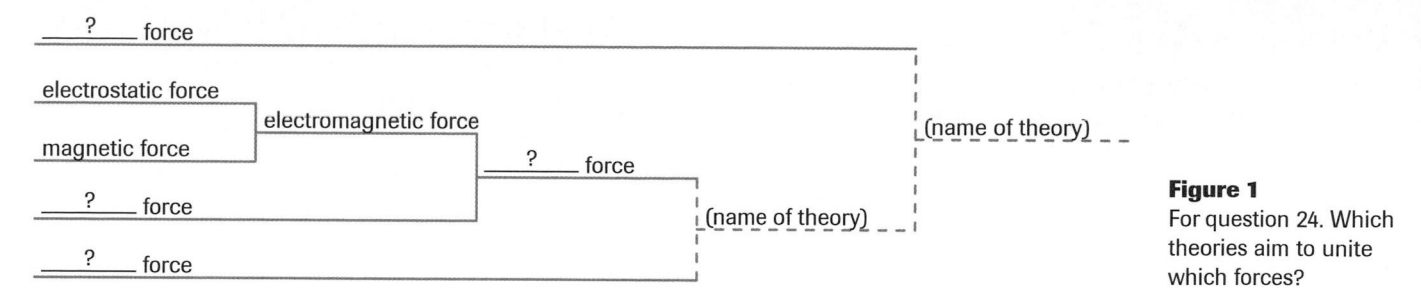

____?____ force

electrostatic force

magnetic force

electromagnetic force

____?____ force

____?____ force

____?____ force

(name of theory)

(name of theory)

(name of theory)

Figure 1
For question 24. Which theories aim to unite which forces?

Applying Inquiry Skills

25. The initial activity of a sample of cobalt-60 is 240 Bq. Graph the activity over a one-year period. (See Appendix C for the half-life.)

26. **Table 1** gives the activity levels of a sample of a radioactive substance at various times.

Table 1

t (h)	*A* (Bq)
0	1000.0
12	786.6
24	618.8
36	486.8
48	382.9
60	301.2
72	236.9
84	186.4
96	146.6
108	115.3

(a) Construct a graph with a curve of best fit.
(b) Calculate the half-life.
(c) Write an equation giving the activity at any time.

27. Place a Geiger-Mueller counter on a stand far away from any radioactive sources. Record the number of counts for a 5-min period. Cover the Geiger-Mueller counter with some aluminum foil and place it back on the stand. Record the number of counts for a 5-min period.
(a) What change did you note in the rate at which radioactive emissions were detected?
(b) Propose a hypothesis to account for the observed differences.

Making Connections

28. Technological breakthroughs often enable corresponding breakthroughs in science.
(a) Give an example of where this is demonstrated in the science of elementary particles.
(b) The technological breakthroughs also have spinoff applications that can be of great social benefit. Give an example of where this is demonstrated by a technology that was developed initially for elementary particle research.

29. Suggest some reasons why one might be reluctant to accept string theory over the standard model.

30. Recall from previous quantum theory work in this text that particles can appear spontaneously from the "quantum vacuum" under appropriate conditions. Recall also that virtual particles, such as virtual photons, can mediate forces.
(a) What are the special conditions that apply to the creation and properties of virtual particles?
(b) How do these special conditions govern the relation between the mass of a virtual particle and the distance over which it can act?
(c) If a virtual particle were massless, what conclusion might reasonably be drawn about the range over which the consequent force can act?

 www.science.nelson.com

Extension

31. Two protons collide, travelling at equal speeds in opposite directions, in the interaction $p + p \rightarrow n + p + \pi^+$.
(a) Determine the total mass of the particles existing before the reaction. Use **Table 1** in Section 13.5.
(b) Determine the total mass of the particles existing after the reaction.
(c) Determine the mass difference. Use this answer to calculate the minimum kinetic energy that the protons need to have to produce the reaction.

PERFORMANCE TASK

The Photovoltaic (Solar) Cell

One of the most important applications of the photoelectric effect is the *photovoltaic cell*, commonly referred to as the *solar cell*. The materials used in photovoltaic cells, such as silicon and gallium arsenide, convert sunlight into electricity. Introduced in the 1950s and based on the same solid-state semi-conductor technology used in transistors and computer chips, this expensive technology was originally used for powering satellites (**Figure 1**). But improvements in the technology over the years have significantly reduced the cost so that it can be applied in many more markets.

Consumer products, such as solar-powered calculators and watches, currently account for about one-third of photovoltaic use. Although the average power output of these cells is in the milliwatt range, consumer products have been an important proving ground for photovoltaic technology.

The largest market for photovoltaics is in remote power applications, areas not served by electric transmission grids, such as cottages, cabins, weather stations, and remote communities in North America and communities in the developing world (**Figure 2**).

The third significant market for photovoltaics is in supplying electricity to electrical transmission grids (**Figure 3**). This can be accomplished either through vast arrays of photovoltaic modules in a centralized location—in the same manner as a traditional power plant—or by decentralized arrays of photovoltaic cells on the roofs of houses and buildings. Electricity produced in this way currently costs over three times that of traditional sources of electrical energy, but with continual improvements in photovoltaic technology, the cost per watt should decrease.

Figure 1
The International Space Station (ISS) uses solar arrays to collect and then convert solar energy to electricity. When exposed to solar energy, photovoltaic cells in the arrays generate small currents of electricity. This powers the station and charges the batteries, which are used when ISS is not in sunlight.

Figure 2
This Mongolian nomad stands beside two solar panels that power lighting and a television inside her tent.

Figure 3
Utility-based, supplemental solar power "farm"

Part 1

In preparation for your selected task, research the Internet and other sources and provide a report, including diagrams, on the following topics:

(a) How do solar cells use the photoelectric effect to convert solar energy to electricity?

(b) How efficient are solar cells? Include methods for enhancing the efficiency.

(c) Compare and contrast photovoltaic technology with other forms of electricity generation, including the impact on the environment.

(d) Briefly summarize the significant advantages and disadvantages of solar power generation.

 www.science.nelson.com

In consultation with your instructor, choose one of the following tasks.

Task 1: Make a Photovoltaic Cell

Using a kit provided by your instructor, you will construct a photovoltaic cell and test its output. Depending on the kit provided, discuss any safety issues with your teacher.

1. Follow the instructions provided for making a photovoltaic cell, keeping a written record of the process.

2. Use your knowledge of the physics of electricity to write up a procedure for testing and measuring the electrical output of the photovoltaic cell. An electrical schematic diagram will be expected as part of your report.

3. Once the photovoltaic cell is operating, use your knowledge of the physics of wave optics to propose to your teacher a way of controlling the intensity and/or colour of the input light. (Equipment and facilities may limit your options.) Then devise a process for measuring the relationship between intensity *or* colour and the output of your photovoltaic cell.

4. Carry out your procedure, graphing the results if possible.

5. Write a formal scientific report of your investigation, including: Materials, Procedure, Analysis, Evaluation, and Synthesis.

Task 2: Using Solar Energy in a Remote Location

You will research the technology required to power a retreat (**Figure 4**) and prepare a written report.

Figure 4

Data Provided

A writer is building a retreat on a small mountain on Vancouver Island, British Columbia, 10 km up a logging road from the nearest town. There is no electrical power available. Heating and cooking energy needs will be met with propane gas, supplemented by an efficient wood stove. The electrical needs are the following: a laptop computer, a 19" television, a VCR, a sound system, a mobile telephone, a satellite/Internet receiver, and one 60-W and three 40-W fluorescent lamps. (The lamps will operate for three hours each evening.)

You must determine:

- the minimum number of hours of sunlight expected in the darkest months of the year for the location
- the average electrical power requirements in a 24-h period
- the size and type of the solar panels needed, the power of the inverter (DC to 110 VAC), and the number and type of storage batteries required
- the water turbine that would provide supplemental power from a nearby mountain stream (vertical fall of 50 m) in the winter months

Your report will outline the equipment needed, the cost of the materials, excluding any special installation costs, and a commentary on the life of the system and maintenance costs. You should demonstrate knowledge of the physics principles involved in the total system.

Analysis

Part 1

Your written report will be evaluated for the following:

- the quantity and accuracy of your research
- the demonstration of the knowledge and understanding of the physics principles involved
- appropriate referencing and crediting
- the quality of the written communication
- the quality of the diagrams submitted
- the societal relationship of photovoltaic technology

Part 2

The evaluation will depend on the optional task selected.

Your Task 1 evaluation will be based on:

- your demonstrated ability to carefully follow instructions
- the viability of your manufactured photovoltaic cell
- the quality of your written report of the investigation

Your Task 2 evaluation will be based on:

- the same criteria as outlined for Part 1

Write numbers 1 to 16 in your notebook. Indicate beside each number whether the corresponding statement is true (T) or false (F). If it is false, write a corrected version.

1. The time interval separating two events is not absolute but relative to the choice of inertial frame.

2. It is possible for a particle with a nonzero rest mass to be accelerated to the speed of light.

3. Rest energy, the product of c^2 and rest mass, can be converted into other forms of energy.

4. Photoelectrons are emitted from a photoelectric material when the frequency of the incident light exceeds the threshold frequency of the material.

5. In the photoelectric effect, the intensity of the incident light does not affect the threshold frequency.

6. The cutoff potential measures the maximum kinetic energy with which photoelectrons are emitted.

7. Coulomb's law, $F_e = \dfrac{kq_1q_2}{r^2}$, does not apply to the forces between charged particles at distances smaller than the size of atoms.

8. The Franck–Hertz experiment revealed that the energy of incident electrons is absorbed by mercury atoms only at discrete energy levels.

9. An α particle is also called a hydrogen nucleus.

10. The neutrino was suggested to resolve the problem of conserving energy and momentum in β decay.

11. For any given energy, less synchrotron radiation results in an accelerator when less massive particles are used.

12. The strong nuclear force can be attractive or repulsive.

13. Because the particles that mediate the weak force are relatively massive, the force acts over a relatively short distance.

14. All hadrons are leptons or mesons.

15. The standard model accounts for every observed particle.

16. Symmetry is frequently applied to scientific theories to predict previously unobserved events.

Write numbers 17 to 25 in your notebook. Beside each number, write the letter corresponding to the best choice.

17. You and your friend are in separate spaceships. In the inertial frame of your ship, your friend recedes from you at $0.9999c$. If you point a laser beam at your friend, and your friend points a laser beam at you, then

(a) each of you sees laser light arrive at a speed of c
(b) each of you sees laser light arrive at a speed of $2c$
(c) neither of you sees light from the other's laser
(d) one of you sees laser light arrive at a speed of c, while the other sees laser light arrive at a speed of $2c$
(e) none of these propositions is true

18. A clock, designed to tick once a second, is in a spaceship moving at a constant speed of $0.5c$ through an inertial frame. You find that the clock is

(a) ticking once a second
(b) ticking at a rate faster than once a second
(c) ticking at a rate slower than once a second
(d) running backward
(e) none of these

19. Classical physics offered a satisfactory explanation for

(a) the deflection of charged particles in an electric field
(b) the diffraction of electrons by crystals
(c) the intensity spectrum of blackbody radiation
(d) the photoelectric effect
(e) matter waves

20. When investigating β decay, the neutrino was postulated to explain

(a) conservation of energy and momentum
(b) conservation of the number of nucleons
(c) counteracting the ionizing effect of radiation
(d) the production of antiparticles
(e) the energy to carry away the β particle

21. Gamma radiation differs from α and β emissions in that

(a) it consists of photons rather than particles having nonzero rest mass
(b) it has almost no penetrating ability
(c) energy is not conserved in the nuclear decays producing it
(d) momentum is not conserved in the nuclear decays producing it
(e) it is not produced in the nucleus

22. How could you distinguish between α and β particles in a cloud chamber?

(a) It would be trivial since only α particles produce visible tracks.
(b) It would be trivial since only β particles produce visible tracks.
(c) It would be impossible to do.
(d) The α particles tend to produce double trails.
(e) The particles bend in opposite directions in a magnetic field.

An interactive version of the quiz is available online.   NEL

GO   www.science.nelson.com

23. The Feynman diagram in **Figure 1** illustrates
    (a) β^+ decay (d) pair production
    (B) β^- decay (e) annihilation
    (c) α decay

down ——→ ————

up ——→ ————

up ——→ ———→ down

W e+

ν

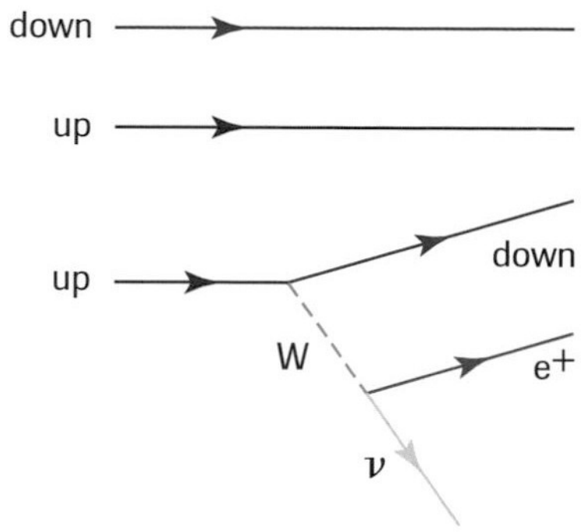

Figure 1

24. The quantum quantity called strangeness was postulated because observation revealed
    (a) opposite charges and production in pairs
    (b) unexpectedly long decay times and production in pairs
    (c) unexpectedly long decay times and opposite charges
    (d) unexpectedly high spin numbers and opposite charges
    (e) unexpectedly low spin numbers and unexpectedly long decay times

25. An example of an impossible quark combination is
    (a) uud   (c) uuu   (e) us
    (b) udd   (d) ud

Write the numbers 26 to 40 in your notebook. Beside each number place the expression or expressions, equation or equations, required to complete the text.

26. Any frame of reference in which the law of inertia holds is called a(n) ___?___ frame. Any frame in which the law of inertia does not hold is called a(n) ___?___ frame.

27. Michelson and Morley's interferometer experiment showed that ___?___.

28. According to the effects of length contraction, a body contracts along the direction of its ___?___.

29. The only mass that can be measured directly is ___?___.

30. Planck proposed that energy is radiated in discrete bundles called ___?___.

31. The threshold frequency for photoelectron emission from a photoelectric material is ___?___ (the same, different) for different metals.

32. The higher the frequency of the light, the ___?___ (higher, lower) the cutoff potential.

33. Matter waves predict the ___?___ that a particle will follow a particular path.

34. A 4.0-eV photon is absorbed by a metal surface with threshold energy 3.0 eV. An electron can be emitted with a kinetic energy in the range of ___?___ eV to ___?___ eV.

35. A continuous spectrum is produced by ___?___. An emission spectrum is produced by ___?___.

36. In the Rutherford scattering experiment, particles were beamed at a thin gold foil. After encountering the gold foil, most of the particles were ___?___.

37. As the electron in a hydrogen atom passes from a higher to a lower orbital, its orbital radius ___?___ (increases, decreases), its speed ___?___ (increases, decreases), and its energy ___?___ (increases, decreases).

38. The half-life, in years, for the decay represented by the graph in **Figure 2** is ___?___.

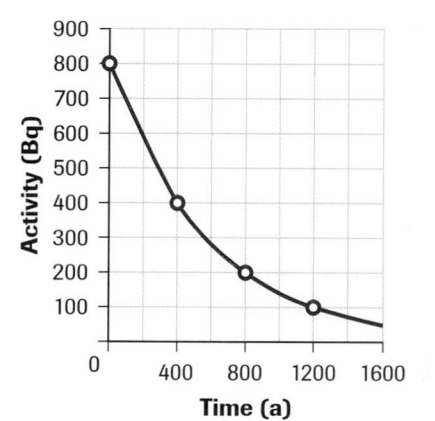

Figure 2

39. We can determine whether a given particle is a meson or a baryon once we know its ___?___.

40. Match the scientist to the discovery or innovation.

α-scattering experiment	Rutherford
radioactivity	Davisson
diffraction of particle	Bohr
energy levels and orbitals in the hydrogen atom	Compton
energy levels in an excited gas	Becquerel
matter waves	de Broglie
particle classification	Planck
momentum of a photon	Einstein
photoelectric effect	Franck
planetary model of the atom	Heisenberg
quanta	Gell-Mann
uncertainty	

Understanding Concepts

1. While stopped at a red light, you notice the car beside you creep forward. You instinctively step on the brake pedal, thinking that your car is rolling backward. What does this say about absolute and relative motion?

2. To whom does the duration of a process seem longer: an observer moving relative to the process or an observer moving with the process? Which observer measures proper time?

3. Explain how the length-contraction and time-dilation equations might be used to indicate that c is the limiting speed in the universe.

4. Give a physical argument that shows that it is impossible to accelerate an object with a nonzero mass to the speed of light, even with continuous force acting on it.

5. A beam of a certain type of elementary particle travels at the speed of 2.80×10^8 m/s relative to Earth. At this speed, the average lifetime of the particles is measured to be 4.86×10^{-6} s. Calculate the lifetime of the particle at rest.

6. You leave Earth for Jupiter, 5.9×10^8 km away. You and mission control synchronize your watches at launch and agree the local time is 12:00 noon. The spaceship's average speed for the trip is $0.67c$ relative to Earth.
   (a) What time do you and mission control claim it is when you reach Jupiter?
   (b) What is the distance from Earth to Jupiter, in the inertial frame of your ship?
   (c) Your ship meets part of its power requirement by collecting hydrogen, at the rate of 1.0×10^{-3} kg/s, from space and converting the mass to usable energy at an efficiency of 10%. What usable power does this system generate?

7. A spaceship passes you at a speed of $0.850c$ relative to Earth. On Earth you measure its length to be 52.2 m. How long would it be when at rest on Earth?

8. A proton is moving at a speed of $0.60c$ with respect to some inertial frame. Calculate its relativistic momentum as measured by an observer in that frame.

9. An electron is travelling at $0.866c$ relative to the face of a television picture tube. Calculate its relativistic momentum with respect to the tube.

10. An electron is accelerated to the speed 2.8×10^8 m/s in a particle accelerator. The accelerator is 3.0 km long according to the physicists using it.

(a) In the frame of reference of the electron, how long does it take to reach the target at the end of the accelerator?
(b) Calculate the electron's momentum when it hits the target.

11. Explain why it is easier to accelerate an electron than a proton to a speed approaching c.

12. Calculate the amount of mass that must be converted to produce 2.3×10^8 J of energy.

13. Calculate the amount of mass that must be converted in order to continuously run a 60-W desk lamp for one year.

14. Calculate the energy associated with a single quantum of X radiation with a frequency of 2.15×10^{18} Hz.

15. In tables listing the properties of elementary particles, sometimes the masses are represented in units of mega electron volts rather than kilograms. What does this mean?

16. Compare the energy of a quantum of "soft" ultraviolet radiation ($\lambda = 3.80 \times 10^{-7}$ m) with a quantum of "hard" ultraviolet radiation ($\lambda = 1.14 \times 10^{-7}$ m). Express your answer as a ratio.

17. Calculate the wavelength, in nanometres, of a photon with an energy of 3.20×10^{-19} J.

18. Using Planck's hypothesis, suggest a reason why no photoelectrons are released from a photoelectric surface until light of sufficiently short wavelength is directed at the surface.

19. Explain the following:
   (a) The threshold frequency is different for different metals.
   (b) Extremely intense red light might fail to liberate any photoelectrons from a surface, but a weakly intense blue light might.
   (c) The photocurrent increases with the intensity of the illumination once the threshold frequency is reached.

20. Barium has a work function of 2.48 eV. What colours of the visible spectrum liberate photoelectrons from a barium surface?

21. Nickel has a work function of 5.01 eV.
   (a) Calculate the threshold frequency for the photoelectric effect.
   (b) Calculate the cutoff potential for radiation of wavelength 1.50×10^{-7} m.

22. Barium has a work function of 2.48 eV. Calculate the maximum kinetic energy of the ejected photons when barium is illuminated by a 452-nm source.

23. When 355-nm light strikes a certain metal, the maximum kinetic energy of the photoelectrons is 1.20 eV. Calculate the work function of the metal.

24. Light of frequency 8.0×10^{14} Hz illuminates a photoelectric surface whose work function is 1.2 eV. Calculate the maximum speed with which an electron reaches the collector, given a retarding potential of 1.0 V.

25. Using the questions below as a guide, compare and contrast the photoelectric effect and the Compton effect.
    (a) What is required to initiate the effect?
    (b) What is the result of the interaction?
    (c) Why does each effect have a significant implication for the nature of light?

26. A thin metal foil is bombarded with X rays in a vacuum. A Compton collision occurs between an X ray photon and an electron in the foil, causing an electron to emerge at some angle to the trajectory of the incident photon, with some kinetic energy and momentum. Describe two characteristics of the emerging photon.

27. Calculate the momentum of a photon whose wavelength is 525 nm.

28. Calculate the momentum of a photon whose frequency is 4.5×10^{15} Hz.

29. Calculate the momentum of a 136-eV photon.

30. An incident photon, of energy 6.0×10^4 eV, initiates a Compton-effect event where the scattered electron has 5.6×10^4 eV of kinetic energy.
    (a) Calculate the energy of the scattered photon.
    (b) Calculate the speed of the electron involved in the event.
    (c) Calculate the momentum of the electron.

31. Calculate the wavelength of a photon having the same momentum as an electron moving at 1.0×10^6 m/s (assume nonrelativistic).

32. In a Franck–Hertz experiment, electrons were accelerated through a potential difference ΔV and then introduced into mercury vapour. After passing through the mercury vapour, the remaining energy of the electrons was measured. Consider only the following prominent energy levels for mercury above the ground state: 4.9 eV, 6.7 eV, 8.8 eV, and 10.4 eV.

    (a) If an electron entered the vapour with energy of 3.0 eV, how much energy might it have after passing through the vapour?
    (b) If an electron entered the vapour with energy of 8.0 eV, how much energy might it have after passing through the vapour?

33. Can an electron in the ground state of hydrogen absorb a photon of energy less than 13.6 eV or greater than 13.6 eV? Explain your reasoning in each case.

34. **Figure 1** in Section 12.5 depicts the energy levels for hydrogen.
    (a) Calculate the wavelengths of the photons emitted in the second Lyman transition and the second Balmer transition.
    (b) Calculate the energy that the atom must absorb if it is to make a transition from $n = 2$ to $n = 4$.

35. A photon has zero rest mass. If a photon is reflected from a surface, does it exert a force on the surface? Explain your answer.

36. Prepare a table comparing the three types of radioactive decay we examined in Section 13.1. Include a description of the particle emitted, how it affects the N and Z numbers of the parent substance, and an example of a material that undergoes that type of radioactive decay.

37. Complete each specification of a nuclear equation. Classify each as an α, β, or γ decay.
    (a) $^{15}_{8}\text{O} \rightarrow ^{y}_{x}\text{Z} + ^{0}_{+1}\text{e} + \nu$
    (b) $^{226}_{88}\text{Ra} \rightarrow ^{y}_{x}\text{Z} + ^{4}_{2}\text{He}$
    (c) $^{231}_{91}\text{Pa} \rightarrow ^{227}_{89}\text{Ac} + ^{y}_{x}\text{Z}$
    (d) $^{214}_{82}\text{Pb} \rightarrow ^{y}_{x}\text{Z} + ^{0}_{-1}\text{e} + \overline{\nu}$
    (e) $^{239}_{92}\text{U} \rightarrow ^{y}_{x}\text{Z} + ^{0}_{-1}\text{e} + \overline{\nu}$

38. Use the information in **Table 1** to calculate the average binding energy per nucleon in copper-65.

Table 1

Name	Rest Mass (u)
electron	0.00055
proton	1.00728
neutron	1.00867
copper-65	64.92779

39. (a) Complete the following equation, which depicts α decay in polonium-214:

$$^{214}_{84}\text{Po} \rightarrow\, ^{y}_{x}\text{Z} + ^{r}_{q}\text{S}$$

   (b) The mass difference between parent and daughters reveals that the decay releases 7.82 MeV. Explain the origin of this energy.

   (c) This energy is released as kinetic energy, shared between the two daughters. Look carefully at your reaction and suggest a reason why this is so.

40. (a) Explain why Geiger-Mueller tubes are less sensitive to γ radiation than they are to α and β particles.

   (b) Identify one device appropriate for detecting weak γ radiation. Explain why this device is more successful than the Geiger-Mueller tube.

41. **Figure 1** depicts the activity of a radioactive sample. Estimate the half-life.

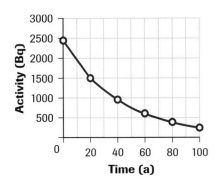

Figure 1

42. A sample of strontium-90 (with a half-life of 28.8 a) is estimated to have an initial activity of 2.50×10^{12} Bq.
   (a) Determine the activity after one half-life.
   (b) Calculate the activity after 5.0 a.

43. A sample of Ra-226 (with a half-life of 1600 a) has an initial mass of 2.50 μg. How much time will elapse before only 1.00 μg remains?

44. A charcoal sample is estimated to have had an initial activity of 2.99 Bq. The present activity is measured to be 1.93 Bq. Estimate the age of the sample.

45. The half-life of a sample is 3.7 a. With initial activity of 450.0 Bq, calculate the activity after 10.0 a.

46. A grand unified theory seeks to unify three forces. Which force is left out?

47. Explain how a synchrocyclotron differs from a cyclotron.

48. Briefly describe how a synchrotron and a linear accelerator respectively accelerate particles. Name two major synchrotrons and one major linear accelerator.

49. Describe the function of the following parts in a contemporary particle detector, such as could be used with a high-energy accelerator: tracking detector, calorimeters, muon chamber.

50. What is the minimum energy of a photon that spontaneously produces a neutron–antineutron pair?

51. Briefly describe β^+ decay using a quark model of the nucleus.

52. What is the quark composition of Λ^0?

53. Gravity is sometimes referred to as "the odd one out." In what sense is the description true?

54. Identify the particle associated with each quark combination:
   (a) udd   (b) sdd

55. Explain how the strong nuclear force is explained in an atomic model that assumes the nucleons are composed of quarks.

56. The Feynman diagram in **Figure 2** shows the result of an interaction between a neutrino and a neutron. The process is a weak interaction, mediated by a W^+ boson. The process gives an electron and another particle. Name the other particle produced in the reaction. Explain your reasoning.

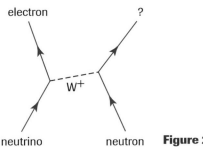

Figure 2

57. Determine which of the following are conserved in each of the reactions specified below: baryon number, lepton number, spin, charge.
   (a) $e^+ \rightarrow \nu + \gamma$
   (b) $p + p \rightarrow p + \bar{n} + n$
   (c) $K \rightarrow \mu + \bar{\nu}_\mu$

58. Use your answers to question 58 to determine which, if any, of the specified reactions can actually occur. Explain your answers.

59. Use conservation of mass, charge, baryon number, and lepton number to determine which, if any, of the following reactions can actually occur:
   (a) $p + e^- \rightarrow n + \nu$
   (b) $n \rightarrow \pi^+ + \pi^-$

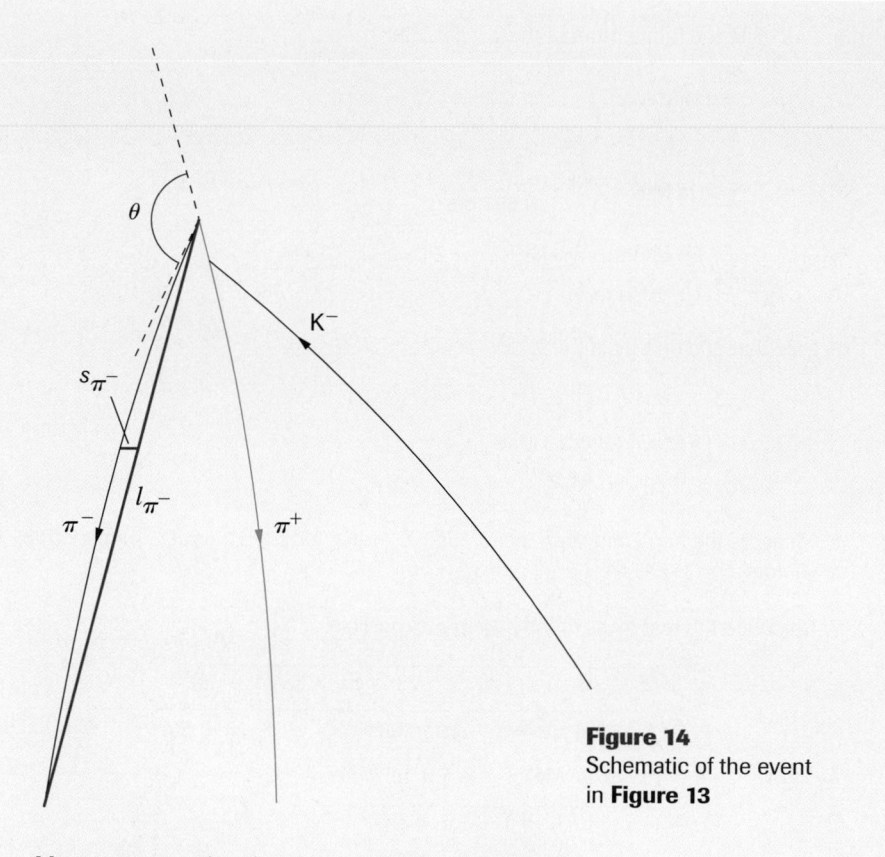

Figure 14
Schematic of the event
in **Figure 13**

Measurements taken from the schematic (**Figure 14**):

$l_{\pi^-} = 8.0$ cm $m_{\pi^-} = 140.0$ MeV/c^2

$s_{\pi^-} = 0.30$ cm $m_{\Sigma^-} = 1197.0$ MeV/c^2

$l_{\Sigma^-} = 0.6$ cm $\theta = 137°$

1. Calculate the radius of curvature of the π^- trajectory.

$$r_{\pi^-} = \frac{l_{\pi^-}^2}{8s_{\pi^-}} + \frac{s_{\pi^-}}{2}$$

$$= \frac{(8.0 \text{ cm})^2}{8(0.30 \text{ cm})} + \frac{0.30 \text{ cm}}{2}$$

$$r_{\pi^-} = 26.8 \text{ cm}$$

2. Calculate the momentum of the π^- particle.

$$p_{\pi^-} = 6.86 \, r_{\pi^-}$$

$$= (6.86 \text{ MeV}/c\cdot\text{cm})(26.8 \text{ cm})$$

$$p_{\pi^-} = 184 \text{ MeV}/c$$

3. Calculate the energy of the π^- particle.

$$E_{\pi^-}^2 = p_{\pi^-}^2 c^2 + m_{\pi^-}^2 c^4$$

$$= (184 \text{ MeV}/c)^2 c^2 + (140.0 \text{ MeV}/c^2)^2 c^4$$

$$= (3.4 \times 10^4 \text{ MeV}^2/c^2)c^2 + (1.96 \times 10^4 \text{ MeV}^2/c^4)c^4$$

$$E_{\pi^-}^2 = 5.4 \times 10^4 \text{ MeV}$$

$$E_{\pi^-} = 2.3 \times 10^2 \text{ MeV}$$

60. (a) List several reasons why the standard model is not considered adequate by some members of the research community.
    (b) What alternatives to the standard model are being contemplated? Briefly describe one such model.

Applying Inquiry Skills

61. Some television remote controls use an infrared beam to send signals to a photodetector on the television. Research the Internet and other sources, and find out how the remote control can send a variety of signals using a single wavelength of light. Present your findings to the class.

 www.science.nelson.com

62. Obtain a watch or clock with a luminous dial. Stop the clock so that the hands do not move. In a darkened room, place some undeveloped photographic film over the clock and cover the apparatus to protect it from surrounding light. Retrieve the film after *several days* have passed and have it developed. Comment on what you see.

Making Connections

63. What implications does the special theory of relativity have for space travel?

64. A photovoltaic solar cell generates electricity. The best cells currently operate at approximately 25% efficiency. How many photons of average wavelength 550 nm would have to be incident on a solar cell each second to supply adequate power to a 60-W bulb?

65. It has been proposed that the momentum of photons could be used in a propulsion system for interstellar spaceships. Calculate the number of photons of average wavelength 5.0×10^{-7} m required to accelerate a spaceship of mass 4.0×10^5 t from rest to a speed of 1.5×10^8 m/s. (Assume that the momentum of all the photons is applied at once. Ignore any relativistic effects.)

Extension

66. Research to find out how the speed of light was first measured with some accuracy. For fun, present a dramatization to the class.

67. Research the work of Stephen Hawking and report on how it builds on the work of Einstein. Record your findings in a brief summary.

68. Research time-dilation effects for a voyager crossing the event horizon around a black hole and for distant observers monitoring the progress of the voyager. Record your findings in a brief report.

69. A Σ^- event was recorded on the bubble chamber photograph in **Figure 3**.
    (a) Identify the event.
    (b) Calculate the rest mass of the invisible X^0 particle formed in the interaction.
    (c) Identify the X^0 particle by comparing its calculated rest mass with the masses of the known particles in **Table 3** of Section 13.6.

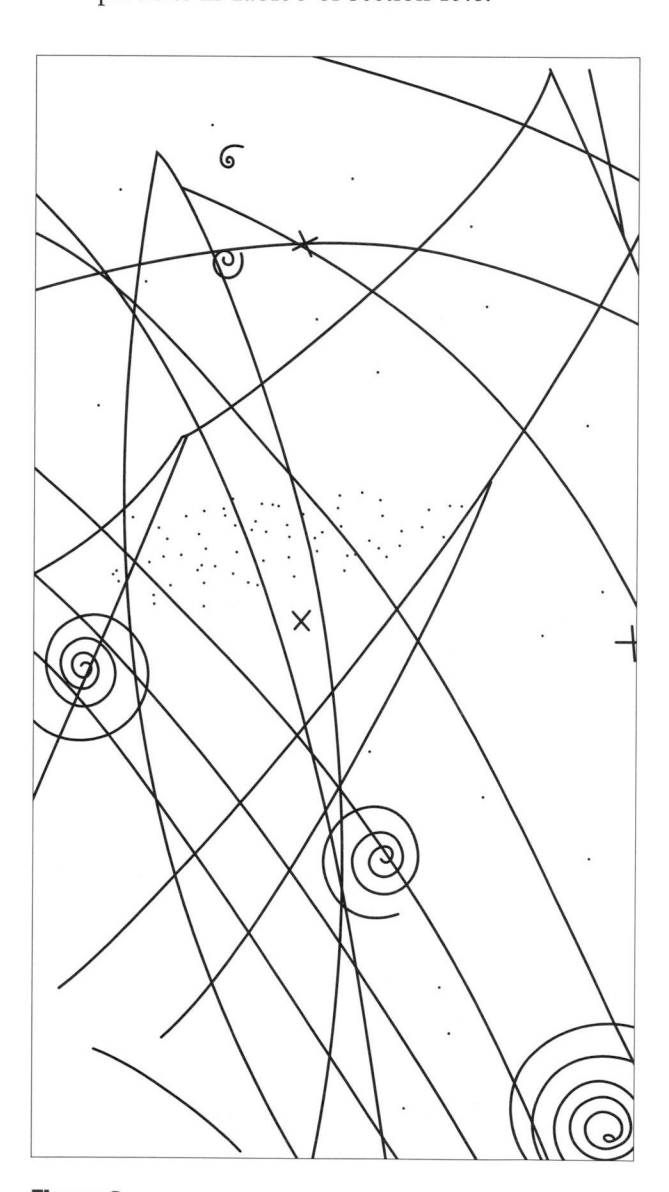

Figure 3

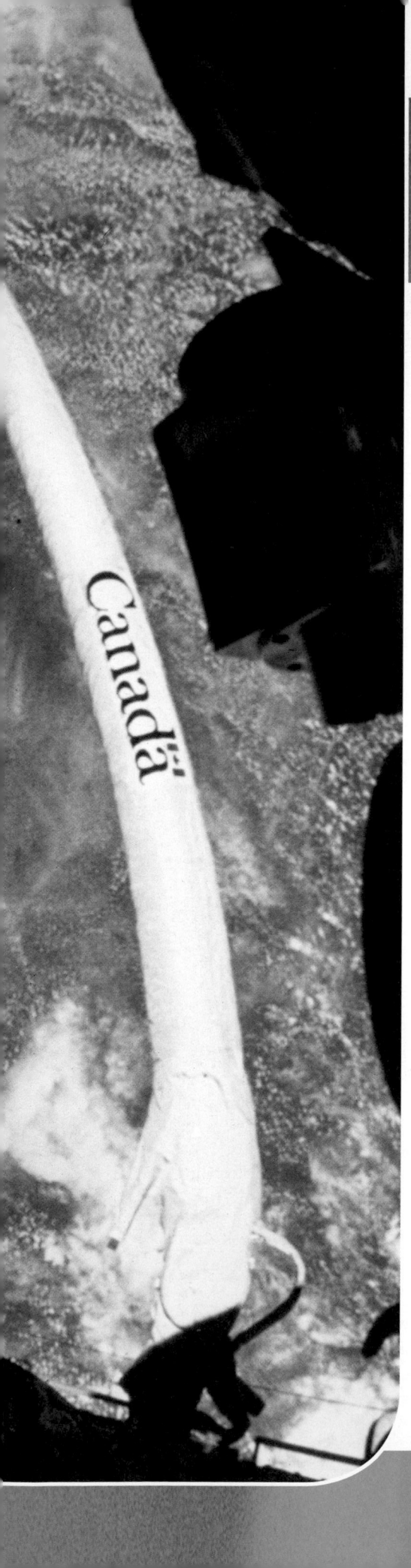

Appendixes

A1 Math Skills

Significant Digits and Rounding Off Numbers

Two types of quantities are used in science: exact values and measurements. Exact values include defined quantities (e.g., 1 kg = 1000 g) and counted values (e.g., 23 students in a classroom). Measurements, however, are not exact because they always include some degree of uncertainty.

In any measurement, the *significant digits* are the digits that are known reliably, or for certain, and include the single last digit that is estimated or uncertain. Thus, if the width of a piece of paper is measured as 21.6 cm, there are three significant digits in the measurement and the last digit (6) is estimated or uncertain.

The following rules are used to determine if a digit is significant in a measurement:

- All non-zero digits are significant: 345.6 N has four significant digits.
- In a measurement with a decimal point, zeroes placed before other digits are not significant: 0.0056 m has two significant digits.
- Zeroes placed between other digits are always significant: 7003 s has four significant digits.
- Zeroes placed after other digits behind a decimal are significant: 9.100 km and 802.0 kg each has four significant digits.
- Scientific notation is used to indicate if zeroes at the end of a measurement are significant: 4.50×10^7 km has three significant digits and 4.500×10^7 km has four significant digits. The same number written as 45 000 000 km has at least two significant digits, but the total number is unknown unless the measurement is written in scientific notation. (An exception to this last statement is found if the number of significant digits can be assessed by inspection: a reading of 1250 km on a car's odometer has four significant digits.)

Measurements made in scientific experiments or given in problems are often used in calculations. In a calculation, the final answer must take into consideration the number of significant digits of each measurement, and may have to be rounded off according to the following rules:

- When adding or subtracting measured quantities, the final answer should have no more than one estimated digit; in other words, the answer should be rounded off to the least number of decimals in the original measurements.

- When multiplying or dividing measured quantities, the final answer should have the same number of significant digits as the original measurement with the least number of significant digits.

Example

A piece of paper is 48.5 cm long, 8.44 cm wide, and 0.095 mm thick.

(a) Determine the perimeter of the piece of paper.

(b) Determine the volume of the piece of paper.

Solution

(a) L = 48.5 cm (The 5 is estimated.)

w = 8.44 cm (The last 4 is estimated.)

P = ?

$$P = 2L + 2w$$
$$= 2(48.5 \text{ cm}) + 2(8.44 \text{ cm})$$
$$P = 113.88 \text{ cm}$$

Both digits after the decimal are estimated, so the answer must be rounded off to only one estimated digit. Thus, the perimeter is 113.9 cm.

(b) $h = 0.095$ mm $= 9.5 \times 10^{-3}$ cm (two significant digits)

V = ?

$$V = Lwh$$
$$= (48.5 \text{ cm})(8.44 \text{ cm})(9.5 \times 10^{-3} \text{ cm})$$
$$= 3.88873 \text{ cm}^3$$
$$V = 3.9 \text{ cm}^3$$

The answer is rounded off to two significant digits, which is the least number of significant digits of any of the original measurements.

Other rules must be taken into consideration in some situations. Suppose that after calculations are complete, the answer to a problem must be rounded off to three significant digits. Apply the following rules of rounding:

- If the first digit to be dropped is 4 or less, the preceding digit is not changed; for example, 8.674 is rounded to 8.67.
- If the first digit to be dropped is greater than 5, or if it is a 5 followed by at least one non-zero digit, the preceding digit is increased by 1; for example, 8.675 123 is rounded up to 8.68.

- If the first digit to be dropped is a lone 5 or a 5 followed by zeroes, the preceding digit is not changed if it is even, but is increased by 1 if it is odd; for example, 8.675 is rounded up to 8.68 and 8.665 is rounded to 8.66. (This rule exists to avoid the accumulated error that would occur if the 5 were always to round up. It is followed in this text, but not in all situations, such as in the use of your calculator or some computer software. This rule is not crucial in your success in solving problems.)

When solving multi-step problems, round-off error occurs if you use the rounded off answer from the first part of the question in subsequent parts. Thus, when doing calculations, record all the digits or store them in your calculator until the final answer is determined, and then round off the answer to the correct number of significant digits. For example, in a multi-step sample problem that involves parts (a) and (b), the answer for part (a) is written to the correct number of significant digits, but all the digits of the answer are used to solve part (b).

Scientific Notation

Extremely large and extremely small numbers are awkward to write in common decimal notation, and do not always convey the number of significant digits of a measured quantity. It is possible to accommodate such numbers by changing the metric prefix so that the number falls between 0.1 and 1000; for example, 0.000 000 906 kg can be expressed as 0.906 mg. However, a prefix change is not always possible, either because an appropriate prefix does not exist or because it is essential to use a particular unit of measurement. In these cases, it is best to use *scientific notation*, also called standard form. Scientific notation expresses a number by writing it in the form $a \times 10^n$, where $1 \leq |a| < 10$ and the digits in the coefficient a are all significant. For example, the Sun's mass is 1.99×10^{30} kg and the period of vibration of a cesium-133 atom (used to define the second) is $1.087\ 827\ 757 \times 10^{-8}$ s.

Calculations involving very large and small numbers are simpler using scientific notation. The following rules must be applied when performing mathematical operations.

- For addition and subtraction of numbers in scientific notation:

  Change all the factors to a common factor, that is the same power of 10, and add or subtract the numbers. In general, $ax + bx = (a + b)x$.

Example

$$1.234 \times 10^5 + 4.2 \times 10^4 = 1.234 \times 10^5 + 0.42 \times 10^5$$
$$= (1.234 + 0.42) \times 10^5$$
$$= 1.654 \times 10^5$$

This answer is rounded off to 1.65×10^5 so the answer has only one estimated digit, in this case two digits after the decimal.

- For multiplication and division of numbers in scientific notation:

  Multiply or divide the coefficients, add or subtract the exponents, and express the result in scientific notation.

Example

$$\left(1.36 \times 10^4\ \frac{kg}{m^3}\right)(3.76 \times 10^3\ m^3) = 5.11 \times 10^7\ kg$$

Example

$$\frac{(4.51 \times 10^5\ N)}{(7.89 \times 10^{-4}\ m)} = 0.572 \times 10^9\ N/m$$
$$= 5.72 \times 10^8\ N/m$$

When working with exponents, recall that the following rules apply:

$$x^a \cdot x^b = x^{a+b}$$
$$\frac{x^a}{x^b} = x^{a-b}$$
$$(x^a)^b = x^{ab}$$
$$(xy)^b = x^b y^b$$
$$\left(\frac{x}{y}\right)^b = \frac{x^b}{y^b}$$
$$a\log x = \log x^a$$

On many calculators, scientific notation is entered using the EXP or the EE key. This key includes the "×10" from the scientific notation, so you need only enter the exponent. For example, to enter 6.51×10^{-4}, press 6.51 EXP +/−4.

Mathematical Equations

Several mathematical equations involving geometry, algebra, and trigonometry can be applied in physics.

Geometry

For a rectangle of length L and width w, the perimeter P and the area A are

$$P = 2L + 2w$$
$$A = Lw$$

For a triangle of base b and altitude h, the area is

$$A = \frac{1}{2}bh$$

For a circle of radius r, the circumference C and the area are

$$C = 2\pi r$$
$$A = \pi r^2$$

For a sphere of radius r, the area and volume V are

$$A = 4\pi r^2$$
$$V = \frac{4}{3}\pi r^3$$

For a right circular cylinder of height h and radius r, the area and volume are

$$A = 2\pi r^2 + 2\pi rh$$
$$V = \pi r^2 h$$

Algebra

Quadratic formula:

Given a quadratic equation in the form $ax^2 + bx + c = 0$,

$$x = \frac{-b \pm \sqrt{b^2 - 4ac}}{2a}$$

In this equation, the discriminant $b^2 - 4ac$ indicates the number of real roots of the equation. If $b^2 - 4ac < 0$, the quadratic function has no real roots. If $b^2 - 4ac = 0$, the quadratic function has one real root. If $b^2 - 4ac > 0$, the quadratic function has two real roots.

Trigonometry

Trigonometric functions for the angle θ shown in **Figure 1(a)** are

$$\sin\theta = \frac{y}{r}$$
$$\cos\theta = \frac{x}{r}$$
$$\tan\theta = \frac{y}{x}$$

Law of Pythagoras: For the right-angled triangle in **Figure 1(b)**, $c^2 = a^2 + b^2$, where c is the hypotenuse and a and b are the other sides.

For the obtuse triangle in **Figure 1(c)** with angles A, B, and C, and opposite sides a, b, and c:

Sum of the angles: $A + B + C = 180°$

Sine law: $\dfrac{\sin A}{a} = \dfrac{\sin B}{b} = \dfrac{\sin C}{c}$

To use the sine law, two sides and an opposite angle (SSA) or two angles and one side (AAS) must be known.

LEARNING *TIP*

Sine Law Caution

The sine law can yield an acute angle rather than the correct obtuse angle when solving for an angle greater than 90°. This problem occurs because for an angle A between 0° and 90°, $\sin A = \sin (A + 90°)$. To avoid this problem, always check the validity of the angle opposite the largest side of a triangle.

Cosine law: $c^2 = a^2 + b^2 - 2ab \cos C$

To use the cosine law, three sides (SSS), or two sides and the contained angle (SAS) must be known. Notice in the cosine law that if $C = 90°$, the equation reduces to the law of Pythagoras.

(a)

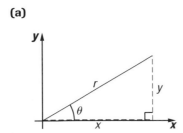

(b)

(c)

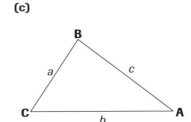

Figure 1
(a) Defining trigonometric ratios
(b) A right-angled triangle
(c) An obtuse triangle

The following trigonometric identities may be useful:

$$\cos \theta = \sin(90° - \theta)$$

$$\sin \theta = \cos(90° - \theta)$$

$$\tan \theta = \frac{\sin \theta}{\cos \theta}$$

$$\sin^2 \theta + \cos^2 \theta = 1$$

$$\sin 2\theta = 2\sin \theta \cos \theta$$

$$\cos 2\theta = \cos^2 \theta - \sin^2 \theta$$

Dimensional and Unit Analysis

Most physical quantities have dimensions that can be expressed in terms of five basic dimensions: mass [M], length [L], time [T], electric current [I], and temperature [θ]. The SI units that correspond to these basic dimensions are kilogram [kg], metre [m], second [s], ampere [A], and kelvin [K]. The square brackets are a convention used to denote the dimension or unit of a quantity.

The process of using dimensions to analyze a problem or an equation is called *dimensional analysis*, and the corresponding process of using units is called *unit analysis*. Although this discussion focuses on dimensions only, the same process can be applied to unit analysis. Both dimensional analysis and unit analysis are tools used to determine whether an equation has been written correctly and to convert units.

Example

Show that the equation for the displacement of an object undergoing constant acceleration is dimensionally correct.

$$\Delta \vec{d} = \vec{v}_i \Delta t + \frac{1}{2}\vec{a}\Delta t^2$$

$$[L] \overset{?}{=} \left[\frac{L}{T}\right][T] + \left[\frac{L}{T^2}\right][T^2]$$

$$[L] \overset{?}{=} [L] + [L]$$

The dimension of each term is the same.

Notice that in the previous example, we can ignore the number $\frac{1}{2}$ because it has no dimensions. Dimensionless quantities include:

- all plain numbers (4, π, etc.)
- counted quantities (12 people, 5 cars, etc.)
- angles (although angles have units)
- cycles
- trigonometric functions
- exponential functions
- logarithms

Derived units can be written in terms of base SI units and, thus, base dimensions. For example, the newton has base units of kg·m/s^2 or dimensions of $[M][L][T^{-2}]$. Can you write the dimensions of the joule and the watt? (A list of derived units is found in Appendix C.)

Analyzing Experimental Data

Controlled physics experiments are conducted to determine the relationship between variables. The experimental data can be analyzed in a variety of ways to determine how the dependent variable depends on the independent variable(s). Often the resulting derived relationship can be expressed as an equation.

Proportionality Statements and Graphing

The statement of how one quantity varies in relation to another is called a *proportionality statement*. (It can also be called a variation statement.) Typical proportionality statements are:

$y \propto x$ (direct proportion)

$y \propto \dfrac{1}{x}$ (inverse proportion)

$y \propto x^2$ (square proportion)

$y \propto \dfrac{1}{x^2}$ (inverse square proportion)

A proportionality statement can be converted into an equation by replacing the proportionality sign with an equal sign and including a proportionality constant. Using k to represent this constant, the proportionality statements become the following equations:

$y = kx$

$y = \dfrac{k}{x}$

$y = kx^2$

$y = \dfrac{k}{x^2}$

The constant of proportionality can be determined by using graphing software or by applying regular graphing techniques as outlined in the following steps:

1. Plot a graph of the dependent variable as a function of the independent variable. If the resulting line of best fit is straight, the relationship is a direct variation. Proceed to step 3.

2. If the line of best fit is curved, replot the graph to try to get a straight line as shown in **Figure 2**. If the first replotting results in a new curved line, draw yet another graph to obtain a straight line.

3. Determine the slope and y-intercept of the straight line on the graph. Substitute the values into the slope/y-intercept form of the equation that corresponds to the variables plotted on the graph with the straight line.

4. Check the equation by substituting original data points.

5. If required, use the equation (or the straight-line graph) to give examples of interpolation and extrapolation.

Example

Use regular graphing techniques to derive the equation relating the data given in Table 1.

Table 1 Velocity-Time Data

t (s)	0.00	2.00	4.00	6.00
$\vec{v}$ (m/s [E])	10.0	15.0	20.0	25.0

Solution

Figure 3 is the graph that corresponds to the data in **Table 1**. The line is straight and has the following slope:

$$\text{slope} = \frac{\Delta \vec{v}}{\Delta t}$$

$$= \frac{25.0 \text{ m/s [E]} - 10.0 \text{ m/s [E]}}{6.00 \text{ s} - 0.00 \text{ s}}$$

$$\text{slope} = 2.50 \text{ m/s}^2 \text{ [E]}$$

The y-intercept is 10.0 m/s [E].

Using $y = mx + b$, the equation is

$$\vec{v} = 2.50 \text{ m/s}^2 \text{ [E] } (t) + 10.0 \text{ m/s [E]}$$

Verify the equation by substituting $t = 4.00$ s:

$$\vec{v} = 2.50 \text{ m/s}^2 \text{ [E] } (4.00 \text{ s}) + 10.0 \text{ m/s [E]}$$

$$= 10.0 \text{ m/s [E]} + 10.0 \text{ m/s [E]}$$

$$\vec{v} = 20.0 \text{ m/s [E]}$$

The equation is valid.

Original graph and variation

First choice to obtain a straight line

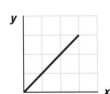

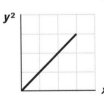

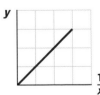

Second choice to obtain a straight line

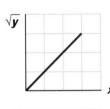

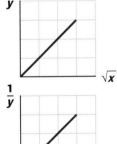

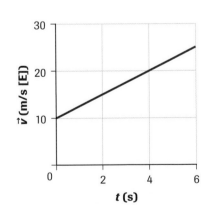

Figure 3
Velocity-time graph

Figure 2
Replotting graphs to try to obtain a straight line

Using $t = 3.20$ s as an example of interpolation

$$\vec{v} = 2.50 \text{ m/s}^2 \text{ [E]} (3.20 \text{ s}) + 10.0 \text{ m/s [E]}$$
$$= 8.00 \text{ m/s [E]} + 10.0 \text{ m/s [E]}$$
$$\vec{v} = 18.0 \text{ m/s [E]}$$

Example

Use regular graphing techniques to derive the equation for the data in the first two rows of **Table 2**.

Table 2 Acceleration-Mass Data

m (kg)	2.0	4.0	6.0	8.0
$\vec{a}$ (m/s^2 [E])	4.0	2.0	1.3	1.0
$\dfrac{1}{m}$ (kg^{-1})*	0.50	0.25	0.167	0.125

*The third row is for the redrawn graph of the relationship.

Figure 4(a) is the graph of the data given in the first two rows of the table. **Figure 4(b)** shows the replotted graph with m replaced with $\dfrac{1}{m}$, which produces a straight line. The slope of the straight line is

$$\text{slope} = \dfrac{\Delta \vec{a}}{\Delta\left(\dfrac{1}{m}\right)}$$

$$= \dfrac{3.2 \text{ m/s}^2 \text{ [E]} - 1.6 \text{ m/s}^2 \text{ [E]}}{0.40 \text{ kg}^{-1} - 0.20 \text{ kg}^{-1}}$$

$$\text{slope} = 8.0 \text{ kg·m/s}^2 \text{ [E]}$$

The slope is 8.0 kg·m/s^2 [E], which can also be written 8.0 N [E].

The y-intercept is 0.0. Using $y = mx + b$, the equation is

$$\vec{a} = 8.0 \text{ kg·m/s}^2 \text{ [E]} \times \dfrac{1}{m}$$

or $\quad \vec{a} = \dfrac{8.0 \text{ N [E]}}{m}$

Verify the equation by substituting $m = 6.0$ kg:

$$\vec{a} = \dfrac{8.0 \text{ kg·m/s}^2 \text{ [E]}}{6.0 \text{ kg}}$$

$$\vec{a} = 1.333 \text{ m/s}^2 \text{ [E]}$$

This value rounds off to 1.3 m/s^2 [E], so the equation is valid.

We can use this equation to illustrate extrapolation; for example, the acceleration when the mass is 9.6 kg the acceleration is

$$\vec{a} = \dfrac{8.0 \text{ kg·m/s}^2 \text{ [E]}}{9.6 \text{ kg}}$$

$$\vec{a} = 0.83 \text{ m/s}^2 \text{ [E]}$$

The acceleration is 0.83 m/s^2 [E].

(a)

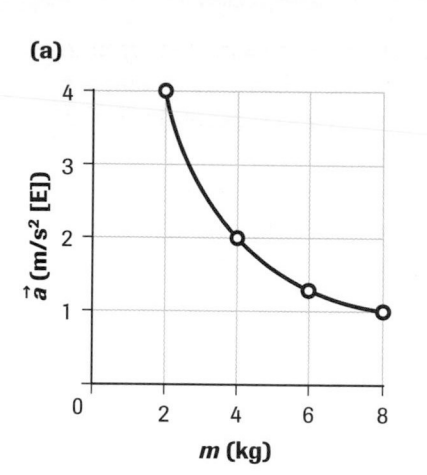

(b)

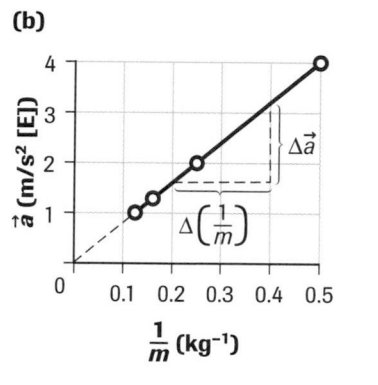

Figure 4
(a) Acceleration-mass graph
(b) Acceleration-$\dfrac{1}{\text{mass}}$ graph

Logarithms

Many relationships in physics can be expressed as $y = kx^n$. As with other mathematical relationships, this type of equation can be analyzed using graphing software. However, another method that provides good results involves log-log graphing. If the relationship is plotted on a log-log graph, a straight line results and the equation of the line can be determined. A log-log graph has logarithmic scales on both axes. The axes can have one or more cycles, and the graph chosen depends on the domain and range of the variables to be plotted. For example, a typical log-log graph may have three cycles horizontally and two cycles vertically.

The steps in deriving an equation involving two variables using log-log graphing techniques are as follows:

1. Label the numbers on the axes of the graph starting with any power of 10, such as 10^{-3}, 10^{-2}, 10^{-1}, 10^{0}, 10^1, 10^2, 10^3, or 10^4. (There is no zero on a log-log graph.)

2. Plot the data on the graph and use an independent scale, such as a millimetre ruler, to determine the slope of the line. This yields the exponent n in the equation $y = kx^n$.

3. Substitute data points into the equation $y = kx^n$ to determine the k value, include its units, and write the final equation.

4. Check the equation by substituting original data points.

Example

Use log-log graphing techniques to determine the equation for the data in **Table 3**.

Table 3 Energy-Temperature Data

T (K)	2.00	3.00	4.00
E (J)	4.80×10^3	2.43×10^4	7.68×10^4

Figure 5 shows the log-log graph of the data in **Table 3**. The slope of the line is

$$\text{slope} = \frac{\Delta y}{\Delta x}$$

$$= \frac{40 \text{ mm}}{10 \text{ mm}}$$

$$\text{slope} = 4$$

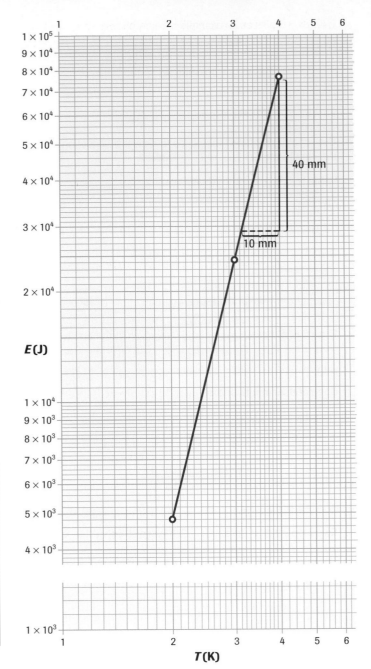

Figure 5
Log-log graph (with a portion removed to save space)

Using the form of the equation $y = kx^n$, where $n = 4$:

$$E = kT^4$$

To determine k, we use the original data:

$$k = \frac{E}{T^4}$$

$$= \frac{4.80 \times 10^3 \text{ J}}{(2.00 \text{ K})^4}$$

$$k = 3.00 \times 10^2 \text{ J/K}^4$$

The final equation is

$$E = 3.00 \times 10^2 \text{ J/K}^4 (T)^4$$

Check the equation using $T = 4.00$ K:

$$E = 3.00 \times 10^2 \text{ J/K}^4 (4.00 \text{ K})^4$$
$$E = 7.68 \times 10^4 \text{ J}$$

The equation is valid.

In the previous example, the values of n and k were calculated once. In student experimentation, the values should be calculated at least three times to improve accuracy.

The log-log graphing technique is particularly useful if three or more variables are involved in an experiment, such as in the centripetal acceleration investigation. The following steps can be applied to obtain the equation relating the variables.

1. Plot the data on log-log graph paper.

2. Find the slope n of each line on the graph, and use the slopes to write the proportionality statements. For example, assume that a depends on b and c such that the slopes are $+3$ and -4 respectively. The proportionality statements are $a \propto b^3$ and $a \propto c^{-4}$, or $a \propto \dfrac{1}{c^4}$.

3. Combine the proportionality statements $\left(\text{e.g., } a \propto \dfrac{b^3}{c^4}\right)$.

4. Convert the proportionality statement into an equation by inserting an equal sign and a constant $\left(\text{e.g., } a = \dfrac{kb^3}{c^4}\right)$.

5. Solve for the constant k by taking an average of three substitutions $\left(\text{e.g., } k = \dfrac{ac^4}{b^3}\right)$.

6. Write the equation and include the units for k.

7. Check the equation by substitution.

Error Analysis in Experimentation

In experiments involving measurement, there is always some degree of uncertainty. This uncertainty can be attributed to the instrument used, the experimental procedure, the theory related to the experiment, and/or the experimenter.

In all experiments involving measurements, the measurements and subsequent calculations should be recorded to the correct number of significant digits. However, a formal report of an experiment involving measurements should include an analysis of uncertainty, percent uncertainty, and percent error or percent difference.

Uncertainty is the amount by which a measurement may deviate from an average of several readings of the same measurement. This uncertainty can be estimated, so it is called the *estimated uncertainty*. Often it is assumed to be plus or minus half of the smallest division of the scale on the instrument; for example, the estimated uncertainty of 15.8 cm is ± 0.05 cm or ± 0.5 mm. The same applies to the *assumed uncertainty*, which is the uncertainty in a written measurement; for example, the assumed uncertainty of the Sun's mass of 1.99×10^{30} kg is $\pm 0.005 \times 10^{30}$ kg or $\pm 5 \times 10^{27}$ kg.

Whenever calculations involving addition or subtraction are performed, the uncertainties accumulate. Thus, to find the

total uncertainty, the individual uncertainties must be added. For example,

$$(34.7 \text{ cm} \pm 0.05 \text{ cm}) - (18.4 \text{ cm} \pm 0.05 \text{ cm}) = 16.3 \text{ cm} \pm 0.10 \text{ cm}$$

Percent uncertainty is found by dividing the uncertainty by the measured quantity and multiplying by 100%. Use your calculator to prove that 28.0 cm $\pm$ 0.05 cm has a percent uncertainty of $\pm 0.18\%$.

Whenever calculations involving multiplication or division are performed, the percent uncertainties must be added. If desired, the total percent uncertainty can be converted back to uncertainty. For example, consider the area of a certain rectangle:

$$A = Lw$$
$$= (28.0 \text{ cm} \pm 0.18\%)(21.5 \text{ cm} \pm 0.23\%)$$
$$= 602 \text{ cm}^2 \pm 0.41\%$$
$$A = 602 \text{ cm}^2 \pm 2.5 \text{ cm}^2$$

Percent error can be found only if it is possible to compare an experimental value with that of the most commonly accepted value. The equation is

$$\% \text{ error} = \frac{\text{measured value} - \text{accepted value}}{\text{accepted value}} \times 100\%$$

Percent difference is useful for comparing measurements when the true measurement is not known or for comparing an experimental value to a predicted value. The equation is

$$\% \text{ difference} = \frac{|\text{difference in values}|}{\text{average of values}} \times 100\%$$

Accuracy is a comparison of how close a measured value is to the true or accepted value. An accurate measurement has a low uncertainty.

Precision is an indication of the smallest unit provided by an instrument. A highly precise instrument provides several significant digits.

Random error occurs in measurements when the last significant digit is estimated. Random error results from variation about an average value. Such errors can be reduced by taking the average of several readings.

Parallax is the apparent shift in an object's position when the observer's position changes. This source of error can be reduced by looking straight at an instrument or dial.

Systematic error results from a consistent problem with a measuring device or the person using it. Such errors are reduced by adding or subtracting the known error, calibrating the instrument, or performing a more complex investigation.

Vectors

Several quantities in physics are vector quantities—quantities that have both magnitude and direction. Understanding and working with vectors is crucial in solving many physics problems.

LEARNING TIP

Geometric and Cartesian Vectors
The vectors in this text are *geometric vectors* in one and two dimensions, which are represented as directed line segments or arrows. *Cartesian vectors* are represented as sets of ordered pairs in one and two dimensions. The properties of both geometric and Cartesian vectors can be extended to three dimensions.

Vector Symbols

A vector is represented in a diagram by an arrow or a directed line segment. The length of the arrow is proportional to the magnitude of the vector, and the direction is the same as the direction of the vector. The tail of the arrow is the initial point, and the head of the arrow is the final point. If the vector is drawn to scale, the scale should be indicated on the diagram (**Figure 6**).

(a)
(b)

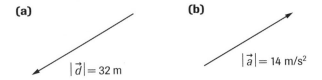

$|\vec{d}| = 32$ m

$|\vec{a}| = 14$ m/s²

Figure 6
Examples of vector quantities
(a) Displacement vector (scale: 1 cm = 10 m)
(b) Acceleration vector (scale: 1 cm = 5 m/s²)

In this text, a vector quantity is indicated by an arrow above the letter representing the vector (e.g., $\vec{A}, \vec{a}, \Sigma\vec{F}, \vec{p}$, etc.). The manitude of a vector is indicated either by the absolute value symbol $|\vec{A}|$ or simply A. The magnitude is always positive (unless it is zero).

Directions of Vectors

The directions of vectors are indicated in square brackets following the magnitude and units of the measurement. The four compass directions east, west, north, and south are indicated as [E], [W], [N], and [S]. Other examples are [down],

[forward], [11.5° below the horizontal], [toward Earth's centre], and [24° N of W] (refer to **Figure 7**).

Directions used in computers and calculators are measured counterclockwise from the $+x$-axis in an x-y coordinate system. Using this convention, the direction [24° N of W] is simply 156°.

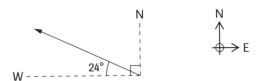

Figure 7
Locating the direction 24° N of W

Multiplying a Vector by a Scalar (Scalar Multiplication)

The product of a vector and a scalar is a vector with the same direction as the original vector, but with a different magnitude (unless the scalar is 1). Thus, $8.5\vec{v}$ is a vector 8.5 times as long as $\vec{v}$ and in the same direction. Multiplying a vector by a negative scalar results in a vector in the opposite direction (**Figure 8**).

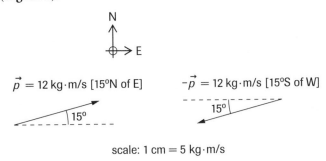

$\vec{p} = 12$ kg·m/s [15°N of E]

$-\vec{p} = 12$ kg·m/s [15°S of W]

scale: 1 cm = 5 kg·m/s

Figure 8
Multiplying the momentum vector $\vec{p}$ by -1 results in the momentum vector $-\vec{p}$.

Components of Vectors

The *component of a vector* is the projection of a vector along an axis of a rectangular coordinate system. Any vector can be described by its rectangular components. In this text, we use two rectangular components because the situations are two-dimensional; three rectangular components are required for three-dimensional situations. Rectangular components are always perpendicular to each other, and can be called *orthogonal components*. (Orthogonal stems from the Greek word *orthos* which means "right" and *gonia* which means "angle.")

Consider the force vector $\vec{F}$ shown in **Figure 9** in which the $+x$ direction is to the left and the $+y$ direction is upward. The projection of $\vec{F}$ along the x-axis is F_x and the projection

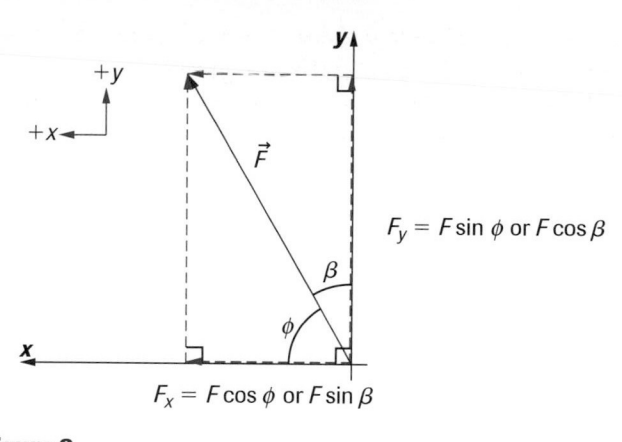

Figure 9
The force vector $\vec{F}$ and its components

along the y-axis is F_y. Notice that although $\vec{F}$ is a vector, its components, F_x and F_y, are not vectors; rather they are positive or negative numbers with the same units as $\vec{F}$. In diagrams, components are often shown as broken or dashed line segments.

Notice that in **Figure 9** there are two angles that indicate each component in terms of the magnitude and direction of the vector. These angles always form a right angle (i.e., in this case $\phi + \beta = 90°$).

It is often convenient to choose a coordinate system other than a horizontal/vertical system or an east-west/north-south system. For example, consider the situation in which a skier is accelerating down a hillside inclined at an angle θ to the horizontal (**Figure 10(a)**). Solving problems related to acceleration and forces is most convenient if the $+x$ direction is the direction of the acceleration, in this case downhill; this means that the $+y$ direction must be perpendicular to the hillside. The corresponding FBD of the skier is shown in **Figure 10(b)**.

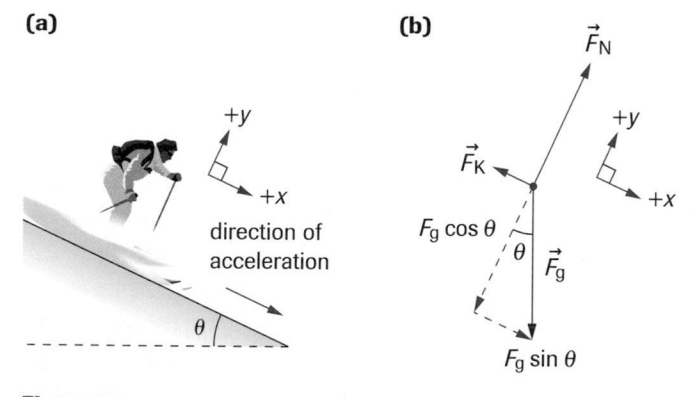

Figure 10
(a) A skier accelerating downhill
(b) The FBD of the skier

Vector Addition

In arithmetic, $3 + 3$ always equals 6. But if these quantities are vectors, $\vec{3} + \vec{3}$ can have any value between 0 and $\vec{6}$, depending on their orientation. Thus, vector addition must take into consideration the directions of the vectors.

To add vector quantities, the arrows representing the vectors are joined head-to-tail, with the vector representing the resultant vector joined from the tail of the first vector to the head of the last vector added (**Figure 11**). In drawing vector diagrams, the vectors can be moved around so that they are head-to-tail. When shifting a vector on a diagram, it is important that the redrawn vector have the same magnitude and direction as the original vector.

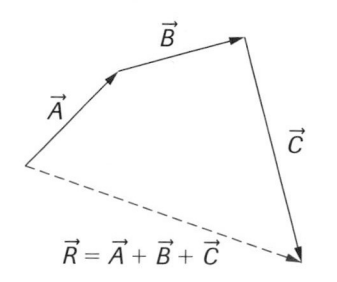

Figure 11
Adding three vectors

The result of adding vectors can be called the vector addition, resultant vector, resultant, net vector, or vector sum. This text uses these terms interchangeably; in diagrams, the resultant vector is a different colour or a different type of line (such as a broken line) to distinguish it from the original vectors.

Vector addition has the following properties:

- Vector addition is commutative; the order of addition does not matter: $\vec{A} + \vec{B} = \vec{B} + \vec{A}$.

- Vector addition is associative. If more than two vectors are added, it does not matter how they are grouped: $(\vec{A} + \vec{B}) + \vec{C} = \vec{A} + (\vec{B} + \vec{C})$.

Example
Use a vector scale diagram to add the following displacements and show that the addition is commutative:

$$\vec{A} = 24 \text{ km } [32°\text{N of E}]$$
$$\vec{B} = 18 \text{ km } [\text{E}]$$
$$\vec{C} = 38 \text{ km } [25°\text{E of S}]$$

Solution

Figure 12 shows the solution using the scale 1 cm = 10 km. The resultant displacement $\vec{R}$ is the same whether we use $\vec{R} = \vec{A} + \vec{B} + \vec{C}$ or $\vec{R} = \vec{A} + \vec{C} + \vec{B}$, thus showing that vector addition is commutative. How would you use this example to show that vector addition is associative?

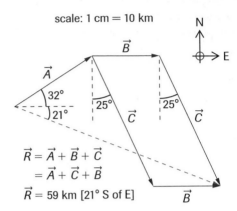

$$\vec{R} = \vec{A} + \vec{B} + \vec{C}$$
$$= \vec{A} + \vec{C} + \vec{B}$$
$$\vec{R} = 59 \text{ km } [21° \text{ S of E}]$$

Figure 12
Vector addition using a vector scale diagram

The accuracy of vector addition can be improved by applying trigonometry. If two perpendicular vectors are added, the law of Pythagoras can be used to determine the magnitude of the resultant vector. A trigonometric ratio (sine, cosine, or tangent) can be used to determine the direction of the resultant vector. If the vectors are at some angle different from 90° to each other, the cosine law and the sine law can be used to determine the magnitude and direction of the resultant vector.

Example

Two forces act on a single object. Determine the net force if the individual forces are

(a) $\vec{F_1} = 10.5$ N [S] and $\vec{F_2} = 14.0$ N [W]
(b) $\vec{F_3} = 10.5$ N [S] and $\vec{F_4} = 14.0$ N [25.5° W of S]

Solution

(a) Refer to **Figure 13(a)**. Applying the law of Pythagoras:

$$\Sigma \vec{F} = \vec{F_1} + \vec{F_2}$$
$$|\Sigma \vec{F}| = \sqrt{|\vec{F_1}|^2 + |\vec{F_2}|^2}$$
$$= \sqrt{(10.5 \text{ N})^2 + (14.0 \text{ N})^2}$$
$$|\Sigma \vec{F}| = 17.5 \text{ N}$$

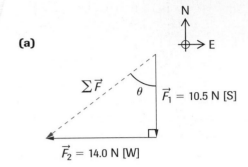

(a)

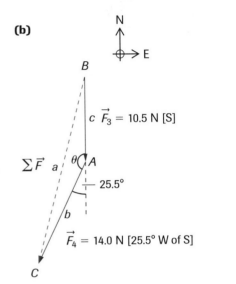

(b)

Figure 13
(a) Forces acting on the object
(b) Determining the net force

The angle θ is found using trigonometry:

$$\tan \theta = \frac{|\vec{F_2}|}{|\vec{F_1}|}$$
$$\theta = \tan^{-1} \frac{|\vec{F_2}|}{|\vec{F_1}|}$$
$$= \tan^{-1} \frac{14.0 \text{ N}}{10.5 \text{ N}}$$
$$\theta = 53.1°$$

The net force is 17.5 N [53.1° W of S].

(b) Refer to **Figure 13(b)**. Applying the cosine law:

$$a^2 = b^2 + c^2 - 2bc \cos A$$
$$a^2 = (14.0 \text{ N})^2 + (10.5 \text{ N})^2 - 2(14.0 \text{ N})(10.5 \text{ N})(\cos 154.5°)$$
$$a = 23.9 \text{ N}$$

Applying the sine law:

$$\frac{\sin B}{b} = \frac{\sin A}{a}$$

$$\sin B = \frac{b \sin A}{a}$$

$$\sin B = \frac{(14.0 \text{ N})(\sin 154.5°)}{23.9 \text{ N}}$$

$$B = 14.6°$$

The net force is 23.9 N [14.6° W of S].

Another accurate method of vector addition is to use the components of the vectors. This method is recommended when adding three or more vectors. To add any number of vectors by components, use the following steps:

1. Define an *x-y* coordinate system, and indicate the +*x* and +*y* directions.

2. Determine the *x*- and *y*-components of all the vectors to be added.

3. Determine the net *x*-component by adding all the individual *x*-components.

4. Determine the net *y*-component by adding all the individual *y*-components.

5. Determine the magnitude and direction of the net vector by applying the law of Pythagoras and/or trigonometric ratios.

Example

Determine the resultant displacement of a dog that runs with the following displacements:

$$\vec{A} = 10.5 \text{ m [E]}$$
$$\vec{B} = 14.0 \text{ m [21.5° E of S]}$$
$$\vec{C} = 25.6 \text{ m [18.9° S of W]}$$

Solution

The sketch of the motion in **Figure 14(a)** indicates that the resultant displacement is west and south of the initial position. For convenience, we choose +*x* as west and +*y* as south. The *x*-components of the vectors are

$$A_x = -10.5 \text{ m}$$
$$B_x = -14.0 \text{ m } (\sin 21.5°) = -5.13 \text{ m}$$
$$C_x = 25.6 \text{ m } (\cos 18.9°) = 24.2 \text{ m}$$

The *y*-components of the vectors are

$$A_y = 0 \text{ m}$$
$$B_y = 14.0 \text{ m } (\cos 21.5°) = 13.0 \text{ m}$$
$$C_y = 25.6 \text{ m } (\sin 18.9°) = 8.29 \text{ m}$$

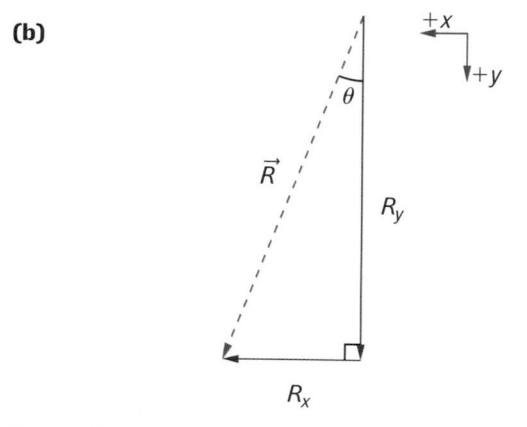

Figure 14
(a) Motion of the dog
(b) Determining the components of the displacements

The net *x*-component is

$$R_x = A_x + B_x + C_x$$
$$= -10.5 \text{ m} - 5.13 \text{ m} + 24.2 \text{ m}$$
$$R_x = 8.6 \text{ m}$$

The net *y*-component is

$$R_y = A_y + B_y + C_y$$
$$= 0 \text{ m} + 13.0 \text{ m} + 8.29 \text{ m}$$
$$R_y = 21.3 \text{ m}$$

As shown in **Figure 14(b)**, the magnitude of the resultant displacement is

$$R = \sqrt{R_x^2 + R_y^2}$$
$$= \sqrt{(8.6 \text{ m})^2 + (21.3 \text{ m})^2}$$
$$R = 23 \text{ m}$$

To find the direction of the resultant displacement:

$$\tan \theta = \frac{R_x}{R_y}$$

$$\theta = \tan^{-1} \frac{R_x}{R_y}$$

$$= \tan^{-1} \frac{8.6 \text{ m}}{21.3 \text{ m}}$$

$$\theta = 22°$$

The resultant displacement is 23 m [22° W of S].

Vector Subtraction

The vector subtraction $\vec{A} - \vec{B}$ is defined as the vector addition of $\vec{A}$ and $-\vec{B}$, where $-\vec{B}$ has the same magnitude as $\vec{B}$, but is opposite in direction. Thus,

$$\vec{A} - \vec{B} = \vec{A} + (-\vec{B}).$$

You should be able to show that $\vec{A} - \vec{B}$ does not equal $\vec{B} - \vec{A}$; in fact, the two vector subtractions are equal in magnitude, but opposite in direction.

Components can be used for vector subtraction. For example, if $\vec{C} = \vec{A} - \vec{B}$ then

$$C_x = A_x - B_x$$

and

$$C_y = A_y - B_y$$

Just as in vector addition, the subtraction of two vectors can be found using a vector scale diagram, trigonometry, or components.

Example

Given that $\vec{A} = 35$ m/s [27° N of E] and $\vec{B} = 47$ m/s [E], determine the change in velocity $\vec{C} = \vec{A} - \vec{B}$ using a vector scale diagram and components of the vectors.

Solution

The vector scale diagram in **Figure 15(a)** shows that $\vec{C} = \vec{A} + (-\vec{B})$ where the vector $-\vec{B}$ is added with the tail touching the head of $\vec{A}$. In this case, $\vec{C} = 23$ m/s [45° W of N]. The x-components of the vectors are

$$A_x = -35 \text{ m/s } (\cos 27°) = -31 \text{ m/s}$$
$$B_x = -47 \text{ m/s}$$

The y-components of the vectors are

$$A_y = 35 \text{ m/s } (\sin 27°) = 16 \text{ m/s}$$
$$B_y = 0 \text{ m/s}$$

(a)

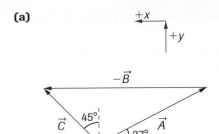

$$\vec{C} = \vec{A} - \vec{B}$$
$$\vec{C} = 23 \text{ m } [45° \text{ W of N}]$$

(b)

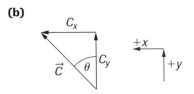

Figure 15
(a) Vector subtraction
(b) Determining the net change in velocity

The net x-component is

$$C_x = A_x - B_x$$
$$= -31 \text{ m/s} - (-47 \text{ m/s})$$
$$C_x = 16 \text{ m/s}$$

The net y-component is

$$C_y = A_y - B_y$$
$$= 16 \text{ m/s} - 0 \text{ m/s}$$
$$C_y = 16 \text{ m/s}$$

As shown in **Figure 15(b)**, the magnitude of the net change in velocity is

$$C = \sqrt{C_x^2 + C_y^2}$$
$$= \sqrt{(16 \text{ m/s})^2 + (16 \text{ m/s})^2}$$
$$C = 23 \text{ m/s}$$

Find the direction of the net change in velocity:

$$\tan \theta = \frac{C_x}{C_y}$$

$$\theta = \tan^{-1} \frac{C_x}{C_y}$$

$$= \tan^{-1} \frac{16 \text{ m}}{16 \text{ m}}$$

$$\theta = 45°$$

The net change in velocity is 23 m/s [45° W of N].

The Scalar or Dot Product of Two Vectors

The *scalar product* of two vectors is equal to the product of their magnitudes and the cosine of the angle between the vectors. The scalar product is also called the dot product because a dot can be used to represent the product symbol. An example of a scalar product is the equation for the work W done by a net force $\Sigma \vec{F}$ that causes an object to move by a displacement $\Delta \vec{d}$ (Section 4.1).

$$W = \Sigma \vec{F} \cdot \Delta \vec{d}$$
$$= \Sigma F \Delta d \cos \theta$$
or $$W = \left(\Sigma F \cos \theta\right) \Delta d$$

Thus, the defining equation of the scalar (or dot) product of vectors $\vec{A}$ and $\vec{B}$ is

$$\vec{A} \cdot \vec{B} = AB \cos \theta$$

where θ is the angle between $\vec{A}$ and $\vec{B}$, A is the magnitude of $\vec{A}$, and B is the magnitude of $\vec{B}$. Notice that $\vec{A}$ and $\vec{B}$ do not represent the same quantities.

A scalar product can be represented in a diagram as shown in **Figure 16** in which an applied force $\vec{F}_A$ is at an angle θ to the displacement of the object being pulled (with negligible friction).

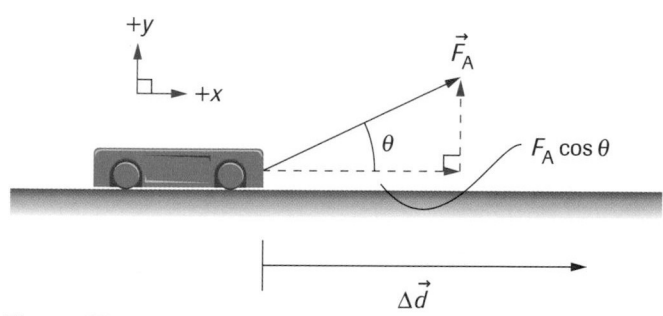

Figure 16
Assuming that there is negligible friction, the work done by $\vec{F}_A$ on the cart in moving it a displacement $\Delta \vec{d}$ is the scalar product, $F_A \cos \theta \Delta d$.

The Vector or Cross Product of Two Vectors

The *vector product* of two vectors has a magnitude equal to the product of the magnitudes of the two vectors and the sine of the angle between the vectors. The vector product is also called the cross product because a "×" is used to represent the product symbol. Thus, for vectors $\vec{A}$ and $\vec{B}$, the vector product $\vec{C}$ is defined by the following equation:

$$\vec{C} = \vec{A} \times \vec{B}$$

where the magnitude is given by $C = |\vec{C}| = |AB \sin \theta|$, and the direction is perpendicular to the plane formed by $\vec{A}$ and $\vec{B}$. However, there are two distinct directions that are perpendicular to the plane formed by $\vec{A}$ and $\vec{B}$; to determine the correct direction you can use the following rule, illustrated in **Figure 17**:

- Right-hand rule for the vector product: When the fingers of the right hand move from $\vec{A}$ *toward* $\vec{B}$, the outstretched thumb points in the direction of $\vec{C}$.

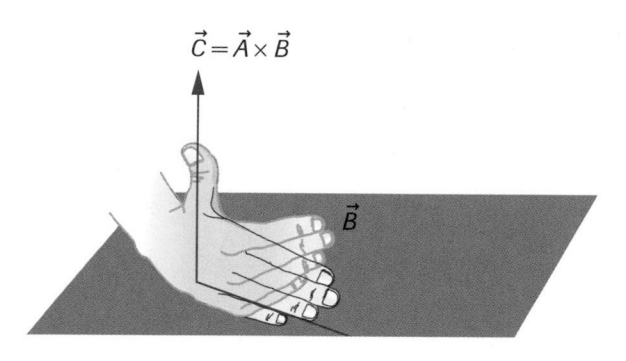

Figure 17
The right-hand rule to determine the direction of the vector resulting from the vector product $\vec{C} = \vec{A} \times \vec{B}$

The vector (or cross) product has the following properties:

- The order in which the vectors are multiplied matters because $\vec{A} \times \vec{B} = -\vec{B} \times \vec{A}$. (Use the right-hand rule to verify this.)
- If $\vec{A}$ and $\vec{B}$ are parallel, $\theta = 0°$ or $180°$ and $\vec{A} \times \vec{B} = 0$ because $\sin 0° = \sin 180° = 0$. Thus, $\vec{A} \times \vec{A} = 0$.
- If $\vec{A} \perp \vec{B}$ ($\theta = 90°$) then $|\vec{A} \times \vec{B}| = AB$ because $\sin 90° = 1$.
- The vector product obeys the distributive law; i.e., $\vec{A} \times (\vec{B} + \vec{C}) = \vec{A} \times \vec{B} + \vec{A} \times \vec{C}$.

LEARNING TIP

Alternative Notation
In advanced physics textbooks, vectors are often written using boldface rather than with an arrow above the quantity. Thus, you may find the dot product and the cross product written as follows:

$\mathbf{A} \cdot \mathbf{B} = AB \cos \theta$
$\mathbf{A} \times \mathbf{B} = AB \sin \theta$

Using Graphing Calculators or Computer Programs

You can use a graphing calculator or a computer-graphing program for several purposes, including finding the roots of an equation or analyzing linear functions, quadratic functions, trigonometric functions, and conic functions. You can also create a graph of given or measured data, and determine the equation relating the variables plotted or solve two simultaneous equations with two unknowns.

Graphing Calculators

Example

A ball is tossed vertically upward with an initial speed of 9.0 m/s. At what times after its release will the ball pass a position 3.0 m above the position where it is released? (Neglect air resistance.)

Solution

Note: The solution given here is for the TI-83 Plus calculator. If you have a different computing calculator, refer to its instruction manual for detailed information about solving equations.

Defining upward as the positive direction and using magnitudes only, the given quantities are $\Delta d = 3.0$ m, $v_i = 9.0$ m/s, and $a = -9.8$ m/s². The constant acceleration equation for displacement is

$$\Delta d = v_i \Delta t + \frac{1}{2} a \Delta t^2$$

$$3.0 = 9.0 \Delta t - 4.9 \Delta t^2$$

$$4.9 \Delta t^2 - 9.0 \Delta t + 3.0 = 0$$

To solve for Δt, we can use the quadratic formula and enter the data into the calculator. The equation is in the form $Ax^2 + Bx + C = 0$, where $A = 4.9$, $B = -9.0$, and $C = 3.0$.

1. Store the coefficients A and B, and the constant C in the calculator:
   - 4.9 [STO▸] [ALPHA] [A]
   - [ALPHA] [:]
   - −9 [STO▸] [ALPHA] [B]
   - [ALPHA] [:]
   - 3 [STO▸] [ALPHA] [C]
   - [ENTER]

2. Enter the expression for the quadratic formula:
   $$\frac{-b \pm \sqrt{b^2 - 4ac}}{2a} :$$
   - [(] [−] [ALPHA] [B] [+] [2nd] [√] [(] [ALPHA] [B] [x²] [−]
     4 [ALPHA] [A] [ALPHA] [C] [)] [)] [)] [÷] [(] [2] [ALPHA] [A] [)]

3. Press [ENTER] to find one solution to the time. To find the other solution, the negative must be used in front of the discimint. The answers are 1.4 s and 0.44 s.

Example

Graph the function $y = \cos x$ for $0° \leq x \leq 360°$.

Solution

1. Put the calculator in degree mode:
   - [MODE] → "Degree" → [ENTER].

2. Enter $y = \cos x$ into the equation editor:
   - Y = [COS] [X,T,Θ,n] [)].

3. Adjust the window so that it corresponds to the given domain:
   - [WINDOW] → $X_{min} = 0$, $X_{max} = 360$, $X_{sel} = 90$ (for an interval of 90° on the x-axis), $Y_{min} = -1$, and $Y_{max} = 1$.

4. Graph the function using the ZoomFit:
   - [ZOOM] [0].

Consider an ellipse, which is important in physics because it is the shape of the orbits of planets and satellites. The standard form of the equation of an ellipse where the centre is the origin and the major axis is along the x-axis is

$$\frac{x^2}{a^2} + \frac{y^2}{b^2} = 1, \text{ where } a > b.$$

The vertexes of the ellipse are at $(a, 0)$ and $(-a, 0)$, as shown in **Figure 18**.

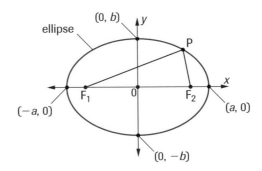

such that $PF_1 + PF_2 =$ constant

Figure 18
An ellipse

Example

Use the "Zap-a-Graph" feature to plot an ellipse centred on the origin of an x-y graph and determine the effect of changing the parameters of the ellipse.

Solution

1. Choose ellipse from the Zap-a-Graph menu:
   - [DEFINE] → Ellipse.

2. Enter the parameters of the ellipse (e.g., $a = 6$ and $b = 4$), then plot the graph.

3. Alter the ellipse by choosing Scale from the Grid menu and entering different values.

Graphing on a Spreadsheet

A *spreadsheet* is a computer program that can be used to create a table of data and a graph of the data. It is composed of cells indicated by a column letter (A, B, C, etc.) and a row number (1, 2, 3, etc.); thus, B1 and C3 are examples of cells (**Figure 19**). Each cell can hold a number, a label, or an equation.

	A	**B**	**C**	**D**	**E**
1	A1	B1	C1		
2	A2	B2			
3	A3				

Figure 19
Spreadsheet cells

To create a data table and plot the corresponding graph, you can follow the steps outlined in the next example.

Example

For an initial velocity of 5.0 m/s [E] and a constant acceleration of 4.0 m/s^2 [E], set up a spreadsheet for the relationship $\Delta \vec{d} = \vec{v}_i \Delta t + \frac{1}{2} \vec{a} \Delta t^2$. Plot a graph of the data from $t = 0$ s to $t = 8.0$ s at intervals of 1.0 s.

Solution

1. Access the spreadsheet and label cell A1 the independent variable, in this case t, and cell B1 the dependent variable, in this case Δd.

2. Enter the values of t from 0 to 8.0 in cells A2 to A10. In cell B2 enter the right side of the equation in the following form: $v_i * t + \frac{1}{2} * a * t * t$ where "$*$" represents multiplication.

3. Use the cursor to select B2 down to B10 and choose the Fill Down command or right drag cell B1 down to B10 to copy the equation to each cell.

4. Command the program to graph the values in the data table (e.g., choose Make Chart, depending on the program).

A spreadsheet can be used to solve a system of two simultaneous equations, which can occur, for example, when analyzing elastic collisions (discussed in Section 5.3). In a one-dimensional elastic collision, the two equations involved simultaneously are

$$m_1 \vec{v}_1 + m_2 \vec{v}_2 = m_1 \vec{v}_1' + m_2 \vec{v}_2'$$ from the law of conservation of momentum

and $$\frac{1}{2} m v_1^2 + \frac{1}{2} m v_2^2 = \frac{1}{2} m v_1'^2 + \frac{1}{2} m v_2'^2$$ from the law of conservation of energy

If the known quantities are m_1, m_2, v_1, and v_2, then the unknown quantities are v_1' and v_2'. To find the solution to these unknowns, rewrite the equations so that one unknown is isolated and written in terms of all the other variables. In this example, enter v_2' in cell A1, enter the first v_1' based on the equation for the law of conservation of momentum in cell B1, and enter the second v_1' (call it v_1'') based on the equation for the law of conservation of energy in cell C1. Then proceed to enter the data according to the previous example, using reasonable values for the variables. Plot the data on a graph and determine the intersection of the two resulting lines. That intersection is the solution to the two simultaneous equations.

A2 Planning an Investigation

In our attempts to further our understanding of the natural world, we encounter questions, mysteries, or events that are not readily explainable. To develop explanations, we investigate using scientific inquiry. The methods used in scientific inquiry depend, to a large degree, on the purpose of the inquiry.

Controlled Experiments

A controlled experiment is an example of scientific inquiry in which an independent variable is purposefully and steadily changed to determine its effect on a second dependent variable. All other variables are controlled or kept constant. Controlled experiments are performed when the purpose of the inquiry is to create, test, or use a scientific concept.

The common components of controlled experiments are outlined below. *Even though the presentation is linear, there are normally many cycles through the steps during an actual experiment.*

Stating the Purpose

Every investigation in science has a purpose; for example,

- to develop a scientific concept (a theory, law, generalization, or definition);
- to test a scientific concept;
- to determine a scientific constant; or
- to test an experimental design, a procedure, or a skill.

Determine which of these is the purpose of your investigation. Indicate your decision in a statement of the purpose.

Asking the Question

Your question forms the basis for your investigation: the investigation is designed to answer the question. Controlled experiments are about relationships, so the question could be about the effects on variable A when variable B is changed.

Predicting/Hypothesizing

A prediction is a tentative answer to the question you are investigating. In the prediction you state what outcome you expect from your experiment.

A hypothesis is a tentative explanation. To be scientific, a hypothesis must be testable. Hypotheses can range in certainty from an educated guess to a concept that is widely accepted in the scientific community.

Designing the Investigation

The design of a controlled experiment identifies how you plan to manipulate the independent variable, measure the response of the dependent variable, and control all the other variables in pursuit of an answer to your question. It is a summary of your plan for the experiment.

Gathering, Recording, and Organizing Observations

There are many ways to gather and record observations during your investigation. It is helpful to plan ahead and think about what data you will need to answer the question and how best to record them. This helps to clarify your thinking about the question posed at the beginning, the variables, the number of trials, the procedure, the materials, and your skills. It will also help you organize your evidence for easier analysis.

Analyzing the Observations

After thoroughly analyzing your observations, you may have sufficient and appropriate evidence to enable you to answer the question posed at the beginning of the investigation.

Evaluating the Evidence and the Prediction/Hypothesis

At this stage of the investigation, you evaluate the processes that you followed to plan and perform the investigation.

You will also evaluate the outcome of the investigation, which involves evaluating any prediction you made, and the hypothesis or more established concept ("authority") the prediction was based on. You must identify and take into account any sources of error and uncertainty in your measurements.

Finally, compare the answer you predicted with the answer generated by analyzing the evidence. Is your hypothesis, or the authority, acceptable or not?

Reporting on the Investigation

In preparing your report, your objectives should be to describe your planning process and procedure clearly and in sufficient detail that the reader could repeat the experiment exactly as you performed it, and to report your observations, your analysis, and your evaluation of your experiment accurately and honestly.

A3 Decision Making

Modern life is filled with environmental and social issues that have scientific and technological dimensions. An issue is defined as a problem that has at least two possible solutions rather than a single answer. There can be many positions, generally determined by the values that an individual or a society holds, on a single issue. Which solution is "best" is a matter of opinion; ideally, the solution that is implemented is the one that is most appropriate for society as a whole.

The common processes involved in the decision-making process are outlined below. *Even though the sequence is presented as linear, you may go through several cycles before deciding you are ready to defend a decision.*

Defining the Issue

The first step in understanding an issue is to explain why it is an issue, describe the problems associated with the issue, and identify the individuals or groups, called stakeholders, involved in the issue. You could brainstorm the following questions to research the issue: Who? What? Where? When? Why? How? Develop background information on the issue by clarifying facts and concepts, and identifying relevant attributes, features, or characteristics of the problem.

Identifying Alternatives/Positions

Examine the issue and think of as many alternative solutions as you can. At this point it does not matter if the solutions seem unrealistic. To analyze the alternatives, you should examine the issue from a variety of perspectives. Stakeholders may bring different viewpoints to an issue and these may influence their position on the issue. Brainstorm or hypothesize how different stakeholders would feel about your alternatives. Perspectives that stakeholders may adopt while approaching an issue are listed in **Table 1**.

Researching the Issue

Formulate a research question that helps to limit, narrow, or define the issue. Then develop a plan to identify and find reliable and relevant sources of information. Outline the stages of your information search: gathering, sorting, evaluating, selecting, and integrating relevant information. You may consider using a flow chart, concept map, or other graphic organizer to outline the stages of your information search. Gather information from many sources, including newspapers, magazines, scientific journals, the Internet, and the library.

Analyzing the Issue

In this stage, you will analyze the issue in an attempt to clarify where you stand. First, you should establish criteria for evaluating your information to determine its relevance and significance. You can then evaluate your sources, determine what assumptions may have been made, and assess whether you have enough information to make your decision.

There are five steps that must be completed to effectively analyze the issue:

1. Establish criteria for determining the relevance and significance of the data you have gathered.

2. Evaluate the sources of information.

Table 1 Some Possible Perspectives on an Issue

Cultural	focused on customs and practices of a particular group
Environmental	focused on effects on natural processes and other living things
Economic	focused on the production, distribution, and consumption of wealth
Educational	focused on the effects on learning
Emotional	focused on feelings and emotions
Aesthetic	focused on what is artistic, tasteful, beautiful
Moral/Ethical	focused on what is good/bad, right/wrong
Legal	focused on rights and responsibilities
Spiritual	focused on the effects on personal beliefs
Political	focused on the aims of an identifiable group or party
Scientific	focused on logic or the results of relevant inquiry
Social	focused on effects on human relationships, the community
Technological	focused on the use of machines and processes

3. Identify and determine what assumptions have been made. Challenge unsupported evidence.

4. Determine any causal, sequential, or structural relationships associated with the issue.

5. Evaluate the alternative solutions, possibly by conducting a risk-benefit analysis.

Defending the Decision

After analyzing your information, you can answer your research question and take an informed position on the issue. You should be able to defend your preferred solution in an appropriate format—debate, class discussion, speech, position paper, multimedia presentation (e.g., computer slide show), brochure, poster, video …

Your position on the issue must be justified using the supporting information that you have discovered in your research and tested in your analysis. You should be able to defend your position to people with different perspectives. In preparing for your defence, ask yourself the following questions:

- Do I have supporting evidence from a variety of sources?
- Can I state my position clearly?
- Do I have solid arguments (with solid evidence) supporting my position?
- Have I considered arguments against my position, and identified their faults?
- Have I analyzed the strong and weak points of each perspective?

Evaluating the Process

The final phase of decision making includes evaluating the decision the group reached, the process used to reach the decision, and the part you played in decision making. After a decision has been reached, carefully examine the thinking that led to the decision. Some questions to guide your evaluation follow:

- What was my initial perspective on the issue? How has my perspective changed since I first began to explore the issue?
- How did we make our decision? What process did we use? What steps did we follow?

- In what ways does our decision resolve the issue?
- What are the likely short- and long-term effects of our decision?
- To what extent am I satisfied with our decision?
- What reasons would I give to explain our decision?
- If we had to make this decision again, what would I do differently?

A Risk–Benefit Analysis Model

Risk–benefit analysis is a tool used to organize and analyze information gathered in research. A thorough analysis of the risks and benefits associated with each alternative solution can help you decide on the best alternative.

- Research as many aspects of the proposal as possible. Look at it from different perspectives.
- Collect as much evidence as you can, including reasonable projections of likely outcomes if the proposal is adopted.
- Classify every individual potential result as being either a benefit or a risk.
- Quantify the size of the potential benefit or risk (perhaps as a dollar figure, or a number of lives affected, or in severity on a scale of 1 to 5).
- Estimate the probability (percentage) of that event occurring.
- By multiplying the size of a benefit (or risk) by the probability of its happening, you can assign a significance value for each potential result.
- Total the significance values of all the potential risks, and all the potential benefits and compare the sums to help you decide whether to accept the proposed action.

Note that although you should try to be objective in your assessment, your beliefs will have an effect on the outcome—two people, even if using the same information and the same tools, could come to a different conclusion about the balance of risk and benefit for any proposed solution to an issue.

A4 Technological Problem Solving

There is a difference between scientific and technological processes. The goal of science is to understand the natural world. The goal of technological problem solving is to develop or revise a product or a process in response to a human need. The product or process must fulfill its function but, in contrast with scientific problem solving, it is not essential to understand why or how it works. Technological solutions are evaluated based on such criteria as simplicity, reliability, efficiency, cost, and ecological and political ramifications.

Although the sequence below is linear, there are normally many cycles through the steps in any problem-solving attempt.

Defining the Problem

This process involves recognizing and identifying the need for a technological solution. You need to clearly state both the question(s) that you want to investigate and the criteria you will use as guidelines to solve the problem and to evaluate your solution. In any design, some criteria may be more important than others. For example, if the product solution measures accurately and is economical, but is not safe, then it is clearly unacceptable.

Identifying Possible Solutions

Use your knowledge and experience to propose possible solutions. Creativity is also important in suggesting novel solutions.

You should generate as many ideas as possible about the functioning of your solution and about potential designs. During brainstorming, the goal is to generate many ideas without judging them. They can be evaluated and accepted or rejected later.

To visualize the possible solutions it is helpful to draw sketches. Sketches are often better than verbal descriptions to communicate an idea.

Planning

Planning is the heart of the entire process. Your plan will outline your processes, identify potential sources of information and materials, define your resource parameters, and establish evaluation criteria.

Seven types of resources are generally used in developing technological solutions to problems—people, information, materials, tools, energy, capital, and time.

Constructing/Testing Solutions

In this phase, you will construct and test your prototype using systematic trial and error. Try to manipulate only one variable at a time. Use failures to inform the decisions you make before your next trial. You may also complete a cost-benefit analysis on the prototype.

To help you decide on the best solution, you can rate each potential solution on each of the design criteria using a five-point rating scale, with 1 being poor, 2 fair, 3 good, 4 very good, and 5 excellent. You can then compare your proposed solutions by totalling the scores.

Once you have made the choice among the possible solutions, you need to produce and test a prototype. While making the prototype you may need to experiment with the characteristics of different components. A model, on a smaller scale, might help you decide whether the product will be functional. The test of your prototype should answer three basic questions:

- Does the prototype solve the problem?
- Does it satisfy the design criteria?
- Are there any unanticipated problems with the design?

If these questions cannot be answered satisfactorily, you may have to modify the design or select another solution.

Presenting the Preferred Solution

In presenting your solution, you will communicate your solution, identify potential applications, and put your solution to use.

Once the prototype has been produced and tested, the best presentation of the solution is a demonstration of its use—a test under actual conditions. This demonstration can also serve as a further test of the design. Any feedback should be considered for future redesign. Remember that no solution should be considered the absolute final solution.

Evaluating the Solution and Process

The technological problem-solving process is cyclical. At this stage, evaluating your solution and the process you used to arrive at your solution may lead to a revision of the solution.

Evaluation is not restricted to the final step, however, it is important to evaluate the final product using the criteria established earlier, and to evaluate the processes used while arriving at the solution. Consider the following questions:

- To what degree does the final product meet the design criteria?
- Did you have to make any compromises in the design? If so, are there ways to minimize the effects of the compromises?
- Are there other possible solutions that deserve future consideration?
- Did you exceed any of the resource parameters?
- How did your group work as a team?

A5 Lab Reports

When carrying out investigations, it is important that scientists keep records of their plans and results, and share their findings. In order to have their investigations repeated (replicated) and accepted by the scientific community, scientists generally share their work by publishing papers in which details of their design, materials, procedure, evidence, analysis, and evaluation are given.

Lab reports are prepared after an investigation is completed. To ensure that you can accurately describe the investigation, it is important to keep thorough and accurate records of your activities as you carry out the investigation.

Investigators use a similar format in their final reports or lab books, although the headings and order may vary. Your lab book or report should reflect the type of scientific inquiry that you used in the investigation and should be based on the following headings, as appropriate.

Title

At the beginning of your report, write the number and title of your investigation. In this course the title is usually given, but if you are designing your own investigation, create a title that suggests what the investigation is about. Include the date the investigation was conducted and the names of all lab partners (if you worked as a team).

Purpose

State the purpose of the investigation. Why are you doing this investigation?

Question

This is the question that you attempted to answer in the investigation. If it is appropriate to do so, state the question in terms of independent and dependent variables.

Prediction/Hypothesis

A prediction is a tentative answer to the question you are investigating. In the prediction you state what outcome you expect from your experiment.

A hypothesis is a tentative explanation. To be scientific, a hypothesis must be testable. Hypotheses can range in certainty from an educated guess to a concept that is widely accepted in the scientific community. Depending on the nature of your investigation, you may or may not have a hypothesis or a prediction.

Experimental Design

If you designed your own investigation, this is a brief general overview (one to three sentences) of what was done. If your investigation involved independent, dependent, and controlled variables, list them. Identify any control or control group that was used in the investigation.

Materials

This is a detailed list of all materials used, including sizes and quantities where appropriate. Be sure to include safety equipment and any special precautions when using the equipment or performing the investigation. Draw a diagram to show any complicated setup of apparatus.

Procedure

Describe, in detailed, numbered steps, the procedure you followed in carrying out your investigation. Include steps to clean up and dispose of waste materials.

Observations

This includes all qualitative and quantitative observations that you made. Be as precise as appropriate when describing quantitative observations, include any unexpected observations, and present your information in a form that is easily understood. If you have only a few observations, this could be a list; for controlled experiments and for many observations, a table will be more appropriate.

Analysis

Interpret your observations and present the evidence in the form of tables, graphs, or illustrations, each with a title. Include any calculations, the results of which can be shown in a table. Make statements about any patterns or trends you observed. Conclude the analysis with a statement based only on the evidence you have gathered, answering the question that initiated the investigation.

Evaluation

The evaluation is your judgment about the quality of evidence obtained and about the validity of the prediction and hypothesis (if present). This section can be divided into two parts:

- Did your observations provide reliable and valid evidence to enable you to answer the question? Are you confident enough in the evidence to use it to evaluate any prediction and/or hypothesis you made?

- Was the prediction you made before the investigation supported or falsified by the evidence? Based on your evaluation of the evidence and prediction, is your hypothesis or the authority you used to make your prediction supported, or should it be rejected?

The leading questions that follow should help you through the process of evaluation.

Evaluation of the Experiment

1. Were you able to answer the question using the chosen experimental design? Are there any obvious flaws in the design? What alternative designs (better or worse) are available? As far as you know, is this design the best available in terms of controls, efficiency, and cost? How great is your confidence in the chosen design?

   You may sum up your conclusions about the design in a statement like: "The experimental design [name or describe in a few words] is judged to be adequate/inadequate because ... "

2. Were the steps that you used in the laboratory correctly sequenced, and adequate to gather sufficient evidence? What improvements could be made to the procedure? What steps, if not done correctly, would have significantly affected the results?

   Sum up your conclusions about the procedure in a statement like: "The procedure is judged to be adequate/inadequate because ... "

3. Which specialized skills, if any, might have the greatest effect on the experimental results? Was the evidence from repeated trials reasonably similar? Can the measurements be made more precise?

   Sum up your conclusions: "The technological skills are judged to be adequate/inadequate because ... "

4. You should now be ready to sum up your evaluation of the experiment. Do you have enough confidence in your experimental results to proceed with your evaluation of the authority being tested? Based on uncertainties and errors you have identified in the course of your evaluation, what would be an acceptable percent difference for this experiment (1%, 5%, or 10%)?

State your confidence level in a summary statement: "Based upon my evaluation of the experiment, I am not certain/I am moderately certain/I am very certain of my experimental results. The major sources of uncertainty or error are ... "

Evaluation of the Prediction and Authority

1. Calculate the percent difference for your experiment.

$$\% \text{ difference} = \frac{\left| \text{difference in values} \right|}{\text{average of values}} \times 100\%$$

   How does the percent difference compare with your estimated total uncertainty (i.e., is the percent difference greater or smaller than the difference you've judged acceptable for this experiment)? Does the predicted answer clearly agree with the experimental answer in your analysis? Can the percent difference be accounted for by the sources of uncertainty listed earlier in the evaluation?

   Sum up your evaluation of the prediction: "The prediction is judged to be verified/inconclusive/falsified because ... "

2. If the prediction was verified, the hypothesis or the authority behind it is supported by the experiment. If the results of the experiment were inconclusive or the prediction was falsified, then doubt is cast upon the hypothesis or authority. How confident do you feel about any judgment you can make based on the experiment? Is there a need for a new or revised hypothesis, or to restrict, reverse, or replace the authority being tested?

   Sum up your evaluation of the authority: "[The hypothesis or authority] being tested is judged to be acceptable/unacceptable because ... "

Synthesis

You can synthesize your knowledge and understanding in the following ways:

- Relate what you discovered in the experiment to theories and concepts studied previously.

- Apply your observations and conclusions to practical situations.

B1 Safety Conventions and Symbols

Although every effort is undertaken to make the science experience a safe one, there are inherent risks associated with some scientific investigations. These risks are generally associated with the materials and equipment used, and the disregard of safety instructions that accompany investigations and activities. However, there may also be risks associated with the location of the investigation, whether in the science laboratory, at home, or outdoors. Most of these risks pose no more danger than one would normally experience in everyday life. With an awareness of the possible hazards, knowledge of the rules, appropriate behaviour, and a little common sense, these risks can be practically eliminated.

Remember, you share the responsibility not only for your own safety, but also for the safety of those around you. Always alert the teacher in case of an accident.

In this text, chemicals, equipment, and procedures that are hazardous are highlighted in red and are preceded by the appropriate Workplace Hazardous Materials Information System (WHMIS) symbol or by ✋.

WHMIS Symbols and HHPS

The Workplace Hazardous Materials Information System (WHMIS) provides workers and students with complete and accurate information regarding hazardous products. All chemical products supplied to schools, businesses, and industries must contain standardized labels and be accompanied by Material Safety Data Sheets (MSDS) providing detailed information about the product. Clear and standardized labelling is an important component of WHMIS (**Table 1**). These labels must be present on the product's original container or be added to other containers if the product is transferred.

The *Canadian Hazardous Products Act* requires manufacturers of consumer products containing chemicals to include a symbol specifying both the nature of the primary hazard and the degree of this hazard. In addition, any secondary hazards, first aid treatment, storage, and disposal must be noted. Household Hazardous Product Symbols (HHPS) are used to show the hazard and the degree of the hazard by the type of border surrounding the illustration (**Figure 1**).

![Corrosive symbol]	**Corrosive**
	This material can burn your skin and eyes. If you swallow it, it will damage your throat and stomach.
![Flammable symbol]	**Flammable**
	This product or the gas (or vapour) from it can catch fire quickly. Keep this product away from heat, flames, and sparks.
![Explosive symbol]	**Explosive**
	Container will explode if it is heated or if a hole is punched in it. Metal or plastic can fly out and hurt your eyes and other parts of your body.
![Poisonous symbol]	**Poisonous**
	If you swallow or lick this product, you could become very sick or die. Some products with this symbol on the label can hurt you even if you breathe (or inhale) them.

Danger

Warning

Caution

Figure 1
Household Hazardous Product Symbols (HHPS)

Table 1 The Workplace Hazardous Materials Information System (WHMIS)

Class and Type of Compounds	WHMIS Symbol	Risks	Precautions
Class A *Compressed Gas* Material that is normally gaseous and kept in a pressurized container		• could explode due to pressure • could explode if heated or dropped • possible hazard from both the force of explosion and the release of contents	• ensure container is always secured • store in designated areas • do not drop or allow to fall
Class B *Flammable and Combustible Materials* Materials that will continue to burn after being exposed to a flame or other ignition source		• may ignite spontaneously • may release flammable products if allowed to degrade or when exposed to water	• store in properly designated areas • work in well-ventilated areas • avoid heating • avoid sparks and flames • ensure that electrical sources are safe
Class C *Oxidizing Materials* Materials that can cause other materials to burn or support combustion		• can cause skin or eye burns • increase fire and explosion hazards • may cause combustibles to explode or react violently	• store away from combustibles • wear body, hand, face, and eye protection • store in proper container that will not rust or oxidize
Class D *Toxic Materials Immediate and Severe* Poisons and potentially fatal materials that cause immediate and severe harm		• may be fatal if ingested or inhaled • may be absorbed through the skin • small volumes have a toxic effect	• avoid breathing dust or vapours • avoid contact with skin or eyes • wear protective clothing, and face and eye protection • work in well-ventilated areas and wear breathing protection
Class D *Toxic Materials Long Term Concealed* Materials that have a harmful effect after repeated exposures or over a long period		• may cause death or permanent injury • may cause birth defects or sterility • may cause cancer • may be sensitizers causing allergies	• wear appropriate personal protection • work in a well-ventilated area • store in appropriate designated areas • avoid direct contact • use hand, body, face, and eye protection • ensure respiratory and body protection is appropriate for the specific hazard
Class D *Biohazardous Infectious Materials* Infectious agents or a biological toxin causing a serious disease or death		• may cause anaphylactic shock • includes viruses, yeasts, moulds, bacteria, and parasites that affect humans • includes fluids containing toxic products • includes cellular components	• special training is required to handle materials • work in designated biological areas with appropriate engineering controls • avoid forming aerosols • avoid breathing vapours • avoid contamination of people and/or area • store in special designated areas
Class E *Corrosive Materials* Materials that react with metals and living tissue		• eye and skin irritation on exposure • severe burns/tissue damage on longer exposure • lung damage if inhaled • may cause blindness if contacts eyes • environmental damage from fumes	• wear body, hand, face, and eye protection • use breathing apparatus • ensure protective equipment is appropriate • work in a well-ventilated area • avoid all direct body contact • use appropriate storage containers and ensure proper non-venting closures
Class F *Dangerously Reactive Materials* Materials that may have unexpected reactions		• may react with water • may be chemically unstable • may explode if exposed to shock or heat • may release toxic or flammable vapours • may vigorously polymerize • may burn unexpectedly	• handle with care avoiding vibration, shocks, and sudden temperature changes • store in appropriate containers • ensure storage containers are sealed • store and work in designated areas

B2 Safety in the Laboratory

General Safety Rules

Safety in the laboratory is an attitude and a habit more than it is a set of rules. It is easier to prevent accidents than to deal with the consequences of an accident. Most of the following rules are common sense.

- Do not enter a laboratory or prep room unless a teacher or other supervisor is present, or you have permission to do so.
- Familiarize yourself with your school's safety regulations.
- Make your teacher aware of any allergies or other health problems you may have.
- Listen carefully to any instructions given by your teacher, and follow them closely.
- Wear eye protection, lab aprons or coats, and protective gloves when appropriate.
- Wear closed shoes (not sandals) when working in the laboratory.
- Place your books and bags away from the work area. Keep your work area clear of all materials except those that you will use in the investigation.
- Do not chew gum, eat, or drink in the laboratory. Food should not be stored in refrigerators in laboratories.
- Know the location of MSDS information, exits, and all safety equipment, such as the fire blanket, fire extinguisher, and eyewash station.
- Use stands, clamps, and holders to secure any potentially dangerous or fragile equipment that could be tipped over.
- Avoid sudden or rapid motion in the laboratory that may interfere with someone carrying or working with chemicals or using sharp instruments.
- Never engage in horseplay or practical jokes in the laboratory.
- Ask for assistance when you are not sure how to do a procedural step.
- Never attempt unauthorized experiments.
- Never work in a crowded area or alone in the laboratory.
- Report all accidents.
- Clean up all spills, even spills of water, immediately.
- Always wash your hands with soap and water before or immediately after you leave the laboratory. Wash your hands before you touch any food.
- Do not forget safety procedures when you leave the laboratory. Accidents can also occur outdoors, at home, or at work.

Eye and Face Safety

- Wear approved eye protection in a laboratory, no matter how simple or safe the task appears to be. Keep the eye protection over your eyes, not on top of your head. For certain experiments, full face protection (safety goggles or a face shield) may be necessary.
- Never look directly into the opening of flasks or test tubes.
- If, in spite of all precautions, you get a chemical in your eye, quickly use the eyewash or nearest cold running water. Continue to rinse the eye with water for at least 15 min. This is a very long time—have someone time you. Have another student inform your teacher of the accident. The injured eye should be examined by a doctor.
- If you must wear contact lenses in the laboratory, be extra careful; whether or not you wear contact lenses, do not touch your eyes without first washing your hands. If you do wear contact lenses, make sure that your teacher is aware of it. Carry your lens case and a pair of glasses with you.
- If a piece of glass or other foreign object enters your eye, seek immediate medical attention.
- Do not stare directly at any bright source of light (e.g., a piece of burning magnesium ribbon, lasers, or the Sun). You will not feel any pain if your retina is being damaged by intense radiation. You cannot rely on the sensation of pain to protect you.
- When working with lasers, be aware that a reflected laser beam can act like a direct beam on the eye.

Handling Glassware Safely

- Never use glassware that is cracked or chipped. Give such glassware to your teacher or dispose of it as directed. Do not put the item back into circulation.
- Never pick up broken glassware with your fingers. Use a broom and dustpan.
- Do not put broken glassware into garbage containers. Dispose of glass fragments in special containers marked "Broken Glass."

- Heat glassware only if it is approved for heating. Check with your teacher before heating any glassware.

- If you cut yourself, inform your teacher immediately. Embedded glass or continued bleeding requires medical attention.

- If you need to insert glass tubing or a thermometer into a rubber stopper, get a cork borer of a suitable size. Insert the borer in the hole of the rubber stopper, starting from the small end of the stopper. Once the borer is pushed all the way through the hole, insert the tubing or thermometer through the borer. Ease the borer out of the hole, leaving the tubing or thermometer inside. To remove the tubing or thermometer from the stopper, push the borer from the small end through the stopper until it shows from the other end. Ease the tubing or thermometer out of the borer.

- Protect your hands with heavy gloves or several layers of cloth before inserting glass into rubber stoppers.

- Be very careful while cleaning glassware. There is an increased risk of breakage from dropping when the glassware is wet and slippery.

Using Sharp Instruments Safely

- Make sure your instruments are sharp. Surprisingly, one of the main causes of accidents with cutting instruments is the use of a dull instrument. Dull cutting instruments require more pressure than sharp instruments and are therefore much more likely to slip.

- Select the appropriate instrument for the task. Never use a knife when scissors would work better.

- Always cut away from yourself and others.

- If you cut yourself, inform your teacher immediately and get appropriate first aid.

- Be careful when working with wire cutters or wood saws. Use a cutting board where needed.

Electrical Safety

- Water or wet hands should never be used near electrical equipment.

- Do not operate electrical equipment near running water or any large containers of water.

- Check the condition of electrical equipment. Do not use if wires or plugs are damaged, or if the ground pin has been removed.

- Make sure that electrical cords are not placed where someone could trip over them.

- When unplugging equipment, remove the plug gently from the socket. Do not pull on the cord.

- When using variable power supplies, start at low voltage and increase slowly.

Waste Disposal

Waste disposal at school, at home, or at work is a social and environmental issue. To protect the environment, federal and provincial governments have regulations to control wastes, especially chemical wastes. For example, the WHMIS program applies to controlled products that are being handled. (When being transported, they are regulated under the *Transport of Dangerous Goods Act*, and for disposal they are subject to federal, provincial, and municipal regulations.) Most laboratory waste can be washed down the drain, or, if it is in solid form, placed in ordinary garbage containers. However, some waste must be treated more carefully. It is your responsibility to follow procedures and dispose of waste in the safest possible manner according to the teacher's instructions.

First Aid

The following guidelines apply if an injury, such as a burn, cut, chemical spill, ingestion, inhalation, or splash in eyes, happens to yourself or to one of your classmates.

- If an injury occurs, inform your teacher immediately.

- Know the location of the first-aid kit, fire blanket, eye-wash station, and shower, and be familiar with the contents/operation.

- If you have ingested or inhaled a hazardous substance, inform your teacher immediately. A Material Safety Data Sheet (MSDS) will give information about the first-aid requirements for the substance in question. Contact the Poison Control Centre in your area.

- If the injury is from a burn, immediately immerse the affected area in cold water. This will reduce the temperature and prevent further tissue damage.

- In the event of electrical shock, do not touch the affected person or the equipment the person was using. Break contact by switching off the source of electricity or by removing the plug.

- If a classmate's injury has rendered him/her unconscious, notify the teacher immediately. The teacher will perform CPR if necessary. Do not administer CPR unless under specific instructions from the teacher. You can assist by keeping the person warm and reassured.

Table 1 Système International (SI) Base Units of Measurement

Quantity	Quantity Symbol	SI Base Unit	Unit Symbol
length	$L, l, h, d, w, r, \lambda, \Delta\vec{d}$	metre	m
mass	m	kilogram	kg
time	t	second	s
electric current	I	ampere	A
thermodynamic temperature	T	kelvin	K
amount of substance	n	mole	mol
luminous intensity	I_v	candela	cd

Table 2 Metric Prefixes and Their Origins

Prefix	Abbreviation	Meaning	Origin
exa	E	10^{18}	Greek *exa* – out of
peta	P	10^{15}	Greek *peta* – spread out
tera	T	10^{12}	Greek *teratos* – monster
giga	G	10^9	Greek *gigas* – giant
mega	M	10^6	Greek *mega* – great
kilo	k	10^3	Greek *khilioi* – thousand
hecto	h	10^2	Greek *hekaton* – hundred
deca	da	10^1	Greek *deka* – ten
standard unit		10^0	
deci	d	10^{-1}	Latin *decimus* – tenth
centi	c	10^{-2}	Latin *centum* – hundred
milli	m	10^{-3}	Latin *mille* – thousand
micro	μ	10^{-6}	Greek *mikros* – very small
nano	n	10^{-9}	Greek *nanos* – dwarf
pico	p	10^{-12}	Italian *piccolo* – small
femto	f	10^{-15}	Greek *femten* – fifteen
atto	a	10^{-18}	Danish *atten* – eighteen

Table 3 The Greek Alphabet

Upper Case	Lower Case	Name	Upper Case	Lower Case	Name
A	α	alpha	N	ν	nu
B	β	beta	Ξ	ξ	xi
Γ	γ	gamma	O	o	omicron
Δ	δ	delta	Π	π	pi
E	ϵ	epsilon	P	ρ	rho
Z	ζ	zeta	Σ	σ	sigma
H	η	eta	T	τ	tau
Θ	θ	theta	Υ	υ	upsilon
I	ι	iota	Φ	ϕ	phi
K	κ	kappa	X	χ	chi
Λ	λ	lambda	Ψ	ψ	psi
M	μ	mu	Ω	ω	omega

Table 4 Some SI Derived Units

Quantity	Symbol	Unit	Unit Symbol	SI Base Unit
acceleration	$\vec{a}$	metre per second per second	m/s^2	m/s^2
area	A	square metre	m^2	m^2
Celsius temperature	t	degrees Celsius	°C	°C
density	ρ, D	kilogram per cubic metre	kg/m^3	kg/m^3
electric charge	Q, q	coulomb	C	A·s
electric field	$\vec{E}$	volt per metre	V/m	$kg \cdot m/A \cdot s^3$
electric field intensity	$\vec{\varepsilon}$	newton per coulomb	N/C	$kg \cdot m/A \cdot s^3$
electric potential	V	volt	V	$kg \cdot m^2/A \cdot s^3$
electric resistance	R	ohm	Ω	$kg \cdot m^2/A^2 \cdot s^3$
energy	E	joule	J	$kg \cdot m^2/s^2$
force	$\vec{F}$	newton	N	$kg \cdot m/s^2$
frequency	f	hertz	Hz	s^{-1}
heat	Q	joule	J	$kg \cdot m^2/s^2$
magnetic field	$\vec{B}$	weber per square metre (Tesla)	T	$kg/A \cdot s^2$
gravitational field	$\vec{g}$	newton per kilogram	N/kg	m/s^2
momentum	$\vec{p}$	kilogram metre per second	kg·m/s	kg·m/s
period	T	second	s	s
power	P	watt	W	$kg \cdot m^2/s^3$
pressure	P	newton per square metre	N/m^2	$kg/m \cdot s^2$
radiation activity	A	becquerel	Bq	s^{-1}
speed	v	metre per second	m/s	m/s
velocity	$\vec{v}$	metre per second	m/s	m/s
volume	V	cubic metre	m^3	m^3
weight	$\vec{F}_w$	newton	N	$kg \cdot m/s^2$
work	W	joule	J	$kg \cdot m^2/s^2$

Table 5 Physical Constants

Quantity	Symbol	Approximate Value
speed of light in a vacuum	c	3.00×10^8 m/s
universal gravitation constant	G	6.67×10^{-11} N·m²/kg²
Coulomb's constant	k	9.00×10^9 N·m²/C²
charge on electron	$-e$	-1.60×10^{-19} C
charge on proton	e	1.60×10^{-19} C
electron rest mass	m_e	9.11×10^{-31} kg
proton rest mass	m_p	1.673×10^{-27} kg
neutron rest mass	m_n	1.675×10^{-27} kg
atomic mass unit	u	1.660×10^{-27} kg
electron volt	eV	1.60×10^{-19} J
Planck's constant	h	6.63×10^{-34} J·s

Table 6 The Solar System

Object	Mass (kg)	Radius of Object (m)	Period of Rotation on Axis (s)	Mean Radius of Orbit (m)	Period of Revolution of Orbit (s)	Orbital Eccentricity
Sun	1.99×10^{30}	6.96×10^8	2.14×10^6	—	—	—
Mercury	3.28×10^{23}	2.44×10^6	5.05×10^6	5.79×10^{10}	7.60×10^6	0.206
Venus	4.83×10^{24}	6.05×10^6	2.1×10^7	1.08×10^{11}	1.94×10^7	0.007
Earth	5.98×10^{24}	6.38×10^6	8.64×10^4	1.49×10^{11}	3.16×10^7	0.017
Mars	6.37×10^{23}	3.40×10^6	8.86×10^4	2.28×10^{11}	5.94×10^7	0.093
Jupiter	1.90×10^{27}	7.15×10^7	3.58×10^4	7.78×10^{11}	3.75×10^8	0.048
Saturn	5.67×10^{26}	6.03×10^7	3.84×10^4	1.43×10^{12}	9.30×10^8	0.056
Uranus	8.80×10^{25}	2.56×10^7	6.20×10^4	2.87×10^{12}	2.65×10^9	0.046
Neptune	1.03×10^{26}	2.48×10^7	5.80×10^6	4.50×10^{12}	5.20×10^9	0.010
Pluto	1.3×10^{23}	1.15×10^6	5.51×10^5	5.91×10^{12}	7.82×10^9	0.248
Moon	7.35×10^{22}	1.74×10^6	2.36×10^6	3.84×10^8	2.36×10^6	0.055

Table 7 Atomic Masses of Selected Particles

Name	Symbol	Atomic Mass (u)
neutron	n	1.008 665
proton	p	1.007 276
deuteron	d	2.013 553
alpha particle	α	4.002 602

Table 8 Data for Some Radioisotopes

Atomic Number (Z)	Name	Symbol	Atomic Mass (u)	Decay Type	Half-Life
1	tritium hydrogen-3	^3_1H	3.016 049	β^-	12.33 a
4	beryllium-7	^7_4Be	7.016 928	γ	53.29 d
6	carbon-11	$^{11}_6\text{C}$	11.011 433	β^+	20.385 min
6	carbon-14	$^{14}_6\text{C}$	14.003 242	β^-	5730 a
8	oxygen-15	$^{15}_8\text{O}$	15.003 065	β^+	122.24 s
11	sodium-22	$^{22}_{11}\text{Na}$	21.994 434	β^+, γ	2.6088 a
14	silicon-31	$^{31}_{14}\text{Si}$	30.975 362	β^-, γ	157.3 min
15	phosphorus-32	$^{32}_{15}\text{P}$	31.973 908	β^-	14.262 d
16	sulfur-35	$^{35}_{16}\text{S}$	34.969 033	β^-	87.51 d
19	potassium-40	$^{40}_{19}\text{K}$	39.96 400	β^-, β^+	1.28×10^9 a
27	cobalt-60	$^{60}_{27}\text{Co}$	59.933 820	β^-, γ	5.2714 a
38	strontium-90	$^{90}_{38}\text{Sr}$	89.907 737	β^-	29.1 a
43	technetium-98	$^{98}_{43}\text{Tc}$	97.907 215	β^-, γ	4.2×10^6 a
49	indium-115	$^{115}_{49}\text{In}$	114.903 876	β^-, γ	4.41×10^{14} a
53	iodine-131	$^{131}_{53}\text{I}$	130.906 111	β^-, γ	8.04 d
61	promethium-145	$^{145}_{61}\text{Pm}$	144.912 745	γ, α	17.7 a

Table 8 continued

Atomic Number (Z)	Name	Symbol	Atomic Mass (u)	Decay Type	Half-Life
75	rhenium-187	$^{187}_{75}$Re	186.955 746	β^-	4.35×10^{10} a
76	osmium-191	$^{191}_{76}$Os	190.960 922	β^-, γ	15.4 d
82	lead-210	$^{210}_{82}$Pb	209.984 163	β^-, γ, α	22.3 a
82	lead-211	$^{211}_{82}$Pb	210.988 734	β^-, γ	36.1 min
82	lead-212	$^{212}_{82}$Pb	211.991 872	β^-, γ	10.64 h
82	lead-214	$^{214}_{82}$Pb	213.999 798	β^-, γ	26.8 min
83	bismuth-211	$^{211}_{83}$Bi	210.987 254	α, β, β^-	2.14 min
84	polonium-210	$^{210}_{84}$Po	209.982 848	α, γ	138.376 d
84	polonium-214	$^{214}_{84}$Po	213.995 177	α, γ	0.1643 s
85	astatine-218	$^{218}_{85}$At	218.008 68	α, β^-	1.6 s
86	radon-222	$^{222}_{86}$Rn	222.017 571	α, γ	3.8235 s
87	francium-223	$^{223}_{87}$Fr	223.019 733	β^-, γ, α	21.8 min
88	radium-226	$^{226}_{88}$Ra	226.025 402	α, γ	1600 a
89	actinium-227	$^{227}_{89}$Ac	227.027 749	α, β^-, γ	21.773 a
90	thorium-228	$^{228}_{90}$Th	228.028 716	α, γ	1.9131 a
90	thorium-232	$^{232}_{90}$Th	232.038 051	α, γ	1.405×10^{10} a
91	protactinium-231	$^{231}_{91}$Pa	231.035 880	α, γ	3.276×10^4 a
92	uranium-232	$^{232}_{92}$U	232.037 131	α, γ	68.9 a
92	uranium-233	$^{233}_{92}$U	233.039 630	α, γ	1.592×10^5 a
92	uranium-235	$^{235}_{92}$U	235.043 924	α, γ	7.038×10^8 a
92	uranium-236	$^{236}_{92}$U	236.045 562	α, γ	2.3415×10^7 a
92	uranium-238	$^{238}_{92}$U	238.050 784	α, γ	4.468×10^9 a
92	uranium-239	$^{239}_{92}$U	239.054 289	β^-, γ	23.50 min
93	neptunium-239	$^{239}_{93}$Np	239.052 932	β^-, γ	2.355 d
94	plutonium-239	$^{239}_{94}$Pu	239.052 157	α, γ	24 119 a
95	americium-243	$^{243}_{95}$Am	243.061 373	α, γ	7380 a
96	curium-245	$^{245}_{96}$Cm	245.065 484	α, γ	8500 a
97	berkelium-247	$^{247}_{97}$Bk	247.070 30	α, γ	1380 a
98	californium-249	$^{249}_{98}$Cf	249.074 844	α, γ	351 a
99	einsteinium-254	$^{254}_{99}$Es	254.088 02	α, β^-, γ	275.7 d
100	fermium-253	$^{253}_{100}$Fm	253.085 174	α, γ	3.00 d
101	mendelevium-255	$^{255}_{101}$Md	255.091 07	α, γ	27 min
102	nobelium-255	$^{255}_{102}$No	255.093 24	α, γ	3.1 min
103	lawrencium-257	$^{257}_{103}$Lr	257.099 5	α	0.646 s
104	rutherfordium-261	$^{261}_{104}$Rf	261.108 69	α	65 s
105	dubnium-262	$^{262}_{105}$Db	262.113 76	α	34 s
106	seaborgium-263	$^{263}_{106}$Sg	263.116 2	α	0.9 s
107	bohrium-262	$^{262}_{107}$Bh	262.123 1	α	0.10 s
108	hassium-264	$^{264}_{108}$Hs	264.128 5	α	0.00008 s
109	meitnerium-266	$^{266}_{109}$Mt	266.137 8	α	0.0034 s

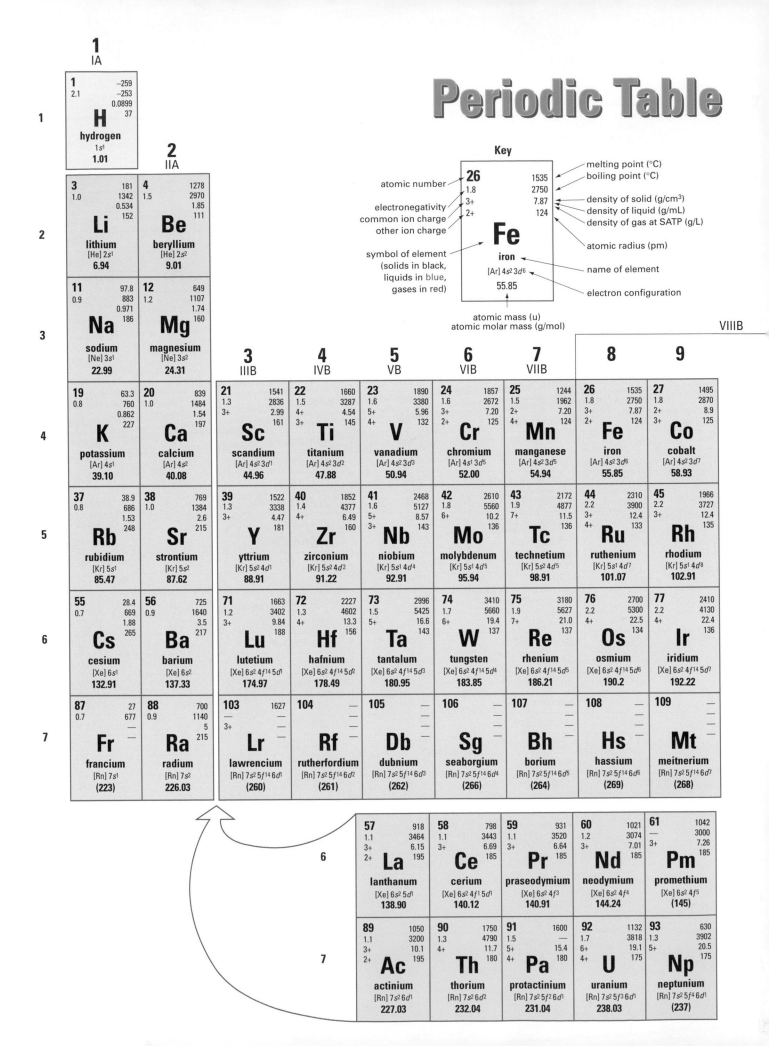

Periodic Table

Key

atomic number	**26**	1535 — melting point (°C)
	1.8	2750 — boiling point (°C)
electronegativity	3+	7.87 — density of solid (g/cm³)
common ion charge	2+	— density of liquid (g/mL)
other ion charge		124 — density of gas at SATP (g/L)
symbol of element	**Fe**	— atomic radius (pm)
(solids in black,	iron	— name of element
liquids in blue,	[Ar] 4s² 3d⁶	
gases in red)	55.85	— electron configuration

atomic mass (u)
atomic molar mass (g/mol)

of the Elements

18 VIIIA

Group 13 IIIA	14 IVA	15 VA	16 VIA	17 VIIA	18 VIIIA

Period 1

2 — -272, -269, X 0.179, 50 — **He** — helium — $1s^2$ — **4.00**

Period 2

5 2300, 2.0, 2550, X 2.34, 88 — **B** boron — [He] $2s^2 2p^1$ — **10.81**

6 3550, 2.5, 4827, X 2.26, 77 — **C** carbon — [He] $2s^2 2p^2$ — **12.01**

7 -210, 3.0, -196, 1.25, 70 — **N** nitrogen — [He] $2s^2 2p^3$ — **14.01**

8 -218, 3.5, -183, 1.43, 66 — **O** oxygen — [He] $2s^2 2p^4$ — **16.00**

9 -220, 4.0, -188, 1.70, 64 — **F** fluorine — [He] $2s^2 2p^5$ — **19.00**

10 -249, —, -246, X 0.900, 62 — **Ne** neon — [He] $2s^2 2p^6$ — **20.18**

Period 3

13 660, 1.5, 2467, 2.70, $^{3+}$ 143 — **Al** aluminum — [Ne] $3s^2 3p^1$ — **26.98**

14 1410, 1.8, 2355, X 2.33, 117 — **Si** silicon — [Ne] $3s^2 3p^2$ — **28.09**

15 44.1, 2.1, 280, 1.82, 110 — **P** phosphorus — [Ne] $3s^2 3p^3$ — **30.97**

16 113, 2.5, 445, 2.07, 104 — **S** sulfur — [Ne] $3s^2 3p^4$ — **32.06**

17 -101, 3.0, -34.6, 3.21, 99 — **Cl** chlorine — [Ne] $3s^2 3p^5$ — **35.45**

18 -189, —, -186, X 1.78, 95 — **Ar** argon — [Ne] $3s^2 3p^6$ — **39.95**

Period 4

10	11 IB	12 IIB

28 1455, 1.8, 2730, $^{2+}$ 8.90, $^{3+}$ 124 — **Ni** nickel — [Ar] $4s^2 3d^8$ — **58.69**

29 1083, 1.9, 2567, $^{2+}$ 8.92, $^{1+}$ 128 — **Cu** copper — [Ar] $4s^1 3d^{10}$ — **63.55**

30 420, 1.6, 907, $^{2+}$ 7.14, 133 — **Zn** zinc — [Ar] $4s^2 3d^{10}$ — **65.38**

31 29.8, 1.6, 2403, $^{3+}$ 5.90, 122 — **Ga** gallium — [Ar] $4s^2 3d^{10} 4p^1$ — **69.72**

32 937, 1.8, 2830, $^{4+}$ 5.35, 121 — **Ge** germanium — [Ar] $4s^2 3d^{10} 4p^2$ — **72.61**

33 817, 2.0, 613, 5.73, — **As** arsenic — [Ar] $4s^2 3d^{10} 4p^3$ — **74.92**

34 217, 2.4, 684, 4.81, 117 — **Se** selenium — [Ar] $4s^2 3d^{10} 4p^4$ — **78.96**

35 -7.2, 2.8, 58.8, 3.12, 114 — **Br** bromine — [Ar] $4s^2 3d^{10} 4p^5$ — **79.90**

36 -157, —, -152, X 3.74, 112 — **Kr** krypton — [Ar] $4s^2 3d^{10} 4p^6$ — **83.80**

Period 5

46 1554, 2.2, 2970, $^{2+}$ 12.0, $^{4+}$ 138 — **Pd** palladium — [Kr] $4d^{10}$ — **106.42**

47 962, 1.9, 2212, 10.5, $^{1+}$ 144 — **Ag** silver — [Kr] $5s^1 4d^{10}$ — **107.87**

48 321, 1.7, 765, $^{2+}$ 8.64, 149 — **Cd** cadmium — [Kr] $5s^2 4d^{10}$ — **112.41**

49 157, 1.7, 2080, $^{3+}$ 7.30, 163 — **In** indium — [Kr] $5s^2 4d^{10} 5p^1$ — **114.82**

50 232, 1.8, 2270, $^{4+}$ 7.31, $^{2+}$ 140 — **Sn** tin — [Kr] $5s^2 4d^{10} 5p^2$ — **118.69**

51 631, 1.9, 1750, $^{3+}$ 6.68, $^{5+}$ 141 — **Sb** antimony — [Kr] $5s^2 4d^{10} 5p^3$ — **121.75**

52 450, 2.1, 990, 6.2, 137 — **Te** tellurium — [Kr] $5s^2 4d^{10} 5p^4$ — **127.60**

53 114, 2.5, 184, 4.93, 133 — **I** iodine — [Kr] $5s^2 4d^{10} 5p^5$ — **126.90**

54 -112, —, -107, X 5.89, 130 — **Xe** xenon — [Kr] $5s^2 4d^{10} 5p^6$ — **131.29**

Period 6

78 1772, 2.2, 3827, $^{4+}$ 21.5, $^{2+}$ 138 — **Pt** platinum — [Xe] $6s^1 4f^{14} 5d^9$ — **195.08**

79 1064, 2.4, 2808, 19.3, $^{1+}$ 144 — **Au** gold — [Xe] $6s^1 4f^{14} 5d^{10}$ — **196.97**

80 -39.0, 1.9, 357, $^{2+}$ 13.5, $^{1+}$ 160 — **Hg** mercury — [Xe] $6s^2 4f^{14} 5d^{10}$ — **200.59**

81 304, 1.8, 1457, $^{1+}$ 11.85, $^{3+}$ 170 — **Tl** thallium — [Xe] $6s^2 4f^{14} 5d^{10} 6p^1$ — **204.38**

82 328, 1.8, 1740, $^{2+}$ 11.3, $^{4+}$ 175 — **Pb** lead — [Xe] $6s^2 4f^{14} 5d^{10} 6p^2$ — **207.20**

83 271, 1.9, 1560, $^{3+}$ 9.80, $^{5+}$ 155 — **Bi** bismuth — [Xe] $6s^2 4f^{14} 5d^{10} 6p^3$ — **209.98**

84 254, 2.0, 962, $^{2+}$ 9.40, $^{4+}$ 167 — **Po** polonium — [Xe] $6s^2 4f^{14} 5d^{10} 6p^4$ — **(209)**

85 302, 2.2, 337, —, X 142 — **At** astatine — [Xe] $6s^2 4f^{14} 5d^{10} 6p^5$ — **(210)**

86 -71, —, -61.8, X 9.73, 140 — **Rn** radon — [Xe] $6s^2 4f^{14} 5d^{10} 6p^6$ — **(222)**

Period 7

110 — **Uun** ununnilium — [Rn] $7s^2 5f^{14} 6d^8$ — **(269, 271)**

111 — **Uuu** unununium — [Rn] $7s^2 5f^{14} 6d^9$ — **(272)**

112 — **Uub** ununbium — [Rn] $7s^2 5f^{14} 6d^{10}$ — **(277)**

113

114 — **Uuq** ununquadium — [Rn] $7s^2 5f^{14} 6d^{10} 7p^2$ — **(285)**

115

116 — **Uuh** ununhexium — [Rn] $7s^2 5f^{14} 6d^{10} 7p^4$ — **(289)**

117

118

Lanthanides (Period 6)

62 1074, 1.2, 1794, $^{3+}$ 7.52, $^{2+}$ 185 — **Sm** samarium — [Xe] $6s^2 4f^6$ — **150.36**

63 822, 1527, $^{3+}$ 5.24, $^{2+}$ 185 — **Eu** europium — [Xe] $6s^2 4f^7$ — **151.96**

64 1313, 1.1, 3273, $^{3+}$ 7.90, 180 — **Gd** gadolinium — [Xe] $6s^2 4f^7 5d^1$ — **157.25**

65 1356, 1.2, 3230, $^{3+}$ 8.23, 175 — **Tb** terbium — [Xe] $6s^2 4f^9$ — **158.92**

66 1412, —, 2567, $^{3+}$ 8.55, 175 — **Dy** dysprosium — [Xe] $6s^2 4f^{10}$ — **162.50**

67 1474, 1.2, 2700, $^{3+}$ 8.80, 175 — **Ho** holmium — [Xe] $6s^2 4f^{11}$ — **164.93**

68 1529, 1.2, 2868, $^{3+}$ 9.07, 175 — **Er** erbium — [Xe] $6s^2 4f^{12}$ — **167.26**

69 1545, 1.2, 1950, $^{3+}$ 9.32, 175 — **Tm** thulium — [Xe] $6s^2 4f^{13}$ — **168.93**

70 819, 1.1, 1196, $^{3+}$ 6.97, $^{2+}$ 175 — **Yb** ytterbium — [Xe] $6s^2 4f^{14}$ — **173.04**

Actinides (Period 7)

94 641, 1.3, 3232, $^{4+}$ 19.8, $^{6+}$ 175 — **Pu** plutonium — [Rn] $7s^2 5f^6$ — **(244)**

95 994, 1.3, 2607, $^{3+}$ 13.7, $^{4+}$ 175 — **Am** americium — [Rn] $7s^2 5f^7$ — **(243)**

96 1340, —, 3110, $^{3+}$ 13.5 — **Cm** curium — [Rn] $7s^2 5f^7 6d^1$ — **(247)**

97 986, —, $^{3+}$, $^{4+}$ 14 — **Bk** berkelium — [Rn] $7s^2 5f^9$ — **(247)**

98 900, —, $^{3+}$, $^{4+}$ — **Cf** californium — [Rn] $7s^2 5f^{10}$ — **(251)**

99 860, —, $^{3+}$ — **Es** einsteinium — [Rn] $7s^2 5f^{11}$ — **(252)**

100 1527, —, $^{3+}$ — **Fm** fermium — [Rn] $7s^2 5f^{12}$ — **(257)**

101 1021, 3074, —, $^{2+}$, $^{3+}$ — **Md** mendelevium — [Rn] $7s^2 5f^{13}$ — **(258)**

102 863, —, $^{2+}$, $^{3+}$ — **No** nobelium — [Rn] $7s^2 5f^{14}$ — **(259)**

C

Physics Nobel Prize Winners

For more information on the physics Nobel Prize winners and their work, check out the official Nobel Foundation Web site at http://www.nobel.se/physics/laureates. Canadian citizens or those scientists doing their work primarily in Canada are indicated by a maple leaf.

2001 Eric A. Cornell (1961–), Wolfgang Ketterle (1957–), Carl E. Wieman (1951–)

2000 Zhores I. Alferov (1930–), Herbert Kroemer (1928–), Jack S. Kilby (1923–)

1999 Gerardus 't Hooft (1946–), Martinus J.G. Veltman (1931–)

1998 Robert B. Laughlin (1950–), Horst L. Störmer (1949–), Daniel C. Tsui (1939–)

1997 Steven Chu (1948–), Claude Cohen-Tannoudji (1933–), William D. Phillips (1948–)

1996 David M. Lee (1931–), Douglas D. Osheroff (1945–), Robert C. Richardson (1937–)

1995 Martin L. Perl (1927–), Frederick Reines (1918–1998)

1994 Bertram N. Brockhouse (1918–) 🍁 , Clifford G. Shull (1915–2001)

1993 Russell A. Hulse (1950–), Joseph H. Taylor Jr. (1941–)

1992 Georges Charpak (1924–)

1991 Pierre-Gilles de Gennes (1932–)

1990 Jerome I. Friedman (1930–), Henry W. Kendall (1926–), Richard E. Taylor (1929–) 🍁

1989 Norman F. Ramsey (1915–), Hans G. Dehmelt (1922–), Wolfgang Paul (1913–1993)

1988 Leon M. Lederman (1922–), Melvin Schwartz (1932–), Jack Steinberger (1921–)

1987 J. Georg Bednorz (1950–), K. Alexander Müller (1927–)

1986 Ernst Ruska (1906–1988), Gerd Binnig (1947–), Heinrich Rohrer (1933–)

1985 Klaus von Klitzing (1943–)

1984 Carlo Rubbia (1934–), Simon van der Meer (1925–)

1983 Subramanyan Chandrasekhar (1910–1995), William Alfred Fowler (1911–1995)

1982 Kenneth G. Wilson (1936–)

1981 Nicolaas Bloembergen (1920–), Arthur Leonard Schawlow (1921–1999), Kai M. Siegbahn (1918–)

1980 James Watson Cronin (1931–), Val Logsdon Fitch (1923–)

1979 Sheldon Lee Glashow (1932–), Abdus Salam (1926–1996), Steven Weinberg (1933–)

1978 Pyotr Leonidovich Kapitsa (1894–1984), Arno Allan Penzias (1933–), Robert Woodrow Wilson (1936–)

1977 Philip Warren Anderson (1923–), Sir Nevill Francis Mott (1905–1996), John Hasbrouck van Vleck (1899–1980)

1976 Burton Richter (1931–), Samuel Chao Chung Ting (1936–)

1975 Aage Niels Bohr (1922–), Ben Roy Mottelson (1926–), Leo James Rainwater (1917–1986)

1974 Sir Martin Ryle (1918–1984), Antony Hewish (1924–)

1973 Leo Esaki (1925–), Ivar Giaever (1929–), Brian David Josephson (1940–)

1972 John Bardeen (1908–1991), Leon Neil Cooper (1930–), John Robert Schrieffer (1931–)

1971 Dennis Gabor (1900–1979)

1970 Hannes Olof Gösta Alfvén (1908–1995), Louis Eugène Félix Néel (1904–2000)

1969 Murray Gell-Mann (1929–)

1968 Luis Walter Alvarez (1911–1988)

1967 Hans Albrecht Bethe (1906–)

1966 Alfred Kastler (1902–1984)

1965 Sin-Itiro Tomonaga (1906–1979), Julian Schwinger (1918–1994), Richard P. Feynman (1918–1988)

1964 Charles Hard Townes (1915–), Nicolay Gennadiyevich Basov (1922–), Aleksandr Mikhailovich Prokhorov (1916–2002)

1963 Eugene Paul Wigner (1902–1995), Maria Goeppert-Mayer (1906–1972), J. Hans D. Jensen (1907–1973)

1962 Lev Davidovich Landau (1908–1968)

1961 Robert Hofstadter (1915–1990), Rudolf Ludwig Mössbauer (1929–)

1960 Donald Arthur Glaser (1926–)

1959 Emilio Gino Segrè (1905–1989), Owen Chamberlain (1920–)

1958 Pavel Alekseyevich Cherenkov (1904–1990), Il'ja Mikhailovich Frank (1908–1990), Igor Yevgenyevich Tamm (1895–1971)

1957 Chen Ning Yang (1922–), Tsung-Dao Lee (1926–)

1956 William Bradford Shockley (1910–1989), John Bardeen (1908–1991), Walter Houser Brattain (1902–1987)

1955 Willis Eugene Lamb (1913–), Polykarp Kusch (1911–1993)

1954 Max Born (1882–1970), Walther Bothe (1891–1957)

1953 Frits (Frederik) Zernike (1888–1966)

1952 Felix Bloch (1905–1983), Edward Mills Purcell (1912–1997)

1951 Sir John Douglas Cockcroft (1897–1967), Ernest Thomas Sinton Walton (1903–1995)

1950 Cecil Frank Powell (1903–1969)

1949 Hideki Yukawa (1907–1981)

1948 Patrick Maynard Stuart Blackett (1897–1974)

1947 Sir Edward Victor Appleton (1892–1965)

1946 Percy Williams Bridgman (1882–1961)

1945 Wolfgang Pauli (1900–1958)

1944 Isidor Isaac Rabi (1898–1988)

1943 Otto Stern (1888–1969)

1939 Ernest Orlando Lawrence (1901–1958)

1938 Enrico Fermi (1901–1954)

1937 Clinton Joseph Davisson (1881–1958), George Paget Thomson (1892–1975)

1936 Victor Franz Hess (1883–1964), Carl David Anderson (1905–1991)

1935 James Chadwick (1891–1974)

1933 Erwin Schrödinger (1887–1961), Paul Adrien Maurice Dirac (1902–1984)

1932 Werner Karl Heisenberg (1901–1976)

1930 Sir Chandrasekhara Venkata Raman (1888–1970)

1929 Prince Louis-Victor Pierre Raymond de Broglie (1892–1987)

1928 Owen Willans Richardson (1879–1959)

1927 Arthur Holly Compton (1892–1962), Charles Thomson Rees Wilson (1869–1959)

1926 Jean Baptiste Perrin (1870–1942)

1925 James Franck (1882–1964), Gustav Ludwig Hertz (1887–1975)

1924 Karl Manne Georg Siegbahn (1886–1978)

1923 Robert Andrews Millikan (1868–1953)

1922 Niels Henrik David Bohr (1885–1962)

1921 Albert Einstein (1879–1955)

1920 Charles-Edouard Guillaume (1861–1938)

1919 Johannes Stark (1874–1957)

1918 Max Karl Ernst Ludwig Planck (1858–1947)

1917 Charles Glover Barkla (1877–1944)

1915 Sir William Henry Bragg (1862–1942), William Lawrence Bragg (1890–1971)

1914 Max von Laue (1879–1960)

1913 Heike Kamerlingh Onnes (1853–1926)

1912 Nils Gustaf Dalén (1869–1937)

1911 Wilhelm Wien (1864–1928)

1910 Johannes Diderik van der Waals (1837–1923)

1909 Guglielmo Marconi (1874–1937), Carl Ferdinand Braun (1850–1918)

1908 Gabriel Lippmann (1845–1921)

1907 Albert Abraham Michelson (1852–1931)

1906 Sir Joseph John Thomson (1856–1940)

1905 Philipp Eduard Anton von Lenard (1862–1947)

1904 Lord (John William Strutt) Rayleigh (1842–1919)

1903 Antoine Henri Becquerel (1852–1908), Pierre Curie (1859–1906), Marie Curie (1867–1934)

1902 Hendrik Antoon Lorentz (1853–1928), Pieter Zeeman (1865–1943)

1901 Wilhelm Conrad Röntgen (1845–1923)

No prizes were awarded in 1916, 1931, 1934, and from 1940–1942.

This section includes numeric and short answers to questions in Section Questions, Chapter and Unit Quizzes, and Chapter and Unit Reviews.

Chapter 1

Section 1.1 Questions, p. 17
4. (a) 4.97×10^2 s
   (b) 2.56 s
5. (a) 0.0 m/s; 5.0 m/s
   (b) 2.5 m/s [E]; 11 m/s [W]; 0.31 m/s [E]
   (c) 0.0 m/s; 2.5 m/s
   (d) 11 m/s [W]
8. (a) 87 m
   (b) 0.73 m/s
   (c) 65 m [43° S of E]
   (d) 0.54 m/s [43° S of E]
10. See Table 3 below.

Section 1.2 Questions, pp. 30–31
3. (a) 1.54 (km/h)/s [E]
   (b) 0.427 m/s² [E]
5. (b) 13 m/s² [W]
7. 12 m/s [E]
8. 28 m/s
10. (a) 15 m/s [fwd]
    (b) 25 m [fwd]
11. (a) 2.0×10^{15} m/s² [E]
    (b) 1.0×10^{-8} s
12. 1.05×10^4 m [fwd]
13. (a) 2.1×10^2 m/s [fwd]
    (b) 2.7×10^{-3} s
14. (a) 45 s (from graph)
    (b) 75 s
    (c) 900 m
15. 0.76 m/s² [31° E of N]
16. 3.45 (km/h)/s [52.7° W of S]

Section 1.3 Questions, p. 40
3. (a) 27 m/s; 97 km/h
   (b) 31 m/s; 1.1×10^2 km/h
4. Java: 1.336 m; London: 1.330 m
5. 2.9×10^3 m/s; 1.1×10^4 km/h
6. (a) 1.3 s
   (b) 13 m/s [up]
   (c) 6.8 s
7. 9.6 m/s [down]
8. (a) 1.1 s
10. No; 7.10 m

Section 1.4 Questions, pp. 50–51
3. 29 m/s [horizontally]
4. (a) 0.71 s
   (b) 17 m
   (c) 25 m/s [16° below the horizontal]
   (d) 0.38 m
5. (a) 0.87 s
   (b) 2.3 m
   (c) 11 m/s [75° below the horizontal]
6. 54°, 74°, 44.4°
7. (a) 1.6×10^2 s
   (b) 1.2×10^5 km
   (c) 31 km
8. (a) 1.1×10^2 m
   (b) 24 s
   (c) 6.2×10^2 m
11. (a) 22 m

Section 1.5 Questions, p. 57
2. (a) 4.0×10^1 m/s [53° N of W]
   (b) 74 m/s [44° N of W]
3. (a) 0.56 m/s
   (b) 0.94 m/s [downstream, 53° from the initial shore]
   (c) upstream, 42° from the shore
4. 3.5×10^2 km/h [34° E of S]
5. (a) approximately 32 km/h

Chapter 1 Self Quiz, p. 63
1. F	8. F	15. (d)
2. F	9. F	16. (c)
3. F	10. T	17. (e)
4. T	11. F	18. (e)
5. F	12. (a)	19. (c)
6. T	13. (d)	
7. T	14. (b)	

Chapter 1 Review, pp. 64–67
1. (a) 27.8 m/s
   (b) 3.5×10^2 km/h
2. (a) $L \times T^{-1}$
   (b) $(L/T^3) \times T$
   (c) $(L/T^2) \times T \times T$
8. (a) and (b) 3.1×10^2 m [7.4° N of E]

9. (a) 7.0 km [28° N of W]
   (b) 11 km [18° N of W]
10. (a) about 2×10^3 m [down] (assuming that people are sitting down to dinner)
    (b) approximately 0 m (assuming people are asleep in beds and beds have random directions)
11. 52.426 m/s
12. (a) 64 m
    (b) about 13 car lengths (assuming 1 car is 5 m)
13. (a) 1.2×10^2 s
    (b) 21 m/s
15. (a) 2.3 m/s
    (b) 1.6 m/s [33° below the horizontal]
16. (a) 17 m [29° E of S]
    (b) 2.7 m/s [29° E of S]
18. (a) 0.53 km
    (b) 2.4 (km/h)/s
19. (a) 21 m/s² [fwd]
    (b) 25 m/s
    (c) $2.1|\vec{g}|$
20. 1.0×10^5 m/s² [fwd]
21. 533 m/s [fwd]
22. 6.1 m/s [up]
23. (a) 16 s
    (b) 12 s
24. 3.9 m/s² [53° W of S]
25. 54 m/s [E]
26. 0.34 s and 3.1 s
28. (a) 3.50×10^4 m/s; 1.26×10^5 km/h
    (b) 2.23×10^4 m/s
    (c) 1.02×10^{-2} m/s²
30. (a) 0.50 s
    (b) 0.3 m
    (c) 19 m/s [15° below the horizontal]
31. 29 m/s [horizontally]
33. 2.6×10^2 km/h [60° E of S]
34. (a) 0.50 m/s
    (b) 0.94 m/s [downstream, 58° from the near shore]
    (c) upstream, 51° from the near shore
35. 5.5×10^2 km/h [15° S of W]
36. 8.9 m above
38. (a) 5.2° above the horizontal
    (b) 0.89 m/s²
40. (a) 2.0 min
41. (a) 0.87 s
46. 62 m/s
47. (a) 2.9×10^2 m
    (b) 16 s
48. (a) [7.5° W of S]
    (b) 14 s
50. 2.0 km/h

Chapter 2

Section 2.1 Questions, p. 76
4. 1.3 N [71° below the horizontal]
5. (a) and (b) 6.4 N [39° S of W]
   (c) and (d) 4.9 N [60° S of E, to two significant digits]
6. 5.0×10^1 N [30° N of W, to two significant digits]

Section 2.2 Questions, p. 87
1. 0 N
2. 19 N [up]
3. 6.6×10^2 N [up]
4. 3.51×10^{15} m/s²
5. (a) 4.3×10^3 m/s² [up]
   (b) 2.8×10^3 N [up]
   (c) 4.4:1
6. 28.0 g
7. (b) 9% decrease
9. 1.96 N
11. (b) 58 kg
    (c) 1.1 m

Section 2.3 Questions, pp. 95–96
2. 0 N
3. (a) 9.80 N
   (b) 29.4 N
   (c) 78.4 N
4. (a) 2.9×10^7 N
5. (a) 1.2 m/s²
   (b) 3.9×10^2 N
   (c) 0.15 m
6. (a) 2.5 N
   (b) 1.8 N; 6.7 N
   (c) 3.1 N [54° above the horizontal]
7. (a) 0.744 m/s²
   (b) 12.0 N
   (c) 21.8 N
8. (a) 25 kg
   (b) 86 N
9. 8.8°
10. (a) 0.273 m/s²
    (b) 30.7 N
11. (a) 1.0 m/s²
    (b) 56 N
    (c) 56 N
    (d) 0.84 m

Section 2.4 Questions, pp. 106–107
2. 3.7×10^3 N; 0.76 m/s²
3. (a) $\mu_K = \tan \phi$
   (b) $a = g(\sin \phi - \mu_K \cos \phi)$
4. (b) 8.6 m/s²

Section 2.5 Questions, p. 111
2. (e) 1.9 m/s²
   (f) 2.2×10^{-2} N

Table 3 Data for Question 10 (for Section 1.1)

Speed	Reaction Distance		
	no alcohol	4 bottles	5 bottles
17 m/s (60 km/h)	14 m	34 m	51
25 m/s (90 km/h)	20 m	50 m	75
33 m/s (120 km/h)	26 m	66 m	99

Chapter 2 Self Quiz, pp. 115–116

1. T	8. F	15. (d)
2. F	9. T	16. (b)
3. F	10. T	17. (a)
4. F	11. F	18. (b)
5. F	12. (a)	19. (b)
6. T	13. (d)	20. (e)
7. F	14. (b)	21. (e)

Chapter 2 Review, pp. 117–119

6. 5.8 m/s²
7. (a) 0.213 m/s²
   (b) 2.41×10^{-2} N
8. (a) 1.4 m/s²
   (b) left string: 2.9×10^2 N; right string: 3.4×10^2 N
9. 729 N [27.0° above the horizontal]
10. (a) 18.3 N
    (b) 70.1 N
14. (a) 96 N
    (b) 1.3 s
15. 4.4 kg
16. 13 m
17. (c) 4.6 m/s²
19. 21.2 cm/s
20. 27.0 kg
21. $\mu_S = \dfrac{mg}{F_{app}}$
23. (a) 2.9×10^3 N
24. (a) 4.2 m/s
    (b) 1.9×10^3 N
25. (a) 2.7×10^2 N
    (b) 43 N
26. 3.02×10^{-2} m

Chapter 3

Section 3.1 Questions, p. 127

3. (a) 9.19 m/s²
   (b) 5.2 m/s²
4. (a) 3.4×10^{-2} m/s²
5. 0.50 Hz
6. 75 m
7. 3.8×10^8 m
9. (a) 3.4×10^5 g

Section 3.2 Questions, p. 138

2. 22.4 m/s
3. 3.2×10^2 N
4. (a) 9.3×10^{22} m/s²
   (b) 8.4×10^{-8} N
5. (a) 1.96 N
   (b) 2.22 N
6. (a) 3.8 m/s
7. 1.1 N; 0.54 N
9. (b) 21 m/s
   (d) 2.0 g

Section 3.3 Questions, p. 144

2. 3.1×10^2 N
3. $(\sqrt{2} - 1)r_E$
4. 4.1×10^{-47} N
5. (a) 6.8×10^{-8} N [W]
   (b) 7.9×10^{-7} N [42° S of W]

6. (a) 3.5×10^5 m from Earth's centre
8. (c) 4.23×10^7 m

Section 3.4 Questions, p. 151

3. 9.02:1
4. (a) 2.42×10^4 m/s
   (b) 1.99×10^{30} kg
5. (a) 4.69×10^4 km
   (b) 4.05×10^4 km
6. (a) 1.2×10^2 s
   (b) 8.3×10^{-3} Hz

Chapter 3 Self Quiz, pp. 157–188

1. T	9. F	17. (c)
2. F	10. T	18. (c)
3. T	11. T	19. (b)
4. F	12. (c)	20. (b)
5. F	13. (d)	21. (c)
6. T	14. (e)	22. (e)
7. T	15. (a)	23. (d)
8. T	16. (e)	

Chapter 3 Review, pp. 159–161

4. 1.4×10^2 m
5. 0.11 cm/s²; 2.4×10^{-4} cm/s²; 1.3×10^{-7} cm/s²
6. 5.4 s
8. (b) 7.5 m/s
   (c) 1.4×10^2 N
9. (a) 5.44×10^3 m/s
   (b) 1.6×10^2 a
10. 2.70×10^2 N
11. (a) 0.25
13. (b) 1.7 N; 6.2 N
    (c) 2.7 m/s
15. 15 times
16. 5.0 r_E
17. 4.21×10^{-10} N
18. 1.3×10^{-2} m/s²
19. 4.82×10^{20} N at an angle of 24.4° from the line to the Sun
20. (a) 9.92×10^5 N
21. 1.9×10^2 units
22. (c) 1.65 m/s
    (d) 0.567 Hz
25. 9.80 m/s²
26. 85 m
27. 8.0 m
28. D

Unit 1 Self Quiz pp. 164–166

1. T	9. F	17. (c)
2. F	10. T	18. (a)
3. T	11. F	19. (c)
4. T	12. F	20. (b)
5. F	13. (c)	21. (c)
6. T	14. (e)	22. (e)
7. T	15. (b)	23. (d)
8. F	16. (e)	24. (d)

25. (a) 3
    (b) 3
    (c) 2
    (d) 2
26. (a) 30.3 m/s

(b) 1.19×10^6 m/s
(c) 3.4×10^{-3} m/s²
(d) 5.7×10^4 m/s²
(e) 1.28×10^{-3} m/s²
27. direction and relative magnitude of the wind
28. brake pedal, gas pedal, and steering wheel
29. westward and down; down
30. unchanged
31. 26 m/s [71° E of N]
32. $\vec{v}_{CE}$
33. zero
34. zero
35. (a) LT^{-2}
    (b) LT^{-1}
    (c) MLT^{-2}
    (d) $L^3M^{-1}T^{-2}$
    (e) LT^{-2}
    (f) dimensionless
    (g) T^{-1}
    (h) M^{-1}
36. Newton's first law of motion
37. decreases
38. noninertial; fictitious forces; centrifugal force
39. $m(a - g)$; $m(a + g)$
40. mass; weight; 6.0
41. (b)
42. (g)
43. (e)
44. (a)
45. (a)
46. (c); (d)

Unit 1 Review, pp. 167–171

6. (a) 0.71 m/s; 0.79 m/s
   (b) both 0.50 m/s [45° N of E]
7. 6.1 times farther on the Moon
9. (a) 0.43 km
   (b) 3.0 (km/h)/s
   (c) 1.0×10^3 N
10. (a) 0.60 m/s
    (b) 0.32 m [N]
    (c) 0.13 m/s [N]
11. (a) 1.5 cm/s
    (b) 1.5 cm/s [horizontally left; 1.5 cm/s [30° right from up]
    (c) 1.2 cm/s [down]
12. 27 m/s [32° S of E]
15. 2.5×10^2 N
16. 1.4 r_E
17. 9.7×10^2 N
19. 1.1×10^2 m
20. (a) 2.42×10^4 m/s
    (b) 1.88 Earth years
21. (a) 16 m/s [down]
    (b) 16 m/s [left]
    (c) 16 m/s [30° up from left]
22. (a) 7.04 m/s²
    (b) 1.73×10^{-3} m/s²
23. (a) 3.2×10^3 N
    (b) 3.2×10^3 N

24. (c) 0.87 m/s² [E]
25. 0.47
26. 3.9 m/s²
27. (a) 7.6×10^2 N
    (b) 4.5×10^2 N
    (c) 6.1×10^2 N
33. 3.6 kg
35. (a) 0.30 s
    (b) 0.042 s
37. 95.0 m
38. (a) 0.83 s
    (b) 4.1 m/s
39. 1.3 m to 5.1 m
    415.6 m
41. 5.6 m
42. 0.13 s
46. (a) 3.0×10^4 km/h
    (b) 4.8×10^3 km
48. (a) 4.5 m/s
50. short by 1.1 m

Chapter 4

Section 4.1 Questions, p. 183

5. (a) 1.7×10^3 J
   (b) -1.7×10^3 J
6. 27.9°
7. (a) 6.3×10^2 N; 0.088
   (b) -2.1×10^3 J
   (d) 1.4×10^3 J

Section 4.2 Questions, p. 188

2. 2.43×10^5 J
3. (a) 3.21×10^5 J
   (b) 32%
   (c) 7.8×10^4 J
4. 11 m/s
5. 0.60 kg
6. (a) 3.09 J
   (b) 4.18 m/s
7. 18 m/s
8. 4.7 m/s

Section 4.3 Questions, p. 194

2. (a) 2.1×10^3 J
   (b) 3.4×10^2 J
3. (a) 4.29 J; 0 J
   (b) 0 J; −4.29 J
4. 15 m
5. (a) −97 J
   (b) 97 J
   (c) 97 J
7. (a) 7.43×10^{15} J
   (b) 6.52 times greater

Section 4.4 Questions, pp. 201–202

2. (a) 0.056 J
   (b) 0 J
   (c) −0.056 J
   (d) 0.056 J; 1.5 m/s
3. 11 m/s
4. (a) 6.10×10^6 J
   (b) 13.6 m/s
5. (a) 4.9 m/s
   (b) back to the original vertical height
6. 17.5°

7. 2.4 m
8. (a) and (b) 0.34
9. (a) 3.5×10^5 J
   (c) 1.2×10^3 kg
   (d) 0.61
10. (a) -2.0×10^2 J
    (b) 1.8×10^2 J
    (c) 2.0×10^2 J

Section 4.5 Questions, pp. 218–219
5. 0.042 m
6. 1.8 N
7. 229 N
8. 2.0×10^{-2} m
9. (a) 0.962 [down]; 3.33 m/s² [down]
   (b) 0.151 m
10. 6.37 m/s
11. (a) 91 N/m
    (b) 0.40 J
12. 2.0×10^1 N/m
13. 0.38 m
14. 0.14 m
15. (b) 0.10 m
    (c) 1.0×10^3 N/m
    (d) 9.1 m/s
17. 6.4×10^4 N/m
18. 7.8×10^{-2} m

Chapter 4 Self Quiz, p. 225
1. T   9. F
2. F   10. (c)
3. F   11. (c)
4. F   12. (e)
5. T   13. (d)
6. T   14. (e)
7. T   15. (a)
8. F   16. (d)

Chapter 4 Review, pp. 226–229
9. (a) -49.1 J
   (b) 49.1 J
10. 32°
11. (a) 1.29×10^3 J
    (b) 1.29×10^3 J
    (c) 8.14×10^3 J
12. 5.6 m
13. 8.90 m/s
14. (a) 2.5×10^{12} J
    (b) 3×10^3 people
15. (a) -2.9×10^2 J
    (b) 2.9×10^2 J
    (c) 2.9×10^2 J
16. (a) 9.2 m/s
17. (a) 29 m/s
    (b) 29 m/s
18. (a) 2.3×10^2 N; 1.3×10^2 N
    (b) 1.4 m/s (c) 2.0×10^2 J
19. 1.0×10^4 m/s
20. 8.40 m/s
21. 42 J
22. (a) 239 N/m
    (b) 35.9 N
    (c) 2.69 J; 10.8 J
23. 0.32 m
24. 0.21 kg

25. (a) 0.053 J
    (b) 0.50 m/s
    (c) 0.33 m/s
    (d) 0.053 J
32. (a) 19.8 m/s
    (b) 20.4 m/s
34. (a) 1.12 mg
    (b) 1.12 $mg\Delta y$
35. 0.079 m
36. 0.019 J
37. 2.0 m
38. 8.4 m/s
39. 12 units

Chapter 5
Section 5.1 Questions, p. 238
3. (a) 77 N·s [E]
   (b) 1.1 N·s [forward]
   (c) 3.5×10^2 N·s [down]
   (d) about 0.12 N·s [S]
4. 2.4 m/s [W]
5. 1.6×10^4 N [W]
6. (a) 0.66 kg·m/s [left]
   (b) 0.66 N·s [left]
7. (a) 1.1 kg·m/s [backward]
   (b) 1.1 N·s [backward]
   (c) 0.45 N [backward]
8. 1.8 m/s [backward]
9. 3.0 m/s [N]
10. (a) 11 kg·m/s [up]
    (b) 1.7×10^3 N [up]

Section 5.2 Questions, pp. 244–245
5. 1.9 m/s in the original direction of cart's velocity
6. 5.8 m/s [N]
7. 4.95 m/s [E]
8. (a) 2.34×10^4 kg·m/s [W]; 2.34×10^4 kg·m/s [E]
   (c) zero
9. 82 kg
10. 0 m/s

Section 5.3 Questions, p. 253
4. 3.1 m/s forward and 0.4 m/s backward
5. $\dfrac{m}{2}$
6. 11 m/s
7. (b) $\dfrac{mv}{(m + M)}$
   (d) $h = \dfrac{m^2 v^2}{2g\,(m + M)^2}$
   (e) $v = \left(\dfrac{(m + M)}{m}\right)\sqrt{2gh}$
   (f) 6.6×10^2 m/s

Section 5.4 Questions, pp. 258–259
2. 66° from the initial direction of the neutron's velocity
3. 55 kg
4. 1.7 m/s [47° S of E]
5. (a) 0.22 kg
   (b) 1.3×10^{-4} J

Chapter 5 Self Quiz, pp. 267–268
1. F   9. T   17. (b)
2. T   10. F   18. (c)
3. F   11. (e)   19. (a)
4. F   12. (d)   20. (d)
5. T   13. (d)   21. (a)
6. T   14. (d)   22. (d)
7. F   15. (e)
8. F   16. (d)

Chapter 5 Review, pp. 269–271
7. 8.1×10^2 kg·m/s; 7.9×10^2 kg·m/s
8. 25 m/s
9. 3.2×10^5 N [E]
10. (a) 1.7 N·s [horizontally]
    (b) 28 m/s [horizontally]
11. 1.00 m/s
12. 0.619 km/s
13. 1.90×10^2 m/s [toward Jupiter]
15. 0.08 m/s [N] for the 253-g car; 1.88 m/s [N] for the 232-g car
16. (b) 3.0 m/s; 4.0 m/s
17. 0.561
18. 3.00 m/s [W]
19. (a) 2.3 m/s
    (b) 2.5 m/s
20. (a) 0.80 m/s
    (b) 7.8 N
21. 3.4×10^3 km/h
22. 2.0 m/s [22° S of W] (See Table 1 below.)
31. (a) $v_1' = \dfrac{v_1(m_1 - m_2)}{m_1 + m_2}$;
       $v_2' = \dfrac{2mv_1}{(m_1 + m_2)}$
    (b) $v_1' = 0$; $v_2' = v_1$
    (c) $v_1' = v_1$; $v_2' = 2v_1$
    (d) $v_1' = -v_1$; $v_2' = \dfrac{2m_1 v_1}{m_2}$
32. 3.4×10^2 m

Chapter 6
Section 6.1 Questions, p. 277
2. (a) 3.99×10^3 N [toward Earth's centre]
   (b) 1.77 m/s² [toward Earth's centre]
3. 7.3×10^{-2} N/kg [toward Earth's centre]
4. (a) 3.0×10^6 m
   (b) 2.8×10^3 N
5. 11.2 N/kg
6. (a) 0.61 m/s² [toward Earth's centre]

   (b) 2.9×10^2 N [toward Earth's centre]
7. (a) 2.6×10^3 km
   (b) 0.24 N
8. 0.75 r_E

Section 6.2 Questions, p. 284
4. 1.8×10^8 s
5. 1.6 times
6. 4.0×10^1 h
7. 9.2×10^6 m

Section 6.3 Questions, p. 294
3. (a) -1.7×10^{10} J
   (b) 5.4×10^3 m/s
4. 1.4×10^9 J
5. (a) -1.18×10^{11} J
   (b) 5.88×10^{10} J
   (c) -5.88×10^{10} J
   (d) 7.74×10^3 m/s
6. (a) -3.03×10^{10} J
   (b) 1.52×10^{10} J
   (c) -1.52×10^{10} J
   (d) 94%
7. (a) 6.18×10^5 m/s
   (b) 4.37×10^4 m/s
8. 1.68×10^3 m/s
9. 5.22 M_S
11. (a) 8.86 mm

Chapter 6 Self Quiz, pp. 298–299
1. T   10. F   19. (e)
2. T   11. (a)   20. (c)
3. T   12. (d)   21. (c)
4. T   13. (c)   22. (d)
5. F   14. (d)   23. (c)
6. F   15. (a)   24. (c)
7. F   16. (c)   25. (a)
8. F   17. (a)   26. (e)
9. T   18. (d)

Chapter 6 Review, pp. 300–301
3. 5.1×10^4 km
4. 0.318 N/kg
5. 4.23×10^{-3} N/kg [1.26° from the spacecraft-to-Earth line]
6. 3.3×10^{23} kg
7. (a) 1.22 r_E
   (b) 0.22 r_E
8. (a) 3.1×10^5 km
   (b) 2.1 d
9. 1.08×10^{11} m
10. (a) 1.21×10^4 km
    (b) 9.92×10^7 J
11. (a) 2.64×10^3 m/s
    (b) 8.17×10^9 J
12. (a) -3.99×10^8 J
    (b) $+3.99 \times 10^8$ J
    (c) 2.82×10^2 m/s
13. -5.33×10^{33} J

Table 1   Data for Question 22 (Chapter 5 Review)

Component	1	2	3
Mass	2.0 kg	3.0 kg	4.0 kg
Final Velocity	1.5 m/s [N]	2.5 m/s [E]	2.0 m/s [22° S of W]

14. (a) 4.23 km/s
(b) 2.37 km/s
15. (a) 2.3×10^8 m/s
(b) 77% of the speed of light
16. (a) 1.1×10^{26} kg
17. (a) 1.7×10^5 m/s
19. 3.2×10^{14} m
20. (a) and (b) 1.48×10^{14} m³/s²
(c) 1.49×10^{14} m³/s², yes
(d) 0.557 d, 1.48×10^{14} m³/s²; 7.52×10^4 km, 1.48×10^{14} m³/s²; 8.67 d, 1.48×10^{14} m³/s²; 5.84×10^5 km, 1.48×10^{14} m³/s²; See also completed Table 1 below.
22. (a) 1.6×10^3 kg
(b) 1.0×10^{11} J
(c) 1.2×10^4 m/s
(d) 5.0×10^3 m/s
24. 40 min
25. 7.9×10^7 s
26. $E = kT^{-\frac{4}{3}}$

Unit 2 Self Quiz, pp. 304–306
1. F   11. F   21. (e)
2. T   12. F   22. (d)
3. F   13. T   23. (c)
4. F   14. F   24. (a)
5. T   15. (c)   25. (c)
6. F   16. (c)   26. (a)
7. F   17. (a)   27. (d)
8. F   18. (d)   28. (d)
9. F   19. (e)
10. F   20. (c)
29. (a) Galileo Galilei
(b) Johannes Kepler
(c) James Prescott Joule
(d) Tycho Brahe
(e) Robert Hooke
(f) Karl Schwartzschild
30. (a) work
(b) force constant of a spring
(c) impulse
(d) force
(e) thermal energy
(f) mass of Earth
31. completely inelastic collision; equals; completely inelastic collision

32. zero
33. singularity; Schwartzschild radius
34. (a) A
(b) E
35. (e), (g), (h), (j), (k), (d), (b), (a), (m)

Unit 2 Review, pp. 307–311
9. 11 m
10. (a) 1.0×10^1 J
(b) 2.0×10^1 J
(c) 2.0 m/s [W]
11. (a) 10.0 kg
(b) 2.50×10^3 N [E]
12. 71 kg·m/s
13. 0.60 m
14. (a) 1.00×10^{-2} J
(b) 8.00×10^{-2} J
(c) 0.671 m/s
17. 31 N
18. 3.8 kg
19. (a) 2.7 J
(b) 0.60 m/s [W]
(c) −1.6 J
(d) 2.2×10^2 N/m
20. 0.20 m
21. (a) 0.42 m/s [left]
(b) 0.87 m/s [left]
(c) 0.38 m/s [left]
22. 2.8 s
23. 1.6 kg
24. $\dfrac{2m}{3}$
25. 11 m/s [37° S of E]
26. (a) 9.1 m/s [26° N of W]
(b) 31%
27. 4.9 m/s [12° W of N]
31. 8.06 m/s²
32. 0.69 g
33. 5.95×10^{-3} N/kg [toward the centre of the Sun]
34. (a) 6.16 a
(b) 1.62×10^4 m/s
35. (a) 1.74×10^{14} m³/s²
(b) 1.09×10^8 m
(c) 8.42×10^4 km
36. 1.90×10^{27} kg
37. (a) 4.23×10^3 m/s
(b) 2.12×10^3 m/s
(c) 3.67×10^3 m/s
(d) 2.39×10^{-19} J

38. (a) 2.4×10^2 m
41. (a) 2.8×10^2 N/m
43. (a) 2.3×10^{-2} J; 2.1×10^{-2} J
(b) -8.5×10^{-3} N
46. (a) 2.9×10^{41} kg
(b) 1.5×10^{11} stars
47. 0.26 m/s [right] for both balls
48. (a) 0.80 m/s [N]
(b) 0.64 J
(c) 1.6 N [S]
(d) -4.8×10^2 J
49. 3.4×10^2 m
50. (a) 744 N/m; 15.3 kg
(c) 2.3 kg
52. 2.4×10^2 N

Chapter 7
Section 7.2 Questions, pp. 335–336
3. 4.5×10^{-2} N
4. (a) 2.67×10^{-14} N
(b) 3.6×10^4 N
(d) 3.6×10^4 N, 3.6×10^3 m/s²
(e) 3.6×10^4 N, 3.6×10^3 m/s²
5. 1.3×10^{-4} C
6. 3.9×10^{-6} C
7. 0.20 N [right], 1.94 N [right], 2.14 N [left]
8. 2.2 N, 1.4 N
9. on the line joining them, 0.67 m from the 1.6×10^{-5} C
10. 55 N/m
13. (a) 5.7×10^{13} C

Section 7.4 Questions, pp. 358–359
1. 4.3×10^{-9} C
2. −0.40
7. 4.0×10^{-5} m
8. (a) -3.6×10^{-2} J
(b) 1.0×10^4 V, 3.3×10^4 V, 2.8×10^3 V
9. (a) 1.1×10^{-6} C
(b) 7.1×10^5 N/C

Section 7.5 Questions, p. 364
1. (a) 1.1×10^{14}
(b) 0, 1.1×10^5 V
(c) 1.2 N
2. (b) 2.9×10^8
3. (a) 1.9×10^{-18} C
(b) 12
4. 1.7×10^{-15} C
5. (a) 8.4°
(b) 0.50 N
8. (a) 4.5×10^5 C
(c) 1.6×10^{-18} kg

Section 7.6 Questions, p. 371
1. (a) 2.1×10^7 m/s
(d) 4.8×10^5 m/s
2. (a) 1.0×10^{-18} J
(b) 1.9×10^6 m/s
(c) 1.6 cm

3. (a) 4.5×10^{-6} m
4. 7.7×10^{-12} J
5. (a) 1.8×10^{-3} m
(b) 2.7×10^5 m/s
(c) 5.1°

Chapter 7 Self Quiz, p. 377
1. F   6. T   11. (b)
2. F   7. (b)   12. (b)
3. T   8. (e)   13. (b)
4. F   9. (e)
5. F   10. (e)

Chapter 7 Review, pp. 378–381
4. 1.0×10^{-3} N
5. 2.4×10^{-9} m
6. (a) 8.2×10^{-8} N
(b) 3.6×10^{-47} N
(d) 2.2×10^6 m/s, 1.5×10^{-16} s
7. (a) 21 N away from negative charge
(b) 59 N toward positive charge
(c) 91 N toward positive charge
12. (a) 6.0 N/C [right]
(b) 4.3×10^{-3} N [left]
13. 3.2×10^7 N/C [right]
14. 5.8×10^5 N/C [right]
15. (a) 4.2×10^3 N/C
(b) 2.9×10^{-3} N
(c) 2.9×10^{-5} N
(d) 6.9×10^{-9} C
18. 2.1×10^5 N [55° up from the left], 0, 1.7×10^8 V
19. 8.1×10^6 V
20. 43 J
21. 4.0×10^{-15} J
22. 2.3×10^{-13} J
23. 2.3×10^4 N/C
24. 2.0×10^2 V
26. 5.1 m
27. 4.7×10^{-19} C, ±3 electrons
28. 49 V
29. -3.6×10^3 V, 9.0×10^3 N/C [toward sphere]
30. 1.3×10^7 m/s
31. 5.9×10^3 V
32. 68 V
33. (a) 1.0×10^7 m/s
(b) 1.6 cm, to the left
(c) 0 m/s
34. 1.6×10^{-14} m
35. (a) 0.41 cm
(b) 8.0×10^7 m/s [4.7° up from the right]
45. (a) 1.0 mm
(b) 1.5×10^{-3} m

Chapter 8
Section 8.2 Questions, pp. 402–403
2. 1.5×10^{-12} N [up]
3. 8.4×10^{-4} m

Table 1 Data of Several Moons of the Planet Uranus (for question 20 Chapter 6 Review)

Moon	Discovery	$r_{average}$ (km)	T (Earth days)	C_U (m³/s²)
Ophelia	*Voyager 2* (1986)	5.38×10^4	0.375	1.48×10^{14}
Desdemona	*Voyager 2* (1986)	6.27×10^4	0.475	1.48×10^{14}
Juliet	*Voyager 2* (1986)	6.44×10^4	0.492	1.48×10^{14}
Portia	*Voyager 2* (1986)	6.61×10^4	0.512	1.48×10^{14}
Rosalind	*Voyager 2* (1986)	6.99×10^4	0.556	1.48×10^{14}
Belinda	*Voyager 2* (1986)	7.52×10^4	0.621	1.48×10^{14}
Titania	Herschel (1787)	4.36×10^5	8.66	1.48×10^{14}
Oberon	Herschel (1787)	5.85×10^5	13.46	1.48×10^{14}

Section 8.3 Questions, p. 407
1. (a) 90°
   (b) 0.67 A
   (c) 0 N
2. 2.5×10^{-4} N [up]
3. 1.0 N

Section 8.4 Questions, p. 414
1. 3.2×10^{-6} T
2. 1.6×10^{-3} T
3. 1.5×10^{-3} T
4. 5.8×10^{-4} N
9. (a) 230 A

Chapter 8 Self Quiz, p. 427
1. F   6. T   11. (a)
2. T   7. F   12. (d)
3. T   8. (b)   13. (a)
4. T   9. (b)
5. F   10. (b)

Chapter 8 Review, pp. 428–429
6. 0.22 T
7. 1.6 A
8. 6.1×10^{-13} N [down]
9. 2.7×10^{-14} N
10. 9.6×10^{-6} T [S]
11. 2.4×10^{-17} N horizontally toward the wire
12. 1.5×10^{-2} T
13. 0.70 A
14. 0.90 N
15. 7.4×10^{3} A
16. 1.0×10^{10} C/kg
17. 5.2×10^{6} m/s
18. 3.4×10^{-27} kg
19. (a) 2.9×10^{5} m/s
    (b) 7.1 m

Unit 3 Self-Quiz, pp. 432–433
1. T   10. T   19. (a)
2. F   11. F   20. (b)
3. F   12. F   21. (a)
4. T   13. T   22. (d)
5. T   14. F   23. (e)
6. T   15. (b)   24. (c)
7. F   16. (b)   25. (a)
8. T   17. (c)   26. (c)
9. F   18. (d)

27. (a) field
    (b) inverse square
    (c) magnetic
28. (a) perpendicular
    (b) coaxial
    (c) electric potential energy
    (d) energy, momentum
29. parabolic, circular
30. decrease in magnitude, increases, increases or decreases

Unit 3 Review, pp. 434–437
2. (a) 1.1×10^{3} N [toward the negative charge]
   (b) 3.7×10^{2} N [toward the negative charge]

(c) 1.6×10^{7} N/C [away from the positive charge]
(d) 6.6×10^{6} N/C
(e) 0.49 m
4. 5.8×10^{-7} N [toward the nucleus]
7. 6.7×10^{3} N/C
9. 5.3×10^{7} m/s
11. (a) 2.8×10^{-12} N
12. 3.1 A
13. (a) 3.2×10^{-9} T [down]
    (b) 0 T
14. 3.1 A
15. 1.18 A, 2.36 A
16. (a) 6.0×10^{4} m/s
    (b) 4.1×10^{-2} m
17. 2.0×10^{-4} T [down], 2.5×10^{-5} T [up]
19. (a) 58 A [in opposite directions]

Chapter 9
Section 9.1 Questions, p. 452
1. (a) 24°
   (b) 3.8 cm
2. (a) 24 cm/s, 18 cm/s
   (b) 1.3
3. (a) 44°
   (b) 1.1
   (c) 5.4 cm
4. 22 cm/s, 13 cm/s
5. 34°
6. 19.9°
8. 67°
9. 24°

Section 9.2 Questions, p. 454
3. 6.3×10^{-4} m

Section 9.3 Questions, p. 460
3. 2
5. 2.0 cm, 12 cm/s
7. 1.25 m
8. 1.0 cm, 1.0 cm, 1.0 cm
9. (a) 169 Hz
   (b) 8.00 m, 10.00 m, 12.00 m
   (c) 4th
11. (a) due north, N49°E, N49°W
    (b) N49°E, N49°W

Section 9.4 Questions, p. 468
5. 4.50×10^{8} m/s

Section 9.5 Questions, p. 475
5. 16
6. (a) 4.2×10^{2} nm
   (b) 8.0×10^{-3} m
7. (a) 5.4×10^{-7} m
   (b) 4.4×10^{-4} m
8. 4.4×10^{-7} m
9. 1.1°, 2.2°, 3.3°

Section 9.6 Questions, p. 479
3. 5.4×10^{-7} m
4. 7.50×10^{14} Hz to 4.00×10^{14} Hz
5. 1.0°
6. 1.2×10^{-5} m

Chapter 9 Self Quiz, pp. 488–489
1. F   9. F   17. (d)
2. T   10. F   18. (c)
3. F   11. (b)   19. (c)
4. F   12. (d)   20. (c)
5. F   13. (a)   21. (a)
6. F   14. (d)   22. (d)
7. T   15. (b)   23. (e)
8. F   16. (e)

Chapter 9 Review, pp. 490–491
3. 0.88
8. 1.92
9. 13.4°
10. 5.9×10^{-7} m
11. 6.6×10^{-7} m
12. 3.8 mm
13. 15.4 cm
15. (a) 1.3×10^{-4} m
    (b) 0.43°
16. 6.6×10^{-7} m
17. 12 nm
18. 631 nm
19. 621 nm
20. 28 mm
21. 2.4 mm
26. 17°
27. (b) 26 cm
28. 9.7 km
29. 2.8×10^{-5} m
30. 7 cm
31. 25 m/s
32. 8.3 MHz

Chapter 10
Section 10.2 Questions, p. 507
2. 5.41×10^{-7} m
3. 5.57×10^{-5} m
4. 6.34×10^{-7} m
5. (a) 9.2°
   (b) 18.4 cm
6. 12.2°
7. 63.3 cm
8. 3.5×10^{-5} m
9. (a) 9.0°
   (b) 12

Section 10.3 Questions, p. 511
2. 6.5°
3. 518 nm, 593 nm, 737 nm
4. 10.0°
5. 9.00×10^{3} lines/cm
7. 1.10

Section 10.4 Questions, p. 519
3. 112 nm, 225 nm
4. (a) 104 nm
   (b) 207 nm
5. 6.0×10^{-7} m
6. 3.0×10^{-3} cm
7. 94.8 nm

Section 10.5 Questions, p. 524
3. 3.90×10^{-6} m
4. 199 nm

5. 103 nm
6. 380 nm
7. 1.30×10^{2} nm

Section 10.7 Questions, p. 529
2. 8.36×10^{-5} m
3. 5.21×10^{-7} m
4. 171 nm
5. 719 nm

Section 10.8 Questions, p. 539
1. (a) 1.67×10^{10} Hz
   (b) 9.38×10^{-3} m
   (c) 5.00×10^{6} m
   (d) 4.62×10^{14} Hz
2. 0.12 s
3. 42°

Chapter 10 Self Quiz, p. 545
1. F   5. T   11. (c)
2. (a) F   6. F   12. (c)
   (b) T   7. T   13. (d)
   (c) T   8. T   14. (d)
3. F   9. F   15. (e)
4. T   10. (d)   16. (e)

Chapter 10 Review, pp. 546–547
2. 6.2×10^{-7} m
3. 1.3×10^{-6} m
4. 6.00×10^{-7} m
5. 8.3×10^{-5} m
6. (a) 1.28×10^{-6} m
   (b) 589 nm
7. 46.1°
8. 69.4 cm
9. 3.9×10^{-6} m
10. 596 nm
11. 1.70×10^{5} lines/cm
14. 1.14×10^{-7} m, 8.02×10^{-8} m
15. 222 nm
16. 1.10×10^{2} nm, 329 nm
17. 218 nm
18. 7.10×10^{2} nm
19. 6.9×10^{-5} cm
20. 97.8 nm
22. (a) $3.5 \times 10^{-5°}$
    (b) 56°
24. 1.13×10^{5} Hz
29. (a) 28.5°
    (b) 45.7°
30. 4.86×10^{-7} m, 3
31. 73

Unit 4 Self Quiz, pp. 550–551
1. T   9. (e)
2. T   10. (c)
3. F   11. (e)
4. T   12. (d)
5. T   13. (d)
6. F   14. (b)
7. T   15. (b)
8. F   16. (e)
17. period
18. source
19. $\dfrac{\lambda}{w}$

20. nodal
21. out of phase, wavelength
22. medium
23. transverse
24. greater
25. $\sin \theta_n = \dfrac{n\lambda}{w}$
26. greater
27. larger
28. **Matching** (See Table 1 below.)

Unit 4 Review, pp. 552–555
2. 259 nm
4. (a) 2.4 cm
   (b) 24 cm/s
5. (a) 3.0 cm
   (b) 2.5 Hz
7. (a) 6.7×10^{-7} m
8. 16.6:1
9. 5.70×10^{-7} m
10. 1.15×10^{-5} m
11. 6.65 mm
12. 5.2×10^{14} Hz
13. 1.9 cm
14. 8.20×10^{-4} m
15. 0.66 mm
16. 3.00×10^{-4} m
20. 6.5×10^{-7} m
21. (a) 0.21°
   (b) 22°
22. 4.20×10^{-3} m
23. (a) 33°
24. 6.3×10^{-6} m
25. 32 mm
26. 5.3 mm
27. 0.5
30. 35 cm
31. 5.74×10^{-7} m
32. (b) 3.33×10^{-7} m
33. 5.30×10^{-7} m, 7.77×10^{-7} m
34. 90.6 nm
35. 102 nm
36. 183 nm, 366 nm
37. 1.93×10^{-7} m
38. 596 nm
39. (d) 442 nm
40. 1.18×10^{-5} m
41. 283
42. 3.3×10^{-5} m

43. 5.89×10^{-4} m
46. 11.7 cm
50. 13 m
51. (a) 1.0×10^4 m, 6.7×10^3 m
   (b) 1.1×10^{-2} m, 1.1×10^{-2} m
52. 3.0 cm
53. 6.67×10^3
54. 1.2×10^{-7} m
55. 9.1×10^{-4} m

Chapter 11
Section 11.2 Questions, p. 579
6. (a) 1.6×10^{-5} s
   (b) 6.5×10^2 m
   (c) 92 m
7. 42 a
8. 115 m
9. (a) 66.7 m
   (b) 1.2×10^6 m
   (c) 4.8 s
10. (b) 0.436 m³
   (c) 1.67×10^{12} kg·m/s
11. 8.71×10^{-9} kg·m/s
12. (a) $0.89c$
   (b) $0.40c$
   (c) $0.10\,c$ to $0.15\,c$

Section 11.3 Questions, p. 584
2. 9.0×10^{16} J
3. 2.91×10^{16} kg
4. 1.8 kg
5. 1.95×10^{-10} J
6. (a) 2.84×10^{-30} kg
   (b) 1.60 MeV
7. \$3.8 × 10⁹
8. 8.36×10^6 km
9. 24 MeV

Chapter 11 Self Quiz, pp. 588–589
1. F   7. (a) T
2. T   (b) T
3. T   8. T
4. (a) T   9. T
   (b) F   10. F
   (c) T   11. F
5. F   12. (d)
6. F   13. (c)

14. (d)   19. (a)
15. (a)   20. (b)
16. (b)   21. (d)
17. (e)   22. (b)
18. (a)   23. (a)

Chapter 11 Review, pp. 590–591
8. 123 m
9. 2.28×10^3 km
10. 523 m
11. 1.4
12. 1.58×10^{-30} kg·m/s
13. 8.7×10^{-30} kg
14. 1.05 kg
15. 0.615 MeV
16. 1.0 MeV
17. (a) 6.49×10^5 J
   (b) 1.4:1
18. 1.39×10^{20} stars
19. (a) 1.13×10^{27} kg
   (b) 5.75×10^{-5}:1
20. (a) 1.1×10^{16} kg
   (b) 1.1×10^{13} m³
21. (a) 2.06×10^4 months
   (b) 4.30×10^3 homes
24. 1.34×10^{-21} kg·m/s
25. $0.87c$
26. $0.943c$
27. 1.80×10^8 m/s

Chapter 12
Section 12.1 Questions, pp. 608–609
8. 1.63×10^{-18} J, 10.2 eV
12. 1.1×10^{15} Hz
13. 2.00×10^2 nm
14. 1.38 eV
15. (a) 1.5×10^{15} Hz
   (b) 9.9×10^{-19} J, 6.2 eV
   (c) 3.3×10^{-27} kg·m/s
16. (a) 2.65×10^{-25} kg·m/s
   (b) 2.91×10^5 m/s
   (c) $E_{\text{K electron}} = 3.86 \times 10^{-20}$ J, $E_{\text{photon}} = 7.96 \times 10^{-17}$ J
17. 2.36×10^{-9} eV, 4.23×10^{-7} eV
20. 1.85×10^{16} photons
21. (a) 2.0×10^{-23} J
   (b) 4.2×10^{27}

Section 12.2 Questions, p. 620
4. (a) 2.6×10^{-11} m
   (b) 6.1×10^{-10} m
   (c) 9.1×10^{-16} m
5. 5.49×10^{-12} m
6. 3.3×10^{-24} kg·m/s, 1.1×10^{-32} kg
7. 6.6×10^{-26} kg
8. 5.5×10^{-10} m

9. (a) 5.29×10^{-15} m
   (b) 4.70×10^{-12} J
   (c) 2.94×10^7 eV
10. 1.5×10^4 eV

Section 12.3 Questions, p. 625
3. 4.4×10^{-40}:1
4. 5.1×10^{-14} m
5. 6.1×

Section 12.4 Questions, p. 638
6. 543 nm
7. (a) 1.25×10^{-4} J
   (b) 3.98×10^{14} photons

Section 12.5 Questions, p. 649
2. (a) 12.1 eV
   (b) 12.1 eV, 10.2 eV, 1.9 eV
3. 3.4 eV
4. 412 nm, 7.3×10^{14} Hz
5. 4
6. (a) 3.32×10^{-10} m
7. 5.2×10^{-9} N

Section 12.6 Questions, p. 653
3. (a) 3.07×10^{-34} m
   (b) $\pm 1.76 \times 10^{-32}$ kg·m/s

Chapter 12 Self Quiz, pp. 659–660
1. F   9. T   17. (e)
2. T   10. T   18. (d)
3. F   11. F   19. (d)
4. T   12. (d)   20. (e)
5. F   13. (b)   21. (d)
6. F   14. (c)   22. (d)
7. T   15. (b)   23. (a)
8. F   16. (a)   24. (b)

Chapter 12 Review, pp. 661–663
4. 5.04×10^{-7} m
5. 1.0×10^{-19} J, -0.64 eV
6. 1.67 eV
7. 1.62×10^{-27} kg·m/s
8. 2.68 eV
9. 1.00×10^{-11} m
10. 582 nm
11. (a) 2.88×10^{-10} m
   (b) 2.88×10^{-10} m
21. 64×
24. 2.1×10^{-10} m
25. (a) 2.8×10^{17} photons
   (b) 9.3×10^8 photons/cm³
29. (a) 2.7 eV
   (d) 6.6×10^{-34} J·s
30. 547 nm
34. 4.8×10^{-23} kg·m/s
35. 2.33×10^2:1
36. 9.1×10^{-9} m
37. 2.7×10^{-6}:1

Table 1 (for Unit 4 Self Quiz question 28)

Scientist	Discovery or Innovation
Gabor	holography
Grimaldi	diffraction of light at two successive slits
Hertz	creation and detection of radio waves
Huygens	wavelet model for propagation of wave fronts
Land	commercially viable polarizing filters
Maxwell	mathematical theory of electromagnetic waves
Marconi	transmission of radio signals
Michelson	interferometer
Newton	particle theory of light
Poisson	diffraction of light around a small disk
Young	two-slit interference

Section 13.1 Questions, p. 676

1. See Table 1 below.
2. (a) $^4_2$He, α decay
   (b) $^0_{-1}$e, β decay
   (c) $^4_2$He, α decay
   (d) $^0_{-1}$e, β decay
   (e) $^0_{-1}$e, β decay
   (f) $^0_{-1}$e, β decay
   (g) $^4_2$He, α decay
   (h) $^4_2$He, α decay
3. (a) $x = 82, y = {}^0_{-1}e$
   (b) $x = 214, y = 84$
   (c) $x = 226, y = 88$
   (d) $x = {}^4_2$He
   (e) $x = {}^3_1$He
   (f) $x = 141$
6. $E = 1.02 \times 10^8$ eV
   $E_n = 7.30 \times 10^6$ eV
7. (a) $^{14}_6C \rightarrow {}^{14}_7C + {}^0_{-1}e + \bar{v}$
   (b) 1.56×10^5 eV

Section 13.2 Questions, p. 686

1. (a) 3.8×10^8 Bq
   (b) 1.5×10^{10} a
2. $t_{1/2} = 3.8$ h
3. 6.47×10^8 a
4. 1.24×10^4 a

Section 13.3 Questions, p. 698

3. (a) 2.0×10^7 m
   (b) 0.067 s

Section 13.4 Questions, p. 704

5. (a) β decay
   (b) W boson and Z boson
8. (a) electromagnetic, weak, gravity
   (b) electromagnetic, weak, gravity
   (c) weak, strong, gravity
   (d) electromagnetic, weak, strong, gravity
   (e) weak
9. 2.5×10^{-18} m to 2.2×10^{-18} m

Section 13.5 Questions, p. 712

1. (a) anti-kaon (K^-)
   (b) pi minus (π^-)
   (c) sigma zero (Σ^0)
   (d) sigma plus (Σ^+)
7. (a) u$\bar{s}$
   (b) uds

Section 13.7 Questions, p. 732

10. 2.0×10^{28} eV;
    2.0×10^{17} eV

Chapter 13 Self Quiz, p. 375

1. T	7. F	12. (d)
2. F	8. F	13. (a)
3. T	9. F	14. (a)
4. F	10. (b)	15. (e)
5. T	11. (c)	16. (c)
6. T		

Chapter 13 Review pp. 736–737

2. (a) $x = 212, y = 82$
   (b) $x = 234, y = 90$
   (c) $x = 82$
   (d) $x = 49, y = 16$
   (e) $x = +1, y = 0, z = e$
   (f) $x = 6, y = 13, z = C$
5. (a) $^{239}_{94}Pu \rightarrow {}^{235}_{92}U + {}^4_2He$
   (b) 5.24 MeV
6. (a) 4.61 mg
   (b) 23 h
7. 1382 a
20. (a) 7.3×10^8 C/kg
    (b) 2.2×10^{-28} kg
26. (b) 35 h
31. (a) 1876.6 MeV/c^2
    (b) 2.165823 u
    (c) 0.151271 u,
    1.62×10^{-4} MeV, or
    1.2×10^{18} J

Unit 5 Self Quiz, pp. 740–741

1. T	10. T	19. (a)
2. F	11. F	20. (a)
3. T	12. F	21. (a)
4. T	13. T	22. (e)
5. F	14. F	23. (a)
6. T	15. T	24. (b)
7. F	16. T	25. (e)
8. T	17. (a)	
9. F	18. (c)	

26. inertial, noninertial
27. ether does not exist
28. length
29. rest mass
30. quanta
31. different
32. lower
33. probability
34. 0, 1.0
35. heated solid, electrically excited gases
36. not deflected
37. decreases, increases, decreases
38. 400 a
39. spin
40. **Matching** (See table below.)

Unit 5 Review, pp. 742–745

5. 1.74×10^{-6} s
6. (a) 12:49 P.M., 1:06 P.M.
   (b) 7.9×10^8 km
   (c) 2.6×10^{16} J
7. 99.1 m
8. 3.8×10^{-19} kg·m/s
9. 4.73×10^{-22} kg·m/s
10. (a) 3.8×10^{-6} s
    (b) 7.1×10^{-22} kg·m/s
12. 3.1×10^{-9} kg
13. 2.1×10^{-8} kg
14. 1.42×10^{-15} J
16. 3.33:1
17. 622 nm
21. (a) 1.21×10^{15} Hz
    (b) -3.28 V

22. 0.27 eV
23. 2.30 cV
24. 6.2×10^5 m/s
27. 1.26×10^{-27} kg·m/s
28. 9.9×10^{-27} kg·m/s
29. 9.86×10^{-24} kg·m/s
30. (a) 0.4 eV
    (b) 1.4×10^8 m/s
    (c) 1.1×10^{-22} kg·m/s
31. 7.3×10^{-10} m
32. (a) 3.0 eV
    (b) 3.1 eV, 1.3 eV, 8.0 eV
34. (a) 12.1 eV
    (b) 2.55 eV
37. (a) $x = 9, y = 15, Z = N$
    (b) $x = 90, y = 222, Z = Rn$
    (c) $x = 2, y = 4, Z = He$
    (d) $x = 83, y = 214, Z = Tl$
    (e) $x = 93, y = 239, Z = Np$
38. 8.762 MeV/nucleon
39. $x = 82, y = 210, Z = Pb,$
    $q = 2, r = 4, S = He$
41. 30 a
42. (a) 1.25×10^{12} Bq
    (b) 2.22×10^{12} Bq
43. 2.10×10^3 a
44. 3.62×10^3 a
45. 69 Bq
64. 6.67×10^{20} photons
65. 4.5×10^{43} photons
69. (b) 9.5×10^2 MeV/c^2
    (c) n^0 particle

Matching (for Unit 5 Self Quiz question 40)

α-scattering experiment	Rutherford
radioactivity	Becquerel
diffraction of particle	Davisson
energy levels in the hydrogen atom	Bohr
energy levels in an excited gas	Frank
matter waves	de Broglie
particle classification	Gell-Mann
momentum of a photon	Compton
photoelectric effect	Einstein
planetary model of the atom	Rutherford
quanta	Planck
uncertainty	Heisenberg

Table 1 (for Section 13.1 question 1)

Type of Emission	Mass	Charge	Speed	Penetrating Power	Ionization Ability
α	6.68×10^{-27} kg	2+	up to 6.67×10^7 m/s	5 cm of air	yes
β	9.31×10^{-31} kg	β^- negative β^+ positive	6.67×10^7 m/s to 3×10^8 m/s	3–6 mm of aluminium	yes
γ	none	none	3×10^8 m/s	30 cm of lead	yes

Glossary

A

absolute index of refraction the index of refraction for light passing from air or a vacuum into a substance

absorption spectrum the lines of missing colour in a continuous spectrum, at the same frequencies as would be emitted by an incandescent gas of the same element

acceleration ($\vec{a}$) rate of change of velocity

acceleration due to gravity ($\vec{g}$) acceleration of an object falling vertically toward Earth's surface

air resistance frictional force that opposes an object's motion through air

air wedge the air between two pieces of optically flat glass angled to form a wedge

alpha (α) **particle** a form of radiation consisting of two protons and two neutrons, emitted during α decay

ampere (A) SI unit of electric current; $\dfrac{F}{l} = 2 \times 10^{-7}$ N/m

Ampère's law Along any closed path through a magnetic field, the sum of the products of the scalar component of $\vec{B}$ parallel to the path segment with the length of the segment, is directly proportional to the net electric current passing through the area enclosed by the path.

angle of incidence (θ_i) the angle between the incident wave front and the barrier, or the angle between the incident ray and the normal

angle of reflection (θ_r) the angle between the reflected wave front and the barrier, or the angle between the reflected ray and the normal

angle of refraction (θ_R) the angle between the normal and the refracted ray, or between the refracted wave front and the boundary

apparent weight the net force exerted on an accelerating object in a noninertial frame of reference

artificial gravity situation in which the apparent weight of an object is similar to its weight on Earth

average acceleration ($\vec{a}_{av}$) change in velocity divided by the time interval for that change

average speed (v_{av}) total distance of travel divided by total time of travel

average velocity ($\vec{v}_{av}$) change of position divided by the time interval for that change

B

back-glare the reflection of light from the back of eyeglass lenses into the eyes

Balmer series series of wavelengths emitted in transitions of a photon from higher energy levels to the $n = 2$ state

baryon number a property of an elementary particle; quarks have a baryon number of $\dfrac{1}{3}$

becquerel (Bq) the SI unit for radioactivity; $1 \text{ Bq} = 1 \text{ s}^{-1}$

Bernoulli's principle Where the speed of a fluid is low, the pressure is high. Where the speed of the same fluid is high, the pressure is low.

beta (β) **particle** negatively charged particles emitted during β^- decay (electrons); positively charged electrons (positrons) emitted in β^+ decay

binding energy the amount of additional kinetic energy needed by a mass m to just escape from a mass M (gravitation); the energy required to break up the nucleus into protons and neutrons (matter)

blackbody an object that completely absorbs any radiation falling upon it

blackbody radiation radiation that would be emitted from an ideal blackbody

black hole a very dense body in space with a gravitational field so strong that nothing can escape from it

bosons according to the standard model, the particles responsible for the fundamental forces of nature

bottom the sixth type of quark

C

central maximum the bright central region in the interference pattern of light and dark lines produced in diffraction

centrifugal force fictitious force in a rotating (accelerating) frame of reference

centrifuge rapidly-rotating device used for separating substances and training astronauts

centripetal acceleration instantaneous acceleration directed toward the centre of the circle

centripetal force net force that causes centripetal acceleration

charge-coupled device (CCD) a semiconductor chip with an array of light-sensitive cells, used for converting light images into electrical signals

charm the fourth type of quark

coefficient of kinetic friction (μ_K) the ratio of the magnitude of the kinetic friction to the magnitude of the normal force

coefficient of static friction (μ_S) the ratio of the magnitude of the maximum static friction to the magnitude of the normal force

coherence property of light in which photons have the same frequency and polarization, travel in the same direction, and are in phase

coherent light light of one wavelength, in phase (e.g., laser light)

colour property assigned to quarks, keeping them in different quantum states to avoid violation of the Pauli exclusion principle

completely inelastic collision a collision in which there is a maximum decrease in kinetic energy after the collision since the objects stick together and move at the same velocity

Compton effect the scattering of photons by high-energy photons

conservation of mass–energy the principle that rest mass and energy are equivalent

constructive interference occurs when waves build each other up, producing a resultant wave of greater amplitude than the given waves

continuous spectrum a spectrum showing continuous (not discrete) changes in intensity

Coriolis force fictitious force that acts perpendicular to the velocity of an object in a rotating frame of reference

coulomb (C) SI unit of electric charge; $1 \text{ C} = 1 \text{ A·s}$

Coulomb's law The force between two point charges is inversely proportional to the square of the distance between the charges and directly proportional to the product of the charges.

cutoff potential smallest potential difference sufficient to reduce the photocurrent to zero

D

damped harmonic motion periodic or repeated motion in which the amplitude of vibration and the energy decrease with time

daughter nucleus the nucleus of an atom created as a result of radioactive decay

de Broglie wavelength the wavelength associated with the motion of a particle possessing momentum of magnitude p: $\lambda = \dfrac{h}{p}$

decay constant the proportionality constant that relates the rate of decay of a radioactive isotope to the total number of nuclei of that isotope

destructive interference occurs when waves diminish one another, producing a resultant wave of lower amplitude than the given waves

difference in path length in an interference pattern, the absolute value of the difference between the distance of any point P from one source and the distance of the same point P from the other source: $\left| P_1S_1 - P_1S_2 \right|$

diffraction the bending effect on a wave's direction as it passes through an opening or by an obstacle

diffraction grating device whose surface is ruled with close, equally spaced, parallel lines for the purpose of resolving light into spectra; transmission gratings are transparent; reflection gratings are mirrored

displacement ($\Delta \vec{d}$) change in position of an object in a given direction

domain theory of magnetism theory that describes, in terms of tiny magnetically homogeneous regions ("domains"), how a material can become magnetized: each domain acts like a bar magnet

double refraction the property of certain crystals (e.g., calcite) to split an incident beam of light into two

dynamics the study of forces and the effects they have on motion

E

Einstein's photoelectric equation $E_K = hf - W$

elastic collision a collision in which the total kinetic energy after the collision equals the total kinetic energy before the collision

elastic potential energy (E_e) the energy stored in an object that is stretched, compressed, bent, or twisted

electric field ($\vec{\varepsilon}$) the region in which a force is exerted on an electric charge; the electric force per unit positive charge

electric potential (V) the value, in volts, of potential energy per unit positive charge; $1 \text{ V} = 1 \text{ J/C}$

electric potential difference the amount of work required per unit charge to move a positive charge from one point to another in the presence of an electric field

electric potential energy (E_E) the energy stored in a system of two charges a distance r apart; $E_E = \dfrac{kq_1q_2}{r}$

electroweak (gauge) theory theory that unifies the electromagnetic and weak nuclear forces

emission spectrum a spectrum that a substance emits with its own specific set of characteristic frequencies

energy levels the various discrete values of internal energy that an atom can possess

equilibrium property of an object experiencing no acceleration

escape energy the minimum kinetic energy needed to project a mass m from the surface of mass M to just escape the gravitational force of M

escape speed the minimum speed needed to project a mass m from the surface of mass M to just escape the gravitational force of M

ether the hypothetical medium, regarded as not directly observable, through which electromagnetic radiation was thought to propagate

event horizon the surface of a black hole

F

fermions according to the standard model, the particles from which all matter is composed; subdivided into leptons and quarks

Feynman diagram a space-time diagram that depicts the interactions of charged particles

fictitious force an invented force used to explain motion in an accelerating frame of reference

field of force A field of force exists in a region of space when an appropriate object placed at any point in the field experiences a force.

field theory the theory that explains interactions between bodies or particles in terms of fields

first excitation energy the smallest amount of energy an atom is capable of absorbing

flavours categories of quarks: up, down, and strange

fluid substance that flows and takes the shape of its container

fluorescence the process of converting high-frequency radiation to lower-frequency radiation through absorption of photons by an atom; when the light source is removed, the fluorescence stops

force ($\vec{F}$) a push or a pull

force constant (k) the proportionality constant of a spring

force field space surrounding an object in which a force exists

force of gravity ($\vec{F}_g$) force of attraction between all objects

frame of reference coordinate system relative to which motion is observed

free-body diagram (FBD) diagram of a single object showing all the forces acting on that object

free fall the motion of an object toward Earth with no other force acting on it than gravity

friction ($\vec{F}_f$) force that resists motion or attempted motion between objects in contact; acts in direction opposite to motion or attempted motion

G

gamma (γ) **ray** high-frequency emission of (massless, chargeless) photons during γ decay

gauge bosons the class of particles that interact through the electroweak force; contains the photon and the W and Z bosons

Geiger-Mueller tube an instrument that detects and measures the ionization from α and β particles

gluons hypothetical chargeless, massless particles believed to carry the strong nuclear force

grand unified theory (GUT) a theory that attempts to combine the strong, weak, and electromagnetic forces into a single theory

gravitational field exists in the space surrounding an object in which the force of gravity exists

gravitational field strength ($\vec{g}$) amount of force per unit mass

gravitational potential energy (E_g) the energy due to elevation above Earth's surface

graviton the hypothetical particle predicted to carry the gravitational force

ground state the lowest energy state of an atom

H

hadrons the class of particles that chiefly interact through the strong nuclear force; contains the neutron, the proton, the pion, and other particles of large mass

half-life a measure of the radioactivity of an isotope; the time $t_{1/2}$ needed for half the atoms in any sample of that isotope, prepared at any instant, to decay

Heisenberg's uncertainty principle If Δx is the uncertainty in a particle's position, and Δp is the uncertainty in its momentum, then $\Delta x \Delta p \geq \dfrac{h}{2\pi}$ where h is Planck's constant.

Higgs boson the theoretical particle X predicted to carry a fourth fundamental force field in the GUT unification of the electromagnetic and strong and weak nuclear forces

hologram the three-dimensional image formed as a result of interference of (transmitted or reflected) coherent light

Hooke's law the magnitude of the force exerted by a spring is directly proportional to the distance the spring has moved from equilibrium

horizontal range (Δx) the horizontal displacement of a projectile

Huygens' principle Every point on a wave front can be considered as a point source of tiny secondary wavelets that spread out in front of the wave at the same speed as the wave itself. The surface envelope, tangent to all the wavelets, constitutes the new wave front.

I

ideal spring a spring that obeys Hooke's law because it experiences no internal or external friction

impulse the product $\Sigma\vec{F}\Delta t$, equal to the object's change in momentum

incoherent light light of one or more wavelengths, out of phase (e.g., white light)

induced charge separation distribution of charge that results from a change in the distribution of electrons in or on an object

inelastic collision a collision in which the total kinetic energy after the collision is different from the total kinetic energy before the collision

inertia the property of matter that causes an object to resist changes to its motion

inertial frame of reference a frame in which the law of inertia is valid

instantaneous acceleration acceleration at a particular instant

instantaneous speed speed at a particular instant

instantaneous velocity velocity at a particular instant

interference fringes the light (**maxima**) and dark (**minima**) bands produced by the interference of light

ionization energy the energy required to liberate an electron from an atom

ionizing radiation radiation at the limit at which ionization can occur, at frequencies higher than ultraviolet

isochronous recurring at regular intervals even when some variable changes; for example, the period of a pendulum is isochronous with respect to variations in the mass of the bob

isolated system a system of particles that is completely isolated from outside influences

J

joule (J) SI derived unit for measuring forms of energy and work; equal to the work done when a force of 1 N displaces an object 1 m in the direction of the force

K

Kepler's first law of planetary motion Each planet moves around the Sun in an orbit that is an ellipse, with the Sun at one focus of the ellipse.

Kepler's second law of planetary motion The straight line joining a planet and the Sun sweeps out equal areas in space in equal time intervals.

Kepler's third law of planetary motion The cube of the average radius r of a planet's orbit is directly proportional to the square of the period T of the planet's orbit.

kinematics the study of motion

kinetic energy (E_K) energy of motion

kinetic friction ($\vec{F}_K$) force that acts against an object's motion

L

laminar flow stable flow of a viscous fluid where adjacent layers of a fluid slide smoothly over one another

laser acronym for Light Amplification by Stimulated Emission of Radiation; source of monochromatic, coherent light

law of conservation of baryon number The total baryon number before a particle interaction equals the total baryon number after.

law of conservation of charge The total charge (the difference between the amounts of positive and negative charge) within an isolated system is conserved.

law of conservation of energy For an isolated system, energy can be converted into different forms, but cannot be created or destroyed.

law of conservation of linear momentum If the net force acting on a system of interacting objects is zero, then the linear momentum of the system before the interaction equals the linear momentum of the system after the interaction.

law of electromagnetic induction An electric current is induced in a conductor whenever the magnetic field in the region of the conductor changes with time.

law of magnetic poles Opposite magnetic poles attract. Similar magnetic poles repel.

length contraction the shortening of distances in a system, as seen by an observer in motion relative to that system

Lenz's law When a current is induced in a coil by a changing magnetic field, the electric current is in such a direction that its own magnetic field opposes the change that produced it.

leptons the class of particles that interact through the weak nuclear force; contains the electron, the muon, the tauon, and the three types of neutrino

linear momentum ($\vec{p}$) the product of the mass of a moving object and its velocity; a vector quantity

Lyman series series of wavelengths emitted in transitions of a photon from higher energy levels to the $n = 1$, or ground, state

M

magnetic force field the area around a magnet in which magnetic forces are exerted

matter waves the name given to wave properties associated with matter

meson the elementary particle originally predicted to be responsible for the strong nuclear force; now a class of particles

metastable state of sustained excitation by electrons in which they can remain excited for comparatively long times

momentum of a photon defined as $p = \dfrac{h}{\lambda}$

monochromatic composed of only one colour; possessing only one wavelength

muon an elementary particle; a mu meson

N

net force ($\Sigma \vec{F}$) the sum of all forces acting on an object

Newton's first law of motion (law of inertia) If the net force acting on an object is zero, that object maintains its state of rest or constant velocity.

Newton's law of universal gravitation The force of gravitational attraction between any two objects is directly proportional to the product of the masses of the objects, and inversely proportional to the square of the distance between their centres.

Newton's rings a series of concentric rings, produced as a result of interference between the light rays reflected by the top and bottom of a curved surface

Newton's second law of motion If the external net force on an object is not zero, the object accelerates in the direction of the net force. The acceleration is directly proportional to the net force and inversely proportional to the object's mass.

Newton's third law of motion For every action force, there is a simultaneous reaction force equal in magnitude, but opposite in direction.

nodal line a line of destructive interference

noninertial frame of reference a frame in which the law of inertia is not valid; a frame that is accelerating relative to an inertial frame

nonionizing radiation radiation at or below the limit at which ionization can occur, at frequencies lower than ultraviolet

normal a straight line drawn perpendicular to a barrier struck by a wave

normal force ($\vec{F}_N$) force perpendicular to the surfaces of objects in contact

O

optical activity property of a substance whereby a transparent material rotates the plane of polarization of transmitted light

P

pair production the creation of a pair of particles (an electron and a positron) as a result of a collision of a high-energy photon with a nucleus

Paschen series series of wavelengths emitted in transitions of a photon from higher energy levels to the $n = 3$ state

Pauli exclusion principle states that no more than one particle can occupy any one quantum state

phosphorescence the property of some materials that allows them to emit light after excitation has been removed

photodiode a semiconductor in which electrons are liberated by incident photons, raising the conductivity

photoelasticity the property of a material that, when analyzed, reveals the material's stress distributions

photoelectric effect the phenomenon in which electrons are liberated from a substance exposed to electromagnetic radiation

photoelectrons electrons liberated in the photoelectric effect

photon the quantum of electromagnetic energy whose energy is hf

pion an elementary particle; a pi meson

Planck's constant constant with the value $h = 6.63 \times 10^{-34}$ J·s; represents the ratio of the energy of a single quantum to its frequency

plane-polarized a wave that can vibrate in one plane only

polarization confining the vibrations of a wave to one direction

polarizer a natural (e.g., clouds) or artificial (e.g., filters) means to achieve polarization

Polaroid a plastic, light-polarizing material

poles the regions at the end of a magnetized body at which magnetic attraction is strongest

population inversion the condition in which more atoms are in a metastable state than in the ground state

position ($\vec{d}$) the distance and direction of an object from a reference point

positron a particle identical to an electron but with a positive charge; also called an antielectron

principle of complementarity to understand a specific experiment, one must use either the wave theory or the photon theory but not both

principle of electromagnetism moving electric charges produce a magnetic field

projectile an object that moves through the air, along a trajectory, without a propulsion system

projectile motion motion with a constant horizontal velocity and a constant vertical acceleration due to gravity

proper length (L_s) the length, in an inertial frame, of an object stationary in that frame

proper time (Δt_s) the time interval between two events measured by an observer who sees the events occur at one position

Q

quanta packets of energy; one quantum is the minimum amount of energy a particle can emit

quantum chromodynamics (QCD) theory that describes the strong interaction in terms of gluon exchanges on the part of quarks and antiquarks

quantum electrodynamics the study of interactions of charged particles in terms of virtual photons

quantum mechanics mathematical interpretation of the composition and behaviour of matter, based on the wave nature of particles

quarks elementary particles making up hadrons

R

radioactive dating a technique using known properties of radioactive materials to estimate the age of old objects

radioactivity the spontaneous emission of electromagnetic (gamma) radiation or particles of nonzero mass by a nucleus

radio waves electromagnetic waves in the frequency range 10^4 to 10^{10} Hz; used in radio and TV transmission

rectilinear propagation of light the term used to describe light travelling in straight lines

refraction the bending effect on a wave's direction that occurs when the wave enters a different medium at an angle

relative velocity velocity of an object relative to a specific frame of reference

resolution the ability of an instrument to separate two images that are close together

rest mass mass measured at rest, relative to the observer

S

satellite object or body that revolves around another body

scalar quantity quantity that has magnitude but no direction

scanning electron microscope a type of microscope in which a beam of electrons is scanned across a specimen

scanning tunnelling electron microscope a type of microscope in which a probe is held close to the surface of the sample; electrons "tunnel" between the sample and the probe, creating a current

scattering the change in direction of particles or waves as a result of collisions with particles

Schwartzschild radius the distance from the centre of the singularity to the event horizon

scintillation tube an instrument that detects and measures the energy delivered to a crystal by incoming γ photons

secondary maxima the progressively less intense bright areas, outside the central region, in the interference pattern

simple harmonic motion (SHM) periodic vibratory motion in which the force (and the acceleration) is directly proportional to the displacement

simultaneity the occurrence of two or more events at the same time

singularity the dense centre of a black hole

solenoid a coiled conductor used to produce a magnetic field; when a current is passed through the wire, a magnetic field is produced inside the coil

space station an artificial satellite that can support a human crew and remains in orbit around Earth for long periods

special theory of relativity 1. *The relativity principle:* all the laws of physics are valid in all inertial frames of reference. 2. *The constancy of the speed of light:* light travels through empty space with a speed of $c = 3.00 \times 10^8$ m/s, relative to all inertial frames of reference.

spectroscope an instrument that uses a diffraction grating to visually observe spectra

spin the quantum property of particles denoting rotational motion; each particle has its own spin number

spontaneous emission emission of a photon by an electron as a result of the absorption of a quantum of energy by an atom; the electron moves spontaneously to a lower energy level in a relatively short time ($\sim 10^{-8}$ s)

standard model the theory that unites quantum chromodynamics with the electroweak theory; it holds that all matter is composed of fermions and bosons

static friction ($\vec{F}_S$) force that tends to prevent a stationary object from starting to move

stationary state the orbit of an electron in which it does not radiate energy

stimulated emission process in which an excited atom is stimulated to emit a photon identical to a closely approaching photon

strangeness a property of certain particles that chiefly interact through the strong nuclear force yet decay through the weak nuclear force

streamlining process of reducing turbulence by altering the design of an object

strong nuclear force the force that binds the nucleus of a stable atom

T

tangent a straight line that touches a curve at a single point and has the same slope as the curve at that point

tension ($\vec{F}_T$) force exerted by materials, such as ropes, fibres, springs, and cables, that can be stretched

terminal speed maximum speed of a falling object at which point the speed remains constant and there is no further acceleration

thermal energy (E_{th}) internal energy associated with the motion of atoms and molecules

threshold frequency (f_0) the minimum frequency at which photoelectrons are liberated from a given photoelectric surface

time dilation the slowing down of time in a system, as seen by an observer in motion relative to the system

top the fifth type of quark

total internal reflection the reflection of light in an optically denser medium; it occurs when the angle of incidence in the denser medium is greater than a certain critical angle

transmission electron microscope a type of microscope that uses magnetic lenses fashioned from circular electromagnetic coils creating strong magnetic fields

transmutation the process of changing an atom of one element into another as a result of radioactive decay

transverse wave periodic disturbance where particles in the medium oscillate at right angles to the direction in which the wave travels

turbulence irregular fluid motion

U

unification scale the limit (10^{-30} m) specified by the GUT below which only one force is predicted to exist, in place of the separate electromagnetic and strong and weak nuclear forces

uniform circular motion motion that occurs when an object has constant speed and constant radius

unpolarized a wave that vibrates in all directions perpendicular to the direction of travel

V

vector quantity quantity that has both magnitude and direction

velocity ($\vec{v}$) the rate of change of position

virtual photon the exchange photon in an electromagnetic interaction; virtual in the sense of being unobservable

viscosity internal friction between molecules caused by cohesive forces

W

W boson short-lived elementary particle; one of the carriers of the weak nuclear force

wave front the leading edge of a continuous crest or trough

wave–particle duality the property of electromagnetic radiation that defines its dual nature of displaying both wave-like and particle-like characteristics

wave ray a straight line, drawn perpendicular to a wave front, indicating the direction of transmission

weak nuclear force the weak force in a nucleus thought to be associated with β decay

weight the force of gravity on an object

work (W) the energy transferred to an object when a force acting on the object moves it through a distance

work function the energy with which an electron is bound to a photoelectric surface

Z

Z boson short-lived elementary particle; one of the carriers of the weak nuclear force

▸ Index

Index

Index

Index

W

Waste disposal, safety, 773
Wave equation, 448, 477, 530
Wave front, **444**. *See also* Diffraction; Huygens' principle; Refraction
Wavelength, 444. *See also* De Broglie wavelength; Dispersion and dispersive media
    and atomic energy levels, 630–37
    and colour, 476
    in interference, 512–17
    lab activity, 482–86, 510, 540–41
    and nodal lines, 456–58
    in refraction, 448, 451
    and spectroscope, 510
Wave nature of matter, 613
Wave-particle duality, **612**
    for electromagnetic radiation, 610–12
    for matter, 615–16
Wave ray, **444,** 447
Wave speed, 444
    in refraction, 448, 451–52

Wave theory of light. *See* Light, wave theory of
Wave transmission
    ripple tank, 444–45
W boson, **702**
Weak nuclear force, 672, **701**
    as boson-mediated, 701–2
Weight, **84**
    apparent, **148**
Wind direction, symbols, 53
Wind speed, 53
Wind tunnel testing, 103–4
Wind turbulence, 103
Work, **178**
    in electric field, 352, 367
    in gravitational field, 181
    in magnetic field, 394
    positive, zero, negative, 179–82, 185, 197–99, 394
    units, 178
Work-energy theorem, **185**, 190. *See also* Energy, law of conservation of

Work function, **601,** 601–2
Workplace Hazardous Materials Information System (WHMIS), 770

X

X (Higgs boson), 729
X rays, 538
    in Compton effect, 605–6
    diffraction, 615
    in electromagnetic spectrum, 532

Y

Young, Thomas, 469. *See also* Double-slit diffraction
Yukawa, Hideki, 700

Z

Z boson, **702**

▸ Credits

Unit 1 Opener Page x: NASA/Science Photo Library; Page 1 inset: Dr. Kimberly Strong

Chapter 1 Opener Page 5 Main: CP Picture Archive (Christof Stache), inset photos: Allsport, bottom: Boreal; Page 6: © Adam Woolfitt/Corbis/Magma; Page 10: Stewart Cohen/Image Network; Page 17 left: Dick Hemingway, centre: © AFP/Corbis/Magma; Page 32 both: © Corbis/Magma; Page 33: © Loren Winters/Visuals Unlimited; Page 34: Courtesy of U.S. Geological Survey; Page 38: © Corbis/Magma; Page 39: © InterNetwork Media/PhotoDisc; Page 41: CP Picture Archive (Ingrid Bulmer); Page 42: © Loren Winters/Visuals Unlimited; Page 46: Boreal; Page 51: Dick Hemingway; Page 52: © George Hall/Corbis/Magma; Page 60: CP Picture Archive (Andre Forget)

Chapter 2 Opener Page 69: Table Mesa Prod/Index Stock; Page 77: © Leonard de Selva/Corbis/Magma; Page 81: Photo provided courtesy of Bombardier Inc.; Page 95: NASA; Page 97: C. Lee/PhotoLink/PhotoDisc; Page 117: © Corbis/Magma

Chapter 3 Opener Page 119: © Bill Aron/Photo Edit; Page 122: CP Picture Archive (Chuck Stoody); Page 135 left: © Bettman/Corbis/Magma, right: © Andrew Brookes/corbisstockmarket/First Light; Page 137: © Joe Schwartz (www.joyrides.com); Page 139 left: © Allan E. Morton/Visuals Unlimited, right: NASA; Page 140: Mary Evans Picture Library; Page 146: NASA; Page 147: NASA; Page 149: NASA; Page 154: © Roger Ressmeyer/Corbis/Magma; Page 155 top: © Tom McCarthy/Photo Edit, centre: © Richard T. Nowitz/Photo Edit, bottom: Keith Brofsky/PhotoDisc; Page 156: Kelly-Mooney/Corbis/Magma; Page 162 top left: Robin Smith/Stone, top right: Nelson Thomson Learning, lower left: Nelson Thomson Learning, lower right: David Buffington/PhotoDisc; Page 170: © Roger Ressmeyer/Corbis/Magma; Page 171: © Richard T. Nowitz/Corbis/Magma

Unit 2 Opener Page 172: Mark Segal/Index Stock; Page 173: Dr. Judith Irwin; Page 174: Walter Geiersperger/Index Stock; Page 175: CP Picture Archive (Joe Cavaretta)

Chapter 4 Opener Page 177: Photo courtesy of Skyjacker Suspensions. Phil Howell took this Rock Ready action shot on the lower Helldorado trail in Moab, Utah during the Easter jeep Safari, 2000. www.skyjacker.com; Page 184: © Charles Philip/Visuals Unlimited; Page 188: © Christine Osborne/Corbis/Magma; Page 189: © Sally Vanderlaan/Visuals Unlimited; Page 194: A. Marsh/First Light; Page 197: © Tony Freeman/Photo Edit; Page 202: © Joe Schwartz (www.joyrides.com); Page 203: Karl Weatherly/PhotoDisc; Page 224: Al Hirsch; Page 227: © Jeremy Horner/Corbis/Magma

Chapter 5 Page 231 both: Dick Hemingway; Page 232: CP Picture Archive (Mike Ridewood); Page 244: Ryan McVay/PhotoDisc; Page 246: Nelson Thomson Learning; Page 248 top: NASA, centre: © Charles O'Rear/Corbis/Magma, bottom: Boreal; Page 253: Boreal; Page 266: Akira Kaede/Photo Disc; Page 271: Boreal

Chapter 6 Opener Page 273: Material created with support to AURA/STScI from NASA contract NAS5-26555;Page 280 © Bettman/Corbis/Magma; Page 295 top: © Roger Ressmeyer/Corbis/Magma, centre: CP Picture Archive, bottom: Nicholas Pinturas/Stone; Page 296: NASA; Page 297: NASA; Page 302 top left: Manrico Mirabelli/Index Stock, top centre: © Bettman/Corbis/Magma, top right: Brooklyn Productions/The Image Bank, lower left: Markus Boesch/Allsport Concepts, lower centre: Chase Jarvis/PhotoDisc, lower right: Steve Mason/PhotoDisc; Page 310: Romilly Lockyer/The Image Bank

Unit 3 Opener Page 312: © Michael S. Yamashita/Corbis/Magma; Page 313: Dr. Marie D'Iorio; Page 316: © SIU/Visuals Unlimited

Chapter 7 Opener Page 317: © Gene Rhoden/Visuals Unlimited; Page 326: © Tony Arruza/Corbis/Magma; Page 329: © Gene Rhoden/Visuals Unlimited; Page 330: © Brian Sullivan/Visuals Unlimited; Page 338: Courtesy of ANCOart; Page 339: David Parker/Science Photo Library; Page 340: Harold M. Waage/Princeton University; Page 341: Harold M. Waage/Princeton University; Page 344: Ontario Power Generation -Lakeview Generating Station; Page 345 top: Dr. John D. Cunningham/Visuals Unlimited, bottom: Van de Graaf generator—Museum of Science, Boston; Page 346: Harold M. Waage/Princeton University; Page 355: top: © Gene Rhoden/Visuals Unlimited, centre: © Gregg Otto/Visuals Unlimited; Page 357: Image by Chris Johnson, Rob MacLeod and Mike Matheson. Reprinted by permission; Page 359: © Steve Callahan/Visuals Unlimited; Page 360: © Bettman/Corbis/Magma; Page 378: © Lester V. Bergman/Corbis/Magma; Page 381 top: Harold M. Waage/Princeton University, centre left: Andy Freeberg Photography, centre right: Resonance Research Corporation, Baraboo, Wisconsin

Chapter 8 Opener Page 383: Superstock; Page 384: © Werner H. Muller/Corbis/Magma; Page 385 both: Richard Megna/Fundamental Photographs; Page 386: Sargent-Welch Fundamental Photographs; Page 388 both: Richard Megna/Fundamental Photographs; Page 389 left: Courtesy Arbour Scientific, right: Richard Megna/Fundamental Photographs; Page 390: James King Holmes/Science Photo Library; Page 391: D. Balkiwill-D. Maratea/Visuals Unlimited; Page 392 top both: Richard Megna/Fundamental Photographs, bottom all: Richard Megna/Fundamental Photographs; Page 397 all: Richard Megna/Fundamental Photographs; Page 399: NASA; Page 400: © Roger Ressmeyer/Corbis/Magma; Page 401: NASA; Page 402: Fundamental Photographs; Page 406: © Michael S. Yamashita/Corbis/Magma; page 420: Courtesy of Frontier City; Page 425 top left: Maximilian Stock Ltd/ Science Photo Library, top right: CC Studio/Science Photo Library, bottom: Stone; Page 430 top left: NASA, top right: © Corbis/Magma, centre left: Dick Hemingway, centre right: Corbis/Magma, bottom: © Roger Ressmeyer/Corbis/Magma

Unit 4 Opener Page 438: Dr. Jeremy Burgess/Science Photo Library; Page 439: Research In Motion

Chapter 9 Opener Page 442: M. Cagnet, M. Francon, J.C. Thierr, *Atlas of Optical Phenomena: Supplement*, Springer-Verlap © 1971; Page 443: © AFP/Corbis/Magma; Page 445: Richard Megna/Fundamental Photographs; Page 450: D.C. Heath and Company; Page 451: Dave Starrett; Page 453: Dave Starrett; Page 455: D.C. Heath and Company; Page 456: D.C. Heath and Company; Page 457: D. C. Heath and Company; Page 462 both: Richard Megna/Fundamental Photographs; page 463: Alfred Pasieka/Science Photo Library; Page 464: © Corbis/Magma; Page 467a,b: M. Cagnet, M. Francon, J.C. Thierr, *Atlas of Optical Phenomena*, Springer-Verlag © 1962; c: Ken Kay/Fundamental Photographs; Page 469: © Bettman/Corbis/Magma; Page 470: D.C. Heath and Company; Page 474: © Stefano Bianchett/Corbis/Magma; Page 475: M. Cagnet, M. Francon, J.C. Thierr, *Atlas of Optical Phenomena*, Springer-Verlag © 1962; Page 476: D.C. Heath and Company; Page 477: David A. Hardy/Science Photo Library; Page 483: D.C. Heath and Company; Page 492: © Karen Tweedy-Holmes/Corbis/Magma

Chapter 10 Opener Page 493: Richard Megna/Fundamental Photographs; Page 494: © Lester V. Bergman/Corbis/Magma; Page 495: Diane Hirsch/Fundamental Photographs; Page 496: Robert

Above: map locates the kingdom of Sikkim, north-east of India. Left: harvesting barley in the lowlands of neighbouring Nepal, once covered with forests, but now permanently under cultivation.

Map below shows the three great cereal areas of the world in A.D. 1500, based on the cultivation of wheat, maize, and rice. The three areas had remained independent up to that date.

food in the grain or seed of a group of annual grasses that are called, in their cultivated form, the *cereals*. Some of these species, such as sorghum and millets, have rather small grains, but are still widely cultivated in parts of Africa and Asia, and here and there in other parts of the world. In the cool, damp north, oats and rye come into their own. But the kings of the cereals are the large-grained temperate crops, wheat and barley; in warmer regions, rice; and, the most generous of all, maize. As late as A.D. 1500, wheat, rice, and maize divided the world into three huge regions. Maize, unlike the others, is a product of the New World, where agriculture began quite independently at least as early as the fourth millennium B.C., though probably long after the first farmers of Jericho.

Cereals in use today are profoundly different from their wild ancestors: their seeds do not fall when they are ripe —a suicidal arrangement for a wild plant, but extremely convenient for harvesting; in the more advanced kinds (of wheat and barley, for instance), the precious grains are easily separated from their protecting sheaths by threshing; and the grains themselves are very much bigger. These changes were brought about by man in two ways, as Charles Darwin pointed out: namely, by methodical selection of seeds from plants with desired characteristics, and by unconscious selection, which he defined as "the preservation by man of the most valued, and the destruction of the least valued individuals, without any conscious intention on his part of altering the breed."

It is difficult now to know how great a part each of these two processes played in the early development of agriculture. It is the same with all other human innovations, as far back as fire control. Palaeolithic hunters are unlikely to have been as sophisticated as 20th-century Oregon Indians; they may actually have burnt land to get a better view of the game, but more probably they went on doing it because, quite mysteriously, hunting went better after they did so. This is the crude slow process known to modern scientists as *conditioning*; you tend to repeat what you were doing (much of it in fact useless and irrelevant) before something good happened, and this is transmitted to later generations as unquestioned tradition. The rapid creative process, whereby an individual sees the advantage of doing something, and convinces others, can hardly have been important before the last glaciation. Both the slow and the rapid processes have been going on ever since, and in early periods we cannot disentangle them.

Methodically or unconsciously, in the eighth millennium B.C. man certainly changed the wild wheat and barley that grew in the Near and Middle East (and nowhere

33

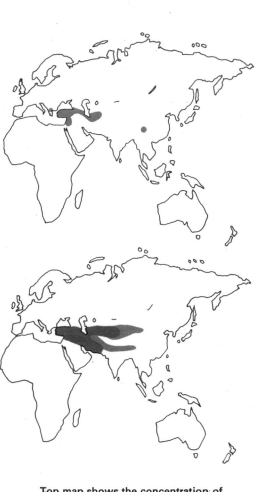

Top map shows the concentration of cereals (barley and wild wheat) in the near Middle East. Lower map shows the distribution of wild goats (blue) and wild sheep (red) which were the next animals to be domesticated after dogs.

Above: five carbonized grains of wheat (of both varieties) found at Jarmo, Iraq. They date from about 6000 B.C. Above right: carbonized grain of the flower part of a wild barley, also from Jarmo.

Drawings right show (from the left) one variety of wild barley and two varieties of wild wheat.

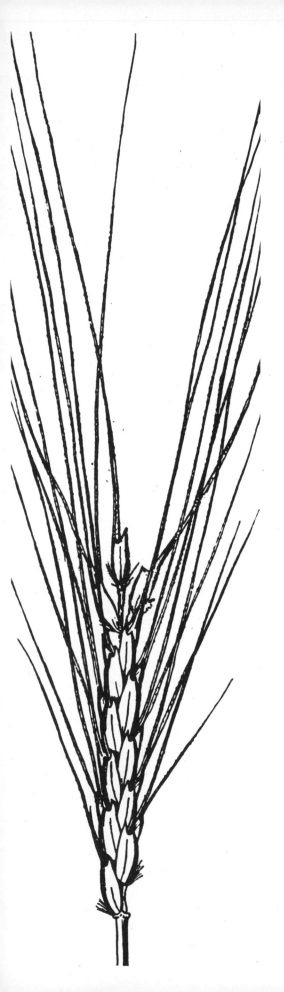

else). We can actually see the transition in remains or traces of wheat and barley from the ancient sites. About the same time in the same places, man began to change animals too. He began both to graze and to breed them under his own control. First came goats and sheep, native to these or nearby regions; later, cattle and asses. And so, from the outset, we find mixed farming: eating the grains of cultivated grasses, or letting farm animals eat grass, and using the animals for horn, hide, meat, and (probably later) milk.

The new way of life at once brought a rising population —which in itself would vastly increase man's impact on the landscape. The higher numbers and new opportunities could be, and were, used in two ways. First, certain peoples were able to build the first cities and the first civilizations because of the new surplus. This naturally happened in three favoured regions near the pioneering farming areas: specifically, in the three rich, fertile river valleys of the Nile (Egypt), the Tigris and Euphrates (Iraq), and the Indus (Pakistan). It happened with quite astonishing speed; in the fourth millennium B.C., there were already elaborate cities, highly organized societies, a host of specialized crafts and trades, and, above all, the art of writing. Meanwhile, elsewhere in the immensely well-endowed Near and Middle East region of this period, others had begun the smelting of metals, and along with civilization came the Bronze Age.

The second process was the spread of the new techniques of agriculture, and, in due time, of the arts of civilization, into Europe, Asia, and Africa, from the Near and Middle East, so neatly situated at the intersection of the three Old World continents.

The Clearing of the Continents
In the 1837 edition of his *Guide for Emigrants to the West* (deservedly a best-seller), a Baptist missionary called John Mason Peck described the process he had watched in Indiana, Illinois, Missouri, and Michigan for nearly 20 years. His account will apply in broad outline to the great movements that cleared all the continents of the earth. "Three classes, like the waves of the ocean, have rolled one after the other. First comes the pioneer, who depends chiefly upon the natural growth of vegetation . . . and the proceeds of hunting. His implements of agriculture are rude, chiefly of his own make, and his efforts directed mainly to a crop of corn [maize] and a 'truck patch' . . . a rude garden . . . . The next class . . . purchase the lands, add field to field, clear out the roads, throw rough bridges over the streams, put up hewn log houses . . . occasionally plant orchards, build mills, school houses, court houses, etc., and exhibit the pictures and forms of plain, frugal,

Gilgamesh, hero of an epic poem of Ancient Iraq, holding a lion he has captured. At one stage in the poem, Gilgamesh journeys into a large, mysterious cedar forest to fight a terrifying monster. Stripped of its legendary trimmings, the journey commemorates the first expeditions of the Ancient Iraqui peoples to find wood for their cities.

civilized lives. Another wave rolls on. The men of capital and enterprise come . . . . The small village rises to a spacious town or city . . . . All the refinements, luxuries, elegancies, and fashions are in vogue . . . ." Here, in miniature, is the history of agricultural man.

Even the first of these waves needs to clear land for crops; the second, and more abundantly the third, begin to need wood, for building, furniture, and—notably where metals are smelted and industries are arising—fuel. The first book in history is the story of Gilgamesh, king of Uruk (in Iraq) in the third millennium B.C., and his expedition to a cedar forest in Syria or Iran to get timber for his city. In the folk-lore of most countries, as indeed in the epic of Gilgamesh itself, the forest is a place of mystery and challenge, where knights hunt monsters and where younger sons seek their fortunes. Let us briefly see what man has done to it, beginning with Europe, where the change has been most complete.

Long before the first literate civilization was arising in Iraq, the new technique of agriculture began to spread from the Near East, carried by pioneers who were on the move by the end of the sixth millennium B.C. One wave, partly sea-borne, poured westward from the Levant to found farming settlements along the coasts and islands of the Mediterranean. Another passed through Asia Minor (modern Turkey) into the Balkans. From there one pioneer group went up the Danube valley; these Danubians, as we call them, spread right across Europe as far as Belgium. They colonized only one kind of soil, which forms a corridor across the continent; this was the soil known as *loess*—fine powdery stuff, ground long before by the glaciers and spread by winds. Loess is naturally well-drained and easy to till with simple hoes, and was at that time covered by a woodland less dense than the surrounding forest. The Danubians, who had few animals except pigs, cleared a piece of ground, grew wheat and barley till the soil was exhausted (in about 10-25 years), and then moved on, to return later when the soil had recovered. They cut plenty of timber, building wooden houses 90 feet long. As their numbers rose, the surplus population (perhaps younger sons, as in the folk tales) pressed ever farther west into the forest: by 4220 B.C. they had reached Magdeburg. In the wake of the pioneers, towns sprang up, and a trading network developed, reaching right back to the Mediterranean—a piece of African ivory found its way to Worms in Germany.

About the time the Danubian advance came to a halt, before 3000 B.C., two other movements had occupied the lighter soils and thinner woodlands of northern and western Europe. One separate group, also coming from

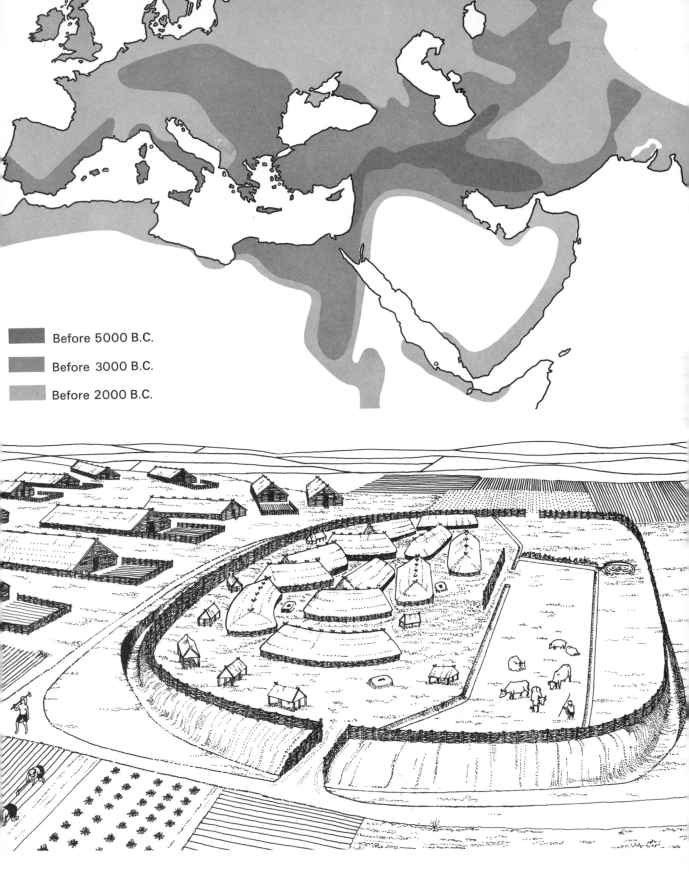

Top: the spread of agriculture from its origins in the Near and Middle East eventually covering most of Europe by about 2500 B.C.

Before 5000 B.C.

Before 3000 B.C.

Before 2000 B.C.

Above: a Neolithic village of the Danubian people, near Cologne. The defensive ditch was probably dug only when the site was occupied for the second time, and land was running short.

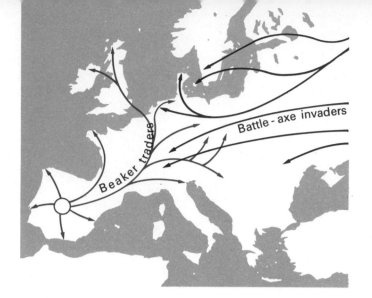

Map shows routes taken by the Beaker traders from Spain around 2000 B.C. and the routes of the Battle-axe invaders from central and southern Russia. Note their convergence in central Europe.

Drawing of a Beaker burial in England, uncovered by building excavations. Beaker burials were often marked by circular mounds, or barrows; these are still recognizable features in parts of the countryside.

the south-east, pushed into Denmark. Meanwhile, from the now well-peopled Mediterranean, seafaring pioneers ventured up the coasts to penetrate Spain, France, Switzerland, and the British Isles; these people were mixed farmers, with cattle and sheep as well as crops. Some of these western pioneers brought a cult of great stone grave monuments that are still dotted around the coastal areas of western Europe.

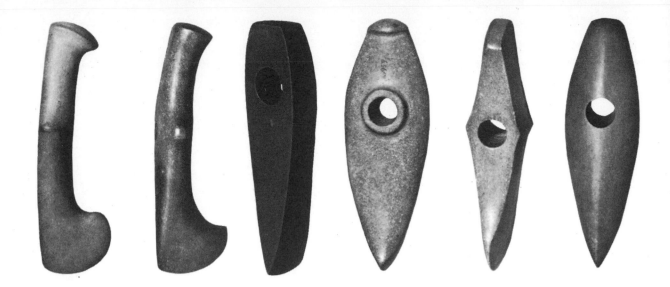

The elegant, finely worked battle-axes of polished stone that gave the Battle-axe people of southern Russia their name.

Below: beaker with a corded design from near Leipzig, Germany. It is 5½ inches high.

By the time the Bronze Age began to reach Europe, around 2000 B.C., the lighter soils were covered with farms and prosperous settlements. About this time, two new waves broke upon Europe. Up the Atlantic coasts sailed a trading people known from their drinking-vessels as the Beaker folk; while in southern Russia there arose a group of mixed farmers with an emphasis on livestock (especially sheep), known from their finely shaped stone weapons as the Battle-axe people. These may well have been the first people of Indo-European culture, from which derive the languages and dominant cultures of India, Iran, and all Europe. The Battle-axe people spread rapidly over Europe, favouring sandy soils less fertile than loess, bringing quantities of sheep, and apparently establishing themselves as joint leaders, with the Beaker merchants, of complex new societies. With the spread of the Celts, Germans, and Slavs in the Iron Age of the first millennium B.C., the peopling of Europe was almost complete. Two last incursions from Asia, in the first millennium A.D., planted the Bulgars in Bulgaria and the Magyars in Hungary, and finished the story; all other newcomers were sooner or later driven out.

We know all these peoples from the tools and other articles they left behind. What kind of Europe did they live in? From various evidence, notably from pollen sequences (p. 29) preserved in Danish and Irish bogs, we can trace the changing vegetation of Europe in the fourth interglacial. At first, tundra sprang up in the rear of the retreating ice-sheets. In the Boreal, as the temperature rose, there appeared forests, first of softwoods such as pine and birch, then of pine and hazel, finally a forest of oak, elm, and other hardwood trees. As the Atlantic period began, in about 5000 B.C., Europe was completely covered, all but its mountain tops, with this forest of oaks and their companions, thinning a little on loess or chalk downs, but dense elsewhere; a happy deer-hunting

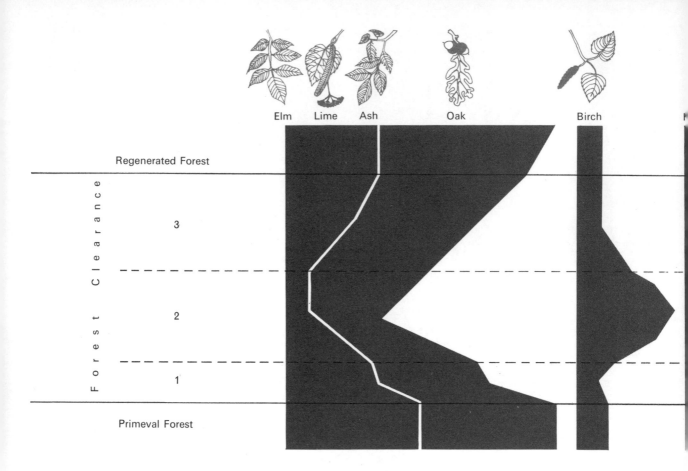

Elm Lime Ash Oak Birch

Regenerated Forest

Forest Clearance

3

2

1

Primeval Forest

ground for scattered groups of Mesolithic "natives." This forest might have survived in full (or nearly—the hunters were burning it in places) until about 500 B.C., when the colder Sub-Atlantic period (still with us) would have turned much of it gradually back to pinewoods. But from about 5000 B.C. it had to contend with agricultural man; and by the end of the Atlantic period, in about 2000 B.C., he was there to stay.

The pollen in the bogs tells two stories. First, we can see what happened when early settlers (like the Danubians) cleared land, used it, and left, to return later. As such a sequence starts, the oak forest reigns. Then comes a layer of charcoal—the settlers have burned a clearing. The oak and its companion trees shrink; the light-loving birch appears, grasses spread, and suddenly there appear the cultivated cereals and their fellow-travellers, the weeds (notably plantains). After a while, the trend is reversed: crops and weeds vanish, grasses retreat, the forest returns—the settlers have moved on. In due course, the whole sequence is repeated several times on the same spot.

The second pollen story tells of the doings of people with more grazing animals (like the Battle-axe people on their sandy soils). It begins as before; but this time the forest never returns, its tentative seedlings trampled by cattle or browsed by sheep; grasses and clovers take

▭ Graig Lwyd   ▭ Penwith Re

■ Tierebulliagh   ■ Langdale

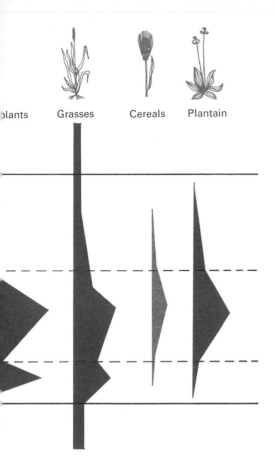

plants Grasses Cereals Plantain

Diagram above, based on pollen samples from bogs in Denmark, shows the agricultural effects of forest clearance round about 2500 B.C. Width of shading represents percentage of various pollens. As forest was cleared (primeval forest to stage 1) big trees declined and herbaceous plants increased. The great increase of birch pollen during stage 2 suggests that clearings were burned, because birch seeds need light for germination, which would be afforded by the clearings. At this time cereals and weeds appeared. As the farmers moved to new areas, large trees reappeared and the regenerated forest was eventually very much like the primeval forest. Above right: photo taken during the Danish experiment in which three men using Neolithic stone axes cleared 600 square yards of forest in four hours.

Left: some of the main Neolithic stone axe factories in Britain, and (smaller symbols) sites where axes from these factories have been found. Cornish axes (not marked) are also widely distributed.

over—the materials for pastures and hay meadows. In this way arose the broad grassland heaths of northern and western Europe, and probably even the great grassy plain of Hungary and much of the south Russian steppe. Even in the surviving forests, elm trees declined: their shoots and leaves were used for cattle fodder.

In the great pioneer movement that cleared the forest from so much of Europe, fire was one tool; the other, no less indispensable, was the axe-head of polished flint or hard stone. These axes were indeed superb tools. In a recent experiment in Denmark, a genuine Neolithic axe-head was fitted into an accurate modern copy in ashwood of an original Neolithic haft. With this instrument, three men cleared 600 square yards of silver-birch forest in four hours; more than 100 trees were felled with one axe-head that had not been sharpened for about 4000 years.

The huge demand for these axes was met by an elaborate industry and trade. On chalk downs, flint-miners drove shafts 40 feet deep, and cut horizontal galleries; by the light of lamps in niches, they levered out the flint with antler picks and shovelled it up with the shoulder-blades of cattle. At Grime's Graves in Norfolk, England, 34 acres were mined, with hundreds of shafts, each sunk by shifting up to 5000 cubic feet of chalk.

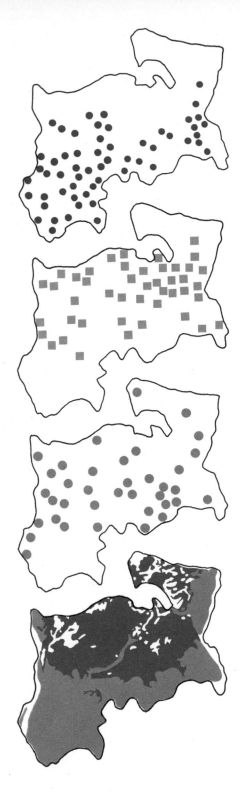

Evidence of forest clearance from place-names in Middlesex, England. Top map marks place-names, mostly Saxon, which do not indicate woodland; here the Saxons settled on land previously cleared. Second map locates later place-names indicating wood; here they cleared for the first time. In the bottom map, light brown indicates light gravelly soils, and dark brown, clay soil, scene of the later clearances. Third map shows woodland according to Norman records of 1086, and suggests that there were still heavily wooded tracts.

Meanwhile, in other areas, expert prospectors tracked down outcrops of suitable hard stone; they found one (of a rock called *porcellanite*) at Tievebulliagh, County Antrim, so small that it was missed by the Geological Survey of Ireland until archaeologists traced the Neolithic trade route. Near such sites, or near flint-mines, regular axe-factories were set up, from which manufactured axe-heads were carried far and wide by travelling salesmen: the axe-heads of Tievebulliagh were exported as far as the London area.

By the end of the Neolithic, an agricultural economy reigned over Europe, and, except in the far north, the way of life of the Mesolithic deer-slayers was plainly redundant. How could they find a place in the new economy? In the British Isles at least, there is evidence that the redundancy problem was brilliantly solved. The Mesolithic hunters knew the country, were used to long-distance travel, and were superbly skilled workers in stone; so they played a key part in the clearance by taking over the industry and trade in axe-heads.

Throughout the Bronze and early Iron Ages (when metal was still expensive for peasants), from about 2000 B.C. to A.D. 500, not much more clearing was done in northern and western Europe. On the areas already won, settlement became fixed and more intensive; towns grew into cities, and civilization began to spread from the south. But vast tracts of dense woods still covered the heavy clay soils; Caesar tells of men travelling through the German forest for two months without finding an end to it. In the last centuries of this period, and most spectacularly in the sixth century A.D., there was a human *retreat* all over continental Europe, from the Mediterranean to Sweden (see Chapters 10 and 11).

By the eighth century A.D., however, the advance began again. The emperor Charlemagne was telling his officials "whenever they found capable men, to give them wood to clear." This time, with iron tools, the peasants began to clear the dense forests and to till the clay soils and the difficult uplands. The story has been pieced together from the useful evidence of place-names and from a mass of documents (for we are now in the age of written history and legal record). The Anglo-Saxons, for instance, began by cultivating the easy soils already tilled in Roman Britain; later, these indomitable farmers began to tackle the heavy clay (frequently stumbling, to judge from the characteristically fractured limbs of their skeletons). By the Norman Conquest, there was still plenty of forest left. On the continent, up to about this time, there were human obstacles; many lords were brutally struggling to preserve the woods for hunting, and when the Count of Vendôme found unauthorized clearings in his woods, he

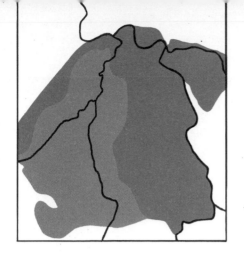

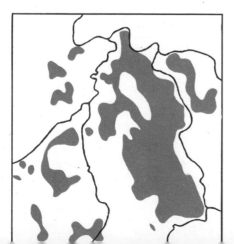

Above: clearing of woodland in Europe, from an 11th-century manuscript. Left: maps of an area of about 350 square miles around Hofgeismar, Germany, showing extent of forest. Top map, about A.D. 500, distinguishes between light and dense forest. By 1290 (second map) much forest clearance had been done and map marks forest of varying density. By 1430 (third map) forest had crept back in many places; situation in 1950 (bottom) shows more forest than 700 years ago.

pulled down the houses and pulled up the crops. But from the 11th to the 13th centuries A.D., the tide of settlers surged forward in the greatest forest clearance yet.

The advance was led by monks, at first the Benedictines, later the Cistercians, who had 500 abbeys by the end of the 12th century, each a focus of forest clearance and up-to-date agriculture. The Order of Hospitallers alone settled 40 villages near Murat on the river Garonne between 1100 and 1110. And by now many lords, eager to extend their jurisdiction, began looking for settlers to carve more lands from the forest. They had to offer inducements, in the form of greater freedom than peasants enjoyed elsewhere. Thus the lords who colonized the Grisons in Switzerland from upper Valais offered their settlers, the "free Valaisians," the right to elect their local administrator. In northern France, agents toured the markets, reading out charters full of tempting liberties to attract settlers to the hard work of clearing some new slice of forest. So, just as happened centuries later in the U.S.A., it was the more independent folk who struck out as pioneers. The most adventurous of all, attracted by the best terms, went east where the Germans were forging into the forests of Prussia and Austria in a tremendous drive eastward through the lands of the Slavs. "Locators"

Recent forest clearance in Europe. Below: a scene in England in 1853, showing trees being cut down and a drainage system being installed in the clay soil. Right: maps of central Europe compare areas covered by forest in about A.D. 900 and in A.D. 1900. Scale of the maps is about 100 miles to the inch.

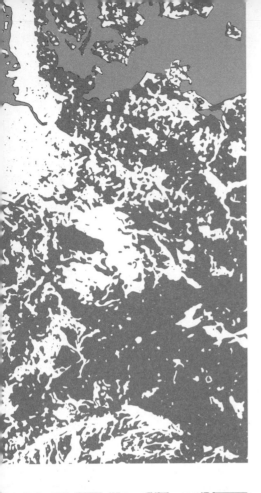

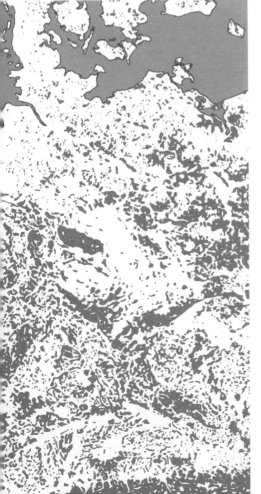

scouted likely bits of forest, recruited settlers, and reaped their reward in fat land grants and trading rights. But the Slavs themselves were clearing too. Place-names in French, German, and Czech all tell the same story of new settlements in the woods. Everywhere new villages and towns arose: more than 100 towns were founded in England alone between 1100 and 1300. It was not long before the "men of capital and enterprise" moved in, to form great new trading cities, notably in northern Germany. It was an age of tremendous excitement and enthusiasm. In 1222, Caesarius of Prüm summed up the work of the past century: "many forests were felled, villages founded, mills erected, taxes ordained, vines planted, and an infinite amount of land reduced to agriculture."

Then, in the 13th century, there was another staggering human retreat, for reasons we shall see later. It has been estimated that one quarter of the cultivated land in Germany was abandoned, and back came the forests. But again the advance was soon resumed. From the 16th century onward, the lost ground was steadily regained. In the course of the 19th century, Sweden alone quadrupled her cropland at the expense of her forests. And over much of the period, the demand for wood boomed as never before. Indeed, in this period, forests were increasingly

Land clearance by women in England during World War II. Home-produced food becomes important during wartime and all available land is utilized.

planted to meet the demand. But there is no doubt about the general outcome—a prodigious shrinkage of the forests. What all the pauses and retreats and renewed advances means, we shall see in later chapters. But nobody could doubt that the pattern of European vegetation since 5000 B.C. is predominantly the handiwork of man.

The clearing of Asia and Africa seems to have lagged behind the clearing of Europe (the continent most easily reached from the Near East source). Through Iran, the techniques of agriculture spread into the Indus valley (Pakistan) in the fourth millennium B.C., to form the basis of the third great early civilization (after Iraq and Egypt). From there, further advance into the Indian subcontinent seems to have been slow. But the Indians made important innovations; in the north-west, they bred zebu cattle; farther south, they began to breed rice, the rich indigenous cereal of the Old World tropics, and they spread this technique to south-east Asia and Indonesia. Meanwhile, probably via the oases of Turkestan, agriculture reached northern China from the Near East in the third millennium B.C.; at first millet was grown, later wheat. From India, rice cultivation may have reached more southern Chinese regions in the second millennium B.C. The Chinese, like the Europeans, began their clearance in the broad loess lands of their north-west, and later spread into the fertile lower valley of the Yellow River; it was not until the first millennium B.C. that they opened up the lands of the Yangtze, and not until the first millennium A.D. that they penetrated the forests to the south of it, where even today large tracts of wild country remain.

While agriculture was being carried westward by the Danubians, it was also spreading into southern Russia, where impressive signs of wealth were evident long before western Europe grew rich. In Greek and Roman times, the great steppe seems still to have carried much forest, but much had already been cleared for crops. The black earth north of the Black Sea supported flourishing principalities, grown rich from the export of grain. Much of the political history of classical Athens (fifth century B.C.) turned on her need to control the Black Sea trade routes, for access to the granary that fed her. But after a promising start, the history of Russia was repeatedly distorted by unremitting movements of peoples westward from Asia through the steppe. After a long period of chaos, Russia advanced again in the early Middle Ages, basing a prosperous league of princedoms and city-states on the great river systems between the Black Sea and the Baltic. In this age, when the Russians were in close touch

Dark red on this map of China indicates loess areas; light red indicates areas having a soil of similar properties.

Plan of the Russian city of Novgorod in the 15th century. The city had great importance as a European trade centre in the early Middle Ages.

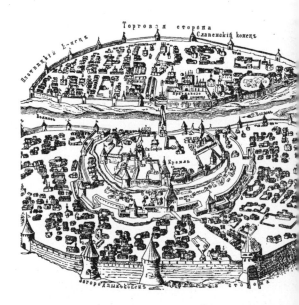

Opposite, top: pot found at Baluchistan, to the north-west of India, featuring the Zebu cattle. Bottom: excavated ruins of Mohenjo-Daro, city on the Indus that flourished about 2500 B.C.

with the rest of mediaeval Europe, they pressed on into the enormous forests, their princes recruiting settlers just as in the west. But the Mongol invasion of the 13th century A.D. devastated much of Russia and cut off the rest from Europe, dominating it for centuries and grievously slowing agricultural advance. It was not until the late 18th and 19th centuries that Russia made her own mighty expansion, clearing forests, pioneering the vast lands of central Asia, driving steel ploughs into the great grassland steppe, and eventually, in the 20th century, pushing cultivation into the deserts beyond.

In Africa, meanwhile, the spread of agriculture seems to have taken two steps. In the third or second millennium B.C., agriculture spread south from Egypt to Sudan, and west along the great savannah belt that spans the continent between the Sahara desert and the tropical rain-forest. Unlike the Egyptians, who grew wheat and barley —typical near East crops—the Sudanese grew sorghum and millet, characteristic small-grained native cereals of Africa that could stand the continuous heat; they also became herdsmen. Agriculture soon stretched from end to end of the belt, but it did not yet penetrate the particularly stubborn tropical rain-forest to the south.

Iron technology, discovered in Asia Minor in the second millennium B.C., probably became established in eastern Sudan in the fourth century B.C., in the reign of King Harsiotef of Kush—the great Sudanese kingdom that had conquered and briefly ruled Egypt a few centuries earlier. By the first century B.C., Meroe, capital of Kush, was an industrial city surrounded by huge slag-heaps. By

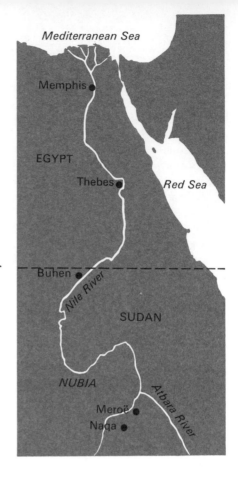

Map locates Meroë in Sudan, near the junction of the Atbara River and the Nile. Below: some of the slag-heaps of Meroë, evidence of the extensive iron-smelting industry there round about the first century B.C.

Coloured area on map shows where Bantu languages are spoken in Africa today.

Below: iron hoe blades made by the Jo Luo people of southern Sudan. The Jo Luo process iron in six-foot-high clay furnaces, probably very similar to those used in Meroë 2000 years ago. These blades were sometimes used as money.

this time, too, iron technology had reached the Nok people in northern Nigeria. In the first half of the first millennium A.D., western Sudan developed its earliest great empires. During this period a Sudanese group in Nigeria, whom we call the Bantu, must have begun to cultivate the yam, a tuber plant that yields more than twice as much food energy per acre as the small-grained cereals, and is suited for cultivation in the rain-forest. With yams and iron tools, the Bantu proceeded to people half a continent. Just as Indo-European languages came to dominate from Ireland to India, so Bantu languages are spoken through almost the whole of central and southern Africa. Those who colonized the easier plains or highlands beyond the rain-forest often turned or returned to other crops, but some of these tribes even today devote special rituals to the yam. By the European Middle Ages, the Bantu had built great empires in Rhodesia, where later they raised the colossal palace walls of Great Zimbabwe. Though the story here lacks the rich documentation of Europe, the Bantu in their spread undoubtedly cleared great areas of forest.

From the 16th century onward, the great stream of European emigration began, rising to a flood in the 19th century with the industrial era. The emigrants' numbers were greater and their equipment better than that of any earlier pioneers, and so the 19th century saw the most spectacularly rapid clearances of all. In New Zealand (where the Maoris had already burnt a good deal of forest into grassland) and Australia, settlers concentrated almost entirely on the making, improvement, or

North America

U.S.S.R.

China

Europe

Africa

Asia

South America

Oceana

50

other areas

forest

meadow

agriculture

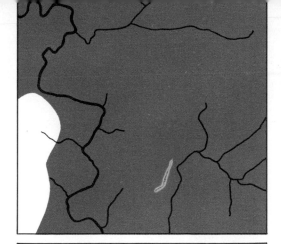

re-making of grasslands for pasture. But the clearance of vast lands for crops has a final and stirring chapter—the colonization of the United States of America.

In the 18th century, the Americans were still confined to the East Coast states. As the 19th century opened, the great move west began. One drive in the south carried tobacco and cotton crops, grown by slaves on huge plantations. A second drive in the north was made by independent pioneer small farmers. The two drives converged at their western edge (in Kansas, for instance), where disputes between farmers and slave-owners over new lands formed a starting-point of the great north-south conflict that finally broke out into the Civil War. By then, the two movements had between them cleared a huge area of forest.

In the south, the advance of the huge plantations swept the forest away in great swaths. In the north, the small farmers cleared more gradually but no less surely. What happened to the forest can be illustrated by its history in Cadiz Township, Green County, Wisconsin, carefully surveyed five times between 1831 and 1950. Changes that took millennia on the map of Europe were completed in Green County in 120 years, as illustrated on this page. In Europe, land was cleared in order of its fertility, giving an irregular pattern of clearings; in Wisconsin, the earlier land-holdings were arbitrarily allotted in square blocks, so that even the few copses left in 1950 tended to have geometrically straight edges: man's handiwork is plainer than ever. The few surviving wood-lots actually became denser and better established, thanks to fire protection, and this is the pattern over the whole forest belt and the mixed savannah on its fringe.

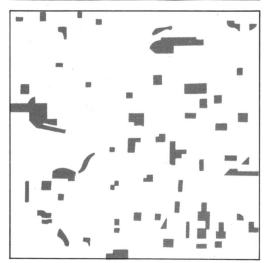

Like the first European clearance, this drive through the forest was made possible only by the production of thousands of axes, this time of steel. We do not know the names of the inventors and "men of enterprise" who created the stone-axe industry of Neolithic Europe. In the American clearance, we are better informed.

In the early 19th century, the newly independent Americans were desperately short of skilled labour. To

Opposite page: world land utilization. Size of rectangles is in proportion to the land area they represent. Divisions within them are similarly in proportion to the amount of land covered by (left to right in each case) permanent cropland, permanent pasture or meadow, forest, and other landscape. The circle shows the world picture. Such features as the high proportion of cropland in Europe and the particularly small area of forest in China at once stand out.

Right: changes in wooded area in Cadiz Township, Wisconsin, during settlement. Shading in top diagram shows forest in the area (of about 35 square miles) in 1831. Second diagram shows wooded areas in 1882—less than one third of the forest of 1831. (Geometrical patterns arose because of arbitrary allotting of land.) By 1902 (third diagram) the wooded area, now only one tenth that of 1831, began to reflect the topography of the area. Current forest areas (fourth diagram) are mostly confined to rocky outcrops and thin-soil hilltops.

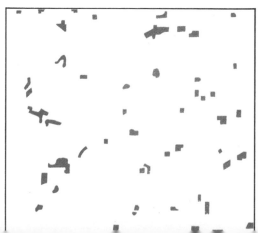

Portrait of Elisha King Root, pioneer of mass production in axe-making. He later applied his new techniques to other industries.

by-pass the shortage, a handful of American technologists took a great new step, and gave the world a fundamentally new technique of mass production. An early field of application was in the provision of large numbers of steel axes of uniform shape and temper. In 1826 Samuel and David Collins of Connecticut assembled a few expert blacksmiths at South Canton, Ohio, and installed a few machines (such as trip-hammers) to lighten their labours. In 1832 they engaged a new foreman, Elisha King Root. Root analysed all the stages of axe-making, divided them among specialist operators, and introduced at South Canton every possible device for standardizing each job: for instance, a whole batch of 100 axe-heads was hung on a drum revolving in a furnace, so that each would receive identical heat treatment in tempering the steel. Methods such as this resulted in a mass production of uniform axes stamped with the Collins trade-mark; without them, the pioneers could never have cleared the forests. Root's solution of the problem of producing the axes helped to advance the American method of mass production, so basic to our present way of life.

In the mid-19th century, the pioneers emerged from the forests into the great grassland belt that ran across North America from south to north, ending in the prairie provinces of Canada. Much of this grassland was itself ready-made by the Indians. Now, oddly enough, once you have cut and burnt the trees, forest soils are relatively easy to cultivate, some by iron, some even by stone tools. The tough sod of the grasslands is another matter. A single plant of the grass family (actually a cultivated grass, rye) was once grown for four months in a box with less than 2 cubic feet of earth. It grew 20 inches high; underground, the root system had developed 378 *miles* of roots! The tangled sod of old grassland, bound together by miles of grass-roots, can be cut only by steel ploughs, developed only in the second quarter of the 19th century. And so, despite all its millennia of forest clearance, Europe had never before been able to tackle the grasslands of Hungary and southern Russia, which were actually cleared for crops at almost the same time as American pioneers cleared theirs. They drove rapidly into the grass belt, continuing to grow maize at first and then turning to wheat in the drier land farther west. Once the sod could be ploughed, the flat or gently rolling prairie was far more thoroughly cleared than more rugged forest land; over huge areas, all trace of the original vegetation was totally destroyed. Over millions of acres in the Middle West, we know the original vegetation only in the way we know it in some of the African and Asian savannahs, by a modern equivalent of fetish groves—the strip of grass fenced in on either side of the railway tracks.

With this last sudden spread of cropland into the grass, we come to the end of our clearance story. Some advance of cropland continues, notably in Africa, and it may be possible to plough farther into some deserts, but there is reason to believe that man is already cultivating almost the whole area of land best suited for agricultural crops, and, indeed, he is now actively protecting or even enlarging the remnants of forest. The upshot of man's activity is clearly seen in a report published in 1962 by the United Nations. (The report was used to prepare the diagram on p. 50.) More than 10 per cent of the entire land surface of the earth is seen to be under crops; most of this would certainly be forest, and the rest grassland, if man had not come to clear it. As for the remaining grassland and forest, we must assume a considerable gain by grass over trees as another of man's doings. Here is the massive and visible evidence of mankind's impact on nature.

The man-made landscape of the central part of the United States—mile upon mile of cultivated fields laid out in neat rectangles.

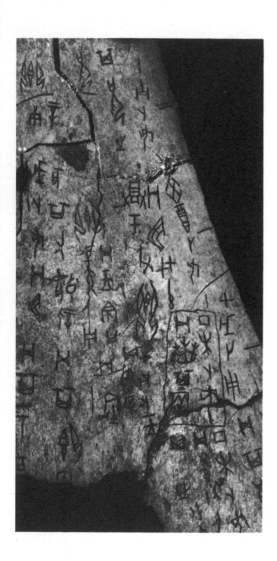

The earliest known form of Chinese writing, incised on a piece of bone. It probably dates from the 12th century B.C.

The gift of Prometheus was the first great breakthrough in man's relations with nature; as we have seen, he began at once to make his mark on the land surface. With the new increase of security and leisure so gained, he first spread over the world; and then, in the fourth glaciation, he began suddenly to make rapid progress in handling his surroundings. Very likely, this was the result of a new development of human language, which facilitated the rapid spread of innovations made by creative individuals. By the dawn of the fourth glaciation, this had led to the second great breakthrough—agriculture. From then on, advances in communication, and hence in the growth and spread of knowledge, came thicker and faster than ever.

These new advances in communication began with writing, which evolved in the fourth millennium B.C. At first it was essentially what we call ideographic, each symbol representing some object or activity or idea. For such writing, which the Chinese still practise today, an enormous number of symbols (more than 50,000 in Chinese) are needed, all of which have to be learned by a really literate person. In the second millennium B.C., alphabetic writing was invented in the Near East. By means of a couple of dozen symbols, put together in endless ways, any number of objects or activities or ideas could be expressed. Alphabetic reading and writing is easily and quickly learned. Early in the last century, a gifted Cherokee Indian called Sequo-yah realized the advantages of the writing activities of Europeans. Knowing only that the thing was possible, he set out to give his tribe the art of writing. At first he thought there would have to be a written symbol for each word. Then he realized (it can only be called genius) that letters should represent sounds, combined in any number of ways. In 1821, he submitted to the tribal council an alphabet of 85 letters for the Cherokee language. The council accepted the idea and within seven years were producing two newspapers in Cherokee; Sequo-yah was made an honorary chief by his own people, and received a financial grant from Congress. The Austrian botanist and language-student Stephan Endlicher named the giant redwood trees of California *sequoias* in honour of this wise red man. The striking fact is that Cherokee children could now learn to read and write their language *in a few days*. When the ancient forerunners of Sequo-yah made their discovery in the second millennium B.C., reading and writing ceased to be the monopoly of a few professionals, and could be used to exchange knowledge between many people.

The actual process of writing was still laborious, and for a long time this limited the number and cheapness of copies of written works. Then in the sixth century A.D., the Chinese invented block-printing. The earliest known

Portrait made in 1838 of the Cherokee
Indian, Sequoyah. He is pointing to the
alphabet he devised for his people.

The Chinese invented movable-type printing. But it was almost as cumbersome as block printing because of the large number of symbols in the Chinese script. Compare part of a Chinese typesetter's case, above, with that of a typesetter working in an alphabetic script (top).

printed work is a notice "Beware of the Dog," dating from A.D. 594. Like ideographic writing, block-printing was a limited gain; every page of a book had to be made into a block as a completely new undertaking.

But just as the alphabet made writing easy and flexible, so the invention of movable type made printing infinitely easier, for now a printer had only to make type for a few letters, and set it up in any required combination. It was in about A.D. 1050 that a Chinese labourer called Pi Sheng invented movable type; but in China, where the language was ideographic anyway, the gain was not obvious. Printing reached Europe, where the languages were

ascensianu.

Above: the earliest surviving example of block printing; it composes Buddhist charms printed between A.D. 762 and 769 from wooden blocks. Left: engraving of a printing press from the title page of a book printed by Jacobus Badius Ascensius in Paris in 1507.

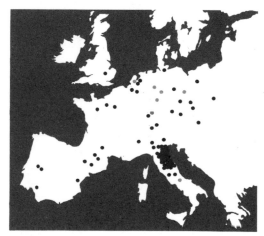

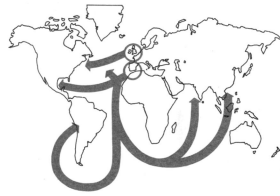

Upper map: arrow marks Europe's first printing press, set up by Johann Gutenberg in Mainz in about 1450. By 1465 printing had started in Holland, Italy, and France (green dots). Fifteen years later there were presses all over Europe (black dots). Lower map shows the spread of presses to Spanish, Portuguese, Dutch, French, and English overseas territories by 1638.

For centuries, man's only real sources
of power had been the muscles of men and
animals, and wind and water (right). Then
came the great technological breakthrough
and new sources of power were discovered.
Coal was the first. Coal can boil water
to produce steam, and many steam-engines
were developed, able to do tasks formerly
impossible or which had required many
men. Below: James Watt's steam-engine
of 1788, used for pumping water.

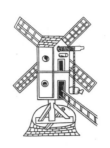

alphabetic, in the 12th century, but since it was only block-printing, book production was still laborious. By the end of the 14th century, however, Pi Sheng's discovery (improved by the Koreans) reached Limoges, and with the combination of the alphabet and movable type, an astonishing new advance began. After fire and agriculture, this was the third great step in human progress—the technological breakthrough.

To gain control over nature, man needs physical energy. Agriculture, by providing a surplus, freed some human beings to expend energy in new ways, as well as, of course, to think. But until the end of the Middle Ages, the only sources of energy or power were human and animal muscles and some locally available natural forces such as gravity, water, and wind (used in such devices as mills and sailing ships). From the technological breakthrough arose new sources of power—coal, oil, atomic energy—driving machines that could do the work of many men or animals. Meanwhile, mass production, and its successor automation, began freeing human beings from even the routine of controlling their machines. With the growth of really systematic science and technology, man acquired an altogether new confidence and capacity to understand and control the complex workings of nature, and so to influence his surroundings as never before, and to create the conditions of modern life.

A key factor in the Industrial Revolution was the substitution of machines to do work normally done by man. In a poor country like India many tasks are still done by hand, even projects like dam building (above). By contrast, in technological societies whole engineering processes can be controlled by machines (below) in the charge of just a few men.

3 The Forest Farmers

Everyone knows that the technological breakthrough began in Europe a few centuries ago. Why did it happen there? We can dismiss any notion that the Europeans are inherently wiser or more creative than other peoples. Nearly all the early discoveries on which the European achievement was based were made by other peoples outside Europe. Agriculture itself came from the Near and Middle East, partly because of the concentration there of useful plants and animals. Writing came from Iraq, and the alphabet from the Phoenician trading cities on the coast of Lebanon and from neighbouring peoples. Iron was first worked in the mountains of the Near East. Modern mathematics depends on the system of numbers worked out in classical India and further improved by Arabs and Persians. Block and type printing, cheap paper,

Map shows how the Sahara, a desert for the last 5000 years, largely cut off the rest of Africa from outside influence, though some civilizations, such as Zimbabwe, did arise. Map also marks possible routes of the first colonizers of the Americas; they probably came from the Middle East, India, China, and Siberia, and may well have crossed overland from Siberia to Alaska during the last glaciation when there was a much lower sea-level. When the ice retreated, America was cut off from the Old World.

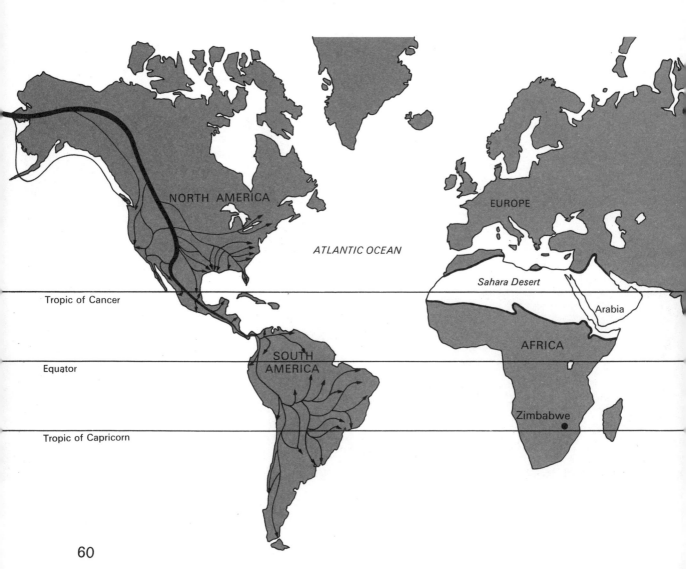

the compass and gunpowder came from China, which in the 15th century A.D. was technically far in advance of Europe. Horses were probably tamed by peoples of Central Asia. The civilizations of India and the Middle East leaned heavily on the skill and enterprise of metal miners in the heart of Africa. Clearly enterprise and inventiveness are not European monopolies. Nor have the Europeans been specially constructive and peaceful; their history reeks of blood.

This list, a small selection, shows how important a part was played by the spread of discoveries (and materials) made by anciently established peoples. From this, however, America could not benefit. Soon after it was first colonized, the retreat of the ice and the rising sea-level completely cut off America from the rest of mankind. A few Bronze Age or Celtic adventurers may have landed in the New World, and Vikings certainly did; but none of these adventures came to anything. Until certain advances in navigation and shipbuilding were made (chiefly by the Chinese, though finally exploited by Europeans), America evolved in total isolation.

Most of Africa, too, was somewhat isolated, though not by an ocean. The ice ages, bringing cold to the temperate zones, brought also the pluvial ages to the tropical regions, when heavy rainfall spread far north and south of the equator. The last interglacial, accordingly, meant the drying-up of once well-watered regions. When it began, the Sahara was covered with fertile stretches occupied by peoples skilled in engraving drawings on rocks. As late as the third millennium B.C., large herds of cattle were grazed in lower Nubia, where, according to the British archaeologist A. J. Arkell, ". . . desert conditions are so severe today that the owner of an ox-driven water-wheel has difficulty in keeping one or two beasts alive throughout the year." From about the fourth millennium B.C., the Sahara began to turn into a vast desert, which merchants died trying to cross.

The Americans and the Africans were thus more or less thrown back not only on their own unaided inventiveness, but also on their own natural resources. Africa was desperately short of *native* useful plants. America was richly endowed with useful plants (such as maize and

Maize is a plant of American origin; it was an important factor in the advance of early American civilizations. The illustration above is the first European drawing of the plant, taken from Leonhard Fuchs's *De Historia Stirpium*, of 1542.

TVRCICVM
FRVMENTVM.
Turckifch korn.

Right: plan of the area known as The Temple at Zimbabwe (see map opposite), a city that rose and fell within the last thousand years. It controlled the production of superbly wrought iron that cities on the coast exported across the Indian Ocean. The Temple itself was nearly 300 feet across at its widest part. Key to numbers on diagram: (1) parallel passage; (2) conical tower; (3) platform; (4) enclosures with remains of huts.

61

potatoes), but desperately short of useful animals: the horse, for instance, though actually evolved on the plains of North America, had been completely wiped out, possibly by a great epidemic, about the time man arrived. The wonder is that both the Americans and the Africans were able to build great civilizations at all.

Europe's easy access to other parts of the Old World was one reason for her success. But much has also depended on the forms of agriculture adopted by human societies, and hence on their relations with nature. These forms are immensely diverse in detail. But, on the whole, after the pioneer clearance, human societies have followed three different agricultural pathways, and these three pathways can be traced in three great climatic divisions of the world. Very roughly, we can think of these as the wet regions, the dry regions, and the ideal region—Europe. We begin with the wet regions, the hot damp rain-forests of the tropics.

The Forest Fallow

The belt called the tropics lies on either side of the equator, is more than 3200 miles wide, and contains about 40 per cent of the earth's surface (including waters, which make up about three quarters of the area). It receives more than half the world's total rainfall, and it is extremely hot. Much of it is covered by dense rain-forest.

Now we saw that the Danubians, the first pioneers of Europe, practised what has been called shifting cultivation

Below: two sketches made in 1883 of farming in Finland. Left picture shows a felled woodland being fired; right picture shows the fired land being ploughed. The ancient Finnish epic *Kalevala* speaks of "the hoe among the pine roots"; later the plough could be used here, for the tree stumps are far enough apart.

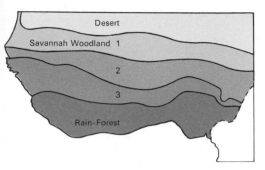

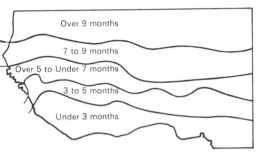

Maps of tropical West Africa show how vegetation is linked to climate. Upper map shows the transition from desert, through three stages of savannah with progressively less grass and more trees, to dense rain-forest near the equator. Lower map shows the number of months in the year with less than one inch of rain (dry season).

—that is, they cleared a plot, burned it, grew crops there for a while among the stumps and roots, left it to revert to forest, and moved on. And in fact, as John Mason Peck (see page 35) was later to notice in North America, this has always tended to be the first stage of clearance. In regions outside the wet tropics, it is normally followed by a wave of more permanent settlement, with other kinds of agriculture. This has been true all over Europe, except in the damp spruce and pine forests of the far north. Here shifting cultivation was still going on in Russia in the late 19th century, and in Sweden till 1918; in Finland it has continued to this day. By the 18th century shifting cultivation had evolved into a systematic method: the farmers grew crops (oats and rye) on a plot for 4 to 6 years, let the land grow back into forest, and then returned 20 or 30 years later to use it again. But the amount of food yielded by this practice was always small, the trees became more and more valuable as timber for the peoples farther south (as their own forests disappeared), and shifting cultivation in the far north is dying out.

But in the tropical rain-forest all over the world, this freezing of agriculture at its first pioneering stage happened on a grand scale, and resulted in a great agricultural system. In 1957, it was estimated by the Belgian agriculturalist P. De Schlippé that shifting cultivation was being practised on over 13 million square miles of land, by 200 million people—nearly one person in ten of the

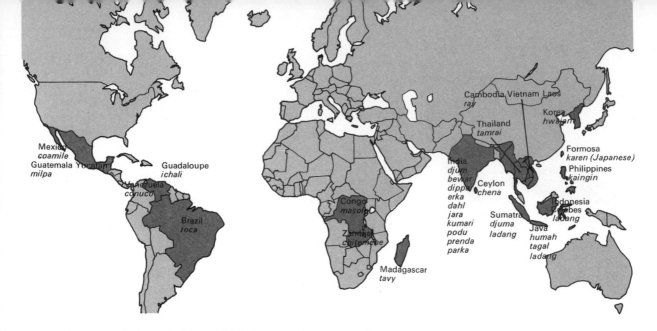

then population of the world. The practice ranges from haphazard use of one casual clearing after another to agricultural systems of extraordinary subtlety and complexity, like those of the Zande people in the Sudan or the Hanunóo people of Mindoro Island in the Philippines. But more often than not, it is a systematic alternation (*rotation*), in which a given plot of land is cleared, burned, used for crops, left unused (*fallow*) to turn back into forest (*bush*), used again, left again, and so on. This is called *bush fallow rotation*. It has arisen again and again, often independently in different places, all over the tropics. Everywhere it is basic to the whole way of life of the people who work it, and they have given it a whole series of names, usually referring both to the system and to a plot of land so used (see map). English-speaking scientists, seeking to impose order on this rich diversity of names, have begun to call the typical plots in all these places *swiddens* (from an old English country word for burned clearings), and the system *swidden farming*.

Above right: map locating the position of Mindoro Island in the Philippines, and, far right, the territory in the south-east part of the island that is occupied by the Hanunóo. The small area marked Yagaw is where the swidden-farming techniques of the Hanunóo were studied in detail.

The Way of the Tropics

It is fair to use one word, for everywhere in the tropics the sequence of work on a swidden is the same. First, an area of forest is chosen (sometimes very carefully). Then it is cleared: small saplings, creepers, and underbrush are slashed cleanly away, some of the big trees are trimmed of their branches, others felled (a dangerous moment in these giant forests), leaving sizeable stumps. The work may be divided up, as among the Hanunóo; men do the heavy felling, women the lighter slashing, and small boys climb to the tops of trees to trim them. All debris is cut up small and spread evenly over the swidden. The whole operation is timed so that debris can dry out during the short dry season. The more careful farmers clear strips around the swidden as firebreaks. Harold C.

Right: a slashed area of swidden in Yagaw, prior to burning. The swidden is in an area where clearings have been made previously. In the background, part of a primary forest is visible.

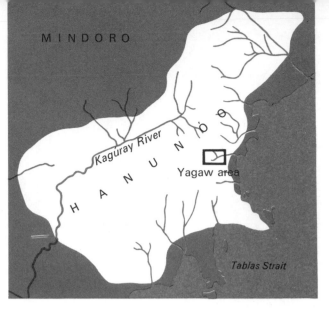

Left: a Hanunóo man felling a large tree with an axe. He is standing on a wooden scaffolding specially constructed for the purpose. Only men participate in the tree-felling, which can sometimes be a dangerous task. Opposite page, top: a woman planting taro in a cut but unburned swidden. She makes a hole with the planting stick, then drops in a young taro plant from her basket. Such root crops as these can survive later burning of the area; most crops are planted after burning.

Conklin, the American anthropologist, lived for several years with the Hanunóo; in 1953-55, during the burning of more than 150 swiddens, less than one acre of neighbouring bush was burned by accident. When he remarked on this, they simply said, "All our swiddens have fire-breaks." Not all peoples are as meticulous as these undoubted masters of the art of swidden farming. At all events, when the debris is tinder dry, the swidden is set ablaze from several places, and in an hour or so it has burned out, leaving a thick layer of ash.

Now begins the sowing and planting of crops. The ground is prepared for seeds by simple tools, hoes or digging-sticks. The people of temperate lands are used to seeing fields laid out with a single crop—wheat, barley, potatoes, etc.—but tropical swidden farming is quite different. A large number of different crops are grown all together, sown or planted and harvested in turn in a continuous sequence through the long wet season, when there is always something to be done and something to be eaten. Just as the hunters of Lascaux were great zoologists, so some of the swidden farmers are no mean botanists. The Hanunóo recognize not only different plant species, but different types or varieties within many of them. Western scientists distinguish about 1200 plant species in the Hanunóo lands of Mindoro Island; all the Hanunóo people themselves can recognize 1600 different kinds of plant, and treat them all differently. More than 400 are bred, by sowing seeds or planting parts that can reproduce new plants; others are destroyed as useless weeds; others, though reproducing themselves, are more or less cultivated, protected from fire when the swidden is burned by being wrapped around with green plant materials. Among such experts a swidden is a regular botanical garden.

Below: firing a swidden with a bamboo torch. During the few days before firing, the Hanunóo clear a fire path around the swidden to minimize the risk of fire spreading to the surrounding forest. Opposite page: Indians from near the Essequibo River, Guyana, firing a field cut about a month previously. Here, the dried branches have to be constantly lighted with a torch.

66

Usually, however, there is one main food plant that gets special attention and is the object of elaborate rituals. Often this is a cereal—maize in America, millets or a local kind of rice in parts of Africa, rice in the East. Sometimes it is a starchy root crop, like the yam in much of Africa; and this is always so on the Pacific islands, for the peoples there seem to have left their original homes in Asia before the coming of rice. Besides the main crops, each society may grow other cereals and root crops in the swidden, and usually too there are leguminous plants rich in protein—we shall come across legumes again later on. A variety of small plants provide spicy tastes or medical remedies. And finally, there may be fruit trees that, as they grow, provide shade for the new sprouts of the returning forest.

Map shows Yagaw area of Mindoro between 1953 and 1955. Dark blue shows 1953 swiddens; mid-blue, 1954 swiddens; and light blue, 1955 swiddens. Primary forest is shown in dark grey, re-grown forest is white, and grassland is light grey. Capital letters are settlement sites.

After a time, the swidden is gradually abandoned, and the forest grows back. Only when the land has been forest again for some time (bush fallow) will the swidden farmers return to it and clear it afresh; meanwhile, they are clearing and using other swiddens elsewhere in the forest. Timing varies in different places, but when swidden farming is working efficiently the bush fallow period is always considerably longer than the period the land is cleared and used for crops. Among the Hanunóo, the intensive cropping period averages 2-4 years, and the bush fallow 8-10 years. In Sierra Leone, the cycle is 2 years cropping, 12-15 years fallow; in Ceylon, 1-3 years cropping, 8-20 years fallow; in New Guinea, 1 year cropping, 15-20 years fallow. Everywhere the older traditional systems follow this pattern of a long bush fallow period.

In some places we find special versions of the bush fallow rotation. A famous one is the *chitemene* system, most advanced in Zambia. This is basically a bush fallow rotation, usually with finger millet as the main crop. But besides clearing the swidden itself, the farmers cut off branches from trees in the forest for some distance around, bring them to the swidden, and burn them with the rest of the debris. We shall see that this refinement probably has real value. The chitemene system is found in fact all over East and Central Africa as far north as Sudan and northern Nigeria; the first European to describe it (in 1866) was the great missionary-explorer David Livingstone, who saw it on the Rovuma River in Malawi. The Indian systems called *parka* and *dippa* are similar, too. In Sudan, several tribes have found another trick. Instead of burning the debris on a swidden, they leave it to the termites; in four months these formidable little animals reduce it to a powder. The Dinka people enrich the debris with branches from the forest around (as in the chitemene system), and let termites pulverize the lot.

Swidden farmers of the tropics have two kinds of neighbours. In the flood plains of rivers, settled agriculture has developed, using the same land for crops year after year. This is based on certain properties of the soils, on irrigation (a subject of Chapter 5), and (except on steep slopes or where farms are only tiny plots) on the use of the plough, drawn by oxen or buffaloes. The stumps of tropical rain-forests grow too close together to admit cattle and ploughing, so swidden farmers still use the hoe and digging-stick. In the East, where settled farming is common, swidden farmers have largely been driven up into the hills; in Africa, where river flood plains are less favourable for settled farming, they spread wider.

The other neighbours of the swidden farmers live on the edge of the rain-forest, where the dry seasons lengthen and the country turns gradually into grassland. They are nomadic (wandering) herdsmen, driving their flocks around in search of pasture and water. A few swidden farmers (like the Hanunóo) keep small grasslands near at hand and raise a few cattle, but in general, domestic animals form no part of swidden farming, and swidden farmers and stock-raising nomads live quite apart; we shall see that this splitting of the two original foundations of agriculture (crops and herds) has always been unfortunate. Since in the tropics both groups are very busy and continually on the move, especially the nomads, they have not been able to integrate into one system of farming or society. In the East, farmers and nomads are rather strictly divided by the boundary of rain-forest and grassland. In Africa, vast areas of open woodland and savannah are dominated by "the rulers of Africa"—the terrible blood-sucking tsetse flies that carry a number of deadly diseases to both man and his animals. The human diseases so spread are being brought under control by drugs, but the cattle diseases are still an unsolved problem, and wherever the tsetse rules, herds must leave or die. In the absence of herdsmen, swidden farmers can often spread for hundreds of miles outside the rain-forest, and so Africa is above all the continent of bush fallow rotation.

Chitemene cultivation in Zambia, a variation of bush fallow rotation. Branches are cut from trees over a wide area, collected in piles, and burned on the area to be cultivated, so providing more fertilizing ash.

Tsetse flies are still found in a large area of Africa (marked blue on map above) and the diseases they transmit to animals are one reason why herdsmen occupy relatively little of that continent.

4 The Tropical Cul-de-sac

In the 19th and early 20th centuries, when European agriculturalists assumed control of farming in the tropics (for instance, the British and Belgians in Africa, and the Dutch in Indonesia), they were shocked by the apparent inefficiency of the traditional farming systems they found there. Accustomed to the economic and highly productive agriculture developed (as we shall see) in Europe, and not realizing how this had happened, they observed that bush fallow rotation used a great deal of land and labour to produce very little food. They assumed that swidden farming was a crude and primitive system, used only because local peasants knew no better. And so, in many parts of the wet tropics, often with the best intentions in the world, Europeans set about clearing the forest for good, ploughing the land, sowing one or two crops in each field, and growing them repeatedly year after year. But in man's interplay with nature, the road to famine is often paved with good intentions. At first the harvests were splendid, but after a few years they fell and fell, and eventually the land became unusable. This happened, for instance, in Malaya, Sierra Leone, Uganda, and the Congo. The chastened Europeans began to realize that there were reasons for swidden farming, after all.

They might have inferred this from the fact that this system of bush fallow rotation had arisen and persisted (often independently) in so many different places in the wet tropics. Even local differences in detail are closely related to local conditions of topography, climate, and natural vegetation. In all the islands of Melanesia (in the Pacific), for instance, six different forms of swidden farming have been found, with different crops, used in six different settings (lowlands, foothills, highlands, and so on). In each island, the people of each region have evolved the same way of exploiting it. Swidden farming and its various forms may have come about by slow unconscious experience of crop and land success or failure; in some places at least, really observant individuals may have played a more creative part—legends of gifted ancestors are common enough. Today, true, the farming systems often largely, and always to some extent, kept up by unthinking traditions and rituals. But there is sometimes method even in the rituals, and people like the Hanunóo can often give perfectly practical reasons for the things they do. At all events, in the 1930s, scientists began to study the special conditions of farming in the wet tropics,

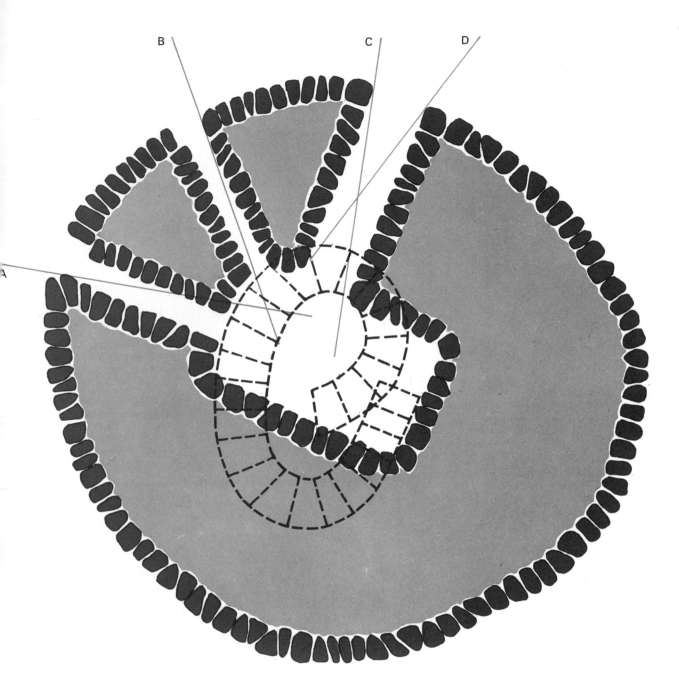

The Mayan civilization of Central America arose between the third and eighth centuries A.D.; based on swidden farming, it achieved great skill in numbers and astronomy. Its sudden collapse is the story of the tropical cul-de-sac, told in this chapter. Left: two views of the observatory in the Mayan city of Chichen Itza; above: plan showing astronomical sight lines (A, south; B, setting of moon, March 21; C, west, and sunset at equinoxes; D, sunset at summer solstice).

and they discovered that bush fallow rotation, properly conducted, has its point. With all the wealth of modern scientific knowledge and technical equipment, the problem of farming these lands more productively is still a formidably difficult one, far from solved; and the wonder is that local pioneers and peasants, lacking all this, produced a system so well suited to their surroundings. To understand how it works and what it does, we shall have to look at the problem of soil fertility.

The Living Soil

Soil looks simple stuff, but it is one of the most complicated things in the world. It is made up, near the surface, of three components: minerals, organic matter (made from the chemical remains of dead plants and animals), and millions of small living organisms ranging in size from viruses and bacteria to the relatively mighty earthworms. The mineral part, also present lower down, is made from the rocks of the earth's surface, ground into small particles (sand), smaller ones (silt), and very small ones (clay), and moved from place to place by wind, water, or glaciers. The organic matter, starting as dead organisms, becomes a sort of paste, called *humus*, between the mineral particles, coating each of them. The amounts of different-sized mineral particles and humus, among other things, determine the structure of the soil, whether it forms into visible "crumbs" (much bigger than the mineral particles), between which air and water can enter and move freely, or becomes a sticky mass. When air and water are present in the right balance, soil supports unimaginable numbers of live organisms. In an acre of soil, there may be up to half a million earthworms; in a square yard, up to 20 million tiny threadworms; and in a saltspoonful, up to 4000 million bacteria; and many other kinds of organisms are present too. These busy organisms, as they feed and excrete and die, make the soil a scene of ceaseless chemical change; some of them make organic matter and break it down again. All of this is true for soils everywhere.

The green plants, on which we and our livestock depend, get materials for energy and growth from air and soil. From the air, they get oxygen and some water. Also, by means of the green chlorophyll in their leaves, they can use the energy of sunlight to take carbon dioxide from the air, discard the oxygen (so surrounding the earth with

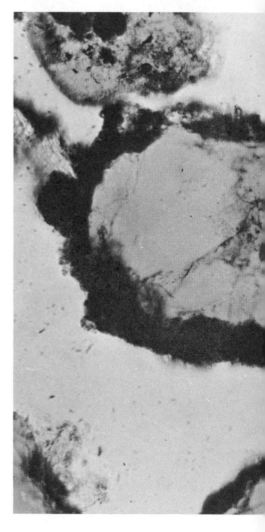

Left: section through a cocoa-root system in a well-drained upland soil in Ghana. Note how the root exploits the soil layers by forming a mat of roots near the surface, penetrating deep, and dividing into fibrous ends on reaching the gritty clay.

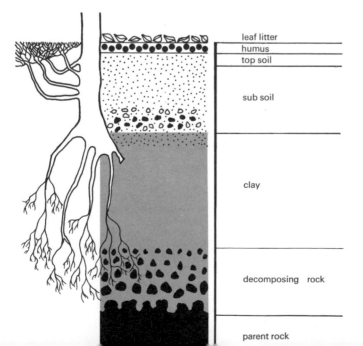

leaf litter
humus
top soil

sub soil

clay

decomposing rock

parent rock

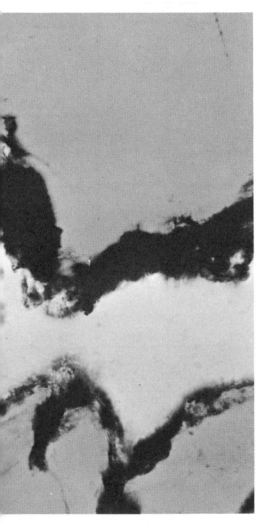

a breathable atmosphere for themselves and all other life), and use the carbon to build up energy-storing carbohydrate compounds—sugars, starch, and others. From the soil, through their roots, they get most of their water, and supplies of a number of vital mineral elements—nitrogen (for making protein, the main material of living bodies), phosphorus (for making nucleic acids, the "blueprints" for all other processes), potassium, calcium, magnesium, sulphur, and other elements needed in smaller amounts. Most of these elements got into the soil originally from the "parent" rocks of which the soil mineral particles are the powdered remains. Nitrogen, however, is another matter.

There is plenty of nitrogen in the air, but plants cannot use free nitrogen; they can only take it from certain compounds containing it—ammonia and nitrates. But air enters the soil through the spaces between crumbs, and here the nitrogen is extracted and turned into elaborate compounds by three groups of bacteria. Two of these (*Clostridium* and *Azotobacter*) live free in the soil; the third group (*Rhizobium*) begins its life in the soil, waiting for the arrival of roots of plants of the family Leguminosae (legumes), or a few other plants about which little is known. These roots release a substance that stimulates rhizobia to swim up to the roots and go inside. Once within the root, they multiply, and the legume makes them at home in a little bulge (a root nodule), where they live in a mutually profitable partnership, the legume providing sugars and the rhizobia nitrogen compounds. When the legume dies, these compounds are left in the soil.

Many mineral elements in the soil, such as potassium and calcium, are stored on the surface of the smallest mineral particles (clay); others, especially nitrogen itself,

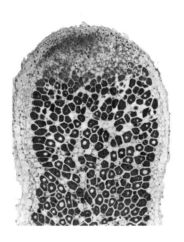

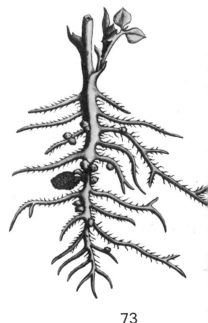

The skeleton of soil is formed of particles of highly resistant, inert rock. Top photo shows clay particles, each less than two thousandths of a millimetre across. The particles are coated with organic matter humus, seen clearly in the lower photograph.

Right: drawing by 17th-century Italian anatomist Marcello Malpighi shows nodules on root of bean plant. Photo above shows root nodule and the concentration of boron (dark), an element essential for the development of nodules on leguminous plants.

73

are stored in the organic matter. For, once the soil is occupied by plants, it becomes a going concern. All the plant food elements (including carbon from the air, which most soil organisms could not otherwise use) are continually being returned to the soil in the dead bodies of plants and animals. Some microbes build nitrogen from these sources into *organic matter*, in which form the nitrogen is unusable by plants but safely stored. Other microbes break the organic matter down into nitrates, which plant roots can use. Others are liable to grab the nitrates and turn them back to free nitrogen, which returns to the air. Thus arises an elaborate roundabout called the *nitrogen cycle*.

The trouble about nitrates is that they are easily washed out of the surface soil into lower depths where most plant roots cannot reach them, or from where they are drained away to the nearest stream. To achieve the right balance of activity of all the various microbes for successful agriculture is quite a trick. For instance, crops are sometimes grown especially as "green manures" for other crops, their dead leaves and stems being worked into the soil to add to the organic matter. Sometimes this actually does more harm than good, for if soil microbes are given too much carbon from such plant remains, they use their surplus energy on the organic matter originally present, making so much nitrate that a lot is washed away or broken down by other microbes before the main crop can get the benefit of it. On the other hand, if the microbes are too idle, the nitrogen is safely stored in organic matter and inaccessible for the plants. Ideally, a balance between these extremes is to be achieved.

The Uses of the Forest Fallow

In the wet tropics, two special conditions are present. First, the heat makes all microbes very active, so the nitrogen cycle revs up. Second, the very heavy rainfall in the long wet season is especially liable to wash (*leach*) nitrates into the lower depths, and also other necessary minerals, particularly where there is too much sand and not enough clay to hold them. Such soils, which tend to become rather acid, are called leached soils. They occur in damp sandy places even in Europe, under heaths and pinewoods, but are especially widespread in the wet tropics. In the flood plains of rivers, however, water does not easily drain away, and here less leaching occurs. If, as in Africa, the great rivers bring down soil from other tropical regions that have been leached themselves, this does not help much. But if, as elsewhere, the great rivers come from richer soils outside the tropics, their flood plains are highly fertile. As we have seen, settled agriculture appeared in the flood plains of the east; so bush

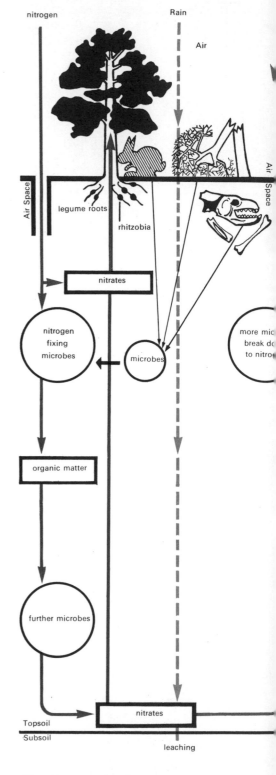

The nitrogen cycle. Plants cannot use free nitrogen; they have to obtain it from nitrogen compounds (nitrates), which are manufactured by bacteria in the soil. Right: in tropical rain-forests, although nitrates and useful mineral elements are liable to be washed into the lower soil depths, the deep tree roots recover them and make possible a lush growth, as in this forest in the Congo.

74

fallow rotation was clearly evolved for leached tropical soils.

The rain-forest has several ways of dealing with the problem presented by these soils. To begin with, the trees continually and rapidly return large quantities of dead matter to the soil—some of it woody material, that holds plant food elements tenaciously. The microbes go at it very fast, and leaves and other debris are broken down so rapidly that there is little litter on the rain-forest floor (such as you find piled up in temperate forests), and little humus in the soil. But the rapid turn-over makes the rich forest vegetation possible: forest trees can flourish even on a ledge thinly covered with soil, where less lavish plants would soon fail through not returning enough dead matter to the soil. The Hanunóo never make a swidden on such ledges, even when they see vigorous forest growth there, because they know it would not work. Where soil is deep but leached, the trees have another advantage: they throw down very deep roots (down to eight feet in some species) to bring up leached elements from the lower soil layers. Finally, the rain-forest is full of leguminous trees (which make up 50 per cent of all plant species in forests of Ghana and Central America), and the rhizobia in their roots counteract the loss of nitrogen by leaching. Legumes and their rhizobia evolved in the later Mesozoic period, when there were no polar ice-caps, and when the wet tropics and their leached soils spread much farther than they do today; they only later made good in temperate regions. They are one of the largest families of seed plants, with 13,000 species ranging from little clovers to giants of the forest; many are useful food crops, and, owing to their special power of winning nitrogen, they are rich in protein. Some legumes are used as swidden crops: the Hanunóo, for instance, grow pigeon-peas, mung beans, lima beans, ground-nuts, and several other legumes.

When man clears the trees and the land is occupied by smaller plants with surface root systems (grass or crops), the turn-over of plant matter is reduced or stopped. Not enough dead matter returns to the soil, and elements leached downward cannot be recovered: hence the eventual crop failures. The *first* crop on a swidden does fine, because it has the benefit of the long bush fallow. The

An expedition led by the British explorer Sir Henry Stanley threads between the towering trees of an African forest. In such forests, there is a rapid turnover of vegetation, and the dead matter—even the large tree trunks—soon decays, so aiding further tree growth.

Koompassia Excelsa, a leguminous tree in South America. As many as half the plants in a tropical rain-forest are nitrogen-providing legumes, and help to make up for nitrogen lost by leaching.

elements drawn up the deep tree roots are lavished on the surface soil of the clearing when the tree debris is burned. Farmers who practise chitemene (see Chapter 3) are even making use of supplies from elsewhere in the forest around. Experiments in Zambia have shown that chitemene ashes enrich the soil with phosphorus, potassium, and calcium, and make it less acid.

Early European experts had been horrified by the practice of burning debris on the swidden. They pointed out that during the fire large amounts of nitrogen must be vaporized and returned to the air, and claimed that the fire must destroy much of the organic matter of the forest soil. But, as long ago as 1932, the British agriculturalist G. Milne took up the defence of swidden farming, and listed a number of advantages of burning; and later work has fully vindicated him. In 1948, for instance, an experiment in growing rice on forest clearings near Njala in Sierra Leone showed that, when all the debris was removed, the first year's yield of rice was very low. If the debris was removed, and burned somewhere else, and the ash brought back and spread over the clearing, the yield was higher. But it was more than twice as high again if the debris was burned on the spot. So not only the ash but the actual burning is valuable. Similar results have been obtained with finger millet in Malawi in 1935–37, and in a long series of experiments in Zambia from 1932 to 1950. In 1959, G. Baldanzi, who was himself in Brazil comparing the benefits of burning vegetation or ploughing it into the soil, surveyed the whole history of burning as an agricultural method, right back to the comment of the poet Virgil in the first century B.C.: "It has often paid to set fire to sterile fields." He concluded that the burn affects only the topmost layer of the soil, and destroys little organic matter; that it improves soil structure; and that it kills or encourages exactly the right microbes to get the best possible balance of the nitrogen cycle in the soil. Once again, it seems, the swidden farmers were, without knowing the mechanism of the process, on the right track.

After a few years (three in Vietnam, four in Sudan, for instance), crop yields from a clearing fall to negligible amounts, and only another long bush fallow will restore the leached elements and repair the nitrogen cycle again. So the normal timing of bush fallow rotation is vindicated. The only exception so far recorded in a swidden region is in a rather dry (and therefore less leached) area in Ceylon, where, in experiments in 1948, it was found that a long bush fallow was unnecessary, and crops could be grown on a clearing for some time. Yet here, too, the swidden farmers practised their rotation (1–3 years cropping, 8–20 years fallow).

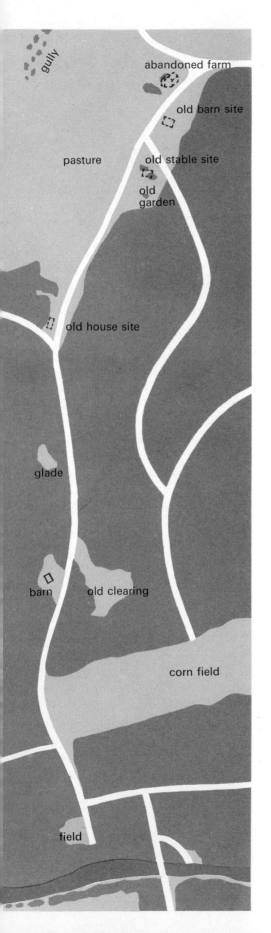

The reason is interesting, and suggests that swidden farmers elsewhere may have got the benefit of restoring soil fertility by doing their rotation from a quite different motive. After a year or two a swidden is so completely overgrown by weeds (which compete with and crowd out food crops) that the labour of weeding it becomes altogether too much; as a result, farmers have had to abandon the clearing some time before soil exhaustion would have brought about crop failure. When the trees grow back, bringing deep shade, the weeds die out, and by the time the swidden is cleared again, they will take a year or two to get a new foothold. The appearance of weeds in the first place was a direct result of cutting down the trees and opening the clearing to the sunlight.

We think of weeds as useless *wild* plants, but this is only a half-truth. Many weeds of temperate lands, where only one or two crops are grown on otherwise bare soil, are almost as man-made as the crops themselves: we call them "weeds of cultivation." Before agriculture, a few of them eked out a precarious existence on the few spots (such as river-banks) where nature left the soil bare, as these species need it to be. Man provided unprecedented amounts of bare soil: he opened Pandora's Box, and out came the weeds and flourished exceedingly. In the pollen sequences of Europe, a weed-like plantain is as unmistakable a sign as wheat of the presence of agricultural man. And man also spread weeds over wide areas when their seeds got mixed up with those of his crops; excavations at Caerleon in Wales in 1964, for instance, showed that the Romans had brought certain weeds to Britain in grain consignments.

Many weeds, however, are simply grasses that were already common before man arrived. Unlike some other things out of Pandora's Box, they have not been an unmixed curse. Oats and rye, for instance, appeared as weeds in the first European wheat and barley fields (wild rye grows today as a weed in the wheatfields of Afghanistan). They became better and better fitted for cultivated life, without any conscious human intention, so that when the pioneers reached the cold north, where the oats and rye did better than wheat and barley, man began to sow them deliberately as crops, So we owe both porridge and one kind of whisky to one-time weeds.

Two maps of an area in America show (right) geographical features and land use, and (left) occurrence of pokeweed (dots). Like most weeds, the plant thrives on open soil, and is therefore native only along the flooded soil of river banks. Note how it has been spread by man to his garden sites and cultivated land, where it is classed as a weed.

In tropical swiddens, weeds are essentially the plants of the grasslands, especially grasses themselves, and they flourish in clearings because man, by removing shade and reducing soil fertility, is tipping the balance in their favour: the forest trees, so lush once their cycle is established, cannot get started if the soil has become too poor. Short cropping periods and long bush fallows ensure that the forest can always return. Experts like the Hanunóo deliberately take care, by protecting certain trees from the burn and by planting new ones, to maintain enough shade to keep grasses at bay till the forest is recovering properly. But for even the least knowledgeable swidden farmers, the time to stop cropping is obvious: it is the time when grasses and other weeds are getting out of hand. Stopping at this point ensures the recovery of the forest, and by so doing it ensures the restoration of soil fertility.

It also ensures the continued *existence* of the soil. For, when the Europeans made their bare ploughed fields in the wet tropics and kept them under cultivation, not only did fertility decline, but often, too, the soil was actually lost by excessive erosion. Natural soil erosion is the gradual removal of the surface of the soil by wind, water, or glaciers, which carry it to streams and so either to their lower reaches and mouths (forming rich flood plains and deltas) or on into the ocean. This natural erosion is going on all the time at an appreciable rate. Natural soil erosion is the normal process whereby soil is distributed over the land, and it makes the river valleys lush with soil from the rocks of the mountains. On a world estimate made by the earth scientist Jean Corbel in 1964, something

Above right: meadow fescue showing root system. Grasses have an advantage over trees in dry country because they have a far larger root system in proportion to leaf area and their roots are nearer the surface. The roots thus take all available moisture from brief rain-storms so that none reaches the tree roots deeper down.

Upland rice growing on land in Sumatra which had been used the previous year for tobacco. Note the carefully preserved bushes and trees; these prevent erosion, and allow the forest to re-establish itself quickly before grasses can get a foothold. After about eight years of forest another tobacco crop is grown.

This area in San Rafael de Mucuchies in the Venezuelan Andes has suffered severe erosion following continual cultivation. Although wheat is still planted in some parts, most of the slope is quite useless for crop growing.

like 10,000 million cubic yards are eroded every year. This soil loss is naturally balanced by the equally gradual wearing away of the rocks beneath to form new soil; the two processes together maintain a roughly constant thickness of soil on the lands of the world, and the persistence of plants continually renews the fertility of surface soil. But whereas the provision of new soil cannot be hastened by man, the erosion of old soil *can*, when he exposes bare earth to the unbridled action of wind and water. When this happens, the soil may simply be lost, and we cannot wait millennia for new soil to form—we have to eat tomorrow.

Destructive soil erosion becomes a real menace on level plains swept by fierce winds, or in places, especially with steep and irregular slopes, where rain is very heavy. On the central plains of North America, owing to the pattern of air movement around the two ends of the coastal mountain chain and up from the Caribbean, furious winds and tornadoes are common; here the whole soil surface may be whipped up as a dust-cloud, leaving only lifeless subsoil or even bare rock. All over the wet tropics (where, as we have seen, swidden farming is commonest on the steep and irregular slopes of the hills), raindrops come down like volleys of bullets. As they hit the soil in exposed areas, bits of it splash into the air, while the rest is beaten into a compact, waterproof state. Instead of sinking into the soil, rain-water tends to run off down the nearest slope, carrying bits of soil with it. The whole top layer may be washed away by this "runoff" (sheet erosion), or the escaping water may dig itself gullies that deepen and widen as bigger and bigger soil fragments, or even rocks, are torn away and batter the floor and sides of each gulley. By such vicious spirals, the living soil of an open field may be washed right away, and carried to streams, to rivers, to the sea itself, silting up harbours and making treacherous bars across river-mouths.

There are several ways of protecting soil from destructive erosion, even in the wet tropics. One method is to spread on the soil surface a layer of material (such as dead plant matter) to take the first force of the rain (or wind): for this, English-speaking farmers have the expressive word *mulch*. Better still, however, is a cover of living vegetation. A forest cover is best of all: it intercepts heavy raindrops, letting them fall gently on to a soil that can absorb all this moisture and release water in a trickle, deep down, to issue as springs. But any continuous plant cover is a great help against erosion; and that is why lowered soil fertility, which eventually means that only a few plants can grow in patches on otherwise bare soil, itself brings soil erosion in its train.

The Hanunóo people of the Philippines know something of all this from tribal experience. They take enormous care when choosing a new swidden site, and may discuss it for months, up to three years in advance of clearing. They use only firm soils on regular slopes, not too steep, and classify soils into many categories, rated in order of fertility: their ratings have been found to agree well with the results of scientific analysis of these soils. As a final check, they drive a bamboo stick into the ground. If the soil does not come up the hollow interior of the bamboo, the site is abandoned. They regard this as purely a ritual activity, but obviously the outcome of the test must depend on soil structure, and therefore must have practical importance.

While the swidden is being cultivated, the great variety of crops grown together, some upright, some creeping, ensures that every foot of soil is covered with vegetation. The period when a swidden is first cleared and exposed

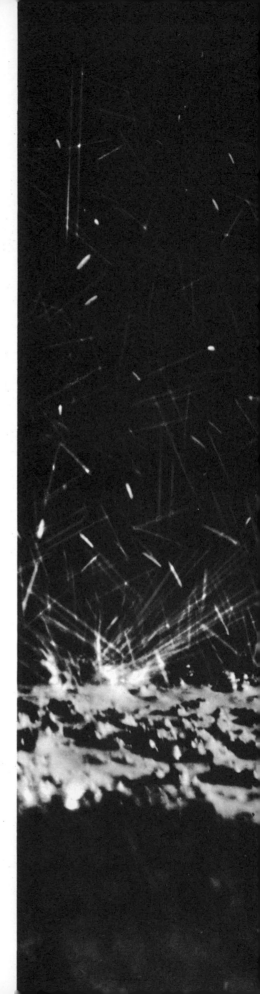

Left: heavy tropical rain strikes
unprotected soil, throwing the fine soil
particles into the air. These particles
fall back to earth, filling the spaces
between the larger particles. This
prevents water sinking into the soil;
instead it runs off in a flood,
eroding the soil as it goes.

Hill on the island of Mindoro shows,
in the background, climax rain-forest
where clearance is ritually prohibited
by the Hanunóo; were clearance to take
place, the steep slopes might well
erode. Such patches of forest provide
a source of seeds for regrowth on
cleared areas.

Map of South-East Asia showing population density as follows: over 200 persons per square mile (darkest blue), 50–200, 10–50, and under 10 (lightest blue). Swidden farming is practised in the lower density areas.

Hanunóo family eating rice and bananas. Swidden farming produces only enough food for present needs, and so works only if population density remains very low.

to the winds is critical; but, as we have seen, when they slash down the plant cover, the farmers take care to spread debris evenly over the soil surface as a mulch. Teen-agers, who find this spreading job less fun than slashing, are supervised by older Hanunóo, who give them their first "lectures" on soil erosion and how to prevent it.

The Dilemma

When all has been said of the real merits of swidden farming the fact remains that in some respects early European visitors were right about some things. It does use a great deal of land and labour to produce a very low yield of food. Even the food yields of the Hanunóo from cropped swiddens, which are about 1300 pounds per acre, are not high by the standards of permanently settled agriculture. The yield of swidden rice in Sierra Leone in 1964, probably typical for this way of farming, was about 775 pounds per acre of cropped land: all advanced rice-growing settled farmers manage to produce several thousand pounds, and one prize-winning Japanese farmer has raised 11,879 pounds per acre! But of course, apart from the low yield on the swidden itself, most of the land at any given time is unproductive bush fallow; so a given area of land will support few swidden farmers. There are about 50 Hanunóo per square mile, but this is an unusually high density; on an estimate made in 1957, the average number is 15. This means that swidden farmers take up not much less room than hunters, who in very good conditions may reach a population density of 2–3 persons per square mile.

When Europeans brought modern medicine to the wet tropics, and often (like the British in India and Burma) peace from local feuds as well, the populations of swidden farmers began to rise. The results showed all too clearly that swidden farming will work *only* if the population stays very low. In 1940, J. A. van Beukering of the Java Department of Economic Affairs estimated that swidden farming could support, at the very most, 125 people per square mile; and this figure has been generally accepted. Whenever populations became denser than this, things started going wrong. To feed the extra mouths, peasants had to have more land under crops and less under bush fallow. On any given plot, the cropping period became longer and/or the fallow period shorter. By 1964 the bush fallow period in parts of Sierra Leone had shortened from 12–15 years to 3–4 years. The reduced periods were often too short to enable the forest to recover and restore soil fertility. Hence, with populations rising all over the wet tropics, land became less and less fertile.

Over vast areas, especially where the dry season was fairly long and swiddens were repeatedly burned after the

If swiddens are repeatedly burned, the forest may never return and grass may move in. Once such cogonals get a foothold the land becomes useless to the swidden farmer because the matted root system below the surface defies his simple tools and continually shoots up grass. Photo below shows cogon grass established in Mindanao, in the Philippines.

original clearing, grass won the battle against trees, the forest failed, and swiddens were covered with tall grasses, especially *Imperata* (cogon) in the East and *Hyparrhenia* in Africa. These new grasslands, or *cogonals*, cover 18 per cent of the whole land surface of the Philippines, spread far and wide in Vietnam, and are common all over the tropics. Modern agriculturalists are only ` just beginning to find ways of using them; for swidden farmers (except in parts of Africa, where a grass fallow rotation gives modest returns with much burning) they are a dead loss: grasses from an established sod of roots and suckers are merciless weeds. Elsewhere, notably on the hills of Africa, India, and Burma, soil erosion took its toll, removing large areas (especially in India) from any kind of productive use.

In the annual reports of the Department of Agriculture

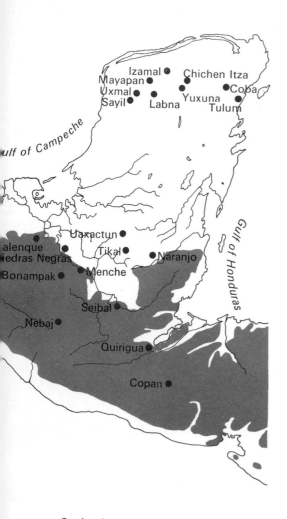

On the above map of southern Mexico and Guatemala are marked the early Mayan sites on the uplands (coloured) and also the sites the Mayas later moved to, in the Yucatan peninsula in the north. Below: bas-relief from an altar at Copan, showing astronomer-priests at the great congress in A.D. 503.

of Northern Rhodesia (now Zambia) from 1933 onward, we can follow the progress of a heroic attempt to conserve the land by controlling the length of chitemene fallow; in the end, it disappears from the reports, and one supposes that population pressure was too much for the agriculturalists. In the Congo, where another controlled system was introduced, interest also seems to have shifted to other kinds of farming. All over the wet tropics, scientists are trying new methods, often using legumes for cover and soil fertility conservation, sometimes planting particular trees to make artificial bush fallows. With all the resources of modern science, they may eventually solve the problem of productive tropical farming, at least when farm animals, with their manure, can be integrated with it. What emerges clearly from the whole story is the fact that swidden farming in past ages could never support population increase without incurring the nemesis of lost fertility, invading grassland, and soil erosion.

We can now finally understand why the agricultural system of the wet tropics could not produce the sustained advance of cities and civilization that led to the technological breakthrough. With all its merits, it is still to a great extent a passive submission or adjustment to natural conditions. To begin with, although some swidden farmers have settled homes (like the Hanunóo, who live in small groups and make swiddens within a radius of about 500 yards from their houses), many, perhaps most, move their homes as well as their plots; both ways of life are found side by side in Malaysia. Even when settled, swidden farmers must work continuously as a small, self-contained group, and such groups are difficult to integrate into societies larger than tribes. But the critical factor is the low food yield per unit of land area. Even the Hanunóo can spare only about 10 per cent of their hard-won food to trade for beads and salt with the people of the coast. To support the full-time specialists needed for cities and civilization, a large surplus is indispensable; and in the lands of swidden farming this surplus could be won, for a time, only by putting more land under crops—hence shortening fallows and inviting all the consequences we have seen.

Some enterprising peoples have tried to escape from the impasse. Two ancient civilizations in Asia (the Khmers of Cambodia and the people of Anuradapura in Ceylon) are thought to have been based at least partly on swidden farming, and to have succumbed to the invasion of cogonals. Both civilizations certainly used some irrigation as well, and may have met other disasters we shall consider later. But one great civilization is known to have been based entirely on swidden farming, and we may illustrate the insoluble dilemma of this way of life

Drawing of a stone pillar at Copan. This city was the great astronomical capital of the Old Mayan Empire and was the site of the great congress.

with the story of the tragic fall of the early Mayas in Central America.

The great cities of the Early Empire of the Mayas were built in the relatively healthy uplands of Guatemala, Honduras, San Salvador, and southernmost Mexico, from the third to the eighth century A.D.—Uaxactun, Tikal, Yaxchilan, Palenque, and above all Copan, scene of a great congress of Mayan astronomers (as their own records tell) convened on September 2, 503, to reform the calendar. The need for accurate timing in farm operations has always made astronomy the earliest civilized science. The early Mayas (who had ideographic writing) were remarkable in this respect; they appear to have invented the modern number system independently of the Indians and Arabs, and they could compute astronomical events to an accuracy of one day in 33 years. Moreover, they seem to have been at least relatively free from the obsession with human sacrifice that infected all the other American civilizations, and reached appalling proportions in Mexico. The early Mayas were, indeed, the hope of America.

But in the eighth and ninth centuries, the cities of the Early Empire were abandoned one by one, and the Mayas retreated to build new ones in the fever-ridden jungles of Yucatan, where (according to a peasant proverb) it rains 13 months in the year. The later Mayas were constantly on the move; under Mexican influence, their societies were riddled with human sacrifice (always a symptom of present or past famine, since it is a brutal way of having fewer mouths to feed), and their once promising civilization gradually decayed.

Three reasons have been suggested for the abandonment of the cities of the Early Empire, and all turn on the fatal dilemma of swidden farming. Some scholars think they succumbed to soil erosion: a study of soil fertility on a Guatemalan hillside (where swidden farming, here *milpa*, is still going on) led one agriculturalist, in 1960, to predict erosion here if the population rose to any extent; and we know that the Mayas moved from steep hillsides to flatter lowlands. Others think the Mayas' fields were invaded by

cogonals, both around the early cities and later in Yucatan; in the course of centuries the forest climax finally triumphed again over the grass in man's absence, so that today the fantastic Mayan cities are buried in jungle. Yet others have emphasized the social effects of soil exhaustion. Some peasants seem to have remained when the city folk left; perhaps the peasants, seeing their lands exhausted by the hungry mouths of the cities, revolted and drove out these city people who ruled but did not mix with them.

On any of these views, the Mayan tragedy shows the ultimate dilemma of the wet tropics. Man here had entered a cul-de-sac of history, from which he could never emerge till others elsewhere had brought civilization to the final breakthrough. If we wonder why, all over the wet tropics, bush fallow rotation continued to work for so long, the answer is that the system worked because populations remained small. And if we ask why this was so, the answer is simple and grim: in the wet tropics, for reasons we shall see, people died young.

Copan sculpture of a youthful Mayan god, patron of the precarious cultivation of maize, on which the cities depended for food. Their demands probably exhausted the capacity of swidden farming and the civilization collapsed. Now the Mayan cities are overgrown by forests (right), visited only by archaeologists.

5 The Dry Belt

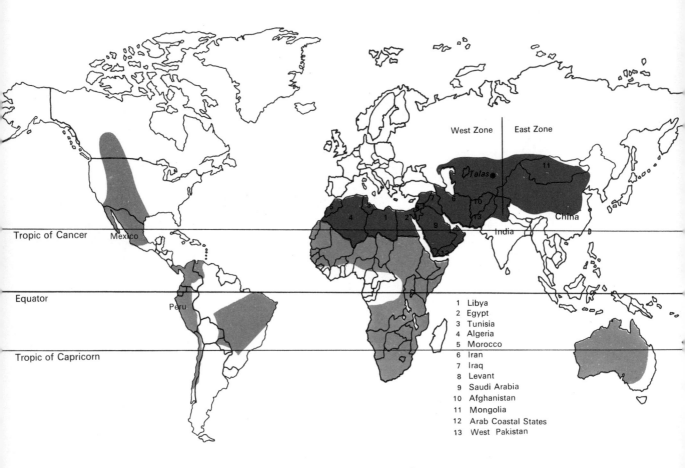

1	Libya
2	Egypt
3	Tunisia
4	Algeria
5	Morocco
6	Iran
7	Iraq
8	Levant
9	Saudi Arabia
10	Afghanistan
11	Mongolia
12	Arab Coastal States
13	West Pakistan

From the wet tropics, with their poor, leached soils and their cruelly handicapped agriculture, we now turn to a very different group of regions—the great dry belt. Here the soils are generally rich, the promise of success appears much greater, and in fact splendid civilizations have flourished at times when most of Europe was barbarous and illiterate. Yet in the long run the progress of mankind was thwarted here, too, by nature, though in a much more complicated way.

The first of this group of regions is a continuous belt right across the Old World, running from the north coast of Africa through the Near and Middle East, bending north around the Himalayas through the vast lands of Central Asia, to end on the plains of northern China. In the course of history, it has tended to divide into two zones. The eastern zone was dominated by the influence of Chinese civilization, shaped by thinkers like Confucius. The western Zone, stretching from Morocco to Central Asia,

The dark red areas on this map indicate the lands of the dry belt we are primarily concerned with in this chapter. Light red areas mark other arid regions. The river Talas in Central Asia roughly divides the eastern area of Chinese influence from the western Islamic zone.

Two great figures of the dry belt. Above right: the prophet Mohammed, seventh century A.D., from a 15th-century Turkish manuscript. Right: Confucius (figure on right) c. 551–497 B.C. Illustration is from a 19th-century painting.

was eventually united only by the culture of Islam, the way of life founded by the Arab prophet Mohammed in the seventh century A.D. The boundary between the two can roughly be set in Turkestan, where the Arabs defeated the Chinese at the battle of the River Talas in A.D. 751 but were unable to invade China. The close cultural connection between the two zones is evident from the fact that in 1939 there were reported to be 48,104,240 Muslims (Mohammedans) in China, or about one Chinese in ten. Nevertheless, the two zones had rather different histories, as we shall see.

The great subcontinent of India lies partly in the dry belt, and its past history has been disastrously influenced by that of the belt as a whole. The grasslands and savannahs of Africa echo the main story at a distance. Other dry regions cover large areas of North and South America, and almost the whole of Australia. Hindus, Chinese, and Muslims in turn only just failed to reach Australia, and so that far continent played no part in history till the coming of Europeans in the 17th century A.D. But the American civilizations of Mexico and Peru had much in common with their counterparts in the Old World dry belt.

Rainfall over all these regions is not prolonged enough to leach plant food out of the surface of the soils, which are often richly fertile, unlike those of the tropical forests. The problem here is just the reverse; and the critical factor for plant life is *lack* of water. The total amount of rainfall per year varies widely even between places close together. For instance, there are $20\frac{1}{2}$ inches of rain per annum at Jerusalem but only $1\frac{3}{4}$ inches at Máan in the desert of Jordan, less than 120 miles away. Rainfall generally increases with height above sea-level, and it also tends to fall with distance from the coast. But throughout the entire belt, rainfall is liable to be irregular, and above all it is restricted to one part of the year: at Jerusalem, for instance, all but $\frac{2}{5}$ inch of the rain falls between November and May. The long dry season presents a formidable obstacle to the growing of even one crop in each year. Over favoured parts of the belt, there are permanently flowing streams, notably the great rivers Nile, Euphrates, Tigris, Indus, and the Yellow River. But over vast tracts, like the Sahara and the Rub al Khali desert of Arabia, there are only *wadis*—beds that carry raging torrents (swift to erode soils) during the brief rains, but are dry for the rest of the year.

91

Above: map of Arabian peninsula shows the distribution of its many wadis. After winter rain-storms these river-beds become raging torrents that erode away soil in the hills where they rise. This silt, deposited on the plains, blocks up many wadis before they reach the sea. In summer, (below), with no rain to water them, wadis are as dry as the barren landscape around them.

In the pluvial period corresponding to the fourth glaciation, the Sahara desert was full of life, and fresh-water shells from that age bear witness to permanent rivers in the heart of the Rub al Khali. It is generally agreed that the dry belt became dry early in the fourth interglacial. A more difficult question is that of the changes in humidity and rainfall over the dry belt during the five millennia or so of recorded human history. It used to be thought that the course of human civilization here was shaped in a simple way by alternating periods of wetter and drier climate. It now seems unlikely that such regular and drastic oscillations really occurred. Certainly the fortunes of dry-belt man are not simply related to climatic change.

The level of water in the ground is good evidence of the total amount of annual rainfall. In several places in Jordan, the construction of Roman wells shows that the level of water in them (and hence in the ground) was the same in Roman times as it is in the present century, and the same thing has been observed in Byzantine wells in the Negev desert of Israel. So rainfall must have been the same when the Romans and Byzantines ruled these regions (first century B.C. to seventh century A.D.) as it is today. Yet, as we shall see, at that period Jordan and Israel were at the height of their prosperity, and covered with productive farms, while by the early 20th century A.D. they were a scene of utter desolation. So their societies clearly did not go up and down because of climatic cycles. True, small fluctuations in rainfall are constantly observed in modern times. We may well suppose that a run of bad drought years may often have secondarily intensified the action of other factors. That other factors were of importance we shall find as we study the tragic upheavals of human civilization in the dry belt.

Water and Work

Throughout all recorded history, over most of these regions, agriculture was either impossible or dangerously unreliable for farmers depending only on rainfall to water their crops. Nevertheless, it was precisely here that human civilizations first appeared. The agriculture on which these civilizations rested was achieved by controlling the distribution of water in such a way as to supply it to crops in the dry season—in other words, to irrigate them. The water used for irrigation might be rain naturally stored in the ground and tapped by artificial wells or natural springs, like the spring that made possible the early success of irrigated agriculture in the oasis of Jericho. Or rainwater could be caught and channelled as it ran off the surface of the land downhill toward the sea.

The greatest opportunities for irrigation were presented in the great river valleys; but here the control of water

meant not only getting it to the crops, but also getting it away from them when necessary (drainage), and preventing destructive floods. Once launched on the technology of water control, man could go further, sending water over long distances by aqueducts or digging great canals to link up rivers for boat and barge transport of food and other goods. Thus, from scratching crude channels in the earth to lead water from some brook to his plot, man in the dry belt graduated to such feats of engineering as the Grand Canal linking the Yangtze and the Yellow River, completed by the seventh century A.D.

From the river valleys of the dry belt, the technique of irrigation spread in due course up into the hills and deep into the deserts; it also spread into regions outside the belt, in or near the tropics, where soils were fertile enough

The ancient civilizations controlling the Near East opened up large areas of desert by means of long-distance aqueducts, like this Roman one near Caesarea in Israel. Plentiful water supplies made this city a prosperous commercial and artistic centre for a thousand years.

to grow warmth-loving rice, vastly productive when flooded with water during part of its growing period. In some of these regions, such as Thailand and southern China, irrigation made possible the growth of two rice crops every year, thus doubling the productivity of the land. Water-controlling or "hydraulic" societies (as the historian Karl A. Wittfogel has called them) developed in southern China, south-eastern India, South-East Asia, and Indonesia, as well as in the lands of the dry belt. From the records compiled by FAO of land areas irrigated in 1962, it appears that the dry belt and the tropics are still the principal homes of irrigation. The one great irrigating country outside both regions is Japan, just warm enough for rice; here, as we shall see, conditions have been unusual.

The agricultural system based on water-control was prodigiously efficient and productive. To begin with, soil erosion by runoff water was automatically controlled. In the valley plains, uncontrolled eroding floods were prevented, and the water was gently led from field to field, so that it sank gently into the soil of each, depositing on the surface just the right amount of fertile silt brought down from the hills—an annual supply of mineral food for the crops. On the steep slopes of the hills, rain-water was likewise trapped and controlled as it ran downward, by the

Below: rice terraces in Indonesia. Over many parts of the world, man learned to terrace steep slopes; he thus prevented soil erosion and was able to irrigate hill land. The picture shows how the water drains from level to level flooding the rice in each plot.

construction of walled steps or terraces. The steps of these terraces were straight and regular; the horizontal lines followed irregular natural contours, making man's control of nature visible in a beautifully composed landscape. By the first millennium B.C., such terraces covered many areas —for example the slopes of the Lebanon, of southern Arabia, and of such remote spots as the island of Luzon in the Philippines; later they appeared in Peru, in East Africa from Sudan to Rhodesia, and in many other regions.

The water-controllers no longer had to shift their ground like swidden farmers. A field once cleared was potentially cleared for ever, annually refertilized by the silt, but protected from the danger of erosion. The ground was not encumbered by tree roots or stumps, the crop was sown or planted in neat rows for easy access of small water-channels, and the farmer could work meticulously over the soil to prepare it for seeds and keep it free of weeds. By the third millennium B.C., the ox-drawn plough had appeared in both Egypt and Iraq, to make furrows; in Iraq it was sometimes equipped with a hopper (funnel) through which seeds were dropped behind the share (blade). In this millennium too, the Iraquis in their written records distinguished different varieties of the same crop (e.g. late-ripening barley and early-ripening barley), which

The invention of the plough meant efficient soil preparation and, especially, weed control on settled land. Below: model of an Egyptian plough, c. 2000 B.C., with one man to drive it and another to guide the oxen. The Kassite plough from Iraq (above), from a clay tablet, 14th century B.C., was more sophisticated; the seed was sown through a hopper attachment.

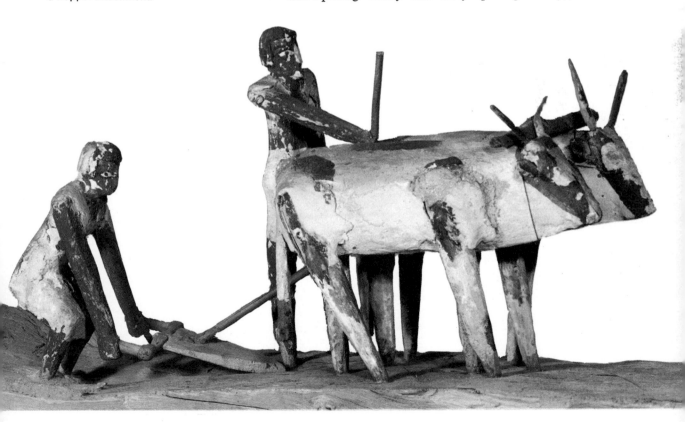

Detail from *The Harvesters* by Peter Breughel the Elder (1520–69). With plentiful regular rainfall European farmers have always found life easier than hydraulic peasants. Harvesting leaves time to enjoy a hearty meal among the rain-fed crops.

they must have selected for sowing in different places.

An agricultural manual already widely known in 1700 B.C. describes the elaborate sequence of operations on a farm on the lower Euphrates. To begin with, the farmer had to irrigate the field, making sure the water did not rise too high. Then the water was drained off, and oxen driven over the field to trample the weeds; afterwards the surface was carefully levelled by men with mattocks, and worked over with a harrow. After thorough ploughing, harrowing, raking, and breaking the clods with hammers, barley was sown, using a plough with a seed-hopper; the seeds had to be dropped into the hopper at a uniform rate. Some more clod-breaking, and the barley was left to grow. The next job was to scare off the birds. The growing crop had to be irrigated three times, at stages defined by the exact height of the plants. Then the farmer had to watch out for a disease that would turn the barley red; but if all was well, he could give a fourth irrigation, which should increase the final grain yield by ten per cent.

Farming as intensive and productive as this was seen nowhere outside the hydraulic societies until the final technological break-through in Europe; even in the early 19th century A.D., Justus von Liebig, the founder of agricultural chemistry, asserted that Europe was in its agricultural infancy by comparison. With high yields on land all permanently in use, hydraulic agriculture supported a very high density of population. In the first century B.C., for instance, the wheat and barley fields of Egypt probably maintained about 725 people per square mile. In the early 20th century A.D. (before industrialization had really started there), the average for the whole province of Shansi in northern China, growing wheat and millet, was 183 people per square mile and that for the whole rice-growing province of Chekiang in southern China was 554 people per square mile. By contrast, in the 16th century A.D., the province of Holland in the Netherlands was unusually densely peopled for Europe—at 95 people per square mile! .

The irrigated land produced a huge food surplus that supported cities of hundreds of thousands of people. Ur and Babylon in Iraq already had populations of this order in the second millennium B.C.; so did Cuzco (in Peru) and Mexico City before the coming of Cortez. In the later history of the Old World dry belt, cities as big as Babylon were common. Except for ancient Rome (importing food from the dry belt), no cities in Europe reached this scale until the technological breakthrough. With such a surplus and such cities, it is no wonder the hydraulic societies of the dry belt were the ones that launched civilization, and that they carried it to great heights of technical and cultural achievement.

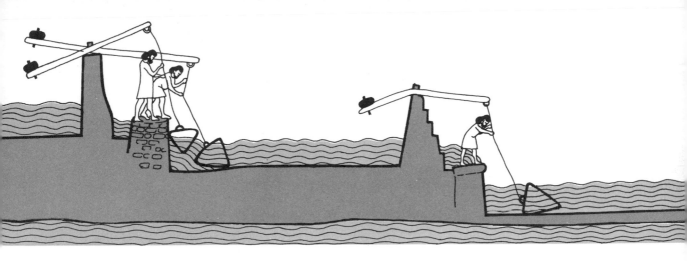

But these achievements were made at a price. Hydraulic agriculture is obviously far more economical of land than swidden farming, but it is even more demanding of labour. The early manual summarized above shows how much attention the farmers of ancient Iraq had to give to water control—a whole set of chores that could be omitted in lands (such as those of Europe) where a farmer could generally depend on rainfall throughout the year. In the early 20th century A.D., wheat-farmers in the Chinese province of Hopeh spent 58·5 per cent of their working time on operations with water. Similar calculations made in other parts of China and in Pakistan showed that work done by the dry-belt farmer on water control alone took up more time than *all* the work done (on his own farm) by a rainfall farmer in mediaeval Europe; and on top of this,

Above: Assyrian peasants operating a shaduf to raise water from canal to irrigation channels (picture redrawn from a relief in the palace of Sennacherib, 7th century B.C.). This simple mechanism —a bucket on a pole, counter-balanced by a weight—demanded constant labour from the operator who lowered the bucket into the canal, and typifies the amount of labour involved in water control in the dry belt.

Below: drawing by a traveller in 18th-century China, where men and women were sometimes harnessed to the plough with animals in the continual struggle to feed the huge labour force.

Chinese Husbandmen, from Nieuhof

the hydraulic farmer generally did a good deal more work on actual cultivation (ploughing, weeding, and so forth). This alone meant a life of unremitting toil for the peasants of the dry belt.

But watering and cultivating their fields by no means exhausted the duties of farmers of the hydraulic civilizations. The great engineering works for irrigation, drainage, and flood control, the canals and the aqueducts, all depended on the part-time labour of the peasants, whenever they could be spared from the farms, and the full-time labour of any of them who could be spared for long periods. These waterworks had to be built in the first place, and then the banks or dikes had to be continually

Egyptians not employed on maintaining irrigation works were used in time-consuming projects like the one below—building and moving the 22-foot-high alabaster statue of Prince Thuti-hotep. Overseer (on knee of statue) directs, and a scribe (centre) records the process. Symbolically, statues of great rulers always towered, with god-like proportions, over their subjects.

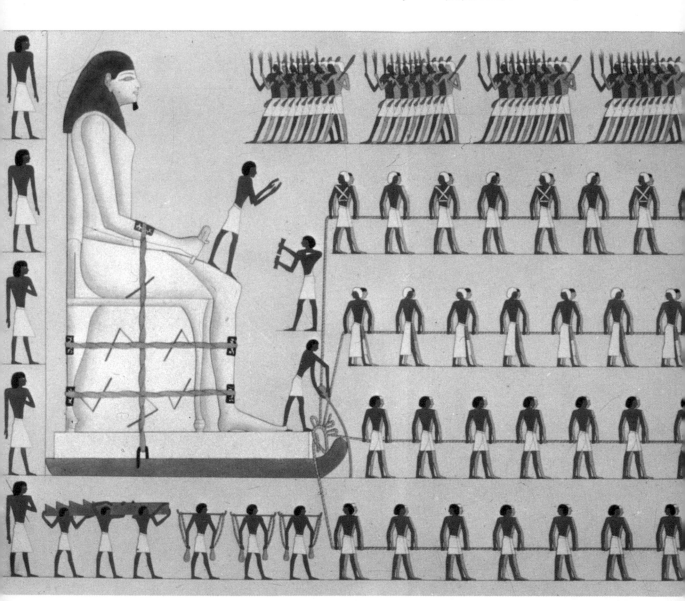

maintained and repaired, and the channels continually kept clear of silt, which every year threatened to clog them and obstruct the flow of water. The mass labour of thousands, or even millions, of people governed the whole character of the hydraulic society.

This mass labour was enlisted by the state as and when required, by compulsory drafts. What this meant for the individual is made vivid for us by a little bit of pottery found at Sbeita (modern Shivtah) in the Negev. On it, in A.D. 600, a Byzantine official had inscribed a dated receipt, which reads: "To Flavius Gormos, son of Zacharias: you have completed one compulsory work for the reservoir." How many shifts Gormos served, and how many such receipts he once treasured, we do not know. But we do know that receipts like this featured in the lives of fantastic numbers of human beings. In principle, the entire population was subject to these drafts.

A book written under the Sui Dynasty (about A.D. 600) describes the labour force used to build part of the Grand Canal of China. It is summarized thus by Joseph Needham, the British biologist and scholar of Chinese: "Some 5,500,000 workers, including all commoners in certain areas between the ages of fifteen and fifty, assembled, and worked under the guard of 50,000 police. Every fifth family was required to contribute one person to participate in the supply and preparation of food. Those who could not or would not fulfil the demands made on them were 'punished by flogging and neck-weights'; some had to sell their children. Over two million men were said to have been 'lost'."

Those impressive figures of population density now appear in another light. To control these swarming, overcrowded masses, to assemble them for forced labour operations and organize their work, to handle the vast stores of surplus grain that began to be gathered in state granaries for feeding the labour gangs, a special kind of state was evolved. At the head of it was a dictator, the king or emperor, with absolute rights over the lives of all his subjects; he often towers over them, larger than life, in his portraits.

An example from ancient Persia gives us some idea of the exalted position occupied by the ruler. In 470 B.C., the Athenian statesman Themistocles, exiled by the Athenian people, took refuge in the domains of the Great King of Persia. Eventually he sought an interview with the Great King. He made his approach through a Persian officer called Artabanus. This officer was prepared to help, but wanted to make sure the Greek would commit no terrible breach of court etiquette, as this would get his sponsor into trouble. He asked for a promise that Themistocles would prostrate himself in the Great King's presence. For, as he

Absolute rulers were vitally necessary to organize and control the massive populations of hydraulic societies—rulers like Naram-Sin (above), 23rd century B.C., leading his Iraqi soldiers into battle, and the Chinese Emperor Wu-Ti (late 6th century A.D.) of the Northern Chou dynasty (below).

Above: account tablet of third dynasty of Ur, listing the quantities of barley produced by various farmers in the reign of Shulgi. Invention of writing grew out of the need for records of food supplies and work in progress, but long remained a skill confined to a bureaucratic elite.

Below: 19th-century line drawing of the legendary emperor Shun consulting oracles with his ministers. Among them is Yü the Great, later emperor, revered as the founder of hydraulic civilization in China.

is said to have explained, "it is the habit of the Greeks, we are told, to honour, above all things, liberty and equality; but amongst our many excellent laws, we account this the most excellent, to honour the king and to worship him."

In hydraulic societies, would-be liberal reformers occasionally appeared at the top (where there was leisure to think of such things), for example, King Urukagina of Lagash in Iraq (25th century B.C.) and the Caliph Al Mamun of Baghdad (9th century A.D.), but their efforts were doomed to frustration. In all their millennia of history, the hydraulic societies never even dreamed of democracy, with laws made and changed by popular consent and binding all governments, with personal freedom from arbitrary arrest, confiscation, torture, and execution by state officials. No individual, however highly placed, wealthy, or useful to society, was safe from ruin or death at the whim of a ruler. All were slaves. Until modern times, the numerous revolutions of the dry belt were fought deliberately to change masters.

However absolute his power, no one man can actually run the lives of millions of people. The ruler worked through enormous bureaucracies of state officials, supported by the surplus wrung from the peasants. This executive class, particularly in the earlier periods, made contributions of vital importance to human progress. The greatest achievement of the hydraulic societies was the invention of writing in Iraq. This was needed for keeping the copious inventories and records of food stores and rations, equipment issues, labour gangs, projects, schedules, targets, and work progress. Once writing was available, it could serve for the exchange and recording of technical discoveries, and also for great literature, of which the first known example is the story of Gilgamesh from Iraq. But the hydraulic societies failed to discover alphabetic writing. Writing long remained ideographic, hard to learn, and restricted to the bureaucrat class; the mass of the people was illiterate, and expected to remain so.

Enormous strides were taken in sciences with obvious immediate practical applications, such as applied mathematics (for computing stores, land survey, and engineering), astronomy (for predicting seasons, notably the annual Nile flood), and, of course, hydraulic engineering, in which the Chinese are outstanding experts even today. But pure fundamental scientific research, of no obvious immediate practical advantage to the state, had to wait for the emergence elsewhere of societies where at least some individuals enjoyed personal freedom. And once the bureaucracy had settled in, its officials more and more lost interest in anything but red tape, a little literary scholarship, and keeping everything exactly as it was, so that they could go on running it for ever.

Above: carved mace-head showing Pharaoh Khasekhamui cutting a dike to release Nile flood water into irrigation channels c. 3000 B.C., an annual event of paramount importance. Failure of the water supplies, water shortage, and the ensuing bad harvest would reduce thousands of peasants to starvation level like those (below) on a bas-relief in the temple of King Unis at Sakkara, about 2350 B.C.

The ultimate justification of the whole system lay in water control, and the state came to be identified with this. This can be illustrated all over the dry belt. The founder of the first dynasty of the area that later expanded into the Chinese Empire was called Yü. We know of him only from legends, but some other early legends of China have been found to be based on fact. Yü was revered as the creator of great works for water control. Another example comes from Egypt. Every year, the Pharaoh himself performed the ceremony of cutting the dikes to admit the flood water to the crops; the Pharaoh Khasekhamui is shown doing so in a relief carved on the head of a mace. Again, the archives of the kingdom of Mari on the upper Euphrates (late third to early second millennium B.C.) include a letter from a high bureaucratic official, apologizing to the king for delay in obeying a summons to the court; he explains that his services were urgently needed to supervise irrigation works. As he pointed out (and it must have been a platitude even then), "if the waters are interrupted, the land of my lord will starve."

Once established, the system developed a momentum of its own. The status of rulers and bureaucrats depended entirely on the control of mass labour and the disposal of large stocks of food. Therefore, they sought more and more labour and food, and they came to feel that this was the indispensable basis of civilization. Peasants were encouraged to breed like flies and to depend absolutely on the government surplus stocks, raised by taxing the peasants themselves. Populations rose dangerously, until any disturbance to the agricultural foundations of the system

(such as collapse of an important waterwork) emptied the granaries and caused frightful famines. Any attempt to invent and apply labour-saving machinery was discouraged as superfluous and subversive. This was a factor of great importance in blocking a further breakthrough. In a famous phrase of the British scientific writer Ritchie Calder, the traditional way of doing a large-scale job was to use "a million men with teaspoons." When no immediate large-scale waterworks were in prospect, the vast armies of workers were employed on impressive but unproductive projects such as the Pyramids of Egypt and the Great Wall of China.

At first the hydraulic societies were fairly small states. But if you tap a river in one place, you may deprive somebody lower down its course. Disputed water rights provoked wars. And then the increasing demand for more and more food-stocks and manpower to control led logically to the expansion of victorious hydraulic states into huge empires, linking larger and larger areas by ever more ambitious hydraulic schemes. These empires, built at the cost of frightful wars between rival states, became especially well-developed in the valleys of great rivers,

Below: the fertile strips of land along the banks of the Nile where hydraulic society developed very early, relying on the annual floods. The photo above of part of this strip shows how peasants still utilize every inch of the rich alluvial soil, their animals grazing on small patches of land among the crops.

whose waters could best be controlled in a co-ordinated manner all along their course. The earliest empire was that of Egypt, founded at the end of the fourth millennium B.C. to control the compact strip of irrigated land in the valley of the Nile. The hydraulic empire of China finally embraced great river valleys and much more. But by the time these empires were widespread, another consequence of the mass labour system had brought into being the hydraulic society's most deadly enemies, and given a final stamp to the history of the dry belt.

Cain and Abel

We have already met one pair of legendary brothers, Prometheus and Epimetheus. In the Book of Genesis, we are told of another pair of brothers, Cain and Abel. Their story is the story of the dry belt. Of these two, "Abel was a keeper of sheep, but Cain was a tiller of the ground."

In its beginning in the neolithic Near East, agriculture was mixed farming, based on the combined use of crops and herds. But the growth of specialized, irrigated, crop agriculture in the hydraulic societies gradually divided people into two groups: farmers and herders. And it tended to drive the herders out into the wilderness. In this sense, Cain, the farmer, is accurately made the aggressor. We have seen how intensively the peasant had to work during the whole growing period of his crops. The passage of the seasons, however, would in theory have left him free to vary his work and diversify his farming, by keeping sheep or cattle on his farm. But, for every hour of his time that was not urgently required for growing the food surplus, the state needed him on the mass labour projects. It could not permit him any other occupations. He did indeed maintain a few beasts, oxen or buffaloes, to draw his plough and his carts. But maintenance of a sizeable herd of cattle or sheep, for meat, milk, hides, or wool, was out of the question. Moreover, livestock needs plenty of room to graze, and as the population rose and farms huddled closer together and shrank to smaller plots, there was simply no room for stock.

One immediate penalty was the loss of animal manure that provided valuable organic matter for the soil and food for the plant crop. The few draught animals did not produce sufficient manure to fertilize the croplands. One answer to the problem was the fertile silt from irrigating waters. Another was the use of green manure, that is, a plant crop grown especially to be ploughed back into the soil as food for the main crop. This technique, fully worked out, is described in Chinese documents from 1134 B.C. onward. In general, the hydraulic farmer could secure enough nourishment for his crops and organic matter for his soil without the manure from a large herd.

Cain the farmer, disposing of the corpse of Abel, the shepherd; from a Persian manuscript.

Another disadvantage of total specialization on crop farming was the disappearance of meat from the peasant diet. Human energy is supplied mainly by the carbohydrates in food, and we have seen that the coming of agriculture meant unprecedented supplies of carbohydrate food from the grains of cereal crops or, in some regions, from starchy tuber crops. But man also needs protein for growing and maintaining the structure of his body; and for this purpose various kinds of protein, having different combinations of component substances called *amino acids*, are required in correct balance. Animal food is a good protein source, and the efficient Mesolithic hunters were adequately supplied. The new large populations based on Neolithic agriculture needed to make up their protein partly from their small herds of farm animals and partly from crops. Protein makes up only 6-14 per cent of cereal grains, and an exclusively cereal diet is liable to cause protein deficiency.

A solution to this problem came about through growing legumes. Legume grains (various peas and beans, ground-nuts, and other crops) have a protein content of 17-25 per cent (38 per cent in the useful soy-bean of the Far East). This high protein content is probably related to their special capacity for obtaining nitrogen (the crucial element in protein), which, as we have seen, comes in so useful for conserving soil fertility, and makes them invaluable as green manures. Moreover, cereal proteins are short of some amino acids (such as lysine) but well supplied with others (such as methionine), while legume proteins are rich in the former and poor in the latter. When maize (cereal) and cow-peas (legumes) in different ratios are fed to young rats, it is found that a 50-50 combination gives the best protein balance; for man, too, the cereal-legume combination provides a balanced protein diet without meat.

When cereal crop agriculture began, it was accompanied in every continent by the growing of legumes. Lentil beans were grown at Halicar in Turkey in the sixth millennium B.C. They were especially common in ancient Egypt, where lentil soup preparation is the subject of a fresco from the reign of Rameses III (late second millennium B.C.). The scale of lentil production in Egypt under the Romans was impressive. When an already ancient Egyptian granite obelisk was shipped to Rome as a souvenir for the Emperor Caligula (early first century A.D.), tons of lentils were used as packing. Remains of peas have been found in a Swiss Neolithic village of the fifth millennium B.C., and broad beans in another Swiss site of the second millennium B.C. Remains of kidney beans dating from 4000 B.C. or earlier occur in caves in Mexico, and kidney beans, lima beans, and a jar of ground-nuts have been found in Peruvian tombs. Manuals on how to grow soy-beans were among the earliest Chinese books (second millennium B.C.).

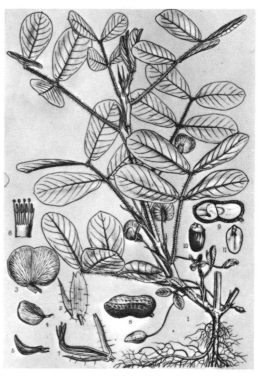

With little space for grazing animals and little time to tend herds, the hydraulic farmer depended almost entirely on crops for food. However, legume grains with a high protein content from plants such as the soy-bean *Glycine hispida* (left), groundnut *Arachis hypogaea* (top), and pea *Pisum sativum* (above), could provide him with an adequately balanced diet when combined with cereal crops.

In due course, all these crops were spread far and wide, and lentils, broad beans, and kidney beans are now almost world-wide.

It seems to have been realized very early that legumes were a food substitute for meat. The first recorded nutritional experiment is described, with admirable scientific precision, in the Book of Daniel. At the end of the seventh century B.C., Nebuchadnezzar, the Chaldean king of Iraq, sacked Jerusalem and carried off most of the Hebrew upper classes to Babylon. The most promising children he decided to bring up in his palace, to be trained into competent Babylonian bureaucrats. He instructed his chief eunuch, Ashpenaz, to feed them for three years from the royal table, after which he intended to inspect their health and educational progress. Among these young students was the prophet Daniel. He realized that the planned diet would include meat that was not kosher (not permitted by the laws of Moses, because not prepared in the Hebrew way); and he asked Ashpenaz, who liked him, if the Hebrew children could be excused. The official objected that if they did not eat the fine nutritious meats they would be less healthy-looking than the other palace children by the time of the king's inspection: "Then shall ye make me endanger

Below: map compiled by the FAO in 1964 showing total intake of protein per head per day in various parts of the world. Blue sections indicate animal protein, red shows other (plant) protein. Diet of rich countries such as Britain and U.S.A. contains much more protein than that of dry-belt Asia and Africa, and a large proportion of it is animal protein. Now, as in the past, inhabitants of dry belt depend mainly on plants for protein.

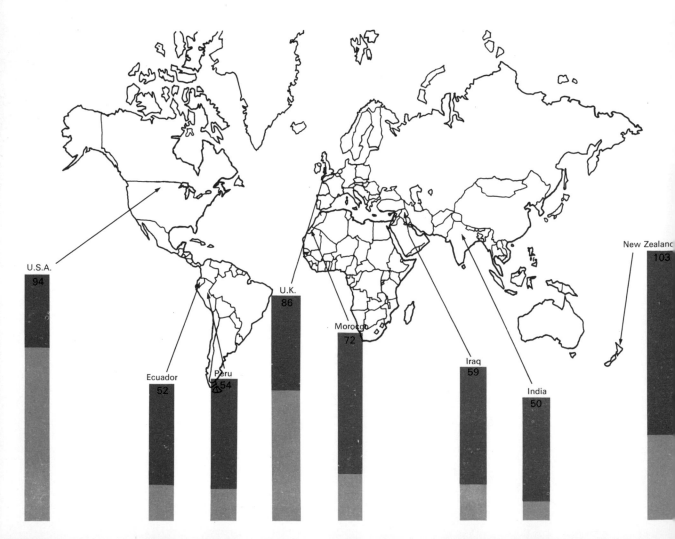

my head to the king." The intelligent young Hebrew persuaded Melzar, a subordinate eunuch in charge of catering, to let the Hebrew children live on beans and water for ten days, and observe the result. "And at the end of ten days, their countenances appeared fairer and fatter in flesh than all the children which did eat the portion of the king's meat." So Daniel and his friends were allowed to stick to their leguminous diet.

The royal table of Babylon was certainly supplied with plenty of meat. On account of its scarcity, what meat there was in the hydraulic societies found its way to the larders of the king and the top officials of the bureaucracy. Meat became, and has remained, one of the most universal status symbols in human civilization. In later history influenced by Europe, meat became associated with wealth in money. The Greeks (in the fifth century B.C.) described a new-rich self-made man thus: "now he doesn't like lentils any more." An FAO survey made in A.D. 1964 shows that meat goes with higher incomes today, not only as between individuals but also as between the more and less developed nations (see map). The average New Zealander gets $2\frac{1}{2}$ ounces of actual animal protein per day, the average Indian $\frac{1}{3}$ ounce. In the U.S.A., animal protein makes up 70 per cent of all the protein in the nation's diet; in India it makes up only 12 per cent. Peasants of the dry belt, today as for so many millennia in the past, must make up most or all of their protein from cereal and legume crops.

Being condemned to live on cereals and beans was thus unpleasant but not altogether a disaster for the peasants of the hydraulic societies. In the long run, a different consequence of the absence of herds was to prove a far heavier penalty for the hydraulic societies as a whole.

In some at least of the hydraulic societies, the state did maintain some livestock, and a few of the peasants were split off from the rest to keep them. At Ur, around 2000 B.C., the state was able to profit from a considerable textile industry, based on the wool of sheep. But as the two forms of *food* production drew further and further apart, separate herding societies of outcasts or adventurers began to form beyond the borders of the hydraulic states. The peasants had taken first pick of the river valleys, and the herders had to be content with grasslands on the outskirts of the desert. These "pastures of the wilderness," as the prophet Joel called them, are pastures in the wet season only. When the dry season comes, the grass is withered by heat and drought, and there is no water for the animals to drink. So the way of life of the herders, like that of the peasants, was forced into a special pattern by the seasonal shortage of water. They evolved a system called *transhumance*. In the wet season, they grazed their herds on the "pastures of the wilderness"; in the dry season, they moved

Above: transhumant herdsman travelling across the barren land of the Levant with his small flock of goats in search of fresh grazing land.

107

Ashurbanipal, king of Assyria
(660–c. 630 B.C.), on a lion hunt. Kings
originating from herding communities
conquered and ruled hydraulic societies
but continued to hunt and eat meat, a
peaceful pastime that prepared them for
war. Below: Arab nomads, at war with
Ashurbanipal, fleeing on fast camels
(from a relief in a palace of Kuyunjik).

into the wetter hills or the river valleys where grass still grew. The herders of Syria to this day move their flocks in summer to the Antilebanon mountains or to the upper valleys of the Euphrates or the Orontes. This yearly pattern of transhumance meant that the herders could not settle in permanent homes; their way of life diverged more and more from that of the settled peasant. But their dry-season need for the hills and river valleys drove them into head-on collision with the expanding hydraulic societies, which needed just these regions all year round. The borders of the hydraulic states became the scene of repeated conflict.

The restless herders could never develop the elaborate paraphernalia of hydraulic civilization. But their way of life, which often included some hunting and gathering to supplement their food supplies, taught them mobility, resourcefulness, knowledge of large tracts of country, and efficient, flexible combined action. These qualities made them formidable in war. They became robbers and raiders. Sometimes, a herder chief and his henchmen actually conquered a hydraulic state. Their descendants were absorbed by the more complex society they now governed, and became typical kings and nobles of hydraulic societies. In this curious interaction, the ruling dynasties of the great kingdoms and empires were repeatedly supplied from the outcast groups beyond their borders. In the second and

first millennia B.C., lower Iraq (for instance) was successively ruled by Amorite, Kassite, and Chaldean dynasties, all typical kings of civilized states, but all originating from herding communities outside the valley. Throughout history, the kings and nobles of civilization have betrayed their ultimate pastoral origin in two ways. They practised hunting as a sport, monopolizing extensive game preserves; and, as we have seen, they ate quantities of meat.

While some herders moved in on civilized societies and became meat-eating rulers otherwise utterly remote from their ancestors, others began to develop a new kind of society in the open steppe or desert. Transhumance had prepared them for a wandering life, and in due course they took the next logical step, and became true nomads, migrating over much greater distances in search of water and grass. Instead of just commuting between summer and winter pastures, they now roamed over whole continents. Cut off from any close contact with civilization, other than a mixture of trading and raiding, these wild nomads of the steppe evolved a mode of life different in many ways from that of the hydraulic societies.

The transition to full nomadism was made possible by taming and harnessing fast riding animals, the horse and the camel. Between 1000 and 900 B.C., horse-riding nomads began to appear on the steppes of Central Asia; it is

By 1000 B.C. man rode the horse as well as the camel. Square on the map (above) marks the area where the Scythians, the first great horse-riding people, originated. They built their nomadic civilization on the speed and mobility of the horses that carried them across the steppes of Asia. Below: Scythian horseman, c. 500 B.C., on a cloth found in a burial chamber in the same area.

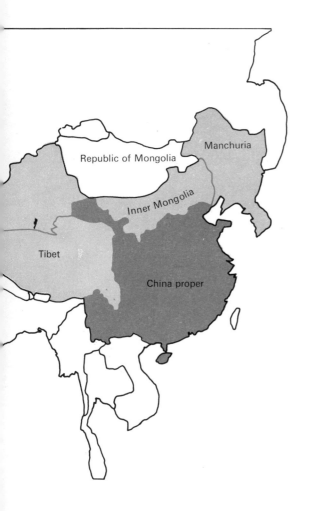

China proper (dark blue), originally composed of hydraulic societies within the Great Wall, has always been much more densely populated than the surrounding states of China (light blue) and the Republic of Mongolia, both inhabited by nomadic tribes. In time, the 18 central provinces have absorbed the surrounding states to form modern China.

thought that the earliest were the people called Scythians, between the rivers Volga and Irtysh. Horses had already been used for centuries (by the Hittites, for instance) to draw chariots, but the great new step was to saddle and train them for fast riding. This new technique, and the nomadic way of life, spread all over Central Asia in the course of the first millennium B.C. Meanwhile, in the deserts of Arabia, other herders had learned to ride camels. In about 1100 B.C., as we read in the Book of Judges, the hosts of Midian descended on Israel, camel-mounted; and early in the first millennium A.D. camel nomadism began to spread into North Africa.

The most striking difference between nomad and hydraulic societies was in numbers. The area of China within the Great Wall has been calculated as 1,532,795 square miles. The combined area of Outer Mongolia (now an independent state) and Inner Mongolia (now part of China), dominated until recently by the pastoral way of life, has been calculated as 914,100 square miles, or about three fifths the area of China. Yet the population of the two Mongolias in the 1930s, not counting recent farmer migrants from China, has been estimated as roughly 2,000,000, while that of China itself was estimated at the same time as roughly 450,000,000. So the number of Chinese per square mile was about 150 times the number of Mongols. The difference had persisted throughout history.

The life of the nomads was based entirely on their herds, which provided meat, milk produce, and hides and fleeces for clothing, harness, and even the tents that served them as homes. To support the large herds, they grazed them for a time on one area, and then moved to another. Just as the forest farmers were always moving on to fresh woods, steppe nomads were always in search of pastures new. They needed even more land than the forest farmers, and their populations were even less dense. On the steppe, as in the forest, numbers had to be kept low if the system was to work.

A moderate amount of grazing is often good for the grasses and clovers that are most nutritious and palatable for stock. Periodic removal of their leaves stimulates them to grow again, more vigorously than before. Grazing animals have preferred them for millennia, so they are now best fitted to respond to the stimulus. Under moderate grazing, they often spread at the expense of less nutritious plants. If the number of stock on a given area is just right, the good grass on any given part of it is stimulated and also periodically rested. But if this stocking rate rises too high, the whole area will be continuously grazed, and good grasses will have no chance to rest and grow lush. They will begin to die out, and be replaced by the less nutritious

The effect of overgrazing on good pasture land is clearly shown by these four photographs of the same area of land in Oregon, U.S.A., over a period of years. At first, with moderate grazing, there is a preponderance of perennial grasses, providing excellent range conditions for livestock.

Intensive grazing reduces the quantity of perennial grasses, and the proportion of scrub increases. Grazing conditions can still be termed "good."

Continued utilization by livestock soon reduces the pasture to "fair" as perennial grasses become scarce and weeds and sage-brush increase.

Finally, only poor vegetation—shrubs, weeds, and annual grasses—covers the land, and patches of bare ground invite soil erosion from wind or rain.

Above: nomads breaking camp in order to move on across the steppes of Central Asia. Their tents are made of animal skins stretched over poles, easily folded away and transported. Drawing from Ashley's *Voyages and Travels*, (1745).

plants they formerly crowded out. The land will be overgrazed.

The effects of overgrazing have been observed in recent years in many countries of the dry belt (such as Iraq, Israel, and the Yemen), but they have been most thoroughly studied in the dry western states of the U.S.A., where much overgrazing went on in the 19th and early 20th centuries A.D. The sequence of events can be illustrated by studies of ranges in southern Idaho. If grassland is grazed at a moderate rate, it is plentifully covered with nutritious perennial grasses that go on growing year after year. With heavier grazing, the perennials are killed off, and replaced by tougher but less nutritious annual grasses that die every year and grow again from seeds. If the grazing pressure increases further, the annuals are killed before they can set seed, and are replaced by unpalatable shrubs, notably the sage-brushes called *Artemisia*, growing in scattered clumps over otherwise bare, dry, easily eroded desert.

As less-nutritious plants take over, the animals need a larger area to get the same amount of nourishment. In Idaho, when perennials cover 50 per cent of a site, one cow can be supported on $3\frac{1}{2}$ acres; when they cover 25 per cent, she needs 5 acres; when they cover only 5 per cent, she needs 15 acres; and when the land turns to desert, no cattle can be raised there at all. So overgrazing is a vicious cycle. Too many animals overgraze the land till it supports fewer than it did to begin with, so the overgrazing gets worse; as more land turns to desert, the rest is grazed more heavily than ever.

As long as nomads and their herds were few enough over a given area, they could graze each part of it just the right amount before going on to the next. But the balance was more precarious for them than for forest farmers because of the effects of drought. Drought has effects rather like those of overgrazing. A few good years, and herds began to increase. A few bad years, and the effects of overgrazing were added to the effects of drought: the combination was deadly.

The distribution of springs for watering the animals was another critical factor. On the Moghan steppe in northwestern Iran, where transhumant herders today bring their flocks down from the hills in winter, areas around springs and streams are always overgrazed. As long as there was plenty of room, the nomads could solve their problems by migrating long distances at times of crisis. But the nomads became so specialized for moving over long distances that they lost many opportunities for insurance against bad years. Their migratory way of life discouraged staying in one spot long enough to raise a food crop for themselves or a fodder crop like hay that could be stored for difficult periods, or even to dig a well. They became more and

The rich fertile land of the valleys
in the Altai Mountains of Central Asia
draws the herdsman and his flocks from
great distances when land on the hills
and plains becomes barren and parched.
Above: nomadic herdsmen make use of
this good pasture land today.

The plight of the Karamoja people in
Uganda today spotlights problems arising
when numbers of stock increase sharply.
Overgrazing leads to wars between
tribes looking for new grazing land.

The Karamoja fortify their villages
(above), building a compound to protect
the cattle, and they also develop
warrior skills. Below: Karamoja boys
learning to throw spears.

more dependent on natural supplies of water and grass.

The hair-trigger balance was easily tipped. Stock was
the only wealth of the nomads. (It is the main status symbol
in many dry parts of Africa today.) So there was a constant
temptation to increase the numbers of stock beyond safe
limits. We have seen what happened to the forest farmers
when they increased their numbers or tried to produce a
large surplus. When the numbers of the nomads or their
herds rose too far, the result could be more dramatic:
events on the steppe always moved fast.

A survey in 1962 of the Karamoja district of Uganda
casts some light on what must have happened when stock
became too numerous. Because of modern veterinary
control of cattle diseases in Karamoja, the population of
cattle in this district had risen steeply during the last few
years. According to the report: "As pasture deteriorates
from overgrazing, tribes begin to jostle. . . . With population growth, inter-sectional conflict has increased, because groups, deprived of their traditional grazings, move

elsewhere to survive." As a result, there had been serious deterioration of law and order.

Karamoja is a limited district, where a civilized modern government frowns on range wars. In the vast open steppe, with no such restriction, disputes over pasture and water took a different course. Tribes, jostled by neighbours, jostled others in turn, in a chain reaction spreading across continents. If other conditions favoured it (especially conditions on the borders of the hydraulic states), the result could be a forcible gathering of tribes into great empires, exactly as happened between hydraulic states disputing water rights. But the empires of the steppe formed a great deal faster. The conquered did not have to be reorganized and integrated into an alien bureaucracy. They just joined the horde. So a small group could grow by combining all its neighbours into one great army, through a snowball process in which each conquered group swelled the conquerors' numbers

The rulers of these hordes allotted pastures, migration routes, and watering rights to their subjects. But they also had to be expert generals. The horde needed unified command, and nomad emperors were even more absolute than the hydraulic kings. Just as those kings found themselves equipped with mass labour, which they turned to any use they could, so the steppe emperors found themselves at the head of formidable armies, spoiling for action and eager to invade the lands of the farmers, and convert as much as possible to pasture. They descended on the hydraulic societies like locusts, with equally destructive results. There was nothing stable about the restless hordes, and they could build nothing permanent. They subsided again into fragments when the force of their explosion was spent. But the explosion itself happened again and again. Outside the great inert hydraulic empires, the nomads were always poised like a time-bomb, waiting to go off next time they fused into a horde. This fusion reaction supplied the final ingredient of human history in the dry belt.

Despite their far smaller total population, the nomads attacked the teeming millions of civilization with devastating effect. They used the principle of the American Civil War general who explained his victories with the words: "I get there fustest with the mostest men." Their terrific mobility enabled them to concentrate hundreds of thousands of men at a single point, where they suddenly appeared in overwhelming force. To terrified peasants and city folk, they seemed innumerable swarms, like the Midianites, who "came up with their cattle and their tents, and they came as grasshoppers for multitude; for both they and their camels were without number: and they entered into the land to destroy it."

Above: Tunisian horseman at a festival. Fast mounted hordes of this kind played a decisive part in the history of the dry belt.

6 The World of Cain

In the dry regions of America, the absence of horses and camels meant the absence of nomad hordes, and so the hydraulic societies had the field to themselves. But they also had all the drawbacks of isolation from resources, ideas, and events in the rest of the world. In the Valley of Mexico, the farmers evolved a unique form of water control. On the marshy borders of a lake, they gathered mud to make an island, held it together with walls of reeds, and planted trees whose roots slowly bound it into a solid mass: the *chinampa*, or "floating garden." The lake itself provided irrigating water, and every year fresh mud was piled on to the surface by the farmers (like the fertilizing silt brought down by rivers in more usual irrigation systems). A grid of islands and canals grew steadily into the lake. At Xochimilco the vegetables for Mexico City are grown today by peasants on chinampas made and tended by the ancient technique, and over large areas of Lake Texcoco that have been exposed by modern drainage work, the outlines of ancient chinampas may still be seen.

While rivers make for unity, lakes preserve isolation. The Mexicans remained scattered in separate city-states, making only transient alliances. Sometimes powerful cities exacted tribute from weaker ones. But none of these dominant cities ever ruled a bureaucratic empire beyond its own borders. Within each city-state, however, the Mexicans developed most of the characteristic features of hydraulic civilization. They had priest-bureaucracies with kings at their head, huge pyramid-like buildings erected by mass labour, ideographic writing (which they may have taught the Mayas), and an impressive command of practical sciences such as astronomy. But their isolation left surprising gaps: they had to meet the firearms of the Spanish invaders with weapons of the Stone Age.

While the surplus from their "floating gardens" encouraged them to build cities and civilization, the Mexicans still relied, outside the lakes, on swidden farming, which many of them practise to this day. They were thus at a halfway stage between the two systems. The resulting mixed societies had a population increase of the hydraulic kind, but an agricultural base inadequate to support this increase. As a result, they experienced the most dreadful population problem in all history, with the following results. The Toltecs, or Master Builders (as their successors justly called them), began to build the greatest Mexican civilization in the 6th century A.D.; by the end of the

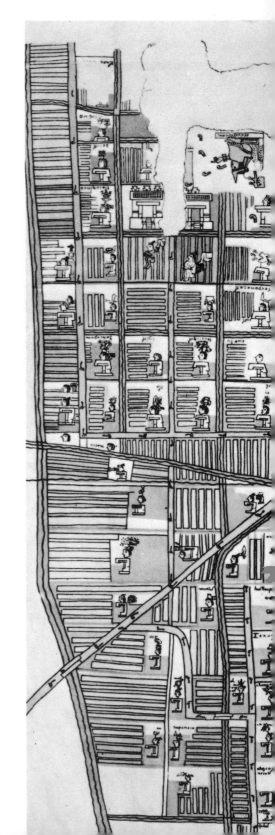

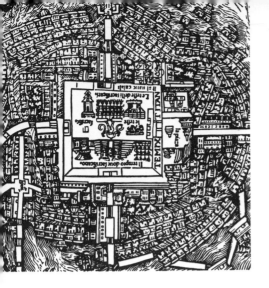

10th, it had gone the way of the Mayan Early Empire (see Chapter 4), probably for similar reasons. But the population problem built up again, and land exhaustion drove the tribes around in restless migrations. In the 15th century A.D., the city-states of the Aztecs, a group of recent immigrants into the valley, became dominant and levied tribute on the rest. By this time, there had evolved a system of perpetual wars between city-states, fought not for conquest but for the capture of victims for holocausts of human sacrifice. On the grisly skull-rack that towered over the city of Tenochtitlan, a Spanish soldier counted several thousand human skulls; and a Mexican manuscript records the deaths of 20,000 victims at a single ceremony. These massacres certainly controlled the population, at the cost of untold suffering and the steady decay of Mexican civilization. In the 16th century, the Spaniards, aided by the rebellious vassals of the Aztecs, brutally finished it off.

In South America, on the western slopes of the Andes, irrigation took a more conventional and successful form. It was widely spread, and involved elaborate terracing of the hillsides, and water control in many small valleys, dominated by the high central plateau of Peru. Throughout the first millennium A.D., a number of city-states emerged to make important advances in technology

Left: Mexican map of chinampas—floating gardens formed by linked artificial islands. Human figures indicate occupied individual plots and footprints mark roadways. Cities like Tenochtitlan (above) were also built on this plan, surrounded by water. In the centre is the skull-rack for the relics of human sacrifice. Below: Mexican warriors in their elaborate and decorative armour with stone-age weapons—obsidian blades fixed into spear-heads.

(notably metallurgy) and civilization. Then, around the 12th century A.D., on that strategic plateau, the Inca people emerged as a conquering power.

Our knowledge of Inca history is almost entirely derived from chroniclers writing after the Spanish conquest, such as Garcilaso de la Vega, son of a Spanish knight and an Inca princess. But the accounts are supported by the condition of the country when the Spaniards arrived. The Incas were entirely specialized for war and for the control of hydraulic agriculture. They overpowered tribe after tribe, bringing them large-scale irrigation and efficient farming methods at the price of unconditional submission. They sent out exploring parties to find new peoples with useful technologies, and systematically conquered them. The Inca Empire spread like a cancer: progress in other directions stopped dead wherever they ruled, for all other peoples were reduced to abject slavery.

The Inca nobles, who made up the imperial bureaucracy, ran the imperial economy with impressive efficiency. Canals of hewn stone hundreds of miles long, tunnelled in places through the mountains, brought irrigation water from glacier lakes to the driest areas. The distribution of the grain surplus in their granaries, along magnificent roads, amply insured against local crop failures. Their subjects were probably better, and certainly more regularly, fed than they have ever been since. The emperors are even said to have controlled the birth-rate, by regulating the number of recruits to the corps of sacred (and compulsory) virgins. But all this was achieved by creating the nearest possible approach to a human ant-hill. Men and women were divided into ten age-groups, each with its allotted

Above: Inca terracing in Peru. Their highly efficient agricultural system allowed the Incas to build up surpluses against famine and store them in huge granaries. Photo above right shows ruins of a large rectangular granary. An old irrigation channel runs from bottom right of picture, around one side of granary, disappearing top right.

■	1st to 4th Inca
▨	5th to 6th Inca
▦	7th to 8th Inca
≡	9th Inca
‖‖	10th Inca

Right: three farming scenes from a Peruvian manuscript. From left to right: September, maize is planted in fields divided by neat irrigation channels; November, the shoots are irrigated from a reservoir; July, the crop is stored away in the granary.

Left: map illustrates spread of Incas in South America, showing how the successive emperors (who were also called "Incas") added to the empire.

TRAVAXO
RA TARPVMITAN

TRAVAXA
3ARACARPAIIACOMVC

TRAVAXA
3ARAPAPAAPAICVIAIMO

tasks. Parents were permitted to care for their children up to the age of two; the job was then assigned to little girls just old enough to walk. Once full-time work began (at nine, for the boys) it continued till death. Food and clothing were prescribed in detail, and virtually everything that was not compulsory was forbidden.

In this mechanical and dreary bureaucracy, there was no writing. It seems that the invention of writing was a joint product of hydraulic agriculture and trade. The people of Iraq, who invented it in the Old World, had to trade for the timber, metal, and other raw materials their valley lacked. In the New World, the Toltecs and Early Mayas (who both used writing) traded profitably with each other. The Incas had no use for trade; they only conquered. They kept all their records by means of the *quipu*, a kind of computing apparatus, made of a long rope with 48 cords attached, and a further 39 cords of different colours attached to these. Knots were placed at intervals, according to a highly elaborate code of programming, and the whole contrivance could store extremely complex administrative or military information. It was probably even harder to learn than ideographic writing. It could not be used for composing literature; but literature, or any other product of the individual imagination, had no place in the Inca Empire.

The ninth emperor, Pachacutec (late 15th century), was given to making maxims, which his officials were expected to learn by heart. "The peace of a nation," he is said to have pronounced, "comes from the obedience of all its subjects." An inveterate tendency of peasants to work harder on their own land than on the state's was dealt with by the penalty of hanging. Overt rebellion (specially prevalent among more civilized peoples, recently conquered) was generally punished by burning or stoning, but Huayna Capac (the last emperor before the Spanish invasion) varied this by impaling everyone on the rebel

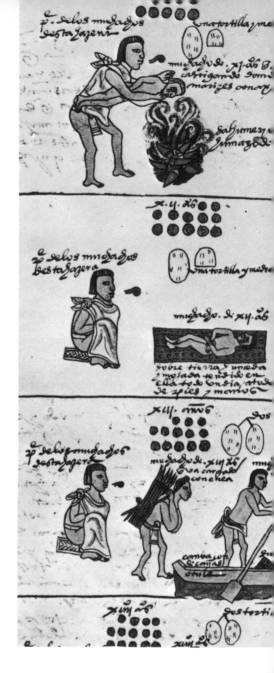

Above right: the training of children in the American hydraulic societies was very strictly organized. Dots at top of pictures indicate child's age; ovals indicate maize-cakes a child was allowed per day. Top line: children punished by being held over smoke. Second line: boy bound naked on damp ground as punishment; girl sweeping floor. Bottom line: boy carrying rushes and punting canoe; girl learning to make maize-cakes.

120

island of Puna, and drowning another 2000 rebels in a lake.

When Francisco Pizarro landed at Tumbes (opposite Puna) in 1529, he told the local chiefs that he had come to bring them the law of his king, the most powerful in the world. They made no comment: they had heard that story before, less than a century earlier, in fact, from the envoys of the Inca Empire. Now every year their young men were drafted to the Inca mining camps in the mountains. The Incas were so hated by the recently subdued coastal peoples that the Emperor Atahualpa, when he heard of the Spaniards' arrival, dared not send his army down to deal with Pizarro on the coast. Instead, he offered to receive the Spaniards at his capital, like brothers (an unfortunate turn of phrase, for Atahualpa killed his own half-brother, the legitimate Emperor Huascar, after making the victim watch his wives being tortured to death). On November 15, 1532, in the Inca city of Cajamarca, 164 Spaniards (with horses, muskets, and artillery) defeated some 30,000 Inca soldiers and captured Atahualpa (whom they later killed). The empire of several million people promptly accepted its new masters. An empire of slaves easily changes hands.

The Spanish conquerors of Peru were simply robbers. The priceless gold art treasures of the Incas, the loot of centuries, went into the melting pot: on June 18, 1533, more than two tons of gold and silver were split between the Spanish invaders, their backers at Panama, and their boss back in Europe, the robber Emperor Charles V of Hapsburg. By the time more responsible administrators arrived from Spain, the agricultural system of the Incas was in ruins. The people had lost their economic security, and had acquired private masters in place of the Inca State. But the invaders cannot be held responsible for the halting of human progress in this area: that had already happened. It was the tragic destiny of mankind in a dry region, commanded by a central plateau, where a hydraulic empire evolved in total isolation from the rest of the world.

Far left: a quipu—long rope with a series of coloured cords attached, knotted in different places—used by the Incas for calculating and keeping records.
Left: quipu in use outside a granary.

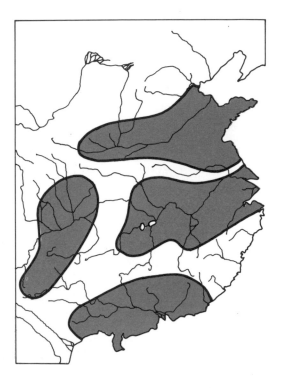

Map shows successive main areas of Chinese agriculture—around the Yellow River, lower and upper Yangtze, and the river valleys near Canton—where hydraulic civilization flourished using rivers for irrigation. The rice needed by the cities was produced on estates like that shown below.

Mandarins and Mongols

In the dry belt of the Old World (see p. 90), the hydraulic societies had the benefit of repeated exchange of ideas and materials with each other and the lands outside the belt. But they also had nomads to contend with. By the 16th century A.D., when the European breakthrough was beginning, the western zone of this belt was already in ruins, as we shall see in Chapter 7. In the eastern zone, however, the Chinese were still technologically far in advance of Europe: nevertheless, they too were already on the downward path.

The land of China is a great continuous mass, uniformly fitted for hydraulic agriculture. On the Yangtze and further south, irrigation provides rice agriculture in subtropical conditions. On the northern plains, rainfall is limited and irregular, but the Yellow River and its tributaries supply perennial waters for the irrigation of wheat and millet. But as you go north-westward and northward, into Turkestan and Mongolia, rainfall declines further, and instead of the rivers draining perennially into the sea, you find seasonal streams running inland to lose themselves in the sands of the desert. Except in oases separated by great tracts of desert or steppe, river irrigation is not feasible. Thus the farmers of China and the herders of the steppe confronted each other for millennia across the blurred border between two adjacent regions, each uniform for hundreds of miles. Supported in depth by her huge resources of food and manpower, China was bound to prevail in the end. But her compact mass also engendered a self-sufficient pride that made her civilization rigid and (on the world scale) almost parochial. In the eastern zone, Cain finally conquered Abel; but it was a costly and a sterile victory.

The modern Chinese historian Chi Chhao-Ting has made sense of much Chinese history in terms of certain key areas of food production. The first of these is the tract of loess soil on the upper Yellow River. On this soil, as in Europe, Chinese agriculture began. For the irrigation and flood control that make up hydraulic agriculture, loess had a special advantage in the early stages: it was soft, and easily banked up or dug into canals with quite primitive tools. As the Chinese gained increasing mastery of hydraulic engineering, they were able to tackle the problem of regulating the devastating floods of the lower Yellow River; and once controlled, this flood plain was richly fertile. Once water control was perfected on the wheat and millet plains of the north, it could be extended to the rice region on the lower Yangtze, potentially the most productive of all. Later, it could spread to the Szechwan plateau on the upper Yangtze, and last of all to the Canton region in the far south.

In the early first millennium B.C., Chinese civilization had already reached the Yangtze River. This China was divided into little hydraulic states, each busy completing the water control system within its own borders. Everywhere the same pattern grew up, of identical "cells" of irrigated land (several in each state), each controlled by a walled city as its nucleus, housing the collected grain surplus to feed its labourers and garrison. The states were so similar that a class of professional literate bureaucrats arose, able to move around offering their services to one prince after another. The greatest of these was Confucius (551–479 B.C.), who composed the philosophy of bureaucratic life that was later to govern China for two millennia and more. Democracy and progress had no place in the Confucian scheme, but it found room for human feelings and the arts of civilized life; and its founder was himself a humane and civilized man.

As each prince completed the irrigation of his domain, he sought to develop larger schemes of water control,

Above: modern Chinese peasants tilling the soil near Nanking on the Yangtze. The rich loess soil (see map on page 47) is easy to work and only light tools are necessary to turn it. For this reason, cave-dwellers in the northern area around the upper Yellow River have been able to dig out chambers in loess banks and inhabit them, from the Neolithic Era to the present day.

which would bring him more grain, peasants, soldiers, and power. In centuries of war, state swallowed state. By the end of the fourth century B.C., the few princes left began to build great walls around their territories. It was futile. China was now so uniform that the process of unification had to reach its logical conclusion. At last there were only two great rival states in the field, Ch'in on the western loess part of the northern plain, and Ch'u on the lower Yangtze. That great rice area had still to develop its full productive potential, and the long-established hydraulic agriculture of Ch'in gave it victory. In 221 B.C., the king of Ch'in became Shih-huangti, first Emperor of All under Heaven.

In the increasingly bloody last phases, the state of Ch'in had taken the lead in organization for total war. After each successful campaign, the Ch'in set a price on the head of every member of the defeated state's armed forces. In 364 B.C., for instance, they took 60,000 heads; in 318, 82,000. The Ch'in left a name execrated for millennia in China; it is a singular irony that we know the country by their name. The architect of the Ch'in state system, which they eventually imposed upon all China, was the professional bureaucrat Kung-sun Yang, Lord of Shang. He expounded the system very clearly in his *Book of Lord Shang*. This book reads like a satire, but he meant every word. He defined "virtue" as unquestioning obedience to the state. The worst deviations from virtue, according to him, were care for old people, not working (at farming or war—nothing else counted as work), personal ambition, a taste for beauty, and love. The people were to be adjusted to total obedience by inflicting severe punishment for even the slightest deviation; then the really serious crimes, like art or love, would never occur. When actually executing a criminal, it was important to find out what death he most feared, and then inflict it. Anyone failing to denounce a friend for law-breaking was sawn in half.

Human beings (and even the higher animals) cannot in fact be trained to this extent by punishment without resisting or breaking down, and the Ch'in had the additional problem of demobilizing the colossal army that they had used to conquer their neighbours. The Ch'in system, born of war and water control at their most exclusive and extreme, lasted exactly one year after the death of Emperor Shih-huang-ti in 210 B.C. The people rose as one man. After a destructive civil war between rival candidates for the empire, a former village official called Liu Pang disposed of all his rivals, and in 202 B.C. he founded the Han dynasty, destined to endure for over 400 years.

The followers of Confucius at once emerged from hiding. The (relatively) humane and flexible bureaucracy they formed was able to survive all onslaughts for over two millennia. Confucius had dreamed of allotting posts in

Above: map shows the base areas of the states of Ch'in and Ch'u which absorbed all the others. By 221 B.C. the king of Ch'in had conquered Ch'u, and he became Shih-huang-ti, the first emperor of China. The thick dark lines within states represent walls.

Below: extent of the empire of the Han dynasty, founded 202 B.C. by Liu Pang. After the death of Shih-huang-ti the peasants revolted and the Han eventually introduced a more humane bureaucracy.

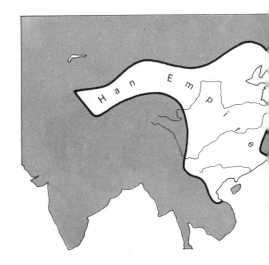

the government on merit alone, by public examinations open to all. The Han began this system, perfected later by the T'ang dynasty. Only those fully accepting all the Confucian precepts passed their examinations and became officials, and when some of them later became examiners, they naturally saw to it that only those . . . and so on. The system was inflexibly resistant to any kind of fundamental change. The examinations were open to all in theory; but in practice nobody had time to learn written Chinese except the sons of the land-owning gentry. So the gentry and the bureaucrats fused into one class, which ruled China: the Mandarins.

Once established, the system survived through the rise and decline of the Han, the T'ang, the Ming, the Chhing (Manchu), and many lesser dynasties. Each dynasty rose and fell in a population cycle. The Mandarins wanted more land to be cultivated and more peasants to work it. This would yield them rent as owners and taxes as officials, both paid in grain. They wanted no long-distance trade or industry to disturb the bureaucratic routine, still less labour-saving machinery. The peasants were encouraged to raise large families solely for land and water labour. For a while, the reclamation of land and repair of water works, ruined in the civil wars, supported a growing population. Then the labour force began to outgrow the food resources. The state increased taxes, but also began to lose its authority. The Mandarins, in their double role of landlords and bureaucrats, became corrupt, and falsified returns, squeezing out more in rent and less in taxes. The government weakened further. The combined rent and taxes became too oppressive, and peasants deserted the land and began to revolt. Finally the government collapsed, there was an interval of destructive civil wars, and a new dynasty arose to start the cycle all over again.

When the Han collapsed in A.D. 220, China was not yet solidly unified and there was still room for development. For a long time the country was divided between the northern plains and the now fully developed regions of the Yangtze River. Then the Sui dynasty (A.D. 581–618), almost as brutal and short-lived as the Ch'in, linked the Yangtze and the Yellow River by the Grand Canal. The grain wealth of the rice region could now be brought to a capital in the north, and the ensuing T'ang dynasty (A.D. 618–906) raised Chinese civilization to its greatest heights, for instance in poetry and the visual arts. After that the system was complete and closed, and each succeeding population cycle eroded the civilization, and left it more feeble than before.

The T'ang capital had to be in the north (despite the greater wealth of the Yangtze region in the south), because by this time the nomads were on the scene. According to

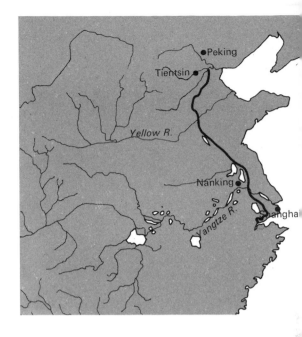

The Grand Canal (marked on map, above) was built during the period of the Sui dynasty (A.D. 581–618) to link the Yangtze and the Yellow River. Improved communications simplified political control, and rice from the prosperous lower Yangtze could be transported to the north to support new capitals near the border.

Below: ink drawing of a horse, a fine example of T'ang art (A.D. 618–906).

the patriotic historians of the Han, civilized China had always fought in self-defence against barbarian hordes, and the Great Wall was built to keep them out. This picture has been demolished by the much-travelled and Mongol-speaking American geographer, Owen Lattimore. By careful analysis of the Han historics themselves, he has shown that Chinese civilization called its own worst enemies into being.

Chinese civilization could spread southward without impediment, for that way irrigation was always easy because of the permanent rivers. Northward, where the streams dwindled, there came a zone where irrigation failed. Mixed farming was possible here, but we have seen (p. 103) that a hydraulic society in extreme form (as it was in China) could not tolerate large herds of stock. Chinese governments therefore tried to draw a line beyond which Chinese civilization stopped. The people of the border, in fact not a line but a broad zone, were constantly tempted to indulge in the un-Chinese activity of herding. Partly to occupy his too large army, but mainly to discourage this temptation, Shih-huang-ti combined the northern walls of several former states into the Great Wall of China. It was not built to keep nomads out; it was a Stone Curtain to keep his subjects in, under the full control of the state. Meanwhile the border peoples had been driven out—China wanted no part of these mixed farmers. They had no option but to take to the open steppe, and develop a nomadic life as specialized in its way as China's.

Scarcely was the Great Wall built, when the nomad horde took shape. The herders of Central Asia are divided by language into the Turks in the west and the Mongols in the east, but we do not know the language of the first nomad neighbours of China, the Hsiungnu. Their first known leader, Tumen, retired into the steppe in the reign of Shih-huang-ti. Disliking his son Modun, he sent him as a hostage to another steppe people farther west, and then attacked them. Modun escaped, and became a popular hero, and his father had to give him command of 10,000 horsemen. Modun trained his men to fire at anything at which he himself fired a whistling signal arrow. He shot his own favourite horse, his own favourite wife, and a fine horse of his father's, and put to death all who failed the tests. He then felt ready to go hunting with his father. When he fired at Tumen, all his men fired too; so all were guilty, and Modun became the first steppe emperor. The whistling arrow of Modun shows how much importance such rulers attached to human life.

The Han and the Hsiungnu waged hot or cold war for centuries. Even in Modun's time, the nomads became such a problem that at one point the Chinese attempted to appease them by giving Modun a Han princess in marriage.

Above: the Great Wall of China at Nan Kon pass near Peking. This fortified wall, 1400 miles long, was first completed by Shih-huang-ti to contain his subjects rather than to keep out the barbarian hordes. Below: the Great Wall and other walls at various times in history, showing how the effective border continually changed.

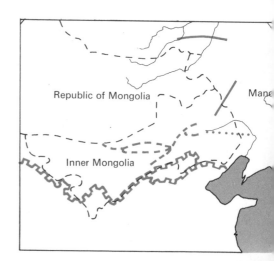

From that time on steppe chieftains claimed a right to the Chinese throne. Nearly all the later dynasties came from outside China: the founder of the T'ang dynasty, greatest of the Sons of Heaven, was descended from the Sons of the Wolf (the Turks). But these successful conquerors, who took over in the chaotic civil wars of the Chinese population cycle, were usually border chiefs. In the border zone, nomad leaders settled down as Chinese allies, and Chinese generals deserted to become steppe raiders. This zone was always a focus of disturbance, because it could never fit in with either the Chinese or the nomad way of life. The Great Wall was repeatedly rebuilt along different lines, enclosing more or less of the border zone. Conditions here began to determine the timing of both Chinese and nomad cycles. The establishment of the Chhing dynasty (A.D. 1644–1911) was a typical border operation. The Chhing (Manchus) were Manchurian chieftains who made their successful bid for China with the support of some Mongol tribes and the traitorous Chinese commander-in-chief, Wu San-kuei, who had estates in the Chinese part of Manchuria.

The nomads themselves, even in hordes, were often prepared to trade rather than raid, like the substantial Mongol horde of Altan Khan, who earned the Chinese

Below: a Mongol horseman, painted on a 14th-century silk scroll. The army of the Emperor Modun consisted of such warriors, equipped with strong bows and sturdy horses.

title of "Obedient and Loyal Prince" by this change of habits. But the Mandarins disliked trade. Exporting grain was a waste of good rent, and importing anything but luxuries would unsettle the Chinese way of life. They generally denied the nomads trade, forcing them back on their own resources, with all the dangers of overgrazing that this entailed (p. 110). In A.D. 1162, the resulting time-bomb was ready to go off.

That year a boy called Temujin was born, son of a minor Mongol chief; he died in 1227 as Genghis Khan, Emperor of the Earth. He had acquired the largest empire in history, stretching from Iran to Korea. He did so by uniting the Mongols, and eventually most of the Turks, into one vast horde. Under his orders, they turned large agricultural areas of Asia for ever into "pastures of the wilderness" (see p. 107): for instance, the whole northern half of Afghanistan, then the empire of Khwarizm. There was no immediate population problem in these areas, for the population was annihilated. The Mongol horde found a way to redress the balance of numbers between nomads and hydraulic civilizations. The great cities of Merv and Herat, for instance, were depopulated to the last child (after inducing the citizens to lay down their arms by promising to spare their lives). The whole of northern China would have suffered the same fate, had not the Mandarin Yehlü Ch'uts'ai convinced Genghis of the advantage of leaving it cultivated and taxing it to finance wars elsewhere. As it was, in the course of their conquest and occupation of China, Genghis and his successors are said to have reduced its population by 40,000,000.

Every former conqueror of part or all of China had been unable to govern without the Mandarins, so China had always remained culturally Chinese, wherever its emperors

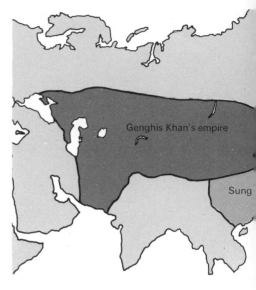

Map shows Genghis Khan's empire at his death (1227), stretching from the Black Sea to northern China. The Sung empire in southern China was finally conquered by his grandson, Kublai Khan, in 1279.

Hulagu, another of Genghis Khan's grandsons, carved out his own empire after ravaging Iraq and Syria. Below: illustration of an anecdote told to Marco Polo: on taking Baghdad, Hulagu locked up the avaricious caliph with locked up the avaricious Caliph with his huge store of gold and left him to starve, reproving him for not spending more on defences. In fact Hulagu massacred caliph and citizens after promising not to kill them.

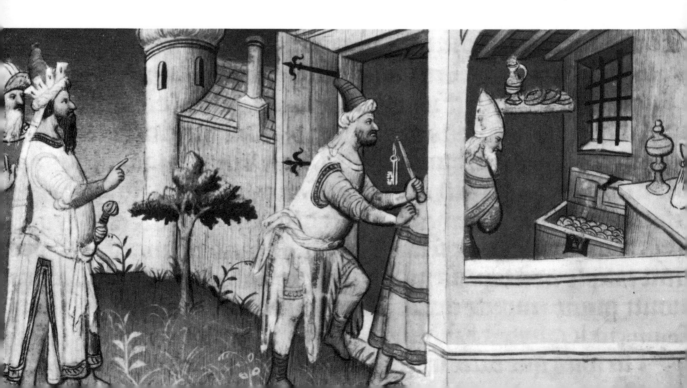

came from. Genghis and his grandson Kublai (who had conquered all China from the Sung dynasty by 1279) made a serious attempt to destroy Chinese civilization. They imported Turkish and Persian bureaucrats, and even the odd roving European, like Marco Polo of Venice. Literate Turks were ordered to construct a Mongol script. In his 27 years of high office in China, Marco Polo never encountered the written Chinese language.

But the Mandarins were invincible. The Mongol Empire soon split apart; the Mongol rulers lost touch with the steppes, and those who remained nomads could not rule settled lands. In 1368, a former Buddhist monk called Chu Yuan-Chang drove the Mongols out of China, and founded (for a change) a Chinese dynasty, the Ming. The Mandarins reappeared in a moment, and remained in charge until the 20th century. Under the Chhing, in the 18th century, they finally tamed the Mongols. They succeeded in bribing the Mongol chiefs to settle down. Then they imported the monastery system from Tibet into Mongolia. Each monastery was given some land, and was supported by a Mongol tribe, which was thus anchored to a fixed territory. In this way, the nomadic pattern was finally broken. The Mongol common people ceased to own any sheep and became virtually serfs of princes or monks. Once the flocks were fixed in position, they needed fewer people to look after them, and widespread unemployment followed. By the time of the 20th-century revolutions, over 40 per cent of the Mongol males had become monks, while princes, abbots, and Chinese immigrants ruthlessly exploited the rest. Numbers had finally won out. But by this time the civilization of China itself, originally shaken by Genghis and Kublai, and later eroded by its own population cycles, was in the last stages of decay. Europeans, arriving (at their most destructive) in the breakdown phase of the Chhing cycle, inflicted further suffering on China. But China, unlike Peru, is enormously *big*—too big for any kind of total conquest by a small group of foreigners unfamiliar with the working of a decentralized civil service dispersed through every town and village. Nevertheless, European technology finally broke the age-old pattern, and introduced China to the modern world.

Modern industrial societies have room for all kinds of food production, and the old feud of Cain and Abel is finally being resolved, as the obvious solution of mixed farming brings prosperity to large areas of the steppe. Strangely enough, the technological breakthrough owes something to Genghis Khan, the Emperor of the Earth. The Mongol Empire gave Central Asia the only peaceful century it ever knew; and in that century, along the Khan's splendid military roads, flowed the Chinese discoveries that made Europe's achievement possible.

Genghis Khan built up a fantastic network of communications across his vast empire, and Kublai perfected it. Messengers changed horses at posting stations every 25–30 miles and covered 250–300 miles in a day. Above: messenger arriving before the Great Khan. Detail from an illustration to Marco Polo's account of his travels, in a mediaeval French manuscript.

7 The Wastes of Abel

In the last decades of the 14th century A.D., a Turkish noble called Timur the Lame (Tamerlane) got control of the remains of the Mongol horde. He combined it with infantry, but his use of the combined forces was in the old nomad tradition; he turned southern Afghanistan into wilderness and did his best to smash the civilization of India. At 19 (according to his *Memoirs*) he vowed never to injure a living thing; his foot felt paralysed when he accidentally trod on an ant. This was a passing phase: he made up for it later, when he built a pyramid of 90,000 human skulls on the ruins of Baghdad. Unlike Genghis, he built no empire; he only looted, killed, and passed on.

Early in 1401, Timur was encamped outside the city of Damascus, engaged in the usual procedure of offering reasonable terms in order to disarm the citizens before sacking the city. He received in his tent an envoy from the Mameluke Sultan of Egypt (then the overlord of Damascus). The man who had "volunteered" for this very uncomfortable mission was an eminent professional bureaucrat of mixed Arab and Berber descent, called 'Abd-ar-Rahman ibn Muhammad ibn Khaldun al-Hadrami of Tunis. He had served, successively, the Sultan of Fez, the Emir of Granada, and the Sultan of Boujie, before entering his present employment. The interview of Timur and Ibn Khaldun is recorded in the latter's autobiography. The Berber gave his host a learned but flattering lecture on nomad conquests, and the Turk asked for a detailed gazetteer of North Africa. With his rare gift for survival (he had left Fez, Granada, and Boujie just in time to avoid ruin by court rivals), Ibn Khaldun got out of Damascus alive (and even saved the lives of a few Damascenes). He saved his skin at the cost of a mule, which Timur, with the meticulous attention to detail of the really great looter, had offered to "buy." Ibn Khaldun tactfully gave it to Timur (he tells us), declining a sale. "Timur said, 'I meant only that I would requite you for it with generosity.' I replied, 'Is there any generosity left beyond that which you have already shown me? . . .' He was silent; so was I. The mule was brought to him while I was with him at his council, and I did not see it again."

Bureaucrats and Bedouin

This Ibn Khaldun was the first person to work out in detail the influence of man's relations with nature on human history. Despite a visit to Pedro the Cruel, King of

Castile, he knew virtually nothing about Europe, so he naturally assumed that *all* human history was cyclical and unprogressive, in the manner of the dry belt (which he knew intimately). But his analysis of dry-belt history is astonishingly modern, and the principles set out in Chapter 5 can almost all be found in his books; many of his generalizations, too, are true of all human societies.

He showed that human behaviour is a product of environment and culture, and not of race. He did not know about the Chinese and the Mongols (racially identical, culturally so different), but he had an excellent example in the Arab people. He observed that when Arabs were settled in farms and cities, they created some of the greatest achievements of civilization; but when they were roaming the desert as nomad herders, or *Bedouin*, despite many useful qualities, they were among the most destructive forces on earth, just like their fellow-nomads—Turks, Mongols, Kurds, or Berbers. Step by step, he analysed the course of events in a hydraulic society. He showed how a

In the 14th century Timur the Lame, a Turkish nobleman, swept across the Arab world with the remnants of the Mongol horde, looting and killing. Left: the pillar of skulls he built after the battle of Baghdad. Below: Timur receives the captive sultan Bayazid of the Ottoman Turks.

131

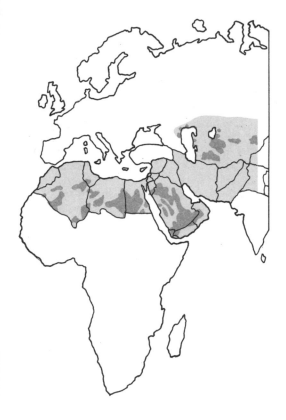

Above: the western zone of the dry belt, usually composed of numerous small states—hydraulic societies surrounded and penetrated by desert—whose need to trade made contact inevitable.

In the western zone, desert and farmland, nomads and farmers, have often been side by side. Below: bedouin tents (foreground) near the settled "bee-hive" mud houses of the peasants.

king cannot rule without a bureaucracy. He noted how population rises, and how at first this makes for greater civilization. But then come higher taxes and general oppression, including forced labour drafts, followed by a weakening of state authority. "Famines increase because many people begin to give up cultivation owing to the increased burden of taxation and the insecurity of property . . . the stocks of agricultural produce begin to fall . . . this will lead to expectations of famine and a rise in the prices of agricultural produce. . . ." And then, as the state weakens and revolts break out, nomad invaders pour in. They easily conquer, because the nomad life gives them great solidarity. But when they become rulers of civilized states, they lose this quality, and the whole cycle starts all over again. In his own North Africa, the Almoravides and Almohads had provided two especially clear-cut cycles; these desert groups, part Arab, part Berber, invaded the coastal strip, became civilized, declined, and were invaded in turn. All his conclusions, indeed, were based on the collection and comparison of facts about different societies known to him. He had studied both sides at first hand, too, thanks to a spell of exile among Berber nomads.

Ibn Khaldun knew little of China, yet his analysis clearly fits the cycles of Chinese history. Yet Chinese agricultural civilization, though more and more decadent, did persist, while the civilizations of the western zone (see map left) were everywhere in ruins by the 20th century A.D. By that time, with the sole exception of Egypt (uniquely favoured in its narrow valley by the gentle slope and the perennial Nile flood), every country in the western zone was predominantly pastoral, and their populations had shrunk accordingly. The empty deserts of North Africa are dotted with the ruins of populous Roman cities. In the time of the great Abbasid caliphs (eighth to ninth centuries A.D.), Iraq had a population of over 30,000,000; by the 20th century, it had less than 5,000,000. Afghanistan was the seat of great empires like the Ghaznavids (11th century A.D.); according to an F.A.O. report, less than three per cent of its land was under crops in 1964. Everywhere Abel conquered Cain, and destroyed the foundations of civilization.

The eastern zone, as we have seen, is divided into two great blocks, roughly China and Mongolia. But in the western zone, as the map shows, there are many scattered regions of easy irrigation, which are divided, surrounded, and interpenetrated by deserts. This had the advantage of making long-distance trade a necessity. The western zone was never so uniform as China, and mutual trade brought a certain flexibility and variety to its civilized societies. One of Ibn Khaldun's most interesting studies, his analysis of price movements and business cycles, finds no application in the world of the Mandarins; they would have been outraged by his belief in the dangers of overtaxing private business enterprise. The western zone societies never had quite the withdrawn parochialism of China, and their literature has a glamour and excitement unknown to "the Empire of All under Heaven."

But the nearness of the wilderness meant that Cain and Abel were everywhere near neighbours. The hydraulic societies of the western zone were terribly vulnerable. The hosts of Midian prowled around, waiting their chance, always ready to encroach with their flocks. Worst of all, the Near East civilizations were between two fires—Bedouin in the south, Turks and Mongols in the north. The climate was fiercer, hotter, and drier; the desert was always near in that sense too, ready (as we shall see) to encroach on the heels of the herders. The Bedouin has been called, not the child, but the father of the desert. An F.A.O. survey in 1962 reported that all the deserts in Iraq are man-made. With his customary insight, Ibn Khaldun noticed that a country (in the dry belt) that has been depopulated becomes drier; we shall see why later on. In the western zone, the scales were weighted against the farmer Cain.

Only for a brief century (around A.D. 700) has the whole western zone been under one empire (the Umayyad caliphate), though ever since then it has shared a common culture: Islam. At all other times it has been a kaleidoscopic pattern of states and empires, with continually changing rulers and frontiers. But we can sample its history by studying one typical region, the Levant (Israel, Jordan, Lebanon, and Syria), where the story of man and nature has been pieced together by the Israeli archaeologist A. Reifenberg.

Agriculture began early here (at Jericho, for instance— see p. 32), and by the tenth century B.C. King Solomon of Israel was buying timber and hiring technicians from Tyre (in what is now Lebanon) by the annual export of 150,000 sacks of wheat. In the eighth and seventh centuries B.C., from their central position on the upper Euphrates, the Assyrians united Iraq, the Levant, and Lower Egypt with a brutality worthy of the Incas or the Ch'in, but were equally efficient in extending irrigation. The more civilized Persian Empire (sixth century on) keenly encouraged agriculture, and the Greeks, who ruled most of the Levant under the Seleucid dynasty (fourth century on), introduced advanced agricultural science and a network of populous cities. Meanwhile the Nabataean Arabs covered Jordan with fertile farms. Under the Romans, who took over in the first century B.C., cultivation pushed out into the deserts and reached its widest extent in the history of the Near East. Hebrew agricultural writers a couple of centuries later knew that soil is progressively more exhausted by beans, barley, wheat, and flax, and used the

Map above shows modern divisions of Levant—Israel, Jordan, Lebanon, and Syria. Their history typifies that of the western zone of the dry belt.

In the second millennium B.C. the Levant was a prosperous agricultural region, partly covered by cedar forests. Below: chiefs of Lebanon felling the cedars, used extensively for building, at the command of their Egyptian overlords.

Above: bronze Roman coin struck to commemorate the Bar Kochba War, A.D. 132–5, in Israel. The date-palm symbolizes the region's fertility in Roman times.

Below: modern dam at Kurnub, on site of an older Byzantine dam, visible further upstream. This was one of a series used to collect flood water and trap silt before it clogged irrigation channels.

most exacting crop (flax) in field trials to estimate soil fertility in different places. From the fourth to the seventh centuries A.D., the Byzantine Empire maintained Levantine water control and agriculture in excellent condition.

Archaeologists have brought out the contrast between the flourishing condition of the Levant in these ancient times and its ruinous state by the 20th century A.D. The plain of northern Syria has been called "the Land of Dead Cities." Near Qal'at Sim'an (capital of the district in the fifth century A.D.), the ruins of 42 ancient towns lie scattered among the 14 villages still occupied. The plain is littered with ruined oil- and wine-presses, now standing forlorn in the desert: there is one whole ruined factory for olive oil production. (The hill of Testaccio on the banks of the Tiber in Italy is made up of remains of huge broken jars that once contained the wine and oil imported to Rome from this now deserted region.) In the valley of the Jordan, a wilderness by the 1900s, ruins of more than 70 ancient settlements have been found; early in the second millennium B.C., as we read in the Book of Genesis, "Lot lifted up his eyes, and beheld all the plain of Jordan, that it was well watered every where . . . even as the garden of the Lord."

The wealth of the ancient Levant was based on splendid works of water control, most of them now ruins. The rapid spread of the Hebrews over the uplands of Israel (in the late second millennium B.C.) was achieved by the invention of a waterproof mortar, for lining the walls of great cisterns to hold rain-water. The spread of cultivation into the desert in Roman and Byzantine times was achieved by new devices, like the complex damming of wadis (as at Kurnub in the Negev) to control floods, fill reservoirs, and trap silt in special compartments. Most ingenious of all were the *foggaras* or chain-wells, which gathered many small trickles of water into a great flow, and were used to irrigate desert settlements for opening up caravan trade across the Negev and Syrian deserts. A foggara system at Qadeym in Syria delivered enough water to irrigate 625 acres. These desert stations are ruins today.

At the confluence of the Jordan and Jezreel valleys stood the city of Scythopolis (Beisan), the seat of a bishop in the fourth century. Around it grew palms, fruit-trees, and flax for linen, thanks to aqueducts bringing water from springs in the hills to a reservoir 13 feet deep and 60 square miles in extent. A report to the (British) Mandatory Government of Israel describes this region in 1931: "Large areas . . . were uncultivated and covered with weeds. There were no trees, no vegetables. . . . The fellahin's (peasants') lot was an alternation of pillage and blackmail by their neighbours, the Bedouin. These latter occupied the other part of the sub-district in similar conditions;

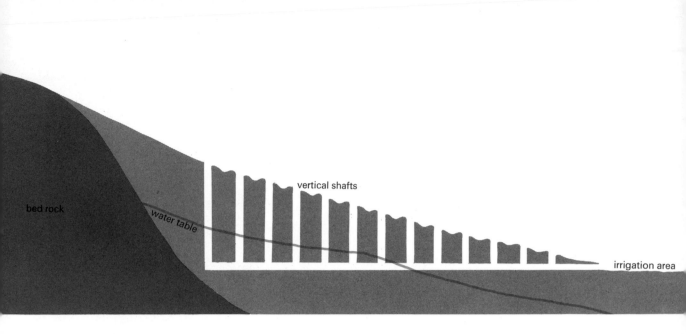

bed rock

water table

vertical shafts

irrigation area

except that cultivation by these nomads was even more scanty. In the spring the countryside was a mass of wild flowers; at other times of the year a waste of weeds and thorn bushes. Only the roughest tracks existed, and these became impassable in winter. . . . Raids and highway robberies formed [the Bedouin's] staple industry."

In ancient times, extensive forests, now vanished, covered much of the Levant. There is no trace today of the great oak forest of Ephraim, where, in the battle between King David and his son Absalom, "the wood devoured more people that day than the sword devoured." The Dead Cities of the north Syrian plain were built with so prodigal a use of timber that the area must have been covered with woodlands: it now has none at all. Most famous of all were the great cedar forests of Lebanon. Forty ships brought this weatherproof timber from Lebanon to Egypt in the reign of the Pharaoh Snefru (third millennium B.C.). By the fourth century B.C., the Greek botanist Theophrastus was talking of a scarcity of timber for ships in the eastern Mediterranean. But there were enough cedars left for the Roman general Pompey to build a large fleet with them in the first century B.C. In the reign of the Emperor Hadrian (second century A.D.), there was still a great state forest in Lebanon: many of its boundary stones have been found, but between them today lies only a treeless, eroded waste. All that remains of the mighty cedars of the Lebanon is a single grove (sacred, as usual) of about 400 trees. Less than one per cent of the Levant is woodland today.

The forests clearly survived ruthless exploitation for timber by the ancient peoples. What finished them was without doubt the encroachment of the Bedouin. As overgrazing turned more and more land into desert, the herders

Above: diagram of a foggara. Many vertical shafts were sunk below the water table (level of water in the ground); trickles from all of the shafts were collected in the underground channel connecting them, producing a sizeable flow. Although many foggaras are now choked with silt, some have been cleared and are in use today.

Victims of Bedouin overgrazing, the cedars of the vast Lebanon forest have been reduced to a single sacred grove.

moved in on the forests (whenever they could) and cut down the trees to provide more pasture. Even here, the grass withered every year at the end of the dry season, so sheep and goats wrought further destruction by eating the young tree shoots. The Hebrews of Roman times knew the connection between sheep and goats and the destruction of forests. "Those who rear these small cattle," wrote Rabbi Akiba, "and cut down good trees . . . will see no sign of blessing." Once denuded of forest, the land was soon turned into desert by overgrazing.

Forests prevent violent runoff, erosion, and floods, and store water for gradual release down slopes (see p. 82). The removal of vegetation brought severe erosion and the eventual drying-up of large regions, where there was no longer enough soil to hold the storm-waters after the wet season had passed. Soil erosion was further unleashed by the destruction of the terraces so carefully constructed to control it; and destruction of the larger irrigation works was still worse, resulting in severe floods and the silting up of the wadis into marshes. The ancient Hebrews well understood the perils of erosion. When their prophets envisaged real catastrophe, they foretold the fall of terraces; and in the Book of Proverbs an oppressor of the poor is likened to "a sweeping rain which leaveth no food."

The effects of soil erosion can be seen all over the Levant in the loss of soil in the uplands and the accumulated deposit of silt that has raised the level of the lowlands. An air photograph of Khirbet Hass, one of the Syrian Dead Cities, shows the boundary walls of many fields, now completely eroded. The foundations of the upland church of Musabbak, obviously completely buried when it was built, are now exposed to a height of four and a half feet. The now desert country of Jordan is covered with the ruins of terraces, some of them in places where almost all soil has been washed away since they were ruined. In Israel, where terrace relics also abound, five feet of earth have been deposited by floods on the low-lying Roman road near Tell ed-Duweir since the third century A.D., and the Roman theatre at Beit-Shan is covered by silt to the top seats. It has been estimated that, since Roman times, enough soil to make over 1500 square miles of good farmland has been washed off the western slopes of the Judaean hills.

The ruin of the Levant, typical for the whole western zone, took place in several stages. Ibn Khaldun's population cycle was well into its last stages by the end of Byzantine rule in the seventh century A.D. The tax on a peasant's annual produce was one fifth in the first century B.C., one third in the first century A.D., and one half by the fourth century A.D., and forced labour drafts became more and more oppressive under the Byzantines. The peasants began to desert the land, and the government seriously

Above: ruined terraces in Israel. Many were destroyed, and their soil eroded, following the Arab invasion of the 7th century A.D.

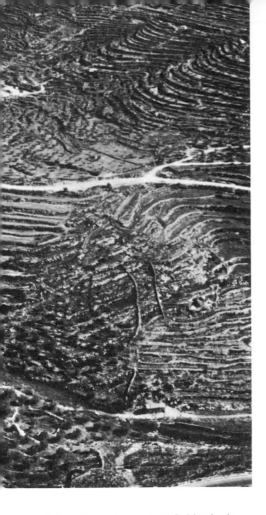

Below: Crusader castle at Byblos in the Lebanon. By the time of the Crusades the supply of wood had been exhausted and the Europeans had to build in stone.

weakened. In the sixth century A.D., a terrible catastrophe (see Chapter 11) drastically reduced the population, and by the next century the stage was set for a nomad invasion; and in due course the nomads appeared, from Arabia.

The coastal strip of southern Arabia had been a prosperous agricultural region since long before the days of Solomon's ally, the Queen of Sheba. The vigorous sea trade of the coastal cities encouraged the pastoral Bedouin of the hinterland to raid less and to take up caravan trade across Arabia. This delayed the development of a typical nomad cycle. Much of this prosperity (and the rising population it encouraged) was based on the Marib Dam, on the uplands of the south coast, probably the greatest in the ancient world, built by the Arabs in the eighth century B.C. In A.D. 450, the Marib Dam broke, and within a century the coastal irrigation systems were totally dislocated. The result was a major population crisis. Peasants turned Bedouin, and trade broke down. The Arabs began to look elsewhere for a living. In A.D. 636, the desperate Bedouin horde overran the Levant, and the next year they overthrew the second Persian Empire.

The Arabs soon established a civilized empire from the Atlantic to central Asia, ruled from Damascus by the Umayyad caliphs who at once became typical hydraulic potentates. But the invasion itself had been devastating, and much destruction dates from that time. The Kurnub Dam in the Negev was wrecked and the whole Negev was permanently overrun by the Bedouin. The Dead Cities of Syria were abandoned. The forests began to dwindle: by the time the Crusaders reached the Dead Cities region, they had to build in stone. The sudden outburst of soil erosion is well illustrated at a place near Jisr Jindas. The position of a ruined Roman bridge here shows that more than 13 feet of silt must have been deposited before an Arab bridge was built above at the same spot.

This was, however, by no means the end of Levantine agriculture. Under the Umayyad caliphs, much was done to repair the damage to irrigation works. The Abbasid caliphs, who destroyed the Umayyad dynasty in A.D. 750, ruled a somewhat reduced empire from Baghdad in Iraq. Much influenced by their Persian ministers, the Barmakids, they raised Near East civilization to new heights. The greatest of all the caliphs was Abdallah al-Mamun (A.D. 809–833), who performed a supreme service to human progress in financing the translation by Syrian experts of the surviving literature of the Greeks. The caliphs devoted special attention to irrigation works on the Euphrates, in Iraq and the Jezire region of Syria. The district of Raqqa, in the Jezire, was famous for its oil, its gardens, and a favourite palace of al-Mamun's father, Harun al-Rashid of *Arabian Nights* fame. The Arab writer Ed-Damishqi described it as one of the most beautiful places in the world.

The Euphrates runs between high banks well above the level of the plain, and is dangerously liable to flood at the wrong times. Irrigation therefore had to be based on permanent canals, mainly concerned with flood control. The canals leaked, and too much water entered the soil. The water level in the soil rose, bringing various minerals, dissolved in it, to the surface layers; here the water evaporated, leaving a poisonous accumulation of mineral salts in the surface layer of soil used by the crops. This process, called *salinization*, is said to have ruined three million acres of land on the Indus River in Pakistan, where conditions are similar. It probably began to affect Iraq and the Jezire region by the time of the Abbasids. But there were plenty of other troubles in store besides this one.

The Abbasid caliphate collapsed into insignificance with the infiltration of Turks into Persia. From the later ninth century A.D. onward, the Near East collapsed into a chaos of transient and shifting kingdoms, engaged in perpetual wars. An Arab geographer of the 10th century A.D. put his finger on one serious consequence; he wrote that southern Jordan was still fertile and rich, but added ominously that the Bedouin already had the upper hand and were ruining everything. When the Crusaders took over most of the Levant at the end of the 11th century, it was still rich in wheat, vines, and sugar-canes (introduced by the Arabs), and there was even a forest at Sharon in Israel big and thick enough to delay the advance of Richard Coeur de Lion, King of England. The Crusaders (few and exposed) conciliated their peasant subjects by lowering taxes—to one half of the annual produce! But the wars became fiercer now; Saladin the Kurd, the Crusaders' chief enemy, devastated Israel in 1189. The end was nigh.

In 1258, Hulagu the Mongol, grandson of Genghis Khan, sacked Baghdad and advanced into the Levant: this is probably why Raqqa is a waste-land, and why, of 4000 square miles of cultivable land in the Jezire, only 20 per cent is cultivated today; over the rest, Bedouin now graze (or over-graze) among the silted-up canals. The Mongols, however, were halted at last by the Turk Baybars, general of the army of the (Turkish) Mameluke Sultan of Egypt. Hulagu and Baybars met, appropriately enough, at the Pool of Goliath near Jerusalem. The Turkish giant beat the Mongol one, and Hulagu retreated to Persia. The Mamelukes, having thus saved the Levant from one destroyer, utterly ruined the coastal areas themselves, in the course of expelling the last of the Crusaders. In 1280, the German pilgrim Burchardus still found some crops growing in Israel; but by the end of the 15th century, after a raid by Timur the Lame, the pilgrim Felix Fabri reported that Israel was a desert.

Ancient systems of agriculture restored to use today. Above: experimental runoff farm at Avdat in the Negev desert. Below: heaps of gravel have been removed to allow the soil to harden into a crust, thus encouraging runoff.

138

The Ottoman Turks took over the Near East in 1506, when there was not enough of civilized society left to turn them into normal hydraulic rulers. Their taxes were a new experience even for that suffering region. By the late 18th century, the peasants were handing over two thirds of their annual produce, and forced to borrow money at 30 per cent interest. They steadily deserted what was left of the farmland. At the start of the Turkish occupation, there were more than 3000 taxable villages in the pashalik (province) of Aleppo; 300 years later, there were only 400. By the 18th century, Israel was so overrun by Bedouin that it was impossible to travel in safety from Gaza to Acre. Incredibly, taxes continued to rise till the end of the Turkish Empire in 1918. By that time the last forests had been cut down, to escape a severe tax on growing trees.

The coming of European technology has begun to show that the tragic retreat of agriculture in the western zone is not irreparable. It is interesting, and a tribute to the early civilizations, that modern development schemes so often follow in their track. The Tunisians are finding that the most promising sites for irrigation development are those around the ruined Roman cities. In 1938 the French restored a great dam on the Orontes built by the Egyptians in the second millennium B.C. But the most intriguing example of applied archaeology comes from the Negev desert in Israel. A team of Israeli scientists (an archaeologist, two botanists, and an engineer) examined about 100 sites, some as old as the 10th century B.C., but most of Roman or Byzantine date, where the ancients had established runoff farms. Just as the chain-well collects small trickles of water from the ground, so the runoff farm collects small trickles of water down slopes on the surface. Each farm needed a catchment area of about 20 times its own area. The farms were placed among hills covered with a kind of loess soil that forms a crust when wetted, so that nearly all the rain runs off and does not sink in. The ancient farmers carefully cleared gravel away to expose the soil, to ensure crust formation. The water trickled down the channels from all around the farm, and was concentrated on to walled terraces in the farm area itself. In 1958 an ancient farm at Shivtah (Sbeita) was reconstructed, with terraces, walls, and channels, and in 1959 the same thing was done at Avdat (Abde). In two drought years, young trees planted at Shivtah made excellent growth. In the exceptionally severe drought of 1960, when large acreages of barley suffered total crop failure in areas further north with twice as much rainfall, a respectable crop of barley (half a ton per acre) was grown at Avdat. Both farms are still thriving, typical of a renaissance of agriculture that allows us to end on an encouraging note the painful story of man and nature in the dry belt.

Modern agricultural experiments on the sites of ancient farms have shown how primitive methods of water control once made the Levant a fertile area. Above: resulting crop on the farm near Avdat (see picture opposite). Neglect and overgrazing destroyed the fertility of the Levant, but such experiments prove that redevelopment could restore former agricultural prosperity.

8 The European Adventure

"No free man shall be taken or imprisoned or deprived of his estates or outlawed or exiled or in any way impoverished, nor will we go against him or send anyone against him, except through the legal judgment of his equals or the law of the land." These are the words of Clause 39 of Magna Carta, the Great Charter, signed by King John of England. He had no intention of abiding by this charter, which was extorted by a group of powerful landowners, who wanted a free hand to plunder and terrorize everybody else. Yet it has captured the imagination of the English-speaking peoples, who celebrated its 750th anniversary

Right: King John of England out hunting. His subjects had a harder life. The rough justice being meted out to them in the drawing below (from the historian Matthew Paris), was one aspect of the king's power that Magna Carta (A.D. 1215) purported to limit, in protecting the individual against arbitrary arrest and punishment.

with great pomp on June 10, 1965. This kind of document has no counterpart in the history of the dry belt.

The salient features of Clause 39 of Magna Carta are the assertion of two old ideas in Europe: the jury system, and the supremacy of secular (as opposed to ritual) law over the state. The first English parliament, summoned 50 years later by the cruel would-be dictator Simon de Montfort, asserted another old European principle: the right of subjects to control the making and changing of the laws binding on the state.

All three principles made their first appearance in the empire of the Hittites (18th-12th centuries B.C.) in Asia Minor (modern Turkey). Significantly, torture and mutilation were absent from Hittite judicial penalties, except for slaves, and then only for theft or arson. Immunity from torture is a good measure of freedom.

Asia Minor is intermediate in climate between the dry belt and Mediterranean Europe; in the international agencies of the modern United Nations, Turkey figures as part of the Near East in some contexts, as European in others. The Hittites (Indo-European invaders) seem to have practised mixed farming; a typical Hittite farm, occupied by five people, had pastures as well as vineyards and orchards, and carried 2 oxen, 22 sheep, and 23 goats, as well as the 6 oxen used for draught. Typical hydraulic society did not develop in Asia Minor until it was absorbed into the Persian Empire in 546 B.C. But the Hittites were too near the dry belt to develop for long in the direction of greater freedom.

When we come to Europe proper, we find all three principles of European law fully realized in the democracy of Athens. In 621 B.C., the people compelled one of their ruling nobles (Draco) to write down a law-code. This Code of Draco was said to be written in blood, so many offences carried the death-penalty; but not long after (about 594 B.C.), the laws were changed by the great statesman Solon, acting on a mandate from the whole Athenian people, and democracy was born.

A body of carefully worked-out and reliable law (as opposed to the whims of a king or his officials) was the only possible basis for large-scale private business enterprise, and in the critical centuries of the breakthrough in late mediaeval Europe it was the businessmen who had the greatest incentive to launch modern technology. But this is not all. Different attitudes to law in society affect the way in which people think about nature. In Europe, by A.D. 1665, the term "law of nature" already appeared as a cliché in the first volume of the *Philosophical Transactions* of the Royal Society; and Joseph Needham has traced the metaphor back through the European Middle Ages to Athens in the fifth century B.C., where the word *astronomy*

From the 17th century A.D. onward, Europeans explicitly tried to discover and manipulate the "laws of nature." Newton (above) established basic principles of mechanics; in America Franklin (below, experimenting with kites in a thunderstorm), was one of the pioneers in the study of electricity.

(star law) was already in use. If nature had laws, then man was not subject to her whims; he could promote his own interests (just as in a human society) by discovering these laws and manipulating them. It was in this spirit, explicitly, that scientists like Boyle and Newton, in the 17th century A.D., set about establishing the fundamental principles of chemistry and physics; and it was this systematic science that accomplished the technological breakthrough.

In the 19th century, when systematic science began to pay off in a spectacular way (for instance, in bringing electricity under human control), it was often thought that progress in human societies was inevitable. In a sense this is true, provided that stresses in the society's relations with nature do not *either* reduce it to chaos *or* force it to specialize—that is, to remain fixed at a particular level. The tropical forest societies were forced, by heat and excessive rainfall, to specialize at a technically simple, tribal level. The hydraulic societies were forced, ultimately by restricted rainfall, to specialize at a much higher technical and cultural level, but one that stopped short of modern technology. The Europeans, forced into neither blind alley, inevitably went on to the technological breakthrough. The natural factors that stopped advance outside Europe have been relatively easy to define; the factors that permitted continued advance in Europe are much more complex.

Since the drought of 1959 (serious by European standards) every country in Europe has taken to practising some irrigation. But this is a refinement to ensure the very high yields of modern intensive agriculture, and it is done with modern labour-saving machinery. Europe has always had enough rain in the crop-growing seasons to make farming perfectly practicable without irrigation in all but a few years: indeed the occasional disastrous crop failures in Europe (e.g. 1594–7) have often resulted from *too much* rain at the wrong time.

The successful invaders of Europe, from the Battle-axe folk to the Germans (see Chapter 2), either were already mixed farmers or became so at once. Europe has practised mixed farming since the Neolithic, and has produced no nomad hordes; her story is that of Cain and Abel, Brothers, in successful partnership. Mixed farming gives scope for a great diversity of farming systems, varying in the ratio of stock to crops, and in the kinds of animals and plants raised. It can thus be adjusted in detail to fit changing circumstances in space and time. The most obvious visible difference between Europe and such countries as Egypt or China was always the extraordinary diversity of the farming landscape. With this went a diversity of behaviour that made for vigorous local institutions, and continually resisted the uniform bureaucratic order so easily imposed in the dry belt.

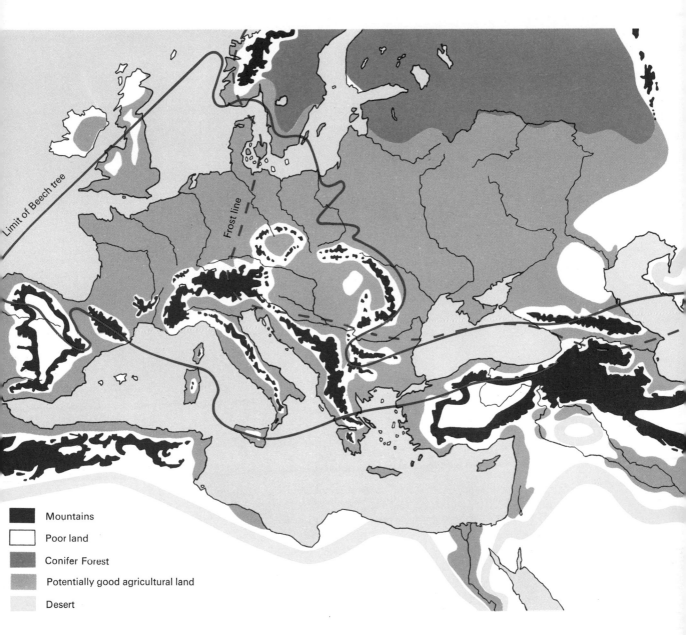

■	Mountains
□	Poor land
▨	Conifer Forest
▨	Potentially good agricultural land
▨	Desert

Map labels: Limit of Beech tree · Frost line

Divided by mountain chains, but criss-crossed by rivers and bounded by a very long coastline, Europe was well-equipped for trade, and each small region, with its special form of mixed farming and associated industries, had something different to offer the others. The division of the continent into many separate and diverse units, whether small tribes or great modern nations, generally favoured the freedom of merchants, technicians, and scientists, who were welcome everywhere and could pack up and move on if they felt oppressed. They evolved a sense of comradeship that often led to the pooling of different technical experiences, and hence to the rapid progress of techniques.

Bounded by a long coastline and criss-crossed by rivers, Europe is an ideal area for trading. Beech-line encloses area where farming is easiest, with plentiful rainfall and not too much frost. Mediterranean Europe, to the south of this line, is warmer but drier, and eastern Europe, beyond the frost line, suffers continual frosts for at least one month of the year.

Gordon Childe (p. 12) has observed that all this can be traced at all epochs: among the technicians of Bronze Age Europe (second to first millennium B.C.), who were more inventive and original in tool design than their civilized contemporaries in the Near East; among the traders and thinkers and technicians who circulated between Ancient Greek cities and between mediaeval or Renaissance states; and finally among "the natural scientists who from the days of Galileo and Newton to A.D. 1945 freely exchanged information and ideas by publication, correspondence and visits, regardless of political frontiers." British and French scientists, for instance, were calmly co-operating with each other throughout the Napoleonic Wars.

Wars between all its territorial units have been a major interruption to European progress. They sprang from the relative infertility of Europe. The soils were generally not badly leached; and their fertility was relatively easily maintained by alternating crops with different demands, by using legumes in these rotations, by animal manure from the stock, and by resting the fields as bare fallows. Most European land slopes too gently for serious erosion risk from the moderate rain-storms, and it is too broken up and sheltered for serious wind erosion. So Europe was better off than the tropical forest peoples. But, without every resource of modern agricultural science, European land could not begin to compare for fertility with the irrigated valley fields of the dry belt. Hence Europe before the technological breakthrough could not afford large cities. Her problem was to produce the large surplus that the hydraulic societies easily acquired—but only by mass labour, and hence at the cost of flexibility and freedom.

The surplus was won, in part by the gradual improvement of farming methods, and in part by tapping the surplus of the rich neighbours of Europe in the dry belt, through a combination of trade and predatory exploitation. This made for a highly unstable economy. A prey to repeated population problems whenever her numbers outran her own resources, Europe has always vibrated with social tensions, engendering bloody class conflicts and predatory wars. Besides these endless disturbances, Europe has had major population cycles. But, in the north of the continent, the temperate climate has caused no irreparable damage in the troughs of the cycles; after the human collapse, the forest came back, but unlike the desert, it was easily cleared again when things improved. Nor was there any unchanging social order like Confucian bureaucracy, to which the cycles incessantly returned. So, whereas in the dry belt technology declined at every cycle, in Europe it advanced. As Gordon Childe has put it, "no trough ever declines to the low level of the preceding one, each crest out-tops its last precursor."

Above: the Emperor Henry VI besieging Naples (A.D. 1194). European states attacked each other and neighbouring dry-belt states in the search for more land when their own proved insufficient to feed rising populations, and Europe abounded in fortified castles like the one (below) at Bingen on the Rhine.

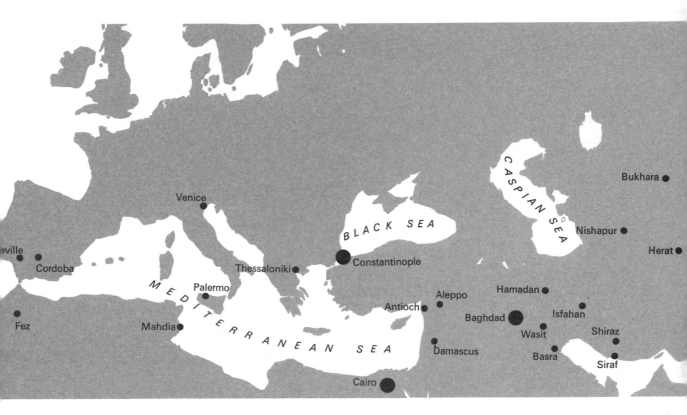

By climate and geography, Europe is divided into three regions: north-western, eastern, and Mediterranean. Eastern Europe can roughly be defined as that region deep in the continent where frost prevails for at least one month of winter. Mediterranean Europe is the part south of the southern limits of the beech tree; it has a dry summer, and is intermediate in climate between the dry belt and the lands to the north. But the winter and spring rains persist long enough for growing one winter crop, harvested at leisure in the warm, dry summer. Irrigation, including terracing, was introduced into Greece, Italy, and Spain in the first millennium B.C.; but it was neither indispensable nor widespread, and did not dominate these societies as it did those of the dry belt. North-western Europe (including northern Italy) enjoys relatively mild winters and rain throughout the year: here irrigation was hardly used until modern times.

Eastern Europe was exposed to the nomad hordes of Central Asia, and this and Byzantine influence distorted its history and retarded its development. Mediterranean Europe suffered in various ways from its nearness to the dry belt, and as we shall see, it was in a serious decline by the 17th century A.D., just when the breakthrough was beginning. Creative individuals from eastern and Mediterranean Europe made great contributions to the subsequent

Above: map of Europe and the Near East, marking largest towns in 11th century A.D. Significantly, all are situated in, or near, the dry belt. European towns remained limited in size compared with those created and supported by hydraulic societies—like Baghdad and Cairo. The first large towns in mediaeval Europe, such as Venice, grew up as trading centres.

145

advance of science; but today these regions are intermediate in technological development (and in average income per head of population) between the advanced countries of north-western Europe and the now relatively poor countries of the dry belt and the tropics. It was left for north-western Europe to take the second step and make the breakthrough; but this region began its civilized career very late in the day, and the European adventure story really begins in the Mediterranean.

Glories and Grandeurs

In the early sixth century B.C., there lived in the Greek city-state of Miletus, on the west coast of Asia Minor, a prosperous trader called Thales. On his business trips abroad, he made a point of collecting scientific information: geometry from Egypt, astronomy from Babylon. Back at home, he had plenty of leisure to think about these things. The theory he worked out was that everything is made of water. This sounds primitive, but so will Einstein's relativity theory two-and-a-half millennia from now. Thales worked out his theory in sufficient detail for others to disprove it, and so improve on it by further observations. His significance is that he was the very first person known

Greek pure science formed the basis of modern European thought, and the foundations of modern geometry were laid by thinkers like Pythagoras and Euclid. Their work first reached European civilization via the Moslem world. Below: two versions of Pythagoras's theorem—(left) page from an Arabic commentary of about A.D. 1250 on Euclid's *Elements*; (right) page of an English text-book of 1888.

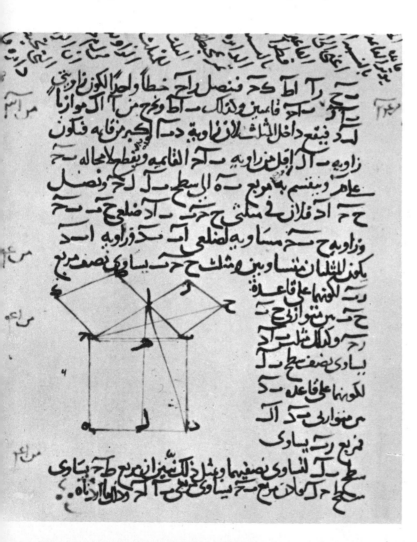

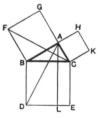

82   EUCLID'S ELEMENTS.

PROPOSITION 47. THEOREM.

In a right-angled triangle the square described on the hypotenuse is equal to the sum of the squares described on the other two sides.

Let ABC be a right-angled triangle, having the angle BAC a right angle:
then shall the square described on the hypotenuse BC be equal to the sum of the squares described on BA, AC.

Construction. On BC describe the square BDEC; I. 46. and on BA, AC describe the squares BAGF, ACKH.
Through A draw AL parallel to BD or CE; I. 31. and join AD, FC.

Proof. Then because each of the angles BAC, BAG is a right angle,
therefore CA and AG are in the same straight line. I. 14.

Now the angle CBD is equal to the angle FBA, for each of them is a right angle.
Add to each the angle ABC:
then the whole angle ABD is equal to the whole angle FBC.

to have engaged in what the Greeks called philosophy, and what we call pure or fundamental science. That is, he tried to understand the basic workings of nature, with no immediate practical application in mind.

As we now well know, pure science is not a waste of time, but this was naturally less obvious to the friends of Thales, and the story goes that one of them asked him what was the point of this kind of thinking. Thales did not reply, but he began to concentrate his new orderly way of thinking about nature on some problems of weather and plant growth. A few years later, during the winter, he quietly bought up every oil-press in the territory of Miletus. That summer the olive crop was a record one, and Thales made a fortune. In his love of pure science and the ruthless logic of his business methods, Thales well represents "the glory that was Greece and the grandeur that was Rome."

The nation we now know as ancient Greece was formed by groups of Indo-Europeans, invading from the north in several waves during the latter half of the second millennium B.C., and fusing with the native inhabitants of mainland Greece, the Aegean and Levantine islands, and the west coast of Asia Minor. Greece, a miniature of Europe, is split by mountains into many small regions; in these, as well as on the islands and on the peninsulas of Asia Minor, many small city-states evolved. They acquired a share of the Near East surplus by piracy and, increasingly, by trade. The territories of these city-states were small and the land poor, so that the Greeks had a persistent population problem. From about the eighth century B.C., they began partially to solve it by founding daughter-cities, or colonies, all around the coasts of the western Mediterranean and the Black Sea.

In the sixth century B.C., the continuing population problem in Greece itself caused increasing social disturbance. The city of Athens took the lead in a new kind of solution. She abandoned hope of feeding herself entirely

Above: olive gatherers, on a Greek vase (sixth century B.C.). Olive oil and pottery were the vital exports that enabled Athens to import wheat.

The Greeks tried to solve their population problem by founding colonies all round the Mediterranean (black dots on map below). The Phoenicians, from the Levant, did the same, and built a great trading empire on their network of ports (white dots).

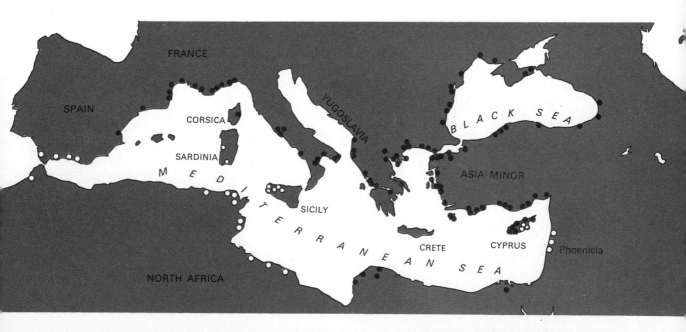

The Phoenicians were the first to use efficient alphabetic writing (top line, above). This was adapted by the Greeks for their own use; they added letters for vowels. Next two lines show parts of two Greek alphabets.

In the first millennium B.C. the Phoenicians dominated trade in the Mediterranean. Below: Phoenician ship, and map of their trade routes. Solid lines indicate known trade routes, and broken lines, probable ones.

from her territory of Attica, and became the first mainly industrial city, producing manufactured goods, especially cheap pottery, for export to the civilized Near East and to lands as far away as central Russia western Germany, and northern France. With this and lucrative oil exports from her olive crop she was able to pay for imports of wheat, chiefly from south Russia.

Through the creative work of Solon and of the still more inspired statesman Cleisthenes (active in the last decade of the sixth century B.C.), Athens became a civilized democracy. In the fifth century B.C., attracting gifted people from all over Greece, the city achieved the greatest concentration of creative activity (in science, literature, history, drama, and the visual arts) in the history of mankind. The democratic system, involving paid official posts and the responsibility of officials to paid juries (both open to all), soon spread to other city-states. It lasted longest in Athens (until 261 B.C.). The city's vulnerable position (its dependence on food imports from far away) was eased by the presence at Laurion in Attica of the richest silver mines in the ancient world, which paid for a powerful war fleet.

The progress in Greece was made possible by the development of two inventions made outside Europe—the alphabet and coinage. Trade is the joint result of diversity in nature, such as the uneven distribution of metals on or near the earth's surface, and the organization of human societies. Within China, for instance, once the country was organized in uniform hydraulic style, there was no point in the peasants exporting cereals to each other. In the Near East of the second millennium B.C., by contrast, the developing societies were not yet highly uniform, and the volume of trade steadily expanded. This necessitated a more flexible and easily-learnt method of writing, and by the end of the second millennium, after many experiments in various parts of the Levant, an efficient alphabet was in use in the Phoenician cities on the coast of Lebanon.

These Phoenicians were the first sea-traders and the greatest navigators of the ancient world. They were at first tolerated (as neutral traders) but were later dominated by the great inland empires. Their basic insecurity must have arisen from their dependence for food on the very narrow strip of land between the Lebanon mountains and the sea. They became totally specialized for trade, employing other people both to grow food and to fight, and their population problem (far worse than that of the Greeks) left them with an almost New-Worldly addiction to human sacrifice. These traits persisted in the colonies they planted on the Mediterranean coasts at about the same time as the Greeks, especially in the great city of Carthage in Tunisia (founded about 800 B.C.), which by about 600 B.C. had assumed leadership over all the Phoenician trading cities in the

western Mediterranean. But though Phoenician civilization became static, their alphabetic writing was recognized by other states as a great innovation, and quickly spread to other languages. The Greeks, in particular, added letters for vowels (necessary in Indo-European languages) and had developed several alphabets by about 700 B.C.; in 403 B.C., they finally agreed on one standard alphabet for all Greek-speaking peoples. In the seventh century B.C., writing had already ceased to be a prerogative of bureaucrats: ordinary Greek mercenaries (with the age-old vandalism of tourists) were scratching their names on the ancient statues in Egyptian temples.

During the eighth century B.C., a state called Lydia had appeared in western Asia Minor. The area was rich in gold, and the gold-bearing river Pactolus crossed the centre of its capital city, Sardis. For their foreign trade, the Lydians invented the gold coin, a small unit of uniform weight and purity, while at the same time they may have begun to use cash, instead of barter, in retail food transactions. For cash they used handfuls of gold dust, just as was done up to modern times in the market-place of Bida in Nigeria, where gold was also plentiful. The new idea of coined money was eagerly adopted by the Greeks, who (during the sixth century B.C.) introduced cheaper coins of silver and bronze. This had far-reaching effects. One was an entirely new feature of town-planning, first fully developed at Athens—a central space, where scientists and travellers strolled and chatted, and where one could buy or sell anything from a ship's cargo to a quick snack. This was the market-place.

Gordon Childe has pointed out the analogy between breaking down ideographic characters into an alphabet and breaking down costly ingots into coined money. Together, letters and coins brought literacy and business within the reach of many, and made both political and social democracy conceivable. In a society dominated by money, some people at least could have leisure and freedom from state and social pressures; if many squandered the opportunity, some used it to develop pure science.

The invention of coins, together with alphabetic writing, boosted development of trade in Mediterranean Europe. Above: ten-drachma piece from Syracuse in Sicily, fifth century B.C., showing head of Arethusa, and, on the other side, a charioteer. In Greek cities, the market-place became a focal point, where all commodities were bought and sold at prices varying according to supply and demand. Right: reconstruction of the market-place in the city of Assos, Asia Minor.

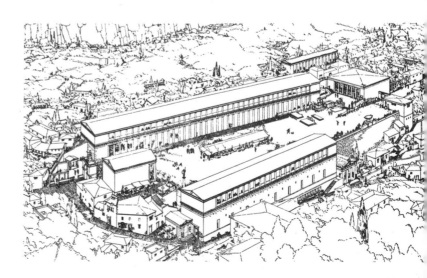

The market-place brought with it a fundamental change in the relations of human societies to nature. The civilized societies of the Near East had long been using relatively small quantities of precious metal (because of its rarity) to symbolize larger quantities of food surplus. But American scholars, reinterpreting the writings of the ancient Near East, have recently concluded that, until Greek times, merchants made their living by taking fixed commissions for their work, and not by buying cheap and selling dear. In the Greek market-places, prices were free to move up or down instantly, as demand or supply increased. From the fifth century B.C. to the 19th century A.D. the history of Europe was largely influenced by the price of food, especially of cereals. The Greeks were alarmed to find that prices rose steadily with rising population (and hence food demand) in the fifth and fourth centuries B.C. Prices were also affected by the amount of precious metal in circulation as money: they rocketed at the end of the fourth century, when Alexander the Great looted the treasure-hoard of the Persians and put it into circulation. The Greeks themselves never understood what had happened.

The problem they failed to solve was their dependence on the dry belt societies, whose food surplus they needed to feed their expanding population. Greek civilization failed because it was infected by the hydraulic way of life. The virus that carried the infection was the institution of slave labour. The wealth of Athens rested on the foreign slaves who worked, until they literally dropped dead, the silver mines of Laurion. Slavery rotted the Greek societies in several ways. It supplied a constant temptation to make war on each other (they sometimes hesitated to enslave their fellow Greeks, but not when it came to the pinch). The permeation of the Greek states by cheap slave labour prevented the free labourers (who worked side by side with slaves, for instance, to build the Parthenon at Athens) from effective bargaining for wages. The one modern social institution conspicuously lacking in the Greek and Roman world (otherwise so much more modern in spirit than any other time and place) was the trade union. Instead, the use of slaves made manual work (other than farming) seem more and more degrading. The free lower classes lost interest in wage increases, and struggled only for landed property. The result was a ceaseless and bitter class war within the city-states, encouraging ideological wars between them.

Cheap slave labour also meant a lack of interest in the application of science to labour-saving machinery or the development of new sources of power. Contempt for manual labour prevented Greek scientists from tackling the one science where they would have had to dirty their hands—chemistry. Ignorance of this crucial subject set an

Above: coin bearing head of Alexander the Great, the Macedonian ruler who conquered the Near and Middle East. Map above right shows extent of his empire.

Like the Greeks, the Romans depended on slaves for most manual labour. Below: part of a Roman funeral monument dedicated to Publius Satur of Capua. The three figures at the foot represent the selling of a slave (central figure), and were probably a reminder that this public figure started life as a slave.

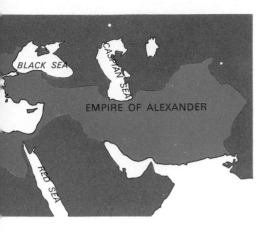

EMPIRE OF ALEXANDER

absolute limit on Greek scientific advance, and caused it to stop short of the breakthrough. The lack was remedied later, partly by the Arabs and partly by mediaeval European scientists, who simply loved getting their hands dirty.

Once thoroughly infected with slave labour, Greek democracy withered. The Greeks ended by succumbing completely to the dry belt way of life. In the fourth century B.C., after a long succession of wars, the Greeks were forcibly united by Philip II, ruler of Macedonia, a half-Greek state of landowning squires. His son Alexander the Great used both Greeks and Macedonians to conquer the Near and Middle East as far as Pakistan. On the conqueror's death in 323 B.C. his Macedonian marshals fought each other for his empire, which finally settled into the great Kingdoms of Macedonia, Syria, and Egypt, several smaller princedoms, and the surviving independent Greek city-states, notably Rhodes, all by now oligarchies with a democratic facade but voting rights firmly restricted to the rich.

Mainland Greece was on the wane; other peoples had adopted the industries of Athens and Corinth, and made their own pottery, so the privileged position of those cities was lost. (The same thing will happen in due course to the developed societies of the present day.) Greeks poured into the new Near East states to staff their bureaucracies,

Desire for more slaves and more silver, and inability to feed their growing populations, drove the Greek city states to make war on each other. Below: vase painting of Greek warriors fighting with swords and spears.

founding many cities but becoming completely absorbed by hydraulic civilization. Even the free Greek cities were now quite prepared to worship allied kings in their temples, a thing unthinkable before.

Under royal patronage, especially in Egypt under the Ptolemy dynasty, the traditional dry belt sciences (such as astronomy and agricultural science) were pursued with spectacular success, thanks to the insights of the new pure science: we have already seen that they raised Near East agriculture to its zenith by the time of the Roman Empire. But pure scientific activity gradually dwindled, finding a last glory in the work of Archimedes of Syracuse in Sicily (287–212 B.C.), often considered the greatest physical scientist in history. Painting and sculpture flourished exceedingly through the third century B.C., but literature and drama, more sensitive to the loss of democratic freedom, decayed at once.

The Greek states, large and small, settled down to a condition of limited but almost permanent mutual warfare. At a congress of Greek states in 217 B.C., amidst the usual half-hearted planning for a United Greek Nations Organization, one delegate (Agelaus of Naupactus) advised his colleagues to watch out for the "cloud in the West." Here a total war was on between Carthage and a league of Italian peoples headed by the city of Rome.

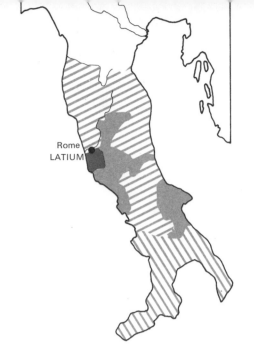

■	500 B.C.
■	300 B.C.
▨	290 B.C.
▧	275 B.C.

152

Map opposite illustrates spread of Roman League in Italy between the fifth and third centuries B.C. The Romans subdued neighbouring states and then treated them as allies in wars against fresh foes. By 275 B.C. Italy was thus welded into one strong unit.

Commanding cheap slave labour, Greek and Roman factory owners alike were uninterested in machinery, and processes remained simple as in the Roman bakery below left (depicted on a baker's tomb). Lower strip shows animals grinding corn and bakers who kneaded the dough by hand. On upper strip workers weigh and dispatch the bread.

The dark areas on the map below show extent of the Roman Republic at the height of its territorial expansion in the first century B.C.

Italy is the Mediterranean country most favoured by nature, with a broad plain running down the west coast, in places very fertile by European standards. In the centre of this belt, a new kind of society of farmers was emerging: the city-state of Rome. Around 509 B.C., this community of mixed farmers threw out their Etruscan overlords and formed the Roman Republic. From the beginning, the governing council, the "Senate," was monopolized by the biggest landowners, but their subjects retained all the independence of farmers owning their land. The Republic combined iron discipline in war with unusual personal freedom from state control in all other contexts. The smaller farmers pressed stubbornly, but with remarkably little violence, for practical reforms. The most spectacular move of this unusual lower class was in 449 B.C., when they set up their own Republic, ignoring the old one; the Senate gave in, and accepted some of the new officials (the tribunes of the people) as permanent elements in its state. In general, the Senators resisted every change, but as each reform became law, they abided by it; the people, in return, never embarrassed the Senate when the Republic was in danger.

When the Romans defeated another Italian people in war, they used similar principles. The losers became their allies, accepting the authority of the Roman Senate in war, but absolutely free from interference in civil matters, and

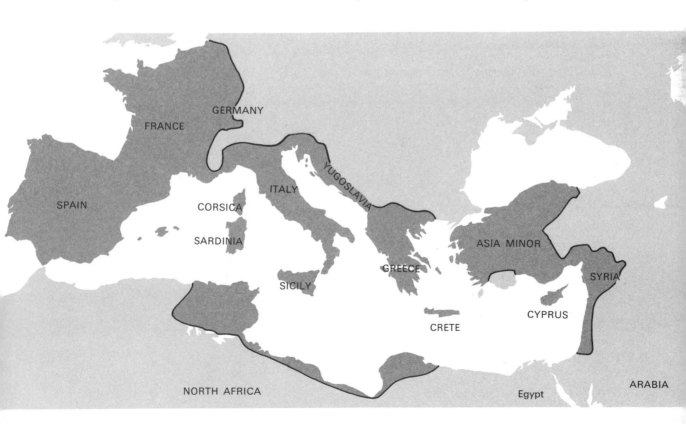

entitled to a share of allied loot. It is not surprising that during the fourth century B.C. the Romans united all Italy into an invincible league.

In the third century B.C., the Romans wiped out the Carthaginian Empire; in the second century B.C., they gained control of the entire Greek world; in or soon after the first century B.C., they conquered north-western Europe. Vast quantities of loot had gathered at Rome; Roman war contractors had made fortunes; the Romans proceeded to invent the business corporation (a legal "person" independent of the actual people composing it) and the stock market (where the public could buy shares in, for instance, shipping companies). Free private enterprise was without limit, and not even in the 19th century A.D. was the power of money so absolute, with all the callous injustice that implies.

Meanwhile Rome had caught the virus of slavery from the Greeks and the dry belt. After the wars with Carthage, the new tycoons invested in slave-run plantations, growing vines or olives or raising stock for export; the swelling city itself was fed increasingly on wheat imported as an imperial tax from Sicily, North Africa, and the Near East. When the very destructive conquest of the East Mediterranean was nearly completed, and the supply of war-slaves dried up, the Roman Senate found a technical reason for demilitarizing Rome's most faithful foreign ally, the Rhodian Republic, which had until then kept down the pirates of Asia Minor and Crete. By simple kidnapping, these pirates now kept the slave-trade going for Rome till 67 B.C., when the Romans finally destroyed them for going too far and interfering with the wheat-importing fleets. Julius Caesar replenished the slave-market in the course of conquering

Rich in precious metal plundered from other societies, Roman civilization was entirely organized around money. Even peasants in the provinces, like the ones above, paid their rents in cash. (From a stone sarcophagus of the third century A.D., found in northern France.)

France (58–49 B.C.). In the first and second centuries A.D., the slave supply dwindled, and it was found that slaves did not breed. Slavery began to decline in Europe. But, long before, the Republic as such had ceased to exist (30 B.C.).

Decline and Fall

It was Rome's misfortune that the flowering of her civilization, which produced some wonderful poetry and a vigorous prose literature, coincided with a prolonged and bloody revolution (about 135–30 B.C.). There was a furious struggle for the loot of the empire, partly between Rome and her Italian allies (especially the hill-folk), partly between the noble politicians (who paid heavy bribes to the voters for their lucrative posts, so that they were often heavily in debt, and therefore kept debasing the coinage) and the businessmen (who wanted a stable currency and stable rates of interest on loans). Having shaken off a wild fringe of speculators who were ruining the empire by extortionate exploitation, business won, with the help of a new professional army.

In the first to second centuries A.D., with moderate, stable interest rates for investment, business ruled the Western civilized world, but (because of the tradition of slavery) without any attempt to develop new machines. The rule of business was as drearily unprogressive as any bureaucracy; literature soon decayed. The empire became virtually a federation of city-states each run by businessmen, paying and controlling a common army and police force led by the emperor at Rome. Prolonged peace and large-scale production of cheap goods like pottery (by cheap labour, not machines) raised even the peasants' standard of living, but not enough by comparison with the

Two bas-reliefs from Trajan's column in Rome. Trajan (A.D. 53–117) typifies the imperial ideal of a ruler working hard for the glory and wealth of the business empire. Below left: Trajan addresses Roman army. Below: with his staff he receives barbarian chiefs.
Treated here as equals, the barbarians were to infiltrate the Roman Empire and build new societies on its ruins.

affluent society in the cities, which took little interest in the welfare of those who produced its food. The peasants recruited into the army finally got out of hand, and throughout the third century A.D. they proceeded to wreck civilization in a series of senseless civil wars, in which they raised one general after another to the throne, murdering him when he tried to restrain them from looting the cities. Some sort of order was restored in A.D. 285 by the Emperor Diocletian, who was born a slave and rose from the ranks of the army, but only by imposing a bureaucratic regime of extreme hydraulic pattern, in which everyone was bound to a hereditary occupation.

From the beginning, the Roman Empire was divided into a Latin-speaking Western half (the western Mediterranean and north-western Europe) and a Greek-speaking Eastern half (the eastern Mediterranean and much of the Near East). During the peaceful first to second centuries A.D., as agriculture, industry, and trade revived in the Eastern half, the unrealistic status of the Western half became glaringly obvious. The food surplus in the West was still totally inadequate for supporting so elaborate a civilization. This had been achieved only because money, symbolizing the surplus of the Eastern half (largely its dry belt regions), had accumulated at Rome in the form of loot. But the Romans did not realize this, and continued to import both food and luxuries on a grandiose scale. Their gold and silver flowed inexorably into the Eastern half of

Below: map marks extent of the Roman Empire in A.D. 476. The Western Empire, weakened by years of overdependence on the Eastern Empire for food supplies, had shrunk to a minute fragment (centre); its former territories were being reshaped by barbarians.

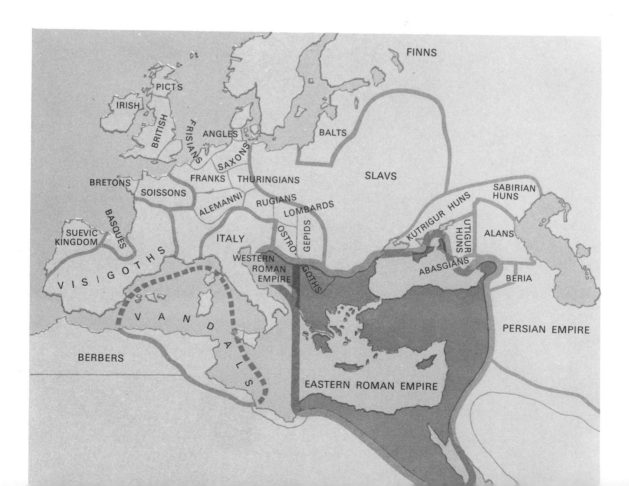

By A.D. 771, the Eastern Empire had become the shrunken Byzantine Empire, based on Constantinople, and was as rigidly organized as any hydraulic society. Expanding Islam was overshadowing Europe.

The Emperor Theodosius I (379–392) formally divided the Empire between his sons who reigned at Rome and Constantinople.

the empire, and some of it went on to India and Afghanistan, to pay for spices, jewels, and Chinese silk. The real importance of Rome steadily declined. Emperors were at first Romans, then Italians, then Westerners, then (throughout the third century A.D.) generals from the region of modern Yugoslavia and Albania, with a few Syrians and even an Arab. Diocletian (born in Yugoslavia) ruled chiefly from his palace at Nicomedia in Asia Minor.

In A.D. 330, Constantine I took the logical step of expanding the city of Byzantium, on the borders of Europe and Asia, into the great new fortress-city of Constantinople (modern Istanbul) as a new capital. When he was fighting his way to the throne (A.D. 312), the armies of Italy, sensing his attitude, put up their last great fight. Normally, in these times, a beaten army simply went over to the winner, but the desperate Italians refused, and the emperor had to forge their weapons into chains.

In the Western Empire, the cities shrank and civilization steadily declined to a level more in keeping with the very small food surplus of Europe. The region split into fragments, which were eventually forged by the Germans into the new kingdoms of Visigothic Spain, Lombard Italy, Frankish France, Belgium and western Germany, and Anglo-Saxon England.

The tragedy of Greece and Rome was a result of a premature attempt to civilize Europe, whose own food surplus was still minute, by drawing on the huge surplus of the dry belt. It could not last. Rome and the West sank into the Dark Ages; Greece and the East were finally absorbed into the dry belt and shared its final ruin under the Turks. But this premature attempt had permanent results. The Romans had codified their new business contract practices, and much else, into a superb body of law, which the Church preserved in the West. In the later Middle Ages, this Roman law aroused great interest among a rising (and characteristically European) class of lawyers, who used it to lay the foundations of the modern business enterprise that organized the breakthrough. The pure science of the Greeks, transmitted via the Islamic peoples (who had made important additions) taught Western Europeans to become scientists themselves, and made the breakthrough possible. Her great statesman Pericles said that Athens was the school of Greece; ancient Greece and Rome were no less the school of modern Western Europe. Finally, it used to be thought that the ancient Greeks and Romans had ruined their natural surroundings in the Mediterranean. But this is far from true, as we shall see when we next consider the momentous history of the European farmers. The ultimate fall of Mediterranean Europe still lay far in the future when in A.D. 476 the (Western) Roman Empire came to its inevitable end.

9 Toward the Breakthrough

A time-traveller from the modern world would feel much more at home among educated Italians of the first century B.C. than he would among the Lombard barons or even the Roman clergy in the seventh century A.D. High civilization had collapsed in the western Mediterranean area, because the local surplus there was quite inadequate to support it. But this does not prove that the resources of the region were already destroyed. The Greeks were undoubtedly brilliant as agricultural scientists, and the Romans, as a result of their peasant origins, took the keenest interest in farming; we have seen what they achieved between them in their territories in the dry belt.

In Greek Egypt in the third, and in Italy in the second and first centuries B.C., sophisticated field experiments were in progress. Elaborate rotations were devised, and the relationship between legumes and soil fertility was well known (though it could not be *understood* without modern chemistry). The engineers of the Ptolemies reclaimed a polder some 200 miles square by draining a lake in the Fayum region; part of it was sown with selected grasses and clovers for pasture. Agricultural textbooks by ancient Greeks and Italians were common, and some survive,

Below: Italian bronze model, from around first century B.C., of plough and oxen used in traditional peasant agriculture. The animals' manure was carefully applied to the fields.

Educated ancient Italians lived in graceful houses like the one below, excavated in Pompeii (from first century B.C.). As the Western Roman Empire crumbled, its highly civilized society was superseded by barbarians, like the Lombards, who "smelled of horses." Above: bronze figure of a Lombard knight.

including the *Georgics*, a popular book in verse by the north-Italian poet Virgil.

The Ptolemies' experts invented a form of what is nowadays called *seed certification*. They selected varieties of each kind of crop, and distributed their seed to the peasants, who were forbidden to sow anything else. Such procedures could not be applied to the free farmers of Italy, and their traditional farming methods were little influenced by the scientists. However, these old methods, though not very productive, do not seem to have been destructive; erosion was carefully controlled, legumes were grown in some places, and animal manure was copiously applied to keep the land fertile.

It is true that the whole of Mediterranean Europe, with its perilously long, dry summers, has suffered severely from erosion and the drying-up of the land through wide-spread destruction of forests and their replacement by useless, patchy shrubs. Many modern conservationists have assumed that the ancient peoples were responsible for deforestation on a grand scale throughout the Mediterranean, though, as we have seen (p. 135), the deforestation of the Lebanon was certainly done much later. One reason for this assumption was the fact that some of the ancient writers were keenly interested in forest conservation, and complained bitterly of the effects of deforestation in certain districts (chiefly the eastern Mediterranean). Plato, for instance, in the fourth century B.C., declared that the land of Attica around Athens had been dried up and eroded by

the destruction of forests in the hills, which had formerly trapped water in their soil to issue in springs and streams: a number of ancient sanctuaries in his time showed where sources had once been, which had dried up. From such examples, the view gained currency in the 19th and 20th centuries A.D. that the whole Mediterranean had been ruined in a similar way. Great stress was also laid on the consequences of overgrazing by goats.

The goat has acquired an evil reputation in Europe; his cloven hoof has become the mark of the Devil. A mobile upper lip and a gift for climbing enable him to eat the young shoots and leaves of bushes and trees, which other stock cannot easily tackle. For the modern enthusiasts of conservation, it seemed to follow logically that overgrazing by goats must destroy both grasses and shrubs or trees, leaving bare soil to be eroded. But the goat is not the only animal with a cloven hoof, and he may have been made a scapegoat—perhaps because goats usually belong to peasants, who can safely be accused of anything, while herds of sheep (which graze very close to the ground) and herds of cattle (which trample plants heavily) have often belonged to the rich. In 1936, the British agriculturalist H. E. Hornby suggested that, since goats will eat the last

Goats feeding on an argan tree in Morocco. Unlike cattle and sheep, goats are well fitted for climbing trees and feeding on them. But they are not necessarily more responsible than sheep and cattle for destroying vegetation.

shrubs left after sheep and cattle "have departed with the last of the grass," they are "merely completing the destruction wrought by sheep, cattle, donkeys and man."

In the whole history of agricultural research, only three experiments have apparently been made to determine the relative destructiveness of heavy grazing by goats and by cattle in regions with long dry seasons. All three were reported during the 1940s, two at Mpwapwa (in Tanzania) by Hornby himself and colleagues, and one at Warmbaths in northern Transvaal, South Africa. In all these experiments, the goats failed to destroy forest or scrub, and did much less harm to grass than cattle, which could leave the soil quite bare in three to four years. In world history, in numbers and economic importance, sheep and cattle have certainly been of overriding importance. Cattle, introduced on a grand scale in the 19th century A.D., were the main agents of erosion in the New World; sheep have dominated the history of both zones of the Old World dry belt, and we shall presently see that the same is true for the western Mediterranean.

The fact that the ancient peoples did *not* ruin this region might be suspected from its subsequent history. Throughout the Dark and Middle Ages, the western Mediterranean was often the most advanced part of western Europe. Naples and Amalfi in southern Italy were the first cities to revive. Brilliant civilizations emerged in the 12th century A.D. in Provence (southern France) and under the Norman kings of Sicily and southern Italy; and Spain made vital contributions to the progress of mediaeval Europe. The climax of the Middle Ages, the Italian Renaissance, had its centre in northern and central Italy, on the borderline between the western Mediterranean and north-western Europe. It was not until the 17th century that the Mediterranean became a backwater.

Provençal civilization was the victim of brutally destructive aggression by its neighbours in northern France: barons in the 13th, royalists in the 17th, and finally revolutionary leaders and their business associates during the French Revolution at the end of the 18th century. But the peoples of Spain and southern Italy really did ruin their own resources, and not in ancient times either. There are many indications from Spanish writers that the deforestation and devastation of once-fertile Spain occurred at the end of the Middle Ages. In southern Italy the question has been settled decisively by factual evidence from an unexpected source—the Royal Air Force. Aerial photography has become a useful archaeological technique, because the outlines of ancient fields, invisible at ground level, are clearly shown in air photographs. The RAF aerial survey of Italy was made during World War II for reasons that had nothing to do with archaeology; but their

Statuette of goat feeding in a thicket, a common motif in Sumerian art, from a royal tomb in Ur, *c.* 2500 B.C.

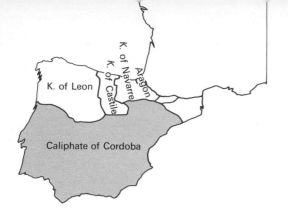

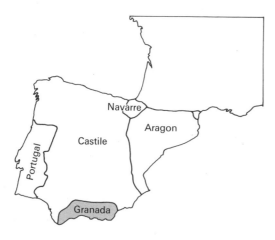

In the 10th century A.D., the Moors ruled over most of Spain (top map), but by the 14th century the kingdoms of Castile and Aragon had expanded and driven the Moors into a small area in southern Spain—Granada (above).

Below: Alphonso the Learned of Castile dictating his book on chess, from a 13th-century manuscript. A patron of science and scholarship, he assembled a team of translators and made Arabic works accessible to the rest of Europe.

study since the war, confirmed by excavations and forgotten documents, has been most illuminating. The pattern of fields under cultivation in southern Italy can be mapped back to the Bronze Age, and it shows that the cultivated area never shrank in ancient times, even in the places most desolate today. A retreat in the sixth century A.D. (as everywhere in Europe) was soon made good again, and the whole of southern Italy was covered with small peasant farms until the 14th century. Then, and only then, did the ruin of southern Italy begin.

The Spanish Tragedy

The course of events in southern Italy and Spain seem to have been very similar, and the two countries were politically related from the 14th century onward. Their story is a tragic one, for they began by playing a crucial part in transmitting ancient science back to western Europe. In the eighth century A.D., the Moors (Arabs and Berbers) overran nearly all Spain and much of Provence. The civilization of the Moors in Spain shared the typical cycles of the dry-belt civilizations of north Africa. At the peaks, it was magnificent. Al-Hakam II, who became emir of Cordoba in A.D. 961, had a library of 400,000 volumes, with a catalogue that filled 44 registers of 50 pages each. He encouraged active research into astronomy, medicine, and agriculture. But at every trough in the Moorish cycles, the Christian kingdoms of Spain (especially Castile, Aragon, and Portugal) pushed back down the peninsula, and by the 14th century had recovered nearly all of it.

During the centuries of intermittent warfare, a cosmopolitan spirit of tolerance often prevailed on both sides. Hence, by the closing years of the 10th century, the first translations of scientific works from Arabic into Latin were compiled at the Benedictine monastery of Santa Maria de Ripoll in Catalonia. From then on, the Christian kingdoms of Spain led the way in making available to western Europe the scientific work of the Greeks, to which Arabs, Persians, and Moors had by now made important additions, either original or derived from India or China. This activity culminated in the court of Alfonso X (the Learned) of Castile, who reigned from 1252 to 1284 at Toledo. Here a team of Christian, Jewish, and Moorish scholars worked together in perfect harmony under this prince; he did for western Europe what al-Mamun had done for Islam. Among the works translated under his auspices was an important 11th-century textbook by the Moor Ibn Bassal on agricultural science. Alfonso was as enthusiastic a patron of practical agriculture as of science and scholarship. He took pains in his decrees to conserve the forests, which in the 14th century were still described (in a book on hunting) as "extensive" all over Castile.

Three centuries later, by the mid-16th century, Castilians and foreigners (e.g. Venetian ambassadors) were describing Castile as a treeless waste. The agriculture of Spain was in ruins, her economy rotten, her civilization decaying, and her people in the grip of the Spanish Inquisition, a system of government reminiscent of the Ch'in, which modern Catholic historians have viewed with as much horror as their non-Catholic colleagues. The agent of this terrible change was the Merino sheep. Through a deadly combination of European and dry-belt factors in this intermediate region, Abel ruined Cain, not by fire and sword, but by the European weapons of money and law.

The fiercely dry summers of Spain and Italy produced in ancient times a system of transhumant stock-raising, almost entirely of sheep, in the midst of the Mediterranean

Merino sheep bred in England. Until the 18th century, the Spanish prevented the export of this breed to the rest of Europe, thus preserving a monopoly of its excellent wool.

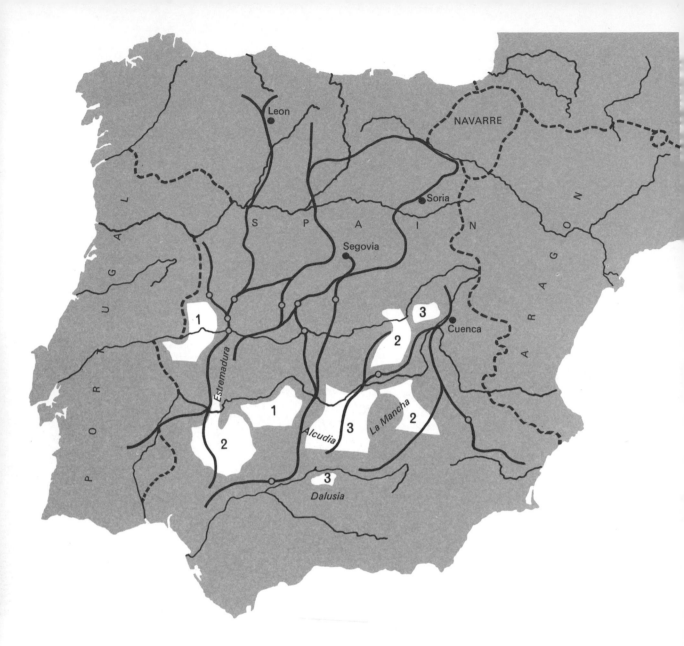

Map shows sheep-walks granted to the Mesta and guaranteed by Alphonso the Learned of Castile in 1273. Sheep grazed on pastures of Estremadura and other southern regions in winter, and in summer were driven to the hills of northern Spain. White patches mark winter pastures owned by military orders of: (1) Alcantara, (2) Santiago, and (3) Calatrava.

civilization of mixed farming. The sheep were grazed in winter on rich level pastures in Estremadura and Andalusia (Spain) and on the coastal plains of southern Italy. In the dry summer they were driven hundreds of miles into the hills of northern Spain and central Italy, along well-marked tracks or sheep-walks. Most Spaniards, even in the 16th century, did not realize that transhumance had anything to do with climate; they thought the march merely kept the sheep fit—and, anyway, it was the traditional thing to do. They actually tried at that time to introduce a transhumant industry on the Caribbean island of Haiti, which has no vast stretches of pasture extending between different climates, and were surprised when it proved a failure.

Ever since the Visigothic kings of Spain (fifth to eighth centuries) the transhumant practice had been protected by royal decrees. The Moors introduced the Merino sheep, with its especially excellent wool. The division of the peninsula between Christians and Moslems cut the transhumant routes in half. But in 1212, at the battle of Las Navas de Tolosa, the Castilians conquered the pastures of southern Spain. In 1273 Alfonso the Learned gave a charter to the Honourable Assembly of the Mesta of the Shepherds, commonly called the *Mesta* (a word of uncertain meaning). This Mesta was a corporation of all the owners of transhumant sheep (as opposed to those kept all year round on the same pastures). Alfonso guaranteed them their three great sheep-walks (each 250 feet wide), but he strictly guarded the rights of the settled farmers along the routes, besides taking pains to ensure conservation of the forests. The importance of the industry lay in the export of Merino wool, which in the early Middle Ages began to replace linen as the main textile for north-western European clothes. From 1303 the customs reports of Southampton, Sandwich, and Portsmouth show Spanish wool imports almost every year.

In the 15th century (for reasons we shall see later) the price of bread fell, and the mixed farming of north-western Europe began to shift its emphasis from crops to stock. In Spain the Mesta began to gain ground and abuse its privileges. Its big chance came with the reigns of Ferdinand of Aragon (1479–1516) and Isabella of Castile (1474–1504), who married, united Spain, conquered the last Moorish state (Granada), and launched a determined policy of destroying local privilege and extending the power of the central government. In November 1476 Rodrigo Manrique died. He was the acting Grand Master of the military Order of Santiago, which owned much of the southern winter pastures and also the income from all taxes on transhumant sheep (by which the Mesta paid for their sheep-walk privileges). Queen Isabella heard the news at Valladolid. She rode at once to the Order's headquarters at Uclès, and proposed her husband as Grand Master. From then on the Mesta and its wool-export trade provided the main revenue of the Crown. But this was not its only attraction for Ferdinand and Isabella. During the reconquest of Spain from the Moors, both the Mesta and the settled landowners and towns on their routes had been bribed with ambiguous and incompatible land-use privileges. Until the 15th century the two parties had a fair working arrangement. But now, by backing the right of the Mesta, a nation-wide corporation, to encroach on privately owned or town lands, including cropland and woods, the monarchs were able to break down the privileges of local bodies and to impose everywhere the authority of the central government. With merciless thoroughness they set out to destroy Spanish (especially Castilian) agriculture

Above: Ferdinand and Isabella, whose marriage united the kingdoms of Castile and Aragon, entering Granada, the last Moorish state to be reconquered in Spain. In strengthening the Mesta, they extended the power of the central government, destroying local privileges.

Above: Jakob Fugger (1412–96), a member of the powerful family of German bankers who leased the southern pastures of Spain as security for loans. Below: Frederick II, Holy Roman Emperor, who promoted the transhumant sheep industry in southern Italy.

for the benefit of the Mesta. A decree of 1489, for instance, greatly widened the borders of the sheep-walks, and prescribed the death penalty for peasants who tried to preserve their old land boundaries. Bringing new land under crops was simply prohibited.

The next king, Charles I, 1516–56 (the Holy Roman Emperor Charles V), was interested in Spain only as a source of money for his endless wars elsewhere in Europe. The wool trade gave him quick returns, and he leased most of the southern pastures to his chief financial backers, the German banking house of Fugger. He gave the Mesta a free rein. The number of transhumant sheep rose from 2,694,032 in 1477 to a peak of 3,453,168 in 1526. By now the Mesta almost ruled Spain. It had close links with the Spanish Inquisition; one of its presidents was also Grand Inquisitor. In 1492, to secure a monopoly of Spanish commerce, the Mesta used its influence at court to obtain the expulsion of the Jews, a mortal blow for Spanish culture as well as for Spanish banking. In 1609–11 the Mesta arranged for the expulsion of the remaining Moorish peasants, who had tried to protect their cropland. In 1639 and 1655 they finished off the Spanish forests by obtaining royal permission to use tree shoots for fodder "in every dry season"—that is, when it did most damage.

By this time, however, the Mesta had lost its grip. From about the mid-16th century, when the population and the price of cereals were rising steeply, the towns and farmers rallied and eventually forced the government to withdraw practical support from the Mesta. As early as 1501, a delegate from the town of Cáceres at the High Court of Valladolid was complaining bluntly of the Mesta's abuses. "Such things," he said (with remarkable courage), "cannot be called just or honest, since they are not for the public good but for the private interests of a favoured few." There was special resentment against the army of legal officials who accompanied the flocks to enforce their privileges. "There is no grandee of Spain," wrote a Spaniard later, in 1616, "who has so many judges and sheriffs to defend him as has the sheep." From about 1550 the numbers of sheep steadily declined, but the tide had turned too late: Spanish agriculture was ruined. Many Spaniards emigrated to the American colonies from the desolate lands, especially Estremadura. The settled landowners themselves, who had been so fiercely discouraged from growing crops, turned to settled sheep-farming, and destroyed the last woodlands.

In southern Italy the pattern of events had been similar, though here the tax on the transhumant flocks had been the main factor. Frederick of Hohenstaufen (the Holy Roman Emperor Frederick II, 1212–50) probably began to enlarge the industry. Alfonso V (1416–58), an Aragonese, continued the process. The vastly lucrative tax

Above: Charles of Parma, enlightened ruler of southern Italy, who became Charles III of Spain in 1759. He opposed power of transhumant organizations in both countries and strove to bring more land under crops.

Below: map of Europe and the Near East in A.D. 737, marking principal towns, trade routes, and products for export. North-western Europe was conspicuously devoid of large towns and natural resources on which prosperity might have been built through trade.

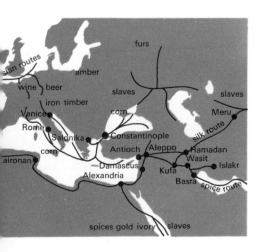

was one of the chief baits that lured France and Spain to fight for possession of Italy during the early 16th century, destroying in the process the Renaissance civilization of northern and central Italy. The Spaniards, who won, naturally continued the system on Spanish lines.

In 1734 Charles of Parma became ruler of southern Italy, and in 1759 he became Charles III of Spain. He gave both countries their first competent government since the Middle Ages. He finally disposed of the transhumant organizations in both countries and did his best to bring more land under crops; the price of cereals was rising again. In a series of patient investigations and reports (1771–83), Charles and his minister Campomanes unravelled the sad story of the ruin of agriculture and civilization in southern Italy and Spain. Their conclusion is summed up in Campomanes's verdict on the powers conferred by governments on the supreme legal officials of the Mesta and its Italian counterpart, by means of which powers these corporations ensured their huge profits. It was, he wrote, "a grant of extraordinary jurisdiction, equivalent to placing a sword in the hands of a madman." The sword had been used. Dry summers and big business had between them finally ruined the western Mediterranean.

The Rise of North-Western Europe

We have seen the regions of the world eliminated, one by one, from the race toward the technological breakthrough, not through any inherent defects in their peoples, but through the limitations imposed by their natural surroundings. And so we come finally to north-western Europe. In the eighth century this region was the most backward, and apparently the least promising, in the world. Its towns had been shrinking steadily throughout the decline of the Western Roman Empire; Autun, for instance (in what is today eastern France) covered 500 acres in the second century, and 25 acres in the fifth. Precious metals, symbols of surplus, had drained away; by the ninth century, gold coins were no longer minted in north-western Europe.

The Scandinavians benefited sporadically from trading and raiding in wealthier eastern Europe. Britain still exported a little tin. The Frankish empire of Charlemagne (A.D. 800 onward), which covered almost exactly the area of the modern Common Market, was poorest of all. The stock-raising Friesians of the northern Netherlands did enough trading to preserve a money economy, but elsewhere transactions relapsed largely into barter, each little district producing barely enough for its own modest needs. Charlemagne could pay for his wars, and for his more constructive attempts to recivilize his empire, only by capturing Slavs and Saxons for export as slaves to Islam,

167

which had access to African gold. In the 9th and 10th centuries devastating raids by Vikings, Magyars, and Moslems further destroyed towns and sapped civilization.

But the turn of the millennium was the turn of the tide for north-western Europe. From then on, unlike all other civilized parts of the world, it never again suffered devastating invasion from outside. The Vikings were tamed, and their descendants became part of the European culture. Financed by the trading cities of Venice and Genoa, north-western Europe even began to thrust back into the Moslem world, in the expansionist wars called the Crusades. Increased trade, and the scientific ideas learned from Islam in peaceful interludes, restored both the money economy and science to Europe. In 1252 gold coins were minted at Genoa: north-western Europe was back in business.

The central problem for the region was that of increasing its own agricultural surplus as a necessary base for any other developments. This was achieved by a series of technical advances that together produced an entirely new farming system. So diverse were European conditions that these advances occurred at widely different times in different places, and in several orders and combinations. Nevertheless, there is one main sequence that was common to large areas and must have been critical for the progress of Europe. This sequence begins with a new kind of plough.

The Mediterranean peoples continued to use the original dry-belt plough, a light instrument that merely scratched the surface of the soil, leaving undisturbed earth between each furrow. The farmers ploughed first in one direction and then at right angles across the first furrows, breaking up the dry clods and keeping the earth as damp as possible. They generally had small, squarish fields, convenient for this cross-ploughing. The early farmers of north-western Europe used the same methods, including small, walled fields. These methods worked fairly well on light, well-drained upland soils, but were almost useless in the damp but much more fertile valleys. Here the soil was heavy and difficult to scratch, and the minerals needed by crops were leached some way below the surface (though not out of reach, as in the tropics). A method was required that would provide better drainage and bring minerals to the surface by deeply disturbing the soil. Because no such method was at hand, both the early natives (e.g. the Celts) and the Italian colonists of north-western Europe could clear and cultivate only the upland soils.

The problem of heavy soil was solved by the invention of a heavy, fixed-mouldboard plough, and its use on very long strip-shaped sections of huge "open fields." The new plough had three parts—the coulter, which cut vertically; the share, which cut horizontally; and the mouldboard, which turned the whole slice of earth over on its side. It

Top: mouldboard plough especially suited to turning heavy soils of north-western Europe (from the 14th century Luttrell Psalter). Farmer ploughed once down centre of field and then round clockwise, the mouldboard turning each slice of earth inward, to produce a field with raised centre and troughs at side, as cross-section above.

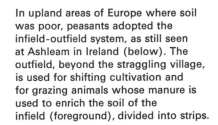

In upland areas of Europe where soil was poor, peasants adopted the infield-outfield system, as still seen at Ashleam in Ireland (below). The outfield, beyond the straggling village, is used for shifting cultivation and for grazing animals whose manure is used to enrich the soil of the infield (foreground), divided into strips.

was usually wheeled and needed several draught animals to pull it. The farmer ploughed down the middle of the strip of field, and then clockwise on alternate sides, always turning the slices inward toward the middle. The result in course of time was a raised ridge along the middle of the field and troughs along the sides. This system provided good drainage and some insurance against weather fluctuations: the crop on the ridge did well in wet years, the crop in the troughs in dry years.

Changes in plough construction seem to have been going on in northern Europe since the early Iron Age, and all combinations of plough and field-shape are found, but the fully developed heavy plough, in use on strips in open fields, first appeared among the Slavs of eastern Europe in the sixth century A.D. In 643 the Latin word *plovum* appears in a northern Italian document (the old scratch-plough was called *aratrum*); by this time the new instrument was probably wide-spread in north-western Europe. Meanwhile the open fields with ridged strips were also appearing. In places (e.g. in the Netherlands) they simply replaced the old Roman square fields; but they also appeared extensively in valley lowlands now cultivated for the first time—for instance, in Britain, where the ash layer (which shows the original clearing of forest by burning) can be dated (by means of radio-active Carbon 14) to around 650–750. Hence the second wave of forest clearance in Europe.

With this new development, the uplands in many places became backward areas. In Ireland, Scotland, and parts of France and Germany, upland farmers evolved their own system, called *infield-outfield*. The outfield was used only for shifting cultivation and mainly left as waste land for grazing animals. The manure of these animals was collected and heaped on the infield, which was cultivated without pause, year after year. This system was certainly the best that could then be used with poor upland soils. It meant a considerable emphasis on stock, and a modified form of it survives in parts of Ireland to the present day.

Now that the rich valleys were opened up, however, the outlook for north-western Europe as a whole was becoming brighter. And on this new land a way was found to achieve an impressive increase in crop production. The Mediterranean peoples had normally used (and continued to use) a simple cropping system called the *two-year rotation*. A winter cereal (wheat or barley) was sown in autumn and harvested early the following spring. The land was then left fallow for more than a year until the next autumn but one, when it was manured and another crop sown. Generally the farm was divided into two parts, with their rotations staggered. This meant that in any one year only half the land was in use, so the surplus produced per unit of area was small. Cereal crops could not be sown

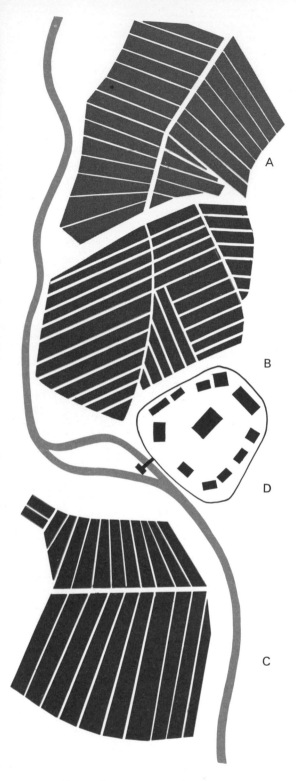

in spring and harvested in summer because there was not enough rain during this period in the Mediterranean region.

When the Italians colonized north-western Europe, they took their traditional two-year cereal rotation with them, not realizing its connection with climate. The Italian naturalist Pliny (A.D. 23–79) tells of an odd accidental discovery by some farmers near the German town of Trier, on the Moselle River. Their winter cereal crop failed. In desperation they sowed another crop in March, and to their surprise they got a harvest. But nobody dared repeat this experiment.

At about this time, however, as pollen studies have shown, Scandinavian and Baltic peoples were practising a two-year rotation with the crop sown in the spring instead of in the autumn of alternate years; here there was plenty of rain in spring, but cold winters discouraged autumn sowing. This system persisted throughout the Middle Ages in the colder regions of Finland and eastern Sweden. In the eighth century A.D., the peoples of the formerly Roman part of north-western Europe came into closer touch (e.g. through their Christian missionaries) with those farther north, and it may be, as the American historian L. White has suggested, that as a result "the Baltic-North Sea spring planting was married to the Mediterranean autumn planting to create a new agricultural system." Certainly a new system, the *three-year rotation*, did appear about this time; it is mentioned in records of the Swiss monastery of St. Gall in 763.

In the three-year rotation wheat or rye was sown in autumn and harvested in late spring. The next year oats, barley, or legumes were sown in early spring and harvested in summer. Then the land was fallowed for a little over a year, and the cycle started again. Usually (though not invariably) three big open fields were used, each being in one of the three states in any given year. Such a farm was worked by a group of peasants, living nearby and contributing draught animals for the heavy plough; each peasant had a set of strips in each field. Some give-and-take was involved, especially for ploughing, but in general each peasant could choose his crops to suit himself. Draught animals and other stock, for meat or wool and to supply manure for the fallow, were grazed on common pasture between or around the fields, and the surrounding woodland supplied timber, firewood, and acorns for pigs.

The three-year rotation spread widely on the open fields during the next three centuries. Though some areas adopted it as late as the 18th century (or never at all), enough farmers changed over to make a very substantial difference to food production. Instead of one half of the land being used in any one year, two thirds were now producing crops. Moreover, since the fallow was generally

Above: diagram of a mediaeval village using the system of crop rotation over three years that was frequently practised in north-western Europe. Agricultural land surrounding the village (D) was divided into three large "open" fields, each one divided into narrow strips cultivated by individual peasants. In a year when field A was left fallow, field B was ploughed in the autumn and sown with wheat or rye, while field C was sown with barley, oats, beans, or peas in the spring.

In the eighth century A.D. the idea of a rigid wooden horse collar was imported into Europe. Above: part of the Bayeux Tapestry showing a horse wearing this type of harness. It allowed an animal to pull four or five times as much weight as did a harness of soft neck-straps like the ones worn by the straining oxen below. These often tended to choke the animal.

ploughed twice, whereas cropland was only ploughed once, in each year, the same amount of ploughing labour would cultivate more land. The inclusion of legumes varied the peasants' diet, and the diversity of crops and growing periods spread the risk of crop failure from bad weather. Finally, the new system could be used to produce an annual crop of oats, a very satisfactory diet for horses.

This oat crop would have been of little use but for the arrival in north-western Europe, some time in the eighth century, of a crucially important invention from Turkestan (perhaps originally from China). Up to this time, horses had been harnessed (for pulling) with a yoke and neck-straps so arranged that every time the animal took the strain it nearly choked. The new invention was the rigid wooden horse-collar. Modern experiments have shown that a team of horses can pull four or five times as much weight with collars as they can with neck-straps. The new invention made both horse-drawn ploughs and horse-drawn wagons really practical. Land transport became more than three times as cheap as in Roman times, which encouraged the growing of crops for distant markets. Horse-power is about one and a half times greater than ox-power, and horses can work faster and longer hours—a vital point for ploughing and harrowing operations in the uncertain weather conditions of north-western Europe. The feeding of plough-horses was made possible by the oat crop in the three-year rotation.

The difficulty of changing over from the two-year system slowed the advance somewhat, but horses were ploughing in Norway by the late 9th century, and by the 11th

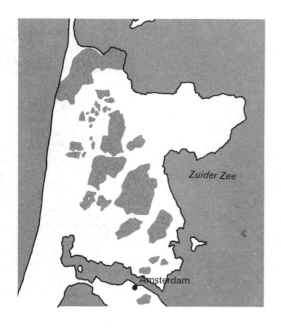

Yellow areas on above map of northern
Holland indicate land reclaimed from
the sea during the 16th and 17th
centuries by draining polders and
building dikes.

Right: two pages from a 15th-century
Shepherd's Calendar. Top: July,
peasants making hay, with insets of the
month's Zodiac signs—Cancer and Leo.
Below: August, harvesting the wheat;
insets of Leo and Virgo, signs for
August. Improved farming methods
brought new confidence, and man began
to mark the seasons by his own changing
activities in controlling nature.

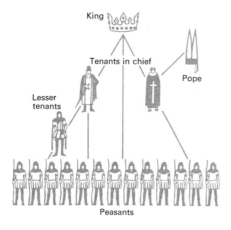

Above: diagram of structure of mediaeval
society. Some peasants were directly
responsible to the king, some to lesser
tenants, and some to the clergy, but all
were jealous of their legal rights.

century the whole new system—heavy plough, horses, oats in a three-year rotation on open fields—was common throughout north-western Europe. One effect of the greater speed of horses was that farmers could live farther from their work; by the 11th century many hamlets were being abandoned and the farmers assembled in villages.

The profound change in farming methods between the 5th and 10th centuries meant a spectacular increase in production for a given amount of labour. One result was the mounting wave of forest clearance (p. 42), together with reclamation of marshes and (in the Netherlands and Belgium) polders from the sea. Another was the surplus that made possible the rise of many new towns and the revival of trade and industry on a greater scale than ever. Most momentous of all was the exuberant confidence and excitement that made the early Middle Ages in north-western Europe the occasion of a profoundly new approach to man's relations with nature (see Chapter 2). Ancient illustrated calendars, for instance, had tended to mark the months with symbols of nature in the different seasons. From the eighth century onward in north-western Europe, as the historian L. White has put it, "the pictures change to scenes of ploughing, harvesting, wood-chopping, people knocking down acorns for the pigs, pig-slaughtering. Man and nature are now two things, and man is master." Man was on his way; given enough know-how, nothing could stop him.

The soldier-landlords and the clergy, who were the masters in the early Middle Ages, lacked the lavish supply of cheap and docile labour available to the hydraulic bureaucrats or the Greek and Roman slave-owners. At this stage their food surplus was much too small for mass labour. Slavery persisted throughout the Middle Ages, but only as a vestige. Since the later Roman Empire, many, if not most, of the people had been serfs, bound to the land, and the knights and clergy often usurped local judicial functions from the royal officials who would otherwise have heard peasants' complaints. This double power led to much oppression: "Injustice stalks the high-roads," wrote the German poet Walther von der Vogelweide at the end of the 12th century. Nevertheless, the north-western European peasants were never anything like as docile as those of the dry belt. True heirs of Rome (thanks partly to the Church, whose power offset that of the feudal knights), the peasants were obsessed with their legal rights, which were numerous and complex.

Many peasants remained free from serfdom throughout the Middle Ages. Forest clearance made for freedom (p. 44); so did the growth of towns, encouraged (as a source of taxes) by the lords. A serf who could escape and stay uncaught for a stipulated period (generally about a

Above: carving on a pillar base in Mainz cathedral symbolizing the burden borne by the lower classes who supported mediaeval society. But this patient resignation was sometimes exhausted. Below: the Swiss Confederacy of free peasants and citizens developed new fighting techniques and often defeated feudal hosts like the Austrians at the Battle of Sempach (1386).

year) in a town, ceased to be a serf: "town air makes free" was a mediaeval German proverb. Even those who remained serfs benefited from the existence of these loopholes. Where stock-raising predominated, the peasants were fairly rich (since stock-raising needed more capital than crop farming), and this made them surprisingly independent. City-states, with more or less freedom, emerged in the industrial and trading regions of Italy and Belgium, and independent peasant federal republics, like the old Roman league, emerged in the stock-raising regions of Switzerland and the northern Netherlands. Against such a background, cheap mass labour was out of the question, even when the population rose steeply from the 11th century onward.

The result was that the peoples of north-western Europe showed an enthusiasm never seen before or elsewhere for power technology and the mechanization of industrial processes. If the Greeks were the first pure scientists, the Mediaevals were the first whole-hearted technologists. They made few completely new inventions, but they showed astonishing energy and versatility in improving processes and applying them on a large scale to a great diversity of purposes. The existence of the wheelbarrow (known in the third century in China, but quite possibly re-invented in Europe, and widely used there) is a homely but significant difference between the mediaeval and ancient worlds. The water-mill is probably a Greek invention (about the first century B.C.), but the Greeks, Romans, and Chinese never used it on a large scale or for anything much besides milling grain. In north-western Europe it is mentioned in the law-codes of the Franks, Visigoths, and Alemanni (of Switzerland and south-western Germany) by the sixth century. In 1086 the *Domesday Book* (William the Conqueror's inventory of English resources) lists 5624 water-mills in about 3000 English villages or towns. The town of Troyes (France) had 11 water-mills in the 11th century, and 41 by the 15th century.

The windmill derives from the Tibetan prayer-wheel (used only for ritual) and was used for milling grain in Afghanistan in the early 10th century. North-western Europe had numerous windmills in many places by the 12th century at least; during the next century 120 were built around the Belgian town of Ypres alone. Perennial streams favoured water-mills in Europe, but the variable winds made windmills difficult to operate; nevertheless, the highly efficient rotating-roof type was developed by the 15th century.

But more striking than number of mills is the variety of uses for water- or wind-driven machinery in the Middle Ages. It was used in the most important industry (textiles) by the 10th century, and during the next five centuries mills,

Above: engraving (*c.* A.D. 1588) of an early type of windmill. The whole building turned with wind direction. Windmills, invented in Asia, were in use in Europe by the 12th century.

Left: drawing in a 13th-century manuscript by Matthew Paris, showing a man pushing a wheelbarrow—a homely illustration of mediaeval technical advance over ancient Europe.

Power from wind- and water-mills was harnessed to more and more mechanical uses, as shown in the two 16th-century engravings on this page. Right: water-wheel turns a shaft with pegs that raise and drop a series of hammers. These might be used for crushing or grinding anything from corn to metal ores. Below: revolving shaft with grindwheels for polishing armour.

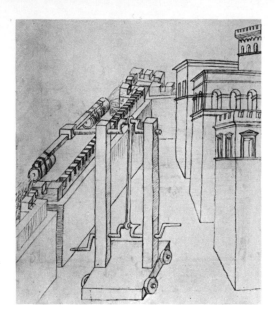

Above: Francesco di Georgio's drawing of about 1500, incorporating the principle of parallel crankshafts. Turning a handle at the foot rotated a mechanism on a higher level.

lathes, trip-hammers, and so forth were adapted for tanning, laundering, sawing, crushing anything from olives to ore; for working the bellows of blast furnaces, the hammers in forges, and grindstones for polishing armour; for use in brewing and in the paint and paper industries. Nor were the engineers content to stop at water and wind. They looked eagerly for other sources of power, and by the 13th century had developed the steam-bellows.

A similar enthusiasm for the applications of driving machinery led engineers to find endless new uses for cranks and cams, and above all to tinker with clock-work (gravity- or tension-driven machinery). This may have arisen independently in China and Europe around the 12th century, but the Chinese did little with it. The Europeans, however, were fascinated. The spirit of these early technicians—worthy ancestors of today's space experts—is summed up in a textbook written by Robert the Englishman in 1271. No clock, wrote Robert, is astronomically accurate, "nevertheless, clockmakers are trying to make a wheel, or disc, which will move exactly as the equinoctial circle does; but they can't quite finish the job. If they could,

Throughout the Middle Ages men were searching for an accurate method of recording time. Below: sketch of an escapement mechanism for a clock, drawn by Villard de Honnecourt. This 13th-century technologist travelled widely, sketching and making notes on new inventions wherever he went.

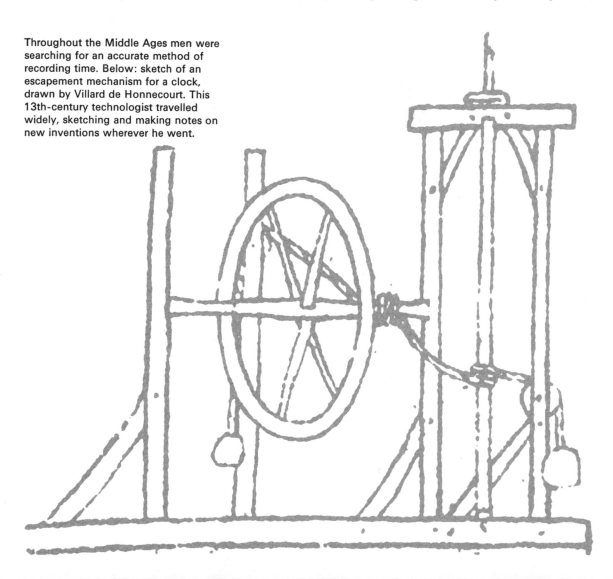

however, they would have a really accurate time-piece." After untiring experiment they cracked the clock problem in the 15th century by inventing the escapement, and the resulting chronometers made possible the long sea voyages that made the world Europe's oyster.

The technologists of those days enjoyed unprecedented prestige. Alfonso the Learned himself wrote proudly about his own back-room wizards, such as Samuel Ha-Levi Abulafia, a Jewish engineer specializing in hoisting devices. The great master-engineers of the Gothic cathedrals were invited all over the continent and treated as V.I.P.s. But it was not only the big names who travelled; a foreman in a salt-works at Salins in eastern France during the early 15th century had studied industrial processes in Burgundy, Lorraine, Provence, Poitou, Germany, Italy, and Spain. Travelling technologists, such as Villard de Honnecourt during the 13th century, kept notebooks on their travels, full of sketches and notes on how to do this and that. Know-how was valued above all. When pure science returned from Greece and Islam, *via* the Spanish translators, and fused with this exciting new technical tradition, there occurred a series of Renaissances, from that of the 12th century to that of the 15th and 16th centuries.

Troubles were in store for Europe and were to lead to dreadful sufferings and convulsions, but the foundations of modern technology were firmly laid by about the 12th century and from then on progress was steady and ever faster. The authentic voice of the Middle Ages echoes down to us in the words of Roger Bacon (1214–94): "Machines may be made by which the largest of ships, with only one man steering them, will be moved faster than if they were filled with rowers; wagons may be built which will move with incredible speed and without the aid of beasts; flying machines will be constructed . . . machines will make it possible to go to the bottom of the seas." The technological breakthrough had begun.

Gothic architecture represents one of the greatest achievements of mediaeval technology. Engineers learnt to build graceful delicate structures that were also strong. Above: fine example of a fan-vaulted roof from Chapter House of Salisbury Cathedral (about A.D. 1280).

Right: miniature of the scholar Roger Bacon, from a 15th-century manuscript. This mediaeval scientist fully realized the significance of the technological breakthrough that was beginning.

10 The Modern World

The new farming system caused, in the 11th to 13th centuries, not only a technological spurt, but a dramatic rise in population that considerably overstepped the rise in production. By the 13th century, this began to have serious consequences. The Crusaders in the Near East were halted by Saladin the Kurd and expelled by Baybars the Mameluke, and north-west Europe began to be overcrowded. The resulting tensions led to ferocious wars, like the Hundred Years' War with England, which devastated France; and bitter social conflicts, like the civil war between businessmen and skilled workers that raged in the towns of Flanders (Belgium) from 1297 to 1328.

Frightful mass lynchings began, the first victims being religious non-conformists, or heretics. In 1231–3, the Chief Inquisitor of Germany, Conrad of Marburg, without the knowledge of the pope, stirred up the German masses like a mediaeval Hitler, and conducted a reign of terror. In the 14th century A.D., the chief lynch victims were Jews

Over-population in 13th-century Europe led to internal wars and persecution of minority groups. In this relief at Naumberg, Germany (below), the high priests paying Judas his 30 pieces of silver wear the special hats that Jews were compelled to wear in the 13th century as a distinguishing mark.

and "witches" (mostly women); the craze for lynching witches persisted on a considerable scale till the 18th century. In the meantime class barriers hardened and it became less easy to enter the feudal aristocracy, while thought and speech, hitherto remarkably free, were increasingly censored.

As the settled populations grew denser, farms were subdivided and became smaller. In Martham (Norfolk), for instance, there were 107 tenant farmers in 1101, and 935 in 1292, with 2021 little plots of land. Such small farms were terribly vulnerable to a run of bad harvests. New class distinctions appeared between well-to-do farmers and the layers of poorer peasants beneath them. Meanwhile the clearing of new land became so urgent, to feed the growing numbers, that areas of poor soil were brought into use, and after a few years crop yields on these began to fall.

Since the 19th century, farmers have generally harvested more than 10 times the amount of wheat grain they have sown. In the 9th century, the ratio was three to one or less. By the 12th century, it had risen to about four to one. When this ratio is low, small changes in it make a big difference. Thus the 12th-century farmer could use three quarters of his (cropped) land for growing food (leaving one quarter for next year's seed), as opposed to two thirds in the 9th century, and he also got the higher yield on the one twelfth of land saved for food production. This is the more important if a large part of the land is fallow, as it still was even under the three-year rotation. That is why the new farming system made such a huge difference, though still not very productive by modern standards. But, by the same token a slight fall in yield was still disastrous. Hence many of the farms on the later and poorer clearings went bankrupt and were abandoned. In Germany literally hundreds of pioneer settlements are known to have been abandoned, and this process began before the great disasters that drastically reduced the population after about 1300.

Even on good and long-settled land, drastic changes occurred. The swelling population demanded more staple food, and therefore more cereal production. The result was a spread of cropland at the expense of pastures and hay meadows, while at the same time more horses and oxen were needed for draught. One result was a modified form of the 3-year rotation, that appeared in the 12th and 13th centuries. The animals were allowed to graze the fallow

Improved farming methods brought increased yields, as shown in these diagrams. Red columns show the yields produced by same amount of seed in 9th, 12th, and 19th centuries. Columns at right show increasing proportion of cropland that could be used to grow food (as opposed to seed for next year). By 19th century, farmers sold the whole crop and bought seed.

9th century

seed sown   yield   cropped land

12th century

seed sown   yield   cropped land

19th century

seed sown   yield

179

field and the stubble on the cropped fields after harvest. Since the individual peasants each owned many small unfenced strips of land, their operations now had to be synchronized, and their freedom to choose their own crops and timings disappeared, a uniform plan being dictated by a manorial or village council.

North-western Europe shows so many differences in local history that it is not too surprising to find one survival into the 20th century of this curious mediaeval farm system: the village of Laxton in Nottinghamshire (England). In 1952 it was taken over by the Ministry of Agriculture (acting as Lord of the Manor) to be a living museum. Its three open fields are worked today by 22 farmers. They meet annually at the "Court Leet of the Manor" and form a 12-man Jury to decide on dates, inspect boundaries, and ensure that their few stretches of permanent pasture and meadow are not infringed by the plough. The controlled three-year rotation on open fields, with most of its traditional techniques, can thus be observed in actual operation with horses today; open-field farming has probably been practised continuously at Laxton at least since the time of Tochi, son of Outi, Lord of the Manor just before the Norman Conquest of 1066.

Above, aerial view of Laxton showing the three open fields, still farmed today: 1. West Field, 3. Mill Field, and 4. South Field, set around village (2).

Above: members of the Jury of Laxton, who are responsible for administration of the three open fields, meeting in South Field (see above) to re-stake boundaries, as they do regularly.

Even the grazing of stubble and fallow did not solve the problem of the lost pastures and meadows. Hay for winter feeding became particularly scarce. In his great poem *Inferno* (Hell), written in 1312–14, Dante expresses the idea of utter dismay by the image of the farmer whose fodder has run out and who looks out of his house to see the fields still white with snow. A more practical note is struck by Walter of Henley, a farm manager turned monk, who in the early 13th century wrote a textbook on farm management. "If you must buy cattle," he writes, "buy them between Easter and Whitsuntide, for then beasts are thin and cheap," having had little to eat during the winter. Some farmers may have had to slaughter some of their stock at the beginning of winter; this and the increasing meat shortage led to meat being stored for long periods to be eaten a little at a time. To preserve it salt was needed; to make it less unappetizing, spices. Salt was available in Europe. The luxury trade in spices from the East Indies (via the Near East) had flourished sporadically since the first century B.C. This trade now assumed greater proportions. Salt and spices produced a terrible thirst; at the end of the Middle Ages the average consumption of beer per head in Sweden was 40 times as great as today.

As the proportion of stock to crops declined, the resulting shortage of manure brought down yields, especially in the poorer, newly cleared lands. People also ate less meat

Below: map of Europe and the Near East in A.D. 1212, marking principal trade routes and commodities exported. Once north-western Europe had begun to prosper and produce a food surplus, natural resources could be exploited and trade developed with dry-belt countries. (Compare map on page 167.)

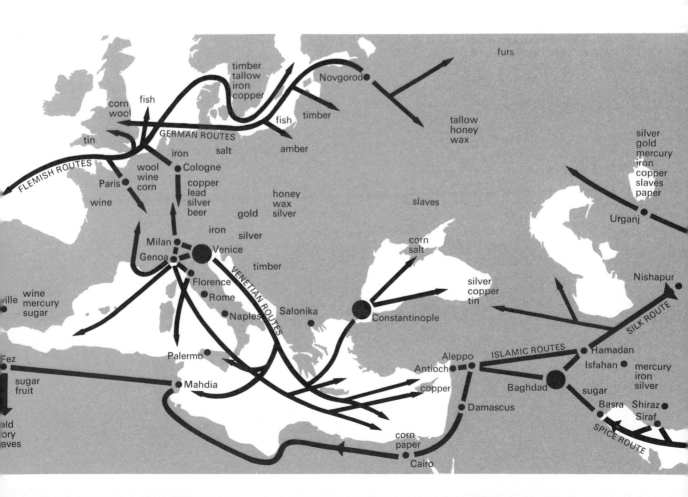

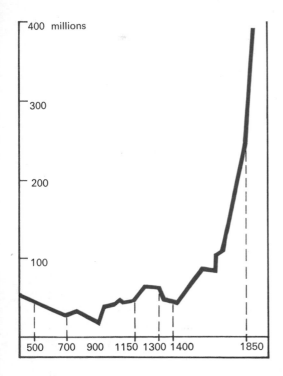

Above: diagram of probable population
of Europe, A.D. 400–1900. Note the
sudden drops around 1000, 1400, and
1650, when malnutrition had undermined
people's health and the death-rate
rose through wars and epidemics.

Black line shows land reclaimed in
Netherlands. Red line marks maximum, and
blue minimum, wheat prices, whose rise
made farming profitable and encouraged
reclamation. (Year 1730 = 100.)

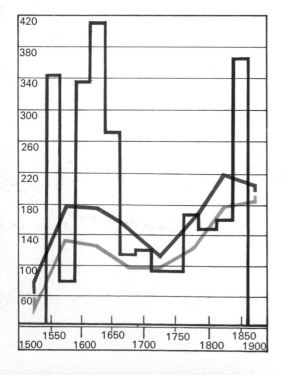

and dairy products, and the new emphasis on oats, together with the controlled choice of crops, may have meant
less production of legumes as spring crops, though the
spring crop field at Laxton has, as it happens, always been
called the Bean Field. There must certainly have been a
lack of protein in the diet, and hence malnutrition, which
undermined the people's health. In 1315–17, there was a
disastrous famine: overpopulation was exacting its price.

The population of north-west Europe reached a trough
in about 1400, and then began to rise again. It continued to
rise until the mid-17th century, stabilized until about the
mid-18th century, and then rose more rapidly than ever
until the 20th century. We can ascribe the rise to a gradual
improvement in agriculture; it took place almost entirely
in the countryside, which supplied a steady flow of recruits
for the growing towns. Its interruption in the 17th century
(like that of the 14th) can be traced to a deterioration in
diet; on the manor of Gripsholm in Sweden, the number of
calories (energy supply from food) dropped by about a
third between 1555 and 1653. In the course of these big
fluctuations in numbers a sequence of linked changes
occurred, which have been assembled into a connected story
by the Dutch economic historian, B. H. Slicher van Bath.

By the 13th century, money and business dominated the
region's history (p. 168). Every time the population rose,
the demand for basic foods rose faster than production,
and the price of cereals, especially wheat, rose too. In the
16th century, the import of precious metals from Mexico
and Peru lowered the value of money relative to that of
cereals, and (since the population was also steeply rising)
the already rising wheat prices positively rocketed, in a
convulsion called the "price revolution." Prices of other
goods (manufactured or dairy products and meat) reacted
less sharply to population change, for these goods were not
essential to life. Hence, when population fell, prices of
animal products were relatively higher than those of cereals.

When wheat prices were relatively high, it paid to clear
or reclaim more land for crops; when they were relatively
low, crop farming paid badly and suffered a depression,
and newly cleared land was abandoned. This is mirrored
in records of polder-making and marsh drainage in the
Netherlands, and in the proportion of cereals in pollen
sequences in several parts of Europe. When wheat prices
were high, mixed farming emphasized crops at the expense
of stock; when they were low, the reverse occurred, and
formerly ploughed land was converted to pasture. The
resulting increase in manure and in protein food helped to
restore crop yields and human health, and start the population rising again. In the 14th–15th centuries, this swing
toward stock-raising was most prominent in Norway and
in England, where hundreds of farming villages disappeared

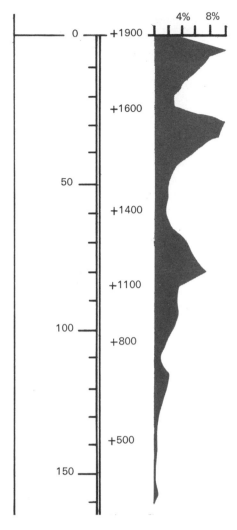

altogether to make room for sheep, so important by this time was the woollen textile industry. In the late 17th and early 18th centuries, the swing from crop to stock farming was about equally extensive in Germany, Austria, Switzerland, Belgium, the Netherlands, France, England, and Ireland. But every time population and cereal prices rose, the pastures were ploughed up again for crops.

In Mediterranean Europe, the swings to stock-raising were disastrous (p. 165). In north-west Europe, where severe summer droughts were rare, mixed farming remained flexible, and its emphasis on crops or stock could easily be reversed. When land was abandoned, some damage was caused by erosion and (in the Netherlands) floods, but no vast areas were transformed into desert. On the contrary, despite much suffering in the agricultural depressions, mixed farming showed steady progress, for each of its components was vigorously developed by turns. The result was the construction of new and very elaborate systems of mixed farming, which at last produced a surplus on something like the dry belt scale.

The pioneers, from the 14th century onward, were the farmers near the populous centres of the textile industry, in northern Italy, north-eastern France, and above all in Flanders (Belgium) and Brabant (the Netherlands).

Their new farming system contained three new ideas. The first was "ley farming" or "convertible husbandry": alternating the same piece of land regularly between temporary pasture (ley) and crops. The second was the use (in rotations) of root crops (e.g. turnips), which were fed to stock kept in sheds. The third was the use of pasture legumes (clovers and lucerne), not just on permanent pastures (the Persians had done this in the fifth century

Counting pollen grains from a section of heathland shows proportion of cereals to other plants grown on the site over the centuries, as on the right of the diagram above, of a piece of land in Holland. Figures on left mark depth dug, in centimetres; centre figures give dates (A.D.) represented by each layer. The three main booms in crop agriculture correspond in time to peaks of population increase.

Diagram (right) shows the gradual development and improvement of mixed farming in north-western Europe. From the 14th century onward, farmers cleared more and more of their land of forest and used an increasing proportion of it for growing varieties of crops for food or stock-feed in more sophisticated rotations. Eventually all land was used productively, with none under fallow.

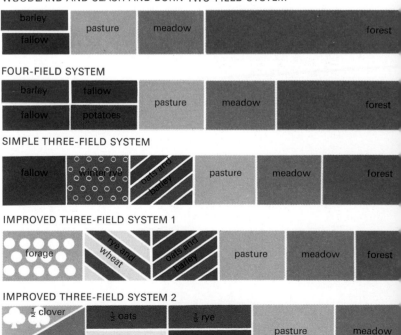

WOODLAND AND SLASH AND BURN TWO-FIELD SYSTEM

barley / fallow | pasture | meadow | forest

FOUR-FIELD SYSTEM

barley / fallow | tallow / potatoes | pasture | meadow | forest

SIMPLE THREE-FIELD SYSTEM

fallow | winter rye | oats and barley | pasture | meadow | forest

IMPROVED THREE-FIELD SYSTEM 1

forage | rye and wheat | oats and barley | pasture | meadow | forest

IMPROVED THREE-FIELD SYSTEM 2

½ clover / ½ root crops | ½ oats / ½ wheat | ¾ rye / ¼ barley | pasture | meadow

From the first to the fifth centuries A.D., India led the world as a trading centre and achieved a high degree of civilization. This fifth-century sculpture of Buddha from the Gupta period (A.D. 300–600), a graceful figure in a fine transparent drapery, typifies the Greek-influenced art of Classical India.

B.C.) but on leys, mixed with grasses, or fitted into rotations. These legumes not only promoted soil fertility but (because they grew during more of the year than grasses) provided winter feed for the animals. At the same time, food legumes (beans, etc.) were emphasized again.

The new system (which provided lavish manure) had many special forms. The so-called "Norfolk Rotation" (modified from a Belgian one used in 1650) was a system of four courses (wheat, turnips, barley, clover), but much longer and more elaborate rotations, often including leys, were also developed. The fallow became shorter and at longer intervals, till it finally disappeared altogether, leaving the land at all times (and therefore the whole cropland at any one time) in use to produce food, directly as food crops or indirectly by feeding animals. At Schmatzfeld in the Harz district of Germany, for instance, the proportion of cropland under fallow at a given time fell from 37.3 per cent in 1592 to 0.8 per cent in 1850. The "new husbandry" spread steadily over north-west Europe. In Austria it had a hero, Johan Christian Schubart, created "Cloverfield Knight of the Holy Roman Empire" by the Emperor Joseph II; in France it had a martyr, the unfortunate Marquise de Marboeuf, guillotined during the Revolution on the muddle-headed charge of sowing fodder crops instead of wheat to feed the people.

The fall of cereal prices in the 17th century had encouraged investment in the new industries emerging from the new technology of north-west Europe (instead of in farming). The substantial surplus provided by the new husbandry supplied labour and capital for the industrialization of north-west Europe in the 18th–19th century. In England, at least, this process is rightly called the industrial "revolution," for it was horrifyingly brutal. Not even Roman slave-owners had overworked children as the new industrialists did. The world now received another lesson in the horrors to be feared from unrestricted private business. But by 1850, the technological breakthrough in Europe was an accomplished fact, and it was to change the life of the whole world.

Toward One World

Until the breakthrough began in Europe, the interlocking cycles of the dry belt and the great currents of trade within and around it had produced a kaleidoscopic pattern, in which peaks of power and/or civilization appeared in different places at different times. Ethiopia was a great power in the sixth, Tibet in the eighth, Lithuania in the 14th century A.D. The world was still divided by shifting but formidable barriers on land or sea.

At almost every period since the Bronze Age, some great region has maintained human progress. After the Greek and Roman decline began, it was the turn of India. The history of this great subcontinent has been intermediate between those of the western and eastern zones of the dry belt. But in the first to fifth centuries A.D., India broke this pattern to become the trading centre of the world, producing great merchant cities where Roman and Chinese wares mingled, and from which expeditions set off east to tap the resources of south-east Asia and Indonesia. Some of these Indian cities were even republics. This civilization, known as Classical India, was brought to an end by a nomad invasion from Central Asia, and India relapsed into the old cycles. The trade of the Indian Ocean returned to the Arabs and Persians, who maintained it until the final decline of the Near East eroded their base. Once Chinese civilization embraced the enterprising coastal peoples of southern China (around Canton), the hatred of the mandarins for private trading enterprise (p. 125) met considerable resistance. In the 15th century A.D., Chinese trading fleets, with the best ships then made, were visiting Africa. But by 1500, the iron bureaucracy had finally won, recalling the Chinese from the mastery of the world's oceans.

Indians, Arabs, and Chinese had great hydraulic civilizations. In Africa south of the Sahara, there were no great fertile flood plains to provide the surplus for such development (p. 74). Nevertheless, the rise of impressive native African empires was achieved by means of a trade surplus, both in the western Sudan, where flourishing textile industries and universities of scholars were to be found, and in eastern Africa. In 1415, at the peak of Chinese enterprise, the Kenyan port of Malindi sent ambassadors (with gifts that included a giraffe) to the Ming emperor in Pekin. In the hinterland, from Kenya to the Transvaal, lived the miners and technicians, creating, thanks to the trade, a non-literate but architecturally magnificent native civilization, culminating in the colossal ruins of Zimbabwe in Rhodesia.

In 1488, the Portuguese explorer Vasco da Gama rounded the Cape of Good Hope; four years later Columbus sailed. From this time on, the kaleidoscope of world

Above: Chinese painting of the giraffe sent to a Ming emperor in Peking by the East African port of Malindi in A.D. 1415 as a present, when trade flourished between the two countries.

Rich mineral deposits—particularly of iron—and great skill in exploiting them, enabled cities of eastern Africa to build up a food surplus through trade, and to support a magnificent civilization in the hinterland. Below: ruins of the great Temple of Zimbabwe, Rhodesia, destroyed in the 17th century but once the prosperous centre of an empire.

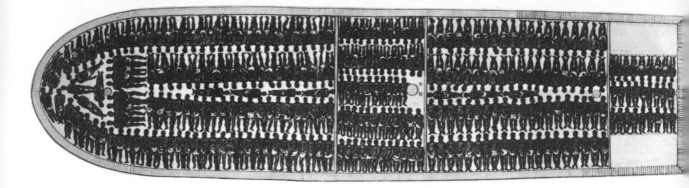

This drawing of a slave ship illustrates the terrible conditions under which slaves were sent from Africa to the New World by British traders. Packed together like cattle, many of them died on the journey.

As late as 1865 the Southern States of America still exploited slave labour to work their plantations of tobacco and cotton, and as domestic servants. Below: engraving of a typical slave sale at Charleston, South Carolina, at that date.

history steadied into a consistent pattern; Europeans dominated the world, but in so doing they brought it together into one system, all of which is now adopting the new technological civilization. The European expansion was in two stages. From about 1500 to about 1850, the Europeans used their technological equipment mainly to control the rest of the world for purposes of trade, loot, and plantation agriculture using slave labour.

Thanks to great sea power combined with an ample home surplus, Britain finally obtained the lion's share of the trade, and this, together with her resources in easily mined coal and iron, made Britain the pioneer of the Industrial Revolution. The plantations were chiefly of sugar-cane in the West Indies, and cotton and tobacco in the south of

the region that became the U.S.A. To staff the plantations with a labour force accustomed to tropical climates, the Europeans (especially the British and Dutch) launched the appalling trade in African slaves, which completed the ruin of African civilizations. Everywhere during this phase the Europeans were brutally destructive and rapacious. Robert Clive, the conqueror of eastern India, wrote in the 1760s that "such a scene of anarchy, confusion, bribery, corruption and extortion was never seen or heard of in any country but Bengal" (he made a fortune himself); but the British in India were no more extreme than other Europeans elsewhere.

Just as wool replaced linen in the 12th–13th centuries, so cotton partly replaced wool in the 18th, and the cotton textile industry of Lancashire was the setting for much of the early machine development in the Industrial Revolution. In 1794, Eli Whitney of Massachusetts invented the cotton gin, a machine for separating the cotton fibres from the seeds; by 1800, U.S. cotton production had risen from 5 to 35 million pounds; and when Whitney died in 1825, it was 225 million pounds. The invention prolonged plantation slavery for half a century, until the maintenance of slaves became unprofitable.

From about 1850, the pattern of colonial exploitation changed. Some at least of the European powers (notably

Above: Eli Whitney of Massachusetts. In 1794 he invented the cotton gin. This machine (below) consisted of a drum with pointed teeth, rotated by hand, that tore away the cotton fibres from the seeds; it did the day's work of several men in an hour. It made slave-worked cotton plantations profitable for fifty years, till erosion reduced the supply of cheap land.

Above: painting of British emigrants leaving Gravesend for the New World. When Europe's population rose steeply in the 19th century, millions emigrated.

Arrows on map above mark the routes followed by the 55 million emigrants who left Europe during the 19th and 20th centuries. The majority (including one eighth of the total population of Ireland) went to the lands opened up in North America in the preceding centuries, but a considerable number chose South Africa, Australia, and New Zealand. Many of the emigrants from the Mediterranean area went to South America.

the British in India) began to provide honest and competent government, and also some preparation for the introduction of industrial technology. By this time advances in transport (railways and steamships) were unifying the world and making mass trade in cheap goods (such as cereal grains) feasible. By this time, too, the population of Europeans was increasing out of all proportion to that of the rest of mankind. It has been estimated that they made up about 22 per cent of the world human population in 1800, and about 35 per cent in 1930.

This huge increase was funnelled into regions hitherto occupied only by small, scattered tribal societies (which were generally ruthlessly displaced), above all in North America. About 377,000 people per year left Europe in 1846–90, about 911,000 per year in 1891–1920, and about 366,000 per year in 1921–9. Between 1846 and 1930, over 50,000,000 Europeans emigrated. In this way were formed the great European societies outside Europe, the largest being the modern U.S.A. and U.S.S.R. Those who stayed in Europe were now fed largely by cereal imports from these newly opened regions. As the American geographer Carl O. Sauer has put it, "the industrial revolution was made possible by the ploughing-up of the great non-tropical grasslands of the world." The supply of space in relatively temperate climates outside Europe began to run out in the early 20th century, when the U.S.A. began to restrict immigration; by this time the European population was levelling off, but there was enough crowding to generate two frightful wars, in which the European powers involved most of the rest of the world.

A rising population accompanied the spread of industrialization from Britain, that is, the change to a state of steadily increasing production by means of machines and inanimate power supplies. The American economist W. W. Rostow has suggested some dates for the initial stages of industrialization in some different countries: Britain, 1783–1802; France, 1830–60; Belgium, 1833–60; U.S.A., 1843–60; Germany, 1850–73; Sweden, 1868–90; Japan, 1878–1900; Russia, 1890–1914; Canada, 1896–1914.

One astonishing feature of this list is the early industrialization of a non-European country, Japan. It is a country with a unique history. Since at least the fifth century A.D., when her written history begins, Japan has practised typical hydraulic agriculture based on rice: "before any business else," says an old Japanese proverb, "draw water to your winter fields." But Japan has no great river systems like the Yellow River, the Ganges, or the Euphrates; her irrigation was based on small streams in a number of districts divided by mountains or inland seas. Hence the Japanese developed the docility of a hydraulic civilization without the centralized bureaucracy.

188

Instead, there evolved a feudal system, in which each district was controlled by a military lord with his knights (samurai). Whereas in the European feudal system the rights of inferiors had great weight at all levels, in that of Japan inferiors had only duties. However, just as pine and poplar may provide a good nursery for beech and sugar maple (p. 20), so in the succession of human history a feudal system may provide a good nursery for a technological society. Because of its small original surplus, Europe could never have started civilization; because of its hydraulic agriculture, and its isolation from influences other than Chinese, Japan could never have made the technological breakthrough. But Europe readily adopted and developed civilized techniques, and Japan adopted modern technology with astounding speed after 1867, when a modernizing party gained control.

For the first half of the 20th century, the Europeans and Japanese remained the only industrial, or developed,

The British brought technological knowledge to India, and railways were built there in the mid-19th century. Engraving shows the first steam-engine for the Peshawar railway being taken across the Indus by boat.

Japan was the first country outside Europe to participate actively in the breakthrough. In 1867 a modernizing party came into power and Japan started to absorb European technology at an amazing rate. Below: opening of the first Japanese railway in 1872.

Above: Indian farmers working with
ox-drawn ploughs in Damodar valley near
pylons of an electrification project.
Outside finance for such projects
is vital to developing countries today.

Below: map marks countries that made
up the Common Market (blue) at end
of 1966. Also named are countries that
had applied to join at that date but
had not been admitted.

nations. This situation is now changing rapidly. The European colonial empires have almost disappeared, though the economic influence of Europeans remains predominant for the time being. The most powerful nations today are the U.S.A. and the U.S.S.R., who combine industrialization with great natural resources within their own large territories. Gradually, however, the countries of the dry belt and the tropics are beginning to develop too. Rostow dates the start of industrialization in China and India at about 1952. Just as Athens lost her privileged status when ceramics industries started elsewhere, so the Europeans will gradually lose their long-sustained predominance, and cannot expect to go on importing raw materials in return for industrial products, which others will soon be making for themselves.

By that time, however, the world will probably be even more integrated than it is today. Meanwhile the problem of speeding development in the developing countries is more urgent, and the developed countries are contributing 3600 million dollars a year to this end. The problem is complicated by the peculiar financial and trading system that has evolved between nations. The nation itself, as a social unit, played an important part in the technological breakthrough. It was a new balance of town and country-side interests, of central and local government, which the ancient city-states had failed to achieve. National organization is spreading everywhere as a precursor of industrialization. But valuable as the national stage has been, it has features that make it increasingly unsuitable for the modern world. These include the subsidies to native producers, tariffs (high duties or limited quotas) against imports from abroad, and the strangling network of international trade balances.

There is little doubt that international organization is on its way. By the 1960s, every urban country in the world, developed or developing, had original scientists and technologists of its own, and all now work together for what is no longer European but world science. The International Geophysical Year in 1957 was an impressive demonstration of a completely co-ordinated world programme. There is already a tendency to set up longer programmes of this kind, like the International Hydrological (Water Study) Decade, which started at the beginning of 1965. While tensions and confusions still obscure international politics, this ceaseless work in the background is gradually making the world one and indivisible.

Progress and Problems

The advance of food production since the breakthrough in north-west Europe has not been without difficulties and set-backs. When the Europeans colonized North

America, they reckoned without the dangers of climates and landscapes less favourable than those they had left behind. In the Southern States of the U.S.A., the planting of rows of cotton or tobacco on bare unprotected soil soon led to catastrophic soil erosion by runoff water. By the outbreak of the Civil War in 1861 usable land was already scarce and expensive (so that slave labour became unprofitable), and the South has been a depressed area ever since.

In the grassland belt of North America, the 19th- and early 20th-century settlers often indulged in reckless overgrazing, or ploughed up the grass and raised crop after crop of cereal without manuring or rotation. The soil was soon exhausted, and the bare fields were unprotected from the terrible gales and cyclones of the region. Disaster struck with the dry period of 1928–37, reaching its climax with the appalling drought of 1934. Masses of soil were whirled up by the winds as dust clouds, to be deposited again in drifts up to 2 feet deep, smothering vegetation elsewhere. In 1934, dust clouds from North and South Dakota blew as far as Washington D.C., bringing the problem of soil conservation visibly to the attention of the Government and Legislature. By that time, according to the U.S. Department of Agriculture, out of the total area of the Continental U.S.A. of 1905 million acres, 1157 million were more or less seriously affected by erosion.

But modern technological man is extraordinarily resilient in the face of such disasters. Within a year of the great drought, both the U.S.A. and Canada had set up special areas for studying the problem, the Vale Project in Oregon and the Melita Reclamation Station in Manitoba. By 1964, both projects had shown the possibility of avoiding erosion on the dry plains and of fully reclaiming eroded land. The station at Melita was sited on land actually abandoned, and has restored much of it to full productive use. Experience in North America, and in

In large tracts of North America overgrazing or continuous farming with the same crop exhausted the land. Bare fields were a prey to water erosion, leaving dry barren gullies (above); or gales and cyclones swept away the topsoil. After droughts, such as the severe one of 1934, high winds whipped parched topsoil into huge dust-storms, smothering vegetation and choking towns. Photo right shows a dust-storm in Kansas (1935).

New Zealand has also been faced with
problems of soil conservation. Right,
above: section of the Tara Hills, South
Island, where effects of overgrazing
were aggravated by a plague of rabbits.
Lower picture illustrates how fertility
was restored to this land by manuring
and seeding with pasture legumes;
serious efforts were made to control
rabbits. The success of this experiment
is particularly striking since this land
is on steep slopes.

Australia, New Zealand, and South Africa (faced with similar problems), has produced an impressive technology of soil conservation. On wind-swept plains, for instance, rows of trees can be planted at intervals as "shelter-belts" to break the force of the winds. The sowing of grasses and especially legumes can gradually reclaim bare soil to fertile cropland. These and other techniques are helping to repair the damage and ensure that it never recurs. In addition, much has been learnt about the effects of grazing in dry regions, which can be applied in the overgrazed Old World dry belt.

All this work is not without surprises. After all we have seen of the effects of deforestation and overgrazing, planting trees might seem always a good idea. Yet in Arizona carefully nurtured cedar and juniper thickets have been shown to waste the region's scarce water and hence lower the carrying capacity for cattle; the trees have to be thinned and pruned. Too many trees can be as bad as too many cattle; the one completely general rule is that too many of *anything* is dangerous.

More spectacular than any disaster has been the advance of agriculture as a direct result of the breakthrough. One obvious new gain was the introduction of more machinery (made of improved metal) and of the new sources of power. Up to and including the 18th century, farmers were still concerned with increasing the ratio of yield to seed, and the chief innovation was the seed-drill, a machine for sowing seeds in rows instead of broadcasting them by hand, which wasted seeds; as early as 1566 the Senate of Venice granted a patent to Camillo Tarello of Lonato for a device of this kind. After about 1800, when the new farming systems had greatly increased yields and the Industrial Revolution was in full swing in Britain, interest turned to machines for harvesting and cleaning the greater amounts of grain quickly and with less labour. The American drive westward was hastened by the reaping

Invention of the seed drill was an important factor in increasing yields: less seed was wasted. Above, woman using early seed drill, from an 18th-century French print.

Below, 19th-century English metal seed drill; seed dropped from box straight down into the furrow.

machine, which Cyrus McCormick of Virginia invented in 1831 and began mass producing in 1845, in the (then) decaying settlement of Chicago. The reaping machine evolved gradually into the combine-harvester, which did everything from cutting to cleaning.

In 1784 James Watt patented steam-powered ploughing, and by 1870 steam-powered tractors were in use. These, however, were heavy and used much fuel and water. In 1892 John Froelich built a tractor powered by an internal combustion engine, and in 1907 Henry Ford began to manufacture such tractors at Detroit; they thus shared the benefits of the system of total mass production he had developed by 1913. Mechanization caused an unprecedented saving in labour. In 1830, using the ordinary plough, harrow, sickles, and flails, it took 144 man-hours to produce 50 bushels of wheat; in the U.S.A. this was reduced to 22 man-hours by 1896, and to 8.25 man-hours by 1930 (with tractors and combine-harvesters). A large labour force was freed for industry; by now in the U.S.A. there are few full-time farmers left. The farm-horse, which served European progress so well in the Middle Ages,

Above: drawing of the first really effective reaping machine, invented by Cyrus McCormick in 1831. Finally replacing hand-scything, this invention dramatically cut down the man-power needed for harvesting.

Diagram below shows how increasing mechanization has cut down the man-hours needed to plough two and a half acres of land. Using an early type of plough with two horses, one man would take 13 hours 42 minutes, but today with a tractor and multi-furrow plough, one man can cover this area in 40 minutes.

13h 42m

12h 3m

5h 57m

4h 19m

Above: illustration from Copeland's *Agriculture, Ancient and Modern* (1866) shows a threshing machine powered by a steam-engine. This machine needed several men to operate it and would be owned by a contractor who leased it out.

has had its day; in the U.S.A. between 1915 and 1940, 11 million horses and mules were displaced by tractors. By 1964, there were too few draught animals left to be counted in agricultural statistics, and there were five million tractors—more than one per farm.

Farm machines have saved mankind much tedious labour, freeing him for other work or increasing his leisure time. For raising food production, however, they have not so far been the most important contribution from the breakthrough. This is clear from the extraordinary story of modern Japan. Unlike Britain and the U.S.A. (or, to a large extent, continental north-west Europe), Japan industrialized without mechanizing her farms or freeing farm labour for industry. She increased her food surplus with the same quantity of farm labour, and this fed a rising population to work her industries. Her farm labour force was 15,500,000 in 1878, and 15,660,000 in 1956–60; meanwhile her total population rose from 36,911,000 to 91,780,000. One reason for this different pattern was the very small size of Japanese farms, which averaged 2.5 acres each in 1878 and 2 acres in 1962. In 1879 the

2h 7m

1h 0m

0h 40m

government began to manufacture farm machinery, but by 1888 the project was dropped; the machines could not be used effectively on such small farms.

Attempts to develop larger farm units and install machines in Japan have been made since World War II; but in 1950, there were still only about 60,000 small tractors in Japan, and even in 1960 only 500,000. Yet average husked rice yield, starting from the high figure of 0.8 tons per acre in 1878 (typical of advanced hydraulic agriculture), was over 1.6 tons by 1962. Of this 100 per cent increase, about 70 per cent was achieved by the 1930s, when there were still virtually no machines. This increase in yields was achieved in Japan by something else: *agricultural chemicals*. These were the fruits of that knowledge of chemistry so lacking in Greek science. They included fertilizers, weedkillers, and pestkillers.

The first of these entirely new developments was the use of chemical fertilizers, the great contribution of the 19th century to agriculture. A number of European scientists established the chemical elements needed by plants. These elements, above all nitrogen, phosphorus, and potassium (NPK), were extracted from natural products and later increasingly synthesized by purely chemical means. Supplied in suitable compounds to crops, they greatly increased, often doubled, yields. World annual consumption of NPK was already about 2 million tons by 1905–6, about 9 million by 1938–9, and about 32.5 million tons by 1962–3. Meanwhile by the 20th century chemists were able to make extremely elaborate compounds, and the age of plastics and synthetics dawned; substances such as nylon, synthetic detergents, and all the plastics now in household use are the things that make our daily life most different from that of all previous generations. By the 1930s, it had been discovered that growth patterns in plants are governed by chemical regulating substances, and new compounds were being made to duplicate some of their actions. In large doses, growth-regulating substances are lethal to plants, and in 1940 it was discovered that some of them kill certain plants more readily than others. The result, especially after World War II, was the synthesis and manufacture of a host of powerful selective weedkillers.

Weeds may include many kinds of plants (see p. 79). However, substances like 2,4-D and MCPA, which spare wild or cultivated grasses, can be used to kill many weeds of cereal crop fields, while TCA and dalapon, relatively lethal to grasses, can be used to kill grass weeds in non-cereal crop fields (e.g. of peas or beet). Some recent weedkillers are even more selective: diallate, if suitably applied, will kill wild oats, a serious weed of wheat and barley fields, without harming the cultivated plants, though the three species are closely related; dicamba will kill some

Increasing use of chemical fertilizers has been an important factor in the development of modern agriculture. Chemical deficiencies produce unhealthy plants. Right-hand plants on this page have been deprived of nitrogen (top), phosphorus (middle), and potassium (below). Fertilizers that correct the balance of these elements help produce healthy plants like those on the left.

grass species but not others, and can be used to change the composition of grassland. Diquat and paraquat will kill everything above ground without deeply penetrating the soil or leaving residues to harm *subsequent* growth; so they can be used when grassland is to be re-sown with improved grasses, without the necessity of ploughing it up.

The new control of weeds is an important factor for increasing production; even carefully cultivated crops could lose 15 per cent of their yield to weeds competing for space and the nutrients in the soil. It is also enormously labour-saving. Weeds dictated the practices of swidden farming; they have been almost as crucial in other types of agriculture. An experiment in India in 1961–2 showed that differences in ploughing methods make relatively little difference to the physical state of the soil, but great differences to yield, in accordance with their effect in suppressing weed growth. Research is going on in Britain to replace ploughing almost entirely by the use of such thoroughgoing weedkillers as paraquat, the more promising because chemical techniques for improving soil structure are also being developed. The need to suppress weeds may have been the main reason for the ceaseless labour of tilling the soil in the past, and perhaps one day the plough itself, so long a vital factor in human progress, will follow the farm-horse into honourable retirement.

After so much attention to man as farmer, citizen, manufacturer, and trader, we may return to man as a hunter. Hunting animals are restrained from exterminating their prey (and hence destroying their food resources) by limits on their own numbers and because the means they evolve for detection and attack are matched by the evolution of comparably effective means of flight, concealment, or defence. Since the breakthrough, man's increase in numbers and advance in technical equipment have been so outstanding that he has been in real danger of reducing game populations to the point where they yield less and less and eventually die out. On land this has been of minor importance, for in the Neolithic, besides developing crop agriculture, man had resolved the problem of overhunting by domesticating the most useful animals and ensuring that they kept up their numbers under his supervision.

Since so little of his food came from hunting the remaining animals, civilized agricultural man has been little troubled by overhunting on land. The principle of domestication has steadily been extended. The feeding-grounds of game in Canada and Africa are being studied with a view to systematic management, just as natural pastures are managed for cattle. Many people regard Africa's wild game as a vital source of animal protein, and by 1962 two farmers in Rhodesia had actually begun to farm game and make it pay.

Man has also used his chemical knowledge to develop selective weedkillers. Applied to a grain field (left of post, top photo) 2, 4–D destroys wild mustard (see untreated plot, right of post). Middle photo: simazine has significantly cut down weeds in corn on the right. Below: dinistro and CDAA have kept weeds out of soy-beans (right), while untreated plot is choked with weeds.

Overhunting in the seas, or overfishing, is another matter. Fishing has remained an important means of food production without interruption since the Upper Palaeolithic. The reliability of fish food from lakes may well have given man one of his first opportunities to settle long enough to grow a crop, and throughout man's subsequent career the volume of fishing has steadily grown, more than ever in the 20th century. The world fish catch was about 21 million tons in 1938, and about 46 million tons in 1963, when it provided 3 per cent of the world's protein food and nearly 10 per cent of the world's animal protein. The breakthrough created both the demand (by population increase) and the technical means for a much bigger world catch than ever before, and the division of mankind into nations led, on the open seas, to unrestricted competition for the game. The result may be illustrated by one of the greatest tragedies in the history of man and nature, the story of whales and whaling.

Man must early have made use of whales stranded on his coasts; a carving of one in northern Norway dates probably from before 4000 B.C. To go out in open boats and hand-harpoon them was a natural step for people whose coasts were often visited by whales. Off-shore whaling was apparently invented independently by several peoples, including the Basques (before A.D. 1150, when it is mentioned in a document) and the Japanese (16th century A.D.); "a whale makes seven villages rich" is an old Japanese proverb. Taught by the Basques, the Dutch and English went farther afield, whaling in the Arctic from the 17th century onward. The great Pacific whaling grounds were opened up from 1789 by the seamen of New England,

For centuries men have been hunting whales for food. Above: a 14th-century seal belonging to the town of Biarritz in France shows men harpooning a whale.

"A whale makes seven villages rich" is an old Japanese proverb. No doubt the villagers in the Japanese painting (below) felt delighted as they hauled up three whales onto the foreshore and cut up the highly prized meat.

especially Nantucket Island. Because of their excellence in handling small boats, men from the Azores were recruited by the New England ships; returning home, the Azoreans founded an off-shore hand-harpoon sperm-whaling industry that survives to this day and has been filmed by the British zoologist Robert Clarke. Between 1863 and 1870, the Norwegian Svend Foyn, with the help of Pastor Hans Esmark, invented the harpoon-gun for tackling the largest whales, hitherto avoided by all except the Japanese; the great Antarctic large-whale industry began in 1904. The development in the late 1920s of the factory ship, which could keep the whales afloat and cut them up on board, completed the whalers' freedom of the open seas right around the Antarctic.

By this series of whaling industries, one whale stock after another was reduced in numbers to the point where it was not worth hunting. The right whales of the north Atlantic and Arctic were so completely overhunted that the whole northern industry had utterly collapsed by 1914. In the west Pacific, 193,000 southern right whales were killed between 1804 and 1817, and 41.25 million gallons of oil from sperm whales were taken in 1830–40; schools of sperm whales, formerly up to 100 each, shrank to about 15. The sperm whales here were only saved from total extinction by the discovery of petroleum in Pennsylvania in 1859, which replaced whale-oil. By 1868 the world whale catch is said to have shrunk to 30. The harpoon-gun and the opening of the Antarctic increased it to 25,673 in 1913, the factory ship increased it further to 54,835 in 1938. The Antarctic rorqual industry, responsible for most of these catches, had drastically depleted the humpback whale by 1913, and the blue whale by 1931, despite warnings by scientists. By 1960, 80 per cent of the world catch consisted of fin whales, the last whales to survive in numbers worth exploiting.

In 1932 the Norwegians and British, then the chief whaling nations, signed the first agreement for restricting catches, but when other nations entered the industry this became ineffective. In 1946 the International Whaling Commission was formed to control world whaling; but the spirit of competition that goes with national organization has prevented it from achieving realistic control in time; the member nations could not even agree on the quota for 1964–5. At a conference at Durham in 1960, R. M. Laws, of the British National Institute of Oceanography, once again reported that survival curves for the blue and fin whales "indicate that at the present rate of exploitation recruitment is insufficient to maintain the stocks." In plain language, the blue and fin whales were dying out.

Fishes are more numerous than whales, and overfishing has had less serious results than overwhaling. By the 20th

Today whales are hunted with more modern equipment than hand harpoons: top photo shows a whale gun—a harpoon containing an explosive charge, mounted on the prow of the ship. Lower photo shows a whale being cut up on a factory ship. Ample storage facilities on such ships make long whaling trips possible.

century, however, rising population and technical advance were causing severe depletion of important commercial sea fishes like cod, haddock, plaice, halibut, and herring. The fish populations of the North Sea rose dramatically after both World Wars (during which fishing there was much reduced). According to the 1964 report of FAO on the State of Food and Agriculture, the leading fishery nations were by this time looking for new grounds on the coasts of developing countries, which were becoming alarmed at the threat to their sea resources from these intruders. However, a new branch of science has developed to tackle the problem of how to fish at a rate that will ensure the highest possible sustained catch, and its recommendations may be applied before it is too late. The potential world fish harvest, if fishing is adequately controlled, has been estimated at about 115 million tons a year, roughly two and a half times the harvest in 1963.

In the long run, however, as on the land, the tendency will probably be to domesticate sea life and turn the oceans (70 per cent of the earth's surface) into a gigantic farm. The farming of freshwater fish is old, and in the flood plains of the Far East freshwater fishes are actually bred as a crop in rotation with irrigated rice. Already much is being done to change the living composition of the smaller inland seas, especially in the U.S.S.R., where not only fish but fish food animals from one sea are used to stock another, just as crop plants are introduced from one region to another on land. In 1939–40, for instance, Soviet scientists took 61,000 specimens of the small worm *Nereis* from the Sea of Azov and put them in the Caspian; by

At Port Erin, Isle of Man, scientists are experimenting in fish farming. Plaice are hatched from eggs in trays (above) and then fed on shrimps. This helps a larger percentage of fish to develop than normal, at a faster rate.

Above: British fishermen in the Baltic landing a catch of herring. Fish forms an important part of our diet today, and as rising populations increase the demand for fish, it is vital that overfishing, which might seriously threaten supplies, should not occur.

When plaice are ready to live on sea-bed they are transferred to enclosed bays where the water is enriched to increase growth. Below: workers at Ardtoe, Scotland, taking fish in polythene bags from the hatchery to the bays.

1956, two or three million tons of *Nereis* were being produced there annually, greatly increasing the food supply, and hence the numbers, of Caspian fishes.

A more radical development is the artificial rearing of sea-bottom fishes from eggs. This was begun in Norway and the U.S.A. in the 1880s, but abandoned by 1952. The fish were reared to their larval stage only, then dumped into the sea. The fish spend this stage in the upper water layers. Our knowledge of conditions in the sea has been greatly increased meantime by marine biologists such as Sir Frederick Russell. The number of larval fishes surviving depends on the minute food organisms in water (which fluctuate with currents and other factors) and is almost independent of the number of larvae to start with. In Britain, after World War II, methods were developed, chiefly by J. E. Shelbourne at Lowestoft, for tank-rearing young plaice to the adult fish stage. At this stage they normally live on the bottom, where the food supply is more constant. The numbers of plaice successfully reared to adulthood were: 1 in 1957, 100 in 1958, 327 in 1959, 1178 in 1960, 2807 in 1961—still only 3.3 per cent of the original eggs. In 1962 there was a big jump to 25,000 reared, more than 50 per cent of the eggs.

By this technique, three developments will be possible: adding adult fish to the natural sea populations, making new nursery grounds where they can grow larger, or complete fish farming up to marketable size. It should be possible to grow plaice to this size in two years under intensive farming, as opposed to four to five years in present natural conditions. Since 1947, British scientists have shown that the fish stocks of Scottish sea-lochs can be increased by applying agricultural fertilizers. In 1965, a Scottish bay was prepared to serve as the first experimental farm for complete sea-fish stock-raising.

But even all this may only be the beginning. The British biologist Sir Alister Hardy has envisaged a true farming of the oceans themselves. Arthur Clarke's novel *The Deep Range* (1957) gives some idea of the possible future here, including domestication of the surviving whales. These ideas are not likely to remain science fiction for long: the sober FAO 1964 report envisages (for a "not far distant" time) such possibilities as "massive engineering operations to plough the bottom of the sea, and the fertilization of the surface waters." Thus man will extend his control of nature from the land to the sea, and realize an old prophecy. For, according to Obed Macy's *History of Nantucket* (quoted by Herman Melville in *Moby Dick*), "in the year 1690 some persons were on a high hill observing the whales spouting and sporting with each other, when one observed; there—pointing to the sea—is a green pasture where our children's grandchildren will go for bread."

11　Pandora's Box

Above: 16th-century French engraving of
serpents flying out of Pandora's box—
symbols of evils that plague mankind.
Man's cultivation of the earth released
a host of unwanted and unexpected evils.

When man began to clear the forest, raise crops and herds, and build cities, roads, and ships, he opened the box of the Earth goddess, and out flew a squadron of merciless enemies. So far we have considered only the least deadly result of the coming of agriculture, the rise of the weeds of cultivation. Another and more serious result was the rise of crop pests, especially insect pests.

That this result is a creation of agriculture appears very clearly from Soviet studies in Kazakhstan, where much of the grass steppe is being ploughed up for wheat. On the steppe before ploughing, there were 199 individual insects per square metre, drawn from 330 species. In the wheat fields, there were 351 individuals per square metre, of which almost all belonged to only 19 dominant species, most of them serious pests of wheat. In the new environment provided by man, the few species fitted for eating wheat had increased to a startling degree; the population of one such species was 280 times greater after a single cropping season than it was before ploughing up.

Such species we call pests. Not only can they reduce a country's whole agricultural production by an average of 10–15 per cent; they can also destroy much larger percentages of particular crops, or in particular years, and so cause devastating crop failures. The synthesis of really efficient chemical insect-killers (insecticides), which kill on contact, has been yet another gain from the technological breakthrough. Their effect on agriculture may be shown by a single example. In an experiment in 1965 at Luzon in the Philippines, spraying lindane to kill insect pests increased the yield of rice by 150 per cent; the pests had been destroying three fifths of the potential rice yield. The first really powerful synthetic compound, DDT, known as a chemical compound since 1873, was discovered during World War II to be an insecticide; it was followed after the war by many others.

There was a big difference between the early uses of weedkillers and insecticides. If the weedkillers had not been selective, they would have killed the crops as well, and could therefore never have been widely used. Killing all insects seemed to matter less, and most of the insecticides developed in the last 30 years have been so generally poisonous that they have destroyed not only most insects but also other animals. The use of chemical insecticides, undoubtedly necessary for increasing food production, has thus raised a whole set of new problems. Compounds like aldrin and dieldrin leave residues in the crops themselves, and although there is no evidence that these have yet been high enough to harm man, they have caused great concern. This is not the only disadvantage, for beneficial animals have certainly suffered from these unselective killing sprays. In a number of Nova Scotia orchards in

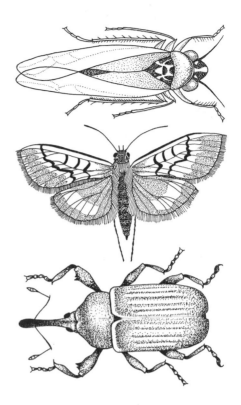

Above: three of the many insects that can cause extensive damage to vital crops. Top to bottom: potato leaf-hopper, European corn borer moth, and boll weevil (which attacks cotton).

Chemical insecticides are important weapons in the war against pests. Below: worker in an anti-locust campaign in the Middle East is helped on with portable apparatus for spraying aldrin.

Above: doctor with pesticide sprayers in a vine-growing village in Bulgaria. Toxic sprays demand that workers wear heavy protective clothing. But such measures will not protect wild life. Below: whitethroat's nest containing a dead chick, probably poisoned by eating a caterpillar killed by pesticide.

the 1940s and 1950s, bees were wiped out by DDT; fortunately, they regained a foothold after its use was stopped. A dearth of bees in parts of Japan has also been ascribed to use of insecticides. Bees are vital for pollinating certain fruit-trees and pasture legumes; the Japanese have had trouble in establishing clovers as a result. Earthworms in pastures also suffer from the sprays; since the work of Charles Darwin we know that their activities improve soil structure, and it has been shown more recently that they help to convert the nitrogen from cattle manure into forms usable by plants.

Yet another difficulty has been the effect upon wild life of insecticides with persistent residues. The chief problem here arises from what scientists call the *food chain*. Animal A eats a plant; animal B eats A, C eats B, and so on. At each stage, the total mass of living matter from an earlier stage gets smaller; the reason is that much of it is converted into energy for food-getting or is excreted, and the amount added to the body-weight of the animal in the next stage in the chain may be as little as 10 per cent. Poisonous chemical compounds, therefore, may accumulate to reach high concentrations in the hunting animals at the end of the chain, either killing them or reducing their fertility. In the north central states of the U.S.A. in the 1950s, DDT sprayed on elm trees to kill bark beetles reached the soil in leaf litter and was eaten by earthworms, which were in turn eaten by robins, of which very large numbers died. Another compound, DDD, was applied at a rate of one part in 50 million to Clear Lake, California, to control the larvae of gnats. It was taken up by small water plants, then eaten by fishes, then by other fishes, and finally by birds (grebes). By this stage in the food chain it had been concentrated 100,000-fold to 2000 parts in a million, and many birds died. Such drastic effects on wild life may have considerable, and often unexpected, repercussions (p. 21).

More directly, unselective insecticides may defeat their own object by destroying insect hunters of pests. Since the drugs are not *equally* poisonous to all insects, the complexities are formidable. In a strictly controlled experiment on lucerne plots in Washington State in 1956–9, the American agriculturalist Wyatt W. Cone studied the effects of three insecticides on populations of three mite species—two pests, *Tetranychus* (A) and *Tydeus* (B), and a third, *Typhlodromus* (C), which preys on the first two. DDT decreased B and C and increased A, because of less hunting by C. Schradan decreased A and C and increased B for the same reason. Dieldrin increased C and thus decreased A and B. In this instance, therefore, dieldrin would be beneficial, but the other two drugs would actually make matters worse.

Biological control works by importing an insect's natural enemies to destroy it. Above: vedalia feeding on fluted scale insects (fluffy white insects in photo), which formerly did great damage to citrus trees in California.

Left: worker examining grubs of Mediterranean fruit-fly stored in trays. In Mexico and southern California large numbers of such grubs are reared and exposed to radioactive cobalt 60, making male flies sterile on hatching. These are released in infested areas. A large proportion of matings consequently produce infertile eggs. This method has been very effective in cutting down numbers of these destructive flies.

Another modern method of controlling pests has been to encourage or introduce their enemies. This has sometimes worked extremely well. In 1868, the fluted scale insect (*Icerya*) reached California on plants imported from Australia, and by 1886 became a devastating pest of Californian citrus orchards. In 1889 its natural enemy, the vedalia (*Rodolia*) was imported from Australia, and by 1900 the pest was almost exterminated. By 1916 it was said that the fluted scale, previously a terrible menace, was of no importance in agriculture since the use of the vedalia. In the 1940s, the use of DDT in California reduced the vedalia population, and the fluted scale reappeared as a pest; use of DDT was restricted in 1948, and the vedalia regained control.

What is most striking is the speed with which all these new problems are being met. Aldrin and dieldrin came into use only in 1950. By 1955 a British government working party was reporting on risks to wildlife from these and other agricultural chemicals; it had also been studying the risks to man since 1950. By 1959, FAO was tackling the residue problem on a world scale, spurred by the fact that nations varied in the residue levels they would permit in food (and could thus block imports from more tolerant nations). All this was long before 1962 when Rachel Carson's book *Silent Spring* caused a public uproar. There has been action in several countries to ban or restrict the use of insecticides with persistent residues, in favour of more poisonous but less persistent ones, such as parathion. By 1964, less poisonous but equally effective compounds like fenitrothion were replacing even these.

It is generally agreed that chemical insecticides are essential if the world population, even at its present level, is to be fed. There is, however, vigorous research to find more selective ones, and also to combine their use with that of natural enemies of pests. In Nova Scotia apple orchards, the Canadian agriculturalist A. D. Pickett and his colleagues have had much success since about 1950 using carefully timed applications of the relatively selective drug ryania, designed to leave hunting insects unharmed to help in controlling the chief pests. The result has been much better control as well as more bees (p. 203).

New, quite different, methods are continually being devised as well, such as the use of ultrasonic or amplified sound broadcasts, which are very effective (for unknown reasons) in reducing the fertility of certain moths; or the

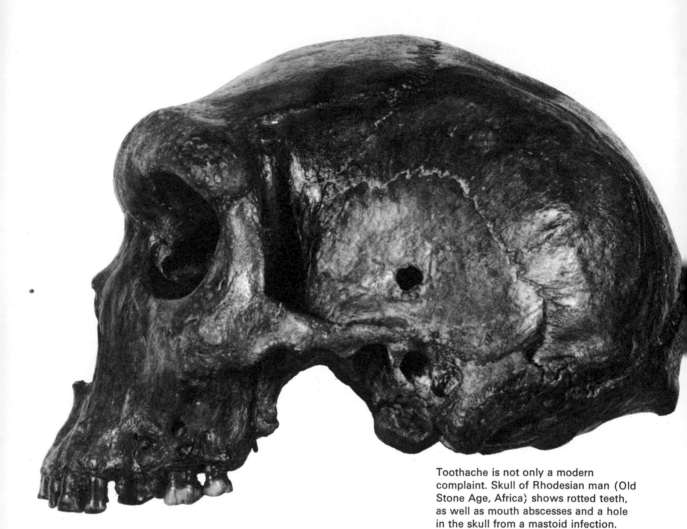

Toothache is not only a modern complaint. Skull of Rhodesian man (Old Stone Age, Africa) shows rotted teeth, as well as mouth abscesses and a hole in the skull from a mastoid infection.

use of the scent of female insects to lure males of the same species into traps. The insecticide story has shown both that man is always liable to have new problems with nature, and that he is now better equipped to solve them than ever before.

Pests, however, are by no means the worst things out of Pandora's Box. For it now seems certain that the coming of most infectious diseases was also a result of man's growing command of his natural surroundings. It is true that from earliest times man suffered from some present-day diseases, and especially from general inflammation of parts of his body, often after an injury. Sinusitis, a result of breathing damp, smoky, or dusty air, which irritates the nose, is an old disease; it has been detected in skulls from all ages, in Dark Age England and France, in ancient Egypt, and even in hunters who lived in a damp cave during the Palaeolithic.

Some diseases, while equally ancient, can be shown to have greatly increased since the coming of agriculture.

Below: rates of tooth decay among four European peoples (3000 B.C. to present day). Note huge rise in highly urban Roman period and in modern times.

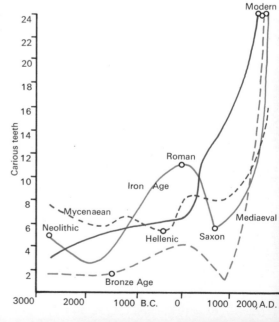

Toothache is as old as mankind. Most of the early Palaeolithic human populations, known to us from bones, showed a proportion of tooth decay, and one specimen of Rhodesian man, who roamed Africa perhaps 15,000 years ago, must have suffered agony from rotting teeth and mouth abscesses, before he was finished off by a mastoid infection of his left ear. Tooth decay depends largely on what you eat, and with the new food habits arising with agriculture came a marked increase in the incidence of this complaint. And tooth decay has been increasingly prevalent ever since. It seems to be above all a disease of city life.

Many of the great specific infectious diseases, however, each caused by one particular type of germ or worm, are real novelties in the story of man and nature. From quite different kinds of evidence, students of parasites and experts on the diagnosis of disease in ancient bones and bodies are agreed that most human diseases have been acquired during the past 10,000 years—that is, since the coming of agriculture. From that time on, new disease problems have continued to arise, in wave after wave; it has been said that they reached their peak throughout the world in the 18th century, but new kinds of outbreaks have occurred even since then. The reasons for all this are complex.

Infectious diseases are due to parasites; the word *parasite* comes from the Greek *parasitos*, meaning someone who comes to dinner. There are enormous numbers of organisms that live on or inside the bodies of other animals, and this way of life is extremely old. Some of these guests earn their keep. A good example is the bacterial population that inhabits a compartment of the gut (especially evolved to house them) in ruminants, such as sheep and cattle, that depend entirely on plant food. These bacteria have the ability, which their hosts lack, of breaking down plant substances such as cellulose and converting them into easily digestible sugars, and this is what makes the ruminant hosts so useful to man. Other organisms can at least live in the bodies of animals without killing or injuring the host, which can thus entertain them all the longer. A healthy guest in a healthy host is the ideal solution for both parties, and when host and guest have been associated over many generations, they often come to make the best of each other. But this compatibility takes time to evolve, and it often happens, especially when a parasite takes to a new host, that the ordinary life-processes of the parasite cause the host damage or even death.

We can divide parasites that are harmful to man into two main groups. The first are the worms, of which there are many kinds. In small numbers they are unimportant, and indeed all human adults entertain a few. But the presence

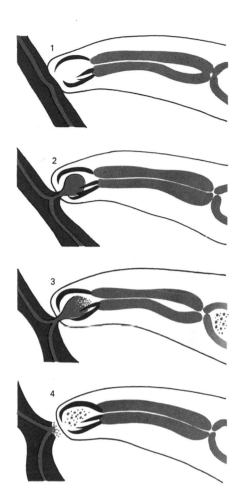

Above: diagram of a hookworm feeding. It clasps intestine wall and this, with blood vessel, is sucked into mouth cavity of the worm, then disintegrated by its juices (3), and the end products are digested. Worm then releases wall (4), leaving blood vessel exposed.

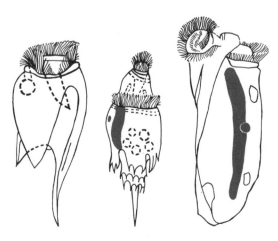

Above: three small parasites that live in the gut of ruminants. Far from harming their host, such organisms are useful in helping to convert cellulose in plant foods into digestible sugars.

of too many specimens in one host individual has serious results. Hookworms, for instance, get into human hosts through the skin and make their way to the gut. Here they fasten on to the gut wall, disintegrate it, and eat the remains, sucking in blood in the process. A single hookworm does little damage in this way, but 500 hookworms can remove nearly half a pint of blood per day. People heavily infected with these parasites become listless, weak, and vulnerable to other diseases. When the people of Puerto Rico were treated intensively for hookworms, their working efficiency increased by more than 60 per cent.

The second main group consists of microscopic organisms: protozoa, bacteria, rickettsias, fungi, and viruses. These are liable to do damage in several ways, especially when introduced into a new host. First, such a parasite during its life may release substances called *endotoxins*, which poison the host tissues. Or, second, after its death it may release other substances called *exotoxins* with the same effect. Or, finally, the parasites may breed and multiply rapidly inside the host, and simply overwhelm the host's life-processes by sheer numbers.

While a parasite may damage its host, the host body may defend itself by various means, especially by producing substances that attack the parasite or its toxins. Each of these "antibodies" usually works only against a particular parasite or toxin. Sometimes they are produced only as long as specimens of the parasite are present; sometimes they are produced in response to the first invasion of parasites and continue to be available, after the attack, for years or even for life. In the latter case, after one attack of the disease the host becomes *immune* for a longer or shorter period: during this period, fresh infection with that particular parasite will cause little or no disease.

Parasite populations may in turn circumvent the defence by developing new strains against which the original antibodies have no effect. The viruses of influenza, in particular, are constantly changing in this way, so that having had one kind of flu is no protection against having another kind later. Moreover, the efficiency of the defence system varies with the general level of health in the host; it may be undermined, for instance, by malnutrition. For this reason, in developing countries where the diet is low in protein, the death-rate from infectious diseases in children 1–4 years old is 20–50 times higher than in the United States and north-western Europe.

The virulence of a parasite (its capacity to cause disease) clearly depends in a complicated way on both host and parasite, and may be continually changing. A microscopic parasite may be present for some time without being able to multiply in the host's body, and hence without doing harm; if a change in the host's health permits it to multiply,

Below: upper picture shows tuberculosis bacteria in spittle (magnified about 600 times). Lower picture shows Asian flu virus (magnified about 200,000 times). This virus attacked Europeans for the first time in 1957, then again in 1965. By the second time, virus had modified, and those who had suffered from it in the first epidemic were no longer immune.

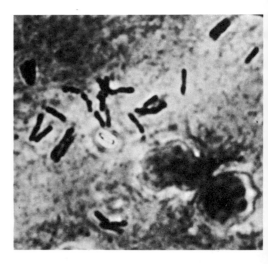

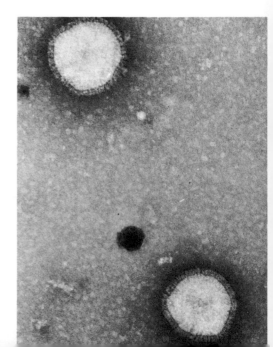

it may cause serious disease. When a parasite first invades a new host population, it may kill many. Those who survive, however, will be partly or wholly immune. If all or most of the host population go on being infected for several generations, most will suffer from the disease early in life, and most adults will be immune. Meanwhile a gradual process of adjustment may have made the symptoms less serious. Eventually, the disease may become a mild childhood illness, like mumps, chicken-pox, and measles in human populations of the northern temperate regions. At one time it was customary in England for the family of a child with such an illness to invite other children to a party, where they could all catch the disease to "get it over." But if these parasites are introduced to populations where they have not been present before, they will cause dangerous disease in people of all ages: this happened when Europeans brought measles to the Eskimos and to the people of Tahiti.

Below, photo of *Trypanosoma gambiense* (magnified about 600 times) in human blood. This protozoan parasite causes sleeping sickness and is carried by tsetse flies from one person to another. Parasite first invades the blood and later attacks the fluid in the brain and spinal cord, thus causing death.

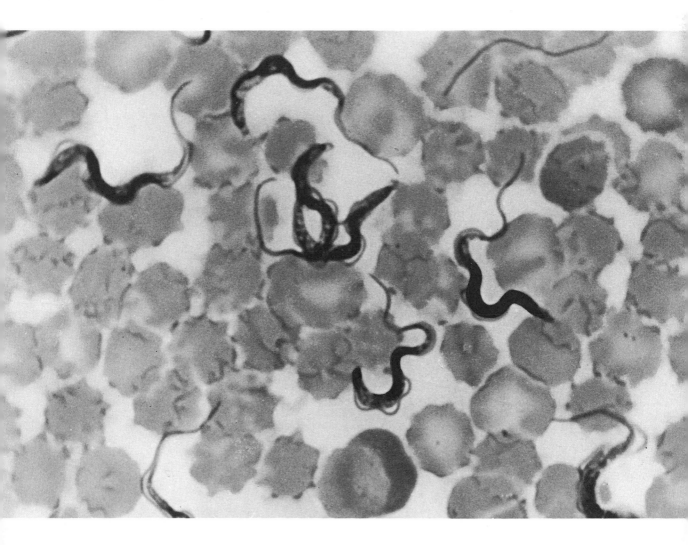

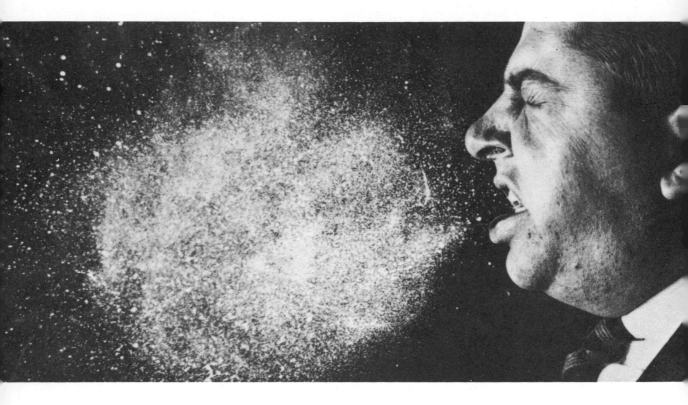

Many parasites can live in more than one host species, while others become specialized for a single host. Unless this specialization is complete, a parasite can move at need from one host species to another. With a new host, the result is likely to be serious disease. Some parasites, especially protozoa and worms, have complicated life-cycles, parts of which are spent in secondary hosts or even as free-living forms; and they may move from one kind of cycle to another. Parasites have evolved a variety of methods of moving between individual hosts. Hence human infectious diseases are spread in a variety of ways.

There are, however, four main ways. First, microscopic parasites may pass into the air when we breathe out, and get into somebody else's lungs: "coughs and sneezes spread diseases," as the posters in England used to proclaim in World War II. This is called *droplet infection*. Second, the parasites may get into the next host when food or drink is contaminated by the corpse or excrement of the previous one. Third, they may be transmitted by close bodily contact. Fourth, they may be carried by other organisms (*vectors*), notably blood-sucking insects. The great variety of transmission methods means that spread of infection depends on an equally great variety of climatic and public health factors, and makes infectious disease a bewilderingly complex problem. Measures effective against one infection may be useless against another, and any

One method of spreading disease is by droplet infection. Above: man with a cold sneezes, expelling air containing microscopic germs. These may pass into the lungs of someone else and infect them—a danger that the Ministry of Health warned the public against in a poster (below) issued in World War II.

WANTED
FOR
SNEEZING
TO THE PUBLIC
DANGER
and coughing without due
care and attention

The Ministry of Health says:-

COUGHS AND SNEEZES
SPREAD DISEASES
Trap the germs in your handkerchief

210

attempt to control the spread of disease in human populations requires considerable knowledge. Until this knowledge was gradually built up, it is no wonder man found infectious disease the most terrifying of all mysteries: he never knew what hit him.

The Perils of Agriculture

Man's troubles must have begun with his earliest successes, the improvements in hunting technique, aided by the first rudiments of agriculture, which enabled him to multiply and spread into the forest. For in the forest there lurked a terrible booby-trap. As man advanced into new areas, he attracted the unwelcome attentions of more and more parasties and vectors, previously comfortably settled among populations of wild animals, most of which had become immune and suffered no disease. Killing or driving away the game left the parasites no alternative but to try the new host instead. Many of them were ready to do so anyway. Today, at least 80 diseases can be naturally transmitted between higher animals and man. New human diseases, introduced from the great "reservoir" of wild life, have cropped up throughout history, and students of parasites see every reason to expect more new human diseases, particularly virus diseases, from this source in the future.

In the jungles of Africa and America, the virus of yellow fever is a parasite of monkeys, and carried from one monkey to another by various species of jungle mosquito. In America, people who wander into the forest to hunt may be bitten by the mosquitoes and catch the virus; on their return they are bitten by the mosquito *Aedes aegypti*, one of that band of blood-suckers that now confines its attentions to human victims. *Aedes* then bites other people in the town or village, and carries the virus through the population, which is smitten with deadly disease. In Africa the monkeys themselves are attracted by human agriculture; they come to raid banana plantations, where they are bitten by another blood-sucker of man, *Aedes simpsoni*, which soon spreads the virus among the villagers. In human history, yellow fever, or Yellow Jack, can fairly challenge comparison as a killer with Genghis Khan or Timur the Lame.

Yellow fever is a disease of the tropics only; the mosquitoes that carry it cannot live for long at temperatures below 68°F. Many (though not all) killer diseases are restricted to particular regions of the world. This is related to the way they are spread. Free-living stages of worms, and many insect vectors of other parasites, can survive only in particular climatic conditions. The differences between the tropics (where, in general, temperature is high and steady, but air moisture varies enormously

Above: howler monkey of South America. In America and Africa, infected monkeys form a reservoir for yellow fever, and virus is carried from monkey to monkey by jungle mosquitoes, which sometimes bite humans. *Aedes aegypti* (below, sucking blood from a human arm) transmits the disease between people.

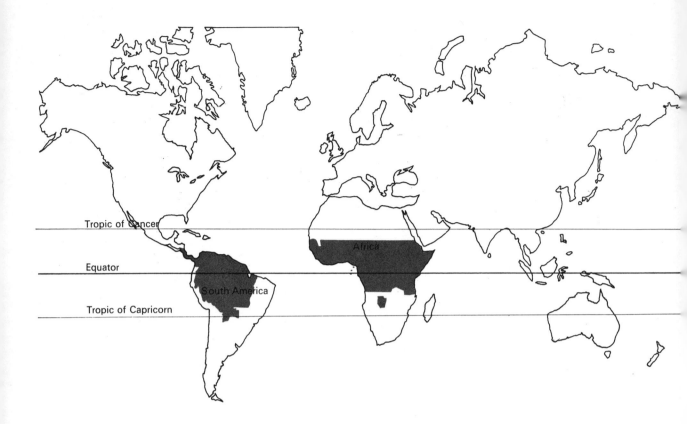

Map above marks areas of Africa and South America where yellow fever is endemic. Mosquitoes carrying this disease can survive only in the hot wet conditions of the tropics.

between wet and dry seasons) and the temperate regions (where it is just the other way round) are extremely important for infectious disease. The temperate regions have a monopoly of several diseases. Those spread as droplets in the air (like the common cold) tend in tropical climates to die without reaching another host individual. Those spread by lice attack people in the temperate regions simply because lice are most comfortable at the temperature of a *warmly clad* human body. But, on balance, the tropics have by far the worst of this bargain. Most of the 80 diseases transmitted from animals to man are tropical; and most of these are African, for tropical Africa is the worst afflicted of all.

The progress of agriculture in the wet tropics exposed the farmers to more and more disasters. It was not only a question of new diseases; in fact, the most striking example involved a disease as old as man. The picture emerges from one of the most ingenious detective stories in science, the story of malaria in Africa. There are certain hereditary conditions of the blood pigments (sometimes called "sickle-cell"), found only in human populations that have been exposed to the protozoan *Plasmodium falciparum*, the most recently evolved and the most deadly malarial parasite of man. The American anthropologist F. B. Livingstone noted the distribution of one of these

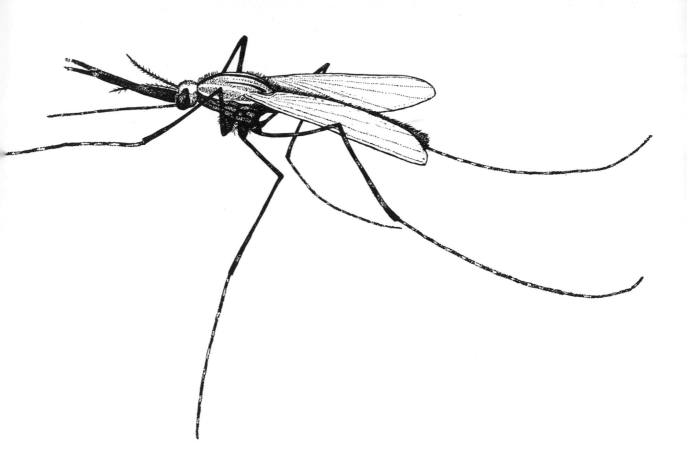

Above: *Anopheles gambiae*, the most deadly species of malarial mosquito, in that it prefers human blood. Mosquitoes breed in sunlit pools, and the clearing of tropical forest created ideal conditions for them.

Below: map shows the way people with a particular hereditary condition of blood pigments, connected with malaria, spread across Africa. In first millennium A.D., yam-growers pushed native peoples westward; in second millennium, rice-growers mixed with natives of areas further west.

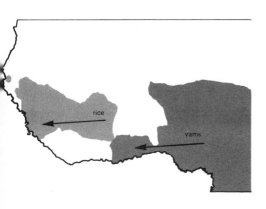

blood conditions in western Africa, and compared it with evidence (chiefly from language distribution) about the movement of peoples in this area. He showed that the condition had spread into western Africa in two waves. In the first wave, migrating and invading peoples drove the original inhabitants before them to the west coast. In the second wave, incoming peoples mixed with local inhabitants and taught them their way of life. Both waves brought with them the practice of clearing the tropical forest for agriculture; the first wave brought the yam (which the Bantu meanwhile were spreading southward, p. 48), and the second wave brought a kind of rice. Later Livingstone established a similar connection in India and south-eastern Asia. From this indirect but perfectly conclusive evidence, it follows that agriculture in the wet tropics creates the conditions for *falciparum* malaria. The villain of this whodunit is the mosquito *Anopheles gambiae*.

All the malarial parasites are carried from person to person by mosquitoes of the genus *Anopheles*. The most deadly species is *Anopheles gambiae*, because it shows the greatest preference for human blood. But it cannot breed without stagnant water or in deep shade. In the forest the soil absorbs water and there are few stagnant pools; there is also deep shade. But when the forest is repeatedly

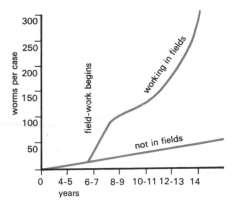

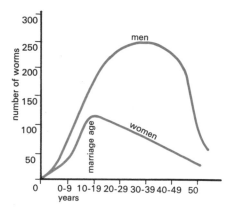

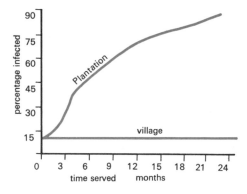

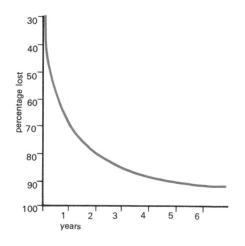

felled, the soil will not absorb water so readily; puddles form after rain, and remain as stagnant breeding sites for the mosquito, unshaded by the missing trees. Any swamps already there are also now exposed to sunlight. Finally, the villages of the farmers abound in wet, stagnant breeding places. In various parts of Africa, *A. gambiae* has actually been seen to abound after forest is cleared and to disappear if the forest is allowed to return; it is virtually confined to the neighbourhood of farming villages. Malaria, which the farmers thus brought upon themselves when they first cleared the forest, has been called the greatest killer of all diseases; when it does not kill, it causes misery and inertia, and drains all the energy and initiative needed for progress.

Another penalty of agriculture in the wet tropics is the hookworm. There are several kinds of hookworm, but they all like hot climates: the few in temperate regions have occurred in mines. The worms get in through the skin, especially of the feet and ankles. These worms are a menace only when many of them enter one person's body (p. 208); this happens when they are rapidly transmitted from the excrement of one host to the skin of another. Human excrement is often used for manure, and in any case, without proper sanitation, it is liable to contaminate the fields around a village. Graphs show in detail that the heaviest infections almost invariably occur in agricultural workers at just the ages when they are busiest in the crop fields. In 1947, it was estimated that some 457 million people were infested with hookworms.

In the village of Keneba in Gambia, medically surveyed in 1950–1, most of the villagers were infected with malaria, and all were loaded with hookworms and several other

Many factors influence the incidence of hookworm disease, but one of the most important is time spent working in fields contaminated by excrement. Left: top graph shows sharp rise in number of worms present in the body when a child starts work in fields. Second graph shows that men are more prone to the disease than women. Third graph: the high proportion of field workers who become infected in a short time compared with those working in village. Bottom graph: length of time worms may live in body.

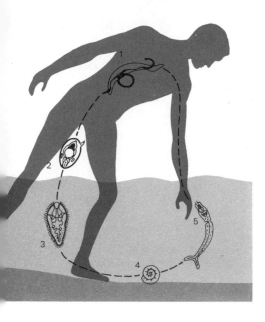

Above: life-cycle of *Schistosoma* worm that causes bilharziasis in man. Adult worms in bladder or intestines of man produce eggs that are passed out in urine. Immature worms hatch in water and invade snail hosts where they develop into cercariae—the infective stage for man—ready to penetrate the skin.

Continuous irrigation channels, also used as watering troughs, like this one in the Sahara (below), risk being contaminated and are a constant threat to health.

kinds of disease-causing worms. In addition, they were suffering from various degrees of malnutrition from lack of the right amount and balance of protein. The authors of the survey concluded that the combined forces of malnutrition and parasitism were "limiting progress and development." This is typical of countless villages in the wet tropics, particularly in Africa.

Malnutrition and disease form a vicious circle. From the nature of the farming system, food is scarce or absent at the time of planting, when the hardest work needs to be done. This critical period often occurs during the first few weeks after the fall of the season's first rain. Not only are the people weak from hunger, but malarial mosquitoes breed and several other diseases are at their worst—all this at a time when a week of inaction means the loss of a fifth of the year's productive work. Farming land shrinks to a small area right around the houses to save the effort of walking to work, and this greatly favours hookworm infestation. If matters go too far, the end may be famine and death for all; or the village, like Keneba, may last for generations at a miserably low level of health. Until the Europeans and the Japanese began the study of tropical medicine, there was no hope of breaking out of the vicious circle.

All this makes the tropical cul-de-sac more intelligible than ever. With the inertia and helplessness of individuals, there grew a terrible stagnation of society, which came to perpetuate and intensify the burden of sickness. The cruelty of tropical nature came to be reflected in a routine social cruelty. Most of these tropical tribal societies have (until modern education disrupts them) ceremonies of initiation, in which the fixed patterns of tribal behaviour are stamped upon teen-agers in an atmosphere of pain and terror, with specially cruel penalties for teen-agers liable to make innovations. Over the ages, the sick crushed the few healthy. The method of swidden farming remained the permanent hall-mark of these societies; and it worked for the simple reason that, except for the Mayas in their early home on the healthy uplands, the populations were too sick to increase. Only with modern medicine and rising populations can we now see it break down.

If disease set the seal on the tropical cul-de-sac, it was no less disastrous in the dry belt. To begin with, the hydraulic societies had to cope with bilharziasis, a disease caused by worms of the genus *Schistosoma*. Like hookworms, they cause considerable loss of blood, pain, and permanent weakness and inertia. The worms spend part of their lives in water-snails, which live in canals, and perfect conditions for the disease are created by continuous irrigation projects. Hence in many places large-scale irrigation has brought this weakening disease upon the

people who practise it. The introduction of continuous irrigation in the Aswan Province of Egypt raised the incidence of bilharziasis in the farmers there from 5 per cent to 75 per cent between 1904 and 1926, and the same development in the Gezira district of Sudan raised the incidence from 1 per cent to 20 per cent in adults and 45 per cent in children between 1948 and 1962. Similar results have been observed in the Baghdad area of Iraq. Eggs of the bilharziasis parasite have been found in the kidneys of mummies, so it was already a plague of ancient Egypt; in 1947, it was estimated that 114 million people were suffering from the disease. Bilharziasis must undoubtedly have helped to keep the peasants of Near Eastern hydraulic societies hopeless and docile.

The story of malaria in the dry belt is more intricate. *Anopheles* mosquitoes of all species breed, as we saw, in stagnant water. In about 1910, the British medical scientist C. A. Bentley made a map of the incidence of malaria in Bengal. The many stagnant river channels and marshy lakes provided perfect conditions for *Anopheles* in the west of the province, where the disease was correspondingly widespread. In the east, vast areas were flooded every year and sodden with rain; here there was too much water flow for the mosquitoes and therefore less malaria. The effect of irrigation on malaria thus depends on its effect on water flow.

The danger lies not in broad canals but in smaller channels choked with weeds, in seepage from canals, and in swamped fields. So, wherever the mosquitoes and the parasites can live, malaria is the inevitable outcome of even temporary neglect or destruction of extensive irrigation works. When wars became intense in the dry belt, or the attacks of the nomads catastrophic, before the people could recover and repair their irrigation canals, malaria moved in and killed, crippled, or expelled them. Bentley made another map of Bengal that showed all too clearly how population declined as malaria moved in. This grim ally, following the camps of the nomads, caused many of the *permanent* devastations of the western zone of the dry belt; malaria from this cause is widespread in Iraq, Afghanistan, and Syria (see Chapter 7). In the north of Ceylon, great irrigation works, built in the Middle Ages, fell into decay, and vast areas became uninhabited until modern times. In Cambodia there arose and flourished in the Middle Ages the hydraulic civilization of the Khmers; its matchless carvings reflect, in this distant jungle, the far-flung influence of Greek art. Chou Ta-Kuan, a Chinese diplomat of the Mongol Empire, has left us an account of this brilliant kingdom, where women received an advanced education and could rise to high administrative office. But even during his visit, the end was near. In the 15th

Darker areas on Bentley's map of Bengal (above) show where malaria was most prevalent (1910). This corresponds to areas with a great deal of stagnant water. Light grey areas on map above right indicate decreasing population, and dark grey expanding population (1901–11).

Below: facade of Angkor Wat, probably the largest religious edifice in the world, built in the first part of the 12th century A.D. by the Khmers. In the 15th century this great hydraulic civilization suffered several barbarian invasions. But malaria was probably the ultimate destroyer of their empire.

century A.D., after a series of barbarian invasions, the Khmers deserted their homeland, and today the forest surges around the fabulous ruins of Angkor. The last invader may well have been the malarial mosquito.

The Dance of Death

When a parasite is always present in some members of a community, it is said to be *endemic*. When it is present in most of them (like malaria at Keneba), it is called *hyperendemic*; when in all of them, *holoendemic*. It is in these conditions that the population can acquire immunity against the diseases caused by at least some parasites. When infectious *disease* attacks many of the people in a community, we speak of an *epidemic*. This can happen in at least three ways. The parasite may be hyperendemic, and something happens (such as a famine) that breaks down the people's immunity, so that the parasites they are already harbouring suddenly make them ill. Or the parasite may be normally endemic in only a few people, or may even infest members of the community only from time to time. In these conditions, the population probably has no immunity at all, and the parasite causes disease in the few people it reaches. Now something happens to make the disease more easily transmitted: conditions arise that favour the vector; a new vector appears; sanitation breaks down, favouring the spread of diseases transmitted in human excrement. Or, finally, a new parasite, which the community has never experienced and against which it has no immunity, is suddenly introduced from outside. In all these circumstances, epidemics can ravage a whole community, and even kill most of its members. If a disease spreads in this way over whole continents, or even the whole world, mankind experiences a *pandemic*, the most terrifying of all disasters.

With the rise of towns and trade—vital elements in the progress of civilization—epidemics and pandemics came into their own. In towns, people are concentrated in large numbers; whereas a disease might spare most of them if they were spread out, it will sweep through them all in a town. The greater the concentration of people, the more difficult sanitation becomes; diseases spread by contact, excrement, or vermin have been the natural scourges of the city. Where people are scattered in self-sufficient communities, epidemics are local; when trade becomes widespread, vectors and parasites are carried over larger areas, ultimately all over the world, and the epidemic becomes a pandemic. Again and again, diseases have been brought into regions hitherto free of them by trading fleets or caravans.

While infectious disease has helped to block the progress of the wet tropics and the dry belt, progress even in the favoured societies of north-western Europe has been slowed by epidemics and periodically halted by a pandemic. The history of civilization is punctuated by these catastrophes; every time society recovered, towns grew, and trade flourished, the danger returned, on an ever-increasing scale.

Throughout civilized history, the supreme ally of infectious disease has been the break-down of social life in revolution and war, more devastating with every larger integration of societies. Sieges and blockades and deliberate crop and herd devastations all engender famine and malnutrition, lowering the people's resistance; the demands and disturbances of war rapidly break down the hard-won benefits of sanitation; and among the ravaged communities, masses of men are carried all over the continents, in the worst possible conditions of camp and warship, to spread far and wide the parasites of infectious disease. Armies and navies were among the first communities to be studied in the dawn of public health research, not only because governments have always had a special interest in the condition of their fighting forces but also because conditions in them were so indescribably bad. Other human barbarities besides war have played a part in spreading disease: the slave trade between Africa and America, with its appalling conditions on the voyage, brought many diseases (possibly including yellow fever) from the Old World to the New.

Two of the chief killers have been *plague* and *typhus*. Plague is a very dangerous disease caused by the bacterium *Pasteurella pestis*. It is originally a disease of wild rodents, and has been observed in over 50 species; it is carried between them by fleas. In all parts of the world, people occasionally catch the fleas and hence the disease, but usually it does not spread; such diseases, occasionally caught in the countryside and not giving rise to epidemics, are called *sylvatic* diseases. The plot thickened when the fleas and the disease passed to the black rat (*Rattus rattus*). Rats are the most tenacious of man's many unwelcome guests. They can live almost anywhere, on almost any diet, and have spread all over the world in the wake of man, their meal-ticket. They eat practically everything man has, and are not above eating man himself. The black rat, which lives in human houses, was from early times man's most inseparable rat companion—traces of black rats have been found on a Neolithic site in Israel.

If large numbers of rats die of plague in a rat epidemic, their fleas look for another host species, and find one conveniently at hand—man. The result is a human epidemic, and since the black rat is a habitual stowaway on ships, this may turn into a pandemic. The two worst pandemics in history were caused in this way. As the

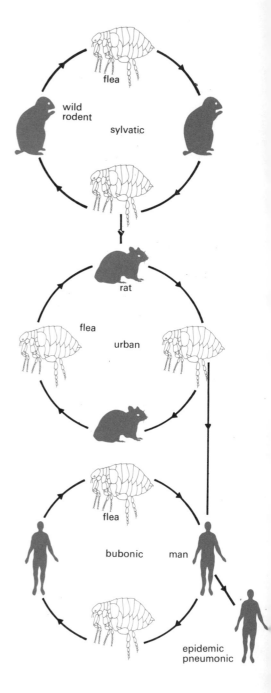

Diagram illustrates development of plague. Sylvatic plague occurs in rural areas among rodents and fleas, who may pass it to urban rats. Urban fleas thus infected may attack humans, who develop bubonic plague. When this invades human lungs (pneumonic plague) it spreads fast by droplet infection as well.

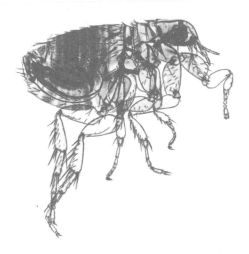

Above, the rat flea, main vector of bubonic plague; and below, the black rat, its usual host. Only when large numbers of such rats die of plague do fleas seek a new host—man.

Chinese poet Shih Tao-nan (1765–92) put it, before he died of plague himself: "Dead rats in the east, Dead rats in the west. . . . Few days following death of the rats, men pass away like falling walls. . . . There in the fields are crops, To be reaped by none; And the officials collect no tax!" What made the plague pandemics so murderous was one further step in the complicated sequence of transmission. The plague infection in man sometimes attacks the lungs, and it can then pass out in human breath and spread not only by fleas but by droplet infection: it is then called *pneumonic* plague, and sweeps like wildfire through a crowded community. An epidemic in Manchuria in 1910 actually started as a sylvatic disease from a local wild rodent, but became pneumonic and spread through slums to kill 42,302 people. The plague pandemics certainly must have involved both black rats and human lungs. Of the two supreme pandemics, that of the sixth century spared Britain,

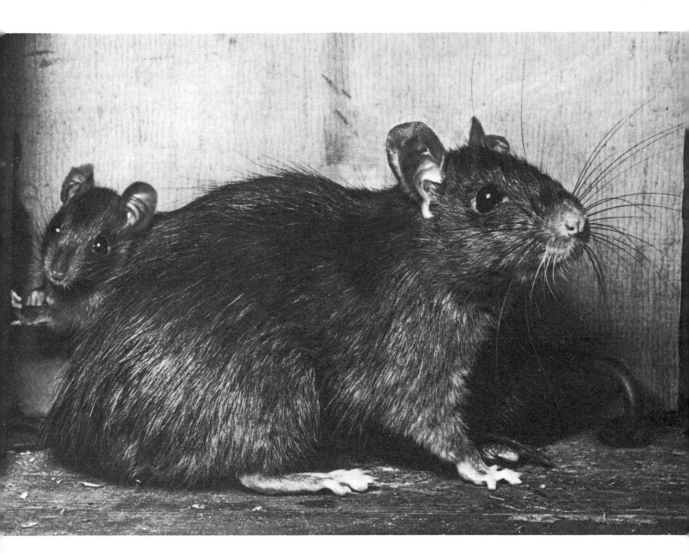

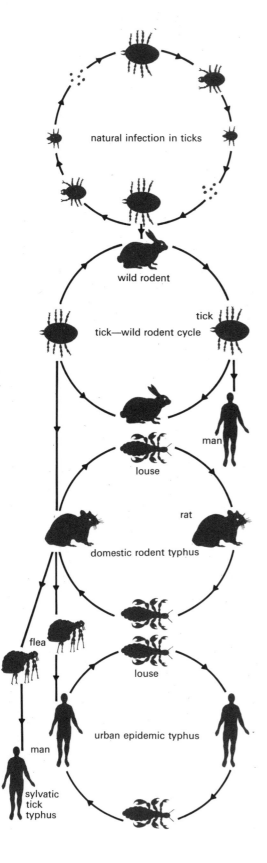

natural infection in ticks

tick—wild rodent cycle

wild rodent

tick

man

louse

domestic rodent typhus

rat

flea

louse

man

urban epidemic typhus

sylvatic
tick
typhus

which the black rat had not yet reached. When the Black Death came in the 14th century, returning Crusaders had already brought the rat to Britain, and this time Britain shared the fate of continental Europe.

Like the virus disease of smallpox (spread by contact), which was probably already epidemic in the Indus valley cities of the third millennium B.C., epidemic plague can probably be traced back to the dawn of city life, though it cannot be recognized with certainty before a Near East outbreak in the second century A.D. A much more recent scourge is epidemic *typhus*, perhaps because it has an even more intricate history of changes in manner of spread. The typhus rickettsia began as a parasite of ticks, which became sufficiently used to it not to suffer disease. From ticks, it began to pass into wild rodents, and occasionally even into human beings, causing the rare sylvatic disease, spotted fever. The next step was the transmission of the organism from rodent to rodent by means of lice, causing murine typhus. Rat-lice will not attack man, but rat-fleas will, and once the disease became established among wild rodents it could reach man in fleas and cause small local epidemics of murine typhus. This became more likely if the rodents affected were rats. This stage may have been reached in the Near East in the early Middle Ages; it seems to have caused its first European typhus epidemic in the monastery of La Cava, near Salerno, in 1083. A dangerous next step occurred when the disease began to pass between *human* lice, greatly favouring its spread in man. It is even more lethal to lice than to man, but before it dies an infected louse has time to move to another human being. This stage seems to have been reached in the 15th century, when typhus was brought by Spanish soldiers returning from Cyprus to the camp of Ferdinand and Isabella of Spain, in their campaign against the last Moorish stronghold of Granada. When the Spanish army was reviewed in 1490, according to Joaquin Villalba, "the generals noticed that 20,000 men were missing from the rolls, and of these 3000 had been killed by the Moors and 17,000 had died of disease."

By the early 16th century, local typhus epidemics were beginning to spread over the continent. A new step was now being taken, the establishment of typhus as a disease of human lice, short-circuiting the rat-fleas altogether, and the setting up of focuses of infection in populations that had had time to acquire some immunity, and could pass it to others who had not. According to Hans Zinsser, the American medical scientist who pieced the whole story together, this stage was probably reached in Hungary, where Europe was at bay against the Ottoman Turks. It may have begun in 1456, when Hunyady was fighting Mohammed II, but it had almost certainly happened by

Diagram of development of typhus from natural infection in ticks via wild rodents to domestic rodents and then to man via fleas. Urban typhus, carried by human lice, causes serious epidemics.

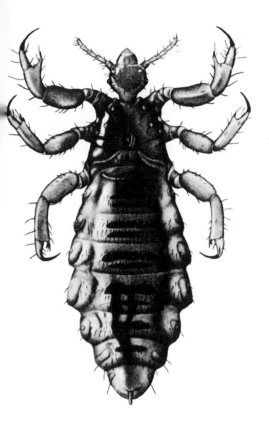

Above: body louse (*Pediculus corporis*), which transmits urban typhus in man.

The network of Roman roads (map below) was an amazing feat of engineering that facilitated trade and communications. It also meant that when an epidemic broke out in one part of the Empire it spread in a way impossible before.

1542, when the Margrave of Brandenburg brought a German army to Hungary's support: in this campaign typhus killed few of the Hungarians and Turks, who had already gained a measure of immunity, but it killed 30,000 of the Margrave's soldiers, and Hungary was known as the graveyard of Germans. The survivors brought typhus back to Germany.

In 1566 the Emperor Maximilian II brought an army of assorted north-western Europeans into Hungary. The resulting typhus epidemic wrecked his campaign, and this time the survivors carried typhus all over north-western Europe; it had reached England by 1577. The infection of Europe was finally completed, in the 17th century, by the Thirty Years' War, which Zinsser has called "the most gigantic natural experiment in epidemiology to which mankind has ever been subjected." When it was over, no corner of the continent was left without its focuses of infection. Armies, deserters, and refugees had roamed all over a Europe ridden by famine and disease. Since by now typhus was firmly united to the louse, its natural focuses from this time on were the most insanitary and crowded places everywhere; it came to be called army fever, ship fever, jail fever, and, most appropriately of all, war fever.

In the first half of the first century B.C., the Roman poet Lucretius, greatest of all popularizers of science, was writing his poem *On the Nature of Things*. Part of the poem tells the epic story of the progress of human society. The poet describes the dawn of agriculture, the domestication of animals, the building of cities, the smelting of metals, and the emergence of civilized institutions. And then, suddenly, he ends with a grim picture of pestilence, modelled closely on the account by Thucydides (who caught it and recovered) of the pestilence of 430 B.C., that murdered the civilization of Athens. Lucretius seems to be saying that this is where human progress stops. However much we achieve, we shall always come up against this impenetrable barrier, the mysterious power of pestilence, which can wipe out in a year the patient work of centuries. The civilization of antiquity, sooner or later, was doomed. It was an astonishing poetic insight, for the ancient world had so far experienced only local epidemics and no pandemic. Yet this was indeed a critical factor that for so long interrupted the advance of even north-western European civilization, breaking it into a jagged curve of dark ages and renaissances.

Lucretius was not immediately vindicated. The first century A.D. was not remarkable for pestilence. But the bomb was only waiting to be ignited. Trade on an unprecedented scale had made the whole Roman Empire one, and linked it with the civilizations of the distant East. The slums grew. The monarchy (a creation of big business)

The first pandemic, perhaps mainly smallpox, struck in the reign of Marcus Aurelius (above), who died of it himself. In the reign of Justinian (below), the first pandemic of plague occurred.

made no attempt to improve the distribution of wealth, comfort, and education. The peasants remained a focus of bitter discontent, ready to explode (as army recruits) into the frightful revolution of the third century (p. 156). And along its splendid lines of communication the Empire had to dispatch troops all over Europe, the Mediterranean, and the Near East, to guard this frontier or that. All the conditions were there for pandemics, and in the second century they began to strike.

The first pandemic struck in the reign of Marcus Aurelius; it was said to have started from a chest looted in a Near Eastern temple, as if it really came out of Pandora's Box. It certainly started in the army of the Near East, in A.D. 165, and spread from Persia to the shores of the Rhine, infecting even German tribes across the frontier. It was probably a whole horde of diseases, each reducing resistance to the others, but the chief killer may have been *smallpox*. It killed the emperor and an unknown number of his subjects; it went on till A.D. 180, paused, and returned in 189, killing 200 people a day in Rome itself. Throughout the third century, the peasants in the armies raged over the Empire, wrecking city life in a holocaust of revenge on the middle classes for their callous indifference to social welfare.

In A.D. 256 the next pandemic came, more extensive than before; it swept from Egypt to Scotland. St. Jerome said it had all but destroyed the human race, and that the earth was returning to deserts and forests. Nevertheless, much evidence (for instance the RAF survey of Italy, p. 161) suggests that the retreat of agriculture during these terrible centuries was limited and temporary, and that from the fourth century onward the population of the Empire continued to increase more than ever.

Then, in 540, there came the first of the two supreme pandemics, mainly *plague*. It lasted for nearly 60 years, and destroyed between one third and one half of the populations of the ancient Mediterranean world. After the year 565, Latin and classical Greek ceased to be living languages. The prophecy of Lucretius had come true: the ancient world was dead.

This time there was no doubt about the retreat in forest clearance (see Chapter 2). But, in north-western Europe, the pandemics had removed some of the conditions that gave them birth. Towns and trade had dwindled. And so the early mediaeval monks and farmers and technologists were free of the dreadful menace that shadowed the Roman Empire. But as trade revived, there were danger signals. Venice paid a price for her trade supremacy: she had 63 plague epidemics in 600 years. But such disasters were still local hazards, and many people must have gone through life without experiencing an epidemic at all. It was in this period that the final steps were taken to make the technological breakthrough a certain prospect.

In the 14th century the rise in population sent everything wrong. Wars intensified, sanitation and morale began to crack. Above all, shortage of protein was reducing the resistance of the people to disease. The northern Dutch, who remained stock raisers and continued to eat meat, were remarkably immune to epidemics; this shows that malnutrition was the crucial factor in what followed. Meanwhile, trade had linked up the whole continent. The population was already going down, and agriculture already retreating. Epidemics were growing more frequent. The way was prepared for the King of Terrors, and in 1347, the Dance of Death began. Plague, the greatest killer of all, appeared in an army of Mongols in the Crimea, and

Map shows how the plague swept across Europe in the 14th century. Lines indicate how far infection had spread at specific dates. In December 1347 the plague had only a small foothold in Mediterranean Europe, where it had arrived from the Near East, but in three years it had engulfed all Europe.

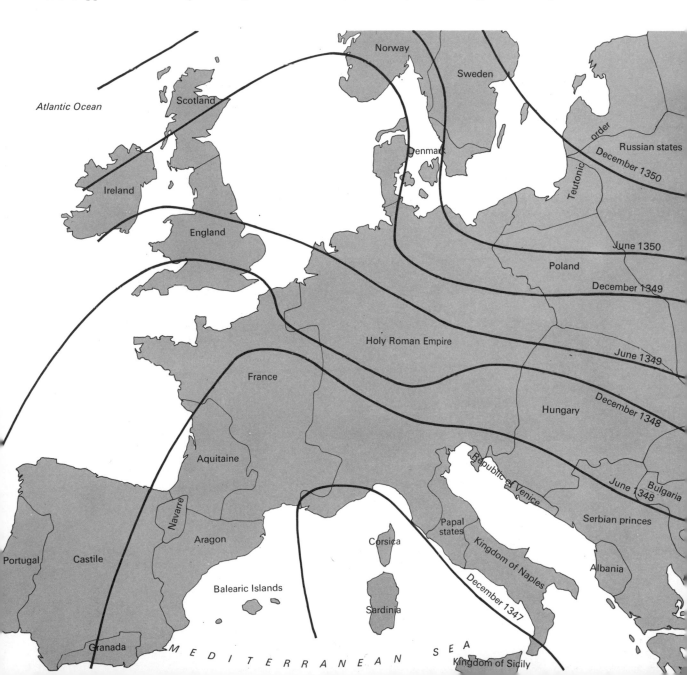

the black rat again carried it all over the civilized world, in the second supreme pandemic, known to history as the Black Death. *In five years, it destroyed between one third and one half of the population of Europe.* Pope Clement VI ordered statistics to be drawn up: the death-roll came to 42,836,486.

Unlike the ancient world, which was rotting when the pandemics struck, mediaeval civilization had passed a threshold of progress and was now certain to make the breakthrough. Recovery was therefore extremely rapid, and science and technology forged ahead with movable-type printing and the Italian Renaissance of the 15th century. By the end of the second century, the people of the Roman Empire had felt that things could only go on getting worse. Mediaeval Europe, on the other hand, saw the end of the Black Death with unbounded joy, and settled down to another bout of progress. People for-gathered at gay parties to exchange plague stories, as they were later to exchange tales of the guillotine or the blitz. The rag trade had a ball: women's dresses were slinky and low-cut, and (despite endless adult grumbling) teen-agers of both sexes *would* wear pointed shoes. But in one respect the result of the second great pandemic was like that of the first. The end of the Black Death ushered in a new world: and the new national languages of Europe suddenly began to take their final shape.

Indeed, from the early Middle Ages onward, European history has a curiously two-fold aspect. On the one hand, there was a surge of progress such as had never occurred elsewhere; on the other, recurrent population crises gave rise to seemingly endless miseries and horrors, in which infectious diseases played a large part. The next three centuries were distinguished by an endless succession of epidemics going the rounds of Europe; in the bigger cities they could be devastating, like the London outbreak of plague in 1665. The new pattern was firmly established by the end of the Thirty Years' War; the endless wars that followed gave Europe little chance to shake it off until Waterloo (1815). From then on, however, systematic improvements in public health began to tell, and rising standards of living began to make people healthier and disease less lethal. Danger lay, however, in the swelling slums of the new big industrial cities, and a new disease took its place on the world stage. *Cholera* is a bacterial disease spread when people are crowded and their excrement gets mixed up with their drinking-water. In 1816 it broke out of its endemic home in India and China, causing four successive pandemics, three of which devastated Europe and North America. After 1875 it began to retreat again, somewhat mysteriously, though improved drainage must have helped. By the 20th century it was

Europeans celebrated the end of the Black Death joyfully. Above: at a feast a more sober guest treads on the long pointed shoes of another. Not all approved the exaggerated new fashions.

Right: spread of cholera, 1816–1923. Before 1816 India was home of the disease. In mid-century, pandemics spread across Europe and America. Retreat of the disease in early 20th century was perhaps encouraged by improved drainage systems, but it still affected much of the East.

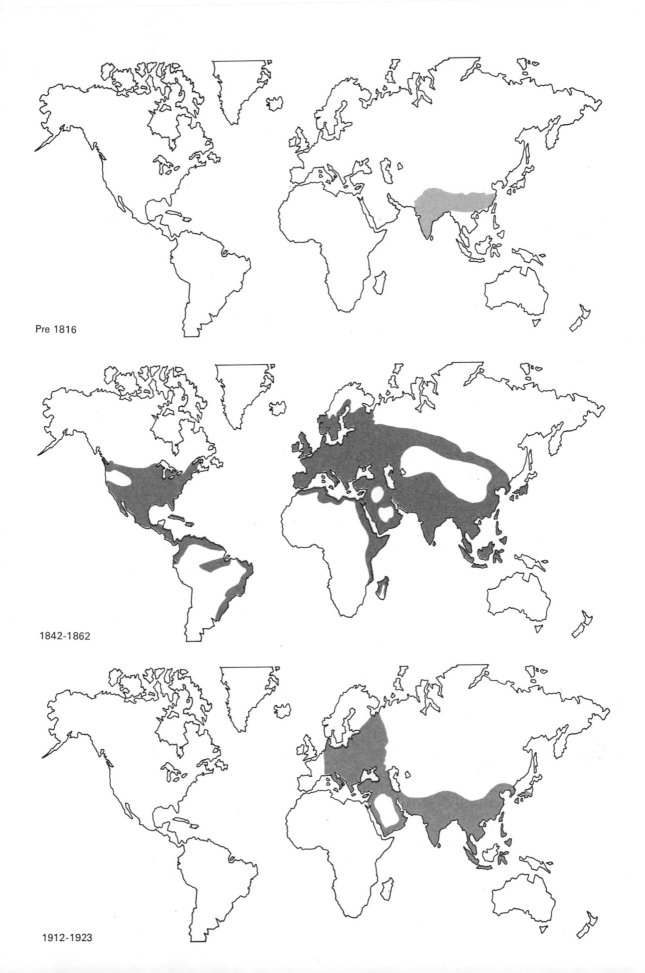

Pre 1816

1842-1862

1912-1923

shrinking back to its homelands: 1923 saw the last cholera epidemic in Europe.

World War I plunged the whole of eastern Europe into a nightmare; with tragic irony, this blow followed on the heels of the discovery in 1909 that typhus was carried by lice. In this new horror, typhus was supported by a coalition of other diseases. The principal sufferer was Russia; according to the heroic Russian physician Tarassewitch, there were probably more than 25 million cases of typhus in Soviet territories between 1917 and 1921, with almost three million deaths. The war must also have affected the health of north-western Europe; it was almost certainly responsible for the last of the pandemics, the influenza outbreak of 1917–9. In the weakened war survivors, the disease was unusually lethal, and about 20 million people died. In Europe, previous epidemics had conferred some immunity; India fared worse. But if this influenza had been as lethal in Europe as the Black Death plague, 1000 million people might have died.

Epidemics and pandemics do more than reduce the population. The testimony of observers (Thucydides, mediaeval writers, Daniel Defoe) is unanimous: pestilence has devastating effects on human behaviour and human society. Distortions of family life are bound to outlast the generation of the pestilence. In general, people become less sociable and more aggressive. Thucydides noted that pestilence destroyed that feeling for law and co-operation on which Athenian democracy was based, and it is easy to trace the degeneration of Athenian politics after 430 B.C. From Athens, the "school of Greece" (as Pericles called her), the effect spread to the pupils: for the next generation, Greek war became more atrocious than ever before or after. War and pestilence are the two sides of a vicious spiral; each encourages the other. As for the Black Death, apart from evidence everywhere of the increase in crime, there is one outstandingly terrible example. Local pogroms of the Jews (often during epidemics) had begun in the time of the early Crusades, when a new kind of suspicion of "non-Europeans" began to play into the hands of a new and rising class of non-Jewish bankers; but these had remained local. When the Black Death got under way, there occurred, all over Europe, a pogrom of pandemic proportions, the greatest before Hitler. Just as the Nazis accused them of fomenting the inflation and depression crises (the real causes of the Nazi outbreak), so in the 14th century the Jews were accused of spreading the plague. As in the previous "epidemic" pogroms (and as in Nazi Germany), there was an obvious criminal motive, which objective mediaeval chroniclers did not miss. "The money of the Jews," wrote one of them, was "the poison which brought about their death." But no such outburst would

have been possible without the conditions created by the Black Death.

We have considered the routine cruelty of tropical tribes, always a prey to sickness (p. 215). A similar routine cruelty, on a more sophisticated level, has characterized the disease-ridden hydraulic societies; here initiation ceremonies were replaced by "deterrent" criminal penalties. Republican Romans recoiled in disgust from the cruel death penalties of the Near East (except those for slaves). Mediaeval Europeans were amazed at the contrast in China between the superlatively conscientious judicial procedures, in which no effort was spared to ensure fair trial, and the revolting nature of the penalties after conviction. Europe has always been more complex, feeling a tension between cruelty and civilized freedom, and repeatedly acting on it. European societies were the first to abolish torture, but at the same time, Europeans have not shrunk from killing on an almost Mongol scale; and the history of Europe is stained with appalling episodes of almost-more-than-Oriental cruelty, like the Thirty Years' War or the Nazi outbreak. The last few centuries have been especially confusing, with real progress interwoven with endless recurrences of cruelty and war. In the long run, the effects of modern medicine and public health, in overcoming the factor of epidemic disease, may be incalculable—unless it is replaced by the no less dangerous factor we shall consider in the final chapter of this book.

The Black Death attacked people of all classes and ages—an idea strikingly expressed by these three groups (left), an early 19th-century copy of a mediaeval dance of death from Basle, Germany. Top, Death takes a merchant; middle, Death leads away an unwilling pope; bottom, Death takes a court jester.

Anxious to find a scapegoat for the Black Death, many people accused the Jews of spreading the plague, and large numbers were killed and their property looted. Below: illustration from Schedel's *Chronicle*, of Jews being burned alive.

12 The Last Problem

Just as new disease problems have arisen from seemingly unrelated changes, such as the rise of towns and trade, so disease problems have sometimes receded as a result of such events; progress in other fields can bring unexpected health bonuses. Two examples are plague and malaria in Europe. Plague had disappeared from all parts of Europe except Turkey by the end of the 17th century A.D., and great plague epidemics never occurred again there. This retreat has never been fully explained, but some of the factors are clear enough. Nutrition improved again from its deterioration in the 17th century. Cotton, more easily laundered than wool, replaced woollen garments on an increasing scale. Houses were more frequently built of stone, and, in at least the more prosperous houses, carpets from the expanding Eastern trade replaced the deplorably insanitary rush floors of the Middle Ages in which layer upon layer of spittle and other filth accumulated.

It now became less easy for the black rat to hide in houses. This weighted the scales against it at about the time when a new rival, the brown rat, was invading from Asia. The brown rat is a Mongol among rodents; it not only competed with the black rat, but assembled in gangs and set about exterminating its enemy. From our point of view, this was eminently satisfactory, for the brown rat, though it can also carry plague, lives in less intimate contact with man than the black one; it inhabits his sewers. On land, the result was an unqualified victory for the brown rat. Only on shipboard did the black rat, better at climbing cables, maintain a foothold. So today, as maps demonstrate, plague is a slum disease of the world's great ports, especially in the least sanitary coastal regions.

Malaria has not always been essentially a tropical disease; it has played its part in the history of Europe. This is especially clear in the Romagna, the area around Rome. Malaria appeared here about 200 B.C., after the second and biggest war with Carthage, when invading troops from North Africa had been in the neighbourhood of Rome. It became really serious in the fourth century A.D., and remained so for about 400 years. This first wave coincided with a pronounced retreat in the agriculture of the Romagna (somewhat ahead of the general European retreat) and a low ebb in the political importance of Rome. Europe has been favoured even in its malarial mosquitoes. Unlike *A. gambiae*, they have not had a special preference for man, or sought out his dwellings. European malaria is

As early as the fifth century B.C. scientists had noted the prevalence of malaria near marshy areas. When Empedocles drained a swamp near Selinus, Sicily, he reduced outbreaks of the disease, and a coin (above) was struck in his honour.

Murine plague is transmitted by black rats, which flourish in insanitary conditions and often infest ships. Inevitably ports are infected, as can be seen on this map, marking areas of Africa affected by the disease in the first half of the 20th century.

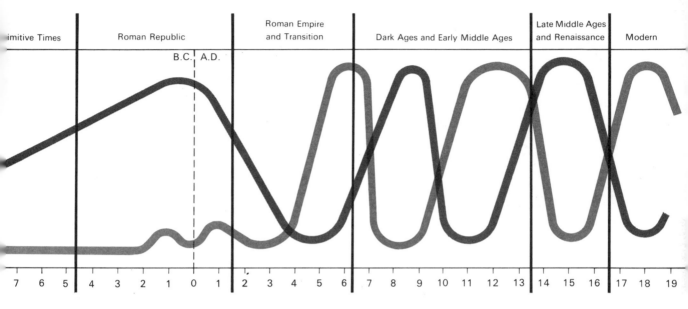

| imitive Times | Roman Republic | Roman Empire and Transition | Dark Ages and Early Middle Ages | Late Middle Ages and Renaissance | Modern |

B.C. | A.D.

7 6 5 4 3 2 1 0 1 2 3 4 5 6 7 8 9 10 11 12 13 14 15 16 17 18 19

(as Hippocrates noticed in the fifth century B.C.) a disease of marsh areas. The Romagna is naturally marshy, but in ancient Roman times it was kept well drained, sometimes by extensive projects. As farming receded, the land returned to marsh and the mosquitoes flourished. As malaria increased, the farmers that survived either became weak and slovenly or left the area. In the seventh century, agriculture here began to recover as part of the general recovery of north-western Europe, and malaria suddenly declined, presumably because of marsh reclamation. Rome took on a new lease of life, and the papacy was at the height of its powers, creating in 800 the Holy Roman Empire. In the 10th century, agriculture declined again and malaria returned; Rome had an increasingly stormy history, which ended when the papacy was forced to remove to Avignon in France. In the late 14th century, the tide turned again; the papacy returned to Rome, and the city played a memorable part in the Italian Renaissance. Malaria declined again during this period. Finally, after the sack of Rome in 1527 and the Spanish domination of Italy, declining agriculture, rising malaria, and a phenomenal crime wave combined to keep Rome insignificant till the 19th century. At every retreat, malaria had made matters worse; at every recovery, its suppression by marsh reclamation had made matters better.

When agriculture (green line) was at a low ebb in the Romagna, malaria (black line) was widespread. The recovery of farming led to reclamation of marshes, reducing malaria. Diagram shows interaction of farming and the disease.

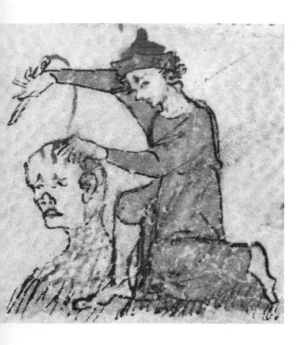

Above: miniature from a 14th-century English manuscript of an early surgical operation. The surgeon, holding his patient down, is suturing, or sewing up, a head wound with a large needle.

Above: mediaeval forerunner of a modern clinic. Physician, left, dresses a wound, while other patients wait for attention. (Belgian MS, 15th century.)

During the last two centuries, long before the World Health Organization (WHO) of the United Nations began its campaign, malaria has been disappearing from north-western Europe. It was gone from England as an endemic disease by 1887, though in 1918 malarious soldiers returning from the war were able to start an epidemic in Kent and Essex. It seems that two main factors have been involved in this improvement. As part of the new advance in agriculture, extensive drainage operations were carried out, thereby reducing the marshy areas in which the mosquitoes breed. Meanwhile, as a consequence of the new farming systems, more cattle were kept indoors through the winter (p. 183). The mosquitoes (especially the most northerly ones, which like shelter) moved from house to byre, and bit cattle instead of man. It appears that these factors, unaided by deliberate control measures, were enough to eradicate malaria in several north-western European countries.

But if we relied on such uncontrolled changes alone, we should probably only be exchanging new diseases for old. The crucial event of the last two centuries has been the advance, thanks to the technological breakthrough, of medicine and public health science. The medical researchers of the ancient Near East, of Greece and Rome, of Islam, and of the European Renaissance made impressive progress in diagnosis and treatment of disease in the individual, the greatest step forward being taken by Hippocrates and his colleagues in Greece during the fifth century B.C. But although Ancient Greeks (and Hebrews) had their suspicions of rats, and although Hippocrates could notice the connection of malaria with marshes, the level of early knowledge of biology was far too low to permit any hope of controlling disease in populations, either epidemic or pandemic. So much and such varied knowledge was needed that this is hardly surprising. Only the work of biologists of the 16th to 19th centuries laid the necessary foundations, and only at the end of the 18th century could the real advance in "death control" begin. Lucretius was right in feeling that man in his own day had no control whatever over pestilence. It was reserved for modern Europe (and Japan) to tackle the problems of public health, epidemic control, and, in due course, tropical medicine.

The Turning Point

Sanitary practices are not in themselves new. Nothing could be more hygienic than the palaces of Minoan Crete (2nd millennium B.C.), and much of the Mosaic Law was admirably sound. Agamemnon, according to Homer, ordered all refuse removed from the Greek camp, because it had offended the gods and thus started a pestilence.

Many reasonable observations about public health were made by ancient and mediaeval scientists. But what was needed was an understanding of the individual diseases, of exactly how they spread, of how to combat vectors, and of how to take advantage of the development of immunity in the body. Man's first major success was in this last area, though it was achieved by trial and error long before the facts were understood. The first great killer to be tackled was one of the very oldest, smallpox. The trick here was to make the body produce antibodies against the disease, by deliberately inducing a mild infection. Preparations used for this purpose are called *vaccines*. They may be live disease parasites, modified by growing them in other animals or cultures where they lose their special virulence for man, or dead ones that still contain the substances necessary to stimulate antibody production. Ideally, they should produce little or no illness, while making the body resistant to natural infection in future. Protection against smallpox (with matter from smallpox sores) had been practised in China and Turkey for some time before it began in Europe. One of the first European "guinea-pigs" was Catherine the Great (1762–96), who summoned Dr. Dimsdale of Hartford to St. Petersburg for the purpose. In 1796, Edward Jenner improved the technique by discovering that the related organism of cow-pox (relatively

In 1796 Edward Jenner discovered that the organism of cow-pox could be used to produce immunity against smallpox. Below: Jenner performing his first vaccination on a small boy. (From a painting by Melingue.)

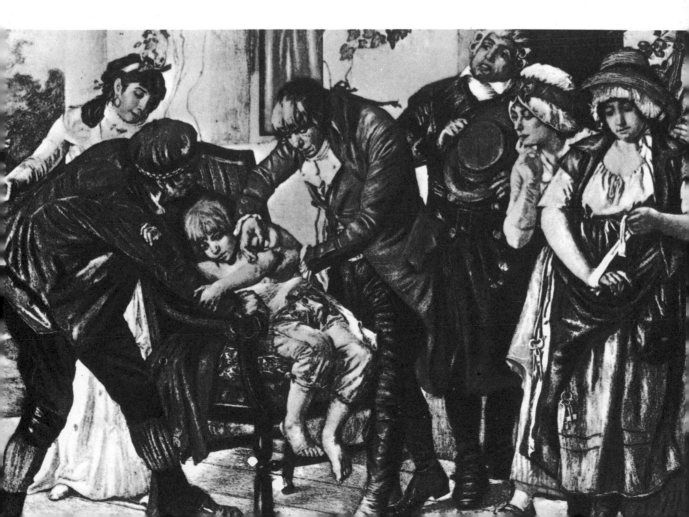

harmless to man) confers immunity against smallpox; cow-pox is called *vaccinia* (from Latin *vacca*, meaning a cow), whence the word "vaccine."

Vaccination became increasingly prevalent in the 19th century and smallpox at last vanished from the roll of great killers. Its elimination in Britain has been almost too successful; vaccination is on the decline as it ceases to seem necessary, and some think there is again danger of smallpox epidemics. Meanwhile, when Pasteur and Koch, in the 1860s and 1870s, began to discover the secrets of infectious disease and its microscopic agents, the principle of vaccination was extended to many other diseases (to some by Pasteur himself): it has been invaluable, for instance, against tuberculosis.

By rendering many or most people in a community artificially immune, vaccination greatly reduces the danger of epidemics. Another approach has been the development of quarantine regulations, as a means of preventing spread of diseases, especially from immune to non-immune parts of the world. This began on common-sense lines. The pioneer state was the Republic of Venice,

German scientist Robert Koch travelled widely to study infectious diseases. Below left, centre figure, he holds a post mortem on an ox at Kimberley, Australia (1900). Below: Louis Pasteur, the French scientist who developed innoculations against anthrax, hydrophobia, and other diseases.

The ancient Cretans had a highly efficient drainage system in the palace at Knossos. Above, Cretan pottery water pipe (about 1800 B.C.). Below: it was not until the 19th century that London fully realized the importance of good sanitation and built proper sewers that did not contaminate drinking water.

which had every reason to fear plague introduction from abroad (p. 222). In 1127 it was enacted that anyone coming from the Levant had to remain in a building called the House of St. Lazarus for 40 days (the word "quarantine" comes from the Italian *quaranta*—forty) before entering the city. Quarantine (always liable to break down in war) remained rather ineffective until modern times, however; for again precise information was needed about each disease. Its rational development has been largely accomplished in the 20th century, and owes most to the work of the League of Nations agencies and the World Health Organization of UNO.

Meanwhile, substantial changes began to take place in systematic public sanitation. It has been said that the great sewers of Roman and Greek cities were essentially storm drains, designed to prevent floods; certainly nobody but the rich had domestic plumbing. In modern Europe there was, for a long time, a definite prejudice against putting human excrement into drains. Until 1815 the discharge of any refuse except kitchen slops into London drains was prohibited by law; in Paris this policy lasted till 1880.

Above: map of Soho drawn up by Dr. John Snow marking houses where cases of cholera occurred in outbreak of 1848. Circles mark drinking-water pumps. When pump in Broad Street was put out of use the epidemic ended, confirming his suspicions of its contaminated water.

Below: U.S. army officials using powder sprays to delouse inhabitants of Naples in typhus epidemic in January 1944. This attack on the vectors of the disease swiftly brought the epidemic to an end.

What spurred the authorities to investigate the problem and change their policy was the succession of cholera outbreaks.

In 1848 Dr. John Snow of Soho, London, made a large-scale map of his practice and marked on it the houses of the 500 cholera victims in the area. These clustered around a hand-pump in what was then Broad Street, and Snow deduced that cholera was spread by contaminated drinking-water. From the mid-19th century onward, human excrement was systematically passed to the drains, and steps taken to dispose of it. This one reform must have been enormously important for all diseases spread by excrement. Other improvements were on the way. Hospitals, formerly a natural focus for epidemics, were reformed by the colossal energy of one tough and bitchy woman. Anyone who doubts the influence of individuals on human history may examine the casualty figures of the armies in the Crimea in 1854–6. The French lost 51 per cent of their wounded, the English 27 per cent; the French lost 25 per cent of their sick, the English 12 per cent. The only factor that the English had and the French had not was Florence Nightingale.

By the 20th century the work of Pasteur and Koch had laid the foundations of the science of infectious diseases; the work of Manson, Laveran, Ross, and others had begun to unravel the complexity of life-cycles and vectors. Large-scale systematic assaults on disease problems began. Work on the Panama Canal was at first halted by disease, especially yellow fever. The builders mounted a vigorous research campaign that (at the cost of several European and Japanese scientists, who took too many risks) ended by identifying Yellow Jack and its vector *Aedes aegypti*. Finally the first grand public health and quarantine operation was mounted during World War I by, of all people, the Kaiser's General Staff. Not conspicuous for their love of mankind, these generals nevertheless realized that if the typhus outbreak of Eastern Europe spread into Germany, the war was lost. We owe it to their Prussian efficiency that not only Germany but the whole of north-western Europe was spared the fate of Russia.

With the coming of the international agencies, first of the League of Nations, then of the United Nations, man's campaigns against infectious disease became world-wide and ever more effective, thanks to the fundamental knowledge now available and to the constant search for more. Even the tropics could begin at last to draw breath. Most spectacular has been the campaign against malaria, which has totally eradicated the disease from vast areas of the earth, and aims at its eradication everywhere. In the control of vector-borne diseases, insecticides have played a great part. Spraying the walls of houses is a crucial part

of the World Health Organization (WHO) campaign against malarial mosquitoes. The new knowledge and techniques even enabled man to come through World War II without the catastrophic disease outbreaks of World War I. Of course, as always, this war came to the rescue of some diseases; it even reintroduced malaria into central Europe, because the deaths of large numbers of cattle drove the mosquitoes back to man. But the typhus epidemic in war-torn Naples in 1943 was quelled remarkably promptly by delousing the population with the insecticide DDT.

As always, there are continual new problems, but dealing with them is no longer a matter of centuries or millennia. That poliomyelitis is an old disease is clear from at least one ancient Egyptian portrait; but it is only now becoming a common illness. It is, in fact, an epidemic disease of *good* sanitation. In insanitary communities, more than 80 per cent of the children acquire immunity before they are four years old. As sanitation improves, people no longer become immune and polio epidemics can occur. They began to be serious as drainage improved in 19th-century Europe, and are appearing in the developing countries as their sanitation improves. Man is coping with this loss of natural immunity by artificial immunization. Thanks to the progress of virus research, when polio became a really alarming threat it took very few years to produce the Salk vaccine.

In another respect, the danger of pandemics is greater now than it ever was before. The speed of air transport gives terrifying opportunities for the spread of diseases

Above: limestone monument from Egypt (about 2000 B.C.) showing the priest Ruma who had an atrophied limb—the result of an attack of poliomyelitis.

Map shows how smallpox epidemic spread by aircraft from Australia and Africa to Europe in 1963. Dots mark small outbreaks, squares large outbreaks. Significantly, large outbreaks occurred along air routes (solid lines). Broken lines mark shipping routes, and dotted line marks coach or train routes.

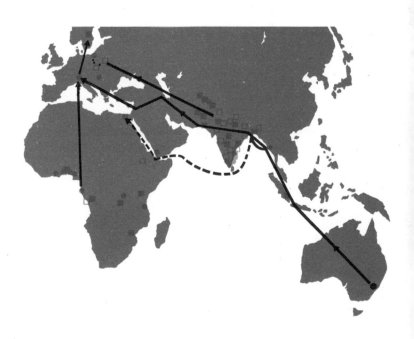

235

between world regions. Experts in the field are haunted by the possibility of yellow fever (always confined to the two sides of the Atlantic) reaching the vast, non-immune populations of Asia. Of 80,716 aeroplanes inspected in the U.S.A. between 1937 and 1947, 28,852 were found to contain insects and related animals. The nightmare became real in 1930, when ships and probably aeroplanes carried *Anopheles gambiae* from Dakar to Brazil, where malaria promptly killed thousands. Swift action by a team of experts had eradicated the mosquito by 1940; but this sort of thing shows what could happen if the ever-more-stringent quarantine precautions of the world broke down —for instance, as a result of war. The 1964 malaria report of WHO shows clearly that the greatest concern of the malaria campaign now is to prevent reintroduction of the disease into countries from which it has been eradicated.

In February 1957 a new influenza virus was isolated in China. In May, the first notification was made to WHO, from Singapore. Within 22 days, cultures of the new organism were sent to Britain, and within a few months a new vaccine was ready for use—just too late. The pandemic of Asian flu had meanwhile hit Britain, making 7.5 million people ill in England and Wales. The death-rate was fortunately extremely low; otherwise a disease with such an attack rate might have been another Black Death. Notification in February would have given time for vaccine production, but no routine machinery existed for China to give this notification, for she was not a member of the United Nations. It is clear that we exclude any country from the work of the international agencies at our peril. Fortunately, China is now already a member of several international scientific organizations. For the impartial organisms and vectors of disease, the world is one and mankind a common host. The lesson is gradually being learnt. It is probably true to say that infectious disease (including disease of crops and herds) is doing more than anything else to force mankind to think and work in terms of international integration.

With all the dangers, old and new, there is no doubt that infectious disease is under control as never before in the history of man. We have passed the germ barrier of Lucretius. Even the tropics are beginning to benefit on a grand scale. In England, average life expectancy at birth in 1550 was 8.5 years; it is now very nearly the biblical three-score years and ten. In such countries as Britain and the U.S.A., the causes of death have changed completely. The dramatic decline of diphtheria and tuberculosis in the 20th century is especially noteworthy. Infectious diseases are no longer at all prominent; their places are taken by cancer and "diseases of old age"—for instance, diseases of the blood-vessel system. These last illnesses are not new

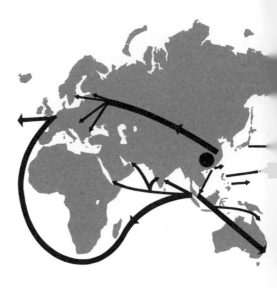

This map shows routes by which Asian flu epidemic of 1957 spread. Probably originating in south-east Asia (black dot), it spread across central Asia to eastern Europe but arrived in Britain by sea. It was then passed on to America.

Below: causes of death in Britain in 1907 and 1963. Deaths from infectious diseases (dark grey) have declined dramatically, while deaths from diseases of heart and blood vessels (dark green) have trebled. Total of deaths from all other diseases (grey) has fallen slightly.

1907

1963

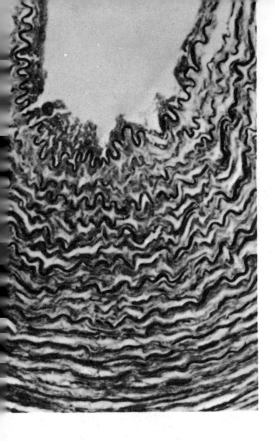

Today, hardening of the arteries is a disease often attributed to the stress of modern life; but evidence of it has also been found in Egyptian mummies, as in this magnified section across an artery of a male mummy.

Growth of the world's population from 10,000 B.C. to A.D. 1950 (figures accurate to within stated margins). Note slow steady climb to 750 million and then, after Industrial Revolution and advances in agriculture and medicine, sharp rise to 2476 million by 1950.

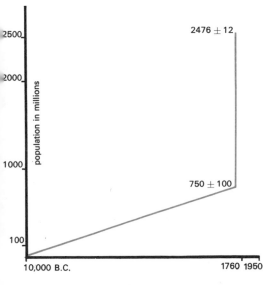

reactions to the strains of modern life, as some suppose—hardening of the arteries attacked at least two Egyptian Pharaohs, Mereneptah and Rameses II; it can actually be diagnosed in tissue sections from mummies. It is simply that most of us, and not just pampered Pharaohs, can now live long enough to die of them. The problems of longevity and cancer are the ones that now lie before biological science. Infectious disease will present continual new problems, and eternal vigilance is the price of public health; but, in principle, this is a problem of the past. What more is there to withhold mankind from continuous progress toward happiness and creative activity? What is left in Pandora's Box? There is indeed one last problem, and by a supreme irony this has appeared as a result of the achievement of modern medicine. It is the problem of population.

A Question of Numbers

At the Brussels International Exhibition of 1958, the British Pavilion contained perhaps the most terrifying exhibit ever put on show. It was a little device like the mileometer on a car dashboard, showing the growing population of the Commonwealth. As the little gadget ticked on and the number steadily increased, mankind's latest problem was presented with startling effect.

Population is a complicated subject, but the rise or fall of a population depends fundamentally on the difference between birth-rate and death-rate, both usually reckoned as numbers per cent (or per thousand) per year. If the death-rate is higher, the population falls; if the birth-rate is higher, the population rises. The trouble is that any rise is by compound interest, since the more people there are, the more they can breed. If a population increases by the same percentage every year, it increases by a constantly greater absolute number. If it rises by two per cent per year, for instance, it more than doubles every generation. A calculation has been made that shows the fantastic implications of all this. If mankind had sprung from a single couple living about 12,000 years ago (shortly before the coming of agriculture), and if there had been one more birth than deaths per hundred per year (a one per cent increase every year), then today the world population would form a sphere of flesh many thousand light-years in diameter, expanding with a velocity many times faster than light.

From the ages at death of fossil remains of Palaeolithic populations, it has been shown that the death-rate was very high, and since man survived, it is assumed that the birth-rate was even higher. About the agricultural civilizations we know rather more than this. Evidence from many sources shows that they generally had very high birth-rates

Sharply rising populations in small
developed countries like Britain are a
very real problem. Above: Liverpool
Street station, London, in the rush hour
with commuters pouring off the trains.

A feature of rising populations is the
increased proportion of people living
in towns. The two maps shown below
illustrate the spectacular spread of
London in the 19th century.

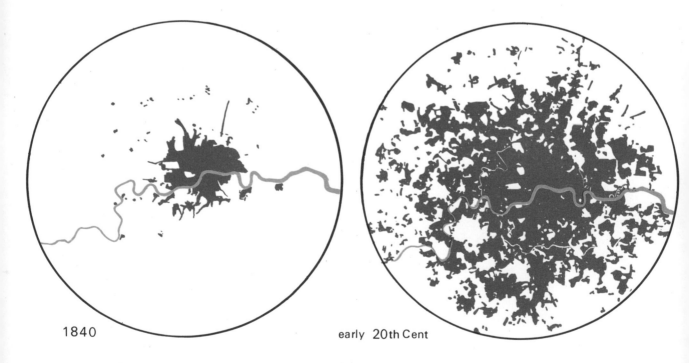

1840

early 20th Cent

of 3.5–5 per cent, and death-rates also high but normally lower, 3–4 per cent. The populations therefore increased by 0.5–1 per cent per year. They did not end up as an expanding sphere of flesh because every so often they were cut down by a catastrophic death-rate of 15–50 per cent.

The agents of death were war, famine, malnutrition, and infectious disease. Hence world population grew relatively slowly; it may have been 2–20 millions in 10,000 B.C., and it has been estimated as 650–850 millions in A.D. 1750.

The technological breakthrough and the Industrial Revolution brought with them a mastery of food production and infectious disease control that reduced the normal death-rate to below 1.5 per cent, and (even more important) drastically reduced the periodic catastrophic death-rates from famine and pestilence. The birth-rate in the developed countries eventually came down to a little above the death-rate, but only after a considerable lag; thus in England and Wales the death-rate was falling steeply before 1820, while the birth-rate began to fall steeply only after 1870. Since in any case the periodic catastrophes were under control, the European population rocketed.

In the developing countries, events were still more spectacular. At a time when they still had the high "agricultural" birth-rate, the coming of modern famine- and disease-control suddenly removed their catastrophic death-rates and reduced their normal death-rates. Between 1891 and 1921, the population of India rose by only 5 per cent. Between 1921 and 1951, when major famines and epidemics were under considerable control, it rose by more than 1 per cent *per year*. In Ceylon, the DDT campaign by WHO against malarial mosquitoes lowered the normal death-rate from 2 to 1.4 per cent in the single year 1946–7; the birth-rate remained over 4 per cent. Hence the annual population increase of Ceylon, which was 0.46 per cent in 1871–80 and 1.71 per cent in 1941–5, rose to 2.74 per cent in 1948. Annual increases of over 2 per cent appeared about the same time in India, China, Central and South America, and other developing areas. Africa, where food and disease problems are tougher, has taken longer to reach this point. In January 1966, however, a new drug, Ambilhar, was announced for use in the cure of bilharziasis. It is said to effect a cure in as little as a week, and may be used by the millions of bilharziasis sufferers in Africa as soon as supplies are available. If bilharziasis is conquered, vast areas of the African dry belt will be opened up by modern irrigation schemes without fear of the consequences, and we can expect a sensational rise in the African populations.

To crown all this, since World War II the birth-rate in developed countries has begun to rise again. In January 1964, the British Minister of Health announced that the "birth-rate in Britain has risen more sharply than any

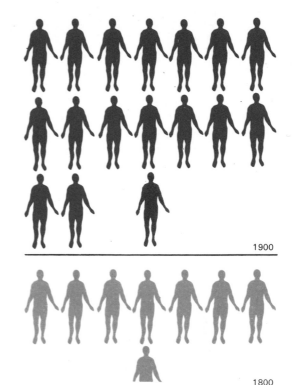

Diagram shows increase in population of Europe in the 19th century. Each figure represents 25 million people. The one coloured grey represents the Europeans who had emigrated by 1900.

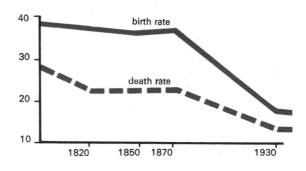

Above: birth- and death-rates per 1000 in England and Wales, 1750–1950. The graphs show the lag between the fall of the death-rate and that of birth-rate. This lag explains the population increase.

239

expert could possibly have forecast," and that births in 1965 would probably reach the figure that experts, a few years earlier, had predicted for 1975.

The minister's experts were not the only people to be taken by surprise. One of the most alarming things about the present rise in world population is the way it outstrips the predictions of experts. The rate of increase itself is continually rising; for India, it was still about 2 per cent in 1960, and 2.8 per cent by 1964. In 1950, Sir Julian Huxley was considered an alarmist when he suggested the world population might reach 3000 million by the year 2000. United Nations estimates prepared in 1951 predicted more than 3000 million by 1980. According to FAO's 1964 Production Yearbook (published in 1965), the world population was in fact 3216 million in 1963. Recent estimates suggest (at the present rate) 22,000 million by the year 2040.

In publications by scientists concerned with food production, one often reads now of a "race" to feed the growing population, and sometimes there is a suggestion that we can win the race. As a result of a fantastic scientific and technological effort, with sharply increasing use of agricultural chemicals, world food production was increased by 10 per cent between 1958 and 1963—a staggering achievement. Yet world food production *per head of population* (and therefore the amount of food per person) was the same in both years, because the population had increased just as much. "Now *here*, you see," said the Red Queen to Alice in *Through the Looking Glass*, "it takes all the running you can do, to keep in the same place." In the Far East and Latin America, food production per head in 1963-4 was actually lower than before World War II. Even at the level of supply we are struggling to preserve, more than half the people in the world are not getting an adequate diet. Moreover, the increase of food production on land is approaching a limit beyond which all our technology cannot push it. Even with the full harvest of the oceans added, we could hardly expect to feed the 22,000 million expected by 2040. In any case, if population increase simply remained at its present rate (let alone became faster), it would sooner or later become that expanding sphere of flesh. Obviously in real life (as opposed to mathematical extrapolation) one of two things must happen: either the birth-rate will come down or the death-rate will go up.

This does not mean that the heroic labours of the food-producers should be slackened. The real race is to "keep in the same place" until the birth-rate can be lowered. Nor is food the only aspect of the problem. At present the population increase is especially disturbing in the developing countries and in small developed countries like Britain,

Above: photo of Golcar, Yorkshire (background), with its industrial and domestic buildings gradually encroaching on the land around it—a dangerous development in a country that already has too little agricultural land to grow food for its population.

Dotted line on graph (right) shows that world production of food has risen steeply in the years 1954–65. But so has population (black line), so that production per head is in fact decreasing slightly. In 1965–66, production per head dropped by about two per cent. (All figures exclude China.)

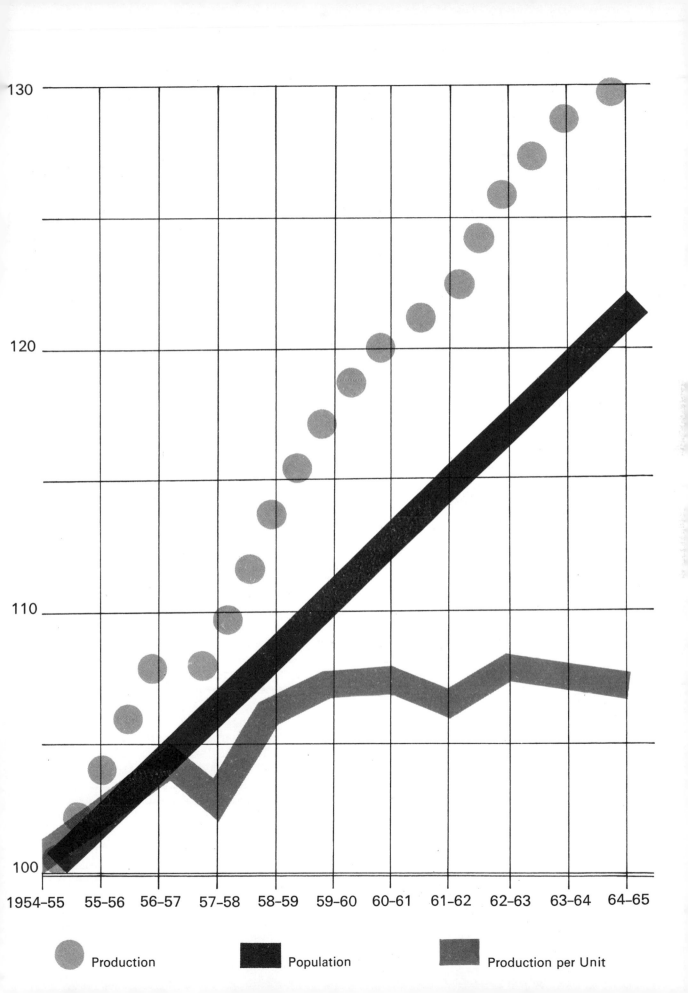

130

120

110

100

1954–55   55–56   56–57   57–58   58–59   59–60   60–61   61–62   62–63   63–64   64–65

Production   Population   Production per Unit

Priests tearing the hearts from live human sacrifices to the Aztec God of War. Nuclear weapons offer a similar solution to the problem of matching population and resources. Can we find a different solution?

the Netherlands, and Japan; the British and Dutch already had only half an acre of farmland per head in 1961, and by 1965 the British Government was talking of building on farmland. The larger developed countries, like the U.S.A. and U.S.S.R., will feel the pinch in due course; already California, for instance, has an increasingly serious water-shortage problem.

All those problems of man's relations with nature that we considered earlier are now trivial if the population is stabilized even at its present level; all are insoluble if it goes on rising much longer. In that case, much evidence suggests that, long before we run completely out of food, tensions due to crowding will erupt in violence and ultimately in wars far worse than those of the 14th and even the 20th centuries. In that case, too, war, followed by famine and pestilence as our vulnerable machinery for food production and public health breaks down, will end in a more catastrophic death-rate than those of the two supreme pandemics, and will throw man's progress back untold centuries. On the other hand, if the population can soon be stabilized or reduced, the prospects for man are golden. Then the work of the food producers will bring rich rewards. Up till now, only a tiny minority of people have ever been able to enjoy comfort, leisure, and education fit for free human beings, supported by the surplus produced by all the rest. Now, for the first time, modern technology and automation could bring these things within the reach of all mankind.

The last problem facing man is, therefore, to reduce the human birth-rate. Population control methods, brutal and painful, have appeared in many human societies, enforced by cruel economic pressure or tribal or state tyranny. The mainland Ancient Greeks killed surplus infants by exposure. The Incas made a proportion of women compulsory virgins for life. Shaka, the Zulu dictator of the early 19th century, made his young warriors compulsory virgins until middle age. Many tribal societies practise surgical mutilation on their members. We cannot afford to reduce the birth-rate at the cost of worse tyrannies than those that blocked the progress of the empires of the dry belt. The problem is, therefore, to discover what makes human beings breed less of their own free will.

The initially falling birth-rate of developed nations suggests one factor: hope. When people expect things to improve, they want the best for their children, and so have fewer. The renewed rise in birth-rate in these same countries may mean that things no longer seem to be improving so fast. This is a powerful argument for making all-out efforts to develop the emerging nations faster and for increasing the opportunities of the under-privileged in the developed ones. A related factor emerges from some very encouraging recent events in Japan. Between 1950 and 1961 a group of Japanese newspapers asked a cross-section of the population: "Do you expect to depend on your children in your old age?" In 1950 more than 55 per cent answered: "Definitely, yes." The proportion giving this answer declined steadily, reaching 27 per cent by 1961, presumably owing to increasing confidence in social services for old people. Now during this same period the Japanese birth-rate actually *fell*, from 2.8 to 1.7 per cent.

There is some hope, therefore, that the birth-rate *can* be reduced in time, if we devote all our research resources to obtaining a general solution of the fundamental problem. After all he has achieved in controlling nature, it would be sad and strange if man proved incapable of this. At all events, we have now reached the most exciting and critical stage in the story of man, and this or the next generation may see the creation of paradise or hell on earth. Which will it be? The question remains an open one, as it was for the poet Sophocles, who wrote these words in his play *Antigone*, produced in Athens about 2400 years ago:

There are many remarkable things, and nothing more remarkable than man; he crosses the sea in the troughs of great waves through the stormy winds of winter; he grinds away the indestructible unwearied earth, eldest of the gods, as his mule-drawn ploughs drive back and forth, year after year.

In the coils of his nets he takes the careless birds and the wild beasts and the beings of the sea; by his devices he tames the shaggy-maned horse and the oxen of the mountains.

He has learned speech and wind-swift thought, and how to live in cities, and to shelter from the bite of frost and the lash of sleet, the all-providing one; baffled by no emergency, only death he cannot escape; but he has found means to avoid diseases hard to control.

Possessing by his skill resources beyond belief, sometimes he comes to harm, sometimes to prosperity.

If we can solve the population problem humanely, the peaceful use of our resources, symbolized by this nuclear power-station, could bring about a paradise on earth.

Index

Page numbers in *italics* refer to captions.

Acknowledgments

Key to picture position = (T) top, (C) centre, (B) bottom, and combinations; for example (TL) top left, or (CR) centre right

6   Philippine Tourist and Travel Association Inc.
10 Museo del Prado, Madrid/ Photo Mas, Barcelona
11 British Museum/Photo John Freeman
12 (T) James Bischoff, *History of Woollen and Worsted Manufactures*, 1842, photographed from a copy in The London Library, with permission
    (C) British Museum/Photo Freeman
    (B) Photo Drummond Young
13 (T) British Museum
    (B) Photo Ashmolean Museum, Oxford
15 British Museum (Natural History)/Photo Behram Kapadia
17 (TR) Musée de l'Homme, Paris
    (B) Geodetic Institute, Denmark. Copyright
18 (T) British Museum
    (B) Radio Times Hulton Picture Library
20 British Museum (Natural History)/Photo Freeman
21 (B) U.S. Forest Service
22 (B) Based on Kenneth P. Oakley, *The Reluctant Society*, British Museum (Natural History), 1955
23 (T) Kenneth P. Oakley, *Man the Toolmaker*, British Museum (Natural History), 1961
    (B) Photo Axel Poignant
24–5 (C) © The Warburg Institute
26–7 Photos R. Rose Innes, Ghana
28 (T) Photo R. Rose Innes, Ghana
    (B) Ghana Survey Department/Aerofilms
29 After Larry Wilson, *In Search of Lost Forests, Forest and Outdoors*, 1952
31 (B) Paul Popper Ltd.
32 (T) Photo Prof. C. von Furer-Haimendorf
32–3 (B) British Museum (Natural History)
34 (BL) Photo Dr. Hans Helbaek
    (R) British Museum (Natural History)
35 British Museum (Natural History)
36 British Museum

37 (T) British Museum (Natural History)
37 (B) Based on C. S. Coon, *Seven Caves*, Jonathan Cape, London, 1957, and Alfred A. Knopf, Inc.
38 (B) From Graham Clark, *Prehistoric England*, Batsford
39 (T) Nationalmuseet, København/Photo Lennart Larson
    (B) British Museum
40 (T & B) British Museum (Natural History)
41 (TR) Nationalmuseet, København/Photo Lennart Larson
42 After J. E. B. Gover, A. Mawer and F. M. Stenton, *The Placenames of Middlesex*, Cambridge University Press, London, 1942
43 (L) After H. Jäger, *Die Entwicklung der Kulturlandschaft im Kreise Hofgeismur*, Göttingen, 1951
    (R) British Museum
44 From G. H. Andrews, *Modern Husbandry: A Practical Scientific Treatise on Agriculture*, 1853
45 (L) After O. Schlüter, *Die Siedlungsräume Mitteleuropas in fruhgeschichtlicher Zeit*, part I, Hamburg, 1952; ("Forschungen zur Deutschen Landeskunde," vol. LXII)
    (BR) Museum of English Rural Life, The University of Reading
46 (T) The American Museum of Natural History, New York
    (B) J. Allan Cash
47 (B) Mansell Collection
48 (B) Photo Basil Davidson
49 (B) Photo Hans Guggenheim
51 After William L. Thomas Jr., *Man's Role in Changing the Face of the Earth*, The University of Chicago Press, 1965
52 Courtesy Firearms Division, Colt's Inc.
53 (T) Fairchild Aerial Surveys Ltd.
54 From Collection of Prof. Ernest K. Smith, now in East Asian Library, Columbia University
55 Courtesy The Library of Congress
56 (T) Photo Behram Kapadia
    (CL) Aldus Archives
56–7 (C) British Museum/Photo Freeman
57 (TR) British Museum
58 (TL) Imperial Chemical Industries
    (TR) British Museum

59 (T) Camera Press/Photo David Channer
59 (B) Courtesy Steel, Peech & Tozer, Rotherham, a branch of The United Steel Companies Limited
61 (TL) British Museum/Photo Freeman
62 Photo courtesy Nationalmuseum, Helsinki
63 (B) Photo courtesy Nationalmuseum, Helsinki
65 (T) Maps based on Harold C. Conklin, *Agriculture in the Philippines*, courtesy the author and Food and Agriculture Organization
    (B) Photo Harold C. Conklin from *Hanunóo Agriculture*, courtesy the author and Food and Agriculture Organization
66 (T & B) Photo Harold C. Conklin
67 (T) Photo Harold C. Conklin
    (B) Photo Clifford Evans and Betty J. Meggers, Smithsonian Institution
68 Based on Harold C. Conklin, *Agriculture in the Philippines*, courtesy of the author and Food and Agriculture Organization
69 (T) William A. Hance, *The Geography of Modern Africa*, Colombia University Press, 1964
70 (T) Office du Livre, Fribourg/Photo Henri Stierlin
72–3 (CT & CB) Rothamsted Experimental Station
73 (CB) Rothamsted Experimental Station
    (BR) British Museum (Natural History)
75 Paul Popper Ltd.
76 From Stanley, *In Darkest Africa*, 1890
77 Photo E. J. H. Corner
78–9 After Jonathan D. Saner, "The Grain Amaranths: A Survey of their History and Classification," *Annals of the Missouri Botanical Garden*, XXXVII, No. 4
80 (T) Photo U.S. Soil Conservation Service
    (B) Karl J. Pelzer, *Pioneer Settlement in the Asiatic Tropics*, American Geographical Society
81 Photo Edward H. Graham
82 Photo U.S. Soil Conservation Service
83 Photo Harold C. Conklin, *Hanunóo Agriculture*, courtesy the author and Food and Agriculture Organization
84 (B) Photo Harold C. Conklin, *Hanunóo Agriculture*, courtesy the author and Food and

Agriculture Organization

85 Karl J. Pelzer, *Pioneer Settlement in the Asiatic Tropics*, American Geographical Society
86 (B) British Museum
87 Photo Loring M. Hewen
88 British Museum
89 F. Catherwood, *Views and Monuments in Central America*
91 (T) Bibliothèque Nationale, Paris
(B) Museum of Fine Arts, Boston (Bigelow Collection)
92 (B) J. Allen Cash, Newsphot Ltd.
93 Photo Felix Gluck
94 Photo S. Bunnag/Food and Agriculture Organization
95 (T) University Museum, Philadelphia
(B) British Museum
96 Metropolitan Museum of Art, New York, Rogers Fund, 1919
97 (B) British Museum/Photo Freeman
98 F. Caillard, *Recherches sur les Arts et Métiers*, Paris, 1831, Bibliothèque Nationale, Paris
99 (T) Musée du Louvre, Paris
(B) Museum of Fine Arts, Boston, Ross Collection
100 (T) British Museum
(B) Prof. Joseph Needham, *Science and Civilization in China*, Vol. II, Cambridge University Press, 1956. Courtesy the author
101 (T) Photo Ashmolean Museum, Oxford
(B) Uni-Dia-Verlag, Stuttgart
102 (T) Photo Jane Garrett
(B) Photo Roger Wood, London
103 Chester Beatty Library, Dublin
104–5 British Museum (Natural History)/Photos Freeman
107 Aldus Archives
108 British Museum
109 (B) Erich Lessing/Magnum Photos
111 Photos U.S. Soil Conservation Service
112 Geographical Projects Ltd.; from *Discovery and Exploration*, published by Paul Hamlyn Ltd.
113 Camera Press/Photo Wu Chun Chang
114 (T) J. Allan Cash
(B) Photo courtesy Alan Root and Anglia Television
115 Photo Paul Almasy
116 From *The Conquest of New Spain*, The Hakluyt Society, Vol. 25, Series 2, Vol. 3, 1910. Courtesy Cambridge University Press
117 (T) British Museum
(B) Bodleian Library, Oxford

118 (T) Camera Press/Photo Alfred Gregory
119 (T) Camera Press/Photo Alfred Gregory
(B) From *Travaux et Mémoires de l'Institut d'Ethnologie de l'Université de Paris*, XXIII, 1936
120 (BR) Musée de l'Homme, Paris
120–1 (TC) Bodleian Library, Oxford
121 (BL) From F. Guamon Poma de Ayala, *Nueva Coronica y Buen Gobierno*
122 (B) British Museum
123 Henri Cartier-Bresson/Magnum Photos
125 (B) Courtesy Lady David
126 (T) Camera Press/Photo Harold Davies
127 Musée Guimet, Paris/Photo J. A. Lavaud
128 (B) Bibliothèque Nationale, Paris
129 Bibliothèque Nationale, Paris
130–1 British Museum
133 (B) Staatliche Museen, Berlin
134 (T) Kadman Numismatic Museum, Tel-Aviv
(B) Georg Gerster
135 (B) Institut Français d'Archéologie de Bayrouth, Liban
136–7 (T) Photo Shabtai Tal, Newsphot Ltd.
(B) J. Allan Cash
138 (T) Photo Lieselotte Evenari, Jerusalem, Israel
(B) Photo Felix Gluck
139 Photo Lieselotte Evenari, Jerusalem, Israel
140–1 (B) By courtesy of the Master and Fellows of Corpus Christi College, Cambridge
141 (T) British Museum
142 (T) National Portrait Gallery, London
(B) Philadelphia Museum of Art. Given by Mr. and Mrs. Wharton Sinkler, reserving life interest
144 (T) Burgerbibliothek, Bern. Cod. 120: Petrus de Ebulo
(B) Photo Lala Ausberg
146 (L) British Museum
147 (T) British Museum
148 (C) Mansell Collection
149 (T & C) British Museum
(BR) After Koldeway: American Archaeological Association Clarendon Press, Oxford
150 (T) British Museum
(B) Museo Provinciale Campano (Caserta), Capua
151 (B) British Museum/Photo Freeman
152 (B) British Museum/Photo Freeman
154 (T) Rheinisches Landesmuseum, Trier
(B) British Museum/Photo Behram Kapadia

155 (B) British Museum/Photo Behram Kapadia
157 (B) Museo de la Real Academia de la Historia/Photo Mas, Barcelona
158 Metropolitan Museum of Art, New York, Rogers Fund, 1909
159 (T) Redrawn from Dürrenmatt, *Schweizer Geschichte*, Hallveg Verlag, Berne, 1957
(B) Italian State Tourist Board
160 UNESCO/Photo Gerda Böhm
161 British Museum
162 (B) El Escorial, Madrid
163 James Bischoff, *History of Woollen and Worsted Manufactures*, 1842, photographed from a copy in The London Library, with permission
165 Photo Mas, Barcelona
166 (T) Bayerischen Staatsgemäldesammlungen, München
(B) Biblioteca Apostolica Vaticana
167 (T) Museo del Prado, Madrid/Photo Mas, Barcelona
168-9 (T) British Museum
(B) V. B. Proudfoot, B.A., Ph.D., F.S.A., University of Durham
171 (T) Musée de la Tapisserie de la Reine, Bayeux/Photo Jean Besse
(B) British Museum
172 (TR & BR) British Museum
173 (T) Bischöflicher Dom und Diozesanmuseum, Mainz
(B) Courtesy Schweizerische Landesbibliothek, Berne
174 (T) The Board of Trinity College, Dublin
(B) British Museum/Photo Behram Kapadia
175 British Museum/Photos Behram Kapadia
176 (T) Biblioteca Nazionale Centrale, Firenze
177 (T) Courtesy The British Travel Association
(B) Bodleian Library, Oxford
178 Photo Eva Bollert
180 (T) Aerofilms & Aero Pictorial Ltd.
(B) From *Laxton: A Guide*. By permission of the Controller of Her Britannic Majesty's Stationery Office. British Crown Copyright
184 Photo Martin Hürlimann
185 (T) The Ralph M. Chait Art Galleries, New York
(B) Rhodesian Government Information Department
186 (T) Aldus Archives
(B) Radio Times Hulton Picture Library
187 (T) British Museum/Photo Freeman
(B) Aldus Archives
188 (T) Mansell Collection

Artists' Credits